34th EUROPEAN SYMPOSIUM ON COMPUTER AIDED PROCESS ENGINEERING / 15th INTERNATIONAL SYMPOSIUM ON PROCESS SYSTEMS ENGINEERING

VOLUME 4

COMPUTER-AIDED CHEMICAL ENGINEERING, 53

34th EUROPEAN SYMPOSIUM ON COMPUTER AIDED PROCESS ENGINEERING / 15th INTERNATIONAL SYMPOSIUM ON PROCESS SYSTEMS ENGINEERING

VOLUME 4

Edited by

Flavio Manenti
"Giulio Natta" Department of Chemistry, Materials and Chemical Engineering, Polytechnic University of Milan, Milan, Italy

Gintaras V. Reklaitis
Davidson School of Chemical Engineering, Purdue University, West Lafayette, Indiana, United States

ELSEVIER

Amsterdam – Boston – Heidelberg – London – New York – Oxford
Paris – San Diego – San Francisco – Singapore – Sydney – Tokyo

Elsevier
Radarweg 29, PO Box 211, 1000 AE Amsterdam, Netherlands
The Boulevard, Langford Lane, Kidlington, Oxford OX5 1GB, UK
50 Hampshire Street, 5th Floor, Cambridge, MA 02139, USA

Notices

Knowledge and best practice in this field are constantly changing. As new research and experience broaden our understanding, changes in research methods, professional practices, or medical treatment may become necessary.

Practitioners and researchers must always rely on their own experience and knowledge in evaluating and using any information, methods, compounds, or experiments described herein. In using such information or methods they should be mindful of their own safety and the safety of others, including parties for whom they have a professional responsibility.

To the fullest extent of the law, neither the Publisher nor the authors, contributors, or editors, assume any liability for any injury and/or damage to persons or property as a matter of products liability, negligence or otherwise, or from any use or operation of any methods, products, instructions, or ideas contained in the material herein.

British Library Cataloguing in Publication Data
A catalogue record for this book is available from the British Library

Library of Congress Cataloging-in-Publication Data
A catalog record for this book is available from the Library of Congress

ISBN (Volume 4): 978-0-443-34092-5
ISBN (Set) :   978-0-443-28824-1
ISSN: 1570-7946

For information on all Elsevier publications visit our website at https://www.elsevier.com/

  Working together to grow libraries in developing countries

www.elsevier.com • www.bookaid.org

Publisher: Candice Janco
Acquisition Editor: Anita Koch
Editorial Project Manager: Lena Sparks
Production Project Manager: Paul Prasad Chandramohan
Designer: Mark Rogers

Typeset by STRAIVE

Contents

Flavio Manenti, Gintaras V. Reklaitis (Eds.), Proceedings of the 34th European Symposium on
Computer Aided Process Engineering / 15th International Symposium on Process Systems
Engineering (ESCAPE34/PSE24), June 2-6, 2024, Florence, Italy
© 2024 Elsevier B.V. All rights reserved. http://dx.doi.org/10.1016/B978-0-443-28824-1.50451-8

A symbolic regression based methodology for the construction of interpretable and predictive thermodynamic models

Sam Kay,[a] Edgar I. Sanchez Medina[b], Kai Sundmacher[b,c], Dongda Zhang[a*]

[a]*Department of Chemical Engineering, The University of Manchester, Oxford Road, Manchester, M1 3AL, UK.*

[b]*Chair for Process Systems Engineering, Otto-von-Guericke University, Universitätsplatz 2, Magdeburg, 39106, Germany*

[c]*Process Systems Engineering, Max Planck Institute for Dynamics of Complex Technical Systems, Sandtorstraße 1, Magdeburg, 39106, Germany*

[*]*dongda.zhang@manchester.ac.uk.*

Abstract

Symbolic regression offers great potential in applied thermodynamics, where traditional modelling efforts have yielded limited improvement. Thermodynamics research revolves around the use of thermodynamic relationships to describe properties such as enthalpy and phase equilibrium amongst others. Yet, these models are often limited to specific temperature and pressure regions, chemical classes and physical states. To address this, we propose a symbolic regression methodology to extend the region of feasibility in which thermodynamic models can be applied reliably. In this study, we generate a residual model, correcting inherent bias within an excess Gibbs energy model by reformulating existing knowledge and introducing new information, namely molecular access systems keys fingerprints (MACCS). To test this approach, a case study was developed, aimed at the prediction of activity coefficients at infinite dilution for a range of temperatures using UNIFAC Dortmund. The results were benchmarked with a Gibbs-Helmholtz graph neural network based method from the literature (Sanchez Medina et al., 2023), in which the advantages and limitations of the proposed symbolic regression based approach were identified, and its interpretibility as well as ease of implementation were well demonstrated. This study, therefore, provides a unique and novel contribution to the field of applied thermodynamics research.

Keywords: Symbolic regression, Thermodynamic models, Interpretable machine learning, Molecular fingerprint, Graph neural network

1. Introduction

To meet the current net zero targets, there has been a drive to more environmentally focused plant design and operation. In this respect, the integration of novel chemical systems, technologies, and "cleaner" energy sources within process operation are essential. A critical focus for sustainable plant development is the separations process, which account for 10-15% of global energy usage (Mutch, 2022), and 40-90% of capital and operating costs within industry (de Haan et al., 2020). Enhancing the design of separation systems necessitates accurate approximations of phase equilibria which requires thermodynamic data derived from many time-consuming and expensive experimental trials. However, the vast experimental space, encompassing all combinations of current and future synthesisable molecules, leaves extensive gaps within available thermodynamic data (Sanchez Medina et al., 2023). To overcome this, predictive models such as the universal quasichemical functional-group activity coefficients method (UNIFAC) were developed and have become a widespread solution to circumvent experimental limitations (Sanchez Medina et al., 2023).

Activity coefficients describe the deviation from ideal behaviour of a substance in a mixture due to intermolecular interactions and size differences. They are of the upmost importance in describing phase equilibria for non-ideal liquid mixtures, and the successful design of a separations system is naturally largely reliant on their accurate retrieval. In chemical engineering, the activity coefficient at infinite dilution (IDAC) is usually of specific interest for its utility: firstly, they can be used to calculate the activity coefficients at finite dilution (Brouwer et al., 2021; Medina & Sundmacher, 2023); secondly, they provide good initial estimates for solvent performance in solvent selection processes (Cheng et al., 2004).

UNIFAC Dortmund is the most commonly applied variant of the UNIFAC predictive model for identifying IDACs. It is not uncommon however, for the predictions made to be inaccurate, particularly in cases where hydrogen bonding or strong hydrophobic interactions are exhibited (Méndez Sevillano et al., 2014). Furthermore, UNIFAC can only maintain its accuracy for systems under specific temperature and pressure conditions (Muzenda, 2013), and its results worsen for very asymmetric molecules and cannot be directly applied to polymer mixtures. Efforts to improve thermodynamic predictions has led to a recent surge in data driven approaches, comprising techniques from matrix completion methods (Damay et al., 2021), to advanced neural networks and transformers (Sanchez Medina et al., 2023). The use of such black box machine learning methods, although accurate, lacks interpretability, limiting physical understanding one may gain from model construction. In recent literature, symbolic regression has proven effective for knowledge discovery, rediscovery of complex physics and in the identification of descriptors for complex systems. Due to its success across a wide array of fields, it is believed that it may offer a unique solution to overcome the persistent interpretability challenges in traditional data-driven modelling.

2. Methodology

2.1. UNIFAC

First, we will cover the structure of the UNIFAC Dortmund model. UNIFAC is partitioned into two terms, one being the combinatorial term which holds the entropic contribution due to molecule size and shape differences. The second being the residual term, which represents the enthalpic contribution, and is dependent on the interactions of the constituent subgroups in the mixture. UNIFAC Dortmund was developed in order to correct structural bias in the combinatorial term, to improve predictions on asymmetric systems, and in the residual term, to enhance the temperature dependance of the model (Lohmann et al., 2001). Yet, even so, there exists much room for improvement when compared to recent data driven applications.

2.2. MACCS Keys

A major characteristic of UNIFAC is its basis in the solution of groups concept, which accounts for the interactions between individual subgroups under the assumption that each subgroup's properties are independent to the rest of the molecule to which it resides on. To enhance UNIFAC's accuracy whilst aligning with its solution of groups foundation, it is proposed to introduce structural information about the molecules under study through MACCS fingerprints.

MACCS fingerprints deconstruct each molecule into subgroups, each of which is compared to one of 166 pre-defined keys, obtaining a value of 1 if present and 0 if not; this way, a distinctly representative fingerprint of each molecule can be found. The dimensions of the MACCS fingerprints are impractical for genetic algorithms like those used in symbolic regression so, dimensionality reduction techniques are employed for concision of the solute-solvent binary system MACCS keys. Specifically, an artificial neural network (ANN) was developed and optimised, using Bayesian optimisation, on the residuals between UNIFAC Dortmund's predictions and the experimentally recorded IDAC values. Then, the final hidden layer was extracted and taken as the reduced input feature space of the MACCS fingerprint in the symbolic regression algorithm. The described methodology is depicted in Figure 1.

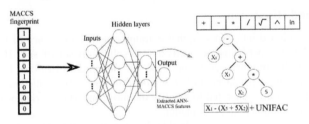

Figure 1 - Symbolic regression methodology using the ANN-MACCS input features.

2.3. Symbolic Regression

We will now cover the concept of genetic algorithms, the cornerstone of symbolic regression. In general, genetic algorithms use a natural selection approach to identify the most fit combination of descriptors. Through successive generations, populations of symbolic equations will become increasingly fit with respect to the objective function, retaining characteristics of the most fit individuals. In this work, individuals within a population are defined via a combination of constants, operators and input variables where the operator space is confined to $(+, -, *, /, \sqrt{}, \exp, \ln)$, in an attempt to reduce the probability of arriving to unphysical expressions.

The symbolic regression algorithm aims to balance model accuracy with model complexity where the complexity is defined as the sum of process variables, operators and constants in the model. In the symbolic regression algorithm, the performance of the symbolic expressions is optimised using the mean squared error (MSE), defined in Eq. (1.1) and comparison between the best models is completed using the mean absolute error (MAE) metric, shown in Eq. (1.2). Each metric is calculated for a functional representation, f, given an input vector $\boldsymbol{x}$ and parameters, $\boldsymbol{\theta}$, for the ith experiment in the output vector $\boldsymbol{y}$.

$$MSE = \frac{1}{N}\sum_{i=1}^{N}(y_i - f(x_i|\theta))^2 \qquad (1.1) \qquad MAE = \frac{1}{N}\sum_{i=1}^{N}|y_i - f(x_i|\theta)| \qquad (1.2)$$

Ideally, it is possible to correct the structure of UNIFAC by making more effective use of the currently provided inputs; hence, statistical features based on said inputs are calculated for use in the symbolic regression model. Explicitly, we target the group interaction parameters, $\boldsymbol{\Psi}$ and the activity of isolated groups in the solution, $\boldsymbol{\Gamma}$ for which we extract statistical representations such as the mean, standard deviation and summation. In addition to these, the group surface area and volume contribution parameters, $\boldsymbol{q}$ and $\boldsymbol{r}$ are provided to account for potential improvements to the model's size and shape contribution. Finally, these inputs are appended to the aforementioned ANN-MACCS representations such that model enhancement can proceed via superior use of prior information as well as the introduction of new information.

2.4. Data Source

The data used in this work consists of a large dataset of binary systems collected as a subset of the DECHEMA Chemistry Data Series Vol. IX, where only datapoints extrapolated from finite dilution phase equilibria measurements were removed due to their tendency to be inaccurate. The data collected consists of experimental IDAC values for a wide range of binary systems.

3. Results and Discussion

The data is partitioned into two sets, that is training and testing, each of which contain 25,075 and 6,457 experiments respectively. A validation set of size 10,075 is then removed from the training set to be used in model construction. To reduce the dimensionality of the input space further, gradient boosting was applied in which feature importance charts were generated to identify the most important variables to be used in the subsequent symbolic regression model.

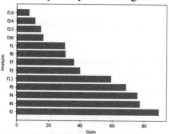

In this figure, features 0 to 11 represent the ANN-MACCS inputs, and any feature above f_{11} relates to a statistical feature based on UNIFAC inputs. The 12 most crucial features were selected for use in the symbolic regression procedure; 9 of which constitute the ANN-MACCS features, whilst variables 30, 23 and 24 denote the solute surface area contribution parameter q_{solute}, and the summation and mean statistics of the activities of isolated groups in the solution respectively. Construction of symbolic expressions using the selected input features prioritised the use the ANN-MACCS features, neglecting the remaining statistics, the three best resulting expressions of

Figure 2 - Feature importance chart depicting importance of the provided input features.

which are shown in Table 1. The finalised expression resulting from symbolic expression was a linear combination of the ANN-MACCS inputs; the average training, validation and testing results are 0.143, 0.170 and 0.171 respectively. In comparison, UNIFAC

Dortmund yields 0.265, 0.266 and 0.267 for the training, validation and testing MAEs. Parity plots of the testing results are shown in figure 3.

Table 1 – Three best performing expressions derived from symbolic regression.

Symbolic Expression		Testing MAE
$\sum a_i \cdot X_i,$	$i = \{2,7,8\}$	0.21
$\sum a_i \cdot X_i + X_3{}^3$	$i = \{2,7,8\}$	0.19
$\sum (a_i \cdot X_i) + b,$	$i = \{0,2,5,6,7,8\}$	0.17

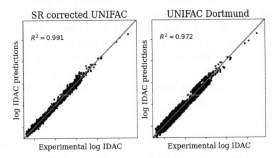

Figure 3 - Parity plot for SR corrected UNIFAC (left) and UNIFAC Dortmund (right).

From Figure 3, in the regions where UNIFAC provides relatively high errors, the generated symbolic expression is consistently able to improve the predictions; this suggests that the symbolic regression (SR) model has an increased spread of binary systems for which it can accurately predict compared to UNIFAC. Secondly, the SR model offers an improvement of 36.0 % with regards to the MAE over UNIFAC Dortmund, clearly indicating an improved capturing of underlying physical phenomena. To assess the SR models performance against literature data driven approaches, we use the work of Sanchez Medina et al., (2023) as a benchmark. Sanchez Medina et al., (2023) combined a graph neural network with the Gibbs-Helmholtz derived expression (GH-GNN) to improve the predictions on IDAC; the results they reported are compared to UNIFAC Dortmund, and the generated SR corrected UNIFAC model in Table 2.

Table 2 - Table comparing the testing MAE for the literature derived GH-GNN, the proposed symbolic regression model and UNIFAC Dortmund

Model	MAE (test set)
UNIFAC Dortmund	0.27
SR corrected UNIFAC Dortmund	0.17
GH-GNN	0.12

From Table 2, UNIFAC Dortmund performs the worst by a large margin, however, there also exists a notable difference in the performance of the proposed SR model and the GH-GNN model. This is to be expected since the architecture of the GNN is much more intricate than of the symbolic regression model, allowing for more system complexity to be captured. Even with this, it is clear that the difference in performance between the literature GH-GNN model and the SR method is much less than the difference between the SR method and UNIFAC Dortmund, this grants justification of the lessened accuracy by potential increases in interpretability.

4. Conclusion

In conclusion, the use of symbolic regression offers a unique solution to the lack of interpretability offered by current "black box" data driven approaches, whilst maintaining a high level of accuracy. The introduction of new structural information into the UNIFAC Dortmund method permitted the establishment of a robust framework in which accurate estimation of complex thermodynamic properties can be made. Furthermore, the application of symbolic regression enables one to identify the statistically most important input features rather easily when compared to other data driven alternatives. This methodology facilitates the extension of UNIFAC Dortmund to a greater range of temperature studies for a larger range of molecules which traditionally would lead to poor performance using UNIFAC Dortmund. Overall, this work demonstrates the combining innovative feature engineering of new structural inputs with dimensionality reduction techniques and symbolic regression based modelling, for the improvement of traditional thermodynamic predictive models.

Acknowledgements

E.I.S.M. is affiliated with the International Max Planck Research School for Advanced Methods in Process and Systems Engineering–IMPRS ProEng at the Max Planck Institute for Dynamics of Complex Technical Systems, Magdeburg

References

Brouwer, T., Kersten, S. R. A., Bargeman, G., & Schuur, B. (2021). Solvent pre-selection for extractive distillation using infinite dilution activity coefficients and the three-component Margules equation. *Separation and Purification Technology*, *276*, 119230.

Cheng, J.-S., Tang, M., & Chen, Y.-P. (2004). Correlation and comparison of the infinite dilution activity coefficients in aqueous and organic mixtures from a modified excess Gibbs energy model. *Fluid Phase Equilibria*, *217*, 205–216.

Damay, J., Jirasek, F., Kloft, M., Bortz, M., & Hasse, H. (2021). Predicting Activity Coefficients at Infinite Dilution for Varying Temperatures by Matrix Completion. *Industrial and Engineering Chemistry Research*, *60*(40), 14564–14578.

de Haan, A. B., Eral, H. B., & Schuur, B. (2020). *Industrial Separation Processes - Fundamentals*. De Gruyter.

Ivan, E., Medina, S., Linke, S., Stoll, M., & Sundmacher, K. (2023). Gibbs–Helmholtz graph neural network: capturing the temperature dependency of activity coefficients at infinite dilution. *Digital Discovery*, *2*(3), 781–798.

Lohmann, J., Joh, R., & Gmehling, J. (2001). From UNIFAC to modified UNIFAC (Dortmund). *Industrial and Engineering Chemistry Research*, *40*(3), 957–964.

Medina, E. I. S., Linke, S., Stoll, M., & Sundmacher, K. (2023). Gibbs–Helmholtz graph neural network: capturing the temperature dependency of activity coefficients at infinite dilution. *Digital Discovery*, *2*(3), 781–798.

Medina, E. I. S., & Sundmacher, K. (2023). Solvent pre-selection for extractive distillation using Gibbs-Helmholtz Graph Neural Networks. *Computer Aided Chemical Engineering*, *52*, 2037–2042.

Méndez Sevillano, D., van der Wielen, L. A. M., Hooshyar, N., & Ottens, M. (2014). MPP-UNIFAC, a predictive activity coefficient model for polyphenols. *Fluid Phase Equilibria*, *384*, 82–88.

Mutch, G. A. (2022). Electrochemical separation processes for future societal challenges. *Cell Reports Physical Science*, *3*(4), 100844.

Muzenda, E. (2013). *From UNIQUAC to modified UNIFAC Dortmund: a discussion*.

Flavio Manenti, Gintaras V. Reklaitis (Eds.), Proceedings of the 34th European Symposium on Computer Aided Process Engineering / 15th International Symposium on Process Systems Engineering (ESCAPE34/PSE24), June 2-6, 2024, Florence, Italy

Investigating the Reliability and Interpretability of state-of-the-art Machine Learning Frameworks for Chemical Retrosynthesis

Friedrich Hastedt,[a] Klaus Hellgardt,[a] Sophia Yaliraki,[a] Antonio del Rio Chanona,[a*] Dongda Zhang[b*]

[a]*Imperial College London, Exhibition Rd, South Kensington, London SW7 2BX, UK*
[b]*University of Manchester, Oxford Rd, Manchester M13 9PL, UK*
a.del-rio-chanona@imperial.ac.uk, dongda.zhang@manchester.ac.uk

Abstract

The discovery of synthesis routes for novel molecules with machine-learning (ML) tools has shown tremendous success in the field of retrosynthesis. Despite this achievement, inconsistent performance evaluation of existing models and the lack of black-box interpretability slow down the adoption within real-life applications and conceal model shortcomings. To address these challenges, we present an automated benchmarking pipeline for model evaluation and introduce an original interpretability study. Our results indicate that purely data-driven models suffer from infeasible reaction predictions and limited model interpretability. Particularly, for simple molecules, we observe that Graph Neural Networks identify critical functional groups within the product molecule, while the popular Transformer architecture fails to recognize the groups. As the molecule increases in complexity, we show that both models propose unfeasible disconnections without providing an interpretable explanation. Conversely, we find that ML frameworks, based on chemical reaction rules, exhibit the best model performance with inherent interpretability. We emphasize the importance of chemically meaningful descriptors as an input to deep-learning models. Our research offers valuable insights that can guide the future advancement of retrosynthesis frameworks within the scientific community.

Keywords: Chemical Retrosynthesis, Machine Learning, Interpretable AI, Graph Neural Networks, Transformers.

1. Introduction

The synthesis of novel molecules is both a costly and time-consuming process. Finding synthesis routes to the target molecule is traditionally carried out by experienced chemists in a retrosynthetic setting. Herein, retrosynthesis refers to the detection of possible disconnection sites in the target molecule to find suitable precursors in a backward fashion. As the number of discovered molecules increases, manual synthesis planning becomes impractical. Corey & Wipke (1969) proposed leveraging computational tools, by encoding reaction rules for automated retrosynthesis. Despite their effectiveness, these expert-based tools face scalability issues, limiting their applicability to handle the growing number of reactions and novel molecules. Segler et al (2017). overcame the limitations of hand-encoded reaction rules by leveraging machine-learning to learn directly from existing chemical reactions within the literature. Their model is capable of directly identifying the best reaction rule (template) from literature precedent. Since their publication, three distinct branches of ML retrosynthesis have emerged: i) Template-based classification (Chen & Jung, 2021), ii) Template-free sequence translation (Liu et al, 2017), and iii) Semi-template graph edit (Sacha et al.,2021). As the naming suggests, the different architectures differ depending on the inclusion or exclusion of reaction templates. Template-based models follow the principle suggested by Segler et. al., that is to assign a specific template to the product molecule (Fig. 1a). Template-free models treat retrosynthesis as a SMILES-to-SMILES translation problem. Nowadays, this is achieved using the Transformer architecture (Fig. 1b). Finally, semi-template models perform edits on the molecular graph to arrive at the reactant molecules. The model identifies the most probable disconnection site (*i.e.,* bond to break) within the molecule, known as the reaction center. This process yields chemically invalid fragments, namely synthons, which are transformed into reactants in the synthon completion step (Fig. 1c).

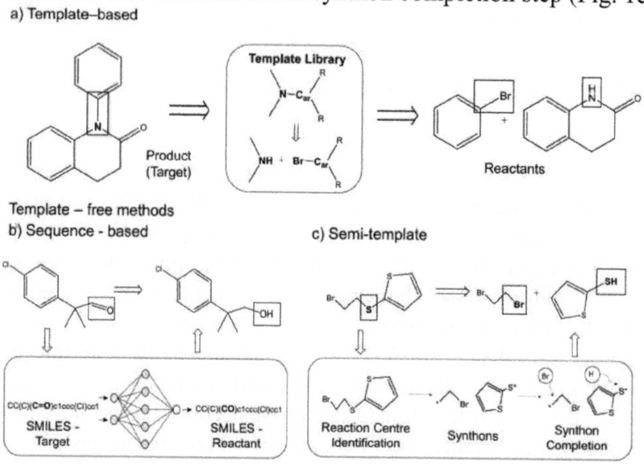

Figure 1: Overview of the three different retrosynthesis architectures.

Whilst each category holds its merit, performance comparison between frameworks has been difficult due to the absence of a robust and impartial evaluation metric. The current evaluation metric, top-k accuracy, biasedly rewards models that effectively recall the reaction provided in the existing dataset. However, it does not measure the ability of retrosynthesis models to propose chemically feasible reactions for unseen molecules. Despite this acknowledged shortcoming, recent research papers continue to utilize the top-k accuracy (due to ease of accessibility) to advertise the superiority of their work over existing models Furthermore, the lack of black-box interpretability conceals current model limitations. This work aims to overcome these challenges by introducing an automated open-source benchmarking pipeline to compare the performance of twelve state-of-the-art frameworks within the three retrosynthesis categories. The pipeline is complemented by an innovative interpretability study with the aim of revealing the extent of chemical knowledge acquired by popular deep-learning architectures.

2. Methodology

2.1 Benchmark Pipeline

The case study for the benchmarking pipeline is based on the open-source USPTO-50k dataset, which is commonly used for evaluating ML-based retrosynthesis frameworks. The benchmarking pipeline comprises several metrics as shown in Figure 2. Each metric measures a different desired property of the framework. While the current metric (top-k accuracy) only checks for the presence of the database (recall), we assess the model's predictions for chemical feasibility, diversity, and validity.

Investigating the reliability and interpretability of state-of-the-art machine
learning frameworks for chemical retrosynthesis

2709

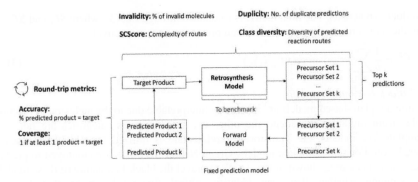

Figure 2: Evaluation metrics for algorithmic benchmarking. The round-trip metrics utilize
a forward synthesis model to compare the target product to the predicted products.

Below we outline the different evaluation metrics employed. As a note, the retrosynthesis model returns k predictions (precursors) per target molecule t. Therefore, the total number of predictions for the test database is $T \cdot k$, where T is the number of molecules within the database ($T = 5007$ molecules). Within this work, k is taken to equal ten.

Round-trip - To check the chemical feasibility of a reaction, experimental validation is desired. However, this is not realisable for $T \cdot k$ reactions. Instead, we employ a fixed synthesis prediction model (inverse problem to retrosynthesis), to predict the reaction outcome for a given precursor set. This ad-hoc replacement allows us to check the cycle-consistency of a reaction. In short, if the target product t is the same as the reaction outcome p for a given precursor set i, the reaction prediction is assumed to be feasible when tested experimentally (Figure 2). The round-trip is scored through the rt-accuracy which measures the percentage of precursor predictions, given set i is cycle-consistent:

$$Acc_{rt,k} = \frac{1}{Tk} \sum_1^T \sum_1^k \mathbb{1}_P \qquad (1) \qquad Dup = \frac{1}{T} \sum_1^T \frac{z_{idv} - 1}{k - 1} \qquad (2)$$

Diversity - For retrosynthesis frameworks designed for synthetic chemists, it is crucial that the system can offer a broad range of reactions covering various fundamental chemical transformations. To measure the diversity of a model's prediction, we classify each reaction per target molecule into ten diverse reaction superclasses from the reaction ontology (RXNO). For each target, the number of diverse reactions is counted, and an average is calculated over all reactions in the database to obtain the diversity metric.

Duplicity - A good retrosynthesis framework should not propose the same reaction twice as this reduces the number of reaction predictions returned by the model. The number of duplicate reactions is calculated through Eq. (2), where z_{idv} equals the number of unique reactions per target molecule:

Invalidity - Similar to duplicate prediction, a retrosynthesis model should not return predictions where the reactant molecules within precursor set i are invalid *e.g.,* violating valency requirements. The invalidity is measured in a similar fashion to Eq. (1), where the indicator function $\mathbb{1}_p$ assumes a value of 1, if all reactant molecules within set i are valid; otherwise, it assumes a value of 0.

Route Complexity – To measure the model's ability to propose less complex and more accessible reactants for a given product target, we utilize a synthetic accessibility metric. Particularly, the metric (SCScore) assigns a higher value to more complex molecules. A good retrosynthesis framework should (in general) reduce the SCScore when going from product to reactants. The final metric is calculated through Eq. (3), where SC_t and $\boldsymbol{SC}_{set\ i}$ are the scores for the target molecule and precursor set i, respectively:

$$\overline{\Delta SC} = \frac{1}{k} \sum_{1}^{k} (SC_t - \max(\boldsymbol{SC}_{set\ i})_k) \qquad (3)$$

2.2 Black-box Interpretability

While template-based models are inherently interpretable due to the inclusion of reaction rules from literature precedent, the other two retrosynthesis categories are not. For template-free models, the Transformer architecture is utilized for SMILES sequence translation. For semi-template models, Graph Neural Networks are employed to predict the reaction centre as shown in Fig. 1c. We unravel the black-box nature of these models by gauging whether they can identify critical functional groups that lead to thermodynamic stabilization of the reaction product over the reactant precursors on six case studies (with two studies presented herein). Below, the methodologies are outlined.

2.2.1 Graph Neural Networks (GNNs)

We train two state-of-the-art *GNN* architectures, namely D-MPNN and EGAT, to identify the reaction center within the product molecule. To find important functional groups that contribute significantly to the model's prediction, we utilize a graph masking algorithm (*GNNExplainer* - Ying et al., 2019). The Explainer identifies nodes (atoms) in the molecule as shown in Figure 3.

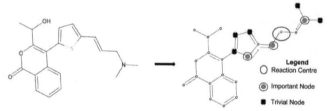

Figure 3: Node importance as identified by the GNNExplainer.

2.2.2 Transformers

To obtain the atom importance from the Transformer, we extract the attention weights from the two different Transformer models, namely vanilla attention, and masked attention. The attention weights hold the importance between tokens (atoms) in product and reactant SMILES sequences. These weights are usually visualised as attention maps in a 2-dimensional space. We plot the attention weights directly on the molecule and infer the atom's importance visually (see Figure 5).

3. Results and Discussion

The benchmarking results are presented in Table 1. Analysing and optimizing each metric individually is unfeasible. Instead, we seek to optimize the rt-accuracy and place soft-constraints on all other metrics given by: $Div \geq 2.5$, $Dup \geq 0.8$, $Inv \leq 10\ \%$ and $\overline{\Delta SC} \geq 0.35$. It is observed that no category performs best for all metrics. However, template-based models are seen to have (overall) the highest rt-accuracy with very low number of invalid and duplicate predictions. Semi-template models have competitive rt-accuracy; however, they suffer from a larger number of invalid predictions. Template-free models exhibit on average the lowest rt-accuracy with low reaction diversity. To reason the inferior performance of semi- and template-free models, we uncover the black-box nature within the interpretability study below.

Investigating the reliability and interpretability of state-of-the-art machine learning frameworks for chemical retrosynthesis

2711

Table 1: Performance comparison for the retrosynthesis categories. Algorithms in **bold** are 2 best within category. <u>Underlined</u> values violate constraints by ≤ 10%. <u>Double-underlined</u> by > 10%

Algorithms	Rt-Accuracy	Diversity	Invalidity	Duplicity	SCScore
Semi-template					
MEGAN	0.78	3.02	<u>10.2</u>	0.90	0.36
GraphRetro	0.77	<u>1.90</u>	7.4	<u>0.47</u>	0.35
RetroXpert	0.46	2.67	<u>18.6</u>	0.91	0.42
G2Retro	0.69	3.06	-	0.98	<u>0.32</u>
Template-free					
Chemformer	0.86	<u>1.23</u>	0.7	<u>0.12</u>	0.47
Graph2Smiles	0.43	<u>2.29</u>	<u>35.8</u>	0.90	0.46
Retroformer	0.68	<u>2.44</u>	8.0	0.83	0.43
GTA	0.72	<u>2.37</u>	6.3	<u>0.76</u>	0.47
TiedTransformer	0.69	2.85	6.0	0.93	0.39
Template-based					
GLN	0.85	<u>2.30</u>	0.2	<u>0.64</u>	0.41
LocalRetro	0.81	3.0	0.5	0.95	0.4
MHNReact	0.78	3.17	0.5	1.0	<u>0.3</u>

The first case study of the interpretability study is a simple amide bond formation (Figure 4, S.1). This amide bond is particularly stabilized due to electron conjugation of the amide group with the carbonyl in the reaction center. The second case study (S.2) is an S_N2 reaction which is stabilized by the stronger C-N bond compared to the C-Br bond. The molecule in S.2 is more complex and contains several possible disconnection sites.

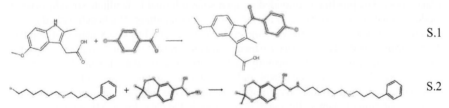

S.1

S.2

Figure 4: Interpretability Case Studies. S.1 – Amide Bond, S.2 – Substitution Reaction.

a) Vanilla Attention – Transformer b) Masked Attention – Transformer c) Node Importance - EGAT d) Node Importance - DMPNN

Figure 5: S.1 - Atom importance for different model architectures.

From Figure 5, it is seen that both GNN models can identify the stabilizing functional group (C-N bond, subplots c/d) whereas the Transformer models do not (subplots a/b). For S.2, no model can provide adequate reasoning for their prediction (Figure 6). In fact, both GNN models propose different disconnection sites compared to Figure 4, S.2. The EGAT model suggests an inefficient benzene ring attachment (subplot e), whereas the D-MPNN suggests a C-C bond formation without providing much interpretability for its prediction (subplots d & f). This shows that when the molecule increases in complexity, purely data-driven models struggle, possibly due to a lack of chemical awareness.

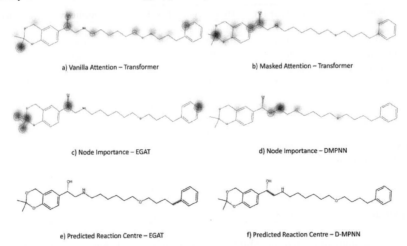

a) Vanilla Attention – Transformer

b) Masked Attention – Transformer

c) Node Importance – EGAT

d) Node Importance – DMPNN

e) Predicted Reaction Centre – EGAT

f) Predicted Reaction Centre – D-MPNN

Figure 6: S.2 - Atom importance and reaction center prediction for different architectures.

4. Conclusions

In this work, we present an automated benchmark pipeline for ML-based retrosynthesis frameworks. The pipeline is provided in open-source format to facilitate straightforward model evaluation and comparison for the scientific community. We benchmarked a vast selection of frameworks on the pipeline and uncovered the black-box nature of popular deep-learning methods. The performance evaluation revealed that "simpler" template-based classification models currently outperform purely data-driven deep-learning frameworks. Furthermore, the GNN and Transformer architectures lack interpretable explanations for their predictions. Future work within the field should therefore focus on the incorporation of chemically aware descriptors in the data-driven ML models such as bond energy or electronegativity. This would render the model more interpretable and likely improve reaction feasibility.

References

Chen, S., & Jung, Y. (2021). Deep Retrosynthetic Reaction Prediction using Local Reactivity and Global Attention. JACS Au, 1(10), 1612–1620.

Corey, E. J., & Wipke, W. T. (1969). Computer-Assisted design of complex organic syntheses. Science, 166(3902)

Liu, B., Ramsundar, B., Kawthekar, P., Shi, J., Gomes, J., Luu Nguyen, Q., Ho, S., Sloane, J., Wender, P., & Pande, V. (2017). Retrosynthetic reaction prediction using neural sequence-to-sequence models. ACS Central Science, 3(10), 1103–1113.

Sacha, M., Błaż, M., Byrski, P., Dąbrowski-Tumański, P., Chromiński, M., Loska, R., Włodarczyk-Pruszyński, P., & Jastrzębski, S. (2021). Molecule edit graph attention network: Modeling chemical reactions as sequences of graph edits. Journal of Chemical Information and Modeling, 61(7), 3273–3284.

Segler, M. H. S., Kogej, T., Tyrchan, C., & Waller, M. P. (2017). Generating focused molecule libraries for drug discovery with recurrent neural networks. ACS Central Science, 120–131.

Ying, R., Bourgeois, D., You, J., Zitnik, M., & Leskovec, J. (2019). GNNExplainer: Generating Explanations for Graph Neural Networks. Arxiv.

Flavio Manenti, Gintaras V. Reklaitis (Eds.), Proceedings of the 34th European Symposium on Computer Aided Process Engineering / 15th International Symposium on Process Systems Engineering (ESCAPE34/PSE24), June 2-6, 2024, Florence, Italy

Application of Artificial Neural Networks in Predicting the Operational Behavior of an Indirect Freezing Desalination System

Caio F. dos Santos,[a] Flávio V. Silva[a]

[a]University of Campinas, Cidade Universitária Zeferino Vaz Av. Albert Einstein, 500, Zipcode 13083-852, Campinas-SP, Brazil

flaviovs@unicamp.br

Abstract

The current and growing shortage of drinking water is a reality across the planet. More than 97% of the water available on the planet is salty and unfit for human consumption or agricultural use. Desalination processes serve as viable alternatives for supplying drinking water in regions facing water scarcity. Typically, areas most impacted by drought are less technologically developed, which hinders the utilization of highly complex processes, such as the reverse osmosis method. Freeze desalination is presented as a simple, affordable, and viable alternative to saltwater treatment processes in drought-affected areas; however, knowledge about the dynamics of the process remains nebulous. In this context, artificial neural networks were developed to predict the fraction of ice formed in the mixture based on the initial NaCl concentration and the NaCl concentration in the brine. The project results indicate that artificial intelligence techniques are effective in predicting the dynamic behavior of the process with an average error of 1.29%.

Keywords: desalination, freezing, neural networks, artificial intelligence.

1. Introduction

The evolution of global warming and poor water resource management, coupled with the planet's increasing population and its demand for clean water, has led to a severe water shortage for approximately 4 billion people for at least one month out of the twelve months in a year. (Jafari Shalamzari and Zhang, 2018; Khatibi and Arjjumend, 2019). The risks of water scarcity are associated with two main factors: the intensive use of water, surpassing its natural replenishment capacity, and human activities that harm the hydrological cycle. Water resources are crucial for the sustainable development of countries.

In this regard, in 2015, the United Nations established the Sustainable Development Goals (SDGs) to guide national policies and international co-operation activities for the next 15 years, in line with the 2030 Agenda. The SDGs consist of 17 objectives aimed at the sustainable development of nations. The sixth goal focuses on ensuring access to clean water and sanitation for all people, regardless of their location.

Considering the guidelines established by the United Nations and the imminent threat of water scarcity and rationing for the global population, water desalination methods are being studied worldwide. These water desalination methods involve processing saltwater to transform it into potable water. In 2017, the capacity of water desalination plants reached a volume of 99.8 million cubic meters per day (GWI, 2018). One of these alternatives is freezing desalination, which proves to be an efficient and viable option for implementation. The potability in terms of sodium chloride concentration is defined by the World Health Organization as values below 0.4 gNaCl/100mL. However, starting from 0.2 gNaCl/100mL, the water exhibits an uncomfortable salty taste. In this work, we will define potability as values below 0.4 gNaCl/100mL. (ORGANIZATION et al., 2011). Although studies on freeze crystallization dated back several centuries, the understanding of ice crystallization and growth in a slurry/mushy ice, salt rejection during the process is still chaotic and unsystematic. For instance, the key parameters affecting the freezing time, cooling rate, cooling source temperature, solution composition, and ice quality are not available despite the numerous reports of experimental studies on FD (Janajreh et al., 2023).

An alternative that can be used in remote areas is freezing desalination, which relies on a well-established cooling system and has low energy costs that can be supplied using clean energy sources such as wind or solar power. Water desalination by freezing systems has been studied and developed worldwide (Barma et al., 2021; El Kadi and Janajreh, 2017; Kalista et al., 2018; Mahdavi et al., 2011; Morillo et al., 2014) and proves to be a simple, cost-effective, and viable alternative for implementation in the Brazilian semi-arid region. Due to being a multivariable and chaotic system, artificial neural networks were employed in constructing the predictive model of NaCl concentration enclosed in ice to determine the best endpoint of the freezing cycle, enabling the methodology to be replicated in indirect freezing desalination equipment.

2. Materials and Methods

2.1. Curve of Concentration Relation with Conductivity and Temperature.

For the execution of freezing cycles, the MK-70 equipment from MLW. It consists of a 15-liter ultracryostat bath that reaches a temperature of -25°C at the surface of the coil and exchanges heat with the saltwater to be frozen. The equipment has a physical limitation of ice formation of up to 80% to ensure upward mechanical agitation.

The monitoring of brine conductivity during the freezing cycles was carried out using the Orion 3-Star conductivity meter from Thermo Scientific. The probe used provides conductivity data in mS/cm and temperature data in degrees Celsius. The temperature sensor is capable of measuring temperatures above -5°C. The solutions were prepared using deionized water and sodium chloride. To develop the predictive model, ten standard solutions of varying concentrations were prepared: 0.05, 0.1, 0.25, 0.5, 1.0, 2.0, 3.0, 6.0, 9.0, and 12.0 grams of NaCl per 100 mL of deionized water. The temperature of the solutions was varied from 1 to 20°C, with conductivity recorded at each temperature. A curve fitting was performed according to Equation 1 to obtain the parameters a, b, c, and d.

$$C[g/100mLH_2O](Cond, T) = a * Cond[\mu S/cm]^b * exp^{(c*T[°C])} + d \qquad (1)$$

2.2. Application of Mass Balance for Determination of Formed Ice Fraction

The initial concentration was varied in 6 ranges: 11, 6.5, 3.4, 1.6, 0.7, and 0.35 grams of NaCl per 100 grams of H2O in fractions ranging from 20% to 80% of ice formation.

Each freezing cycle will provide data on the initial concentration of NaCl, the final concentration of NaCl in the brine, and the final concentration of NaCl enclosed in the ice. From this data, the mass balance of Equation 2 can be applied to obtain the fraction of ice formed in the cycle.

$$\%Ice(C_0, C_{Ice}, C_{Brine}) = 1 - \frac{C_0 - C_{Ice}}{C_{Brine} - C_{Ice}} \qquad (2)$$

2.3 Regressor Artificial Neural Networks Applied to Prediction of Formed Ice Fraction.
The chosen artificial intelligence for building the predictor was the Artificial Neural
Network Regressor, which aims to fit the training data provided during training. The
model's goal is to predict the ice fraction based on the initial concentration of the cycle
and the radio of the dynamic concentration of sodium chloride in the brine described in
equation 3.

$$RSC_{Brine} = \frac{C_{Brine}}{C_0} \tag{3}$$

2.4 Application of Mass Balance for Determining NaCl Concentration in Formed Ice
With this information, it is possible to reapply the mass balance and determine the
concentration of sodium chloride enclosed in the ice, as described in Equation 4.

$$C_{Ice}(C_0, C_{Brine}, \%Ice) = \frac{C_0 - (1 - \%Ice) * C_{Brine}}{\%Ice} \tag{4}$$

2.5 Regressor Artificial Neural Networks Applied to Prediction of Formed Ice Fraction.
The inputs to the Artificial Neural Network (ANN) are the Initial Concentration of the
solution and the Ratio of Salt Concentration in the Brine.
The output of the ANN is the fraction of ice formed and training of the neural network
was carried out in Python, using the SciKit-Learn library, based on the block diagram
shown in Figure 1. The Scikit-Learn is a machine learning tool known for providing
efficient implementations of traditional machine learning algorithms in the Python
programming language.

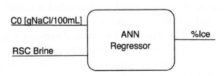

Figure 1 - ANN Regressor Block Diagram

For monitoring the concentration of sodium chloride in the brine during the freezing
process, it was necessary to apply Equation 1, this time fitting the curve at temperatures
below 0°C and obtaining new values for a, b, c, and d. The curve-fitting data was obtained
during the freezing cycles. At the end of the freezing cycles, the brine's conductivity and
temperature data were stored for curve fitting alongside the sodium chloride
concentration values.

2.6 Freezing Cycle Termination Method.
The determination of the termination point for the freezing cycles will be evaluated based
on the maximum quotient of the obtained potable water yield and the number of cycles
required to achieve it, as per Equation 5.

$$Quotient = \frac{\%Productivity}{Cycles} \tag{5}$$

3. Results and Discussions

3.1. Curve of Concentration Relation with Conductivity and Temperature.
Data was collected by correlating the concentration of NaCl in the solution with
conductivity and temperature, and curve fitting was performed according to Equation 1.
The parameters a, b, c, and d were adjusted for two different concentration ranges, one
greater than 2 grams per 100 mL of water and the other less than 2 grams per 100 mL of
water. Table 1 illustrates the parameters for each model.

Table 1 - Predictor Parameters for Concentration, Models 1, 2, and 3.

	Model 1	Model 2	Model 3
Parameter	$C \leq 2g/100mL$	$C \geq 2g/100mL$	$-5°C \leq T \leq 0°C$
a	0.08422454	0.02735635	0.10068852
b	1.10092099	1.37416940	1.02826665
c	-0.02684441	-0.03232585	-0.07030928
d	0.00813535	0.59426096	-0.01505198

The mean percentage errors attributed to models 1, 2, and 3 were 1.427%, 0.963%, and
0.60%, respectively.

3.2 Regressor Artificial Neural Networks Applied to Prediction of Formed Ice Fraction.
Using the data from partial indirect freezing cycles performed, an artificial neural network
with two inputs and one output was designed, as illustrated in Figure 1. The available data
was normalized and divided into training and testing datasets, with a ratio of 19.51% (33
for training and 8 for testing). The training of the neural network was conducted using the
GridSearch tool to determine the best architecture. The hyperparameters that showed the
best performance included three layers with 87, 174, and 87 neurons, respectively, and
the rectified linear unit (ReLU) activation function.
The use of two inputs and one output in building the model allows for the visualization
of a response surface in three dimensions within the operating values of the equipment,
as shown in Figure 2.

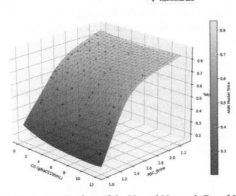

Figure 2 - Response Surface of the Neural Network-Based Model.

It is observed that the network adapted well to the training data without overfitting issues, achieving a mean absolute percentage error of 2.087%.

3.3 Application of Mass Balance for Determining NaCl Concentration in Formed Ice

With an understanding of the system's dynamics, it is possible to determine the moment to conclude the freezing cycle. By applying the mass balance on the response surface of the neural network illustrated in Figure 2, it can be observed in Figure 3 that salt encapsulation is minimally influenced by the increase in the ice fraction produced per cycle.

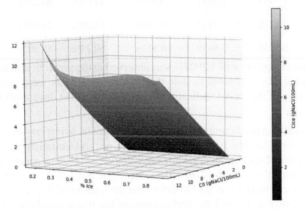

Figure 3 - Response Surface of NaCl Concentration in Ice.

3.4 Freezing Cycle Termination Method.

The conclusion of the freezing cycle was defined as the highest possible ice formation value (80%) in cycles that do not achieve potability. From the definition of the freezing cycle termination point, it is possible to predict the number of cycles required to achieve potability and the corresponding total ice fraction obtained by the system at each of the initial concentrations addressed during the neural network training. The data has been illustrated on Figures 4 and 5.

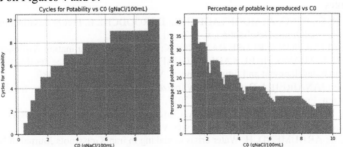

Figure 4 - Number of cycles to achieve potability.   Figure 5 - Process Yield.

3.5 Validation Data.

The validation of the model will be carried out through the desalination of a solution with 3.0265 g NaCl/100mL. The model predicted that potability would be reached in 6 cycles, achieving 0.4 g NaCl/100mL with a yield of 19.26%. The freezing cycles were executed on the equipment, Table 2 illustrates the results obtained in each prediction.

Table 2 - Model validation with real freezing data

Cycle	C0	C Brine	C Ice	% Ice	%Ice Model	% Error
1	3.0265	6.6983	2.1961	81.56%	80.84%	0.8724%
2	2.1786	4.7026	1.5361	79.71%	80.38%	0.8467%
3	1.5455	3.2826	1.1319	80.77%	80.22%	0.6841%
4	1.1303	2.3821	0.8375	81.04%	80.20%	1.0407%
5	0.8239	1.7115	0.6164	81.05%	79.90%	1.4228%
6	0.5936	0.8659	0.4176	60.74%	58.99%	2.8878%

An average percentage error of 1.2924% was observed in the prediction of the ice fraction formed in each cycle. It is valid to state that none of these data were used in the prior training or testing of the model, indicating the robustness of the developed predictor.

4. Conclusions

ANN was effective in predicting the fraction of ice formed, using known input variables such as the initial solute concentration and brine concentration during freezing. The concentration of sodium chloride enclosed in ice crystals was accurately calculated using the predictive model of the ice fraction and a mass balance. The obtained neural model was able to determine the number of freezing cycles required to achieve potability levels and the performance of the freeze desalination process with minimal   error.

Future work could investigate variations in the coil surface temperature or altering the coil's geometry. These variables can be incorporated into neural network training and operated dynamically in the desalination process to achieve better results.

Acknowledgments

The authors would like to thank the National Council for Scientific and Technological Development (CNPq) grant number 131644/2021-1.

References

BARMA, M. C.; PENG, Z.; MOGHTADERI, B.; DOROODCHI, E. Freeze desalination of drops of saline solutions. Desalination, v. 517, p. 115265, 2021.

GWI. DESALINATION & REUSE HANDBOOK: International Desalination Association, 2018.

JANAJREH, I., ZHANG, H., EL KADI, K., GHAFFOUR, N., 2023. Freeze desalination: Current research development and future prospects. Water Research 229, 119389.

KADI, K. E.; JANAJREH, I. Desalination by freeze crystallization: an overview. Int. J. Therm. Environ. Eng, v. 15, n. 2, p. 103–110, 2017.

KALISTA, B.; SHIN, H.; CHO, J.; JANG, A. Current development and future prospect review of freeze desalination. Desalination, Elsevier, v. 447, p. 167–181, 2018.

KHATIBI, S.; ARJJUMEND, H. Water crisis in making in iran. Grassroots Journal of Natural Resources, v. 2, n. 3, p. 45–54, 2019.

MAHDAVI, M.; MAHVI, A. H.; NASSERI, S.; YUNESIAN, M. Application of freezing to the desalination of saline water. Arabian Journal for Science and Engineering, Springer, v. 36, p. 1171–1177, 2011.

MORILLO, J.; USERO, J.; ROSADO, D.; BAKOURI, H. E.; RIAZA, A.; BERNAOLA, F.-J. Comparative study of brine management technologies for desalination plants.Desalination, Elsevier, v. 336, p. 32–49, 2014.

SHALAMZARI, M. J.; ZHANG, W. Assessing water scarcity using the water poverty index (wpi) in golestan province of iran. Water, MDPI, v. 10, n. 8, p. 1079, 2018.

Flavio Manenti, Gintaras V. Reklaitis (Eds.), Proceedings of the 34th European Symposium on Computer Aided Process Engineering / 15th International Symposium on Process Systems Engineering (ESCAPE34/PSE24), June 2-6, 2024, Florence, Italy

Towards Sustainable WWTP Operations: Forecasting Energy Consumption with Explainable Disentangled Graph Convolutional Networks

Louis Allen[a], Joan Cordiner[a],*

[a]The Department of Chemical and Biological Engineering, University of Sheffield, Sheffield, S1 3JD, United Kingdom

*j.cordiner@sheffield.ac.uk

Abstract

Understanding and predicting factors influencing energy consumption in wastewater treatment plants (WWTP) is critically important. Such insights offer opportunities for significant cost savings and can facilitate the operation of more environmentally sustainable processes. Machine learning (ML) has shown promise in modeling the complex non-linear relationships inherent to WWTPs, however many models suffer from interpretability issues limiting their real-world application. Furthermore, conventional ML methods often struggle with long-term forecasting in the face of variable input data, a common challenge in WWTP operations.

Our study proposes a novel approach that combines operating sensor data with core chemical engineering knowledge to address these challenges. We propose a disentangled graph convolutional network tailored for time series forecasting, drawing upon sensor data from a WWTP in Melbourne. This method learns disentangled representations of latent factors within the dataset which can help explain consumption trends, offering insight that can help reduce overall energy use. When benchmarked against traditional ML models, our approach exhibited superior prediction accuracy and model reliability. Our findings underscore the potential of integrating domain-specific knowledge into data-driven methodologies, especially in intricate manufacturing settings. The standout performance of disentangled graph convolutional networks, as evidenced in our study, offers a promising avenue for delivering transparent and actionable energy consumption forecasts, empowering WWTP operators to make decisions that enhance process sustainability.

Keywords: Energy Forecasting, Explainable Machine Learning, Wastewater Treatment

1. Introduction

Wastewater treatment is a critical challenge for urban communities, vital for health and various activities (Ahmad and Chen, 2018). As urban populations grow exponentially, the demand for clean water intensifies, posing global challenges like climate change and increased energy consumption in wastewater treatment, constituting 40% of urban energy usage (Bagherzadeh et al., 2021). Addressing this issue is crucial for sustainable global goals.

Understanding the drivers of high energy consumption is pivotal for reducing overall energy usage in wastewater treatment plants (WWTPs), and long-term energy consumption forecasts are key for informed decision-making (Ahmad and Chen, 2018;

Bagherzadeh et al., 2021). However, forecasting energy consumption in WWTPs is intricate due to the nonlinear nature of the biological reaction process and diverse influencing factors (Li et al., 2019; Jiang et al., 2014).

Machine learning (ML) has shown promise in accurately capturing consumption trends, but concerns persist about model robustness to noise (Picos-Benítez et al., 2020; Bagherzadeh et al., 2021; Alali et al., 2023). Graph convolutional networks (GCNs) offer a novel approach for complex time series forecasting, explicitly leveraging the relational structure of data to capture complex dependencies and patterns (Hu et al., 2022). Combining GCNs with long short-term memory (LSTM) models enhances accuracy in time series forecasting, as demonstrated in financial time series forecasting (Valaskova et al., 2023). However, this graph-based approach has not been applied to energy consumption (EC) forecasting in WWTPs, possibly due to GCN architectures neglecting latent factors, limiting robustness and explainability (Ma et al., 2019).

To address these challenges, this paper introduces DisenGC-LSTM, a novel approach combining disentangled graph convolutional networks with LSTM architectures for accurate and explainable time series forecasting in WWTPs (Ma et al., 2019). DisenGC-LSTM, aims to overcome the limitations of traditional GCNs in neglecting latent factors and compromising model robustness and explainability (Ma et al., 2019).

2. Methodology

2.1. DisenConv Layer

Let $G = (V, E)$ be an undirected graph where V is a finite set of nodes such that $n = |V|$ corresponds to the number of variables in a dataset $\mathbf{X} \in \mathbb{R}^{m \times n}$, where each node u has a feature vector $\mathbf{x} \in \mathbb{R}^m$. E is a set of edges such that $e_{u,v} \in E$ shows the existence of an edge between nodes u and v.

Figure 1 shows the disentangled convolutional layer which outputs a disentangled representation of a node $\mathbf{y}_u = [\mathbf{c_1}, \mathbf{c_2}, \dots, \mathbf{c_K}]$ where $\mathbf{c}_k \in \mathbb{R}^{\frac{h}{k}}$ describes the kth aspect of node u by iteratively searching each of the neighbors of node u and assigning a probability that the nodes are connected due independent factor k ($1 \leq k \leq K$). This is done by projecting the feature vector into different subspaces:

$$\mathbf{z}_{u,k} = \frac{\sigma(\mathbf{W}_k^\mathsf{T}\mathbf{x}_u + \mathbf{b}_k)}{\left|\left|\sigma(\mathbf{W}_k^\mathsf{T}\mathbf{x}_u + \mathbf{b}_k)\right|\right|_2}, \tag{1}$$

where $\mathbf{W}_k \in \mathbb{R}^{m \times \frac{h}{k}}$ and $\mathbf{b}_k$ are the parameters of channel k and σ is a ReLU activation function, h is the size of the output of the DisenConv layer. Since feature vector $\mathbf{x}_u$ may be incomplete for a real world system, we cannot directly map $\mathbf{z}_{u,k}$ to $\mathbf{c}_k$. Instead, Ma et al. propose a neighborhood routing mechanism to iteratively mine information from the surrounding neighbors of node u to construct $\mathbf{c}_k$. We only want to use information pertinent to factor k and therefore should look to only collect information from neighbors of node u connected *because* of factor k. To do this, let $p_{v,k}$ represent the probability that node u and v are connected due to factor k, where $p_{v,k} \geq 0$ and $\sum_{k'=1}^{K} p_{v,k'} = 1$.

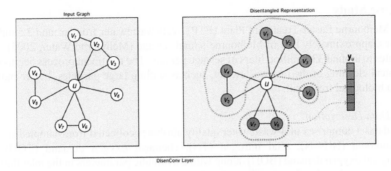

Figure 1: Disentangled convolutional layer (DisenConv) which takes in a graph and produces a disentangled representation of the graph for each node shown here for node u.

The neighborhood routing mechanism iteratively infers a value for $p_{v,k}$ before constructing $\mathbf{c}_k$, starting by initializing $p_{v,k}^{(1)} \alpha \exp(\frac{\mathbf{z}_{v,k}^{\mathsf{T}}\mathbf{z}_{u,k}}{\tau})$ where τ is a hyper-parameter that controls the 'hardness' of the assignment (Ma et al., 2019). The mechanism searches for the largest cluster in each subspace, with the constraint that a neighbor can only belong to a single subspace. Since each channel receives different subsets of neighbors we can maintain that each channel represents an independent factor. The following are completed on every iteration:

$$\mathbf{c}_k^{(t)} = \frac{\mathbf{z}_u^k + \sum_{v:e_{u,v}\in G} p_{v,k}^{t-1}\mathbf{z}_{v,k}}{\left|\left|\mathbf{z}_u^k + \sum_{v:e_{u,v}\in G} p_{v,k}^{t-1}\mathbf{z}_{v,k}\right|\right|_2}, \tag{2}$$

$$p_{v,k}^{(t)} = \frac{\exp(\mathbf{z}_{v,k}^{\mathsf{T}}\mathbf{c}_k^{(t)}/\tau)}{\sum_{k'=1}^{K} \exp(\mathbf{z}_{v,k'}^{\mathsf{T}}\mathbf{c}_{k'}^{(t)}/\tau)}, \tag{3}$$

for each iteration where $t = 2, ..., T$. The iterations output $\mathbf{c}_k = \mathbf{c}_k^{(T)}$ where $\mathbf{c}_k$ is the center of the subspace. This DisenConv layer can be integrated into a recurrent neural network architecture to enhance the accuracy and explainability of time-series forecasting models.

2.2. Time-series Forecasting with DisenConv Layers

Given $G_{\text{WWTP}} = (V, E)$ is an undirected graph representation of a WWTP, $\mathbf{X} \in \mathbb{R}^{m \times n}$ is a dataset such that $n = |V|$ is the number of features in the dataset and m is the number of time steps in the dataset, we aim to forecast the energy consumption of the plant. To do this we integrate the DisenConv layer described above with a long-short-term memory (LSTM) architecture (DisenGC-LSTM) architecture in which latent factors are disentangled through the convolution, and temporal information is learned by the LSTM. This is an adaptation of the GC-LSTM model demonstrated for link prediction by (Chen et al., 2021). The impact of the DisenConv layer can therefore be directly observed by comparing the proposed DisenGC-LSTM model with a GC-LSTM model where the architecture is kept identical apart from the convolution method. The models will be assessed quantitatively using the root-mean-squared error (RMSE) and R^2 value.

3. Case Study

The Melbourne Easter Treatment Plant (ETP) treats wastewater from around 2.5 million homes, approximately half of Melbourne's total sewage (Melbourne Water, 2005). This equates to around 330 million liters of sewage per day. The treatment process begins with physical cleaning of the raw wastewater, such as settling large particles, before moving on to biological treatment.

3.1. Data Description

The dataset comprises of 4 wastewater quality attributes collected from sampled sensors - Ammonia (NH4-N), total nitrogen (TN), chemical oxygen demand (COD) and biological oxygen demand (BOD), along with 2 hydraulic parameters in the inlet flowrate of sewage and outlet flowrate from the plant. Since climate effects have a significant impact on the treatment of wastewater data from the Melbourne airport weather station was joined to give an augmented dataset (Bagherzadeh et al., 2021). This offers an additional 9 features including average temperature (T_{avg}), maximum temperature (T_{max}), minimum temperature (T_{min}), atmospheric pressure (AP), average humidity (H), total precipitation (Pr), average visibility (VIS), average wind speed (WS_{avg}), and maximum wind speed (WS_{max}). Finally, total electricity consumption (EC) is taken via revenue quality meters. This gives a dataset of 16 features with approximately 1000 samples taken across a period of 5 years.

3.2. Graph Data

We format the ETP dataset into a graph that can be read by both the DisenGC-LSTM and GCLSTM models along with the data. While there are many methods of graph construction, from leveraging mechanistic relationships to establish graph edges, to data-driven causal inference methods, the goal of this work is to establish if the DisenConv layer can group important variables into distinct channels that represent latent factors. Therefore, input to the model is a fully connected, undirected graph $G_{WWTP} = (V, E)$ where $|V| = 15$ since each node represents a dataset feature, and $|E| = 105$. Data for the energy consumption is not included in the graph. Instead, this data is supplied as targets for the prediction model to train against.

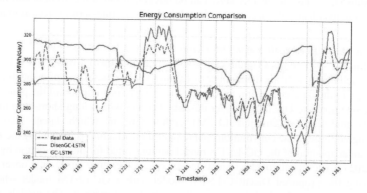

Figure 2: Results from the plotting of the real energy consumption data (MWh/day) against the forecast from the DisenGC-LSTM model (green) and the GC-LSTM model (red), demonstrating the performance of the DisenGC-LSTM model.

3.3. Model Training

The problem is formulated as a supervised machine learning problem in which each of the models is given a set of training data $\mathbf{X}_{\text{train}}$ where $n = 15$ is the number of features of the dataset that each correspond to a node in the graph, and m_{train} is the length of the training dataset. The models are trained to predict a the energy consumption of the plant based on collected training samples $\mathbf{y}_{\text{EC,train}} \in \mathbb{R}^{m_{\text{train}}}$. Prior to training, both the samples and the targets are scaled in the region of [0, 1]. The models were trained on 80% of the available data, with the remaining data split into 3 test sets of 10% each. This is so the results can be validated across 3 testing sets giving a more reliable performance estimate. The models were trained over 100 epochs in which the data was divided into mini-batches of 32 samples. The Adam optimizer was used with a learning rate of 0.001 (Kingma and Ba, 2014). The loss function used was the mean squared error (MSE) between the predicted samples and the training samples. Hyper-parameters for each of the models were tuned using the grid search method.

4. Results & Discussion

Figure 2 shows the forecasts for both the GC-LSTM model and the DisenGC-LSTM model with the proposed disentanglement mechanism. We see that the DisenGC-LSTM model provides a superior forecast. The DisenGC-LSTM forecast (green) fits very closely to the real data (gray) and is clearly able to predict the pattern of the data well, capturing both the trend of the data and largely able to replicate and predict the noise that is seen by the real energy consumption data. For example, between timestamps 1233 and 1263 we see that the DisenGC-LSTM prediction accurately captures the shape of the real data, despite there being variations in the data. This is in contrast to the GC-LSTM model which does not predict the rise in energy consumption across these timestamps. In fact, the GC-LSTM model predicts poorly and, despite capturing rough trends, tends to miss almost all important characteristics of the energy consumption data. Proof of this can be seen when comparing the GC-LSTM prediction to a straight-line forecast taken from the mean average of the training data, as shown in Table 1. We can see that the average forecast actually predicts better, with an RMSE of 20.36 MWh/day compared to 28.37 MWh/day for the GC-LSTM model. Comparatively, the DisenGC-LSTM model achieves an RMSE of just 10 MWh/day, outperforming the GC-LSTM model considerably and showing its effectiveness as a model compared to using an average forecast. The closeness of this fit is also reflected in the R2 scores for both models, where we see the DisenGC-LSTM model achieving an R2 score of 0.66, where the GC-LSTM model has a negative R^2 score showing that a simple averaging model performs better.

Table 1: Summary of results comparing the two run models against a base line average prediction.

Model	RMSE (MWh/day)	R^2
Average	20.36	0.00
GC-LSTM	28.37	-0.15
DisenGC-LSTM	10.91	0.66

5. Conclusion

In this paper we introduced a novel approach by combining graph convolutional networks (GCNs) with disentangled graph convolutional layers for time series forecasting of energy consumption in a WWTP. The DisenConv layer aimed to disentangle latent factors within the graph, providing enhanced accuracy and explainability compared to traditional

GCN models. Our methodology was applied to the Melbourne Eastern Treatment Plant (ETP) dataset, incorporating various wastewater quality attributes, hydraulic parameters, and climate data. The results demonstrated the superiority of the proposed DisenGC-LSTM model over the standard GC-LSTM model. The DisenGC-LSTM accurately captured the complex dynamics of energy consumption, outperforming the traditional graph convolutional model which have historically been shown to exhibit high accuracy. The DisenGC-LSTM model's ability to disentangle latent factors within the graph led to improved forecasting accuracy and a more nuanced understanding of the underlying processes.

This work contributes to the advancement of machine learning applications in the domain of wastewater treatment, offering a promising avenue for optimizing energy consumption in WWTPs. The DisenGC-LSTM model's success opens the door to further exploration of disentangled graph- based approaches for addressing the challenges posed by the intricate and nonlinear dynamics of wastewater treatment processes.

References

T. Ahmad, H. Chen, 2018. Utility companies strategy for short-term energy demand forecasting using machine learning based models. Sustainable Cities and Society401 39, 401–417.
URL https://doi.org/10.1016/j.scs.2018.03.002

Y. Alali, F. Harrou, Y. Sun, 7 2023. Unlocking the potential of wastewater treatment: Machine learning based energy consumption prediction. Water (Switzerland) 15.

F. Bagherzadeh, A. S. Nouri, M. J. Mehrani, S. Thennadil, 10 2021. Prediction of energy consumption and evaluationof affecting factors in a full-scale wwtp using a machine learning approach. Process Safety and Environmental Protection 154, 458–466

J. Chen, X. Wang, X. Xu, J. Chen, X. Wang, X. Xu, 2021. Gc-lstm: Graph convolution embedded lstm for dynamic network link prediction.

Y. Hu, X. Cheng, S. Wang, J. Chen, T. Zhao, E. Dai, 2 2022. Times series forecasting for urban building energy consumption based on graph convolutional network. Applied Energy 307, 118231.

Y. Jiang, W. Fu, L. Mao, F. Ren, L. Yang, J. Xiang, R. Liang, H. Hao, Z. Wang, 2 2014. Influence factors analysis of urban sewage treatment plant on energy consumption. Beijing Jiaotong Daxue Xuebao/Journal of Beijing Jiaotong University 38, 33–37.

D. P. Kingma, J. Ba, 2014. Adam: A method for stochastic optimization. arXiv preprint arXiv:1412.6980.

Z. Li, Z. Zou, L. Wang, 2019. Analysis and forecasting of the energy consumption in wastewater treatment plant. Mathematical Problems in Engineering 2019.

J. Ma, P. Cui, K. Kuang, X. Wang, W. Zhu, 2019. Disentangled graph convolutional networks. pp. 4212–4221.

W. Melbourne Water, 2005. Melbourne water. Social and Environment Data 2006.

A. R. Picos-Benítez, B. L. Martínez-Vargas, S. M. Duron-Torres, E. Brillas, J. M. Peralta-Hernández, 11 2020. The use of artificial intelligence models in the prediction of optimum operational conditions for the treatment of dye wastewaters with similar structural characteristics. Process Safety and Environmental Protection 143, 36–44.

K. Valaskova, A. Lazcano, P. J. Herrera, M. Monge, 2023. Combined model based on recurrent neural networks and graph convolutional networks for financial time series forecasting. Mathematics224 11. URL https://doi.org/10.3390/math11010224

Flavio Manenti, Gintaras V. Reklaitis (Eds.), Proceedings of the 34th European Symposium on Computer Aided Process Engineering / 15th International Symposium on Process Systems Engineering (ESCAPE34/PSE24), June 2-6, 2024, Florence, Italy

Reverse HAZOP: Enhancing Safety Improvements through Natural Language Processing and Text Mining

Seyed Mojtaba Hoseyni [a], Weixiang Han [b], Joan Cordiner [a*]

[a] *University of Sheffield, Chemical and Biological Engineering, Sheffield S1 3JD, UK*
[b] *University of Sheffield, Computer Science, Sheffield S1 4DP, UK*
* *j.cordiner@sheffield.ac.uk*

Abstract

This research presents an intelligent method that uses text mining to enhance the effectiveness of Hazard and Operability Analysis (HAZOP). Despite HAZOP's effectiveness in identifying hazards, its findings are often overlooked and conducting new analysis is time-consuming. Text mining, part of Natural Language Processing (NLP), can analyse safety-related data to identify risks and factors contributing to safety incidents, enabling proactive safety measures. The study introduces a HAZOP analysis data table structure to develop safety inspection checklists and proposes a reverse HAZOP analysis method. Case studies are used to demonstrate the practical application and benefits of NLP and text mining in safety improvements and reverse HAZOP. It highlights the benefits of utilising these technologies in terms of enhanced safety measures, proactive risk management, and improved decision-making.

Keywords: HAZOP, Text mining, Process safety, Risk analysis, Natural Language Processing (NLP)

1. Introduction

HAZOP, having a rich history in process safety since the 1960s, is a reputed method of hazard identification and risk analysis. Safety and risk-prevention is paramount for industrial enterprises. Thus, identification and reflection of accidental faults is essential for constructing preventative control systems which is achieved by conducting HAZOP (Martínez, et al., 2019). Despite its esteem, HAZOPs findings and recommendations from published analysis reports are often overlooked, and therefore not applied. Moreover, the current process of conducting a new HAZOP analysis is often deemed as time-consuming and subjective (Pasman & Rogers, 2016).

On the contrary, NLP employs text mining algorithms to promise organisations incisive acquirement of safety related data from various sources- namely incident, safety and HAZOP reports and maintenance logs. Detection of hidden patterns is optimised, to highlight the contributing factors of safety incidents. Ultimately, it is used as a tool for mitigating proactive developments of robust safety guidelines- bringing forth training needs, and the implementation of preventive maintenance strategies (Robinson, et al., 2021).

This study develops a framework to execute the reverse HAZOP analysis method to validate existing studies. In this paper, real-world examples are used to illustrate the practical application of NLP and text mining techniques in the domain of safety improvements and reverse HAZOP.

The novelty of the research lies in introducing an intelligent approach that utilizes text mining, particularly NLP, to enhance HAZOP. Unique contributions include the development of safety inspection checklists based on a structured HAZOP analysis data table and the proposal of a reverse HAZOP analysis method. These innovations enable the identification of risks and contributing factors to safety incidents, facilitating proactive safety measures. The integration of NLP and text mining enhances decision-making and proactive risk management in industrial settings, marking a distinctive advancement in safety improvement methodologies.

2. Methodology

A novel approach to reverse HAZOP analysis, utilizing data mining techniques, is proposed in this study to uncover intricate relationships within comprehensive HAZOP data sets. These datasets encompass various elements such as process parameters, causes, consequences, guide words, probabilities, severities, and risk levels associated with potential hazards and accident scenarios in the HAZOP report. By computing word frequencies for process parameters, guide words, causes, and consequences, significant attention factors are identified based on high word frequencies. Furthermore, an information inspection table is devised to establish the inspection order. The methodology is structured into three integral components: (1) implementation of text data mining based on the HAZOP report, and (2) word frequency statistical analysis and (3) correlation analysis.

2.1. Data mining on the HAZOP text

Because the analysis results of HAZOP are usually recorded in the form of report text, text data mining can extract the key information from its unstructured, qualitative data (Dang & Ahmad, 2014) - generating it as parameters, deviation safeguards etc. Text data mining is used to prompt the construction of the HAZOP analysis table with the following steps:

2.1.1. Data Preprocessing

Data preprocessing is a crucial step in the data mining and data analysis process of the HAZOP analysis table execution. Raw text data from the HAZOP report data needs to be transformed into a digestible, uniform design. Unstructured data, in the form of text, must first be cleaned and formatted before any conclusive analysis and modelling can be made. Such process involves the manipulation, or dropping of data before it is used to ensure or enhance performance (Jansen, et al., 2023).

2.1.2. Text Clustering Analysis – Latent Dirichlet Allocation (LDA) Model

Latent Dirichlet Allocation (LDA) is a widely-used form of statistical topic modelling-treating documents as a probabilistic distribution sets of words or topics (Jelodar, et al., 2019). Classification is used to succinctly categorise the text into a document, and the words per topic (Blei, et al., 2003). Documents are represented as a mixture of topics, and a topic as a bunch of words. Those topics reside within a hidden/latent layer- hence the name .

Despite its nature, LDA is not a clustering algorithm. Whilst both methods group documents, its process differ. The LDA topic model is based on the intuition that words that belong to a topic tend to appear together in documents (Blei, 2012).

2.2. Word Frequency Statistic

Following the investigation and analysis of the HAZOP nodes, word frequency analysis needs to be explored. Such statistical analysis is commonly used to identify the most frequently used words in qualitative text reports. It is seen throughout various applications- namely NLP, but also search engine optimisation, and content analysis. As such, it can help to highlight key themes and trends. This information can be used to improve the readability and clarity of the report, and therefore identify areas that may require further investigation or clarification (Feng, et al., 2021).

After counting how many times each distinct word appears in a lengthy text, the words are arranged in decreasing order of frequency. Every word in the sample has its rank assigned in that order, and the product of the rank and the frequency is determined to be roughly equal for each word.

2.3. Correlation Analysis

Correlation analysis is another statistical method. In the context of word frequency statistics, correlation analysis can be used to identify and evaluate the relationship/strength between the frequency of different words (variables) in a text.

If a strong positive correlation is determined, the frequency of the word is similar in both texts. Conversely, if there is a strong negative correlation, the frequency of the word is different between the texts (Ricketts, et al., 2022).

3. Results and Discussion

We chose a HAZOP report of a gas turbine unit as a case study. Data tables are built to the nodes of the case study. It briefs the key features relevant to standard HAZOP measures- parameters, guidewords, deviation, causes, consequences, severity, safeguards, likelihood, risk, ref, recommendations. 6 out of the total 46 nodes were selected for this study. The occurrence frequency of each node classification can reveal potential risks associated with specific nodes for plants. These risks can be quantified based on the data table from the HAZOP analysis. As shown in Figure 1, Node 02B and 08 in general, have occurrence time more than 100 times.

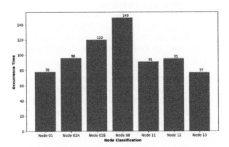

Figure 1. Statistical results of equipment classification

To find the most relevant process parameters and guide words for each node in the HAZOP data table, frequency of each words can be counted and subsequently the words can be sorted by their frequency and use to form deviations. This way, missing any important information can be avoided when analysing the nodes. Figures 2 and 3 show the word frequency statistics of the process parameters and guide words for the nodes respectively.

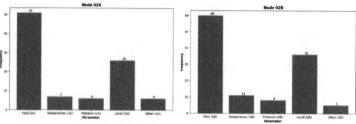

Figure 2. Process parameters' word frequency

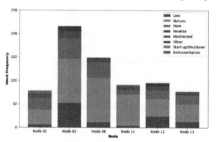

Figure 3. guide words' word frequency

The frequency with which each word occurred in the cause and consequence of the node was counted using the word frequency statistics technique. It is suggested that in order to improve the visibility of the analysis results in this study, at least 20 terms with the highest frequency be chosen as keywords. Table 1 presents the terms in a frequency-descending order to facilitate a better understanding of the causes and effects.

Table 1. Cause and consequence of 'Node 02'

Element	Keywords and word frequency
Cause	('Closed', 75), ('Open', 58), ('Controller', 47), ('MV', 45), ('Discharge', 44), ('Manual', 39), ('Level', 32), ('Valve', 31), ('Cooler', 26), ('Left', 26), ('Blockage', 21), ('Fail', 21), ('Failure', 19), ('Spurious', 18), ('Partial', 18), ('Suction', 18), ('Bypass', 18), ('Error', 17), ('Gas', 16), ('Boot', 16)
Consequence	('Possible', 219), ('Pressure', 213), ('Compressor', 138), ('Suction', 126), ('Explosion', 125), ('Damage', 99), ('Fatalities', 87), ('Gas', 80), ('Fire', 77), ('Less', 72), ('Glycol', 72), ('Separator', 72), ('Surge', 68), ('Rupture', 67), ('Low', 64), ('Ignited', 59), ('Jet', 57), ('Potential', 55), ('High', 52), ('Drum', 52)

Typically, the LDA model is evaluated using perplexity as an index. Figure 4's curve indicates that the number of topics at 7 is at the inflection point; as a result, 7 is the number of clustering subjects that are selected.

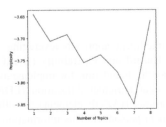

Figure 4. Perplexity Curve

Using clustering analysis, the LDA model is utilised to count the percentage of the seven topics and cluster all of Node 02's causes and effects. Word frequency probabilities are computed, and the top 10 keywords for each topic are used to represent it and arrange the results. Table 2 shows consequence topics for Node 2 with the word frequency probabilities associated with the specific keywords of the consequence topic. Topic names can be defined by looking up each topic's keyword usage.

Table 2. The 'Node 02' consequence topics' clustering analysis

ID	Consequence Topic	Keywords	Probability
0	Piping Failures	Possible, Pressure, May, Back, Fatalities, Less, Design, Piping, Downstream, Process	0.46
1	Flow related anomalies	Flow, Leading, Gas, Loss, Increasing, Scenario, Hazardous, Partial, Production, Wet	0.65
2	Compressor failures	Pressure, Compressor, Suction, Possible, Damage, Low, Surge, Leading, Flow, Explosion	0.16
3	Equipment damage	Compressor, Suction, Flow, Leading, Pressure, Possible, Damage, Surge, Low, Explosion	0.80
4	Pressure related anomalies	Pressure, Possible, Compressor, Damage, Surge, Suction, Low, Flow, Explosion, Leading	0.16
5	Medium failure with Interrupted operation	Compressor, Suction, Pressure, Low, Surge, Damage, Possible, Leading, Flow, Lead	0.92
6	Severe failure	Pressure, Possible, Explosion, Damage, Surge, Compressor, Potential, Fatalities, May, Fire	0.48
7	Abnormal level in suction drum	Pressure, Possible, High, May, Fire, Rupture, Exceed, Upstream, Equipment, Leak	0.62

A contingency table is used to determine whether two aspects of the same analysis data are correlated. From Figure 5, process parameters and guidewords are used. The results show that 'No/ Less' happened the most in 'Flow', following 'Less' in 'Level'.

Guide word / Process parameter	Less	No/Less	More	Reverse	Misdirected	Other	Start-up/Shutdown	Instrumentation	All
Flow	0	94	2	0	15	0	0	0	111
Temperature	6	0	12	0	0	0	0	0	18
Pressure	6	0	8	0	0	0	0	0	14
Level	40	0	22	0	0	0	0	0	62
Other	0	0	0	0	0	11	0	0	11
All	52	94	44	0	15	11	0	0	216

Figure 5. Process parameters and guidewords of 'Node 02'

4. Conclusions

This study introduces an intelligent approach leveraging text mining techniques to augment the efficiency of Hazard and Operability (HAZOP) analysis. The HAZOP analysis data table served as the foundation for implementing both a word frequency statistical algorithm and Latent Dirichlet Allocation (LDA) clustering models. The interrelationships among various HAZOP elements are illustrated, offering valuable insights for safety management personnel. This information can be instrumental in the analysis, prevention, and control of accidents within chemical plants. The findings have substantial implications for enhancing the safety and reliability of production processes in industrial plants. In evaluating the practical application of the proposed approach, it is essential to acknowledge potential limitations and challenges. The generalizability of the findings may be constrained by the specific context and dataset used in this study. Further research and validation across diverse industrial settings are warranted to establish the broader applicability and robustness of the intelligent approach. Addressing these concerns will contribute to a more comprehensive understanding of the method's effectiveness and facilitate its successful implementation across various HAZOP analysis scenarios.

References

Blei, D., 2012. Probabilistic topic models. *Communications of the ACM,* 55(4), pp. 77-84.

Blei, D. M., Ng, A. Y. & Jordan, M. I., 2003. Latent dirichlet allocation. *Journal of machine Learning research,* Volume 3, pp. 993-1022.

Dang, S. & Ahmad, P. H., 2014. Text mining: Techniques and its application. *International Journal of Engineering & Technology Innovations ,* 1(4), pp. 22-25.

Feng, X. et al., 2021. Application of natural language processing in HAZOP reports. *Process Safety and Environmental Protection ,* Volume 155 , pp. 41-48..

Jansen, B. J. et al., 2023. Data Preprocessing. In: *Understanding Audiences, Customers, and Users via Analytics: An Introduction to the Employment of Web, Social, and Other Types of Digital People Data.* s.l.:Springer, Cham.

Jelodar, H. et al., 2019. Latent Dirichlet allocation (LDA) and topic modeling: models, applications, a survey. *Multimedia Tools and Applications,* Volume 78, pp. 15169-15211.

Martínez, B., Rodríguez, M. & Díaz, I., 2019. Automating HAZOP studies using D-higraphs. *Computer Aided Chemical Engineering ,* Volume 46, pp. 553-558.

Pasman, H. J. & Rogers, W. J., 2016. How can we improve HAZOP, our old work horse, and do more with its results? An overview of recent developments. *Chemical Engineering,* Volume 48, pp. 829-834.

Ricketts, J., Pelham, J., Barry, D. & Guo, W., 2022. *An NLP framework for extracting causes, consequences, and hazards from occurrence reports to validate a HAZOP study.* s.l., s.n.

Robinson, C., Brown, S. & Cordiner, J., 2021. Towards Automated HAZOPs. *Computer Aided Chemical Engineering,* Volume 50, pp. 505-510.

Flavio Manenti, Gintaras V. Reklaitis (Eds.), Proceedings of the 34th European Symposium on Computer Aided Process Engineering / 15th International Symposium on Process Systems Engineering (ESCAPE34/PSE24), June 2-6, 2024, Florence, Italy

Developing Purely Data-Driven Multi-Mode Process Controllers Using Inverse Reinforcement Learning

Runze Lin [a,b], Junghui Chen [c,*], Biao Huang [b,*], Lei Xie [a], Hongye Su [a]

[a] *State Key Laboratory of Industrial Control Technology, Institute of Cyber-Systems and Control, Zhejiang University, Hangzhou 310027, China*
[b] *Department of Chemical and Materials Engineering, University of Alberta, Edmonton, AB T6G 2G6, Canada*
[c] *Department of Chemical Engineering, Chung-Yuan Christian University, Taoyuan 32023, Taiwan, R.O.C.*
jason@wavenet.cycu.edu.tw & biao.huang@ualberta.ca

Abstract

In recent years, process control researchers have been paying close attention to Deep Reinforcement Learning (DRL). DRL offers the potential for model-free controller design, but it is challenging to achieve satisfactory outcomes without accurate simulation models and well-designed reward functions, particularly in multi-mode processes. To address this issue, this paper presents a novel approach that combines inverse RL (IRL) and multi-task learning to provide a purely data-driven solution for multi-mode control design, allowing for transfer learning and adaptation in different operating modes. The effectiveness of this novel approach is demonstrated through a CSTR continuous control case using multi-mode historical closed-loop data. The proposed method offers a promising solution to the challenges of designing controllers for multi-mode processes.

Keywords: multi-mode process control, data-driven controller design, inverse reinforcement learning, multi-task reinforcement learning

1. Introduction

In the realm of Industry 4.0 and smart manufacturing, intelligent processes are becoming increasingly crucial in the field of process control. The emergence of AI for science/engineering has provided a visionary direction for a new DRL paradigm that empowers and facilitates modern process industries. In recent years, attention has shifted toward the intersection of DRL and process control within the process industry domain (Nian et al. 2020, Shin et al. 2019). This resulted in significant advancements and applications for both continuous and batch processes. A noteworthy development was the integration of transfer learning into DRL for process control, which aims to enhance its safety and practicality (Lin et al. 2021, Lin et al. 2023, Lin et al. 2024).

Current research has yet to overcome the core challenges of implementing DRL, such as the costly trial-and-error process, low sample efficiency, and exploration instability. Unfortunately, traditional control design methods, like DRL and Model Predictive Control (MPC), have overlooked the vast amounts of closed-loop operating data accumulated in industrial settings, failing to fully leverage its valuable information. However, discovering controller patterns or characteristics from the actual closed-loop data can serve as a solid foundation for DRL transfer learning. Inverse RL (IRL) can make this idea a reality, especially Adversarial IRL (AIRL) (Fu et al. 2017), which reframes learning from demonstrations into a probabilistic inference problem. However, conventional IRL struggles with the inherent multi-mode characteristics in process control because different operating modes result in distinct data distributions that make IRL less applicable in the multi-mode controller design scenarios.

Therefore, this paper proposes a framework for learning a multi-mode process controller based on IRL. Our method organically incorporates adversarial reward learning, variational inference, MaxEnt principle, etc., with the ultimate aim of training a purely closed-loop data-driven controller that can adapt to various operating modes.

2. Preliminaries

2.1. Markov decision process (MDP)
The MDP is defined by a tuple (S, A, p_S, η, r), where S and A represent the state and the action spaces, $p_S : S \times A \times S \rightarrow [0,1]$ denotes the state transition probability, $\eta : S \rightarrow P(S)$ is the initial state distribution, $r : S \times A \rightarrow \Box$ is the reward function.

2.2. Maximum entropy RL and IRL (Levine 2018, Ziebart et al. 2008)
The maximum entropy (MaxEnt) RL objective is defined as:

$$\arg \min_{\pi} D_{KL}(p_{\pi}(\tau) \| p(\tau)) = \arg \max_{\pi} \sum_{t=1}^{T} E_{(s_t, a_t) \sim \rho_{\pi}}[r(s_t, a_t) + H(\pi(a_t \mid s_t))]. \qquad (1)$$

where $H(\pi) = E_{\pi}[-\log \pi(a \mid s)]$ is the entropy-regularization term for the control policy. MaxEnt RL is a type of RL that aims to create a policy that is as random as possible while still achieving the overall objective of a standard RL that maximizes the expected sum of rewards. MaxEnt IRL is a method of IRL that falls under the MaxEnt RL framework. Its objective is to solve the maximum likelihood estimation (MLE) problem as follows.

$$\arg \min_{\theta} D_{KL}(p_{\pi_E}(\tau) \| p_{\theta}(\tau)) = \arg \max_{\theta} E_{p_{\pi_E}(\tau)}[\log p_{\theta}(\tau)] = E_{\tau \sim \pi_E}\left[\sum_{t=1}^{T} r_{\theta}(s_t, a_t)\right] - \log Z_{\theta} \qquad (2)$$

2.3. Adversarial inverse RL (AIRL) (Fu et al. 2017)
AIRL casts optimization of Eq.(2) as a GAN problem, in which the discriminator D_{θ} is:

$$D_{\theta}(s, a) = \left(\exp\{r_{\theta}(s, a)\}\right) / \left(\exp\{r_{\theta}(s, a)\} + \pi_{\omega}(a \mid s)\right) \qquad (3)$$

where $r_{\theta}(s, a)$ is the learned reward function and $\pi_{\omega}(a \mid s)$ is the corresponding policy. The policy π_{ω} in AIRL is trained to maximize $E_{\rho_{\pi_{\omega}}}[\log D_{\theta}(s, a) - \log(1 - D_{\theta}(s, a))]$, which is equivalent to maximizing the objective of a MaxEnt RL policy.

3. Problem statement

3.1. Multi-mode process control problem
A general control system can be characterized as the following state-space form:

$$s_{t+1} \Box p(s_{t+1} \mid s_t, a_t) \qquad (4) \qquad\qquad a_t \Box p(a_t \mid s_t, \omega) \Box \pi_{\omega}(a_t \mid s_t) \qquad (5)$$

where $\pi_{\omega}(a_t \mid s_t) \Box p(a_t \mid s_t, \omega)$ is denoted as a ω-parameterized control policy. Then the evolution trajectory of MDP unfolds from the initial state as follows:

$$p(\tau) = p(s_1, a_1, \ldots, s_T, a_T \mid \omega) = \eta(s_1) \sum_{t=1}^{T} p(s_{t+1} \mid s_t, a_t) \pi_{\omega}(a_t \mid s_t). \qquad (6)$$

However, in process control scenarios, many controlled processes inherently exhibit multi-mode behaviors, meaning they have various operating modes/working conditions. In the case of multi-mode processes, the optimal controllers for each operating mode are not consistent. Now let's describe the control problem for multi-mode processes.

A process system with $M \in \Box^+$ operating modes is given, each associated with a different optimal/near-optimal controller $\pi_E \Box \{\pi_E^0, \pi_E^1, \cdots, \pi_E^M\}$, where the optimal controller for mode m is denoted as π_E^m. π_E will generate M trajectory distributions that are structurally similar. Therefore, the multi-mode process control problem aims to learn a universal controller $\pi_\omega(a_t \mid s_t)$ that can adapt to scenarios with various modes.

3.2. Context-conditional multi-task controller learning problem

In this paper, the contextual policy is used to reframe the multi-task IRL for multi-mode process control design as the problem of solving a context-conditional MDP (Yu et al. 2019). Let $\pi(a_t \mid s_t, m)$ represent the controller for each operating mode, including the latent context variable m as an additional dependence of the policy for each mode. The generative model for the expert trajectory $\tau_E^m \, \square \, \{\mathbf{s}_{1:T}, \mathbf{a}_{1:T}\}_m$ under the m-th operating mode can be defined as follows:

$$s_1 \sim \eta(s_1), m \sim p(m), \pi \sim p(\pi \mid m), a_t \sim \pi(a_t \mid s_t), s_{t+1} \, \square \, p(s_{t+1} \mid s_t, a_t) \tag{7}$$

The marginal distribution of the overall historical dataset composed of different modes can be represented by:

$$\tau_E \sim p_{\pi_E}(\tau) = \int_M p_{\pi_E}(m, \tau) dm = \int_M p(m) p_{\pi_E}(\tau \mid m) dm \tag{8}$$

where $p(m)$ represents the prior distribution of the latent context variable (*i.e.*, the mode-indicating variable), $p(\pi \mid m)$ represents the context-conditional policy, $\eta(s_1)$ and $p(s_{t+1} \mid s_t, a_t)$ respectively denote the probability distributions for the initial state and state transition, and $p_{\pi_E}(\tau \mid m)$ represents the context-conditional trajectory distribution.

Our objective is to learn the control policies and reward functions for each mode. However, in real-world scenarios, the prior distribution $p(m)$ and the conditional trajectory distribution $p_{\pi_E}(\tau \mid m)$ are unknown. We can only observe the marginal distribution $p_{\pi_E}(\tau)$, which makes multi-mode learning particularly challenging.

4. Methodology

4.1. From single-task to multi-task MDP

To apply a multi-task IRL approach to learning controllers from historical closed-loop operating data of multi-mode processes, the original MDP is augmented by a conditional dependency based on $m \in M$, where M represents the value space of the latent context variable m. Now the context-conditional policy can be defined as $\pi : S \times M \to P(A)$, and accordingly, the reward function is modified to $r : S \times A \times M \to \square$.

Expanding upon the MaxEnt RL framework in Eq. (2), in multi-mode scenarios, the optimal context-conditional policy can be computed as:

$$\pi_E^m \leftarrow \pi^* = \arg\max_\pi E_{m \sim p(m), (\mathbf{s}_{1:T}, \mathbf{a}_{1:T}) \sim p_\pi(\cdot \mid m)} \left[\sum_{t=1}^T r(s_t, a_t, m) - \log \pi(a_t \mid s_t, m) \right] \tag{9}$$

where $r(s_t, a_t, m)$ is the mode-specific reward function, and $-\log \pi(a_t \mid s_t, m)$ is the entropy-regularization term for the contextual policies. The context-conditional distribution for the m-th expert trajectory $p_{\pi_E}(\tau \mid m)$ in Eq.(8) can be formulated as:

$$\tau_E^m \sim p_{\pi_E}(\tau \mid m) = p_{\pi_E}(\mathbf{s}_{1:T}, \mathbf{a}_{1:T} \mid m) = \eta(s_1) \prod_{t=1}^T p(s_{t+1} \mid s_t, a_t) \pi_E(a_t \mid s_t, m) \tag{10}$$

Given a set of multi-task demonstrations τ_E *i.i.d.* sampled from the marginal distribution $p_{\pi_E}(\tau)$ defined by Eq.(8) and Eq.(10), i.e.,

$$\tau_E \sim p_{\pi_E}(\tau) = \int_M p(m) \eta(s_1) \prod_{t=1}^T p(s_{t+1} \mid s_t, a_t) \pi_E(a_t \mid s_t, m) dm \tag{11}$$

The context-conditioned multi-task IRL aims to discover historical multi-mode patterns and then learn a multi-mode controller prior in a purely data-driven manner.

4.2. Latent context inference model for multi-task learning

When given the demonstrations from some unknown modes $m \sim p(m)$, $\tau_E^m \sim p_{\pi_E}(\tau \mid m)$, an inference model can be used to estimate the latent context variable $\hat{m} \sim q(m \mid \tau_E^m)$. Subsequently, substituting the inferred mode-indicating variable $\hat{m}$ to the learned reward $r_{\text{IRL}}(s, a, \hat{m})$, the DRL agent, guided by this context-conditional reward, should generate policies similar to those driven by the true underlying reward $r(s, a, m)$.

4.3. Multi-task IRL using context-conditional probabilistic inference

Like Eq.(2), the context-conditional trajectory distribution can be derived as:

$$\tau_\theta^m \sim p_\theta(\tau \mid m) = p_\theta(\mathbf{s}_{1:T}, \mathbf{a}_{1:T} \mid m) = \frac{1}{Z_\theta}[\eta(s_1)p(s_{t+1} \mid s_t, a_t)]\exp\left(\sum_{t=1}^{T} r_\theta(s_t, a_t, m)\right) \quad (12)$$

where the above conditional input m is inferred by an inference model $q_\psi(m \mid \tau)$. Therefore, the primary goal of multi-task IRL is to solve an MLE problem:

$$\arg\min_\theta \mathrm{E}_{p(m)}\left[D_{\text{KL}}(p_{\pi_E}(\tau \mid m) \| p_\theta(\tau \mid m))\right]$$

$$= \arg\max_\theta \mathrm{E}_{p(m), p_{\pi_E}(\tau \mid m)}[\log p_\theta(\tau \mid m)] = \mathrm{E}_{m \sim p(m), \tau \sim \pi_E^m}\left[\sum_{t=1}^{T} r_\theta(s_t, a_t, m)\right] - \log Z_\theta \quad (13)$$

To achieve this goal, AIRL can be used to minimize the KL divergence between the expert trajectory and θ-induced trajectory distributions. However, each trainable term in Eq.(13) is conditioned on the latent context m. Simply optimizing it would ignore m since there is no explicit correlation between τ and m. Thus, the mutual information (MI) is introduced to increase the dependence between the latent context and the induced trajectory. The MI under joint distribution $p_\theta(m, \tau) = p(m)p_\theta(\tau \mid m)$ is given by:

$$I_{p_\theta}(m; \tau) = \mathrm{E}_{m \sim p(m), \tau \sim p_\theta(\tau \mid m)}[\log p_\theta(m \mid \tau) - \log p(m)] \quad (14)$$

where $p_\theta(\tau \mid m)$ is the conditional distribution (Eq.(13)), and $p_\theta(m \mid \tau)$ is the posterior distribution. Eq.(13) indicates the primary goal under the MaxEnt principle, and Eq.(14) provides an additional objective as a kind of regularization term over the latent context variable. Therefore, the overall optimization objective would be formulated as:

$$\min_{\theta, \psi} \mathrm{E}_{p(m)}[D_{\text{KL}}(p_{\pi_E}(\tau \mid m) \| p_\theta(\tau \mid m))]$$

$$-\alpha \cdot I_{p_\theta}(m; \tau) + \beta \cdot \mathrm{E}_{p_\theta(\tau)}[D_{\text{KL}}(p_\theta(m \mid \tau) \| q_\psi(m \mid \tau))] \xrightarrow{\alpha = \beta = 1} \quad (15)$$

$$= \max_{\theta, \psi} - \mathrm{E}_{p(m)}[D_{\text{KL}}(p_{\pi_E}(\tau \mid m) \| p_\theta(\tau \mid m))] + \mathrm{E}_{m \sim p(m), \tau \sim p_\theta(\tau \mid m)} \log q_\psi(m \mid \tau) \quad (16)$$

The first term of matching the conditional distributions is exactly the primary goal of the context-conditional multi-task IRL problem, under the MaxEnt reward learning framework. The second term of maximizing the MI enforces the high correlation between τ and m. And the last term accounts for matching the variational inference approximation $q_\psi(m \mid \tau)$ with the true posterior $p_\theta(m \mid \tau)$ for the latent context.

4.4. Practical implementation for solving multi-task IRL

The first term in Eq.(16) can be achieved using techniques such as AIRL. The only modification needed is to augment the RL state with an additional input dependency, *i.e.*, the latent context m; thus the IRL policy would be $\pi_\omega(a_t \mid s_t, m)$. The second term can be optimized using sampled approximation for $p(m)$ and $p_\theta(\tau \mid m)$. Based on the above analysis, the overall objective of the context-conditional multi-task IRL algorithm is:

$$\min_\omega \max_{\theta, \psi} \mathrm{E}_{\tau_E \sim p_{\pi_E}(\tau), m \sim q_\psi(m \mid \tau_E), (s, a) \sim \rho_{\pi_\omega}(s, a \mid m)} \log(1 - D_\theta(s, a, m))$$

$$+ \mathrm{E}_{\tau_E \sim p_{\pi_E}(\tau), m \sim q_\psi(m \mid \tau_E)} \log(D_\theta(s, a, m)) + \mathrm{E}_{m \sim p(m), \tau \sim p_\theta(\tau \mid m)} \log q_\psi(m \mid \tau) \quad (17)$$

where $D_\theta(s,a,m) = \left(\exp\{r_\theta(s,a,m)\}\right) / \left(\exp\{r_\theta(s,a,m)\} + \pi_\omega(a \mid s,m)\right)$.

Once the training over multi-mode historical closed-loop data is completed, the multi-task IRL-based controller can be used as an initialized multi-mode controller to adapt to unseen operating modes in transfer learning settings.

5. Results & discussion

To demonstrate the effectiveness of the proposed approach, a continuous stirred tank reactor (CSTR) process is chosen as the controlled object as shown in Fig. 1. This system is a jacketed non-adiabatic tank reactor, where a single irreversible and exothermic first-order reaction takes place. The first-principle model is given in detail in (Lin et al. 2023). The control objective is to keep the reaction temperature T close to the setpoint T^{set} by manipulating the valve opening m (coolant feed flow rate).

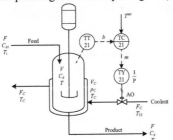

Steady state working conditions: temperature setpoint $T^{\text{set}} = 88$ °C, coolant inlet temperature $T_{Ci} = 27$ °C, feed temperature $T_i = 66$ °C, feed flow rate $F = 7.5 \times 10^3$ m³/s, concentration of reactant in the feed $C_{Ai} = 2.88$ kgmoles/m³.

Fig. 1 Sketch of the CSTR control system   Fig. 2 Details for the CSTR model

In the experiment, two different modes are designed to showcase the multi-mode control scenario: **Mode 1:** Setpoint 88 → 90 °C, and **Mode 2:** Setpoint 88 → 86 °C. An expert PI controller is used to demonstrate expert behavior in controlling the CSTR system. The PI controller is well-tuned to control the two setpoints and handle system disturbances. To increase stochasticity in the expert trajectories, white noise is added to the reactant feed/inlet concentration of the CSTR. A total of 2,112 expert trajectories are collected, each consisting of 300 samples ($Ts = 10$ s, representing the actual system of 3,000 seconds). The typical PI expert demonstrations for the two operating modes are shown in Fig. 3. It can be seen that the expert's control performance is satisfactory.

The state in the RL MDP is designed as $S \square [C_A, T, T_C, b, T^{\text{set}} - T]^T$, the action of RL is the controller output signal (valve opening) $A \square [m]$, and the Trust Region Policy Optimization (TRPO) is chosen as the forward RL training algorithm. For this multi-mode CSTR control problem, the latent context variable in the multi-task IRL agent is selected as the temperature setpoint as it indicates the mode-specific information. The above closed-loop expert demonstrations are used for multi-task IRL training.

The control performances of the trained multi-task IRL agent for the two modes are presented in Fig. 4. The results show that the successfully trained multi-task IRL agent can imitate expert behaviors well and also indicate its adaptability in different modes.

6. Conclusion

This paper proposes a multi-task IRL method to address the multi-mode process control problem. The method first establishes the mathematical formulation of the conditional policy and trajectory distribution using a latent context variable. Subsequently, it combines various techniques, including MaxEnt IRL, mutual information, and variational inference, to achieve context-conditional reward and policy optimization. Experimental results demonstrate the effectiveness of the proposed approach in learning a universal controller that can adapt to diverse scenarios based on historical multi-mode closed-loop data. This approach offers a promising solution for data-driven controller design based on probabilistic inference.

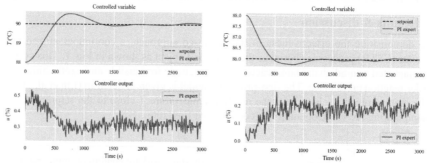

Fig. 3 Control performances of the PI expert demonstrations

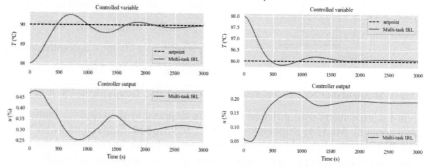

Fig. 4 Control performances of the successfully trained multi-task IRL agent

References

J. Fu, K. Luo and S. Levine, 2017. Learning Robust Rewards with Adversarial Inverse Reinforcement Learning. arXiv:1710.11248 DOI: 10.48550/arXiv.1710.11248.

S. Levine, 2018. Reinforcement Learning and Control as Probabilistic Inference: Tutorial and Review. arXiv:1805.00909 DOI: 10.48550/arXiv.1805.00909.

R. Lin, J. Chen, L. Xie and H. Su, 2021. Accelerating Reinforcement Learning with Local Data Enhancement for Process Control. 2021 China Automation Congress (CAC).

R. Lin, J. Chen, L. Xie and H. Su, 2023. Accelerating reinforcement learning with case-based model-assisted experience augmentation for process control. Neural Networks, 158: 197-215.

R. Lin, Y. Luo, X. Wu, J. Chen, B. Huang, H. Su and L. Xie, 2024. Surrogate empowered Sim2Real transfer of deep reinforcement learning for ORC superheat control. Applied Energy, 356: 122310.

R. Nian, J. Liu and B. Huang, 2020. A review On reinforcement learning: Introduction and applications in industrial process control. Computers & Chemical Engineering, 139: 106886.

J. Shin, T. A. Badgwell, K.-H. Liu and J. H. Lee, 2019. Reinforcement Learning – Overview of recent progress and implications for process control. Computers & Chemical Engineering, 127: 282-294.

L. Yu, T. Yu, C. Finn and S. Ermon, 2019. Meta-inverse reinforcement learning with probabilistic context variables. Advances in Neural Information Processing Systems (NeurIPS 2019).

B. D. Ziebart, A. Maas, J. A. Bagnell and A. K. Dey, 2008. Maximum Entropy Inverse Reinforcement Learning. Proceedings of the 23rd national conference on Artificial intelligence (AAAI), Chicago, Illinois, AAAI Press.

Flavio Manenti, Gintaras V. Reklaitis (Eds.), Proceedings of the 34th European Symposium on Computer Aided Process Engineering / 15th International Symposium on Process Systems Engineering (ESCAPE34/PSE24), June 2-6, 2024, Florence, Italy

Finding advanced MOFs to capture argon from the air through machine-learning and molecular simulation

Xiaoyi Xu, [a] Xu Ji,[b] Yiyang Dai[a*]

[a]School of Chemical Engineering, Sichuan University, Chengdu 610065, China
*daiyy@scu.edu.cn

Abstract

Argon, widely used in industry as inert gas, is colorless and oderless with extremely low chemical reactivity. Traditional method of obtaining this rare gas is fractionation which has some shortcomings such as high energy consumption, high cost and complex production process. Metal-organic frameworks(MOFs), as a class of emerging organic-inorganic hybrid porous materials, have great potential to become new adsorbents of argon. Until now, Computation-ready experimental metal-organic framework(CoRE MOF) database contains 12,020 experimentally synthesized MOFs so that it is like finding a needle in a haystack to discover advanced MOFs through only methods of experimental. This study proposes a high-throughput screening strategy based on machine learning(ML) and grand canonical Monte Carlo(GCMC), which could quickly and precisely discover the MOFs with excellent properties for separating argon and air. At the same time, the addition of ML greatly saved computing power. Firstly, the adsorbent performance scores(APS) of randomly selected 25 % candidates in CoRE database after pre-screening were given by simulating pressure swing adsorption(PSA) process of air on MOF using GCMC. Then, with 23 descriptors characterized structure and chemical properties of MOFs as features and APS as target values, ML models were built to predict the APS of remaining 75 % MOFs. Finally, TOP5 MOFs with excellent adsorption performance were known according to result of sorting all APS. This screening strategy could greatly save calculation cost and improved efficiency of finding high-performance MOFs. Comparing with traditional materials discovery approaches, this work could be faster, more focused and possess more guiding insight for new MOFs adsorbents of argon ahead synthesized in the laboratory.

Keywords: Argon separation, MOF, Grand Canonical Monte Carlo,machine-learning, high-throughput screening, Structure-performance relationship.

1. Introduction

Argon is one of the most abundant noble gases in the air(About 0.932 %). It is colorless, odorless, non-flammable, extremely chemically inactive and innocuous, which has a very wide range of applications.To be specific, argon is used as protective gas for welding processes to prevent welding defects(Phakpeetinan et al.,2016). The argon knife is used for clinical minimally invasive surgical treatment(Camille et al.,2019) and the argon laser is used for the treatment of various eye and skin diseases(Korkmaz et al., 2015). In research and experiments related to the semiconductor industry, argon also has an extremely broad range of applications. To summarize, Argon plays an indispensable role in various fields such as industry, medicine, environmental protection, mining, geology, manufacturing and etc.

Currently, the main method for manufacturing argon is air separation, which involves using low-temperature liquid air distillation to obtain large-scale argon separation based on different boiling points of each component. This production method's drawbacks comprise high energy consumption, high cost, complex and hazardous production process, and an enormous coolant and media requirement throughout(Xu Jin et al.,2006). Pressure swing adsorption separation(PSA) is a gas separation technique known for its excellent low energy consumption, easy operation, cheap regeneration cost, good environmental benefits and great dependability. Thus, through PSA process to capture argon from the air, may offer a fresh approach to resolving the aforementioned issues and enabling argon production.So far, there have been several studies on the application of PSA for argon separation from air, such like Saburo Hayashi et al. developed a secondary pressure swing adsorption system consisting of two molecular sieve zeolite columns which is capable of producing argon from a ternary gas mixture that contains argon, oxygen and nitrogen. The most critical point of this process is the selection of adsorbent. As a new class of super porous nanomaterials connected by metal atoms, organic ligands, and topological structures, metal-organic framework materials (MOFs) have a lot of promise and appealing prospects,which have notable properties like large specific surface area, high porosity, adjustable pore size, robust functionality, and exceptional adsorption activity. With 12,020 MOFs in computationally ready experimental MOF database (CoRE MOF), built by Snurr et al.(2014), it is nearly impossible to find high-performance MOF adsorbents using only methods of experimental synthesis and characterization for all MOFs, which is similar to trying to find a needle in a haystack. Consequently, a rapid screening strategy for superior-performing MOF adsorbents holds immense significance in achieving efficient recovery and capture of argon from air. Molecular simulation-based high throughput computational screening (HTCS) techniques have become powerful tools for accelerating material discovery due to the remarkable advances in computational chemistry and increased computational power(Ramprasad et al.,2017). Experts and academics have conducted a number of studies on the HTCS of MOF materials, including ethane/ethylene separation, hydrogen purification, separation of Cs/Sr, and natural gas purification (CO_2/CH_4).

However, there aren't many studies on inert gases. The majority concentrate on the gas separation of Xe and Kr. Compared to the vast number of MOFs available, existing studies on Ar adsorption and separation mainly focus on specific types of MOFs. Anastasios I. et al.(2004), utilized grand canonical Monte Carlo(GCMC) and equilibrium molecular dynamics to compute the adsorption and diffusion performance of argon in CuBTC MOF. The reports about HTCS on MOFs for argon capture from air are lacking in the relevant literature, which may indicate that promising MOF adsorbent candidates are still to be found. Even so, it would be extremely expensive and time-consuming to perform a molecular simulation for all data. Machine learning(ML) is routinely combined with GCMC in the MOF domain to identify MOFs with exceptional performance from large databases.

Given this, this work presents a high-throughput screening strategy based on ML and GCMC simulation, which is used to efficiently and precisely screen MOFs with the best argon/air separation performance from CoRE MOF database. In order to facilitate calculation, the system is regarded as a three-component mixture of argon, oxygen and nitrogen (0.01:0.78:0.21). The simulated temperature is 298 K, and the adsorption and desorption pressure are 1 bar and 0.1 bar respectively.

2. Model and Method

This section is used to detail the workflow for high-throughput screening of MOFs adsorbents to separate argon from air adsorbents.

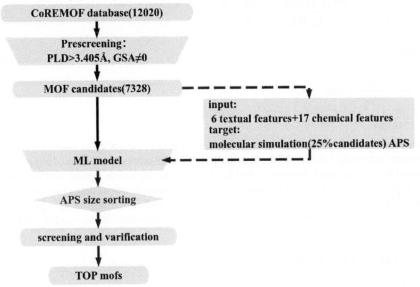

Figure 1 Workflow for high throughput screening of MOFs to separate argon from air

2.1. MOF Database and Pre-screening

The database utilized in this study was CoRE MOF database, which comprised the Crystallographic Information File (CIF) of 12,020 structurally diverse authentic MOFs.

In order to comprehensively characterize MOFs, this research considered both structural and chemical descriptors that had been successfully applied to ML models with great predictive accuracy of various gas systems. The free source software Zeo++ 0.3 calculated six structural descriptors: largest cavity diameter(LCD), pore limiting diameter(PLD), accessible surface area(GSA), volume surface area(VSA), porosity(Φ), and density(ρ). The code proposed by barisoo and ibarisorhan calculated seventeen chemical characteristics: number of atoms per unit cell, metal type, unsaturation, metallic percentage, oxygen to metal ratio, electronegative atoms to total atoms ratio, weighted electronegative per atom, and nitrogen to oxygen ratio. During pre-screening stage, MOFs that clearly could not adsorb argon were eliminated based on the geometric structure analysis; that is those with PLD<0.3405 nm or GSA=0 (the molecular dynamic diameter of Ar is 0.3405 nm). As a result, there were 7,328 MOFs remained in the pre-screened database.

2.2. Grand Canonical Monte Carlo Simulate

Based on RASPA 2.0 software, the GCMC simulation method was used to calculate performance indexes for capturing argon from air. To reduce the time of simulation, all MOFs skeletons were considered rigid structures. The Lennard-Jones(LJ) potential energy parameter of the MOF skeleton atom was taken from the UFF force field, The LJ truncation distance was set to 17 Å. The performance evaluation indexes included working capacity (ΔN, mol/kg), selectivity (S), regeneration performance (R%) and adsorbent performance score (APS), and the calculation formula is shown as follows.

$$\Delta N_{Ar} = \Delta N_{Ar}^{ads} - \Delta N_{Ar}^{des} \tag{1}$$

$$S_{Ar/(O_2+N_2)} = \frac{\Delta N_{Ar}^{ads}/(\Delta N_{N_2}^{ads} + \Delta N_{O_2}^{ads})}{f_{Ar}/(f_{N_2} + f_{O_2})} \tag{2}$$

$$APS = \Delta N_{Ar} \times S_{Ar/(O_2+N_2)} \tag{3}$$

$$R\% = \frac{\Delta N_{Ar}}{\Delta N_{Ar}^{ads}} \times 100 \tag{4}$$

2.3. Model

We constructed five ML regression-prediction models to describe the structure-activity relationship model between MOF descriptors and the adsorption properties of argon. Each model took 6 structural descriptors and 17 chemical descriptors as inputs, and the values of APS as targets. A series of feature engineering operations such as data cleaning, outlier processing, dimensionality reduction, standardization, and normalization were performed on dataset to improve the effect of models. Detailed parameters of the machine learning models are shown in Table .

3. Result and Discussion

3.1. Validation with Literature Data

The applicability and accuracy of the method utilized in this work must be validated before large-scale molecular simulation. The argon single-component adsorption isotherm of IRMOF74 was calculated and compared to experimental isotherm. Besides, we chose 10 % MOFs in CoRE MOF database at random and calculated their working capabilities(including several specific Ar adsorbents with potential) at 298K and 1bar. As shown in Figure 2 and Table 1, the simulation results are in good agreement with the experimental and simulation data reported in the literature, which indicates that the force field and parameter settings used in this article are reliable.

Table 1 Several potential argon MOF adsorbents

MOFname	GUXLIU	BUSQIQ	WOWGEU	CUNXIS	PARMIG	BEKSAM
Simulation	3.624	4.758	4.137	4.837	4.224	5.546
Literature	3.9	4.58	3.89	3.82	3.94	4.98

Finding advanced MOFs to capture argon from the air through
machine-learning and molecular simulation
2741

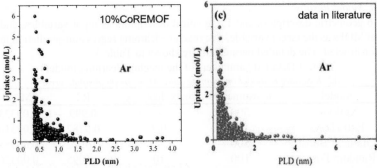

Figure 2 Comparison of 10%CoREMOFs working capabilities with literature

3.2. Simulation Results

25 % MOFs were randomly selected to simulate their adsorption property by GCMC, and APS was sorted to obtain the top 5 MOFs, as shown in Table 2. According to simulation results, the APS of MOF adsorbents in this system is rather minimal. Some probable reasons are as follows: 1. Compared to oxygen and nitrogen, argon level in air is exceptional low. The extremely low adsorption capacity strongly hinders adsorption performance improvement. 2. Under normal conditions, the sequence of preferential adsorption of MOFs for these three mixed gases is: O2>Ar>N2. 3. Oxygen and argon have very similar physical properties, including size, boiling point, and isothermal adsorption heat, resulting in their separation is more difficult.

Table 2 TOP 5 argon MOF adsorbents

name	Ar	S	R %	APS
CUHLUO	0.06565	2.305	86.03	0.1513
AFEKAX	0.03959	2.099	88.45	0.0831
BUFPIC	0.04203	1.551	57.54	0.0652
BIBYAO	0.04604	1.350	79.84	0.0621
EKADIF	0.02093	2.595	88.16	0.0543

3.3. Structure-activity Relationship

The structure-activity relationship of MOFs was drawn based on PLD. As shown in Figure 1, higher performance is more likely to arise in smaller PLD intervals.

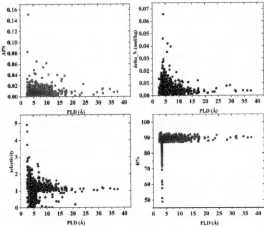

Figure 3 Structure-activity relationship analysis based on PLD

3.4. ML Model Results

Using 6 geometric descriptors and 17 chemical descriptors as input variables, and APS value of MOFs as the target variable, five machine learning regression-prediction models were constructed. The detailed parameters are shown in Table 3.

Table 3 Detailed parameters of the machine learning model

R2: R-Square of model on training data; MAE: mean absolute error

model		n_estimators	max_features	R2	MAE
XgBoost		500	-	0.999	0.00323
ExtraTrees		100	0.7	0.9782	0.00310
Gradient Boost		500	-	0.9522	0.00355
Random Forest		100	10	0.5095	0.00326
Voting	RF	350	0.75	0.8252	0.00308
	gbdt	100	0.5		
	XgB	25	-		
	ET	100	0.75		

4. Conclusion

In this paper, a method that combines ML and GCMC with large-scale calculation for screening 12,020 real MOFs as Ar/ air separation adsorbents is proposed. Firstly, 7,328 MOFs were pre-screened through geometric analysis. 25 % candidates were extracted for molecular simulation calculations, and resulting data was used to build ML models which predicted APS of remaining 75 % MOFs. The results show that simulation data based on GCMC are consistent with experimental and literature data, and are reliable and inspiring. This study found that the argon adsorption capacity of BIBYAO is 5.9803 mol/L, which is much higher than the current working capacity of argon adsorbents. Therefore, our work is highly crucial for future identification of high-performance argon adsorbents. But ML models built on 25 % MOFs data performed poorly on remaining 75% MOFs performance predictions. To improve model's accuracy, we can further screen the modeling features, enlarge the dataset, or adjust the model structure.

References

P. Phakpeetinan, A. Chianpairot, E. Viyanit, F. Hartung, and G. Lothongkum, 2016, Effects of nitrogen and hydrogen in argon shielding gas on bead profile, delta-ferrite and nitrogen contents of the pulsed GTAW welds of AISI 316L stainless steel. Materials Testing, Vol. 58 (Issue 6), pp. 489-494.

P.Camille, H. Eduard, F. Pierre, N. Lars, 2019, Effect of argon and nitrogen atmospheres on the properties of stainless steel 316 L parts produced by laser-powder bed fusion, Materials & Design,Vol. 179, ISSN 0264-1275

S. Korkmaz, F. Ekici, S. Sül, 2015, Argon laser-assisted treatment of benign eyelid lesions, Lasers in Medical Science, 1435-604X

J. Xu, A. Malek, S. Farooq, 2006, Production of Argon from an Oxygen−Argon Mixture by Pressure Swing Adsorption, Industrial & Engineering Chemistry Research,5775-5787

H. C. Gulbalkan, Z. P. Haslak, C. Altintas, 2022, Assessing CH4/N2 separation potential of MOFs, COFs, IL/MOF, MOF/polymer, and COF/polymer composites, Chemical Engineering Journal, 428: 131239

R. Ramprasad, R. Batra, G. Pilania, A. Mannodi-Kanakkithodi, C. Kim, 2017, Machine learning in materials informatics: recent applications and prospects, npj Computational Materials, 2057-3960

Barisoo, Ibarisorhan, 2020, MofFeatures, https://github.com/davidtangGT/MOF-Features

Flavio Manenti, Gintaras V. Reklaitis (Eds.), Proceedings of the 34th European Symposium on Computer Aided Process Engineering / 15th International Symposium on Process Systems Engineering (ESCAPE34/PSE24), June 2-6, 2024, Florence, Italy

Digital Twins of Waste Particles for Waste Bulk Simulations

Karim Khodier,[a]* Alisa Rizvan[a]

[a]*Chair of Waste Processing Technology and Waste Management, Montanuniversitaet Leoben, Franz-Josef-Strasse 18, 8700 Leoben, Austria*
karim.khodier@unileoben.ac.at

Abstract

Targets for reduced greenhouse gas emissions and mandatory future recycling rates, as defined in the European Union's circular economy package require more effective and efficient (mechanical) waste treatment processes, and therefore a better understanding of the processes and affordable metrology for material flow monitoring. Digital twins of waste particles can make a significant contribution by enabling the calibration of more complex discrete element method simulations and the generation of artificial training data for vision-based monitoring. Concrete implementation concepts for these applications are presented in this work. Furthermore, first results on the generation of particle twins, the collection of reference data for intensive DEM properties, and the digitisation of particle geometries are discussed: the former still poses significant challenges, while the latter has already been successfully implemented for some test particles using photogrammetry.

Keywords: Digital twin, DEM, solid waste, mechanical processing, photogrammetry

1. Introduction

Approximately half of global greenhouse gas emissions are caused by the extraction of natural resources (Hellweg et al., 2019). Substituting them with recycled materials can significantly reduce these emissions (Kroell et al., 2023), with a current circularity rate of material use of only 11.5% in the European Union in 2022 (Eurostat, 2023).

The European Union aims to exploit the positive potential of recycling, having set gradually increasing mandatory recycling rates for particular waste streams, for example, a final rate of 65% for municipal waste in 2035 and 70% for packaging waste in 2030 (European Union, 2018). It thus contributes to the achievement of the United Nations (2023) Sustainable Development Goals (SDGs) 11, 12 and 13 (sustainable cities and communities, responsible consumption and production, climate action).

Achieving these increased recycling rates while ensuring economic viability and controlling the emissions from waste management (which itself is responsible for 3% of greenhouse gas emissions; state 2017, acc. Eurostat, 2020), requires more effective and more efficient treatment processes. Improving these processes requires better knowledge of the effects of process parameters (Khodier et al., 2021). This knowledge is still limited for mechanical processing – the first stage of solid waste treatment. Furthermore, approaches aiming at dynamic waste-adaptive processing, such as material-adaptive smart waste factories (Khodier et al., 2019) or digital twins of waste sorting plants (Kroell et al., 2023), require reliable and affordable metrology for material flow monitoring.

While there is an increasing number of empirical studies on mechanical waste processing machines (e.g., Khodier and Sarc, 2021; Küppers et al., 2021; Möllnitz et al., 2021), and material flow monitoring (cf. Kroell et al., 2022), simulation studies on this topic are scarce. One reason is the heterogeneity and diversity of waste particles, which limits simulation to bulk behaviour (Wissing et al., 2017) or specific waste fractions (Anglou et al., 2023).

However, the representation of waste particles in simulations – in the sense of digital twins – is desirable: it enables more sophisticated physical simulations, providing potentially valuable insights into processes that cannot be obtained from data-driven methods. It also enables simulation-based training data generation for machine learning-based metrology and process control.

This work depicts two application concepts, one for calibrating discrete element method (DEM) simulations and one for generating training data for machine learning-based material flow monitoring. Recent results on creating digital waste particle twins for these applications are also presented.

2. Discrete Element Method Calibration

Data-driven models are advancing in the mechanical treatment of solid waste, providing insights and predictions for these processes. While their potential is still being exploited (Sarc et al., 2019), some of their limitations are clear a priori: they cannot cover what is not in the data. Thus, they cannot provide information on machine geometries that have never been built or on plant configurations (in terms of selection and order of processing machines) that do not exist. Physical models, on the contrary, can do just that. And for particles processing, like mechanical waste treatment, DEM is the method of choice.

DEM simulations require calibration of the processed materials. Due to the complexity of this calibration (Coetzee, 2017), typically, only a few material classes are used or the bulk is calibrated as a whole and represented by spheres. This approach does not seem promising for the variety of waste particle shapes and their behavior – for example, on a screen. Representation of the variety of material classes, and particularly shapes, seems necessary. It is also likely to be computationally feasible, given the relatively large particle sizes in waste mechanical waste processing (greater than 30 to 60 mm for many processing steps) and the relatively low particle numbers compared to, for example, powder processes.

The challenge is to collect information on the variety of particles in a waste stream for model calibration. A machine learning-assisted approach has been conceptualised (Figure 1) and is being investigated (Khodier et al., 2023). The idea is to predict particle geometries (e.g., using the Pixel2Mesh approach, Wang et al., 2018) and DEM parameters (e.g., Young's modulus, friction coefficients) from sensor measurements (e.g., RGB, near-infrared, laser-triangulation, induction) of a monolayer of singled particles, comparable to the situation on a sensor-based sorter, using suitable infrastructure, like the Digital Waste Research Lab at the Chair of Waste Processing Technology and Waste

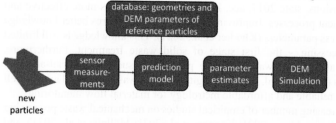

Figure 1: DEM calibration workflow for new particles (Khodier et al., 2023)

Management, Montanuniversitaet Leoben (2023). They can then be used immediately in simulations. The prediction is based on a database of intensive DEM parameters and geometries of known reference particles.

3. Machine Learning-based Material Flow Monitoring

Information on the state of the processed materials at different positions in the processing plant is essential for understanding the processes and their parameters' influences and for developing plants towards dynamic control and utilising digital twins.

To date, the characterisation of material classes is often done using near-infrared sensors (e.g., for polymers, Kroell et al., 2022). However, these sensors are too expensive to justify positioning one for each stream within the plant. In addition, they only see the surface of multilayered bulk materials on transport belt conveyors and hence only provide surface composition data. Therefore, machine learning-based material flow monitoring, using much cheaper RGB cameras, and training the models with bulk mass composition information is desirable. However, current studies focus mainly on spectroscopy (e.g., Zinchik et al., 2021) and applications to monolayers of singled particles (e.g., Kandlbauer et al., 2021).

A fundamental obstacle for bulk applications that aim to predict the mass composition of the bulk, rather than just the surface, is the accessibility of reliable training data. While capturing an image – the features in a machine learning model – is already feasible, providing trustworthy labels, in terms of mass composition, that match the bulk below the surface visible in the image is challenging: there are no reference sensors for this. And extracting matching increments of waste streams for manual analysis is difficult (cf. Khodier et al., 2019), let alone doing so tens or hundreds of thousands of times per measurement position to satisfy the data hunger of deep learning models.

A digital training data generation concept (Figure 2) was therefore developed, again using waste particle twins. In this case, geometry, optical texture, and particle mass information are required. These twins are used in a simulation environment for generating digital bulks in twins of actual measurement setups – e.g., on a belt conveyor. In contrast to DEM simulations, a physics engine (currently in Blender) is used to reduce the computational effort for the multitude of runs (generating many training data rows) and keep texture information to obtain realistic feature sets. The loss in modelling accuracy, compared to a DEM simulation, is assumed to be negligible since realistic bulks but not realistic bulk behaviour simulations are required.

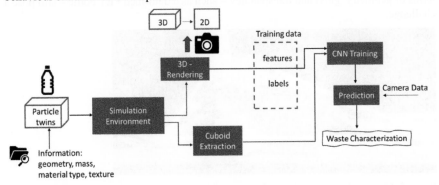

Figure 2: Concept for simulation-based training data generation for material flow monitoring

From these digital bulks, features are extracted by digitally photographing 3D renderings created in the simulation environment. Labels are also obtained by capturing the mass composition within the virtual cuboid under the virtual camera. These feature-label pairs are then used to train a Convolutional Neural Network (CNN) to predict mass composition in real measurement situations.

4. Results and Discussion on the state of Particle Twin Generation

Digitising information about the mass and material type of a particle is trivial. Therefore, research has focused on obtaining information on the intensive DEM parameters of reference particles and digitising particle geometries.

The first approach was to use bulk calibration methods, such as static and dynamic angle of repose (cf. Coetzee, 2017), using different subsets of a total batch of reference particles, and calibrating the intensive particle DEM parameters so that the simulated angles match experimental ones for all subsets. In practice, the entanglement of the waste particles – which causes them not to behave as typical bulk – resulted in unclear angles in the experiments (Figure 3).

Therefore, a new approach has been defined, which is still under evaluation: separation experiments, e.g., drum screening, are performed several times with all reference particles. Their intensive DEM parameters are then calibrated so that the probability of each particle ending up in one or the other fraction (here: coarse or fine fraction) is the same in the experiments and the simulations.

4.1. Particle Geometries

A method for digitising particle geometries – including their texture – has been successfully developed using photogrammetry: 40–50 partially overlapping photos of the particle are taken from different positions around and from above the particle (Figure 4 left). The particle is turned over, and another set of photos is taken. From each set, a model (with a flat bottom) is created in Autodesk Recap Photo, with the size adjusted based on a manual length measurement along one axis, that yields an accuracy of ±5 mm for the other two axes. The resulting two models are then merged into one particle model in Blender. For DEM simulations, the particle meshes are then imported into a DEM simulation environment. In this study, Ansys Rocky was used.

The method has worked well for the first test objects (see Figure 4 right). Well-lit objects with clear contours and simple geometries work better, while more complex objects in terms of geometry, gloss and transparency – such as a deformed PET bottle – still pose a challenge.

Figure 3: Static angle of repose test with two possible angle interpretations

Figure 4: Schematic representation of the camera positions for photogrammetry (left) and a particle 3D model from two perspectives (right)

5. Conclusion and Outlook

The determination of the intensive DEM parameters is still an open question. Here, the presented updated approach, which is based on the probability of the particles ending up in a particular output stream, is examined next. This requires the digitisation of a sufficiently large amount of particle geometries, which is in progress. In addition, a study of the sensitivity of DEM results to particle mesh resolution is underway to enable informed decisions to be made about on the investment of computational costs. Also, once a large number of particle geometries are available, tests on predicting new particles' geometries using an artificial neural network are planned.

Concerning the training data generation for material flow monitoring, first artificial bulks have been created in Blender. Work is currently focused on extracting the labels (the material composition in the imaginary cuboid under the photographed surface). A study has also just started on predicting the mass and volume of particles from singled particle streams, based on training data generated using digital waste twins.

In conclusion, the variety of promising application scenarios for digital twins of waste particles is huge, while much research is still needed to bring them to market.

Acknowledgements

Partial funding for this work was provided by the project Calibration of Discrete Element Simulation Models using Particle Sensor Data and Artificial Intelligence – acronym KalKIDEM – funded by the office of the regional government of Styria within UFO – Unconventional Research. Partial funding for this work was also provided by: The Center of Competence for Recycling and Recovery of Waste for Future (acronym ReWaste F) (contract number 882 512) under the scope of the COMET – Competence Centers for Excellent Technologies – financially supported by BMK, BMAW and the federal state of Styria, managed by the FFG.

References

E. Anglou, Y. Chang, A. Ganesan, S. Nair, C. Sievers, F. Boukouvala, 2023, Discrete element simulation and economics of mechanochemical grinding of plastic waste at an industrial scale, Computer Aided Chemical Engineering (52), doi: 10.1016/B978-0-443-15274-0.50382-6

C.J. Coetzee, 2017, Review: Calibration of the discrete element method, Powder Technology (210), doi: 10.1016/j.powtec.2017.01.015

European Union, 2018, Directive (EU) 2018/851 of the European Parliament and of the Council of 30 May 2018 amending Directive 2008/98/EC on waste.

Eurostat, 2020, Greenhouse gas emissions from waste, https://ec.europa.eu/eurostat/web/products-eurostat-news/-/DDN-20200123-1

Eurostat, 2023, Circular Economy – material flows, https://ec.europa.eu/eurostat/statistics-explained/index.php?title=Circular_economy_-_material_flows (accessed 22/11/2023)

S. Hellweg, S. Pfister, L. Cabernard, H. Droz-Georget, A. Foemelt, M. Haupt, J. Mehr, C. Oberschelp, E. Piccoli, T. Sonderegger, A. Sudheshwar, C. Walker, Z. Wang, 2019, Environmental Impacts of Natural Resource Use, Global Resources Outlook 2019, pp. 64–97, ISBN: 978-92-807-3741-7

L. Kandlbauer, K. Khodier, D. Ninevski, R. Sarc, 2021, Sensor-based particle size determination of shredded mixed commercial waste based on two-dimensional images, Waste Management (120), doi: 10.1016/j.wasman.2020.11.003

K. Khodier, A. Curtis, R. Sarc, M. Lehner, P. O'Leary, P. Pomberger, 2019, Smart solid waste processing plant: vision and pathway, proceedings of the 29th ISWA world congress, Bilbao, 7th-9th October 2019.

K. Khodier, C. Feyerer, S. Möllnitz, A. Curtis, R. Sarc, 2021, Efficient derivation of significant results from mechanical processing experiments with mixed solid waste: Coarse-shredding of commercial waste, Waste Management (121), doi: 10.1016/j.wasman.2020.12.015

K. Khodier, R. Sarc, 2021, Distribution-independent empirical modeling of particle size distributions – coarse-shredding of mixed commercial waste, Processes (9/3), doi: 10.3390/pr9030414

K. Khodier, A.L. Krabichler-Mark, I. Werner, A. Rizvan, Y. Varsh, 2023, Efficient calibration of discrete-element-method simulations for waste applications using particle sensor data and artificial intelligence, proceedings of the 19th international symposium on waste management and sustainable landfilling, Sardinia, 9th-13th October 2023.

N. Kroell, C. Xiaozheng, K. Greiff, A. Feil, 2022, Optical sensors and machine learning algorithms in sensor-based material flow characterization for mechanical recycling processes: A systematic literature review, Resources, Waste Management (149), doi: 10.1016/j.wasman.2022.05.015

N. Kroell, A. Maghmoumi, T. Dietl, X. Chen, B. Küppers, T. Scherling, A. Feil, K. Greiff, 2023, Towards digital twins of waste sorting plants: Developing data-driven process models of industrial-scale sensor-based sorting units by combining machine learning with near-infrared-based process monitoring, Resources, Conservation & Recycling (200), doi: 10.1016/j.resconrec.2023.107257

B. Küppers, I. Seidler, G. Koinig, R. Pomberer, D. Vollprecht, 2020, Influence of throughput rate and input composition on sensor-based sorting efficiency, Detritus (9), doi: 10.31025/2611-4135/2020.13906

S. Möllnitz, B. Küppers, A. Curtis, K. Khodier, R. Sarc, 2021, Influence of pre-screening on down-stream processing for the production of plastic-enriched fractions for recycling from mixed commercial and municipal waste, Waste Management (219), doi: 10.1016/j.wasman.2020.10.007

Montanuniversitaet Leoben, 2023, Digital Waste Research Lab, https://www.avaw-unileoben.at/de/forschung-geraete_und_technikum-digital_waste_research_lab/ (accessed 23/11/2023)

R. Sarc, A. Curtis, L. Kandlbauer, K.E. Lorber, R. Pomberger, 2019, Digitalisation and intelligent robotics in value chain of circular economy oriented waste management – A review, Waste Management (95), doi: 10.1016/j.wasman.2019.06.035

United Nations, 2023, The sustainable development goals report: special edition, ISBN: 978-92-1-101460-0

N. Wang, Y. Zhang, Z. Li, Y. Fu, W. Liu, Y.-G. Jiang, 2018, Pixel2Mesh: Generating 3D mesh models from single RGB images, Computer Vision – ECCV 2018

F. Wissing, S. Wirtz, V. Scherer, 2017, Simulating municipal solid waste incineration with a DEM/CFD method – Influences of waste properties, grate and furnace design, Fuel (206), doi: 10.1016/j.fuel.2017.06.037

S. Zinchik, S. Jiang, S. Friss, F. Long, L., Høgstedt, V.M. Zavala, E. Bar-Ziv, 2021, Accurate characterisation of mixed plastic waste using machine learning and fast infrared spectroscopy, ACS Sustainable Chemistry & Engineering (9), doi: 10.1021/acssuschemeng.1c04281

Flavio Manenti, Gintaras V. Reklaitis (Eds.), Proceedings of the 34th European Symposium on Computer Aided Process Engineering / 15th International Symposium on Process Systems Engineering (ESCAPE34/PSE24), June 2-6, 2024, Florence, Italy

Improved Deep Learning Architectures for the Decomposition of Mixed Integer Optimization Problems

Niki Triantafyllou[a,b], Maria M. Papathanasiou[a,b,*]

[a]The Sargent Centre for Process Systems Engineering, Imperial College London, London, United Kingdom, SW72AZ

[b]Department of Chemical Engineering, Imperial College London, London, United Kingdom, SW72AZ

*maria.papathanasiou11@imperial.ac.uk

Abstract

End-to-end supply chain optimization dictates synchronized, multi-scale, decision-making across various functions, stakeholders, and levels of planning in an organization. This usually leads to NP-hard problems. To tackle the computational challenges posed by large-scale supply chain models, we propose a deep learning-based decomposition methodology of Mixed Integer Linear Programming (MILP) models. Specifically, we train a Convolutional Neural Network (CNN) multi-label classifier with previous solutions of the target MILP model and we use the CNN to approximate the solution of a user-defined complicating variable. We apply our methodology to a MILP model that characterizes investment planning and patient scheduling in the field of personalized immunotherapies. From a modeling perspective, the patient-specific nature of these therapeutics leads to NP-hard problems as the demand increases. We achieve a classifier test set sample-level accuracy for the approximation of the binary variable responsible for investment planning decisions of 89.35%, meaning that the CNN leads to the global optimum solution in 89.35% of the instances in the test set. The results showcase a reduction of up to 81% and 83% in the number of constraints and binary variables for all scenarios examined, respectively.

Keywords: MILP, decomposition, deep learning, supply chain

1. Introduction

A major challenge for end-to-end supply chain optimization is the synchronized, multi-scale, decision-making across the various functions in an organization, the geographically distributed stakeholders, and the different levels of planning; namely strategic, tactical, and operational (Shah, 2005; Grossmann 2005). Holistic supply chain models are usually large, multi-scale, non-linear, and often computationally expensive to solve. Such models are inherently combinatorial due to the many discrete and logical decisions involved. They are typically described as NP-hard problems, which suggests that their solution time increases exponentially with the problem size in the worst case. Optimizing such problems requires effective mathematical formulations, tailored decomposition solution strategies that may compensate global optimality for tractability, and efficient utilization of computational resources (Pistikopoulos *et al.*, 2021).

Machine learning can be leveraged to tackle mixed integer optimization problems by employing various techniques and algorithms. State-of-the-art algorithms often rely on manually crafted heuristics (a) to make decisions (e.g. cutting plane selection on branch-and-bound, or linking variables for full space decomposition approaches), (b) to perform expensive computations (Bengio *et al.*, 2021). Consequently, machine learning emerges as a promising alternative to enhance these decisions more efficiently. Machine learning can contribute to algorithm improvement in two primary ways: (a) by replacing expensive computations with fast approximations (Bertsimas & Stellato, 2022; Triantafyllou *et al.*, 2023) and (b) by addressing algorithmic decisions that heavily depend on expert knowledge and intuition, which may result in suboptimal outcomes (Bonami et al., 2022; Mitrai & Daoutidis, 2023).

In this study, we introduce a decomposition algorithm that leverages Convolutional Neural Networks (CNNs) to approximate the complicating binary variable y_m, $m \in \mathbf{M}$, responsible for investment planning decisions in a personalized medicine supply chain.

2. Methodology

2.1. Decomposition algorithm

The deep-learning-based decomposition algorithm presented here (Figure 1), introduces a novel approach to address computational complexity in Mixed-Integer Linear Programming (MILP) models. The primary objective of the CNN model is to approximate one of the complicating binary variables, reducing computational complexity. The algorithm initiates by taking the MILP model of interest and generating a set of random N problem instances. Subsequently, the MILP is solved for each instance, establishing a comprehensive dataset comprising inputs and corresponding outputs. This dataset is then used for training the CNN classifier.

Once trained, the CNN is employed to make predictions for a target problem instance, approximating the complicating binary variable. The resulting approximation can be leveraged to either fix the variable or reduce the associated relevant set, a decision left to the modeler. Subsequently, the reduced MILP is optimized, and the optimal solution is obtained.

It is important to note, however, that similar to many decomposition approaches, the algorithm does not provide a guarantee of global optimality.

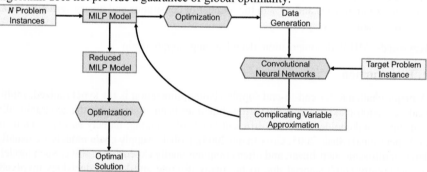

Figure 1. Proposed deep learning-based decomposition algorithm.

2.2. The problem case

To showcase the algorithm's capabilities, an in-house MILP model that describes the CAR T-cell therapy supply chain is used (Triantafyllou *et al.*, 2022). The supply chain superstructure consists of 4 nodes–leukapheresis center, manufacturing site, Quality Control (QC), and hospital. CAR T-cell manufacturing starts at the leukapheresis center, where T-cells are isolated from the patient's bloodstream and are cryopreserved before further processing. The leukapheresis sample is then shipped to the manufacturing facility, where it is genetically engineered. Lastly, the therapy undergoes in-house QC and once product quality and safety are ensured, it is shipped back to the hospital for administration to the patient. We consider 4 leukapheresis sites and 4 hospitals in the UK and 6 manufacturing sites located in the UK, US, and Europe. The manufacturing facilities m have a capacity of 4 (m_1 and m_4), 10 (m_3 and m_6), or 31 (m_2 and m_5) parallel lines. The model considers demand uncertainty by utilizing randomized demand profiles with different probability distributions (Triantafyllou *et al.*, 2023), manufacturing capacity limitations, patient-specificity, and time and location constraints, whilst the objective is to minimize the total supply chain cost. Finally, the total turnaround time is expressed as a non-monetary supply chain metric modeled as a constraint.

2.3. Data Generation

To train and test the CNN multi-label classifier, a comprehensive dataset through the solution of the original MILP model is generated. To train the CNN for global optimality, the MILP is always solved for an optimality gap of 0%. For this, High-Performance Computing (HPC) (Imperial College London) is used, leveraging parallel computing capabilities where the problems are solved over multiple CPUs. The dataset comprises 8,970 problem instances, each representing a unique demand scenario. Patient demands, ranging from 10 to 2400 per year, were solved to optimality with the CPLEX solver to reflect real-world variability. The only parameter that varies throughout the instances is the demand scenario parameter ($INC_{p,c,t}$), where each patient p is assigned to a leukapheresis center c at a specific time point t. For each patient demand, a total of 15 randomized demand profiles were generated, considering splitting equally across: uniform, left triangular, and right triangular distribution. The dataset, incorporating different probability distributions in demand profiles, serves as a robust training ground for ensuring the adaptability and efficacy of our algorithm to demand uncertainty.

2.4. Multi-label classifier

Here, CNNs are responsible for strategic planning by forecasting the optimal supply chain network configuration based solely on the annualized demand (Figure 2). Specifically, the CNN model is designed to forecast both the quantity and the strategic placement of manufacturing facilities to efficiently meet the demand. Employing a multi-label classification approach is crucial for our objectives, as it enables the prediction of multiple manufacturing facilities for each instance, allowing for the consideration of highly decentralized supply chain networks when necessary. Additionally, the model can predict infeasibilities, introducing an extra label for the classifier, in addition to the six candidate manufacturing facilities. By doing this demand profile instances that cannot be fulfilled

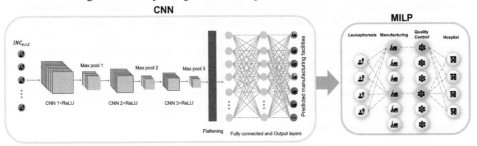

Figure 2. Proposed convolutional neural network architecture for the decomposition of the CAR T-cell supply chain MILP model.

with the available capacity are identified, and therefore the computational expense is decreased by bypassing the construction and solution of infeasible instances.

2.5. Network Architecture

Building upon previous work (Triantafyllou *et al.*, 2023), we employ CNN architectures for improved predicting capabilities. The input features considered for the CNN are the total daily demands for a quarter of a year (90 days), assuming a recurrent demand profile per trimester. The proposed CNN architecture comprises three convolutional layers followed by max-pooling, and two fully connected layers for multi-label classification (Figure 2). Key specifications include:

- 1st Convolutional layer: 32 filters, kernel size 10, followed by max-pooling.
- 2nd Convolutional layer: 64 filters, kernel size 5, followed by max-pooling.
- 3rd Convolutional layer: 128 filters, kernel size 3, followed by max-pooling.
- Fully Connected layers: 256 neurons, ReLU activation, dropout 0.1; 128 neurons, ReLU activation, dropout 0.1.
- Output layer with 7 neurons, where the labels are the 6 manufacturing facilities and the possibility of infeasible solutions due to limited facility capacity as seen in Figure 2.

2.6. Training

The model undergoes training utilizing the Adam optimizer with a learning rate of 0.0001. Binary Cross Entropy with Logits is employed as the loss function. Dropout is applied for regularization. The dataset is partitioned into three subsets: 80% for training, 10% for testing, and 10% for validation. The training process spans 5000 epochs.

3. Results

3.1. Classifier evaluation

The overall performance of the multi-label classification CNN model is measured by *sample level accuracy* and additional extracted metrics from the *confusion matrix,* i.e. *precision*, *recall*, and *F-score* for each class. The ordinary 2-dimensional confusion matrix used in multi-class classification is undefined when it comes to multi-label classification, where each instance can be labeled with more than one class. To overcome this, the multi-label confusion matrix with one extra row (No True Label-NTL) and one extra column (No Predicted Label-NPL) is used.

Sample-level accuracy provides the ratio of totally correctly classified instances to the total number of samples. It is a straightforward metric that gives a general overview of a model's performance and specifically the classifier's performance regarding global optimum complicating variable approximations. For such types of problems usually imbalanced datasets are an inherent challenge that needs to be tackled. In such cases, other metrics such as that account for partial correctness such as the Hamming Loss and the Jaccard Index might provide a more comprehensive evaluation of a model's performance. The evaluation metrics for the trained CNN appear in Table 1. It should be noted that the multi-label classification model is trained with three different demand distributions to better cope with demand uncertainty. This can lead to different supply chain structures for the same yearly demands. Therefore, there is a possible trade-off between model accuracy and robustness to demand uncertainty.

Table 1. Evaluation metrics for the test set.

Label-level accuracy (%)	Sample-level accuracy (%)	Jaccard Index (%)	Hamming Loss (%)
97.29	89.35	97.38	2.71

3.2. Infeasibility and suboptimality

By looking at the confusion matrix in Figure 3, the classifier overall predicts very well. However, in a few cases, it overpredicts the required manufacturing capacity to fulfil the demand by assigning bigger manufacturing facilities than the ones required and sometimes it underpredicts by choosing a smaller facility or failing to add an extra facility. In the former case, the decomposition methodology leads to local optimum solutions, whereas in the latter case, it leads to infeasible solutions. While the model predicts correctly in 86% of the instances that m6 belongs to the optimal supply chain configuration, in 8% of the instances it confuses facilities m6 (10 parallel lines) and m_1 (4 parallel lines) (infeasible solution) and in 5% of the instances, it leads to local optimum solutions by predicting facility m_2 (31 parallel lines) instead of m_6.

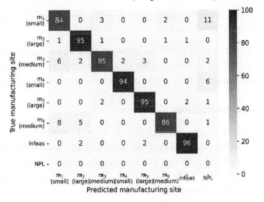

3.3. Computational complexity reduction

The reduced MILP model is solved considering only the subset of manufacturing facilities chosen by the CNN, becoming a subproblem of the original planning and scheduling MILP model. Therefore, the reduced MILP accounts only for detailed scheduling in the supply chain, which entails optimal transport modes for the node-to-node

Figure 3. Normalized multi-label confusion matrix with one extra row for No True Labels (NTL) and one extra column for No Predicted Labels (NPL).

connections, optimal allocation of patient samples in the manufacturing facilities and hospitals, and the optimal utilization of the available parallel lines in the manufacturing sites with the scope of minimizing the therapy cost and return time.

In Figure 4, we present a comparative analysis of the performance between the reduced MILP obtained from the deep learning-based decomposition algorithm and the original MILP. The evaluation is conducted across 12 distinct randomized demand scenario instances from our validation set (100, 200, 500, 1000, and 2000 patients annually), with 4 scenarios for each distribution.

For uniform demand distributions (Figure 4a), the decomposition algorithm consistently achieves the global optimum solution, accompanied by a noteworthy reduction of up to 81% and 83% in the number of constraints and binary variables across all examined scenarios. In the case of the left triangular distribution (Figure 4b), the decomposition algorithm performs very well, yielding global optimum solutions in all instances. Notably, for the instance involving 2,000 patients per year, the CNN classifier deems the problem infeasible, resulting in no solution attempts (Figure 4b) therefore reduced computational time.

Moving to the right triangular distribution (Figure 4c), the decomposition algorithm generates infeasible solutions for the 200 and 500 patient demand scenarios per year, despite the actual feasibility of the problems. This discrepancy is attributed to underpredictions, where smaller facilities than required are assigned. Interestingly, for the

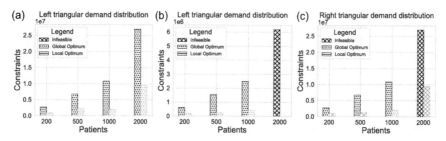

Figure 4. Performance of the deep learning-based decomposition algorithm in comparison to the original MILP model.

scenario with 2,000 patients per year, the classifier predicts feasibility, leading to a 64.7% reduction in the number of constraints. However, upon solving the reduced model, the optimizer (CPLEX) determines the model to be infeasible (Figure 4c).

4. Conclusions

In this study, we employ a deep learning-based decomposition algorithm utilizing a Convolutional Neural Network (CNN) multi-label classifier to address the computational complexity of large-scale supply chain models, exemplified through a personalized medicine supply chain case study. The classifier achieves a sample-level accuracy of 89.35%, signifying the attainment of the global optimum in 89.35% of the random scenarios within the test set. Computational complexity benchmarking between the original MILP and the reduced MILP, generated by the decomposition algorithm, reveals a substantial reduction of up to 81% in the number of constraints. However, the algorithm yields suboptimal or infeasible solutions in 10.65% of the random scenarios within the test set, highlighting the need for future improvements such as the prediction of the k-most likely labels or the introduction of integer cuts.

References

Y. Bengio, A. Lodi, and A. Prouvost, 2021. Machine learning for combinatorial optimization: a methodological tour d'horizon. *European Journal of Operational Research*, 290(2), 405-421.

D. Bertsimas, B. Stellato, 2022. Online Mixed-Integer Optimization in Milliseconds. *INFORMS Journal on Computing*, 34(4), 2229-2248.

P. Bonami, A. Lodi, and G. Zarpellon, 2022. A classifier to decide on the linearization of mixed-integer quadratic problems in CPLEX. *Operations Research*, 70(6), 3303-3320.

I. Grossmann, 2005. Enterprise-wide optimization: A new frontier in process systems engineering, *AIChE Journal*, 51(7), 1846–1857.

I. Mitrai, and P. Daoutidis, 2023. A graph classification approach to determine when to decompose optimization problems, *Computer Aided Chemical Engineering, 52, 655-660*.

E. N. Pistikopoulos, A. Barbosa-Povoa, J. H. Lee, R. Misener, A. Mitsos, G. V. Reklaitis, V. Venkatasubramanian, F. You, R. Gani, 2021. Process systems engineering – The generation next?, *Computers & Chemical Engineering*, 147, 107252.

N. Shah, 2005. Process industry supply chains: Advances and challenges', *Computers and Chemical Engineering*, 29(6), 1225–1235.

N. Triantafyllou, A. Bernardi, M. Lakelin, N. Shah, M. M. Papathanasiou, 2022. A digital platform for the design of patient-centric supply chains, *Scientific Reports*, 12, 17365.

N. Triantafyllou, S. Papaiakovou, A. Bernardi, M. Lakelin, N. Shah, A. Kokossis, M. M. Papathanasiou, 2023. Machine learning-based decomposition for complex supply chains, *Computer Aided Chemical Engineering*, 52, 1655-1660.

Flavio Manenti, Gintaras V. Reklaitis (Eds.), Proceedings of the 34th European Symposium on Computer Aided Process Engineering / 15th International Symposium on Process Systems Engineering (ESCAPE34/PSE24), June 2-6, 2024, Florence, Italy
© 2024 Elsevier B.V. All rights reserved. http://dx.doi.org/10.1016/B978-0-443-28824-1.50460-9

Data-Driven Modeling for Industrial Plants Based on Non-Stationary and Sparsely Sampled Data Streams

Changrui Xie,[a] Yujie Hu,[a] Lingyu Zhu,[b] Han Gong,[c] Hongyang Li,[c] Xi Chen [a]

[a] State Key Laboratory of Industrial Control Technology, College of Control Science and Engineering, Zhejiang University, Hangzhou, Zhejiang, 310027, China
[b] College of Chemical Engineering, Zhejiang University of Technology, Hangzhou, Zhejiang, 310014, China
[c] Zhejiang Amino-Chem Co., Ltd, Shaoxing, Zhejiang, 312369, China
xi_chen@zju.edu.cn

Abstract

In this paper, a robust auto-regressive exogenous regression model and the associated parameter inference algorithm is developed. Student's-t distribution is adopted to accounted for the noise in dealing with outliers. The parameter inference is conducted through the Streaming Variational Bayes (SVB) approach based on sparsely sampled data streams. To address the non-stationarity in data streams, power priors are established for each streaming batch by means of the exponential weighting mechanism. The uncertainty of parameter estimates is accounted for by formulating the problem under a full Bayesian framework. Furthermore, an analytical posterior predictive distribution is approximately derived, enabling the model to provide not only a point estimate but also the associated predictive uncertainty. The effectiveness of the proposed model and the adaptation algorithm is validated through an industrial distillation process.

Keywords: Streaming variational inference, power priors, Student's-t distribution, non-stationary data streams, sparse sampling.

1. Introduction

In industrial processes, quality variables play a crucial role in process monitoring and production optimization. Traditional offline measurement has substantial delays. Data-driven modeling techniques offer an alternative to soft sensing by leveraging easily measurable process variables to model quality variables.[1] Industrial plants continuously generate data streams during production, presenting a challenge in adapting data-driven models to these evolving real-time streams. And the variations in operation conditions can introduce shifts in data distribution, making global models unsuitable for real-time applications. Several adaptive mechanisms, including the moving, window approach, the recursive approach and the Just-In-Time learning approach, have been used to online update the data-driven model.[2-4] Nevertheless, sparse sampling of quality variables and the associated problem of data scarcity pose a considerable challenge to model adaptation. In such circumstances, probabilistic approaches can remedy this issue by accounting for the uncertainty in limited data, yielding more generalizable prediction.[5] They not only provide a point estimate for the quality variable, but also give the associated predictive uncertainty through the posterior predictive distribution. Streaming Variational Bayes (SVB) has been proposed for parameter inference in probabilistic model base on streaming data.[6] It can naturally serve as a Bayesian recursive updating approach for probabilistic models. However, SVB's assumption of data interchangeability across different batches makes it unsuitable for handling non-stationary streams. The power prior approach mitigates the limitations of SVB through an exponential forgetting mechanism.[7] Additionally, the presence of outliers in industrial data streams may cause a considerable impact on the model adaptation. A prevalent method to deal with this problem is using Student t-noise to account for the effect of outliers.[8] Student's-t distribution has a longer tail for explaining the noise and an adjustable parameter named Degree of Freedom (DOF), making it robust to outliers. In this work, we develop a robust probabilistic model for industrial plants by using Student's-t distribution, which is initially identified through variational inference (VI), and continually updated through SVB with power prior approach. Therefore, our model can adapt to variations in the operation condition by using non-stationary and sparsely sampled data streams. Its robustness helps avoid the adverse effects of outliers on model adaptation. The processes of model identification and adaptation are conducted within a full Bayesian framework.

2. Robust Regression Model with SVB and Power Priors

2.1. Model Development

Due to the data scarcity caused by the sparse sampling of quality variables, a simple Bayesian linear regression model is preferred to build the mapping from x_n to y_n:

$$y_n = \boldsymbol{\theta}^T \boldsymbol{x}_n + \varepsilon_n, \quad n = 1, 2, \dots, N \tag{1}$$

where $\boldsymbol{x}_n \in \boldsymbol{R}^M$ denotes the input variables, $\boldsymbol{\theta} \in \boldsymbol{R}^M$ denotes the regression weights, n corresponds to the sampling instance, and ε_n is the noise of the model. In this study, Student's-t distribution is employed to account for the contaminating noise:

$$\varepsilon \sim St(\varepsilon|0, \lambda, d) = \frac{\Gamma((d+1)/2)}{\Gamma(d/2)} (\lambda/\pi d)^{1/2} (1 + \lambda \varepsilon^2/d)^{-(d+1)/2} \tag{2}$$

where λ denotes the precision (inverse of variance) and d denotes the degrees of freedom. $\Gamma(d) = \int_0^\infty z^{t-1} e^{-z} dz$ is the Gamma function. Student's-t distribution can be decomposed into an infinite mixture of scaled Gaussian distributions. Therefore, the likelihood function of the regression model can be yielded as

$$y_n \sim St(y_k|\boldsymbol{\theta}^T \boldsymbol{x}_n, \lambda, d) = \int_0^\infty \mathcal{N}(y_n|\boldsymbol{\theta}^T \boldsymbol{x}_n, (\lambda z_n)^{-1}) \mathcal{G}\left(z_n \left| \frac{d}{2}, \frac{d}{2} \right.\right) dz_n \tag{3}$$

where $\mathcal{N}(\mu, \sigma)$ denotes the Gaussian distribution with mean μ and variance σ, $\mathcal{G}(\cdot)$ denotes the Gamma distribution, and z_n is the intermediate latent variable. A hierarchical Normal-Gamma prior is assigned to the weights $\boldsymbol{\theta}$ and precision λ:

$$p(\boldsymbol{\theta}, \lambda|\boldsymbol{L}) = p(\boldsymbol{\theta}|\lambda, \boldsymbol{L})p(\lambda) = \mathcal{N}(\boldsymbol{\theta}|0, (\lambda \boldsymbol{L})^{-1}) \mathcal{G}(\lambda|a_\lambda, b_\lambda) \tag{4}$$

where $\boldsymbol{L}$ is the precision matrix parameterizing the Normal distribution of $\boldsymbol{\theta}$. We assume $\boldsymbol{L}$ to be a diagonal matrix such that $\boldsymbol{L} = diag(\boldsymbol{\delta}) = diag(\delta_1, \delta_2, \dots, \delta_M)$, where the vector $\boldsymbol{\delta}$ is unknown. This sparse configuration is known as automatic relevance determination (ARD). Conjugate priors are also chosen for $\boldsymbol{\delta}$ and the DOF d:

$$p(\boldsymbol{\delta}) = \prod_{i=1}^M \mathcal{G}(\delta_i|a_\delta, b_\delta), p(d) = \mathcal{G}(d|a_d, b_d) \tag{5}$$

Therefore, the joint probability over all random variables, including y_n, the local latent variable z_n and the global variables $\{\boldsymbol{\theta}, \lambda, \boldsymbol{\delta}, d\}$, can be described hierarchically as

$$p(y_n, \boldsymbol{\theta}, \lambda, \boldsymbol{\delta}, d, z_n|\boldsymbol{x}_n) = p(y_n|\boldsymbol{x}_n, \boldsymbol{\theta}, \lambda, z_n)p(\boldsymbol{\theta}|\lambda, \boldsymbol{\delta})p(\lambda)p(\boldsymbol{\delta})p(z_n|d)p(d). \tag{6}$$

2.2. Parameter Inference

In this study, mean-field variational inference is employed for parameter inference. Thus, the variational posterior $q(\boldsymbol{\theta}, \lambda, \boldsymbol{\delta}, d, \boldsymbol{z})$ can be approximately factored as

$$q(\boldsymbol{\theta}, \lambda, \boldsymbol{\delta}, d, \boldsymbol{z}) \approx q(\boldsymbol{\theta}, \lambda) \left[\prod_{i=1}^{M} \delta_i\right] q(d) \left[\prod_{i=1}^{N} z_i\right]. \tag{7}$$

Through the variational inference, the variational posterior $q(\boldsymbol{\theta}, \lambda)$ can be yielded as

$$q(\boldsymbol{\theta}, \lambda) = \mathcal{N}(\boldsymbol{\theta}|\boldsymbol{\mu}_\theta, \lambda^{-1}\boldsymbol{\Sigma}_\theta)\mathcal{G}(\lambda|\alpha_\lambda, \beta_\lambda) \tag{8}$$

where the hyperparameters in (8) can be calculated by

$$\alpha_\lambda = a_\lambda + N/2, \quad \beta_\lambda = b_\lambda + [\boldsymbol{y}^T \text{diag}(\langle \boldsymbol{z} \rangle_{q_z})\boldsymbol{y} - \boldsymbol{\mu}_\theta^T \boldsymbol{\Sigma}_\theta^{-1} \boldsymbol{\mu}_\theta]/2 \tag{9}$$

$$\boldsymbol{\mu}_\theta = \boldsymbol{\Sigma}_\theta \boldsymbol{x}^T \text{diag}(\langle \boldsymbol{z} \rangle_{q_z})\boldsymbol{y}, \quad \boldsymbol{\Sigma}_\theta = [\boldsymbol{x}^T \text{diag}(\langle \boldsymbol{z} \rangle_{q_z})\boldsymbol{x} + \text{diag}(\langle \boldsymbol{\delta} \rangle_{q_\delta})]^{-1} \tag{10}$$

As for ARD parameter $\boldsymbol{\delta}$, the update equation for each δ_i is given as

$$q(\boldsymbol{\delta}) = \prod_{i=1}^{P} \mathcal{G}(\delta_i|\alpha_\delta, \beta_{\delta_i}), \text{where } \alpha_\delta = a_\delta + \frac{1}{2}, \ \beta_{\delta_i} = b_\delta + \frac{1}{2}\langle \lambda \theta_i^2 \rangle_{q_{\lambda,\theta_i}} \tag{11}$$

Similarly, the variational posterior distribution of the latent variable $\boldsymbol{z}$ can also be yielded. The variational posterior distribution of the DOF d is approximated by utilizing the Stirling's Series.[9] The variational posterior distributions of $\boldsymbol{z}$ and d are summarized as:

$$q(\boldsymbol{z}) = \prod_{n=1}^{N} \mathcal{G}(z_n|\alpha_z, \beta_{z_n}), \quad q(d) = \mathcal{G}(d|\alpha_d, \beta_d) \tag{12}$$

where

$$\alpha_z = \frac{\langle d \rangle}{2} + \frac{1}{2}, \quad \beta_{z_n} = \frac{\langle d \rangle}{2} + \frac{\langle \lambda \rangle}{2}\langle (y_n - \boldsymbol{\theta}^T \boldsymbol{x}_n)^2 \rangle_{q_\theta} \tag{13}$$

$$\alpha_d = \frac{N}{2} + a_d, \quad \beta_d = b_d - \frac{N}{2} - \frac{1}{2}\sum_{n=1}^{N}\left(\langle \log z_n \rangle_{q_{z_n}} - \langle z_n \rangle_{q_{z_n}}\right). \tag{14}$$

The expectation operations are denoted by $\langle \cdot \rangle$ in the aforementioned equations. These equations are iteratively applied to search for the optimal variational posterior distributions over parameters $(\boldsymbol{\theta}, \lambda, \boldsymbol{\delta}, d, \boldsymbol{z})$. After each iteration, the lower bound $\mathcal{L}$ is evaluated as an indicator of training convergence:

$$\mathcal{L} = E_{q_{\theta,\lambda,\delta,d,z}}[\log p(\boldsymbol{y}, \boldsymbol{\theta}, \lambda, \boldsymbol{\delta}, d, \boldsymbol{z}) - \log q(\boldsymbol{\theta}, \lambda, \boldsymbol{\delta}, d, \boldsymbol{z})] \tag{15}$$

2.3. Online Update with SVB and Power Priors

SVB with power prior approach serves as an adaptation mechanism for the regression model, making it capable of accommodating the non-stationarity in streaming data. Upon receiving a new batch $[\boldsymbol{x}_t, \boldsymbol{y}_t]$, the power priors are initially computed and subsequently used for parameter inference within the VI framework. The size of one batch, denoted as P, may be extremely small due to sparse sampling. The power priors for the tth batch is constructed by the exponentially weighted combination of uninformative priors and variational posteriors obtained in the $t - 1^{th}$ batch. Given the predefined forgetting factor ρ, the power priors for d_t, $\boldsymbol{\theta}_t$ and λ_t for the tth batch can be obtained as

$$\begin{aligned} \hat{p}(d_t^{pp}|d_{t-1}, \rho) &= [\mathcal{G}(d_0|\alpha_d^{(0)}, \beta_d^{(0)})]^{1-\rho}[\mathcal{G}(d_{t-1}|\alpha_d^{(t-1)}, \beta_d^{(t-1)})]^\rho \\ &= \mathcal{G}(d_t^{pp}|\alpha_{d,pp}^{(t)}, \beta_{d,pp}^{(t)}) \end{aligned} \tag{16}$$

$$\hat{p}\big(\boldsymbol{\theta}_t^{pp}, \lambda_t^{pp} | \boldsymbol{\theta}_{t-1}, \lambda_{t-1}, \rho\big)$$

$$= \Big[\mathcal{N}\big(\boldsymbol{\theta}_{t-1} | \boldsymbol{\mu}_\theta^{(t-1)}, \lambda_{t-1}^{-1}\boldsymbol{\Sigma}_\theta^{(t-1)}\big) \mathcal{G}\big(\lambda_{t-1} | \alpha_\lambda^{(t-1)}, \beta_\lambda^{(t-1)}\big) \Big]^\rho$$

$$\Big[\mathcal{N}\big(\boldsymbol{\theta}_0 | \boldsymbol{\mu}_\theta^{(0)}, \lambda_0^{-1}\boldsymbol{\Sigma}_\theta^{(0)}\big) \mathcal{G}\big(\lambda_0 | \alpha_\lambda^{(0)}, \beta_\lambda^{(0)}\big) \Big]^{1-\rho} \tag{17}$$

$$= \mathcal{N}\Big(\boldsymbol{\theta}_t^{pp} | \boldsymbol{\mu}_{\theta,pp}^{(t)}, \lambda_t^{pp-1}\boldsymbol{\Sigma}_{\theta,pp}^{(t)}\Big) \mathcal{G}\Big(\lambda_t^{pp} | \alpha_{\lambda,pp}^{(t)}, \beta_{\lambda,pp}^{(t)}\Big)$$

where $\boldsymbol{\mu}_\theta^{(t-1)}, \boldsymbol{\Sigma}_\theta^{(t-1)}, \alpha_\varpi^{(t-1)}$ and $\beta_\varpi^{(t-1)}$ (ϖ is in $\{d, \lambda\}$) are parameters of the posteriors for the $t-1^{th}$ batch; $\boldsymbol{\mu}_\theta^{(0)}, \boldsymbol{\Sigma}_\theta^{(0)}, \alpha_\varpi^{(0)}$ and $\beta_\varpi^{(0)}$ are parameters of the uninformative priors; $\boldsymbol{\mu}_{\theta,pp}^{(t)}, \boldsymbol{\Sigma}_{\theta,pp}^{(t)}, \alpha_{\varpi,pp}^{(t)}$ and $\beta_{\varpi,pp}^{(t)}$ are parameters of the desired power priors for the tth batch. Using the power priors, the update equations for $\boldsymbol{\theta}_t$ and λ_t can be obtained as

$$\boldsymbol{\Sigma}_\theta^{(t)} = \Big[\boldsymbol{x}_t^T \text{diag}(\langle\boldsymbol{z}_t\rangle_{q_t(z)})\boldsymbol{x}_t + \boldsymbol{\Sigma}_{\theta,pp}^{(t)-1} \Big]^{-1} \tag{18}$$

$$\boldsymbol{\mu}_\theta^{(t)} = \boldsymbol{\Sigma}_\theta^{(t)} \Big[\boldsymbol{x}_t^T \text{diag}(\langle\boldsymbol{z}_t\rangle_{q_t(z)})\boldsymbol{y}_t + \boldsymbol{\Sigma}_{\theta,pp}^{(t)-1} \boldsymbol{\mu}_{\theta,pp}^{(t)} \Big] \tag{19}$$

$$\alpha_\lambda^{(t)} = \alpha_{\lambda,pp}^{(t)} + P/2 \tag{20}$$

$$\beta_\lambda^{(t)} = \beta_{\lambda,pp}^{(t)} + \Big[\boldsymbol{\mu}_{\theta,pp}^{(t)T} \boldsymbol{\Sigma}_{\theta,pp}^{(t)-1} \boldsymbol{\mu}_{\theta,pp}^{(t)} + \boldsymbol{y}_t^T (\langle\boldsymbol{z}_t\rangle_{q_t(z)})\boldsymbol{y}_t - \boldsymbol{\mu}_\theta^{(t)T} \boldsymbol{\Sigma}_\theta^{(t)-1} \boldsymbol{\mu}_\theta^{(t)} \Big]/2. \tag{21}$$

The update equations for the latent variable $\boldsymbol{z}_t$ remain the same as (13). The convergence of the training procedure can also be monitored by the *ELBO*.

2.4. Posterior Predictive Distribution

Given a new, unseen sample x_{N+1}, the proposed model provides a posterior predictive distribution for unknown y_{N+1} as:

$$p(y_{N+1} | \boldsymbol{x}_{N+1}, \mathcal{D})$$

$$= \iiint p(y_{N+1} | \boldsymbol{\theta}^T \boldsymbol{x}_{N+1}, \lambda, d) p(\boldsymbol{\theta}|\mathcal{D}) p(\lambda|\mathcal{D}) p(d|\mathcal{D}) \mathrm{d}\boldsymbol{\theta}\mathrm{d}\lambda\mathrm{d}d$$

$$= \iiint N\Big(y_{N+1} | \boldsymbol{\mu}_\theta^T \boldsymbol{x}_{N+1}, \lambda^{-1}(z_{N+1}^{-1} + \boldsymbol{x}_{N+1}^T \boldsymbol{\Sigma}_\theta \boldsymbol{x}_{N+1})\Big) \mathcal{G}(\lambda|\alpha_\lambda, \beta_\lambda) \mathcal{G}\Big(z_{N+1} \Big| \frac{d}{2}, \frac{d}{2}\Big)$$

$$\mathcal{G}(d|\alpha_d, \beta_d) \mathrm{d}\boldsymbol{\theta}\mathrm{d}\lambda\mathrm{d}d$$

$$\approx \int \mathcal{N}\Big(y_{N+1} | \boldsymbol{\mu}_\theta^T \boldsymbol{x}_{N+1}, \lambda^{-1}\big(z_{N+1}^{MAP-1} + \boldsymbol{x}_{N+1}\boldsymbol{\Sigma}_\theta\boldsymbol{x}_{N+1}^T\big)\Big) \mathcal{G}(\lambda|\alpha_\lambda, \beta_\lambda) \mathrm{d}\lambda \tag{22}$$

$$= St\Big(y_{N+1} | \boldsymbol{\mu}_\theta^T \boldsymbol{x}_{N+1}, \frac{\alpha_\lambda z_{N+1}^{MAP}}{\beta_\lambda} [1 + z_{N+1}^{MAP} \boldsymbol{x}_{N+1}\boldsymbol{\Sigma}_\theta\boldsymbol{x}_{N+1}^T]^{-1}, 2\alpha_\lambda\Big) \tag{23}$$

where $\mathcal{D} = [\boldsymbol{x}, \boldsymbol{y}]$ denotes the training set. Note that in (22), we substitute the latent variable z_{N+1} with its *MAP* (Maximum-A-Posterior) estimate in order to derive an analytical solution. Ultimately, the mean and variance of the prediction are given by

$$E[y_{N+1}] = \boldsymbol{\mu}_\theta^T \boldsymbol{x}_{N+1}, \quad \text{Var}[y_{N+1}] = \frac{\beta_\lambda}{z_{N+1}^{MAP}(\alpha_\lambda - 1)} [1 + z_{N+1}^{MAP} \boldsymbol{x}_{N+1}\boldsymbol{\Sigma}_\theta\boldsymbol{x}_{N+1}^T]. \tag{24}$$

When an unseen sample $\boldsymbol{x}_{N+1}$ is received, the posterior predictive distribution for y_{N+1} can be calculated according to (24) using the latest posteriors of parameters.

3. Industrial Application

In this work, a distillation column is employed to evaluate the proposed model. A dataset spanning 25 days was collected from the plant and subsequently partitioned into training, testing, and validation sets in a 2:2:1 ratio by time. We aim to predict the yield concentration at the top of column, named y. The process variables, involving eight

Table 1. Numerical metrics of the predictions given by five models.

Methods	LS	RLS	SVB-PP	Robust SVB	Robust SVB-PP
MSE	191.24	155.88	97.00	207.03	91.63
MAE	156.25	119.43	75.59	145.18	69.13

temperatures at different trays (T_j for $j = 0, ... ,7$) and one inlet flowrate F, are recorded at one-minute intervals and used as input variables. The target variable, i.e., concentration, is measured every five minutes. In this work, a lag of 5min is set for the input variables. Therefore, the regression model is constructed as

$$y[t] = \sum_{i=0}^{4} w_F^{(i)} F[t - i] + \sum_{j=0}^{7} \sum_{i=0}^{4} w_T^{(5j+i)} T_{j+1}[t - i]. \tag{25}$$

Bayesian neural networks can deal with more complex, non-linear relationships, and model uncertainty by assigning probability distributions to the weights and biases. In this work, we prefer to choose a simple linear regression to model the mapping from the process variables to the target variables, due to data scarcity in streaming batches arising from sparse sampling. The optimal value of the forgetting factor ρ is selected as 0.98 after a grid search between 0.95 and 1. Our proposed robust linear regression model with SVB and power priors (Robust SVB-PP) is compared with other four models including a non-adaptive linear model (LS), the recursive least square (RLS) model, the Robust linear regression model with SVB (Robust SVB) and the linear regression model with SVB and power priors (SVB-PP). To evaluate the efficacy of the model adaptation under sparse sampling, only one sample is used for every 4h from the testing set, serving as a streaming batch for online model updates. Table 1 lists the *MSE* and *MAE* of the five models on the testing set. Detailed results as well as predictive uncertainties are presented in Fig. 1, where the sparsely sampled streaming data used for model updates are marked by the star symbols, and three outliers are also noted in the figure.

It is obvious that the robust SVB-PP, SVB-PP and RLS model can address the non-stationarity in the data streams, compared to the LS and Robust SVB model. However, the RLS model and the SVB-PP model are significantly misled by the three outliers, resulting in wrong model updates and terrible predictions. Sparse sampling worsens the problem as it may cost a long time to correct the model back. One potential approach to address this issue is resorting to outlier detection algorithms to identify and exclude outliers before updating the model. However, it is often laboursome to perform outlier detection online. Moreover, the old criterion for outlier elimination, obtained from past batches, may be inappropriate for the new batch due to variations in the industrial platform. And data scarcity may hinder the application of most outlier detection algorithms on a new streaming batch. Instead, our proposed Robust SVB-PP model is inherently robust to the outliers and can respond with high predictive uncertainties. Thereafter, once a normal sample is sampled for model updates, these uncertainties will return to the regular level. These excellent characteristics make our model more robust and informative in industrial applications.

4. Conclusion

In this paper, a Streaming Variational Bayes (SVB) with power prior approach was developed for parameter inference in a robust linear regression model. Non-stationary and sparsely sampled data streams were used for online model adaptation within a full Bayesian framework. The effectiveness of the proposed model and the associated adaptation algorithm was validated through an industrial application. Results show our model can adapt to the variations in operation conditions by using sparsely sampled data, and accomplish higher and more reliable predictive accuracy. Student's-t distribution

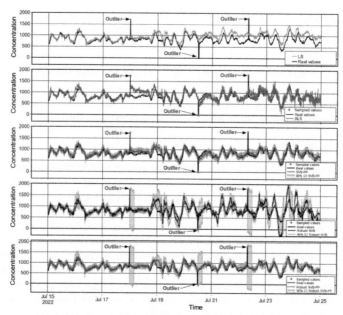

Figure 1. Prediction results given by the five models.

makes it robust to potential outliers in streaming batches. Predictive uncertainties given by the model provide more information on the reliability of the regression model.

Reference

P. Kadlec, B. Gabrys, and S. Strandt, 2009, Data-driven soft sensors in the process industry, *Comput. Chem. Eng.*, vol. 33, no. 4, pp. 795-814.

J. Liu, D.S. Chen, and J.F. Shen, 2010, Development of self-validating soft sensors using fast moving window partial least squares, *Ind. Eng. Chem. Res*, vol. 49, no. 22, pp. 11530-11546.

S.J. Qin, 1998, Recursive PLS algorithms for adaptive data modeling, *Comput. Chem. Eng.*, vol. 22, no. 4-5, pp. 503514.

A. Saptoro, 2014, State of the art in the development of adaptive soft sensors based on just-in-time models, *Procedia Chem.*, vol. 9, pp. 226-234.

C.M. Bishop and N.M. Nasrabadi, 2006, *Pattern Recognition and Machine Learning*, New York.

T. Broderick, N. Boyd, A. Wibisono, A.C. Wilson, and M.I. Jordan, 2013, Streaming variational bayes.

Masegosa A, Nielsen TD, Langseth H, Ramos-López D, Salmerón A, Madsen AL, 2017, Bayesian models of data streams with hierarchical power priors.

M. Svensén and C.M. Bishop, 2005, Robust Bayesian mixture modelling, Neurocomputing, pp. 235-252.

C. Impens, 2003, Stirling's series made easy. *Am. Math. Mon.*, vol. 110, no. 8, pp. 730-735.

Flavio Manenti, Gintaras V. Reklaitis (Eds.), Proceedings of the 34th European Symposium on Computer Aided Process Engineering / 15th International Symposium on Process Systems Engineering (ESCAPE34/PSE24), June 2-6, 2024, Florence, Italy

Adaptive Soft-sensor for Sudden Changes in Process Characteristics Based on Transfer Learning

Kaito Katayama,[a] Kazuki Yamamoto,[b] Koichi Fujiwara[a*]

[a]*Department of Materials Process Engineering, Nagoya University, Furo-cho, Chikusa-ku, Nagoya, 464-8601, Japan*
[b]*AGC Inc., 1-1, Suehiro-cho, Tsurumi-ku, Yokohama, 230-0045, Japan*
fujiwara.koichi@hps.material.nagoya-u.ac.jp

Abstract

Soft-sensors have been widely utilized in various manufacturing processes for predicting important process variables, such as product quality or variables relating to process safety, from other easily measured variables when important process variables cannot be measured online. Highly adequate soft-sensors are necessary for efficient and safe process operation; however, when process characteristics are altered due to a variety of factors, the performance of soft-sensors may deteriorate. Because it is burdensome to update or re-build soft sensors frequently, they should be adapted to such changes automatically. Thus, automatic soft-sensor updating methods for adapting to current process characteristics, such as Just-In-Time (JIT) modelling, have been proposed. Transfer learning (TL) has also been used for updating soft-sensors. The soft-sensors updating methods based on TL have been utilized for adapting quickly to changes in process characteristics, in which operation data collected prior to changes in process characteristics are used as the source domain data, and the current process data are regarded as the target domain data. However, previous methods using TL cannot be applied to sudden and unpredictable changes in process characteristics because TL needs information about the exact timings of characteristic changes.

This study proposes a new adaptive soft-sensor updating technique called the latest sample targeting FEDA (LST-FEDA). In the proposed method, a fixed number of samples close to the query in time are defined as the target domain of FEDA, which is considered a TL method, because samples measured at close sampling points may have similar characteristics. Using a JIT modelling manner with LST-FEDA, soft-sensors are constructed and target variables are predicted for every sample measurement by focusing on some latest samples that may be similar to the query as the target domain in TL. Locally-weighted partial least squares (LWPLS) can be applied for JIT modelling. The proposed method enables soft-sensors to quickly adapt to sudden changes as well as slow changes in process characteristics. The proposed method was applied to the operation data of a vinyl acetate monomer (VAM) process, which showed that the proposed method could maintain its prediction performance even after malfunction occurrence. The prediction performance of the proposed method after the malfunction improved the correlation coefficient by 6.1 % and the root means squared errors (RMSE) by 32.9% on average compared with the previous method. In conclusion, the proposed LST-FEDA can potentially contribute to efficient process operation and reduce the maintenance or updating of soft-sensors in the practical stage.

Keywords: Soft-sensor, Just-In-Time modelling, Transfer learning, VAM process

1. Introduction

In manufacturing processes, various types of hardware sensors have been used to measure process variables; however, product quality or other important variables often have to be measured with periodic offline analysis because some variables, such as product composition, cannot be measured online. It takes some time to perform offline analysis, resulting in delays in process control.

Soft-sensors have been widely used in various manufacturing processes to address this issue (Kadlec *et al.*, 2011). A general soft-sensor uses a regression model predicting a key variable that is difficult to analyze online with hard-sensors from process variables easy to measure online. By inputting a newly measured sample into the constructed soft-sensor, the objective variable is predicted in real-time, which contributes to realizing stable and efficient process operation. However, as process characteristics change due to the aging of manufacturing facilities or periodical process maintenance, the prediction performance of the soft-sensor may deteriorate, leading to declining operation efficacy and safety (Kano and Fujiwara, 2013). It is important for the soft-sensor to rapidly adapt to the current process condition for effective and safe process operation.

To address this issue, an adaptive modelling method, Just-In-Time (JIT) modelling was developed (Atkeson *et al.*, 1997). JIT modelling can handle sudden changes in process characteristics as well as gradual changes by utilizing past process operation information; however, it does not always adapt to abrupt changes when the new process condition is completely unknown, for example, facility malfunction.

Recently, the application of transfer learning (TL) to soft-sensor adaption has been proposed. TL is a machine learning method that transfers information from an experienced similar problem (source domain) to a new problem (target domain) to make the problem easier to solve (Pan and Yang, 2010). Yamada *et al.* (2022) applied a TL technique called frustratingly easy domain adaptation (FEDA) (Daumé III, 2007) to construct soft-sensors for process manufacturing products with multiple grades. They reported achieving accurate predictions of the quality of the target grade product. However, it is difficult to apply conventional TL-based methods to abrupt changes in process characteristics because the onset of such changes should be identified in order to transfer information appropriately.

In order to solve these problems of JIT-based and TL-based methods, this study proposes a new TL method, referred to as latest sample targeting FEDA (LST-FEDA), for JIT modelling. Because it is expected that samples measured at close measurement time have similar characteristics to each other in manufacturing processes, LST-FEDA designates a fixed number of recent samples as the target domain of TL and other past samples as the source domain, which is expected to select suitable samples for soft-sensor update in JIT modelling. Whenever new samples are acquired, the data in the target domain are refreshed by LST-FEDA, and the soft-sensor is reconstructed following the JIT modelling manner. By applying the proposed LST-FEDA to JIT modelling, the soft-sensor can cope handle gradual changes in process characteristics over time, as well as abrupt changes even when there is no historical data similar to the current process condition.

In this study, the usefulness of the proposed method is demonstrated through its application to simulation data of a vinyl acetate monomer (VAM) production process (Machida *et al.*, 2016) generated by a process simulator provided by Omega Simulation Co., Ltd (https://www.omegasim.co.jp/, accessed 2023/08/05).

2. Methods

2.1. Frustratingly easy domain adaptation (FEDA)

FEDA is a domain adaptation learning method, which can be described by a simple expansion of an input variable space (Daumé III, 2007). In soft-sensor design, the source and target domains are operation data before and after the change in process characteristics. FEDA extends the source domain data $X_S \in \mathbb{R}^{N_S \times M}$ and target domain data $X_T \in \mathbb{R}^{N_T \times M}$ as follows:

$$\Phi(X_S) = [X_S \quad X_S \quad \mathbf{0}] \tag{1}$$

$$\Phi(X_T) = [X_T \quad \mathbf{0} \quad X_T] \tag{2}$$

where N_S and N_T are the numbers of source and target domain samples, respectively. $\mathbf{0}$ denotes a zero matrix whose size is the same as X_S or X_T. The common input variable space can be trained from X_S and X_T while spaces specific to the source and target domains be from $\mathbf{0}$ and X_S or $\mathbf{0}$ and X_T, respectively.

While process characteristics gradually change due to aging, JIT modelling is expected to cope with such slow changes. However, process characteristics sometimes suddenly alter by process maintenance or malfunction, with which JIT modelling cannot always cope. Since the former is scheduled, specifying the source and target domains in TL is easy, and FEDA can be used to adapt soft-sensors to the process condition after maintenance. On the other hand, the latter situation is usually unpredictable, and identifying its precise onset is not easy. It is difficult to apply FEDA for such cases because appropriate information transferring requires a proper definition of the source and target domains.

2.2. Latest Sample Targeting FEDA (LST-FEDA)

It can be assumed that samples close to each other in time have similar characteristics to each other except for abrupt changes in process characteristics. The latest adjacent samples for model adaptation can be always selected in JIT modelling while process characteristics gradually change. When abrupt changes in process characteristics occur, historical samples similar to the current condition should be used for model update.

According to the above consideration, this study modifies FEDA for JIT modelling and extends the input matrix $X \in \mathbb{R}^{N \times M}$ as follows:

$$\Phi(X) = \begin{bmatrix} X_{past} & X_{past} & \mathbf{0} \\ X_{new} & \mathbf{0} & X_{new} \end{bmatrix} \tag{3}$$

where N and M are the numbers of stored samples and measured variables, respectively. $X_{new} \in \mathbb{R}^{k \times M}$ is the latest k samples in X as the target domain, and $X_{past} \in \mathbb{R}^{(N-k) \times M}$ is the set difference of X and X_{new}. That is, this modification constraints that the target domain must be the latest k samples only. Following $\Phi(X)$, the query $x_q \in \mathbb{R}^M$ needs to be also modified as follows:

$$\Phi(x_q) = \begin{bmatrix} x_q^\top & \mathbf{0}^\top & x_q^\top \end{bmatrix}^\top \tag{4}$$

Using $\Phi(X)$ and $\Phi(x_q)$, a soft-sensor is updated with JIT modelling manner. This formula is referred to as LST-FEDA.

3. Case study

To evaluate the performance of the proposed LST-FEDA with JIT modelling, we used simulation process data generated from a vinyl acetate monomer (VAM) process model. Forty hours of VAM process operation data were generated, which contained a situation in which a sudden malfunction occurred in the process. At the start of the measurement, the process was operating in a steady state, and 33 hours after the start of the measurement, process malfunctions occurred. The first 30 hours of data were used for training and the remaining 10 hours for test. To verify the prediction performance of the soft-sensors for various types of malfunctions, test data containing five different types of malfunctions were prepared. MAL1 and MAL2 are malfunctions that reduce the feed composition of the feedstock ethylene and acetic acid, respectively; MAL3 and MAL4 are the malfunctions that reduce the feed pressure of the feedstock Ethylene and oxygen, respectively; MAL5 is a malfunction that decreases reaction activity of the reactor due to degradation and sintering of the catalyst bed. The 65 process variables of the VAM process measured every 10 seconds were adopted as input variables of a soft-sensor, and the output to be predicted by the soft-sensor was the mass percent concentration of VAM in the product, which is measured every 30 minutes offline.

We adopted locally-weighted partial least squares (LWPLS) (Kim *et al.*, 2013) as a JIT modeling method, and constructed soft-sensors with the proposed LST-FEDA. In addition, LWPLS-based soft-sensors with and without the conventional FEDA were constructed for comparison However, it is important to note that it is difficult to use the conventional FEDA in real processes when an unpredicted malfunction occurs. Thus, it was assumed that the occurrence of the unpredicted malfunctions was observed for comparison, and the conventional FEDA was applied only when the malfunctions occurred. On the other hand, new information was always transferred in the proposed LST-FEDA. The number of the target domain samples in the proposed LST-FEDA, the number of latent variables Z, and the localization parameter φ in LWPLS have to be determined appropriately as hyper-parameters. In this case study, they were tuned through three-fold time-series cross-validation (S. Arlot and A. Celisse, 2010). In this study, $Z = 3$ and $\varphi = 2$ were selected for LWPLS and LWPLS with FEDA, and $k = 15$, $Z = 35$, and $\varphi = 0.25$ for LWPLS with LST-FEDA.

The prediction results for the test datasets of MAL1 and MAL2 are illustrated in Figures 1 and 2. The vertical dashed line at 180 min denotes the onset of the malfunction. The prediction by any soft-sensor fluctuated significantly shortly after the malfunction occurrence, which lasted for approximately one hour. However, the errors between the measurement and the prediction by LST-FEDA were the smallest of the three soft-sensors.

Table 1 summarizes the prediction performance of the constructed soft-sensors for five test datasets including malfunctions. In order to account for the differences in behaviors after the malfunction, the prediction performances were evaluated in three periods: 0-600

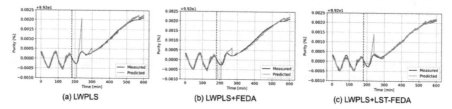

(a) LWPLS   (b) LWPLS+FEDA   (c) LWPLS+LST-FEDA

Figure 1: Prediction results of the soft-sensors in VAM process with MAL1

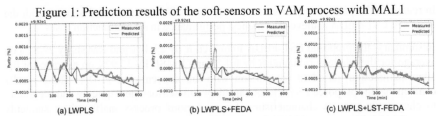

(a) LWPLS   (b) LWPLS+FEDA   (c) LWPLS+LST-FEDA

Figure 2: Prediction results of the soft-sensors in VAM process with MAL2

Table 1: Prediction performances in VAM process

Malfunction	Model	0-600min (the whole period)		180-240min (shortly after malfunction)		240-600min (after malfunction)	
		R	RMSE ($\times 10^{-4}$)	R	RMSE ($\times 10^{-4}$)	R	RMSE ($\times 10^{-4}$)
MAL1	-	0.49	23.6	0.67	74.6	1.00	0.74
	FEDA	0.75	8.90	0.56	28.0	0.99	0.96
	LST-FEDA	**0.99**	**1.22**	**0.91**	**3.49**	**1.00**	**0.44**
MAL2	-	0.59	3.27	-0.51	9.87	0.90	1.19
	FEDA	**0.76**	**2.06**	-0.45	**5.86**	0.95	1.07
	LST-FEDA	0.73	2.28	**-0.45**	6.86	**0.96**	**0.72**
MAL3	-	0.14	8.18	-0.55	25.8	0.80	0.81
	FEDA	0.33	4.11	-0.53	12.7	0.74	0.96
	LST-FEDA	**0.60**	**2.13**	**-0.35**	**6.48**	**0.92**	**0.54**
MAL4	-	0.95	0.84	0.92	1.67	0.96	0.68
	FEDA	0.94	0.79	**0.97**	**0.36**	0.93	0.88
	LST-FEDA	**0.96**	**0.66**	0.93	0.48	**0.96**	**0.66**
MAL5	-	0.92	17.5	-0.27	11.7	0.92	22.1
	FEDA	0.93	17.3	-0.57	9.83	0.92	22.0
	LST-FEDA	**0.93**	**15.8**	**0.19**	**9.08**	**0.93**	**20.1**

min (whole period), 180-240 min (shortly after the malfunction), and 240-600 min (after the malfunction). In this study, the correlation coefficient (R) and the root mean squared error (RMSE) were adopted as evaluation metrics. The best values in each test data are highlighted in bold in Table 1.

The proposed LST-FEDA achieved the best performance in almost all malfunction scenarios except for the whole period in MAL2. According to Figure 1, LST-FEDA successfully suppressed significant fluctuation of the prediction shortly after the malfunction in comparison with other two methods. Moreover, LST-FEDA could appropriately follow the measurement one hour after the malfunction occurrence.

In MAL2, RMSE of LST-FEDA for the whole period was slightly worse than the conventional FEDA. According to Figure 2, LST-FEDA was not able to avoid incorrect prediction deterioration shortly after MAL2 occurred; however, the conventional FEDA also did not make accurate predictions during this period, which suggests that it is impossible for any method to appropriately cope with MAL2 shortly after its occurrence.

In regard to the prediction performance after the malfunction, the soft-sensors with the proposed LST-FEDA achieved the highest performance in all malfunction cases.

In summary, the proposed LST-FEDA improved R by 22.4 % and RMSE by 29.8 % on average for the whole period, and R by 6.1 % and RMSE by 32.9 % on average for the after malfunction period in comparison with the conventional FEDA. These results confirm that the proposed LST-FEDA can adapt soft-sensors more quickly and accurately to changes in process characteristics due to various process malfunctions suddenly occurring.

4. Conclusion

In this study, we propose a new TL method for JIT modeling, referred to as LST-FEDA. The proposed LST-FEDA is an extension of FEDA defining a fixed number of recent samples close to a query in time as the target domain data and other data as the source domain data. By updating the target domain data for every new sample collection, it is possible to construct soft-sensors emphasizing characteristics of recent data more than past data. Thus, soft-sensors constructed with LST-FEDA quickly adapted to sudden changes in process characteristics that cannot be addressed by conventional TL methods.

To verify the performance of LST-FEDA, the proposed LST-FEDA was applied to the operation data of the VAM process. This result clearly showed that LST-FEDA achieved the best prediction performance in almost all malfunction cases in comparison with the conventional methods. The proposed method will contribute to efficient and safe process operation in the future.

In future works, we plan to apply LST-FEDA to real process data and assess its performance comprehensively. Additionally, we aim to refine LST-FEDA further by allowing for more flexible determination of the number of target domain samples.

References

P. Kadlec, R. Grbić, and B. Gabrys, 2011, Review of adaptation mechanisms for data-driven soft sensors, Computers & Chemical Engineering, 35, 1, pp.1-24

M. Kano and K. Fujiwara, 2013, Virtual sensing technology in process industries: trends and challenges revealed by recent industrial applications, Journal of chemical engineering of Japan, 46, 1, pp.1-17

C. G. Atkeson, A. W. Moore, and S. Schaal, 1997, Locally Weighted Learning, Springer Netherlands, Lazy Learning, pp.11-73

S. J. Pan and Q. Yang, 2010, A survey on transfer learning, IEEE Transactions on knowledge and data engineering, 22, 10, pp.1345-1359

N. Yamada and H. Kaneko, 2022, Adaptive soft sensor based on transfer learning and ensemble learning for multiple process states, Analytical Science Advances, 3, 5-6, pp.205-211

H. Daumé III, 2007, Frustratingly Easy Domain Adaptation, ACL Anthology, pp.256-263

Y. Machida, S. Ootakara, H. Seki, Y. Hashimoto, M. Kano, Y. Miyake, N. Anzai, M. Sawai, T. Katsuno, and T. Omata, 2016, Vinyl Acetate Monomer (VAM) Plant Model: A New Benchmark Problem for Control and Operation Study, IFAC-PapersOnLine, 49, 7, pp.533-538

Omega Simulation Co. Lid., https://www.omegasim.co.jp, (accessed 2023/08/05)

S. Kim and R. Okajima and M. Kano and S. Hasebe, 2013, Development of soft-sensor using locally weighted PLS with adaptive similarity measure, Chemometrics and Intelligent Laboratory Systems, 124, pp.43-49

S. Arlot and A. Celisse, 2010, A survey of cross-validation procedures for model selection, Statistics Surveys, 4, pp.40-79

Flavio Manenti, Gintaras V. Reklaitis (Eds.), Proceedings of the 34th European Symposium on Computer Aided Process Engineering / 15th International Symposium on Process Systems Engineering (ESCAPE34/PSE24), June 2-6, 2024, Florence, Italy

Non-Parametric Models for Yield Prediction in a Suzuki-Miyaura Coupling

Pablo J. Salazar,[a] Brahim Benyahia,[a*]

aDepartment of Chemical Engineering ,Loughborough University, Leicestershire, UK
b.benyahia@lboro.ac.uk

Abstract

The yield of a chemical reaction significantly influences efficiency, cost, safety, sustainability, and product quality in the chemical and pharmaceutical industries. Opportunities arise from automated flow chemistry platforms, generating real-time experimental data, for the application of machine learning methods, enhancing insights into reaction performance. In this study, non-parametric models are employed to predict Suzuki-Miyaura coupling reaction yields from 5760 automated flow-synthesis reactions. Non-parametric models, specifically, Gaussian Processes (GPs) with one-hot encoding are utilized, with a comparison of their performance against classic machine learning models, ensemble models, and a two-layer neural network. GPs, particularly those with Automatic Relevance Determination (ARD), demonstrate superiority over the evaluated machine learning models, revealing improvements in R^2 and root mean squared error metrics. The findings underscore the superiority of non-parametric models, especially GPs with ARD, over neural networks when using fractions of the dataset for training and predicting previously unseen reactions. Non-parametric models show potential for accurate yield predictions even with relatively small datasets, promising faster and more effective development of synthetic pathways in the chemical and pharmaceutical industries.

Keywords: Machine Learning, Gaussian Process, Flow Chemistry, Yield Prediction

1. Introduction

The use of algorithms and statistical models in chemical and pharmaceutical research has gained relevance, especially with the rise of High Throughput Experimentation (HTE) and continuous flow platforms. Automated platforms enhance reproducibility, efficiency, and real-time analytical data generation, leading to the rapid acquisition of standardized datasets (Bennett and Abolhasani, 2022). Experimentally obtained datasets, including negative outcomes, provide opportunities to develop realistic models for reaction outcome prediction, reaction condition prediction, and drug discovery (Angello et al., 2022). Model performance is evaluated with unseen test samples, making feature representation and model development active research areas (Pomberger et al., 2022). Chemical reaction yield, comparing obtained product to the theoretical maximum, is vital for optimizing reactions and resource use. The complexity stems from numerous reaction variables and challenges linked to the often small and varied data. This complexity escalates with descriptor and the choice of machine learning model, which directly impacts accuracy. Attaining high accuracy is essential in navigating this intricate process.

To address current challenges in predictive modelling, two benchmarks have been developed for machine learning in predicting reaction yields, namely the works done by Ahneman et al., (2018) on Buchwald-Hartwig amination and Perera et al., (2018) on

Suzuki-Miyaura coupling. The Buchwald-Hartwig dataset was evaluated using various models, among which Random Forests (RFs) demonstrating the best performance. Descriptors' impact was explored through one-hot encoding and random features, affirming the models' capabilities (Chuang and Keiser, 2018). For the Suzuki-Miyaura dataset, a two-layer Neural Network, trained with one-hot encoding, predicted high yields with a subset of the data (Granda et al., 2018). Schwaller et al. (2021) used Natural Language Processing (NLP) models and SMILES representations to train a transformer model (BERT), outperforming RF models on the Buchwald-Hartwig Dataset and showing comparable results on Suzuki-Miyaura. Graph Neural Networks (GNNs) introduced a new dimension, with YieldGNN (Saebi et al., 2023) outperforming BERT and RF models. A GNN with permutation invariance processing (Kwon et al., 2022) outperformed both BERT and its data-augmented version, providing superior yield predictions along with uncertainty estimation.

Graph Neural Networks (GNNs) excel in capturing molecular relationships for superior predictive performance. However, there is an opportunity to enhance predictions further with additional machine learning (ML) models using non-structural descriptors, especially for small datasets like Suzuki-Miyaura. A promising approach is exploring GPs as non-parametric probabilistic models, known for modelling complex relationships and uncertainties, particularly in scenarios with limited data availability (Rasmussen, 2004; Stach et al., 2021).

In predicting reaction yields, GPs perform similarly to RFs regardless of the descriptors used in an HTE dataset of trimipramine (Pomberger et al., 2022). Simple one-hot encoding yields high-performing predictions, with slightly lower error for more complex descriptors. The capabilities of GP models, such as kernel selection and Automatic Relevance Determination (ARD), are yet to be explored in yield predicting models. This work assesses the predictive capabilities of GP models against classic models (k-Nearest Neighbour, Support Vector Machine (SVM)), ensemble models (RF, XGBoost), and a two-layer neural network (Granda et al., 2018) using Suzuki-Miyaura dataset with one-hot encoding. The GP model, with automatic relevance determination, outperforms other models. Evaluating the model on fractions of the dataset confirms its high performance and potential for handling relatively small datasets. Anticipated benefits include more accurate yield predictions, expediting synthetic pathway development in the chemical and pharmaceutical industries.

2. Methods

2.1. Suzuki-Miyaura coupling dataset.

Perera and colleagues (2018) developed and automated flow system for reaction screening of a Suzuki-Miyaura coupling reaction involving the preparation of reaction segments at regular timer intervals and their analysis through high-resolution Liquid Chromatography-Mass Spectrometry (LC-MS). The process involved the injection of stock solution aliquots of the catalyst, reactants, ligands, and bases into a carrier solvent stream. This setup allowed the variation of a complete set of variables including 11 ligands, 7 bases, and 4 solvents, resulting in a total of 5760 reactions.

In the present work, a one-hot vector encoding of the set of variables was applied to explicitly evaluate the performance of machine learning models in the prediction of reaction yields. This type of encoding has been demonstrated to deliver high-quality predictions for reaction yields in previous studies on HTE-generated datasets. An overview of the reaction, along with the specific reactants, ligands, bases, solvents, and reaction conditions as well as an example of the vector encoding are detailed in Fig. 1.

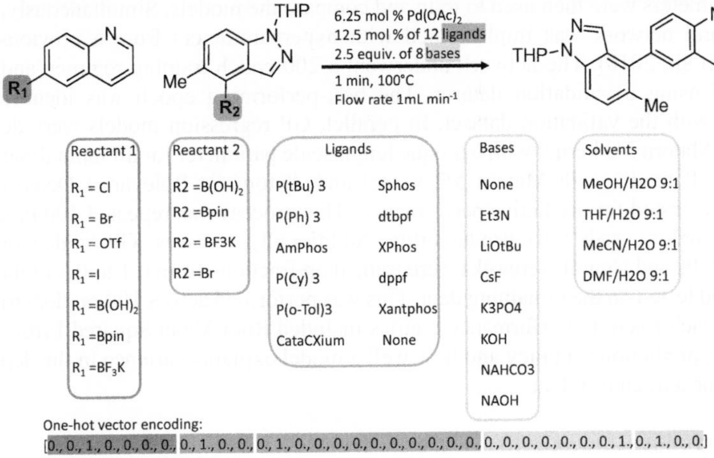

Reactant 1	Reactant 2	Ligands		Bases	Solvents
R_1 = Cl	R2 =B(OH)$_2$	P(tBu) 3	Sphos	None	MeOH/H2O 9:1
R_1 = Br	R2 =Bpin	P(Ph) 3	dtbpf	Et3N	THF/H2O 9:1
R_1 = OTf	R2 = BF3K	AmPhos	XPhos	LiOtBu	MeCN/H2O 9:1
R_1 =I	R2 =Br	P(Cy) 3	dppf	CsF	DMF/H2O 9:1
R_1 =B(OH)$_2$		P(o-Tol)3	Xantphos	K3PO4	
R_1 =Bpin		CataCXium	None	KOH	
R_1 =BF$_3$K				NAHCO3	
				NAOH	

One-hot vector encoding:
[0., 0., 1., 0., 0., 0., 0., 0., 1., 0., 0., 0., 1., 0., 0., 0., 0., 0., 0., 0., 0., 0., 0., 0., 0., 0., 0., 0., 0., 1., 0., 1., 0., 0.]

Fig. 1. Suzuki-Miyaura coupling reaction overview with specifications of the set of variables along with a visual representation of one-hot vector encoding.

2.2. Non-parametric Models

Gaussian Processes (GPs) are non-parametric models known for their flexibility and ability to capture complex non-linear relationships within data. GPs are defined by mean and covariance functions, as expressed in Eq. (1), allowing them to model the entire probability distribution over functions.

$$f(x) \sim \mathcal{GP}\big(m(x), k(x, x')\big) \tag{1}$$

The mean is a function of x, which in practical applications takes to be the zero function, and the covariance $k(x, x')$ expresses the expected covariance of $f(x)$ at the points x, and x'. The covariance function involves hyper-parameters, subject to optimization, capturing the relationships of the encoding of the reactants according to the respective yield of the reactions.

In this study, the evaluation of yield prediction performance led to the identification of the Matern 5/2 covariance with a single lengthscale hyperparameter as the initial effective choice. However, employing Automatic Relevance Determination (ARD), which assigns a lengthscale parameter to each input dimension, yielded an enhancement in predictive performance. The significance of these lengthscales lies in their role in defining the smoothness and oscillatory behaviour of the model. While a shared lengthscale in Matern 5/2 implies a uniform impact across dimensions, ARD's individual lengthscales enable customized adjustments, thereby influencing the contribution of each input dimension to the model's predictive accuracy.

2.3. Experimental Setup

To evaluate non-parametric models for yield prediction, GP models were compared with various machine learning (ML) models using the Suzuki-Miyaura coupling dataset. The data was split into 70% for training and 30% for testing. Hyperparameter tuning was conducted via grid search and five-fold cross-validation, optimized K-Nearest Neighbors, Support Vector Machine Regression, Random Forests, and XGBoost. Optimal hyperparameters were then used to train and compare the models. Simultaneously, a two-layer neural network was implemented with hyperparameters from a previous study (Granda et al., 2018). The network underwent a 200-epoch training regimen and it was evaluated using a validation dataset. The best-performing epoch was identified and retrained with the validation dataset. In parallel, GP regression models were deployed using the Matern 5/2 kernel with a unique lengthscale parameter for all input dimensions. Another GP model with Matern 5/2 kernel and Automatic Relevance Determination (ARD) was tested for predictive performance. This process was repeated 100 times with different random seeds for reproducibility. Additionally, to assess GP models on small datasets, GPs and Neural Networks were trained on fractions from 0.1 to 0.8 of the entire dataset and tested on the remaining data. This was performed across 100 random train/test splits for each fraction. Performance metrics included Root Mean Squared Error and R^2, evaluating prediction accuracy and how well a model explains variance in the dependent variable for unseen test data.

3. Results

3.1. Model Comparison

The best-performing models from each of the 100 70/30 train/test splits were compared. As shown in Fig. 2a, k-Nearest Neighbour demonstrated the poorest predictive performance among all the tested models, while SVM, Neural Networks, and Ensemble models (Random Forest and XGBoost) exhibited similar performance, with their R^2 and RMSE falling within the confidence interval of the Neural Network; Ensemble models performed better. Gaussian Processes with Matern 5/2 showed slightly superior performance to XGBoost. Notably, GP with Automatic Relevance Determination (ARD) demonstrated the best performance, with its 95% confidence interval values surpassing the best possible performance of its counterparts. Additionally, GP models exhibited less variability in performance. Regarding Root Mean Squared Error (Fig. 2b), the results aligned with the R^2 metric, where GP with ARD displayed the lowest error, indicating superior predictive accuracy.

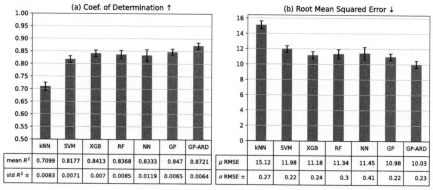

Fig. 2. Predictive performance metrics on test data for the evaluated models. Including the mean and standard deviation across 100 random 70/30 train/test splits for each model. Values and 95% confidence intervals are shown for: A) Coefficient of determination, and B) RMSE.

3.2. Predictive Performance Fractions of the Dataset

The performance of predicting reaction yields was assessed using dataset fractions ranging from 0.1 to 0.8, with the remaining portion used for predictions. Both configurations of GPs were compared with a two-layer neural network, each fraction trained 100 times with different random seeds. Fig. 3 illustrates a performance trend, showing that GP models exhibit significantly better performance when trained with 10% of the dataset. GPs consistently outperform neural networks, as evident in the depicted confidence intervals for each model. Notably, GP with Automatic Relevance Determination (ARD) consistently outperforms both models. It's worth highlighting that GP with ARD, trained with 0.4 of the dataset, achieves slightly better performance than training the neural network and GP model with 0.8 of the dataset.

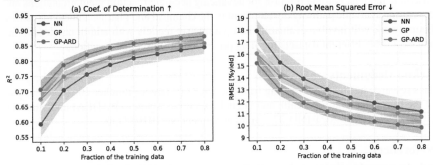

Fig. 3. Predictive performance of training dataset fractions for Neural Network, GP, and GP with ARD models. The shaded regions around each line depict the 95% confidence interval based on 100 tests for: A) Coefficient of determination, and B) Root mean squared error.

4. Discussion

The evaluation of GP models for reaction yield prediction indicates that optimizing a single lengthscale parameter for all input dimensions achieves comparable or superior performance to ensemble models, two-layer neural networks, and transformer-based models reported in previous studies. Optimizing lengthscales for each input dimension significantly impacts the model's ability to discern individual dimensions' influence on predictive accuracy, resulting in substantial performance improvement against all tested models, comparable to GNN-based models known for superior structural information encoding (Saebi et al., 2023). Gaussian processes show adaptability for modelling intricate relationships without a specific functional form, pivotal in datasets with complex patterns or challenging scenarios for traditional ML models. ARD kernels enhance adaptability by automatically adjusting feature relevance, prioritizing those significantly contributing to yield prediction. The non-parametric nature of GPs with ARD proves beneficial in scenarios with varying feature importance, and automatic feature selection within ARD kernels prevents overfitting. This study unveils GPs' intriguing capability to achieve high performance even with small datasets (10% of the total), attributed to their non-parametric adaptability. Despite the reported slightly lower prediction errors with additional descriptors in ML models, the limitation of one-hot encoding lies in its inability to capture physical or chemical information. This study explicitly focuses on the impact of non-parametric models on yield predictions, achieving high performance even with limited dataset fractions. In reaction optimization, accuracy in yield prediction becomes crucial for informed decision-making, anticipating faster and more effective synthetic pathway development in the chemical and pharmaceutical industries.

5. Conclusion

In conclusion, the integration of advanced algorithms and statistical models in chemical and pharmaceutical research, driven by high-throughput experimentation and continuous flow platforms, has yielded significant progress. Benchmark studies on real-time analytical data showcase the potential of innovative approaches, such as Natural Language Processing models and Graph Neural Networks, surpassing traditional models in predicting reaction yields. Furthermore, exploring predictive modelling challenges highlights the efficacy of Gaussian Processes, especially in enhancing accuracy for datasets like Suzuki-Miyaura, even with small sizes. The use of GPs with automatic relevance determination demonstrates superior performance compared to classic and ensemble models, holding promise for advancing accurate reaction yield predictions and expediting synthetic pathway development in the chemical and pharmaceutical industries. Future work will involve evaluating non-parametric models with additional descriptors and exploring different datasets for yield prediction in subsequent reactions.

Acknowledgments

This research has received funding from the UKRI (reference number 10038378) as part of the European Union – Health and Digital Executive Agency (HADEA) under the call HORIZON-HLTH-2021-IND-07 – grant agreement No 101057430.

References

D.T. Ahneman, J.G. Estrada, S. Lin, S.D. Dreher, A.G. Doyle, 2018, Predicting reaction performance in C–N cross-coupling using machine learning. Science, 360, 186–190.

N.H. Angello, V. Rathore, W. Beker, A. Wołos, E.R. Jira, R. Roszak, et al., 2022, Closed-loop optimization of general reaction conditions for heteroaryl Suzuki-Miyaura coupling. Science, 378, 399–405.

J.A. Bennett, M. Abolhasani, 2022, Autonomous chemical science and engineering enabled by self-driving laboratories. Curr Opin Chem Eng, 36, 100831.

K.V. Chuang, M.J. Keiser, 2018, Comment on "Predicting reaction performance in C–N cross-coupling using machine learning." Science, 362, 589–604.

J.M. Granda, L. Donina, V. Dragone, D-L. Long, L. Cronin, 2018, Controlling an organic synthesis robot with machine learning to search for new reactivity. Nature, 559, 377–381.

Y. Kwon, D. Lee, Y.S. Choi, S. Kang, 2022, Uncertainty-aware prediction of chemical reaction yields with graph neural networks. J Cheminform, 14, 2.

D. Perera, J.W. Tucker, S. Brahmbhatt, C.J. Helal, A. Chong, W. Farrell, et al., 2018, A platform for automated nanomole-scale reaction screening and micromole-scale synthesis in flow. Science, 359, 429–434.

A. Pomberger, A.A. Pedrina McCarthy, A. Khan, S. Sung, C.J. Taylor, M.J. Gaunt, et al., 2022, The effect of chemical representation on active machine learning towards closed-loop optimization. React Chem Eng, 7, 1368–1379.

C.E. Rasmussen, 2004, Gaussian Processes in machine learning. Lect Notes Comput Sci, 3176, 63–71.

M. Saebi, B. Nan, J.E. Herr, J. Wahlers, Z. Guo, A.M. Zurański, et al., 2023, On the use of real-world datasets for reaction yield prediction. Chem Sci, 14, 4997–5005.

P. Schwaller, A.C. Vaucher, T. Laino, J.-L. Reymond, 2021, Prediction of chemical reaction yields using deep learning. Mach Learn Sci Technol, 2, 015016.

E. Stach, B. DeCost, A.G. Kusne, J. Hattrick-Simpers, K.A. Brown, K.G. Reyes, et al., 2021, Autonomous experimentation systems for materials development: A community perspective. Matter, 4, 2702–2726.

Flavio Manenti, Gintaras V. Reklaitis (Eds.), Proceedings of the 34th European Symposium on Computer Aided Process Engineering / 15th International Symposium on Process Systems Engineering (ESCAPE34/PSE24), June 2-6, 2024, Florence, Italy

Learning Interpretable Representation of Koopman Operator for Non-linear Dynamics

Deepak Kumar,[a] Vinayak Dixit,[a] Manojkumar Ramteke [a,b] and Hariprasad Kodamana [a,b,*]

[a] *Department of Chemical Engineering, Indian Institute of Technology Delhi, New Delhi, 110016, India*

[b] *Yardi School of Artificial Intelligence, Indian Institute of Technology Delhi, New Delhi, 110016, India*

*kodamana@chemical.iitd.ac.in

Abstract

In this study, we introduce an innovative approach for extracting linear representations from nonlinear dynamical systems lifted to a higher-dimensional space. The Koopman Operator (KO), a powerful tool used to linearize nonlinear dynamics, forms the cornerstone of our approach. However, the analytical identification of KO often presents significant challenges, leading to the reliance on deep learning techniques. These techniques, while powerful, suffer from a lack of transparency due to their 'black-box' nature, thus limiting their broader applicability in scientific domains.

To address this limitation, we employ the Equation Learner (EQL) network in place of conventional neural networks. The EQL, known for its interpretability, is adept at producing explicit mathematical equations that represent the latent embeddings of the system used to convert state variables to lifted space and bring them back to original space. It not only preserves the predictive strength inherent in deep learning models but also infuses the process with the clarity and interpretability typically associated with symbolic regression.

As a practical application of our methodology, we have applied this algorithm to a Continuous Stirred-Tank Reactor (CSTR) example. This implementation successfully linearizes the nonlinear dynamics of the CSTR, demonstrating the efficacy of our approach in a real-world scenario.

Keywords: Koopman Operator, Equation Learner, Data-driven Discovery

1. Introduction

The landscape of scientific exploration and understanding, especially in the realm of complex dynamical systems, is undergoing a significant transformation. Linearizing non-linear dynamics of chemical processes is preferred due to the simplicity and ease of analysis that linear models offer. These models are more computationally efficient and easier to use for real-time process control and optimization. Additionally, linear control theories, such as PID control, are well-established and more straightforward to implement, making them a practical choice for consistent process performance and stability.

The Koopman operator (KO) provides a powerful method for linearizing complex dynamics by transforming a non-linear dynamical system into an infinite-dimensional linear system [Koopman (1931)]. It does this by acting on the space of observable functions of the state, rather than directly on the state itself. This approach allows the dynamics of the system to be described linearly, even though the system itself may be inherently non-linear. By doing so, KO facilitates the use of linear analysis techniques on complex, non-linear systems, making them more accessible and easier to understand and predict.

The analytical identification of KO, crucial for linearizing complex dynamics, presents a substantial challenge due to its infinite-dimensional nature. This complexity makes deriving an exact analytical representation of KO for complex systems a daunting task. However, Autoencoders, renowned for their ability to compress and encode high-dimensional data into a more manageable form, can approximate KO by transforming the intricate, non-linear state space of a dynamical system into a higher-dimensional, linearly analyzable space. This approach enables the application of linear techniques to systems that are fundamentally non-linear.

Despite this innovative application, autoencoders are often viewed as "black boxes," presenting a significant limitation in terms of interpretability, posing a challenge in scenarios where understanding the underlying process is crucial. This lack of transparency and interpretability is particularly problematic in fields where decision-making relies on a clear understanding of the system's behavior, such as in safety-critical applications like chemical engineering. Thus, there is an increasing need for advancements that balance predictive accuracy with transparency and interpretability in these models.

Integrating Equation Learner (EQL) networks into the encoder and decoder components of an autoencoder used for estimating Koopman observables represents a significant advancement in enhancing interpretability [Martius and Lampert (2016)]. EQL networks, known for their capacity in symbolic regression, generate explicit mathematical equations rather than just numerical outputs. This attribute is key to understanding the inner workings of the model. Incorporating EQLs into encoder and decoder transforms these processes into equation-driven operations, thus making the approach of approximating Koopman observables transparent and interpretable.

The use of EQLs means that the Koopman observables are expressed through clear mathematical relationships, elucidating how different variables and states interact within the system's dynamics. This level of clarity is essential, particularly in complex systems analysis, as it allows for a deeper understanding of the interconnections and dependencies within the system. Furthermore, the explicit equations provided by EQLs facilitate thorough analysis and validation, aligning the model's outputs with established physical laws and theoretical principles. Such validation is critical in fields where accuracy needs to be complemented with theoretical conformity.

Moreover, the interpretability and transparency offered by EQL-based autoencoders significantly enhance the trust and usability of these models in practical scenarios. Practitioners and researchers are more likely to adopt models that provide not just accurate predictions but also a comprehensible rationale behind these predictions. This approach combines the predictive strength of machine learning with the much-needed element of interpretability, making these models particularly valuable in applications where understanding the underlying dynamics is as crucial as the predictive accuracy itself.

2. Methodology

2.1. Koopman Theory

Koopman theory states that any nonlinear system can be evolved in a linear system in infinite-dimensional space using KO. This provides an elegant approach to analyse and control nonlinear dynamical systems linearly [Lusch et al. (2018)]. Among the current techniques to estimate the KO, one of the most prevalent is extended dynamic mode decomposition, where the operator is identified from a dataset that is linked either spatially or temporally, depending on the description of the system [Proctor et al. (2016)]. In this methodology, the observables of the system are transformed from their original vector space to a different one which has a higher dimension than the native state [Schmid (2010]. This transformation is deliberately made a nonlinear one and the set of these nonlinear mappings is called the dictionary. In the new higher dimensional vector space, it is theorized that the states evolve linearly.

Let us look at a nonlinear dynamical system in discrete-time domain, which can be represented by

$$x_{n+1} = f(x_n) \tag{1}$$

where $x_n \in R^n$, $f \in R^n$ is a continuously differentiable mapping. Now, let the elements of dictionary be represented by g where, $g \in R^p$, then according to Koopman theory we get,

$$g(x_{n+1}) = K\big(g(x_n)\big) \tag{2}$$

where $g(x) \in R^m$, m is a higher dimensional space, that represents the lifted space. The collection set of all such g is called dictionary denoted by D.

$$D \equiv \boldsymbol{G} = [g_1 \ g_2 \ .....] \tag{3}$$

The next step is to create two vectors at different time steps or states, Y_k and Y_{k+1}, which represent the evolution of the system at a state k and one step after it.

$$Y_k = \begin{pmatrix} g_0\big(x_{(0,k)}, x_{(1,k)} x_{(2,k)} \cdots x_{(n,k)}\big) \\ \vdots \\ g_p\big(x_{(0,k)}, x_{(1,k)} x_{(2,k)} \cdots x_{(n,k)}\big) \end{pmatrix} \tag{4}$$

where $x_{(i,k)}$ is the ith state variable at time step k.

Then we can write,

$$Y_{k+1} = KY_k \tag{5}$$

The KO is then estimated using extended dynamic mode decomposition by the optimization of following expression as problem:

$$min_K \big|\big|Y_{k+1} - KY_k\big|\big|_2 \tag{6}$$

2.2. Equation Learner (EQL) Network

Neural networks are, by definition, black box model that find an unknown relation between the input and the output data set provided. If the data is sufficient enough, it is expected to generalize the results to a new data set provided, which is extrapolation. But black box models are not useful as they don't provide any insight or understanding of the system which is desired in industries for process safety and control. For the purpose of learning approximate analytical representations from the neural network, we implement an EQL framework [Martius and Lampert (2016]. A feedforward L layered deep neural network was implemented. The initial $L - 1$ layers consisted of a linear mapping to a vector $z^{(l)}$ which is further transformed using activation functions and mathematical combinations.

The linear mapping of the layer l can be defined as,

$$z^{(l)} = W^{(l)} y^{(l-1)} \tag{7}$$

Further, the elementary function $f_i^{(l)}$ is operated on i^{th} element of $z^{(l)}$.

$$g_i^{(l)} = f_i^{(l)}(x) \tag{8}$$

where, $f_i^{(l)}(x) \in \{x, sin(x), cos(x), e^x, log(x), \dots\}$

Furthermore, elementary operations like multiply, divide, etc. are applied among selected elements of $g^{(l)}$ as shown in Figure 1.

The parameters of the network that are to be optimized using training can be denoted by θ, where

$$\theta = \{W^{(1)}, \dots, W^{(L)}\} \tag{9}$$

which could be found by minimizing the Mean Squared Error Loss function combined with a regularisation function.

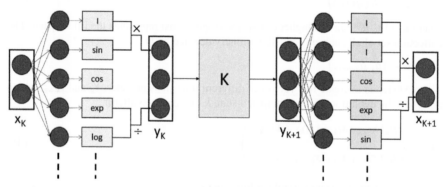

Figure 1: Illustration of integration of Koopman operator and equation learner framework

2.2.1. Interpretable Koopman Operator Estimation

We propose a new method to discover D using EQL as shown in Figure 1. Encoder EQL (J) network is used to encode the original input x_K to lifted inputs y_K which is linearly mapped to its next state y_{K+1} using Koopman operator (K). Furtehr, we use a decoder EQL (L) network to get back the next original inputs x_{K+1} from y_{K+1}. The final loss value is a combination of following losses:

$$L_{\text{reconstruction}} = |x^t - LJ(x^t)|_2^2 \tag{10}$$

$$L_{\text{state estimation}} = |x^{t+1} - LKJ(x^t)|_2^2 \tag{11}$$

$$L_{\text{Koopman observable}} = |KJ(x^t) - J(x^{t+1})|_2^2 \tag{12}$$

$$L_{0.5}^*(w) = \begin{cases} |w|^{\frac{1}{2}}, & if \ |w| \geq a \\ \left(\dfrac{-w^4}{8a^3} + \dfrac{3w^2}{4a} + \dfrac{3a}{8}\right)^{\frac{1}{2}}, & if \ |w| < a \end{cases} \tag{13}$$

In these equations, $||\,.\,||_2^2$ denotes the squared Euclidean norm.

The $L_{0.5}^*$ regularization is designed to be less sensitive to outliers than the $L1$ norm and to promote sparsity more than the $L2$ norm. [Kim et al. (2020)] The $L_{0.5}^*$ is defined as a piecewise function that changes its behavior based on the magnitude of the parameter w relative to a threshold a. In this case study, the regularization is found to work best at $a = 1$.

3. Results and Discussion

The proposed framework's performance in linearizing the dynamics of reversible reaction $A \rightleftharpoons B$ in a Continuous Stirred Tank Reactor (CSTR) under isothermal conditions was evaluated through its ability to predict the concentrations of reactants A, C_A, and B, C_B over time. The encoder part of the network (J) lifts the 2 inputs to 5 inputs and decoder part provides us next states in original space.

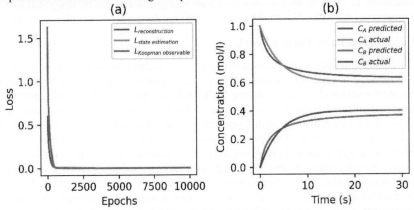

Figure 2: (a) Various training losses vs epochs and (b) State estimation using initial condition and recursive prediction on the training data. Note that training was done for one time step ahead prediction whereas the plots show prediction based on initial conditions only

As shown in Figure 2(a), the convergence of loss metrics, encompassing $L_{reconstruction}$, $L_{state\ estimation}$, and $L_{Koopman\ observable}$ losses, was rapid and stabilized at near-zero values early in the training process. This fast convergence suggested a strong initial learning phase, attributed to the effective architecture and optimization via gradient descent. The stability of these losses at minimal values without overfitting corroborated the architecture's capability to generalize well to the dynamics of the CSTR system.

Complementing the loss metrics, as shown in Figure 2(b), the predictions of reactant concentrations, C_A and C_B, showed a remarkable alignment with the actual data. It also shows the recursive prediction capabilities of the network. Although trained for one-step-ahead predictions, the graph reveals the model's ability to predict the time evolution of C_A and C_B by recursively applying its learned dynamics, starting from the initial conditions and proceeding without further reference to actual data points. The close alignment between the recursive predictions and the actual data underscores the model's robust understanding of the reaction kinetics, capturing the depletion and formation of the reactants over time.

The application of the $L0.5^*$ regularization played a pivotal role in the network's performance, ensuring a balance between model complexity and predictive precision. This regularization likely prevented overfitting, a common challenge in neural network training.

Also, the use of EQL networks in the encoder and decoder segments afforded complete interpretability of the learned transformations. This transparency is a substantial advantage, as it not only validates the internal workings of the model but also provides explicit mathematical formulations of the observable functions governing the reaction kinetics. These formulations offer a deeper analytical insight into the reaction process, enabling a clear understanding of how the model arrives at its predictions.

Our approach, focusing on interpretable, data-driven estimation of the KO via the EQL network, inherently differs from conventional deep neural network (DNN) methods. The core of our methodology is interpretability, a feature typically not prioritized in other linearization techniques. This unique focus makes direct comparisons with other methods less relevant, as they do not share this central aspect of interpretability, crucial in our research for understanding complex system dynamics. Our research aims to set a new benchmark in the field by demonstrating how interpretability can be integrated into the estimation of the KO, offering clear insights into the dynamics of complex systems.

4. Conclusion and Future Work

The combination of a well-designed neural network architecture with EQL networks has demonstrated significant promise in accurately capturing and predicting complex chemical reaction dynamics, offering both predictive power and valuable interpretive insights. Future work should validate the model's effectiveness beyond the training set to ensure that it can generalize to different initial conditions and system perturbations. We propose that the application of our linearized models to specific control contexts represents a significant and promising avenue for future research. This could potentially involve the integration of our methodology into various control scenarios to demonstrate its practical utility and effectiveness. The ability to generate explicit Koopman observables and their inverses also opens up new avenues for leveraging the model in educational settings, where understanding the mechanics of chemical processes is paramount.

References

Schmid, P. J. (2010). Dynamic mode decomposition of numerical and experimental data. Journal of fluid mechanics, 656, 5-28.

Lusch, B., Kutz, J. N., & Brunton, S. L. (2018). Deep learning for universal linear embeddings of nonlinear dynamics. Nature communications, 9(1), 4950.

Li, Q., Dietrich, F., Bollt, E. M., & Kevrekidis, I. G. (2017). Extended dynamic mode decomposition with dictionary learning: A data-driven adaptive spectral decomposition of the Koopman operator. Chaos: An Interdisciplinary Journal of Nonlinear Science, 27(10).

Proctor, J. L., Brunton, S. L., & Kutz, J. N. (2016). Dynamic mode decomposition with control. SIAM Journal on Applied Dynamical Systems, 15(1), 142-161.

Proctor, J. L., Brunton, S. L., & Kutz, J. N. (2018). Generalizing Koopman theory to allow for inputs and control. SIAM Journal on Applied Dynamical Systems, 17(1), 909-930.

Martius, G., & Lampert, C. H. (2016). Extrapolation and learning equations. arXiv preprint arXiv:1610.02995.

Xiao, Y., Zhang, X., Xu, X., Liu, X., & Liu, J. (2020). A deep learning framework based on Koopman operator for data-driven modeling of vehicle dynamics. arXiv preprint arXiv:2007.02219.

Koopman, B. O. (1931). Hamiltonian systems and transformation in Hilbert space. Proceedings of the National Academy of Sciences, 17(5), 315-318.

Kim, S., Lu, P. Y., Mukherjee, S., Gilbert, M., Jing, L., Čeperić, V., & Soljačić, M. (2020). Integration of neural network-based symbolic regression in deep learning for scientific discovery. IEEE transactions on neural networks and learning systems, 32(9), 4166-4177.

Flavio Manenti, Gintaras V. Reklaitis (Eds.), Proceedings of the 34th European Symposium on
Computer Aided Process Engineering / 15th International Symposium on Process Systems
Engineering (ESCAPE34/PSE24), June 2-6, 2024, Florence, Italy

Enhancing real-time data querying in chemical engineering: A bilevel vocabulary-constrained seq2seq approach

Zeheng Zhao, Jinsong Zhao

Department of Chemical Engineering, Tsinghua University, Beijing 100084, China
zh-zhao21@mails.tsinghua.edu.cn, jinsongzhao@tsinghua.edu.cn

Abstract

Real-time interaction between front-line operators and the data stored in SQL databases is an essential part of the intelligent chemical process industry, and NL2SQL (natural language to SQL) is currently lacking in the process industry. First, we constructed an NL2SQL dataset with characteristics of the process industry, which poses challenges to existing NL2SQL algorithms. Next, we proposed a seq2seq model with bilevel vocabulary constraints to adapt to the characteristics of the process industry. The first level is a global restriction to identify the entities and functions used in the SQL output. The second level is a local restriction to limit the range of the next output word determined by BNF (Backus-Naur form) grammar, simplifying the training of the model in complex sentences. On the proposed ChESQL dataset, the Jaccard similarity increased from 69.94 % to 74.10 %, and the exact matching rate increased from 4.36 % to 7.95 %.

Keywords: NL2SQL, natural language processing, seq2seq, machine translation.

1. Introduction

A real-time question-answering system helps in decision-making and improves accuracy in chemical plants. A crucial aspect of the question-answering system is translating NL questions into SQL queries. Our contribution to the NL2SQL system in chemical engineering includes two parts. First, we introduce ChESQL, a new dataset with few precedents in the industrial field, based on an alarm management database from a petroleum refinery. The dataset comprises 500 prototype questions, which are augmented to 2130 NL-SQL pair instances (Figure 1). The dataset exhibits three characteristics: extensive use of MySQL functions for real-time calculations; numerous entities in the dataset, which matches the case in chemical engineering; being derived from real-world problems, which makes it more complex. Second, we propose a seq2seq (sequence-to-sequence) model with bilevel vocabulary constraints (Figure 2) to address these challenges. The first level is global and involves creating a vocabulary subset for the output SQL query. The second level is local and relies on a BNF based on MySQL syntax. By using bilevel constraints, we enhance precision both lexically and grammatically.

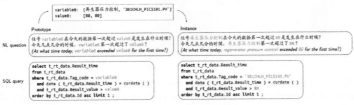

Figure 1: An example in ChESQL, in both prototype and instance forms.

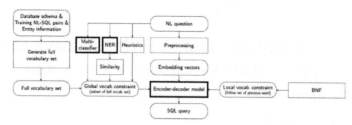

Figure 2: Architecture of the proposed model. Bold blocks represent neural models.

2. Dataset

2.1. Dataset overview

ChESQL is a dataset created specifically for the process industry. The lengths of the 500 distinct SQL queries and 2130 NL questions are shown in Figure 3(a)(b). Figure 1 shows an example NL-SQL pair from ChESQL, and Figure 4 shows another pair from GeoQuery (Iyer et al., 2017), which is a commonly used dataset. Through comparison, it can be seen that in ChESQL, the three characteristics of the process industry mentioned before are reflected. Specifically, first, ChESQL involves more functions (shown in underlined bold). Although the number of functions in ChESQL is limited, they are all related to data processing (such as average and max) or time-related operations in MySQL (such as timediff and curdate), which are naturally required in the process industry. Second, the dataset contains many named entities and numbers (shown in light gray). Moreover, they may have different representations in SQL and NL, and the relation between the two can only be known through definitions but not through the training of neural models. Third, the SQL queries in ChESQL can be complex. On the one hand, the dataset is taken from a real industrial process and verified by engineers. On the other hand, it is a feature of SQL. Simple questions may also have complex expressions, so the length of the SQL queries and NL questions are not always related (Figure 3(c)). In addition to the length, complexity is also reflected in the number of SQL keywords contained in each SQL query (Figure 3(f)). Through comparison with other existing single-domain datasets in Table 1, we see that ChESQL has the highest average count of functions and distinct keywords and the second highest number of distinct SQL query prototypes and NL questions. Please note that although we present ChESQL with NL questions in Chinese, compared to other datasets in English, the difference is only reflected in average NL length, and other comparisons are totally fair.

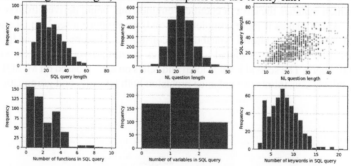

Figure 3: Basic statistics of ChESQL. (a) Histogram of the lengths of 500 distinct SQL queries. (b) Histogram of the lengths of 2130 NL questions. (c) Scatter plot of the lengths of NL-SQL pairs. (d) Histogram of the number of functions in SQL queries. (e) Histogram of the number of variables in SQL queries. (f) Histogram of the number of keywords in SQL queries.

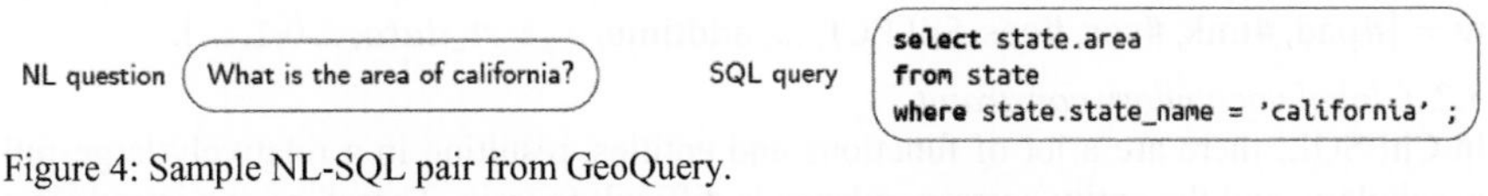

NL question (What is the area of california?)   SQL query

```
select state.area
from state
where state.state_name = 'california' ;
```

Figure 4: Sample NL-SQL pair from GeoQuery.

Table 1: Comparison of ChESQL and other single-field NL2SQL datasets.

Dataset	#SQL	#NL	Ave SQL len	Ave NL len	Ave # of functions	Ave # of variables	Ave # of keywords	Ave # of distinct keywords
ChESQL	**500**	**2130**	24.5	22.8	**1.62**	0.88	7.36	**6.52**
Academic	185	196	37.8	13.2	0.54	1.59	7.46	5.21
ATIS	**947**	**5280**	100.8	10.5	0.22	4.36	19.29	5.50
GeoQuery	246	877	27.8	7.5	0.92	0.44	7.51	4.10
IMDB	89	131	30.5	10.2	0.30	1.34	6.16	4.70
Restaurants	23	378	30.6	10.1	0.35	1.78	6.13	4.09
Scholar	193	817	39.0	6.6	0.70	1.56	8.82	6.41
Yelp	110	128	29.3	9.9	0.45	1.98	6.22	4.63

2.2. Construction of the dataset

The dataset contains 4 tables with a total of 24 columns. The definition of each table is as follows: Table t_rt_info is the tag information table, containing meta-information such as tag codes, and upper and lower alarm thresholds. Table t_rt_data is the real-time data table, containing the timestamps and measured values of tags described in Table t_rt_info. Table t_model_data is the model definition table, which defines the inference models used when an alarm occurs. Table t_inference_data contains the inference results. These four tables are typical as they include the whole process of defining data, obtaining data, defining custom functions, and applying custom functions.

To generate a prototype NL-SQL pair, we first write an NL question and its corresponding SQL query, and then label the words that can be replaced, such as entities and numbers. Then the prototype pair is used to generate more instance pairs by replacing the labeled words. Finally, we check the validity and consistency of SQL queries and the diversity and unambiguity of NL questions.

When splitting the dataset into training and test sets, we use the method described in (Finegan-Dollak et al., 2018), providing question-based and query-based division.

2.3. Evaluation metrics

The evaluation criteria of the dataset include the following three. Jaccard similarity evaluates how close the output SQL query is to the true query in vocabulary, therefore it can test if the NL2SQL system can find out the correct functions and entities. The SQL validity rate evaluates how many output queries are grammatically correct. The exact matching rate assesses how many output queries are identical to the true queries.

3. Model

3.1. Generating the full vocabulary set

Compared to machine translation tasks, the output vocabulary in NL2SQL tasks depends heavily on the dataset, which needs to be decided case by case. As shown in Figure 2, after obtaining the dataset, we added the table and column names according to the table schema, the correspondence between the entities in NL and SQL according to the entity information, and the functions according to the SQL queries in the training set. Then SQL keywords such as SELECT are added. Finally, some values, such as 0, 1, True, and False, and punctuation are added. Together, these make up the full vocabulary set w required for the output in the seq2seq model.

$$w = [\#pad, \#unk, \#sos, \#eos, SELECT, \ldots, addtime, \ldots, t\_rt\_data, \ldots 0, 1, \ldots].$$

3.2. Global vocabulary constraint

In ChESQL, there are a lot of functions and entities, resulting in a relatively large full vocabulary, and the entity correspondence is difficult to train. Therefore, we introduce a first level of vocabulary constraint, sifting out the words for each input NL question. As shown in Figures 2 and 5, multi-classifier and NER are used to accomplish this task.

The multi-classifiers include two separate classifiers, identifying which tables and which functions will be used, respectively. These two types of words have small vocabulary, high frequency in the dataset, and weak correspondence with NL expressions, so the multi-classification strategy is suitable. Once the classification is finished, only the corresponding functions and tables (including the columns in the table) are added to the global vocabulary constraint $\mathbb{W}_{\text{global}}$.

NER is used to identify the entities. Entities have a large vocabulary, low frequency in the dataset, and strong correspondence with NL expression. After NER recognizes the entities, the SQL form of the entities will be added to $\mathbb{W}_{\text{global}}$.

Finally, we use a heuristic approach to identify the numbers. Numbers in NL questions are added directly to $\mathbb{W}_{\text{global}}$.

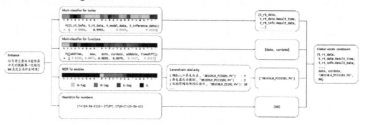

Figure 5: The flow chart for generating global vocabulary constraints from an NL question.

3.3. Local vocabulary constraint

When the model translates NL questions into SQL queries, further restrictions are needed to ensure the validity of the output. Therefore we introduce the second level of vocabulary constraint, which is a local one. BNF can specify the syntax of languages using simple notations, which allows a sentence to be parsed. The follow set $\mathbb{W}_{\text{local},i}$ contains all valid words that can directly follow one word, which is decided after BNF is defined. For example, in MySQL, "SELECT" can be followed by any column but never another "SELECT" or "FROM". This way, the validity of the output SQL query is guaranteed.

3.4. Seq2seq model with bilevel vocabulary constraint

The global and local vocabulary constraints are put into use in the seq2seq model. Denote the 0-1 indicator matrix as I_{global} and I_{local}, each with size $l \times s$, where l is the target length of the output SQL query and s is the size of the full vocabulary set w discussed in Section 3.1. The (i, j)-th element in I_{global} and I_{local} represents if the j-th word in w is allowed for the i-th place in the output SQL query under the global vocabulary constraint $\mathbb{W}_{\text{global}}$ and the local vocabulary constraint $\mathbb{W}_{\text{local},i}$.

When training, we design a loss function that punishes when a word that does not satisfy the bilevel vocabulary constraints has a high output weight. More specifically, the loss function is

$$\text{Loss}(\boldsymbol{O}) = \text{CrossEntropy}(\boldsymbol{O}, \boldsymbol{t}) + \frac{\alpha}{l} \text{Sumsqr}\left(\boldsymbol{O} \otimes \left(\boldsymbol{1} - \boldsymbol{I}_{\text{global}}\right)\right)$$
$$+ \frac{\beta}{l} \text{Sumsqr}\left(\boldsymbol{O} \otimes \left(\boldsymbol{1} - \boldsymbol{I}_{\text{local}}\right)\right).$$

where O is the output weight matrix with size $l \times s$, Sumsqr(A) is the operation of summing all squared values in matrix A, and α and β are two adjustable parameters.

When predicting, for each output token, we mask the words that do not satisfy the bilevel vocabulary constraints, i.e., multiplying the decoder output weight vector d by the 0-1 indicator vectors i_{global} and i_{local} (both with size $1 \times s$ as we predict only one word at a time) before performing the argmax operation.

$$\text{Next\_token\_index} = \text{argmax}(d \otimes i_{\text{global}} \otimes i_{\text{local}})$$

4. Experiment

4.1. Setup

We use ChESQL and query-based split, which results in a training set including 1740 NL-SQL pairs with 408 distinct SQL queries and a test set including 390 NL-SQL pairs with 92 distinct SQL queries. For word embedding, we use chinese-bert-wwm-ext (Cui et al., 2021). For the multi-classifier, we use NeuralNLP (Tencent, 2019), which is a TextRNN framework based on attentioned GRU. For NER, we use NCRF++ (Yang and Zhang, 2018), which is a framework based on BiLSTM-CRF. For the encoder-decoder model, we use a transformer model with the attention mechanism. We train the seq2seq model for 50 epochs, using fine-tuned $\alpha = \beta = 10^{-3}$.

4.2. Results

4.2.1. Multi-classifier and NER

In the multi-classifier, each NL question is labeled by one or multiple classes. And we assess the model label-wise. The result after 20 training epochs is shown in Table 2.

Table 2: Model evaluation for the two multi-classifiers trained separately for tables and functions.

Tables/Functions	Data split	#True labels	#Predict labels	#Right labels	F1-score
Tables	Training	2474	2474	2473	0.9996
	Test	552	558	535	0.9640
Functions	Training	3928	3876	3841	0.9844
	Test	832	828	824	0.9928

In NER, each token in the NL questions is labeled by the BIO tagging. Therefore, the performance of the model can be assessed by its accuracy and F1-score. The result after 20 training epochs is shown in Table 3.

Table 3: Model evaluation for the NER model.

Data split	#All tokens	#Right tokens	Accuracy	F1-score
Train	46926	46889	0.9992	0.9917
Test	10788	10693	0.9912	0.9664

4.2.2. NL2SQL translation

We have the plain seq2seq model as the baseline. The three aforementioned evaluation metrics are listed in Table 4. Both the question-based and the query-based split are used.

Table 4: Model evaluation for the NL2SQL task.

Model	Proposed model with constraints		Baseline seq2seq	
Dataset split	Query-based	Question-based	Query-based	Question-based
Jaccard similarity	0.9772/0.7410	0.9871/0.8181	0.9555/0.6994	0.9561/0.7985
SQL validity rate	1.0000/1.0000	1.0000/1.0000	0.9028/0.5225	0.9707/0.7271
Exact matching rate	0.7826/0.0795	0.8948/0.2535	0.6092/0.0436	0.6939/0.1718

4.3. Analysis

4.3.1. Multi-classifier and NER

From the results in Table 2 and Table 3, we can see that the multi-classifier and NER work with high accuracy. Therefore, these additional modules play an effective role in aiding the seq2seq model in deciding which words are valid.

4.3.2. NL2SQL translation

Compared to the baseline model, our model performed better in all evaluation metrics. Jaccard similarity in the test set increased from 69.94 % to 74.10 % in the query-based split, which means the output of the model contains more correct vocabularies after we add on the global vocabulary constraint. The SQL validity rate achieves 100% in our model in all trials as it is inherited from the local vocabulary constraint. In terms of the exact matching rate, the bilevel vocabulary constraint does improve the performance, e.g., from 4.36 % to 7.95 % in the test set of the query-based split. However, the exact matching rate still has a large potential, as in all setups, this metric exceeds 60 % in the training set and remains below 20 % in the test set. This can be further improved by considering result matching rate, using a larger dataset or even large language models.

4.3.3. Question-based and query-based tasks

Question-based and query-based splits offer challenges at different levels. Question-based split has the same structure of SQL queries in both the training set and test set, so it becomes a classification task rather than a translation task. A query-based split ensures that there are no queries derived from the same prototype in the training set and test set. In all models, the evaluation metrics of the question-based split are better than those of the query-based split. This also shows that in future NL2SQL tasks, we need to place more emphasis on query-based dataset splitting, as it is closer to practical applications.

5. Conclusion

We constructed ChESQL, which is a Chinese NL2SQL dataset in the field of chemical engineering, featuring a large number of entities and functions. We then proposed a seq2seq model with bilevel vocabulary constraints to enhance the NL2SQL translation performance. A global vocabulary constraint narrows down the vocabulary range to aid finding the correct entities and functions. A local vocabulary constraint enables the system to be aware of the grammatical state and thereby generate valid queries. This model outperforms the baseline seq2seq model, improving Jaccard similarity, SQL validity rate, and exact match rate.

References

Cui, Yiming, Che, Wanxiang, Liu, Ting, Qin, Bing, Yang, Ziqing, 2021, Pre-Training With Whole Word Masking for Chinese BERT, IEEE, 10.1109/TASLP.2021.3124365.

Finegan-Dollak, Catherine, Kummerfeld, Jonathan K., Zhang, Li, Ramanathan, Karthik, Sadasivam, Sesh, Zhang, Rui, Radev, Dragomir, 2018, Improving Text-to-SQL Evaluation Methodology, ACL, 10.18653/v1/p18-1033.

Iyer, Srinivasan, Konstas, Ioannis, Cheung, Alvin, Krishnamurthy, Jayant, Zettlemoyer, Luke, 2017, Learning a Neural Semantic Parser from User Feedback. ACL, 10.18653/v1/p17-1089.

TENCENT, 2019, NeuralNLP-NeuralClassifier, https://github.com/Tencent/NeuralNLP-NeuralClassifier.

Yang, Jie, Zhang, Yue, 2018, NCRF++: An Open-source Neural Sequence Labeling Toolkit, Association for Computational Linguistics, 10.18653/v1/p18-4013.

Zhong, Victor, Xiong, Caiming, Socher, Richard, 2017, Seq2SQL: Generating Structured Queries from Natural Language using Reinforcement Learning, arXiv, 10.48550/ARXIV.1709.00103.

Flavio Manenti, Gintaras V. Reklaitis (Eds.), Proceedings of the 34th European Symposium on Computer Aided Process Engineering / 15th International Symposium on Process Systems Engineering (ESCAPE34/PSE24), June 2-6, 2024, Florence, Italy

Long-term Constant Relation Analysis of Variables Based on Bayesian Optimization and SSA and application to the monitoring of non-stationary process

Jingzhi Rao,[a] Chengyu Han,[a] Chong Liu,[a] Wei Sun,[a,*] Jingde Wang,[a]

[a]*College of Chemical Engineering, Beijing University of Chemical Technology, North Third Ring Road 15, Chaoyang District, Beijing, 100029, China*
Corresponding Author's E-mail: sunwei@mail.buct.edu.cn

Abstract

Stationary subspace analysis (SSA) as a long-term constant relationship analysis method has been widely used in non-stationary process monitoring, where traditional multivariate statistical process monitoring (MSPM) is not applicable in that most of them are based on the assumption of the process is stationary. It is considered that the data is a linear summation of stationary and non-stationary sources in SSA and the long-term constant relation between non-stationary variables can be effectively extracted. In the SSA steps, the data should be manually segmented before input, and the number of the stationary sources also needs to be manually determined. If the parameters are not set appropriately, the monitoring results will be compromised. Bayesian optimization (BO) is an effective parameter tuning approach in machine learning, due to the ability to find good points in a search space without many function evaluations. Thus, an SSA-BO non-stationary process monitoring strategy is proposed in this paper. Firstly, the input data is normalized with z-score and divided into N epochs. Then the number of the stationary sources d_s is determined, so that the dimension of projection matrices in stationary and non-stationary subspaces can be determined and they are initialized respectively. The two projection matrices are optimized by conjugate gradient descend. BO are used to search for the optimal combination of parameters thus obtaining the optimal projection matrix with an improved objective function. Finally, monitoring statistics and control limits are constructed with the projections of the original variables in the stationary subspace to enable the non-stationary process monitoring. The proposed method is validated by a numerical case and an industrial case, and the monitoring results demonstrate that optimal parameters combination could be searched by BO.

Keywords: long-term constant relation, non-stationary, fault detection

1. Introduction

Process monitoring is as an effective method to ensure the stability and safety of real-time process operation. A large amount of operation data collected by Distributed Control System (DCS) provides abundant support for data-driven process monitoring methods (Cheng Ji et al., 2022). Multivariate Statistical Process Monitoring (MSPM) has gained considerable attention due to the fact that MSPM doesn't require considerable prior process knowledge and their practical implementations are straightforward. The basic idea of represented MSPM method Principal Component Analysis (PCA), is to project the process data into a low-dimensional subspace that contains the most variance of the original data and accounts for correlations among different variables. Most of

MSPM method are based on the assumption that the process is operated in a pre-defined normal state (Scott, D et al., 2020), which is usually stationary. However, non-stationary variables could exist in large-scale and complex chemical processes, which could be a result of equipment aging, adjustments in normal plans, and external disturbances (Cheng Ji et al., 2022). It brings huge difficulty for MSPM to achieve satisfactory process monitoring performance. To further develop process monitoring methods for non-stationary processes is of great concern.

Many researches have been made to address the issues of non-stationary process monitoring, and representative methods include difference strategies, model adaptive updating strategies and long-term constant relationship analysis. Long-term constant relationship analysis is considered as an effective way for handling non-stationary processes, by which the long-term constant relationship among the non-stationary variables is extracted. Stationary subspace analysis (SSA) is a typical long-term constant relationship analysis method for extracting the stationary and non-stationary components of a high-dimensional signal which was first proposed by Bunau et al (Von Bünau, P et al., 2009). There are two key parameters when establishing the SSA model, number of epochs the data divided N and number stationary sources d_s, which need to be determined manually and will affect the performance of SSA monitoring model. In this regard, optimization algorithms can be hybridized with SSA to tune automatically the parameters, resulting in the optimal parameters combination. Bayesian Optimization (BO) is good choice in optimization of parameters of machine learning algorithms, which has been shown to outperform other prior art global optimization algorithms on a number of challenging optimization benchmark functions (D.R. Jones et al., 2001). Therefore, in order to obtain better monitoring results, BO is adopted to optimize the two key parameters of SSA.

2. Theory and method

2.1. Stationary Subspace Analysis

SSA is a blind source separation approach that factorizes the observed signal $x(t)$ into stationary and non-stationary source based on the Eq. (1):

$$x(t) = As(t) = [A^s, A^n]\begin{bmatrix} s^s(t) \\ s^n(t) \end{bmatrix} \tag{1}$$

where A is an invertible matrix. $s^s(t)$ is the stationary sources and $s^n(t)$ is the non-stationary source. The goal of SSA is to separate the stationary sources and non-stationary sources by estimating a demixing matrix.

$$P = A^{-1} = \begin{bmatrix} P^s \\ P^n \end{bmatrix} \tag{2}$$

$$\begin{bmatrix} s^s(t) \\ s^n(t) \end{bmatrix} = A^{-1} x(t) = \begin{bmatrix} P^s x(t) \\ P^n x(t) \end{bmatrix} \tag{3}$$

where P^s and P^n are the stationary and non-stationary projection matrices.
The specific steps of SSA are as follows:
1. The process data are divided into N consecutive and nonoverlapping epochs, $[X_1, X_2 \dots \dots X_N]$. For any projection matrix P, it is possible to obtain the mean $\mu_{s,i} = P^s \mu_i$ and covariance matrix $\Sigma_{s,i} = P^s \Sigma_i$ of stationary sources in each epoch, thus obtaining the distribution $Norm(\mu_{s,i}, \Sigma_{s,i})$.

2. The distance between the stationary sources and the standard normal distribution is calculated in each epoch which is measured by the Kullback-Leibler divergence D_{KL}. D_{KL} are summed over each epoch to construct an objective function.

$$f(P^s) = \sum_i^N D_{KL}[Norm(\mu_{s,i}, \Sigma_{s,i})\|Norm(0,I)] \qquad (4)$$

corresponds to the following optimization objective:

$$min \sum_i^N D_{KL}[Norm(\mu_{s,i}, \Sigma_{s,i})\|Norm(0,I)] \qquad (5)$$

$$s.t. P^s(P^s)^T = I \qquad (6)$$

The problem is usually solved by the gradient descend method to obtain the optimal stationary projection matrix P^s and stationary sources $P^s x(t)$

3. Similarly, an objective function can be constructed as follows to obtain the optimal non-stationary projection matrix P^n and stationary sources $P^n x(t)$:

$$g(P^n) = \sum_i^N D_{KL}[Norm(\mu_{n,i}, \Sigma_{n,i})\|Norm(0,I)] \qquad (7)$$

corresponds to the following optimization objective:

$$max \sum_i^N D_{KL}[Norm(\mu_{n,i}, \Sigma_{n,i})\|Norm(0,I)] \qquad (8)$$

$$s.t. P^n(P^n)^T = I \qquad (9)$$

2.2. Bayesian Optimization

The goal of BO is to minimize or maximize an objective function in a bounded area. The idea of constructing the BO objective function is as follows:

D_{KL} between an n-dimensional multivariate series and the standard normal distribution can be calculated as follows:

$$D_{KL,M} = \frac{1}{2}[\|\mu_p\|^2 - logdet(\Sigma_p) + Tr(\Sigma_p) - n] \qquad (9)$$

Summed D_{KL} of one of the n-dimensional multivariate series can be calculated with Eq. (10):

$$D_{KL,S} = \frac{1}{2}[\sum_{i=1}^n\|\mu_i\|^2 - \sum_{i=1}^n logdet(\Sigma_i) + \sum_{i=1}^n Tr(\Sigma_i) - \sum_{i=1}^n 1] \qquad (10)$$

where $\|\mu_p\|^2$ is the sum of squares of the means of each series and $Tr(\Sigma_p)$ is the sum of diagonal elements of the original multivariate series.

$$\|\mu_p\|^2 = \sum_{i=1}^n\|\mu_i\|^2 \qquad (11)$$

$$Tr(\Sigma_p) = \sum_{i=1}^n Tr(\Sigma_i) \qquad (12)$$

$$error = D_{KL,M} - D_{KL,S} = \frac{1}{2}[\sum_{i=1}^n logdet(\Sigma_i) - logdet(\Sigma_p)] = \frac{1}{2}log\left(\frac{\Sigma_1\Sigma_2...\Sigma_n}{det(\Sigma_p)}\right) \qquad (13)$$

where $[\Sigma_1\Sigma_2...\Sigma_n]$ are the diagonal elements of Σ_p. Thus the average D_{KL} for each of the n-dimensional multivariate series can be calculated:

$$\frac{D_{KL,S}}{n} = \frac{D_{KL,M} - error}{n} \qquad (14)$$

Considering the stationary source and non-stationary source, the optimization goals of BO is:

$$Max: log\left(\frac{D_{KL,M,n} - error_n}{D - d_s} \Big/ \frac{D_{KL,M,s} - error_s}{d_s}\right) \tag{15}$$

$$s.t. \ N \geq \frac{D - d_s}{2} + 2 \tag{16}$$

where $D_{KL,M,s}$ and $D_{KL,M,n}$ are the overall D_{KL} of stationary source and non-stationary source. d_s is the number of stationary source and D is the dimensions of the original signals. The goal of the BO is to find the optimized parameter combination (N, d_s) to optimize the performance of SSA.

2.3. Monitoring steps

The SSA-BO process monitoring method is divided into two sections, offline modeling and online monitoring. In offline modeling, the input data is normalized with z-score and divided into N epochs and the number of the stationary sources d_s is determined, so that the projection matrices in stationary and non-stationary subspaces can be initialized. The two projection matrices are optimized by conjugate gradient descend. BO are used for searching for the optimal combination of parameters thus obtaining the optimal projection matrix with an improved objective function. Finally, Mahalanobis distance MS and control limits L are constructed with the projections of the original variables in the stationary subspace to enable the non-stationary process monitoring.

In online monitoring, the inputted data are projected into the stationary subspace with the projection matrix obtained in offline modeling. MS is calculated with the stationary series and if MS exceed L, the system will trigger an alarm.

3. Cases and results

3.1. Numerical case

In order to verify the effectiveness of the above objective function, the 5-dimensional stationary source $s^s(t) = [\ s_{1t}{}^s, s_{2t}{}^s \ldots \ldots s_{5t}{}^s]$, the 5-dimensional non-stationary source $s^n(t) = [\ s_{1t}{}^n, s_{2t}{}^n \ldots \ldots s_{5t}{}^n]$ and $A \in R^{10 \times 10}$ are generated randomly, thus obtaining $X = A \cdot [s^s(t), s^n(t)]^T = (x_{1t}, x_{2t} \ldots x_{10t})$. The total number of samples is 3000, the training dataset includes 2000 samples and the rest 1000 samples are divided into the test dataset.

The faults are introduced to x_{7t} at 500th samples, where a random walk process is introduced to the data causing the deviation from its original trend.

Fault Detection Rate (FDR) and False Alarm Rate (FAR) are applied to evaluate the process monitoring performance. FDR and FAR of SSA with different parameter combinations are shown in Figure 1.

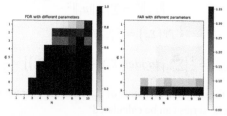

Figure 1 monitoring performance of SSA with different parameters combinations

It can be observed that with d_s increases, FDR will also increase. However, large d_s will lead to high FAR, which means worse performance. In addition, the number of epochs N will have a certain effect on the monitoring results. Thus, BO is performed to search the optimized parameters, the initial number of random searches is set to 20, the number of iterations is 50, and the search interval for d_s is (1,9), the search interval for N is (2,10). The optimized parameters result, $N = 4.434 \approx 4$, $d_s = 5.198 \approx 5$, indicates that number of stationary sources of original signals could be obtained by BO. The monitoring results of SSA with the parameters above are in Figure 2.

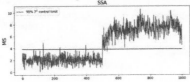

Figure 2 monitoring results of SSA with optimized parameters

It can be observed that when the fault occurs, SSA triggers an alarm and FDR is 0.994, FAR is 0.006, which indicates that the parameters searched by BO is effective.

3.2. Industrial case

In the catalytic reforming process unit of a petrochemical company, the pressure drop at the hot end of the heat exchanger often increases abnormally, which pose a significant safety risk if left unaddressed. A section of historical data with abnormal rise of pressure drop is selected, including 3000 samples, and the sampling frequency is 1 minute, each sample consists of 21 variables.

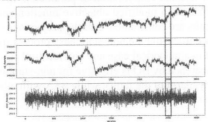

Figure 3 Variation trends of some key variables

As shown in Figure 3, the pressure drop at the hot end of the heat exchanger follows a similar non-stationary trend to that of the circulating hydrogen feed rate. However, around the 2450th sample point, an abnormal increase in the pressure drop at the hot end of the heat exchanger is observed because of the different trends from circulating hydrogen feed rate and stationary naphtha feed rate, which suggests that the fault occurs. To validate the proposed method, the first 2000 samples are used for training the model, while the remaining samples are the test dataset to verify the model. The results of BO are in Table 1.

Table 1 Bayesian Optimization results of industrial case

No	Target	Allowed	N	d_s
1	8.238	True	9.506	14.69
2	15.24	False	2.002	6.744
...	...	...	...	...
56	**11.34**	**True**	**12.03**	**9.217**
...	...	...	...	...
69	8.169	True	12.40	14.22
70	10.47	False	5.526	6.069

The optimized parameters, $N = 12.029 \approx 12$, $d_s = 9.217 \approx 9$. The monitoring results of SSA with different parameters are in Figure 4.

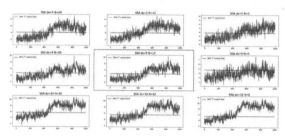

Figure 4 monitoring results of SSA with different parameters

It can be observed from Figure 4 that SSA with the optimized parameters triggers an alarm at 459th sample points, while there are large number of false alarms or miss alarms in the results of SSA with other parameters, which indicates that the parameters searched by BO is effective.

4. Conclusion

In this work, a process monitoring strategy based on SSA-BO is proposed. BO is applied to search for the optimal combination of parameters in SSA thus obtaining the optimal projection matrix with a modified objective function and improved monitoring statistics, and control limits are constructed with the projections of the original variables in the stationary subspace to enable the non-stationary process monitoring. The strategy proposed is also applied in a numerical case and an industrial case. The results show that the parameters of SSA searched by BO is effective for non-stationary process monitoring and it can trigger an early alarm of the faults, while SSA with other parameters results in large number of false alarms or miss alarms.

Acknowledgments

This work was supported by the National Natural Science Foundation of China (grant numbers 22278018).

References

Ji, C., Sun, W., 2022, A review on data-driven process monitoring methods: Characterization and mining of industrial data. Processes,10,2, 335.

Scott, D., Shang, C., Huang, B.,Huang, D.,2022, A holistic probabilistic framework for monitoring nonstationary dynamic industrial processes. IEEE Transactions on Control Systems Technology, 29, 5, 2239-2246.

Ji, C., Ma, F., Wang, J., & Sun, W.,2022, Early Identification of Abnormal Deviations in Nonstationary Processes by Removing Non-Stationarity. In Computer Aided Chemical Engineering, 49, 1393-1398.

Von Bünau, P., Meinecke, F. C., Király, F. C., Müller, K. R.,2009, Finding stationary subspaces in multivariate time series. Physical review letters, 103, 21, 214101.

D.R. Jones.,2001, A taxonomy of global optimization methods based on response surfaces. Journal of Global Optimization, 21, 4, 345–383.

Flavio Manenti, Gintaras V. Reklaitis (Eds.), Proceedings of the 34th European Symposium on Computer Aided Process Engineering / 15th International Symposium on Process Systems Engineering (ESCAPE34/PSE24), June 2-6, 2024, Florence, Italy

Flexibility Analysis Using Surrogate Models Generated via Symbolic Regression

Tim Forster[a], Daniel Vázquez[b], Isabela Fons Moreno-Palancas[a], Gonzalo Guillén-Gosálbez[a,*]

[a] *Department of Chemistry and Applied Biosciences, Institute for Chemical and Bioengineering, ETH Zurich, Vladimir Prelog Weg 1, 8093 Zurich, Switzerland*

[b] *IQS School of Engineering, Universitat Ramon Llull, Via Augusta 390, 08017 Barcelona, Spain*

[*] *Corresponding author: gonzalo.guillen.gosalbez@chem.ethz.ch*

Abstract

Computing the flexibility index to quantify the extent to which disturbances and uncertainties can affect a given process can be very challenging, especially if constraints are hard to describe algebraically or if they are unavailable as closed-form expressions. Here, we tackle the challenge of solving a flexibility index problem in the presence of such constraints by using symbolic regression. In essence, we replace those constraints in the flexibility index problem by an algebraic surrogate built using symbolic regression. This facilitates the solution process of the flexibility index problem by allowing the user to apply off-the-shelf deterministic solvers. We showcase the capabilities of our approach in a case study, discussing the pros and cons of the suggested approach relative to other existing approaches.

Keywords: Uncertainty, Flexibility Index, Symbolic Regression, Surrogate Modelling.

1. Introduction

To continuously satisfy safety, operational or cost constraints, a production process needs to be operable even in the presence of slight disturbances or uncertainties during the operational phase (Grossmann et al., 1983). In a pioneering work, Swaney and Grossmann (1985a, 1985b) introduced a method to compute an index that assesses the flexibility of a given process design under operation, i.e., the ability to continue operation under uncertainty. Due to the deterministic form of the flexibility index problem, it can only be computed if constraints are available as closed-form mathematical expressions. This makes the flexibility index computation challenging if very complex constraints are involved in the model or if the constraints are not available analytically (Floudas et al., 2001). To overcome this challenge, several approaches have been described to assess the feasible space and the flexibility of a model for cases where only input-output data is observed. Some of these works use surrogate models, such as Kriging (Boukouvala and Ierapetritou, 2012), neural networks (Metta et al., 2021), or high-dimensional model representations (Boukouvala et al., 2010). One limitation of such modelling approaches is that the user must assume an *a priori* model structure. Another approach was described by Sachio et al. (2023), where the authors created an available Python package to obtain representations of the design space boundary. Further, Zhao et al. (2021) used derivative free optimization to calculate the flexibility index. Alternatively, analytical equations could be derived using symbolic regression to replace only some of the constraints, which would allow using the originally described flexibility index problem (Grossmann et al., 1983) and state-of-the-art solvers. Building on this idea, our proposed approach relies on the application of a symbolic regression algorithm that finds analytical equations that can reproduce given data precisely. The identified models can subsequently be incorporated in the flexibility problem, thereby simplifying the calculations, and enabling the user to apply off-the-shelf deterministic solvers. This approach allows to decouple the surrogate model training from solving the flexibility index problem. Below, we illustrate the capabilities of our approach applied to a continuous stirred tank reactor, where we discuss the model building time, prediction accuracy of the model, and the solution approach for the resulting hybrid flexibility formulation.

2. Problem Statement

Some process parameters $\theta_k, k \in K$ might be affected by uncertainties. Additionally, some process variables $z_n, n \in N$ could be adjusted to counteract these uncertainties. In what follows, we shall consider a given number of process constraints $f_j(\theta, z), j \in J$. To result in a feasible operation, each of those constraints must be fulfilled, meaning that the inequalities $f_j(\theta, z) \leq 0$ should hold for all constraints. Usually, a nominal operating point $\theta_k^N, k \in K$ is defined for a process, without considering variations in the uncertain parameters. At this point, the question is how far the values can deviate from such a point such that the process remains feasible. A first step to assess the process flexibility, according to Grossmann et al. (1983), could be the evaluation of the worst constraint violation $u = \max\{f_j(\theta, z)\}$, which can be minimized by adjusting the control variable. This leads to the so-called feasibility function $\psi(\theta)$ of the process, defined in Eq. (1):

$$\psi(\theta) = \min_{z} \max_{j \in J}\{f_j(\theta, z)\} \qquad (1)$$

For the case when $\psi(\theta) \leq 0$, the process remains feasible for the given realization of θ, and infeasible otherwise. A modeler might face difficulties to formulate closed-form constraints $f_j(\theta, z)$ when they are very complex to be described, or even inaccessible in an algebraic form (i.e., if the constraints are expressed as a system of ordinary or partial differential equations). In this case, the solution of the system in Eq. (1) is not straightforward. To overcome this challenge, we split the set of constraints J into the two subsets $G \subset J$ and $H \subset J$. The first subset, G, contains the constraints $\hat{f}_j(\theta, z) \leq 0, j \in G$ that are already available as closed-form expressions. On the other hand, subset H contains the constraints $\tilde{f}_j(\theta, z) \leq 0, j \in H$, which are unavailable as closed-form constraints or very difficult to describe. Subsequently, the constraints in H are replaced with closed-form surrogate models that are constructed via symbolic regression.

3. Methodology

3.1. Fundamentals of the Flexibility Index Problem
For the sake of brevity, we do not reproduce here the entire fundamentals of feasibility and flexibility theory. Instead, we refer readers to the original works by Grossmann et al. (1983), Halemane and Grossmann (1983), and Swaney and Grossmann (1985a, 1985b). A short summary of the derivation of the flexibility index problem is given below for the sake of completeness and readability. Originally, Grossmann et al. (1983) proposed an approach to quantify the largest possible uncertainty set $\theta \in T$, such that the process remains feasible over the entire range of θ. For this, the variable δ was introduced, which

can be regarded as a scaled deviation from a nominal point θ^N, such that any realization of θ around that nominal point results in a feasible solution (i.e., the feasibility function $\psi(\theta)$ remains non-positive). For this work, we assume a rectangular form for T given by $T = \{\theta : \theta_k^N - \delta\Delta\theta_k^{min} \leq \theta_k \leq \theta_k^N + \delta\Delta\theta_k^{max}\}$, while other options are documented and compared in literature (Pulsipher et al., 2019). In this rectangular form, the parameters $\Delta\theta^{min}$ and $\Delta\theta^{max}$ represent the minimum lower and maximum upper deviations (Grossmann et al., 2014). This deviation δ is optimized to maximize the area around the nominal operating point θ^N, represented by $T(\delta)$. This results in a bi-level optimization problem, given in Eq. (2), which determines the flexibility index ζ.

$$\zeta = \max_{\delta}\left\{\delta : \max_{\theta}\psi(\theta) \leq 0\right\} \tag{2}$$

After a reformulation of the problem given by Swaney and Grossmann (1985a, 1985b), the application of the Karush-Kuhn-Tucker conditions, and the introduction of an active set strategy by Grossmann and Floudas (1987), the flexibility index problem can be posed as a single-level optimization problem, given in Eq. (3). A summary of these reformulations is comprehensively covered by Pulsipher et al. (2019).

$$\begin{aligned}
\zeta = \min_{\delta} & \; \delta \\
s.t. \quad & f_j(\theta, z) - u + s_j = 0, \qquad \forall j \in J \\
& \sum_j \lambda_j = 1 \\
& \sum_j \lambda_j \frac{\partial f_j(\theta, z)}{\partial z_n} = 0, \qquad \forall n \in N \\
& s_j \leq M(1 - y_j), \qquad \lambda_j \leq y_j, \qquad \forall j \in J \\
& \sum_j y_j \leq |N| + 1 \\
& \theta \in T(\delta), \qquad \delta \geq 0, \qquad \lambda_j, s_j \geq 0, \qquad \forall j \in J
\end{aligned} \tag{3}$$

In this formulation, u, s_j, λ_j, and y_j refer, respectively, to the maximum constraint violation, the slack variables, the Lagrange multipliers, and binary variables of constraint f_j. Furthermore, $|N|$ represents the dimensionality of adjustable process variables, and M a large-enough parameter that acts as upper bound for the slack variables s_j.

3.2. Replacement of Constraints by Surrogate Models

It might be challenging to formulate closed-form constraints $f_j(\theta, z)$ to solve the problem given in Eq. (3). In such a case, we define the two sets of constraints, H and G, respectively, as described in section 2. Subsequently, we replace the constraints $\tilde{f}_j$ (or parts of them) by algebraic surrogates built with a symbolic regression algorithm, where the surrogate functions replacing the constraints $\tilde{f}_j$ will be denoted by $\mathcal{F}_j$. The flexibility index problem in Eq. (3) is therefore reformulated into the hybrid expression in Eq. (4), which combines the backbone of the original flexibility index problem with a data-driven model component for the replaced constraints. As models for $\mathcal{F}_j, j \in H$, we build algebraic expressions using a symbolic regression algorithm that identifies closed-form equations that map specific inputs to observed target variables. This leads to the following model with analytical surrogates embedded.

$$\zeta = \min_{\delta} \delta$$

$$s.t. \quad \hat{f}_j(\theta, z) - u + s_j = 0, \qquad \forall j \in G$$

$$\mathcal{F}_j(\theta, z) - u + s_j = 0, \qquad \forall j \in H$$

$$\sum_{j \in J} \lambda_j = 1$$

$$\sum_{j \in G} \lambda_j \frac{\partial \hat{f}_j(\theta, z)}{\partial z_n} + \sum_{j \in H} \lambda_j \frac{\partial \mathcal{F}_j(\theta, z)}{\partial z_n} = 0, \qquad \forall n \in N \tag{4}$$

$$s_j \le M(1 - y_j), \qquad \lambda_j \le y_j, \qquad \forall j \in J$$

$$\sum_{j \in J} y_j \le |N| + 1$$

$$\theta \in T(\delta), \qquad \delta \ge 0, \qquad \lambda_j, s_j \ge 0, \qquad \forall j \in J$$

4. Case Study

4.1. Software Implementation

The calculations discussed in this work were carried out on an AMD Ryzen 7 Pro CPU and 32 GB of RAM. We used Python v3.10.13 with NumPy v1.26.1, SciPy v1.11.3, and pyDOE v0.3.8 to construct the sampling dataset. The symbolic regression algorithm provided by Guimerà et al. (2020), the Bayesian Machine Scientist (BMS), was used to train the surrogate models. The resulting flexibility index problem was modeled in Pyomo (Hart et al., 2011) v6.6.2 and solved using BARON (Sahinidis, 1996) v22.9.30.

4.2. Continuous Stirred Tank Reactor

We apply the hybrid flexibility approach discussed above to a continuous stirred tank reactor (CSTR). In the reactor, a first order reaction takes place, where a raw material A reacts irreversibly to form a product B. The reaction rate r ($g\ L^{-1}\ s^{-1}$) is calculated through an Arrhenius expression, from the temperature T (K), activation energy E ($J\ mol^{-1}$), universal gas constant R ($J\ mol^{-1}\ K^{-1}$), and a pre-exponential factor k (s^{-1}), i.e., $r = A \cdot (k \cdot 10^{10}) \cdot \exp\{-E/(RT)\}$, where A ($g\ L^{-1}$) is the concentration of the raw material in the reactor. The temperature and volume in the vessel are constant and set to $T = 310\ K$, and $V = 100\ m^3$, respectively. The feed concentration of material A is denoted by A^0 ($g\ L^{-1}$). The feed rate F ($m^3\ s^{-1}$) represents the control variable $z = [F]$ and is bounded between $F \in [\underline{F}, \overline{F}] = [100, 120]\ m^3 s^{-1}$. Additionally, the inlet concentration A^0 and the pre-exponential factor k are regarded as uncertain parameters $\theta = [A^0, k]$ within the bounds $\underline{\theta} = [0.8\ g\ L^{-1}, 5.76\ s^{-1}]$ and $\overline{\theta} = [1.2\ g\ L^{-1}, 8.64\ s^{-1}]$, respectively. The nominal operating point is $\theta^N = [1.0\ g\ L^{-1},\ 7.00\ s^{-1}]$. The goal of the flexibility analysis is to quantify the largest possible rectangular set $\theta \in T(\delta)$, such that the process is still feasible. Besides imposing bounds on the variables, we seek to keep the concentration of B at the outlet of the reactor above a given minimum required concentration $B^{req} = 3 \cdot 10^{-2}\ gL^{-1}$. The mass balances are given in Eq. (5).

$$A \in [\underline{A}, \overline{A}], \qquad B \in [\underline{B}, \overline{B}], \qquad \theta \in [\underline{\theta}, \overline{\theta}], \qquad F \in [\underline{F}, \overline{F}]$$

$$\frac{dA}{dt} = \frac{F}{V}(A^0 - A) - r(k) \quad \text{and} \quad \frac{dB}{dt} = -\frac{F}{V}B + r(k) \tag{5}$$

To identify the surrogate model $\mathcal{F}_h$ – which should map the feed rate, the inlet concentration of A and the pre-exponential factor to the concentration of product B at the outlet of the reactor – the ODE system given in Eq. (5) is solved for different input vectors $[F_i, A_i^0, k_i], i \in$

I with $|I| = 200$ samples, each with $1\ gL^{-1}$ of A and no B as starting conditions in the reactor. A Latin Hypercube Sampling approach was used to generate the $|I|$ samples, of which 80% were used for model training and 20% for model testing. After simulating the reactor for each sample i, the outlet concentration of B was obtained. To train the BMS model, a variety of unary $(\exp(x), \log(x), x^2, x^3, \sqrt{x})$ and binary $(+, -, \div, \times)$ operators were allowed to be selected by the algorithm. 1000 Markov chain Monte Carlo steps were used for model training. The model was allowed to consider up to eight differentiated parameters.

5. Results and Discussion

First, the model building results are discussed, followed by an assessment of the flexibility index calculations. Figure 1 (a) shows the training and testing performance of the identified algebraic model, while Figure 1 (b) summarizes the results of the flexibility index problem.

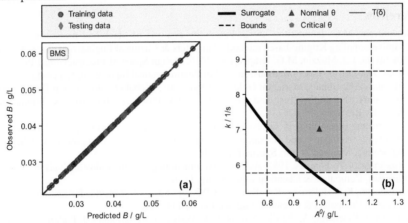

Figure 1 (a) Observed values are plotted against the model predictions. The circles represent the training data, whereas the diamonds correspond the test data. (b) Graphical representation of the solution for the flexibility index problem. The bright shaded area represents the feasible region. The dashed lines represent the bounds of the uncertain parameters θ. The bold solid nonlinear line represents the surrogate constraint which can be influenced by the control variable z. The considered nominal operating point θ^N (triangle) is located in the set $T(\delta)$ (dark-shaded solid-lined box). The critical realization of θ (pentagon) is visualized where $T(\delta)$ touches the closest constraint, which happens to be the surrogate constraint.

For training the BMS model, 2 min were required. The resulting training and testing root mean squared errors were $5.2 \cdot 10^{-8}$, and $3.6 \cdot 10^{-8}$, respectively, and the coefficients of determination were $R^2 = 1.000$ for training and testing, respectively. The model could therefore map the inputs remarkably well to the outputs.

The flexibility index problem could be solved with the identified algebraic model incorporated. Less than one second was required to reach global optimality (zero relative optimality gap). In the optimal solution, the control variable F was at its bound of $100\ m^3 s^{-1}$. The solution provides the maximum allowed deviation of the uncertain parameters such that the process remains feasible. The flexible region $T(\delta^*)$ is therefore spanned by the parameter intervals $A^0 \in [0.92, 1.09]$ and $k \in [6.15, 7.85]$, corresponding to a flexibility index of $\zeta^* = 0.853$.

6. Conclusion

We introduced an approach to compute the flexibility index of a process in cases where constraints are present that are very complex to be described, or even inaccessible in an algebraic form. The original deterministic flexibility index problem is combined with a surrogate model built by symbolic regression. An advantage of the symbolic regression algorithm used, the Bayesian Machine Scientist, is that no aprioristic model structure for the approximated constraints is required. Further, the surrogate model training can be decoupled from the flexibility index problem, which reduces the complexity of the entire solution procedure. The approach was applied to a continuous stirred tank reactor example implementing a chemical reaction. A model that precisely maps the uncertain parameters and control variables to a desired output could be identified, where the closed-form expression then allowed the use of a global solver to solve the resulting hybrid flexibility index problem.

References

F. Boukouvala, M.G. Ierapetritou, 2012, Feasibility analysis of black-box processes using an adaptive sampling Kriging-based method, Computers & Chemical Engineering, 36, 358–368.

F. Boukouvala, F.J. Muzzio, M.G. Ierapetritou, 2010, Design Space of Pharmaceutical Processes Using Data-Driven-Based Methods, Journal of Pharmaceutical Innovation, 5, 119–137.

C.A. Floudas, Z.H. Gümüş, Marianthi G. Ierapetritou, 2001, Global Optimization in Design under Uncertainty: Feasibility Test and Flexibility Index Problems, Industrial & Engineering Chemistry Research, 40, 4267–4282.

I.E. Grossmann, B.A. Calfa, P. Garcia-Herreros, 2014, Evolution of concepts and models for quantifying resiliency and flexibility of chemical processes, Computers & Chemical Engineering, Manfred Morari Special Issue, 70, 22–34.

I.E. Grossmann, C.A. Floudas, 1987, Active constraint strategy for flexibility analysis in chemical processes, Computers & Chemical Engineering, 11, 675–693.

I.E. Grossmann, K.P. Halemane, R.E. Swaney, 1983, Optimization strategies for flexible chemical processes, Computers & Chemical Engineering, 7, 439–462.

R. Guimerà, I. Reichardt, A. Aguilar-Mogas, F.A. Massucci, M. Miranda, J. Pallarès, M. Sales-Pardo, 2020, A Bayesian machine scientist to aid in the solution of challenging scientific problems, Science Advances, 6.

K.P. Halemane, I.E. Grossmann, 1983, Optimal process design under uncertainty, AIChE Journal, 29, 425–433.

W.E. Hart, J.-P. Watson, D.L. Woodruff, 2011, Pyomo: modeling and solving mathematical programs in Python, Mathematical Programming Computation, 3, 219–260.

N. Metta, R. Ramachandran, M. Ierapetritou, 2021, A novel adaptive sampling based methodology for feasible region identification of compute intensive models using artificial neural network, AIChE Journal, 67, e17095.

J.L. Pulsipher, D. Rios, V.M. Zavala, 2019, A computational framework for quantifying and analyzing system flexibility, Computers & Chemical Engineering, 126, 342–355.

S. Sachio, C. Kontoravdi, M.M. Papathanasiou, 2023, A model-based approach towards accelerated process development: A case study on chromatography, Chemical Engineering Research and Design, 197, 800–820.

N.V. Sahinidis, 1996, BARON: A general purpose global optimization software package, Journal of Global Optimization, 8, 201–205.

R.E. Swaney, I.E. Grossmann, 1985a, An index for operational flexibility in chemical process design. Part I: Formulation and theory, AIChE Journal, 31, 621–630.

R.E. Swaney, I.E. Grossmann, 1985b, An index for operational flexibility in chemical process design. Part II: Computational algorithms, AIChE Journal, 31, 631–641.

F. Zhao, I.E. Grossmann, S. García-Muñoz, S.D. Stamatis, 2021, Flexibility index of black-box models with parameter uncertainty through derivative-free optimization, AIChE Journal, 67, e17189.

Flavio Manenti, Gintaras V. Reklaitis (Eds.), Proceedings of the 34th European Symposium on Computer Aided Process Engineering / 15th International Symposium on Process Systems Engineering (ESCAPE34/PSE24), June 2-6, 2024, Florence, Italy

Predicting FTS products through artificial neural network modelling

Federico Moretta[a], Arian Grainca[b], Flavio Manenti[a], Giulia Bozzano[a], Carlo Pirola[b]

[a]*Politecnico di Milano, Department of Chemistry, Material and Chemical Engineering piazza Leonardo da Vinci 32, 20133, Milan (MI), Italy*
[b]*Università degli Studi di Milano, Dipartimento di Chimica, Via Golgi 19, 20133, Milan (MI), Italy*

*arian.grainca@unimi.it

Abstract

Fischer-Tropsch synthesis is essential for converting CO_2 into hydrocarbons, creating sustainable fuels and olefins. However, challenges in production yield and reaction kinetics remain. This study introduces an artificial neural network (ANN) to predict FT synthesis products from specific inputs, including temperature, pressure, GHSV, H_2/CO_2 ratio, and catalyst composition (Fe weight and K as a promoter). The ANN's ability to predict outputs like CH_4, C_{2-4}, C_{5+}, CO_2 conversion, and CO selectivity, without detailed reaction mechanisms, is a key innovation. This approach circumvents complex kinetic models. The network architecture is optimized for minimal error, and results are validated against a comprehensive database.

Keywords: Fischer-Tropsch, Neural Network, Optimization, Modelling.

1. Introduction

Addressing climate change, reducing CO2 emissions from fossil fuels is crucial. The shift towards sustainable initiatives like 'energy transition' presents both environmental and economic opportunities for businesses. Strategies like Carbon Capture and Storage (CCS) and Carbon Capture Utilization (CCU) are pivotal, with CCU gaining attention for converting CO2 into valuable chemicals and fuels (Chung et al. 2023). Power-to-Liquid (PTL) approaches in CCU are significant for producing high-energy-density fuels like methanol, gasoline, and diesel, which are easier to store and transport. Fischer-Tropsch Synthesis (FTS), since 1925, has been effective in generating hydrocarbons like alpha-olefins and linear paraffins from various feedstocks, crucially without sulfur, nitrogen, and aromatic compounds (Mohajerani et al., 2018). The adaptation of CO2-based FTS for fuel production is a notable advancement under stringent environmental regulations (Martín & Cirujano, 2022). Artificial Neural Networks (ANN) play a vital role in the process industry, enhancing equipment failure prediction, maintenance (Nadai et al., 2017), and system optimization. Their application in conventional FT synthesis for process optimization and kinetic modeling has been successful (Adib et al., 2013; Chakkingal et al., 2022; Sharma et al., 1998). This study applies ANN to FT synthesis with CO2 feedstock, aiming to predict the selectivity of key species like CO, CH4, C2-4, and C5+, using Fe-based catalysts promoted with K. To enhance predictions, five networks were developed for each output, based on parameters like catalyst composition, surface area (BET), temperature, and pressure, identified through Kendall correlation coefficient analysis. The ANN's architecture was optimized using a mixed-integer genetic algorithm methodology. Modelling

2.1 Experimental set-up

In the continuous mixing setup employed, the flow rates of hydrogen (H_2, 30 Nml min^{-1}), carbon dioxide (CO_2, 10 Nml min^{-1}), and nitrogen (N_2, 5 Nml min^{-1}, internal standard) were regulated using three Brooks mass flow controllers. These gases were introduced from the top into a packed bed catalytic reactor, which had an internal diameter of 6 mm and was charged with 1 gram of catalyst. The catalyst was held in position by two disks of quartz wool. To ensure the reactor's internal surface was inert, a blank test was conducted. The process of catalyst activation took place at a temperature of 623 K and a pressure of 0.4 MPa over a duration of four hours. During this phase, the reagent flow rate was maintained at 45 Nml min^{-1}, employing the CO_2/H_2 mixture. Following the reaction, liquid products, including water and heavy hydrocarbons (C_{5+}), were condensed in a cold trap equipped with an external cooling jacket set to 278 K. The condensed liquids were then subjected to gas chromatographic analysis. Pressure within the system was kept constant at 2.0 MPa by means of a pneumatic back pressure regulator. To compute the CO_2 conversion rate and product selectives , an Agilent 3000A micro gas chromatograph was utilized. This device measured the peak areas of N_2 and CO_2 (AN2 and ACO2), their respective relative response factors (k), and the inlet flow rates of N_2 and CO_2 (Fin N2, and Fin CO2).Samples of the effluent were collected every two hours for analysis, using the chromatograph equipped with molsieve and QPLOT columns.

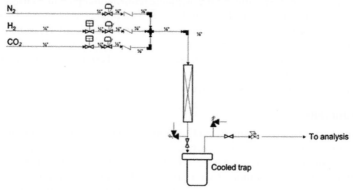

Figure 1: *simplified experimental plant set-up for FT reaction.*

2.2 Neural Network Architecture

The architecture of the ANN is based on the relations between the biases and weight of each node, the neuron activation function, and the training function. Firstly, cascade forward network has been considered, since it relates the output layer weights with an additional weight evaluated from the values of the input variables. It has been seen that it helps to better identify and exploit all the dependences between the input and output variables, given the nature of the system (Zimmermann and Mattedi, 2022). The other network characteristics have been chosen by optimizing the performance of the network. This was done through a genetic algorithm, which selected through a random generation of points (i.e., generation), the best one that minimize the mean square error (MSE) or the network. Both activation functions (AF) and training functions (TF) have been labeled with integers numbers, to be successfully read from the optimizer. Thus, a mixed-integer approach has been used; and the hidden layer have been constrained between 1 and 10 layers. In fact, the variability and quantity of data in the dataset considered is not enough to achieve good performances with high hidden layers number (Ogunbo et al., 2020). Table 1 shows the list of the activation and training functions. The modeling and optimization have been performed through MATLAB©, from which it has also been chosen the type of activation and training function.

Table 1. Labeling of activation and training functions selected for the mixed-integer optimization.

Label	Activation function	Training function	Abbreviation
1	Pure linear	Levenberg-Marquardt	LM
2	Log-sigmoidal	Bayesian regularization	BR
3	Tan-sigmoidal	Quasi-Newton BFGS	QN-BFGS
4	-	Resilient Back Propagation	RBP
5	-	Scaled conjugate gradient	SCG
6	-	Conjugate gradient with Powell/Beale restarts	P/B-CG
7	-	Fletcher-Powell conjugate gradient	F/P-CG
8	-	Polak-Ribiére conjugate gradient	P/R-CG
9	-	One-pass secant	OPS
10	-	Gradient drop-down variable learning rate	GDVLR
11	-	Gradient disc with momentum	GDM
12	-	Gradient Discess	GD

2.2.1 Input variable definition

The input variables to the model have been chosen accordingly to the nature of the catalyst and of the process. Since the aim of the model is to predict the kinetic results and performances of the process, the catalyst composition has been addressed, in terms of density and (ρ_{cat}) and specific surface (BET). Since the active phase and promotor have been fixed *a priori*, the density gathers the information of the catalyst intrinsic composition. Finally, the Kendall correlation coefficients evaluation (Figure 1) confirms the goodness of the dependences between catalyst features and products, which shows that at higher catalyst density, higher chain products are preferred, but at higher BET, lighter hydrocarbons are favored, since increase the selectivity of the catalyst itself in terms of pore dimension and tortuosity. Moreover, two more input variables have been selected: temperature (T) and pressure (P). By defining the state of the system, these are important information since highlights both the sensitivity to the process to produce a certain group of species and the catalyst operational window. At higher temperature, lower chain hydrocarbons are expected, and at higher pressure higher chain hydrocarbons are favored (Chen and Yang, 2019).

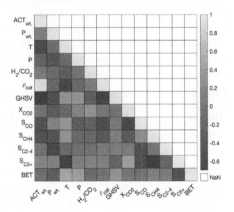

Figure 2: Heatmap of the correlation coefficients of the dataset features

2.3 Dataset Compilation for Artificial Neural Network Training

To facilitate the modeling process through an artificial neural network (ANN), a comprehensive dataset was necessary. This dataset was compiled from a combination of 12 articles (Qingxin Yang, 2021) and experimental results. From these articles, a variety of data points were extracted, encompassing reaction conditions such as temperature, pressure, gas hourly space velocity (GHSV) and ratios of reactants. Additionally, reaction outputs were included, such as: CO_2 conversion and selectivities towards products. The nature of the catalysts used in these studies was also a critical component of the dataset, represented by their densities, which were calculated (Eq. 1)based on the amounts of active metals, promoters and the porosity (φ). The latter was calculated as the average between the experimental values of the catalysts used and literature values taken as standard case (Yulan Zhang, 2015).

$$\rho_{cat} = \varphi \cdot \left(\frac{\% \, K}{100} \cdot \rho_K + \frac{\% \, Fe}{100} \cdot \rho_{Fe} + \frac{100 - \% \, K - \% \, Fe}{100} \cdot \rho_{Ti_2 O}\right) \qquad (1)$$

In total, literature review yielded data for 70 different reaction conditions, providing a robust foundation for the ANN. To complement this, experimental data reflecting similar parameters were incorporated into the dataset. This experimental contribution added 25 unique data sets, ensuring a diverse and comprehensive pool of information for training the neural network. This amalgamation of literature-derived and experimental data forms the backbone of the ANN model, ensuring its relevance and applicability in the context of Fischer-Tropsch synthesis.

2. Results and Discussion

The best architecture for the five networks is found from the optimization (Table 2). Two activation functions, one for the hidden layers (HL) and one for the output layer (OL) are selected. It must be said that the learning rate and normalization of input/output variables are done automatically by the MATLAB© algorithm used for the modeling. The performances of these networks are assessed with the value of the MSE (Table 3). These values are in line with the ones obtained in literature (Fernandes, 2006). As it is possible to notice, the highest performances are reached for X_{CO2} and S_{C2-4} predictions, while the worst one came from the modeling of the S_{C5+}.

Table 2. optimization architecture from the genetic algorithm solution

Output	Symbol	N° HL	AF HL	AF OL	TF
CO_2 conversion	X_{CO2}	9	Log-sigmoidal	Pure linear	P/B-CG
CO selectivity	S_{CO}	2	Pure linear	Tan-sigmoidal	F/P-CG
CH_4 selectivity	S_{CH4}	9	Log-sigmoidal	Pure linear	OPS
C_{2-4} selectivity	S_{C2-4}	4	Log-sigmoidal	Tan-sigmoidal	OPS
C_{5+} selectivity	S_{C5+}	8	Tan-sigmoidal	Tan-sigmoidal	BR

However, despite the MSE gives to this the highest value, the mean prediction error (MPE), evaluated as the relative error between the experimental data and the network calculations, has its highest value on the prediction of the CO selectivity. This is principally due to the intrinsic nature of the ANN when applied on chemical processes.

Table 3. Performance indicators of the networks.

Network	Total epochs	Epoch at minimum MSE	MSE	MPE
CO_2 conversion	16	10	92.87	0.30
CO selectivity	28	22	118.4	0.82
CH_4 selectivity	12	6	112.3	0.58
C_{2-4} selectivity	20	14	81.62	0.19
C_{5+} selectivity	45	44	167.3	0.37

On the other hand, other algorithms have been used for comparison; with particular focus on S_{CO} evaluation. To make the comparisons, MSE has been used as performance indicator. Firstly, Multiple Linear Regression (MLR) and Decision Tree Regression (DTR) are tested, using as independent variable the same used in ANN. Results are shown in table 4.

Table 4. Performance indicators and comparison with other algorithm.

Algorithm	Average MSE	STD.DEV	S_{CO} MSE
ANN	114.5	33.00	118.4
MLR	157.3	36.75	193.1
DTR	138.6	44.30	172.5

As it possible to notice, ANN outperformance the other algorithm tested; MLR, the simplest one, has the lowest score, and this is reasonable since the behavior of the species, including CO, is strongly nonlinear, depending on the thermodynamic of the process. On the other hand, DTR has better score with respect to MLR, but still not performing enough well. This because decision tree can be overwhelmed from the variability of the data, which led to a drastically change in the tree structure during the regression. In conclusion, it is recommended to still use ANN as primary algorithm for the prediction of these parameters and, if possible, evaluate the CO selectivity as a complementary to the other parameters.

3. Conclusions

The application of artificial neural networks (ANN) in this Fischer-Tropsch synthesis study demonstrates a balance of success and challenges. The ANN's ability in predicting CO_2 conversion and C_{2-4} hydrocarbon selectivity, in line with existing literature (Fernandes, 2006), underscores its effectiveness in modeling specific aspects of the synthesis process. However, the model's struggles with accurately predicting longer chain hydrocarbons (SC_{5+}), as reflected by a higher Mean Square Error (MSE), reveal limitations in its capacity to handle the complexities of these reaction pathways. This could stem from data variability, limitations in the network architecture, or insufficient training data. The most significant Mean Prediction Error (MPE) in predicting CO selectivity highlights a critical area of improvement. It suggests the model's limited sensitivity to subtle variations in reaction conditions, a crucial aspect for precise chemical process modeling. This finding calls for a deeper exploration into refining the ANN architecture, possibly integrating more diverse and complex datasets or adopting more sophisticated machine learning techniques. Overall, the study presents a promising yet incomplete picture of ANN's capability in chemical process optimization. Future research should focus on enhancing the model's accuracy across a broader range of outputs and delving into more complex reaction dynamics. Such advancements are essential for realizing the full potential of ANN in this field.

References

Wonsuk Chung, Sunwoo Kim, Ali S. Al-Hunaidy, Hasan Imran, Aqil Jamal, Jay H. Lee, Identification of sustainable carbon capture and utilization (CCU) pathways using state-task network representation, Computers & Chemical Engineering, Volume 178, 2023.

Mohajerani, S., Kumar, A., & Oni, A. O. (2018). A techno-economic assessment of gas-to-liquid and coal-to-liquid plants through the development of scale factors. Energy, 150, 681–693.

Martín, N., & Cirujano, F. G. (2022). Multifunctional heterogeneous catalysts for the tandem CO2hydrogenation-Fischer Tropsch synthesis of gasoline. Journal of CO2 Utilization, 65(August), 102176.

Adib, H., Haghbakhsh, R., Saidi, M., Takassi, M.A., Sharifi, F., Koolivand, M., Rahimpour, M.R., Keshtkari, S., 2013. Modeling and optimization of Fischer–Tropsch synthesis in the presence of Co (III)/Al2O3 catalyst using artificial neural networks and genetic algorithm. J. Nat. Gas Sci. Eng. 10, 14–24. https://doi.org/10.1016/j.jngse.2012.09.001

Chakkingal, A., Janssens, P., Poissonnier, J., Virginie, M., Khodakov, A.Y., Thybaut, J.W., 2022. Multi-output machine learning models for kinetic data evaluation : A Fischer–Tropsch synthesis case study. Chem. Eng. J. 446, 137186. https://doi.org/10.1016/j.cej.2022.137186

Chen, J., Yang, C., 2019. Thermodynamic Equilibrium Analysis of Product Distribution in the Fischer–Tropsch Process Under Different Operating Conditions. ACS Omega 4, 22237–22244. https://doi.org/10.1021/acsomega.9b03707

Fernandes, F.A.N., 2006. Optimization of Fischer-Tropsch Synthesis Using Neural Networks. Chem. Eng. Technol. 29, 449–453. https://doi.org/10.1002/ceat.200500310

Garona, H.A., Cavalcanti, F.M., De Abreu, T.F., Schmal, M., Alves, R.M.B., 2021. Evaluation of Fischer-Tropsch synthesis to light olefins over Co- and Fe-based catalysts using artificial neural network. J. Clean. Prod. 321, 129003. https://doi.org/10.1016/j.jclepro.2021.129003

Nadai, N., Melani, A., Souza, G., Nabeta, S., 2017. Equipment failure prediction based on neural network analysis incorporating maintainers inspection findings. https://doi.org/10.1109/RAM.2017.7889684

Ogunbo, J.N., Alagbe, O.A., Oladapo, M.I., Shin, C., 2020. N-hidden layer artificial neural network architecture computer code: geophysical application example. Heliyon 6, e04108. https://doi.org/10.1016/j.heliyon.2020.e04108

Sharma, B.K., Sharma, M.P., Kumar Roy, S., Kumar, S., Tendulkar, S.B., S. Tambe, S., Kulkarni, B.D., 1998. Fischer–Tropsch synthesis with Co/SiO2–Al2O3 catalyst and steady-state modeling using artificial neural networks. Fuel 77, 1763–1768. https://doi.org/10.1016/S0016-2361(98)00110-0

Takeshita, T., 2012. Assessing the co-benefits of CO2 mitigation on air pollutants emissions from road vehicles. Appl. Energy, Energy Solutions for a Sustainable World - Proceedings of the Third International Conference on Applied Energy, May 16-18, 2011 - Perugia, Italy 97, 225–237. https://doi.org/10.1016/j.apenergy.2011.12.029

Zimmermann, A.S., Mattedi, S., 2022. Feedforward and cascade forward networks for viscosity prediction for binary mixtures of ammonium-based ionic liquids and water. Fluid Phase Equilibria 556, 113416. https://doi.org/10.1016/j.fluid.2022.113416

Qingxin Yang, Andrey Skrypnik, Alexander Matvienko, Henrik Lund, Martin Holena, Evgenii V. Kondratenko,Revealing property-performance relationships for efficient CO2 hydrogenation to higher hydrocarbons over Fe-based catalysts: Statistical analysis of literature data and its experimental validation,Applied Catalysis B: Environmental,Volume 282,2021,119554.

Yulan Zhang, Longlong Ma, Junling Tu, Tiejun Wang, Xinjun Li, One-pot synthesis of promoted porous iron-based microspheres and its Fischer–Tropsch performance,Applied Catalysis A: General, Volume 499, 2015, Pages 139-145.

Flavio Manenti, Gintaras V. Reklaitis (Eds.), Proceedings of the 34th European Symposium on Computer Aided Process Engineering / 15th International Symposium on Process Systems Engineering (ESCAPE34/PSE24), June 2-6, 2024, Florence, Italy

Automated Reaction Mechanism Constructor

Miguel Ángel de Carvalho Servia[a], King Kuok (Mimi) Hii[b], Klaus Hellgardt[a], Dongda Zhang[c*], Antonio del Rio Chanona[a*]

[a]*Department of Chemical Engineering, Imperial College London, South Kensington, London, SW7 2AZ, United Kingdom*
[b]*Department of Chemistry, Imperial College London, White City, London, W12 0BZ, United Kingdom*
[c]*Department of Chemical Engineering, The University of Manchester, Oxford Road, Manchester, M13 9P, United Kingdom*
dongda.zhange@manchester.ac.uk; a.del-rio-chanona@imperial.ac.uk

Abstract

In catalytic reaction engineering, the discovery of reaction mechanisms is paramount but challenging due to the intricate involvement of intermediates and limited prior knowledge. This study introduces a novel approach to generate the smallest feasible reaction mechanism (SFRM) that can accurately represent kinetic data sets. We propose an iterative algorithm based on a rule-based formulation, aiming to uncover the SFRM with minimal prior information about a system. Starting with the simplest conceivable mechanism, the algorithm advances by adding layers of complexity, estimating kinetic parameters, and evaluating mechanisms through the Akaike information criterion (AIC). Once a simpler mechanism demonstrates a smaller AIC value, it is selected as the optimal solution. Applied to the fructose to 5-hydroxymethylfurfural (HMF) mechanism, the methodology successfully uncovered the structure utilized for kinetic rate data generation. This novel framework offers experts a robust foundation for suggesting reaction mechanisms, addressing current limitations in mechanism discovery, emphasizing its utility not as a replacement but as a useful tool for experts.

Keywords: Chemical reaction engineering, automated reaction mechanism constructor.

1. Introduction

Understanding reaction mechanisms is crucial for constructing microkinetic models, which play a pivotal role in various sectors, including business and public policy decision-making. In the business domain, microkinetic models are important tools for chemical engineers to design and theoretically assess the profitability and viability of chemical processing plants. On the public policy-making side, international treaties like the Stockholm Convention on Persistent Organic Pollutants (POPs), aimed at minimizing the production and use of POPs, relied on kinetic models to understand the environmental behavior and degradation of chemicals such as dichlorodiphenyltrichloroethane. These models need to strike a balance between accuracy and dimensionality to ensure interpretability and efficient computational evaluation.

Traditionally, the development of reaction mechanisms and corresponding microkinetic models has been the responsibility of domain experts. Their knowledge is used to propose possible reaction intermediates, and the reaction steps by which they are formed and consumed. However, given the vast number of possible interactions among reactants, intermediates, and products – potentially hundreds of thousands – the manual assembly of these models is not only tedious and error-prone but also incredibly time-consuming.

The uptake of data-driven methodologies and enhanced analytical capabilities, which have significantly increased the amount of available kinetic data, has catalyzed the creation of automated approaches for mechanism development. These have been previously divided into two categories: one relies on combinatorial algorithms to generate all possible reactions based on electronic configuration congruence, while the other generates characteristic reactions of a known reaction class based on the reactants and products involved.

The combinatorial approach, bounded only by electronic congruence, often results in enormous reaction networks that require significant reduction. These large reaction mechanisms compromise computational efficiency and model interpretability, as mentioned. The latter approach generates more tractable networks but is dependent upon pre-existing knowledge of reaction classes, which may not always be accessible. For in-depth discussions on these methodologies, reviews by van de Vijver et al. (2014) and Ratkiewicz and Truong (2005) are recommended.

Both methods present inherent limitations, prompting the need for a 'middle-ground' approach that can construct a minimalistic reaction network without pre-existing system knowledge. This gap motivated our formulation of SIMBA (SImplest Mechanism Builder Algorithm), which aspires to create the smallest feasible reaction mechanism (SFRM) that can accurately explain available kinetic data without prior knowledge. The following sections of this paper are laid out as follows: Section 2 delves into the inner-workings of SIMBA, detailing the iterative construction, optimization, and selection of the SFRM; Section 3 presents the case study employed to validate the approach, including the generation of in-silico data; Section 4 showcases the results where SIMBA successfully uncovers the underlying microkinetic model of the case study; and Section 5 concludes with the primary contributions of the study and proposes enhancements and future research directions.

2. Methodology

SIMBA (SImplest Mechanism Builder Algorithm) is tailored to develop microkinetic models using kinetic data, focusing on identifying the informationally smallest reaction mechanism that accurately describes the available data. It comprises four key phases: (I) reaction chain generation phase, where it proposes increasingly complex reaction mechanisms; (II) ODE system builder phase, translating these mechanisms into microkinetic models represented by ordinary differential equations (ODE); (III) system integration phase, estimating kinetic parameters using an optimization algorithm; and (IV) comparison phase, assessing each model's performance with the Akaike Information Criterion (AIC) to decide if further iterations are necessary. Each phase contributes to SIMBA's goal of efficiently deriving an accurate and minimalistic representation of the kinetic system. The following subsections delve into each of these phases in greater detail.

2.1. Reaction Chain Generation

The initial phase of SIMBA involves the proposition of a series of reaction mechanisms, starting from the most basic possibility and gradually escalating in complexity with each iteration. This reaction chain generation phase begins by assuming reaction stoichiometry is known and discounting termolecular or higher-order interactions due to their relative rarity. For instance, consider a straightforward reaction stoichiometry such as 'A → Y + Z', with A, Y, and Z representing arbitrary reactants and products.

With the reaction stoichiometry known and constraining reactions to be either bimolecular or unimolecular, SIMBA identifies the simplest possible mechanism for this example as a single-step reaction: 'A → Y + Z'. Upon completing the first iteration, the algorithm proceeds to a second iteration, introducing an intermediate, labeled 'B'. This addition broadens the scope of potential mechanisms, now encompassing two-step mechanisms. In this second iteration, SIMBA generates and considers all three feasible mechanisms: (I) 'A → B', followed by 'B → Y + Z'; (II) 'A → B + Y', followed by 'B → Z'; and (III) 'A → B + Z', followed by 'B → Y'.

Should a third iteration be needed, as determined by SIMBA's fourth phase, another intermediate, 'C' in this case, would be introduced. The algorithm then constructs the corresponding possible mechanisms incorporating this new intermediate. At each stage, SIMBA systematically generates all possible reaction mechanisms under the set of constraints and feeds these into the next phase of the algorithm for further evaluation and optimization. This structured approach ensures a thorough exploration of potential reaction pathways, progressively building in complexity, to accurately model the kinetic behavior of the system under study in the simplest way possible.

2.2. ODE System Builder

Following the initial phase of generating reaction mechanisms, SIMBA advances to the next stage: the transformation of these theoretical mechanisms into microkinetic models, each represented by a system of ODEs. This automatic formulation is critical for translating theoretical reaction mechanisms into quantifiable models that we can then optimize and evaluate.

To illustrate this process, Figure 1 depicts the expected inputs and outputs of the ODE system builder, referred to as 'make_system', for two sample reaction mechanisms discussed in the previous subsection. From Figure 1, it is evident that the output of the ODE system builder is a function characterized by unknown kinetic parameters. In the third phase of SIMBA, these unknown parameters are estimated, enabling the proposed microkinetic model to be compared against available kinetic data.

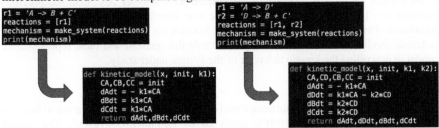

Figure 1: Representation of the inputs required by the ODE builder and its expected output. Two examples of increasing complexity are shown.

2.3. System Integration

In this phase, SIMBA employs an optimization algorithm to estimate the kinetic parameters for each proposed model. The accuracy of these models in representing the kinetic behavior of the system heavily depends on this phase, making it essential for refining the models based on the available experimental data. For solving this optimization problem, commonly known as parameter estimation, in this work we employed the limited-memory bounded Broyden-Fletcher-Goldfarb-Shanno (L-BFGS-B) algorithm. The optimization problem tackled by SIMBA is formally defined as:

$$\theta^* = \underset{\theta}{\operatorname{argmin}} \sum_{i=1}^{n_t} \mathcal{L}\left(\hat{C}\left(t^{(i)}|\theta\right), C^{(i)}\right). \tag{1}$$

In this formulation, θ represents the set of unknown kinetic parameters that need to be estimated; n_t denotes the number of sampling points at which experimental data is available, $\hat{C}\left(t^{(i)}|\theta\right)$ are the predicted concentrations of the observed species at time $t^{(i)}$, based on the model with parameters θ; $C^{(i)}$ are the actual measured concentrations of the observed species at the corresponding time $t^{(i)}$; and $\mathcal{L}$ is designed to compute the sum of squared errors between $\hat{C}(t^{(i)}|\theta)$ and $C^{(i)}$. The L-BFGS-B algorithm's role in this phase is to iteratively adjust the parameters θ to minimize the error computed by $\mathcal{L}$, effectively tuning the model to align with the observed kinetic behavior as close as possible. Once this phase is concluded and the kinetic parameters are estimated, the models can be evaluated and compared against each other.

2.4. Model Comparison

Having developed various microkinetic models with their respective optimized kinetic parameters to best fit the observed data, the final stage in SIMBA involves a quantitative comparison of these models. This comparative analysis is essential to decide whether SIMBA should continue generating new reaction mechanisms or conclude its operation. The decision-making process in this phase employs the Akaike information criterion (AIC) to evaluate and compare the models.

For a given model m with parameters θ_m of dimension d_m, the AIC is computed as follows:

$$AIC_m = 2\ell(\theta_m|\mathcal{D}) + 2d_m, \tag{2}$$

where ℓ represent the negative log-likelihood given a data set $\mathcal{D}$. When comparing two models, m_1 and m_2, the model with the lower AIC value is considered the better one. The choice of the AIC as the model selection criteria is not arbitrary. In fact, in literature, it has been shown that AIC is a great information criterion that tends to perform better than other criteria within the kinetic modeling paradigm (de Carvalho Servia et al., 2023). The usage of AIC is also important because it helps us balance model complexity and overfitting through the penalty term that it includes.

The routine by which we determine if SIMBA terminates or continues is straightforward: if the current iteration n produces a mechanism with a lower AIC than the previous iteration $n - 1$, then SIMBA proceeds to the next iteration $n + 1$; otherwise, SIMBA terminates. This iterative process ensures that SIMBA not only explores a wide range of potential mechanisms but also converges towards the smallest and most representative model in describing the kinetic behavior of the system under study.

3. Case Study

The case study used for the performance analysis of SIMBA is the dehydration of fructose to 5-hydroxymethylfurfural (HMF), catalyzed by [BmimHSO₃][HSO₄]. The overall reaction is show below:

$$C_6H_{12}O_6 \rightleftharpoons C_6H_6O_3 + 3H_2O. \tag{3}$$

A microkinetic model can be developed using the reaction mechanism proposed in Hu et al. (2023), where HMF is formed through three dehydration steps and three different intermediates are produced and consumed. The proposed mechanism is shown below:

$$A \xrightarrow{k_1} B + Int_1$$
$$Int_1 \xrightarrow{k_2} B + Int_2$$
$$Int_2 \xrightarrow{k_3} Int_3 \tag{4}$$
$$Int_3 \xrightarrow{k_4} B + C$$

where A, B and C represent fructose, water and HMF respectively; and Int_1, Int_2 and Int_3 denote the three intermediates that are formed during the conversion of fructose to HMF. To generate the in-silico data set, three computational studies were carried out with the following initial conditions (in molar units): (C_A(t=0), C_B(t=0), C_C(t=0)) $\in$ {(4, 0, 0), (6, 2, 1), (4, 2, 0)}. For each experiment, the concentration of the reactant and products are recorded 30 times, at evenly spaced intervals between time $t_0=0$ h and $t_f=2$ h. The kinetic parameters were defined as: $k_1=1.514$ h^{-1}, $k_2=5.259$ h^{-1}, $k_3=9.352$ h^{-1} and $k_4=2.359$ h^{-1}. Gaussian noise is added to the in-silico measurements to simulate a realistic chemical system. The added noise had zero mean and a standard deviation of 0.2 for all observed species. This noise addition allows the approximation of the response of a real system.

4. Results and Discussion

The implementation of SIMBA on the in-silico data indicated that only three iterations were necessary to identify the smallest feasible reaction mechanism (SFRM) for our study. In other words, the optimal SFRM was discovered during the second iteration, as indicated by the AIC values. For clarity and conciseness, Table 1 presents the microkinetic models, lists the estimated kinetic parameter values, along with the AIC values for the best reaction mechanism of each iteration executed by SIMBA. For reference, the sum of squared errors (SSE) between the in-silico data and the data-generating model is 10.780 M^2, whereas the SSE between the in-silico data and the model discovered by SIMBA is 12.664 M^2.

The performance of SIMBA on the case study of the production of HMF from fructose is promising. Given the stoichiometry and acknowledging the rarity of ter- and higher-order molecular interactions, SIMBA successfully identified the underlying mechanism and microkinetic model that governs the system's dynamics. This achievement underscores SIMBA's potential as an effective tool in kinetic discovery. However, it is crucial to recognize SIMBA's limitations: while it proposes a mechanism with intermediates, it does not chemically identify these intermediates. In our case, deducing the nature of these intermediates is feasible through basic atom balances and fundamental chemical knowledge. Nevertheless, in more complex chemical systems, identifying these intermediates might not be as straightforward, necessitating the insight of an experienced experts. This limitation highlights a notable challenge in the algorithm's application.

Despite this, the results reinforce the utility of SIMBA as a valuable tool for chemists and reaction engineers. It is not a replacement for expert knowledge but rather a tool that can significantly expedite the process of mechanistic discovery. By providing a robust initial 'guess' of the reaction mechanism, SIMBA enables experts to efficiently put together the puzzle pieces of complex chemical processes, potentially shortening the timeline for understanding and optimizing such systems.

5. Conclusions

This study introduces SIMBA, an algorithm encompassing four phases: reaction chain generation, ODE builder, system integration, and model comparison. Tested on the catalyzed synthesis of HMF from fructose, SIMBA successfully identified the smallest feasible reaction mechanism from in-silico data, matching the literature-sourced microkinetic model. This highlights SIMBA's potential in accelerating mechanistic discovery, despite its limitation in not chemically identifying reaction intermediates.

Future research should focus on integrating chemical knowledge into SIMBA, crucial for aiding the discovery of complex systems, and on incorporating uncertainty quantification in model predictions. Enhancing SIMBA in these aspects will significantly improve its effectiveness and reliability in discovering and optimizing microkinetic models, making it a more comprehensive tool for chemists and reaction engineers.

Table 1: The best reaction mechanism at each iteration of SIMBA, along with the corresponding microkinetic model, the estimated kinetic parameters, and the AIC value. It demonstrates that the SFRM was discovered in iteration 2, where the chosen mechanism perfectly matches with the data-generating one.

Iteration	Reaction Mechanism	Microkinetic Model	Estimated Kinetic Parameters	AIC Value
1	$A \xrightarrow{k_1} B + D$ $D \xrightarrow{k_2} B + E$ $E \xrightarrow{k_3} B + C$	$\begin{bmatrix} dC_A/dt \\ dC_B/dt \\ dC_C/dt \\ dC_D/dt \\ dC_E/dt \end{bmatrix} = \begin{bmatrix} -k_1 C_A \\ k_1 C_A + k_2 C_D + k_3 C_E \\ k_3 C_E \\ k_1 C_A - k_2 C_D \\ k_2 C_D - k_3 C_E \end{bmatrix}$	$k_1 = 1.589 \text{ h}^{-1}$ $k_2 = 3.975 \text{ h}^{-1}$ $k_3 = 1.808 \text{ h}^{-1}$	287.030
2	$A \xrightarrow{k_1} B + D$ $D \xrightarrow{k_2} B + E$ $E \xrightarrow{k_3} F$ $F \xrightarrow{k_4} B + C$	$\begin{bmatrix} dC_A/dt \\ dC_B/dt \\ dC_C/dt \\ dC_D/dt \\ dC_E/dt \\ dC_F/dt \end{bmatrix} = \begin{bmatrix} -k_1 C_A \\ k_1 C_A + k_2 C_D + k_4 C_F \\ k_4 C_F \\ k_1 C_A - k_2 C_D \\ k_2 C_D - k_3 C_E \\ k_3 C_E - k_4 C_F \end{bmatrix}$	$k_1 = 1.558 \text{ h}^{-1}$ $k_2 = 4.853 \text{ h}^{-1}$ $k_3 = 9.188 \text{ h}^{-1}$ $k_4 = 2.091 \text{ h}^{-1}$	281.528
3	$A \xrightarrow{k_1} B + D$ $D \xrightarrow{k_2} B + E$ $E \xrightarrow{k_3} B + F$ $F \xrightarrow{k_4} G$ $G \xrightarrow{k_5} C$	$\begin{bmatrix} dC_A/dt \\ dC_B/dt \\ dC_C/dt \\ dC_D/dt \\ dC_E/dt \\ dC_F/dt \\ dC_G/dt \end{bmatrix} = \begin{bmatrix} -k_1 C_A \\ k_1 C_A + k_2 C_D + k_3 C_F \\ k_5 C_G \\ k_1 C_A - k_2 C_D \\ k_2 C_D - k_3 C_E \\ k_3 C_E - k_4 C_F \\ k_4 C_F - k_5 C_5 \end{bmatrix}$	$k_1 = 1.583 \text{ h}^{-1}$ $k_2 = 2.162 \text{ h}^{-1}$ $k_3 = 10.0 \text{ h}^{-1}$ $k_4 = 8.565 \text{ h}^{-1}$ $k_5 = 8.562 \text{ h}^{-1}$	287.931

References

R. van de Vijver, N. M. Vandewiele, P. L. Bhoorasingh, B. L. Slakman, F. S. Khanshan, H.-H. Carstensen, M.-F. Reyniers, G. B. Marin, R. H. West, K. M. van Geem, 2014, Automatic Mechanism and Kinetic Model Generation for Gas- and Solution-Phase Processes: A Perspective on Best Practices, Recent Advances, and Future Challenges, International Journal of Chemical Kinetics, 47, 4, 199-231

A. Ratkiewicz, T. N. Truong, 2005, Automated Mechanism Generation: From Symbolic Calculation to Complex Chemistry, International Journal of Quantum Chemistry, 106, 1, 244-255

M. Á. de Carvalho Servia, I. O. Sandoval, K. K. Hii, K. Hellgardt, D. Zhang, E. A. del Rio Chanona, 2023, The Automtaed Discovery of Kinetic Rate Models – Methodological Frameworks, arXiv

J. Hu, M. Yu, Y. Li, X. Shen, S. Cheng, T. Xu, C. Ge, Y. Yu, Z. Ju, 2023, Dehydration mechanim of fructose to 5-hydroxymethylfurfural catalyzed by functionalized ionic liquids: a density functional theory study, New Journal of Chemistry, 47, 11525-11532.

Flavio Manenti, Gintaras V. Reklaitis (Eds.), Proceedings of the 34th European Symposium on Computer Aided Process Engineering / 15th International Symposium on Process Systems Engineering (ESCAPE34/PSE24), June 2-6, 2024, Florence, Italy

Integrating Knowledge-Guided Symbolic Regression for Model-Based Design of Experiments to Automate Process Flow Diagram Development

Alexander W. Rogers,[a] Amanda Lane,[b] Philip Martin,[a] Dongda Zhang[a*]

[a]Department of Chemical Engineering, The University of Manchester, Oxford Road, Manchester, M1 3AL, UK
[b]Unilever R&D Port Sunlight, Quarry Road East, Bebington, CH63 3JW, UK
*Corresponding author email: dongda.zhang@manchester.ac.uk

Abstract

New products must be formulated rapidly to succeed in the global formulated product market; however, key product indicators (KPIs) can be complex, poorly understood functions of the chemical composition and processing history. Consequently, process scale-up must undergo expensive trial-and-error campaigns that do not guarantee optimality. To accelerate process flow diagram (PFD) optimisation and knowledge discovery, this work proposed a novel digital framework to automatically quantify process mechanisms by integrating symbolic regression (SR) within model-based design of experiments (MBDoE). For each iteration, SR proposed a Pareto front of interpretable mechanistic expressions, and then MBDoE designed a new experiment to discriminate between them while automatically balancing the objective of PFD optimisation. To investigate the framework's performance, a new process model capable of simulating general formulated product synthesis was constructed to generate in-silico data for different case studies. The framework could effectively discover ground-truth process mechanisms within a few iterations, indicating its great potential within the general chemical industry for digital manufacturing and product innovation.

Keywords: knowledge discovery, symbolic regression, model-based design of experiments, interpretable machine learning, process flow diagram optimisation.

1. Introduction

At present, the scale-up of formulated products must undergo expensive trial-and-error campaigns due to the complex, poorly understood link between the final product properties, chemical composition, and processing conditions during manufacture. At this moment, MBDoE is the most promising approach to solving this challenge, whereby a model is used to efficiently guide exploration vs. exploitation of the experimental design space. The general MBDoE framework is flexible. The model used can be a mechanistic, machine learning or hybrid model. Experiments can be designed to yield the most new statistical information for the minimum amount of time and resources or, if formulated as a multi-objective optimisation problem, be designed to simultaneously optimise operating conditions (Franceschini & Macchietto, 2008). However, using MBDoE for PFD development within the formulation and speciality industries remains a severe challenge due to insufficient high-quality data for pure machine learning methods or quantitative descriptions of the complex formulation processes for building hybrid or pure mechanistic models. As such, the best solution is to propose a general framework for automatically discovering good mechanistic models – an approach that would be interpretable. By their construction, analytical expressions can be inspected, debugged, and adapted by expert practitioners to incorporate prior physical knowledge to improve data efficiency or discover new physical knowledge.

The sparse identification of nonlinear dynamics (SINDy) algorithm (Brunton et al., 2016) promotes sparsity among a library of candidate functions to discover ordinary differential equations (ODEs). However, the dynamics must have a sparse representation in the pre-defined library. Genetic algorithms for symbolic regression (SR) explore a much larger space of expressions by selection, mutation, and crossover defined only by a set of input features and mathematical operators (de Franca et al., 2023); as such, SR has helped discover constitutive property relationships (Angelis et al., 2023) and has been applied to discovering kinetic rate models for catalytic processes (Servia et al., 2023). However, without prior knowledge to constrain the solution space, it is very challenging for SR to find accurate expressions for complex systems – even then, the identified expression may represent a local approximation, reducing its physical interpretability. Hence, there have been some, albeit very few, attempts to incorporate prior physical knowledge into SR (Kronberger et al., 2022; Reinbold et al., 2021), so this remains an open challenge. Therefore, this work proposes a novel digital modelling framework integrating SR within MBDoE to aid automatic knowledge discovery and PFD optimisation. This framework is designed to efficiently recover underlying governing equations representing the scale-independent process dynamics through an iterative procedure. To help accelerate system identification and minimise the number of experiments required, the structure of the expressions searched by SR is also constrained based on prior physical knowledge.

2. Methodology

The framework integrating knowledge-guided SR and MBDoE is illustrated in Fig. (1). Starting at Step 1, an initial set of experiments is conducted based on expert experience of important PFD parameters, ϑ , and their lower, ϑ_{lb}, and upper, ϑ_{ub}, bounds.

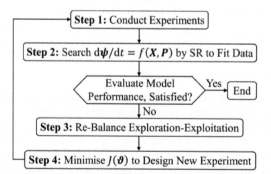

Figure 1: General SR-MBDoE for proposing mechanistic expressions for the underlying system and designing experiments that automatically balance exploration vs. exploitation.

In Step 2, SR identifies a Pareto set of expressions balancing fitting accuracy and complexity for the intrinsic dynamics, $d\psi/dt = f(X, P)$. Where ψ, X and P are vectors of KPIs, chemical concentrations and processing conditions, respectively. In Step 4, MBDoE will design a new experiment to discriminate between the candidate expressions by minimising the multi-objective function, $J(\vartheta)$, which can prioritise knowledge discovery alone or simultaneously explore opportunities for PFD optimisation. These objectives are re-weighted automatically in Step 3 based on the information and optimality gains from the experiment in the prior MBDoE iteration.

2.1. Knowledge-Guided Symbolic Regression

In Step 2, tournament selection promotes and mutates the candidates with the smallest L'_{MSE} from a population of expressions using the Python-Julia library PySR (Cranmer, 2023). In the end, the fittest individuals in the population at each level of complexity were lined up as a Pareto set and scored by the negated derivative of the log-loss with respect to complexity, as in Eq. (1) (Cranmer, 2023). Where L_{MSE} is the mean-square fitting error (MSE) for each expression, while the superscript C is the complexity of the expression. The top scoring expressions represent a balance between fitting accuracy and complexity.

$$\text{Score} = -\Delta\log(L_{\text{MSE}}^{C})/\Delta C \tag{1}$$

However, model selection by parsimony alone does not guarantee that the selected model will extrapolate well, which is key to minimising the number of experiments for system identification; for this, prior knowledge about the nature of the function is necessary.

$$L'_{\text{MSE}} = L_{\text{MSE}} + P \tag{2a}$$

$$P = \begin{cases} \infty, & \text{if } G \notin G' = k(\boldsymbol{X}, \boldsymbol{P}) \times [f(\boldsymbol{X}, \boldsymbol{P}) - b(\boldsymbol{X}, \boldsymbol{P}) \div K(\boldsymbol{X}, \boldsymbol{P})] \\ 0, & \text{otherwise} \end{cases} \tag{2b}$$

Expressions were guided towards structures with physically meaningful interpretations. Appended to L_{MSE} used to evaluate fitness during tournament selection, was a penalty, P, defined in Eq. (2b) to take infinity when the expression, G, was not of the form, G'. Generalisable to PFD optimisation is the assumption of state equilibration, where $k(\cdot)$, $f(\cdot)$, $b(\cdot)$ and $K(\cdot)$ are functions representing the overall rate, forward and backward driving forces, and equilibrium constant for the underlying formulation process, but G' can take other structural forms if different prior knowledge is considered true.

2.2. Multi-Objective MBDoE for PFD Development

In Step 4, MBDoE designs new experiments by minimising the multi-objective function, $J(\boldsymbol{\vartheta})$, in Eq. (3). $J_M(\boldsymbol{\vartheta})$ is the expected information gain, $J_P(\boldsymbol{\vartheta})$ is the objective function for process optimisation, while J_M^{max} and J_P^{max} are normalisation constants. $0 \leq \alpha \leq 1$ systematically balances these objectives and is updated in Step 3 each MBDoE iteration.

$$\min_{\boldsymbol{\vartheta}} J(\boldsymbol{\vartheta}) = \alpha \cdot \frac{J_M(\boldsymbol{\vartheta})}{J_M^{\text{max}}} + (1 - \alpha) \cdot \frac{J_P(\boldsymbol{\vartheta})}{J_P^{\text{max}}} \tag{3a}$$

$$\text{s.t. } \boldsymbol{\vartheta}_{lb} \leq \boldsymbol{\vartheta} \leq \boldsymbol{\vartheta}_{ub} \tag{3b}$$

$J_M(\boldsymbol{\vartheta})$ was estimated as the variance in the final product KPI, $\widehat{\boldsymbol{\psi}}_f$, predicted by simulating the PFD with combinations of the top three scoring kinetic expressions proposed by SR selected by Eq. (1). To balance exploration vs. exploitation automatically, in Step 3, α is re-weighted using Eq. (4) based on the actual information gained, ΔJ_M, by the experiment and how far from optimality, ΔJ_P, was the PFD in the previous MBDoE iteration.

$$\alpha = \frac{\Delta J_M}{\Delta J_M + \Delta J_P} \tag{4}$$

3. Formulation Process Modelling and Case Study

A liquid product, typical of cosmetic and pharmaceutical creams, was used as a case study, and a new mechanistic model was proposed for the first time to approximate its formulation and KPI dynamics. This model was used to run computational experiments and generate in-silico data to test the SR-MBDoE framework.

$$r_1 = k_1 \cdot \dot{\gamma} \cdot (\alpha - T) \cdot [X_A X_W] \cdot H(T - T_K) \tag{5a}$$

$$r_2 = k_2 \cdot \dot{\gamma} \cdot T \cdot \left[X_L X_W - \frac{X_{L^*}}{K_2 \cdot T^{-1}}\right] \tag{5b}$$

$$r_3 = k_3 \cdot \dot{\gamma} \cdot \left[X_L - \frac{X_V}{K_3 \cdot \dot{\gamma} \cdot (T - \beta)}\right] \cdot H(T - T_K) \tag{5c}$$

The model grouped the chemical constituents into five phases (i.e., W, A, L, L^* and V); proposed rate equations for three mechanisms: r_1: $2A + 5W \rightarrow L$ and r_2: $L + 10W \rightleftharpoons L^*$ and r_3: $3L \rightleftharpoons V$; and embedded the kinetics into the recycle emulsification configuration in Fig. (2a). The rates, r_i, in Eq. (5) were functions of X and $P = [T, \dot{\gamma}]$, where T was temperature and $\dot{\gamma}$ was average shear rate, while $H(T)$ was the Heaviside switch function and k_i, K_i, α, β and T_K were constants. At any time, KPI was: $\psi = f(X)$. Fig. (2b) shows the in-silico product KPI profiles for the four experiments that initiated MBDoE in the following case studies. This modelling approach is generally applicable to approximating product formulation by sequential ingredient additions and processing operations.

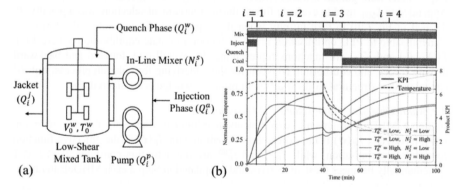

Figure 2: Recycle configuration for product manufacturing (a) and four example in-silico process dynamic KPI profiles (b), where V is volume, Q is volumetric flowrate and T is temperature; the superscripts w, a, s, p and j denote two of the phases, the in-line mixer.

4. Results and Discussion

The SR-MBDoE framework was investigated in Case Study 1 when the sole focus was process knowledge discovery: $\alpha = 1$; then in Case Study 2 when the aim was simultaneous knowledge discovery and PFD optimisation: $\alpha = f(\Delta J_M, \Delta J_P)$. In-silico experiments measured ΔX and P over the in-line mixer each minute where the intrinsic dynamics dominated. For each MBDoE iteration, SR proposed three candidate expressions for each of the three rate equations $r_i = f(X, P)$ (i.e., nine overall); then, a new experiment was designed and conducted by minimising $J(\vartheta)$, expanding the dataset.

Integrating Knowledge-Guided Symbolic Regression and Model-Based
Design of Experiments to Automate Process Flow Diagram Development

2813

4.1. Case Study 1: Process Knowledge Discovery

For each MBDoE iteration (I_{MBDoE}), Case Study 1A proposed a new set of equations from scratch, while Case Study 1B carried over and improved the equations from the previous I_{MBDoE}, representing a trade-off between the risk of inherited biases and computational efficiency. Fig. (3a) and (3b) show the prediction MAPE for the product KPI and fitting MSE for the top three scoring expressions for each rate equation following each I_{MBDoE} for Case Studies 1A and 1B, respectively. To begin with, the "evolutionary pressure" towards the ground truth was weak, and there were too many similarly fitting expressions to search. As more carefully designed experiments were added, the difference in the MSE between correct and incorrect expressions during tournament selection became stronger, encouraging the promotion of better-fitting expressions.

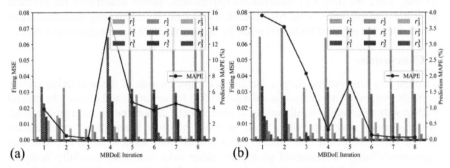

Figure 3: Mean absolute percentage error (MAPE, for prediction) and mean-square error (MSE, for fitting) of the expressions r_i^j proposed at each iteration of Case Studies 1A (a) and 1B (b); i and j index the rate equation and relative complexity. Bars corresponding to the top-scoring expressions used for estimating the MAPE at each iteration are hashed.

In both Case Studies, the MAPE peaked. In Case Study 1B, the ground truth for r_3 was found in $I_{MBDoE} = 4$ but then demoted but not forgotten in $I_{MBDoE} = 5$ in favour of a worse-fitting approximation with an MSE of 0.0086, but its much lower complexity gave it a higher score of 1.3 compared with 1.1 and 0.82 for the other candidates with MSEs of 0.00001 and 0.0009, respectively. The choice of metric to score and select expressions is critical; however, each metric or information criterion (e.g., Akaike, Bayesian and Hannan-Quinn) comes with its own biases. Only carefully designed experiments can reliably discriminate between different hypotheses and identify the correct model structure. Thus, by $I_{MBDoE} = 6$ when the new experiment pushed up the MSE of the approximation from 0.0086 to 0.011, the score ranking flipped, and the ground truth was re-identified. By contrast, the MAPE never recovered in Case Study 1A, suggesting that building complete expressions from scratch is more challenging. So, rather than inherited biases hindering discovery, adding new information by MBDoE incrementally to improve existing expressions can guide SR towards the correct structure more efficiently.

With the constraint (i.e., based on prior knowledge of state equilibration) active, SR successfully yielded physically insightful expressions that could be interpreted in terms of key forward and backward driving force factors. Now, Case Study 1C tested the performance of the SR-MBDoE framework when lifting this constraint. Here, the MAPE decreased from 25.6% to 1.98% and plateaued for $I_{MBDoE} \geq 7$, demonstrating that constraining the search to the correct structure significantly improved fitting accuracy and sped up knowledge discovery when the number of experiments was small.

4.2. Case Study 2: Simultaneous Knowledge Discovery and PFD Optimisation

The aim was to hit a target final product KPI, ψ_t, within a $\pm 3\%$ tolerance of a specific value while minimising total batch time, τ. Initially, MBDoE bounced between exploration ($\alpha > 0.5$) and exploitation ($\alpha < 0.5$). For as long as ΔJ_M was large, and new experiments continued to be informative, then exploration was prioritised. Once ΔJ_M became small ($\alpha = 0.2$ by $I_{MBDoE} = 5$), and new experiments no longer proved to be as informative, then process optimisation was prioritised. If, at any point, the model aimed for and successfully hit on a good recipe (i.e., one that achieved an in-spec KPI), then there would be nothing new to learn or improve about the process within the local vicinity; thus, the next iteration would bounce back to pure exploration. By $I_{MBDoE} = 7$ the nominal total batch time was greatly reduced from $\tau = 100$ min at $I_{MBDoE} = 0$ to $\tau = 57$ min, while the final KPI satisfied the requirement, further evidencing the practical advantage and efficiency of the SR-MBDoE framework. By discovering mechanistic rate expressions, the physical trade-offs made by the optimised PFD were also interpretable.

5. Conclusions

Through two case studies, despite the highly complex nature of the underlying ground truth, the proposed knowledge-guided SR-MBDoE framework could recover the ground truth exactly after only a small number of experiments, demonstrating its great potential. While carrying over expressions from previous MBDoE iterations for modification proved more successful than building expressions from scratch. However, selecting expressions based on statistical parsimony alone risks bias; only carefully designed experiments can reliably discriminate between similarly fitting candidates of different complexities. Then, when the knowledge-guided constraint on the expressions' structure was lifted, the prediction accuracy for the same number of experiments decreased substantially. By synergising human intelligence with the automatic discovery and discrimination of interpretable mechanistic models representing the scale-independent process dynamics, the proposed framework shows excellent potential for accelerating product innovation, scale-up and design of PFDs for producing new formulations.

References

Angelis, D., Sofos, F., & Karakasidis, T. E. (2023). Artificial Intelligence in Physical Sciences: Symbolic Regression Trends and Perspectives. *Archives of Computational Methods in Engineering, 30*(6), 3845–3865. https://doi.org/10.1007/s11831-023-09922-z

Brunton, S. L., Proctor, J. L., & Kutz, J. N. (2016). Discovering governing equations from data by sparse identification of nonlinear dynamical systems. *Proceedings of the National Academy of Sciences, 113*(15), 3932–3937. https://doi.org/10.1073/pnas.1517384113

Cranmer, M. (2023). *Interpretable Machine Learning for Science with PySR and SymbolicRegression.jl.* https://doi.org/10.48550/ARXIV.2305.01582

de Franca, F. O., Virgolin, M., Kommenda, M., Majumder, M. S., Cranmer, M., Espada, G., Ingelse, L., Fonseca, A., Landajuela, M., Petersen, B., Glatt, R., Mundhenk, N., Lee, C. S., Hochhalter, J. D., Randall, D. L., Kamienny, P., Zhang, H., Dick, G., Simon, A., … La Cava, W. G. (2023). *Interpretable Symbolic Regression for Data Science: Analysis of the 2022 Competition* (arXiv:2304.01117). arXiv. http://arxiv.org/abs/2304.01117

Franceschini, G., & Macchietto, S. (2008). Model-based design of experiments for parameter precision: State of the art. *Chemical Engineering Science, 63*(19), 4846–4872.

Servia, M. Á. de C., Sandoval, I. O., Hellgardt, K., Kuok, K., Hii, Zhang, D., & Chanona, E. A. del R. (2023). *The Automated Discovery of Kinetic Rate Models—Methodological Frameworks* (arXiv:2301.11356). arXiv. http://arxiv.org/abs/2301.11356

Flavio Manenti, Gintaras V. Reklaitis (Eds.), Proceedings of the 34th European Symposium on Computer Aided Process Engineering or 15th International Symposium on Process Systems Engineering (ESCAPE34 or PSE24), June 2-6, 2024, Florence, Italy
© 2024 Elsevier B.V. All rights reserved. http://dx.doi.org/10.1016/B978-0-443-28824-1.50470-1

Harnessing Instruction-Tuned Large Language Models to Mine Structured Omics Data for Predicting Chemical Toxicity

Yufan Liu,[a] Guoping Lian,[a,b] Tao Chen[a]*

[a]*School of Chemistry and Chemical Engineering, University of Surrey, Stag Hill, Guildford GU2 7XH, UK*
[b]*Unilever R&D Colworth, Unilever, Sharnbrook MK44 1LQ, UK*
* t.chen@surrey.ac.uk

Abstract

Chemical safety and toxicology are important considerations in designing safer and sustainable products and processes. Omics technologies, including transcriptomics, proteomics, and metabolomics, provide crucial insights into chemical toxicity by identifying molecular-level changes post-chemical exposure and elucidating regulatory pathways. Despite the vast literature on this topic, there's a lack of comprehensive datasets detailing chemical perturbations and their outcomes. A tool that can efficiently and accurately extract structured data from scientific literature is needed. Large Language Models (LLMs) like GPT-4 offer the potential for efficient information retrieval from intricate texts. However, optimising their factuality and desired behaviour often requires labour-intensive human feedback. Addressing this, our work introduces a semi-automated pipeline for structured information extraction from voluminous literature. Initially, literature that contain any type of omics in the title or abstract and mention pathway analysis in the text were obtained from PubMed. Subsequently, GPT-4 was employed to extract data points including omics type, perturbation, perturbation type and study results, from selected literature abstracts in a zero-shot manner. After manual corrections, this data served to fine-tune the GPT-3.5-turbo model. This fine-tuned model then processed a new batch of abstracts, with its output validated by GPT-4. Discrepancies were manually reconciled, and the consolidated data was used to further fine-tune the GPT-3.5-turbo model. Following an iterative process of reconciliation and fine-tuning, the resulting model demonstrated high accuracy and alignment in extracting structured data from literature with minimal human intervention, which holds the potential to accelerate knowledge transformation. Additionally, we present a structured dataset encapsulating omics type, perturbations, perturbation types, results, etc., that can be used for future omics studies.

Keywords: Chemical safety, omics technologies, Large Language Models (LLMs), Structured information extraction, fine-tuning GPT.

1. Introduction

In the field of chemical safety and toxicology, the need to develop safer and more sustainable products and processes is increasingly recognised (Anastas, 2016). The emergence of omics technologies, including transcriptomics, proteomics, metabolomics, and other related disciplines, has significantly enhanced our understanding of the mechanisms underlying chemical toxicity. These technologies provide detailed insights into the molecular-level changes that transpire following chemical exposure, thus elucidating on the complex regulatory pathways within cells (Liu et al., 2023).

The regulatory pathways of a cell are a complex network involving a myriad of biomolecules, each possessing distinct physicochemical properties and engaging in complex, non-linear interactions. Single-omics techniques can measure biomolecules of a specific type, providing a fragmented view of these pathways. Multi-omics approaches enable a more holistic understanding of pathway's response to chemical exposure (Canzler *et al.*, 2020).

Transcriptomics, which focuses on the comprehensive detection of RNAs in the cell, primarily identifies pathway responses through the differential expression of a known set of target genes. Proteomics offers insights into the proteins is particularly valuable for understanding toxicopathic effects and responses, leading to the development of protein-centric adverse outcome pathways (AOPs) and predictive models of toxicological pathways (Madeira and Costa, 2021). Phosphoproteomics, which aims to map and quantify protein phosphorylation, plays a vital role in deciphering the intracellular signalling networks that respond to cellular stresses (Titz *et al.*, 2014). Metabolomics, focusing on a wide array of chemically heterogeneous molecules, has emerged as a pivotal tool in toxicological studies, examining metabolic alterations in cells under chemical exposures (Olesti *et al.*, 2021). On this basis, the fields of toxicogenomics, toxicoproteomics, toxicometabolomics and other fields have been developed to use omics technology to predict toxicity.

Despite these advancements, a significant gap remains in the availability of datasets that encompass the information about chemical perturbation and corresponding real omics data and detailed information about regulatory pathways. Existing databases, such as DrugMatrix, Open TG-GATEs and L1000 (Liu *et al.*, 2023), provide limited information, predominantly in gene expression. While the literature on the use of omics data to explore chemical toxicity mechanisms is growing, the effective extraction of information from these complex datasets is a formidable challenge. The development of large language models (LLMs) like GPT has facilitated the efficient extraction of information from complex, unstructured text sources (Zhu *et al.*, 2023). However, a critical challenge remains in evaluating the accuracy of the outputs generated by LLMs and in ensuring their human alignment. This alignment is crucial to guarantee that the model's outputs are not only precise but also consonant with human values and intentions. Conventionally, such evaluations necessitate intricate training procedures or labour-intensive manual annotation of samples, which are time-consuming (Fu *et al.*, 2023). Therefore, a more expedient and efficient approach is imperative.

In this context, we propose a semi-automated method that enables effective information extraction with minimal human intervention. Our approach has led to the extraction of 10 critical data points, including omics layer, species, biological sample, differentially expressed genes (DEGs), proteins (DEPs), metabolites (DEMs), and regulatory pathways for a range of chemicals. This dataset is poised to be a valuable resource for downstream analysis, offering the potential to unravel the intricate relationships between these data points and to further our understanding of chemical toxicity mechanisms.

2. Methods and results

2.1. Corpus retrieval

Our methodology commenced with the stringent selection of articles from a comprehensive corpus. Criteria for inclusion mandated the presence of specific omics-related terms (proteomics, metabolomics, transcriptomics, phosphoproteomics, multi-omics) in either the title or abstract. Additionally, articles were required to contain the phrase "pathway analysis" within their main text. Exclusion criteria were set to omit articles with any mention of "plant" in the title or abstract, reflecting our study's focus on non-plant organisms. From the PMC database (as of 25th October 2023), we retrieved 13,102 articles in XML format. The retrieved articles were pre-processed to keep the articles with 'article-type' of 'research-article'.

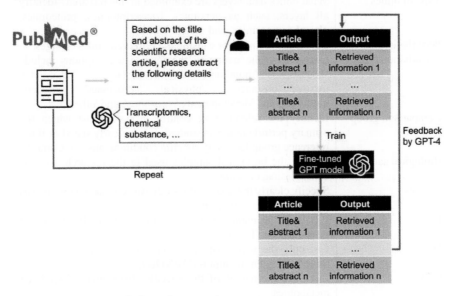

Figure 1 The overview of information extraction

2.2. GPT-4 extraction in zero-shot prompting

GPT-4 API was used for extracting structured information from 150 randomly chosen articles. This process was executed in a zero-shot manner with a structured prompt: 'Based on the title and abstract of the scientific research article, please extract the following details:'.

The prompt was designed to extract key details including (1) Target article: This question is set to know whether this article contains the information we want before extracting information; (2) Type of omics: Different omics layers contain different layers of molecular information; (3) Specific primary perturbation: It is important to know the aim of the article, which is the primary perturbation that causing omics change; (4) Perturbation type: Figuring out what the type of the primary perturbation can help us to do downstream analysis; (5) Comparison group: With this data point, the settings of control group can be acquired; (6) Biological sample: Different biological samples with difference cells composition can convey different information. (7) Species: The same treatment can act differently one different animal; (8) Differentially Expressed Genes (DEGs); (9) Differentially Expressed Proteins (DEPs); (10) Differentially Expressed Metabolites (DEMs). (11) Pathway Enrichment Results: Results in regulatory can help us to understand the mechanism of cellular or tissue's responses to stimulation.

The prompts that describe each task are shown in Table 1. To avoid hallucination, the description of each prompt is ended with "*If the information isn't available, respond with 'Not specified'*".

Table 1 Extracted data points and the description of prompt.

Data points	Prompt
Target article	Is the article focused on omics analysis comparing two conditions (e.g., disease vs. control, treated vs. untreated, treatment A vs. treatment B)?
Type of omics	What omics data layers are examined in this research? Identify all layers, such as genomics, transcriptomics, proteomics, phosphoproteomics, and metabolomics.
Perturbation	Define the main factor causing the observed omics changes.
Perturbation type	Characterize the nature of the main cause. Options include 'disease', 'monomolecular substance', 'Complex mixtures/substance', 'physical processes', 'genetic modifications', 'development', 'resistance', and 'other'.
Comparison group	Identify the reference or control group against which the primary perturbation was studied. If not clearly stated or if the reference group lacks any specific condition, answer 'Control'.
Biological sample	Specify the biological samples used in the research, such as cells, plasma, or urine
Species	Specify clearly the species the study was conducted on, such as Homo sapiens, mouse, rat.
DEGs	List only the names of the specific differentially expressed genes, e.g., ATP2A1.
DEPs	List only the names of the specific differentially expressed proteins, e.g. Paralemmin-3/A6NDB9.
DEMs	List only the names of the specific differentially expressed metabolites.
Pathways	List the biological pathways (excluding individual genes or transcription factors) impacted by the primary perturbation.

Extracted data underwent initial manual validation and formatting, with semicolons delineating multiple comparison groups. The validation classified each answer into three classes, a) Correct: the information is correct and the format is desired; b) Correct but not aligned: Correct information location but not in desired format; c) Wrong: wrong information extracted. The GPT-4 model achieved 83% to 100% in 11 tasks (Figure 2).

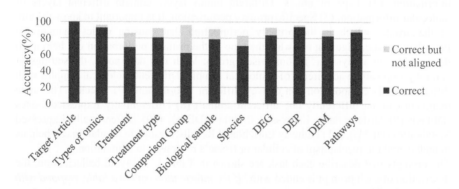

Figure 2 The accuracy of zero-shot prompting in extracting information from 150 articles.

2.3. Fine-tuning GPT model

Two fine-tuned GPT-3.5-turbo models (gpt-3.5-turbo-1106) were developed: one for classification and another for information extraction.

2.3.1. Fine-tuned model for target article identification

The classification model was trained using 150 positive articles from the initial step and 50 negative articles unrelated to omics analysis. The positive examples were labeled with 'True', and negative as 'False'. The prompt was structured as *"You are an expert in Bioinformatics. You are to determine if the study focused on omics analysis comparing two conditions (e.g., disease vs. control, treated vs. untreated, treatment A vs. treatment B) based on article title and abstract provided."* Which is followed by the title and the abstract. The True/False labels were used as expected output to fine tune the model.

2.3.2. Fine-tuned model for information extraction

The preliminary model for information extraction was trained using pairs of titles, abstracts, and their respective extracted information, post manual correction. The prompt used for training contains two parts. The first part is system message, which tells the system the details about the task of extraction, including the return format, JSON, and the 10 data points with the descriptions. The second part is user message, which contains the title and the abstract of the article. The ten time points were used as output to fine-tune the model.

2.4. Validation and correction

After the development of the fine-tuned models for classification and information extraction, these models were employed to process 200 articles. Zero-shot prompting was also employed for this determination. Comparisons were made between the results from the fine-tuned models and GPT-4, with any discrepancies being manually reviewed.

Of these, 169 articles were identified as target papers and used for further information extraction. The results from the fine-tuned models underwent validation using zero-shot prompting GPT-4. The prompt was structed to have two parts, the first part, system message, starts with "Your task is to determine if the student's answers is correct or not. To solve the problem do the following:

- First, work out your own answers to the questions.

- Then compare your solution to the student's solution and evaluate if the student's solution is correct or not." Also indicated the desired answer is "Correct/Wrong". The second part user massage was structured to include the instruction of desired data points extraction, title, abstract, and "student solutions".

The results that were regarded as a wrong answer were validated manually. To understand the performance of both the GPT-4 and fine-tuned GPT-4 model, the output from two model were assessed comprehensively.

Following manual corrections, the consolidated results were used to train two additional fine-tuned models. Step 2.3.1- 2.4 were repeated on both the second and third batch, comprising 200 articles each. This semi-automated fine-tuning process reduced the workload by 72% compared to manually assessing all data points.

2.5. Large-scale information extraction

After three iterations of fine-tuning, the models achieved accuracies of 97% in classification and average accuracies of 97% in 10 tasks in information extraction. The classification model was then applied to the remaining articles in the pool, identifying those relevant for further information extraction. Ultimately, this process yielded data on 1063 monomolecular substances and 758 complex mixtures/substances, alongside corresponding differentially expressed genes, proteins, metabolites, and regulatory pathways.

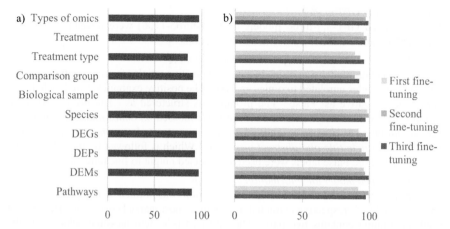

Figure 3 a) The performance of GPT-4 in validating fine-tune model; b) The performance of fine-tuned models in ten tasks of information extraction in three iterations.

3. Conclusions

Our study has successfully demonstrated the integration of advanced computational methods with omics data analysis in chemical safety and toxicology. By developing a semi-automated pipeline using GPT-4 and fine-tuned models, we have streamlined the extraction of critical data from extensive scientific literature, achieving high accuracy in both classification and information extraction. Our findings pave the way for future research in chemical toxicity and safer product development, showcasing the significant role of artificial intelligence in advancing the field of toxicological studies.

Acknowledgement

Y. Liu received a PhD studentship co-funded by Unilever and the University of Surrey.

References

Anastas, N. D. (2016) 'Connecting toxicology and chemistry to ensure safer chemical design', *Green Chemistry*, 18(16), pp. 4325–4331. doi: 10.1039/c6gc00758a.
Canzler, S. *et al.* (2020) 'Prospects and challenges of multi-omics data integration in toxicology', *Archives of Toxicology*. Springer, pp. 371–388. doi: 10.1007/s00204-020-02656-y.
Fu, J. *et al.* (2023) 'GPTScore: Evaluate as You Desire'.
Liu, A. *et al.* (2023) 'Using chemical and biological data to predict drug toxicity', *SLAS Discovery*, 28(3), pp. 53–64. doi: 10.1016/j.slasd.2022.12.003.
Liu, Y., Lian, G. and Chen, T. (2023) 'A novel multi-omics data analysis of dose-dependent and temporal changes in regulatory pathways due to chemical perturbation: a case study on caffeine', *Toxicology Mechanisms and Methods*, 0(0), pp. 1–12. doi: 10.1080/15376516.2023.2265462.
Madeira, C. and Costa, P. M. (2021) 'Proteomics in systems toxicology', *Advances in Protein Chemistry and Structural Biology*, 127, pp. 55–91. doi: 10.1016/bs.apcsb.2021.03.001
Olesti, E. *et al.* (2021) 'Approaches in metabolomics for regulatory toxicology applications', *Analyst*, 146(6), pp. 1820–1834. doi: 10.1039/d0an02212h.
Titz, B. *et al.* (2014) 'Proteomics for systems toxicology', *Computational and Structural Biotechnology Journal*, 11(18), pp. 73–90. doi: 10.1016/j.csbj.2014.08.004.
Zhu, Y. *et al.* (2023) 'Large Language Models for Information Retrieval: A Survey', pp. 1–26.

Flavio Manenti, Gintaras V. Reklaitis (Eds.), Proceedings of the 34th European Symposium on Computer Aided Process Engineering / 15th International Symposium on Process Systems Engineering (ESCAPE34/PSE24), June 2-6, 2024, Florence, Italy

Achieving Flexibility in High Throughput Liquid Handing experimentation by smart System Design

Simon Seidel[a], Peter Neubauer[a], Mariano Nicolas Cruz-Bournazou[a]

[a] Chair of Bioprocess Engineering, Department of Biotechnology, Faculty III, Technische Universität Berlin, Berlin, Germany
simon.seidel@tu-berlin.de

Abstract

Automation and data handling have become essential in the developments of Laboratory 4.0, liquid and robotic object handling, and laboratory digitalization. However, existing systems seldom offer comprehensive and adaptable integrated platforms, restricting seamless integration and flexible experiments. There is a constant need to synchronize hardware automation with data handling and computational workflows to facilitate development of automated lab processes in today's R&D.

Addressing this, we introduce a distributed micro-service based robotic control platform for biolabs, designed to simplify system orchestration for high throughput experiments through features such as easy modifiability, alongside efficient hardware integration. This development includes a hardware-software infrastructure utilizing microservices, digital twins, among others, and incorporates miniaturized systems developed in-house, steering towards meeting the requisites of Laboratory 4.0 and alleviating longstanding challenges faced in automation and digitalization in this sector.

Keywords: Micro-Service Based Infrastructure, Laboratory 4.0, Digital Twin, Laboratory Digitalization, and Integration

1. Introduction

The advancement of liquid handling stations in biolabs has been complemented by the introduction of various auxiliary devices like filtering stations, pumping units, washers, and cooling/heating units, including compact shakers and specialized microscopes. While the integration of physically larger equipment can present challenges, such as pipetting issues and reduced parallel processing capability, the trend is shifting towards smaller-scale, distributed systems(Anantanawat et al., 2019; Haby et al., 2019; Hemmerich et al., 2018; Hertzberg & Pope, 2000; Pereira & Williams, 2007). This trend highlights the need for scalability and flexibility in labs, adopting an edge-focused approach where each device operates semi-independently. Devices such as mini bioreactors, diverse well plates, organ-on-chip systems, and microfluidic devices are well suited to be integrated in such distributed framework. Their integration into an automated platform enhances experimental capabilities and overall lab performance.

We present a comprehensive system designed for high-throughput liquid handling in biolabs. The system integrates diverse technologies and methodologies, including process orchestration, on-demand simulations, and flexible workflow design in Cylc v8 and Apache NiFi. It utilizes a Tecan liquid handler and an array of smart devices for enhanced flexibility and efficiency in experimentation. The paper is structured to first describe the setup and concludes with a demonstration of an experimental run using the entire system.

2. Software, Hardware and Methodology

The comprehensive setup consists of various devices and software which are each described in the following sections. First a hardware description is provided in the section 2.1, then a software description and the methodology is provided in section 2.2.

2.1. Physical setup description

The setup is built in and around a Tecan Evo 200 (Tecan, Switzerland) liquid handler (LiHa). It features a variety of devices, which are physically and virtually integrated. The LiHa pipetting head can pipet eight liquids in any configuration, while the 384 needle head can pipet a large number of liquids in parallel. By placing all devices close to each other in and adjacent to the platform, the given setup can perform high throughput experimentation. The 384 needle washing station (Tecan, Switzerland) can wash and cool the needles, depending on the used liquid, e.g. washing and cooling liquid. The plate reader M1000 (Tecan, Switzerland) measures samples with less than one second per well. The thermal device (inhouse development) can reach temperatures from -20 to 100

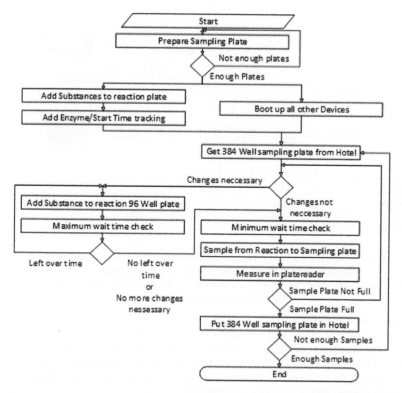

Figure 1: This workflow outlines the procedure for the enzymatic characterization process. Initially, all necessary substances are stored within the liquid handling system. The process is then executed according to a predefined workflow implemented in Cylc v8.

degrees Celsius within 12 independent sections of one 96 well plate. Each section consists of 4 wells, resulting in 48 independently controlled wells.

2.2. Methodology and Software Components

A variety of systems are necessary for the integration of the devices for the process (ref. section 2.2.1). The main central component is the Laboratory orchestration system (ref. section 2.2.2) This system uses an Workflow management (ref. section 2.2.3) and other subsystems (ref. section 2.2.4).

2.2.1. Experiment Procedures

For the purpose of this study, the authors established an enzyme characterization process setup aimed at high-throughput experimentation to demonstrate the performance of the system. The initial phase involves preparing the liquid handling station by adding enzymes, substrates, and stock substances. The system tests different combinations of initial conditions for each enzymatic reaction in a 96 well plate and samples from each well several times. In total 48 reactions are run in parallel. The comprehensive process is outlined in Figure 1.

2.2.2. Laboratory Orchestration

The orchestrator oversees the liquid handling procedures, coordinating equipment such as the Tecan liquid handler, thermal devices, centrifuges, transfer units, wash stations,

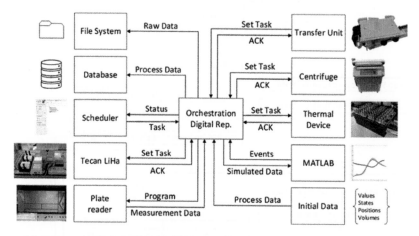

Figure 2: The complete Apache Nifi based communication Infrastructure condensed into one diagram. The laboratory orchestration is the central element for the used automated setup in the biolab. This scheme shows which Software and devices are included into the system and what type of data is being transferred.

and plate readers (ref. Figure 2). It tracks the locations and statuses of components like vials and multi-well plates and maintains records of measurement data and sample origins. Additionally, the orchestrator updates information based on pipetting actions and adjusts for changes in liquid levels and well conditions. It ensures procedural consistency, prevents unfeasible command execution, and handles hard- and software communication through the Apache NiFi based data infrastructure.

2.2.3. Workflow Management and Experiment Execution

Cylc v8 is instrumental in creating dynamic, parallel and cycling workflows that vary in complexity, thereby enhancing the flexibility and integration of the experimental process. Its user interface allows for quick modifications and easy integration of new steps into existing workflows (ref. Figure 1)

2.2.4. Additional Software

MATLAB is utilized for simulating physical, chemical, and biological processes in experiments, using mechanistic models for an optimal design of experiments. It performs estimations and simulations, which are then fed back into the system for efficient experiment management.

Apache NiFi connects the lab's devices, enables the creation of new device connections, data routing between devices and software communication within the digital infrastructure. It features robust data management, data storage during communication failures, and a user interface for troubleshooting and visualization in complex setups. Apache NiFi also facilitates data processing and transformation, ensuring compatibility and seamless communication across various platforms.

3. Results

The performance of the system was evaluated based on its data handling capabilities, flexibility, and the integration of various hardware and software components. The orchestrator efficiently managed real-time data export and analysis, including the

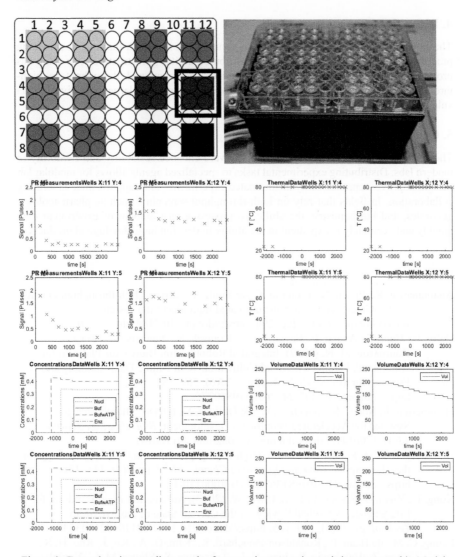

Figure 3: Exemplary intermediate result of an ongoing screening as it is represented in Matlab. The data is from a single 96 well plate 4 well segment is displayed in the upper left scheme and upper right picture. The time zero seconds in the plots represents the time of enzyme addition in the main 96 Well plate. The top four plots on the left show plate reader measurements from 384 Well measurements plates for samples from the four well block. The upper right four plots show the temperature measurements taken during the experiment. The bottom left plots show calculated concentrations from the four wells and the bottom right graphs show the total volume in each of the four wells.

automatic calculation of reaction initiation times. This was tested in an experiment where measurements from three 384-well plates is reassigned online to individual wells in a 96-well plate (ref. Figure 3). The setup can overcome various problems and errors. This adaptability allowed stretching and rerunning of certain steps during the execution.

4. Discussion

The integration of hardware and software components in a high-throughput screening process, as described is enabled using a distributed digital infrastructure. The setup has proven to be effective in enhancing efficiency, accuracy and throughput in high-throughput screenings or characterisation, precisely processing larger and diverse data volumes.

5. Conclusion

The setup of laboratory components and software enhance scalability and flexibility in modern labs. Distributing experimental tasks to specialized agents allows for modular lab design, improves reproducibility in automated experiments, and supports inter-laboratory collaboration. In fields that rely on high-throughput screening, such as pharmacology, genomics, and biochemistry, the ability to process a vast amount of experiment data quickly and accurately is expedient in the ability to develop biotechnological products.

References

Anantanawat, K., Pitsch, N., Fromont, C., & Janitz, C. (2019). High-throughput Quant-iT PicoGreen assay using an automated liquid handling system. *BioTechniques*, *66*(6), 290–294. https://doi.org/10.2144/btn-2018-0172

Haby, B., Hans, S., Anane, E., Sawatzki, A., Krausch, N., Neubauer, P., & Cruz Bournazou, M. N. (2019). Integrated Robotic Mini Bioreactor Platform for Automated, Parallel Microbial Cultivation With Online Data Handling and Process Control. *SLAS Technology*, *24*(6), 569–582. https://doi.org/10.1177/2472630319860775

Hemmerich, J., Noack, S., Wiechert, W., & Oldiges, M. (2018). Microbioreactor Systems for Accelerated Bioprocess Development. *Biotechnology Journal*, *13*(4), 1700141. https://doi.org/10.1002/biot.201700141

Hertzberg, R. P., & Pope, A. J. (2000). High-throughput screening: New technology for the 21st century. *Current Opinion in Chemical Biology*, *4*(4), 445–451. https://doi.org/10.1016/S1367-5931(00)00110-1

Kong, F., Yuan, L., Zheng, Y. F., & Chen, W. (2012). Automatic Liquid Handling for Life Science: A Critical Review of the Current State of the Art. *SLAS Technology*, *17*(3), 169–185. https://doi.org/10.1177/2211068211435302

Leung, C. M., de Haan, P., Ronaldson-Bouchard, K., Kim, G.-A., Ko, J., Rho, H. S., Chen, Z., Habibovic, P., Jeon, N. L., Takayama, S., Shuler, M. L., Vunjak-Novakovic, G., Frey, O., Verpoorte, E., & Toh, Y.-C. (2022). A guide to the organ-on-a-chip. *Nature Reviews Methods Primers*, *2*(1), 33. https://doi.org/10.1038/s43586-022-00118-6

Pereira, D. A., & Williams, J. A. (2007). Origin and evolution of high throughput screening: Origin and circumscribed history of HTS. *British Journal of Pharmacology*, *152*(1), 53–61. https://doi.org/10.1038/sj.bjp.0707373

Zhu, Y., Zhang, Y.-X., Cai, L.-F., & Fang, Q. (2013). Sequential Operation Droplet Array: An Automated Microfluidic Platform for Picoliter-Scale Liquid Handling, Analysis, and Screening. *Analytical Chemistry*, *85*(14), 6723–6731. https://doi.org/10.1021/ac4006414

Flavio Manenti, Gintaras V. Reklaitis (Eds.), Proceedings of the 34th European Symposium on Computer Aided Process Engineering / 15th International Symposium on Process Systems Engineering (ESCAPE34/PSE24), June 2-6, 2024, Florence, Italy

Modelling and stochastic optimization of a three-compartment electrochemical reactor for CO_2 electroreduction to formic acid using neural networks

Jose Antonio Abarca*, Mario Coz-Cruz, Guillermo Díaz-Sainz, Angel Irabien

Departamento de Ingenierías Química y Biomolecular, Universidad de Cantabria, ETSIIT, Avenida de los Castros s/n, 39005, Santander, Spain.
*joseantonio.abarca@unican.es

Abstract

Among different configurations, the three-compartment electrochemical reactor has demonstrated promising results for the CO_2 reduction towards formic acid. To facilitate the technology's scale-up, it is essential to assess the system's performance and identify the most crucial operational variables. Modelling the system also provides valuable insights into tailoring process variables to achieve formic acid that meets specific requirements. In this context, a case study is proposed to address the non-linear optimization problem of installing the CO_2 electroreduction process in a cement industry, aiming to minimize overall cost. Furthermore, various scenarios are considered to evaluate the economic viability of implementing this CO_2 electroreduction technology.

Keywords: CO_2 electroreduction, three-compartment electrochemical reactor, neural network, empirical modelling, non-linear optimization.

1. Introduction

Some of the main challenges facing society are related to climate change and global warming. The anthropogenic emission of CO_2 is a precursor to these phenomena. Various strategies, such as the use of renewable energy sources or improving energy efficiency, are proposed to mitigate these CO_2 emissions. In this sense, CO_2 electroreduction ($ERCO_2$) to value-added products emerges as one of the most promising CO_2 utilization processes from both economic and environmental perspectives (He et al., 2023). This technology transforms the CO_2 molecule into other chemical products (e.g., formic acid, methanol, ethylene) in an electrocatalytic process by applying an external voltage. Additionally, it allows for the storage of energy from renewable sources in the form of chemical bonds (Ozden et al., 2022).

In recent years, several research efforts have focused on developing efficient CO_2 electrolyzers for $ERCO_2$, primarily addressing reactor configuration, catalyst selection (Díaz-Sainz et al., 2023), process variable evaluation (Díaz-Sainz et al., 2021), and electrode fabrication (Abarca et al., 2023). Three-compartment configurations have shown promising results in $ERCO_2$ to formic acid (Yang et al., 2020). These devices offer advantages over conventional one or two-compartment reactors, such as high Faradic Efficiencies toward formic acid, long-term stability, and direct formic acid production (Fernández-Caso et al., 2023). Furthermore, lab-scale commercial devices are available to study the process performance, facilitating the determination of suitable conditions for process scale-up and enabling the development of predictive models that can be useful tools in designing larger-scale electrolyzers.

The cement industry is one of the so-called hard-to-abate sectors, where CO_2 emissions cannot be avoided by conventional strategies, and CCUSs (Carbon Capture Utilization and Storage) are proposed. $ERCO_2$ to formic acid gains special relevance, as this chemical product is typically used for wastewater effluent treatment as a pH-neutralizing reactant. Formic acid production can be tailored by adjusting $ERCO_2$ operational variables to meet industry requirements; hence, optimization work is needed to minimize the overall process cost.

This work aims to develop a predictive model using an artificial neural network (ANN)-based methodology capable of determining optimal conditions for obtaining formic acid with specific specifications via CO_2 electroreduction. Besides, this model is implemented in a case study of the cement industry to optimize the process according to industrial requirements.

2. Methodology

2.1. Experimental set-up

A commercial lab-scale three-compartment electrochemical reactor (Dioxide Materials) is employed to evaluate the influence of different process variables. Specifically, a 3^3-centered experimental design is proposed, analyzing three operational variables; i) CO_2 inlet flow rate, ii) humidity of the CO_2 feed, and iii) the current density applied to the system. Other influencing variables, such as the central compartment inlet water flow rate or anolyte inlet flow rate, are assessed using literature data (Yang et al., 2020). Each experimental point is duplicated to enhance the data quality, ensuring robust inputs to the ANN.

2.2. Model development

A neural-network-based model is created using Neural Designer (Artificial Intelligence Techniques, Ltd) to construct the numerical expressions based on the data input collected during the experimental work with the commercial reactor. The input variables and their levels are presented in Table 1:

Table 1. Variables and different levels of the input variables to the ANN model.

Variable		+	-	O
Central water flowrate (ml min^{-1})	X_1	0.17	0.065	0.12
Current density (mA cm^{-2})	X_2	200	45	90
Cathode water feed (g h^{-1})	X_3	3	0.5	1.5
CO_2 flowrate (l min^{-1})	X_4	0.06	0.02	0.04

As target variables, formic acid concentration and energy consumption (CE) (Eq. 1) are considered.

$$Energy\ Consumption\left(\frac{kWh}{kmol}\right) = \frac{Q \cdot V}{C_{Formate}} \tag{1}$$

Where Q is the total charge supplied to the electrochemical cell (A), V is the absolute cell potential (V), and $C_{Formate}$ is the molar flowrate of formate in the output stream of the electrochemical reactor (mol s^{-1}). The model is normalized to the geometric area of the electrochemical reactor to allow the system performance analysis at different scales.

2.3. Case study

The optimization problem of the system variables is proposed using a cement industry as a case study. A cement plant, located in Cantabria (Spain), with an overall 63.7 l min^{-1} CO_2 emission, is chosen to propose the installation of an $ERCO_2$ system to mitigate CO_2 emissions and recycle CO_2 into formic acid, which is required in the plant as a pH-neutralizing reactant. The overall cost is established as the objective function (OF) to minimize, considering the CAPEX and OPEX of the system.

$$OF = CAPEX + OPEX \tag{2}$$

$$CAPEX = Area \cdot RC/5 \tag{3}$$

$$OPEX = TEC \cdot EP - TCO_2 \cdot (ETS - CC) + (FAD - FA) \cdot FAP \tag{4}$$

In these equations, *Area* is the reactor geometric area (m^2), *RC* stands for the reactor cost (27000 € m^{-2}, based on the previous acquisition costs of electrochemical reactors for CO_2 electroreduction), *TEC* denotes the total energy consumption (kWh), *EP* is the electricity price (0.105 € kWh^{-1}), TCO_2 corresponds to the CO_2 transformed (t), *ETS* signifies the CO_2 emission right cost (81.65 € t CO_2^{-1}), CC is the capture cost (€ t CO_2^{-1}), *FAD* represents the demanded formic acid (t), *FA* indicates the produced formic acid (t), and *FAP* represents the formic acid market price (4100 € t^{-1}). *CAPEX* evaluates the cost of constructing the scaled CO_2 electrolyzer, annualized over five years. *OPEX* considers the cost of the electricity needed in the $ERCO_2$ process, savings related to the non-utilization of CO_2 emissions rights, CO_2 capture cost, and savings on the demand for formic acid from external sources.

This optimization problem is constrained by requirements for product quality, plant characteristics, and limitations in model construction (Table 2). This results in a constrained non-linear optimization minimization problem (MINLP) addressed using the General Algebraic Modelling System (GAMS, GAMS Development Corporation, Washington, DC, USA). A reduced gradient algorithm is applied to solve the MINLP problem, utilizing the CONOPT solver to obtain the optimal solution.

Table 2. Constrained variables for the optimization problem

Variable	Constrain	Up	Low
Central water flowrate (l min^{-1} m^{-2})	Model	0.34	0.13
Current density (mA cm^{-2})	Model	200	45
Cathode water feed (g h-1)	Model	3	0.5
CO₂ flowrate (l min^{-1})	Plant	63.7	-
Formic acid concentration (g l^{-1})	Quality	120	80

Moreover, different sensitivity analyses are conducted to evaluate the impact of parameters such as electricity price, emission right cost, or formic acid price on the economic feasibility of the $ERCO_2$ installation.

3. Results

3.1. Model deployment

The predictive model is constructed using machine learning, where data obtained from the experimental work is utilized to build the ANN architecture. As depicted in Figure 1.a, the ANN consists of several interconnected neurons: i) the scaling layer adjusts inputs to a proper range, ii) the perceptron layer combines and weights the input dataset, transforming it through an activation function into an output, iii) the unscaling layer restores the output to its original units, and iv) the bounding layers restrict the output value. The selection and optimization of neurons are carried out through an iterative process, aiming to achieve the best possible fit to the provided data for building the ANN. The resulting model includes four neurons in the scaling layer (one for each input variable), two perceptron layers with linear and hyperbolic tangent activation functions, and two neurons for both unscaling and bounding layers. The model deployment demonstrates a high level of adjustment, fitting the experimental data with an R^2 of 0.991.

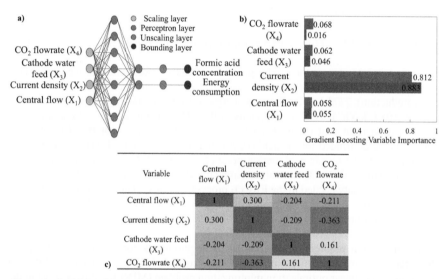

Figure 1. a) ANN architecture for the predictive model, b) Gradient Boosting variable importance coefficient chart, and c) variable correlation matrix

Besides, the significance of the input values concerning each output is assessed through a gradient-boosting approach (Figure 1.b), to examine potential non-linearities in the system. For both output variables, the applied current density (X_2) exhibits the highest impact, with a coefficient exceeding 0.8. Regarding the correlation among different variables (Figure 1.c), it is evident that the correlation values are below 0.4, indicating weak relationships between the different variables. Notably, the most robust correlation is observed between the current density (X_2) and the CO_2 flowrate (X_1), showing an inverse effect of -0.363.

Furthermore, the development of the ANN enables the derivation of an empirical mathematical model that relates the input and output variables. The mathematical expressions defining the architecture of the ANN are manually extracted and implemented as the model equations in the optimization problem presented below.

3.2. Case study

The optimization problem, centered on the cement industry, considers an annual demand of 100 t of formic acid. Furthermore, the chosen CO_2 capture technology for the initial case study is MEA (Monoethanolamine) absorption, recognized as one of the most advanced and competitive systems, with an estimated capture cost of 63 € t CO_2^{-1} (Wang et al., 2017).

In this context, the outcomes reveal that the objective function (overall cost) has a negative value of -76476 € y^{-1}, meaning significant savings with the implementation of the ERCO₂ installation. The CAPEX is estimated at 36228 € y^{-1}, while the OPEX is -112704 € y^{-1}. The positive economic balance is primarily due to OPEX, where savings related to the costs of emission rights make this technology economically viable. The optimal reactor geometric area is determined at 6.71 m^2, producing 9.67 t of formic acid per year, with a concentration of 106.62 g l^{-1}, meeting the required product quality. Furthermore, the operational variables of the three-compartment electrochemical cell are established, with a CO_2 flowrate of 60.3 l min^{-1}, a current density of 200 mA cm^{-2}, a water content in the CO_2 feed stream of 0.5 g l^{-1}, and a water central flow of 0.172 l min^{-1} m^{-2}.

Besides, the influence of external factors on the objective function, such as the electricity price, emission rights price, or formic acid market price, is assessed through different sensitivity analyses, as shown in Figure 2. As observed, variations in electricity prices do not significantly affect the overall cost of the process. This can be attributed to the higher relevance of CO_2 emission and capture and formic acid costs. Regarding the CO_2 emission right cost, economic viability is dependent on its price. In cases where the ETS price is lower than the capture cost per ton of CO_2, the cost becomes positive, indicating that the savings related to a lower CO_2 emission cost do not compensate. However, forecasts for the ETS market in Europe suggest an increase in emission costs, making the ERCO₂ installation more lucrative in the coming years. Finally, for the formic acid price, the effect is inverse, as the price increases, the cost rises. This is related to the fact that only 10 % of the total demand for formic acid from the cement plant is covered by the ERCO₂ process; therefore, the market must be tapped for the rest of the demand, and the cost is strongly affected by price variations.

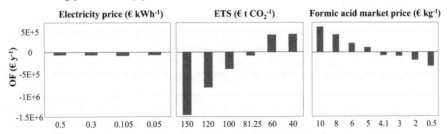

Figure 2. Sensitivity analyses for variations in the electricity, emission right, and formic acid prices.

4. Conclusions

The investigation of the three-compartment electrochemical reactor for ERCO₂ involves the analysis and modelling of various operational variables. This leads to the development of an empirical model based on ANN. It is noteworthy from this variable that the current density applied is the most influential variable affecting performance. This model represents valuable insights for future technology implementation and scale-up.

Within this context, a case study delves into the deployment of an ERCO$_2$ reactor in the cement industry. The optimization of main operation variables and the reactor's geometric area is carried out to align with the requirements of the industrial plant requirements. The results of non-linear optimization results indicate a 6.71 m^2 reactor with the capability to produce 9.67 t of formic acid per year.

Moreover, the economic feasibility of the ERCO$_2$ process is assessed under various scenarios. This involves evaluating the influence of the electricity price, CO$_2$ emission cost, and fluctuations in formic acid prices. Significantly, the CO$_2$ emission cost emerges as the most crucial factor. In accordance with this finding and anticipating the projected rise in emission rights costs, the ERCO$_2$ process's long-term economic viability is ensured in this case study.

Acknowledgments

The authors fully acknowledge the financial support received from the European Union's Horizon Europe research and innovation program under grant agreement No 101118265. Jose Antonio Abarca gratefully acknowledges the predoctoral research grant (FPI) PRE2021-097200 conceded by the Spanish Ministry of Science through the Spanish Research Agency (AEI).

References

J. A. Abarca, G. Díaz-Sainz, I. Merino-Garcia, G. Beobide, J. Albo & A. Irabien, (2023). Optimized manufacturing of gas diffusion electrodes for CO$_2$ electroreduction with automatic spray pyrolysis. Journal of Environmental Chemical Engineering, 11(3), 109724.

G. Díaz-Sainz, M. Alvarez-Guerra, B. Ávila-Bolívar, J. Solla-Gullón, V. Montiel & A. Irabien (2021). Improving trade-offs in the figures of merit of gas-phase single-pass continuous CO$_2$ electrocatalytic reduction to formate. Chemical Engineering Journal, 405, 126965.

G. Díaz-Sainz, K. Fernández-Caso, T. Lagarteira, S. Delgado, M. Alvarez-Guerra, A. Mendes & A. Irabien (2023). Coupling continuous CO$_2$ electroreduction to formate with efficient Ni-based anodes. Journal of Environmental Chemical Engineering, 11(1), 109171.

K. Fernández-Caso, G. Díaz-Sainz, M. Alvarez-Guerra & A. Irabien (2023). Electroreduction of CO$_2$: Advances in the Continuous Production of Formic Acid and Formate. ACS Energy Letters, 8(4), 1992–2024.

F. He, S. Tong, Z. Luo, H. Ding, Z. Cheng, C. Li & Z. Qi (2023). Accelerating net-zero carbon emissions by electrochemical reduction of carbon dioxide. Journal of Energy Chemistry, 79, 398–409.

A. Ozden, F.P. García de Arquer, J.E. Huang, J. Wicks, J. Sisler, R.K. Miao, C.P O'Brien, G. Lee, X. Wang, A.H. Ip, E.H. Sargent & D. Sinton (2022). Carbon-efficient carbon dioxide electrolysers. Nature Sustainability, 5(7), 563–573.

Y. Wang, L. Zhao, A. Otto, M. Robinius & D. Stolten (2017). A Review of Post-combustion CO$_2$ Capture Technologies from Coal-fired Power Plants. Energy Procedia, 114, 650–665.

H. Yang, J.J Kaczur, S.D. Sajjad & R.I. Masel (2020). Performance and long-term stability of CO2 conversion to formic acid using a three-compartment electrolyzer design. Journal of CO$_2$ Utilization, 42, 101349.

Flavio Manenti, Gintaras V. Reklaitis (Eds.), Proceedings of the 34th European Symposium on Computer Aided Process Engineering / 15th International Symposium on Process Systems Engineering (ESCAPE34/PSE24), June 2-6, 2024, Florence, Italy

Towards Self-Consistent Graph Neural Networks for Predicting the Ideal Gas Heat Capacity, Enthalpy, and Entropy

Adem R. N. Aouichaoui,[a] Simon Müller,[b] Jens Abildskov[a*]

[a] *Dept. of Chemical and Biochemical Engineering, Technical University of Denmark, Søltofts Plads 228A, 2800 Kgs. Lyngby, Denmark*
[b] *Institute of Thermal Separation Processes, Hamburg University of Technology, Hamburg, Germany*

ja@kt.dtu.dk

Abstract

Ideal gas heat capacity correlations are indispensable for modelling energy systems and evaluating process efficiency. While most correlations are empirical in nature, few are theoretically motivated, where the model parameters reflect physical quantities relating to the molecule. These however are rarely modelled through quantitative structure-property relationships, which hinders extending their applicability to new compounds. This work provides a realisation of a hybrid model that combines data-driven modelling in the form of a graph neural network that outputs a set of parameters used for the ideal gas heat capacity correlation. The study covered over 22,000 data points across 1,909 organic compounds resulting in a mean absolute error of 31.97 J/mol-K, a mean relative error of 11.63% and a correlation coefficient of 0.97.

Keywords: Graph neural networks, Hybrid modelling, Property prediction, QSPR

1. Introduction

In-silico evaluation of the thermophysical properties of molecules is an important prerequisite to performing large-scale screening of the chemical design space to identify suitable candidates for various applications. Flammability properties such as flash point and autoignition temperatures allow the identification of a chemical's safe processing and storage conditions. Critical point properties can be used in the cubic equation of states to perform P-V-T calculation and identify the process condition of chemicals. Quantitative structure-property relations (QSPRs) are mathematical models that relate the structural information of a given compound to the target property of interest. However, some properties are not only influenced by the structure of a molecule but also by some intensive variables such as temperature, pressure, and composition. Such properties include density, vapour pressure, thermal conductivity, and heat capacities (ideal gas and liquid). The latter plays an important role in modelling energy systems and enables performing energy balances, used in process simulation and technology evaluation.

2. Heat Capacity Correlation

The heat capacity of ideal gases (Cp^*) is defined as the amount of energy required to change the temperature of one mole of vapour by one degree assuming no intermolecular interactions. Most correlations developed are polynomial or exponential correlations as a function of the temperature, with a set of compound-specific constants determined through regression. In this work, we focus on the model developed by Aly and Lee (1981), which is derived from statistical mechanical formulae along with a series of assumptions and simplifications. This implies that the parameters used to develop the correlation have physical meaning, bringing the model closer to a true first-principle model. Based on a series of assumptions ("Born-Oppenheimer approximation for nuclear and electronic wave functions, the use of harmonic oscillator for vibrational motion and a decoupling of the vibrational and rotational motions with the grid rotator"), the total molecular energy can be separated into translational, rotational, and vibrational energies. Aly and Lee reduced the contribution to the overall C_p^* to contributions from the most dominant vibrational characteristic temperature ($C_{p,v}$), an electronic contribution ($C_{p,e}$) and a contribution from internal bond rotation ($C_{p,r}$) as seen in Eq.(1)

$$C_p^* = C_{p,v} + C_{p,e} + C_{p,r} \tag{1}$$

The contribution to the heat capacity from vibrational energy is expressed in Eq.(2),

$$C_{p,v} = B\left[\frac{C/T}{\sinh(C/T)}\right]^2 \tag{2}$$

Where B is a constant and C is a characteristic temperature. The contribution to the heat capacity from electronic energy is expressed in Eq.(3),

$$C_{p,e} = D\left[\frac{E/T}{\cosh(E/T)}\right]^2 \tag{3}$$

Where D and E are similar to Eq.(2) are a constant and characteristic temperature respectively. The contribution from the internal rotational bond is assumed constant for each compound as seen in Eq.(4).

$$C_{p,r} = A \tag{4}$$

Combining Eq.(2)-Eq.(4) yields the expression for C_p^* seen in Eq.(5).

$$Cp^* = A + B\left[\frac{C/T}{\sinh(C/T)}\right]^2 + D\left[\frac{E/T}{\cosh(E/T)}\right]^2 \tag{5}$$

An analytical solution can readily be obtained to calculate the enthalpy and entropy of ideal gases through the fundamental relations relating these quantities to the heat capacity seen in Eq.(6). Integration constants are not of any concern as enthalpy and entropy are expressed as differences (Δ) w.r.t. a reference state.

$$H^* = \int Cp^* \, dT \quad \& \quad S^* = \int \frac{Cp^*}{T} \, dT \tag{6}$$

Despite the integral role the property plays, QSPRs for predicting this quantity are few, especially for the ideal gases. Many still rely on the group-contribution (GC) method developed by Benson et al. (1969) and Joback and Reid (1987). Benson defined 250 groups and 40 corrections for nearest neighbors achieving 4-6 J/mol-K as an absolute error. Meanwhile, Joback and Ried defined 41 groups capable of describing organic compounds containing rings, sulfur, halogens, and nitrogen. The ideal gas heat capacity was modelled as a cubic polynomial in temperature with four coefficients (a, b, c, and d) which are modelled as a linear function of the group contributions. The study covered 288 compounds yielding a mean absolute percentage error of 1.59% and a mean absolute error of 5.9 J/mol-K. One advantage of developing QSPRs for this purpose is that solely the structural information is needed alongside the desired temperature for evaluation. However, one drawback of the GC methods is their linear nature, complex group identification procedure and inability to account for missing contributions. The recent surge in machine learning (ML) has renewed interest in developing QSPR capable of extracting relevant structural information and generating molecular descriptors from general molecular identifiers such as the SMILES (simplified molecular input line entry system).

3. Data-Driven Quantitative Structure-property Relation (QSPR)

Graph neural networks (GNNs) have emerged as viable candidates for ML models to predict a wide range of thermophysical properties with great accuracy (Aouichaoui et al., 2023b). These models take as input a graph representation and by staking convolutional layers (also known as message passing layers), the information embedded (also known as latent/hidden representation) in the nodes (representing atoms) and edges (representing bonds) is transferred internally (operations called message and update functions) and aggregated (also known as readout) to produce a vector representation of the molecule. This vector is used as an input to a multi-layer perceptron (MLP) to produce the target output. While GC methods can be seen as white-box models, GNNs are completely black-box with very little interpretable aspect. This might hinder their wider applicability as the model trend when extrapolating is not known. It has been shown that such models, despite having good performance metrics, might produce nonsensical results when extrapolating such as melting points being above boiling points (Aouichaoui et al., 2023b). This is largely due to the models not being constrained by physical laws. Recent trends in data-driven modelling have emphasized the need to add logic to govern the learnings of the model and to constrain it to generate meaningful and consistent outputs. Semi-parametric hybrid modelling combines data-driven and mechanistic modelling and has proven to generate accurate and physically meaningful outputs (Medina et al., 2022). In this work, we present one realization of hybrid modelling using GNNs for functional property prediction, in this case, the ideal gas heat capacity.

4. Methods

4.1. Decoupled Serial Hybrid Modelling Framework
The hybrid modelling approach proposed herein uses five individual GNNs to predict the five parameters (A, B, C, D and E) needed for the C_p^* correlation shown in Eq.(5). The framework "decouples" the initial identification of the five parameters, which are predetermined initially through least-square fitting using a range C_p^* values at different temperatures. A schematic of the framework can be seen in Figure 1.

4.2. Graph Neural Network Model: Attentive Fingerprint (AFP)
The attentive fingerprint (AFP) model by Xiong et al. (2020) uses the attention mechanism to enable the model to learn weights when aggregating messages across the molecule. This enables the model to focus on important substructures relevant to the target property. The attention mechanism consists of three steps: alignment (combines the hidden representation of a node with that of its neighbours), weighting (assigns a weight coefficient summing up to one through a softmax activation) and context (produces an

update to the node). This mechanism is applied on a node level and graph level as an alternative approach to readout. The algorithm can be found in the work by Xiong et al. (2020). The molecular information chosen for featurizing the graph is commonly used in GNN modelling and is identical to those used by Aouichaoui et al. (2023).

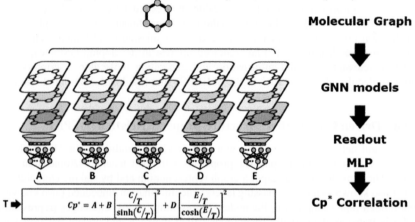

Figure 1: Decoupled serial hybrid modelling framework for the ideal gas heat capacity

4.3. Data

The data used in this work are obtained from the Design Institute for Physical Properties under the American Institute of Chemical Engineers (AIChE-DIPPR) (Rowley et al., 2019). A total of 1,909 organic compounds containing halogens, nitrogen, and sulphur with at least five measurements (a total of 22,962 data points) and temperature ranges from 25K to 6000K were chosen. The data covered experimental (88 compounds) and predicted values, with the main prediction method being density function theory (DFT) calculations using B3LYP/6-311+G(3df,2p) frequency evaluation.

4.4. Model development

Initially, the correlation parameters in Eq.(5) were determined through least squared error fitting using differential evolution (Storn and Price, 1997). A constraint was set that all parameters had to be positive since they represent characteristic temperatures. Then, five GNNs were trained independently using the same 90%-5%-5% randomly split compounds for training, validation and testing respectively. The models were trained for a maximum of 500 epochs and used early stopping to safeguard against overfitting. The model was trained using the ADAM optimizer with a scheduled learning rate similar to the study by Aouichaoui et al., (2023). The hyperparameters consisted of the number of node-level and graph-level message-passing layers as well as the length of the final representation produced. The number of MLP layers was fixed to 2 with the hidden layer being half of the length of the molecular feature produced. The hyperparameters were determined using a grid search where the number of layers ranged from one to four, while the length of the molecular feature vector could take the values 1024, 512, 256 or 128.

5. Results & Discussion

The preliminary fit of the parameters for Eq.(5) was successful yielding an overall coefficient of determination (R^2) of 0.99, while the MAE and MRE were 0.93 J/mol-K and 0.43 % respectively. The lowest R^2 was 0.93, while the maximum MAE and MRE were 10.20 J/mol-K and 4.5 % respectively. Table 1 shows the same metrics for predicting the five parameters through the GNNs. The model with the lowest validation MAE is chosen from the grid search.

Table 1: Performance metrics of the GNN on the parameters C_p^* correlation: first value corresponds to that for training, the second for validation and the third for testing.

Metric	A	B	C	D	E
R^2	0.926	0.955	0.523	0.889	0.106
	0.904	0.906	0.390	0.420	0.087
	0.938	0.958	0.125	0.918	0.028
MAE	4.02	8.90	219.30	10.16	317.82
	3.90	9.91	305.38	13.69	250.24
	5.44	11.75	336.342	11.97	344.08
MRE	24%	12%	18%	22%	35%
	27%	14%	26%	23%	37%
	28%	12%	26%	18%	36%

Table 1 clearly shows that the GNN only succeeded in modelling the A, B and D parameters satisfactorily (the low validation R^2 was due to an outlier). For the remaining parameters (C and E), the model fails to reproduce the results. This could indicate that there is no apparent relation between the structure and the determined C and E parameters, despite Eq.(5) being theoretically motivated. Therefore, we hypothesize that there are potentially multiple set of parameters that provides similar results due to collinearity and as such some of the determined values do not necessarily reflect the desired physical quantities. However, the endpoint of interest is C_p^* as such, these were evaluated using the predicted parameters. Figure 2 shows a parity plot for the predictions from regressing the parameters (using differential evolution) and those obtained from predicting the parameters (using GNN).

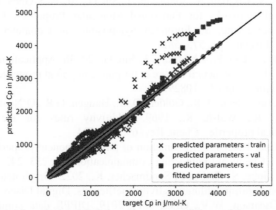

Figure 2: Parity plot for calculated Cp* through parameter fitting and the parameter prediction

The results obtained showed surprisingly much better results than the individual parameter fitting. The hybrid model achieved an overall R^2 of 0.97, an MAE of 31.97 J/mol-K and an MRE of 11.63%. The accuracy of the obtained C_p^* stands in contrast with that of C and E, this can be attributed to i) deviations cancelling out, ii) the worst predicted parameters (C and E) are part of a quotient and thus their numerical value might not be affected by the errors or iii) the contribution from the quotients is negligible. Further insights can be obtained using sensitivity and collinearity analysis and will be the subject of future work. Compared to the GC methods, the results obtained cover a larger space, while achieving slightly lower performance metrics. This can be due to uneven data splitting (bias), the goodness of fit of the individual parameters or inconsistencies in the data. The obtained results were compared to a purely data-driven approach using GNN on a smaller subset of the data used herein (only experimental), which obtained an R^2 of 0.99, MAE of 1.65 J/mol-K and MRE of 1.1% (Aouichaoui et al., 2023a). using the same subset of data, the current model achieves an R^2, MAE and MRE of 0.96, 22.36 J/mol-K and 14.22% respectively. While the metrics favour the data-driven approach, it is important to note that the training methods were fundamentally different and as such it is not entirely possible to conclude which method is better.

6. Conclusions

The study presented a hybrid model for the ideal gas heat capacity that combines five GNNs to predict five compound-specific constants which are used in a theoretically motivated correlation. The results showed that the final prediction is good despite the presence of large errors on two of the five parameters. This can potentially be due to collinearity between the parameters. The presented model can predict the functional properties of various organic compounds solely based on the structural information and the state variable (in this case the temperature). This could potentially be extended to cover other similarly obtained properties such as densities and vapour pressure.

References

Aly, F.A., Lee, L.L., 1981. Self-consistent equations for calculating the ideal gas heat capacity, enthalpy, and entropy. Fluid Phase Equilibria 6, 169–179.

Aouichaoui, A.R.N., Cogliati, A., Abildskov, J., Sin, G., 2023a. S-GNN: State-Dependent Graph Neural Networks for Functional Molecular Properties, Computer Aided Chemical Engineering, 33 European Symposium on Computer Aided Process Engineering. Elsevier, pp. 575–581.

Aouichaoui, A.R.N., Fan, F., Abildskov, J., Sin, G., 2023b. Application of interpretable group-embedded graph neural networks for pure compound properties. Computers & Chemical Engineering 176, 108291.

Benson, S.W., Cruickshank, F.R., Golden, D.M., Haugen, G.R., O'Neal, H.E., Rodgers, A.S., Shaw, R., Walsh, R., 1969. Additivity rules for the estimation of thermochemical properties. Chem. Rev. 69, 279–324.

Joback, K.G., Reid, R.C., 1987. Estimation of pure component properties from group-contributions. Chemical Engineering Communications 57, 233–243.

Medina, E.I.S., Linke, S., Stoll, M., Sundmacher, K., 2022. Graph neural networks for the prediction of infinite dilution activity coefficients. Digital Discovery 1, 216–225.

Rowley, R.I., Oscarson, W.V., Giles, N.F., 2019. DIPPR data compilation of pure chemical properties.

Storn, R., Price, K., 1997. Differential Evolution – A Simple and Efficient Heuristic for global Optimization over Continuous Spaces. Journal of Global Optimization 11, 341–359.

Xiong, Z., Wang, D., Liu, X., Zhong, F., Wan, X., Li, X., Li, Z., Luo, X., Chen, K., Jiang, H., Zheng, M., 2020. Pushing the Boundaries of Molecular Representation for Drug Discovery with the Graph Attention Mechanism. J. Med. Chem. 63, 8749–8760.

Flavio Manenti, Gintaras V. Reklaitis (Eds.), Proceedings of the 34th European Symposium on Computer Aided Process Engineering / 15th International Symposium on Process Systems Engineering (ESCAPE34/PSE24), June 2-6, 2024, Florence, Italy

Prototype of Automated Physical Model Builder: Challenges and Opportunities

Shota Kato* and Manabu Kano

Graduate School of Informatics, Kyoto University, Yoshida-honmachi, Sakyo-ku, Kyoto 606-8501, Japan
*shota@human.sys.i.kyoto-u.ac.jp

Abstract

In the process industry, physical models are indispensable, yet current models sometimes compromise accuracy or incur substantial computational costs. Such cases require new physical models, but the traditional approach to building physical models is reliant on expert knowledge and is time-consuming. This necessitates the development of a new efficient physical model building methodology. Our research aims to establish automated physical model builder, AutoPMoB, which builds physical models from manufacturing process literature. The realization of AutoPMoB requires developing several methods, including those for collecting documents related to the target process and accurately extracting information for physical model building from the documents. In this study, we develop an AutoPMoB prototype, employing a large language model alongside a model building approach previously proposed in our research. The prototype's application to a continuous stirred tank reactor showed its capability to extract necessary data accurately, although the initial attempts did not yield the anticipated models. Subsequent modifications in unifying expressions led to successful model building, underscoring the effectiveness of our system in leveraging literature for physical model building. Advancing AutoPMoB towards practical deployment necessitates specific enhancements, particularly in methods for equivalence judgment of definitions, retrieval of relevant documents, integration of non-documentary information, and domain-specific adaptation.

Keywords: Artificial intelligence, Physical model, Digital twin, Natural language processing, Process modelling.

1. Introduction

Physical models are crucial in the process industry and serve multiple purposes, including process design and process operation. Although these models can be incorporated into existing tools, there are times when their accuracy is lacking or they are computationally expensive. In such instances, a new physical model must be built. To overcome the time-consuming and costly nature of traditional iterative model building, we aim to develop automated physical model builder, AutoPMoB [Kato and Kano (2022)].

Figure 1 presents an overview of AutoPMoB. The system automatically builds a physical model of the target process in three steps: 1) it retrieves relevant documents, 2) extracts and standardizes the necessary information for model building from these documents, and 3) builds, validates, and ranks model candidates based on this standardized information. To actualize AutoPMoB, we have proposed methods to optimize performance at each step, including a method to judge the equivalence of two differential algebraic equations [Kato et al. (2023)] and a method for automatically generating physical model candidates from multiple equations [Kato and Kano (2023)].

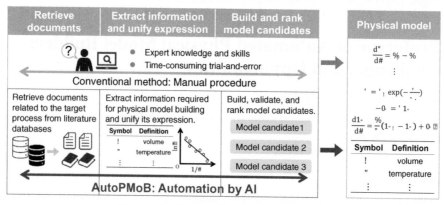

Figure 1 A schematic diagram of AutoPMoB.

Information extraction from documents has been facilitated by advancements in natural language processing (NLP), particularly methods that leverage the Transformer architecture [Vaswani et al. (2017)]. Recently, large language models (LLMs), which have extensive parameters trained on vast datasets, have emerged as a particularly potent technology. LLMs have exhibited superior performance in various tasks, including information extraction [Han et al. (2023)].

This study integrates an LLM with our model candidate building method [Kato and Kano (2023)] to develop a prototype. Besides, we apply this prototype in a case study to assess its usefulness, identify current challenges, and propose solutions for further enhancement.

2. Methods

2.1. Prototype of AutoPMoB

The prototype receives information necessary for building a physical model from the user: the target process and variables to be included in the model. Users must prepare TeX-formatted documents about the target process. The prototype then extracts mathematical equations and variables, which include variable symbols and definitions, from these documents, judges the equivalence of the extracted information to standardize expressions, and generates physical model candidates. We use an LLM for extracting information and judging the equivalence of variable definitions. After this extraction and standardization, we build model candidates using the methods we previously proposed [Kato and Kano (2023)].

2.1.1. Information Extraction and Equivalence Judgment of Variable Definitions

This study targets TeX documents, wherein mathematical equations are incorporated within equation environments, and variables outside of equations are displayed in inline formats (e.g., enclosed in \$, like \$t\$). We extract mathematical equations and variable symbols from these documents using a pattern-matching method capable of accurate extraction. Since variable definitions are typically phrases within a sentence, they are challenging to extract using only a rule-based method [Schubotz et al. (2017)]; therefore, we employ an LLM-based approach that understands word meanings for accurate extraction of variable definitions from the documents.

The efficiency of LLMs improves with well-designed input, known as prompts. We implement few-shot learning, which incorporates multiple examples into the prompt

---

Prompt:

Read the given sentence carefully, and extract the definition of the variable symbol. Answer the extracted definition in the format <"symbol":"definition"> without any explanation. If no definition exists, then just answer <"symbol":"NO DEFINITION">.

Symbol: "\Delta H"

Sentence: In the above equations, F is the feed flow rate to the reactor, V_r is the reactor volume, \Delta H is the heat of reaction, Q is the manipulated rate of heat input, and ρ and c_p are the density and specific heat capacity of the fluid in the reactor, respectively.

Answer: <"\Delta H":"the heat of reaction">

... (More examples are omitted here.)

Symbol: "C_A"

Sentence: The outlet temperature (T) and the concentration (C_A) are controlled using proportional integral (PI) controllers by manipulating the inlet coolant flow rate (F_c) and the feed flow rate (F), respectively.

Answer:

- -

Expected Output:

<"C_A":"the concentration">

Figure 2 An example of prompts for variable definition extraction

[Brown et al. (2020)]. As Han et al. (2023) noted that ChatGPT's information extraction performance diminishes with the increase in the variety of output information, we crafted distinct prompts for the tasks of information extraction and equivalence judgment. These prompts include a task description, output format, examples, and a test case based on the ones by Han et al. (2023). Figure 2 illustrates a prompt example for extracting variable definitions, featuring a symbol and a corresponding sentence for each instance. For judging the equivalence of variable definitions, we input the symbol, its definition, and an equation that includes them.

2.1.2. Model Candidate Building

We apply the physical model building algorithm [Kato and Kano (2023)] to create models that fulfill the user-defined requirements. This method inputs a set of equations alongside the user's specifications and yields sets of equations that align with these requirements. The requirements consist of variables that must be included in the model and whose values can be freely determined. Desired model candidates are generated by amalgamating equations to match the degree of freedom with the difference between the number of equations and the number of variables.

2.2. Experimental Settings

We evaluated the prototype's ability to automatically build the preferred physical model of a continuous stirred tank reactor (CSTR). We prepared nine documents using the following procedure: 1) we obtained nine papers relevant to the CSTR in PDF format, 2) converted them into TeX format with InftyReader [Suzuki et al. (2003)], and 3) manually revised them to accurately represent the original papers. Only the modeling sections from each paper were used in document preparation. Table 1 enumerates the used papers, and Figure 3 presents the equations from Papers 1 and 2.

Table 1 List of papers used in case study

No.	DOI
1	10.1016/j.cherd.2019.09.009
2	10.1016/j.jlp.2016.05.023
3	10.1016/j.jlp.2012.10.003
4	10.1016/S0005-1098(01)00083-8
5	10.1252/jcej.07WE187
6	10.1109/EPEPEMC.2010.5606563
7	10.1016/j.compchemeng.2005.11.008
8	10.1109/ICEFEET49149.2020.9187017
9	10.1109/IICIRES.2017.8078297

$$-r_A = k(T)c_A = k_o \exp(-\frac{E}{RT})c_A \tag{1}$$

$$\frac{dc_A}{dt} = \frac{F}{V}(c_{A,in} - c_A) - r_A \tag{2}$$

$$\frac{dT}{dt} = \frac{F}{V}(T_{in} - T) + \frac{h_r}{\rho c_p}r_A - \frac{UA_r}{V\rho c_p}(T - T_j) \tag{3}$$

$$\frac{dT_j}{dt} = F_{cw}\frac{\rho_w}{m_o}(T_{cw} - T_j) + \frac{P}{c_w m_o} + \frac{UA_r}{c_w m_o}(T - T_j) \tag{4}$$

$$-r = KC_A^2 \tag{5}$$

$$K = K_0 \exp(\frac{-E}{RT(t)}) \tag{6}$$

$$\frac{dC_A(t)}{dt} = \frac{F}{V_r}(C_0 - C_A(t)) - K_0 \exp(\frac{-E}{RT(t)})C_A(t)^2 \tag{7}$$

$$\frac{dT(t)}{dt} = \frac{F}{V_r}(T_0 - T(t)) - \frac{\Delta H}{\rho c_p}K_0 \exp(\frac{-E}{RT(t)})C_A(t)^2 + \frac{Q(t)}{\rho c_p V_r} \tag{8}$$

Figure 3 Part of equations included in documents. Equations (1)-(4) are in document 1, and equations (5)-(8) are in document 2.

We determine that the prototype has successfully built models if it, given the nine documents and user-defined requirements, outputs models capable of computing the values of all variables in the equations. Additionally, we assess the prototype's ability to correctly extract variable symbols, definitions, and equations, and to ascertain their equivalence.

3. Results and Discussion

3.1. Experimental Results

The accuracy, precision, and recall of variable definition extraction were 74.1%, 75.9%, and 95.3%, respectively. In the equivalence judgment of variable definitions, no equivalent pairs with different variable symbols were identified as equivalent (Recall=0%). Moreover, for pairs with the same variable symbol and definition, only about half were correctly identified as equivalent when they appeared in different equations (Recall=47.4%).

In model candidate building, the prototype successfully built a physical model from each document by using the set of variables it contained. However, it failed to generate a model candidate by integrating equations from different documents because the notations were not standardized.

3.2. Discussion

Analyzing the LLM output for variable definition extraction revealed that most errors were due to definitions not matching the correct ones precisely. Despite the LLM occasionally altering expressions or generating definitions not present in the text, it accurately extracted variable definitions from the nine documents. Variable definition extraction performance may decline for more specialized or niche processes, as Han et al. (2023) reported that the performance of ChatGPT is lower for specialized tasks than for general ones. A method is needed to ascertain when LLMs should be employed for variable definition extraction and to devise a proficient extraction technique for expertise-demanding processes.

For variable definition equivalence judgment, we provided the symbols for the two variable definitions and the equations incorporating those symbols. Although judging equivalence solely on variable definitions proved challenging, the optimal input strategy remains undetermined. Enhancing LLM performance could involve incorporating more context of the definitions into the prompts or leveraging external knowledge, which warrants further investigation. Additionally, the equivalence judgment method becomes computationally expensive as the number of documents increases, since the method judges the equivalence of all possible combinations. Developing a more efficient method for processing a larger number of documents promptly is essential for future progress.

To assess model candidate building, we manually standardized the expressions in two documents (1 and 2 in Table 1). After the standardization, the prototype was able to yield the required physical models that could compute all variables within the models. Presently, the algorithm requires users to specify variables; future improvements will aim to enable the method to build models without user-specified variables.

3.3. Challenges

Overcoming three key obstacles is essential for the realization of AutoPMoB.

3.3.1. Document Retrieval

Although this study presupposed the availability of documents relevant to physical modeling, locating such documents in practice is often arduous and financially burdensome. Furthermore, finding documents for physical model building is challenging because current search engines lack the capability to specifically search for mathematical formulas. The goal is to create a system that efficiently retrieves the necessary documents for model construction tailored to the target process and the objectives of model building.

3.3.2. Integration of Non-literature Information

Not all literature, including academic papers and textbooks, provides the complete data needed for physical model building. In instances where literature falls short, the incorporation of non-literature data, like ontologies and other databases, becomes valuable. Additionally, the nature of information, such as its novelty and reliability, varies by source, necessitating strategies to manage each type of data effectively.

3.3.3. Adaptation for unknown processes

Information extraction and equivalence judgment performance of NLP-based methods tend to deteriorate when applied to unfamiliar processes, such as new or specialized ones.

Where similar data exists, transfer learning may offer a viable solution; hence, a major challenge is to identify how documents about different processes relate and to devise a method capable of delivering high performance even in the absence of target process data.

4. Conclusions

In pursuit of establishing automated physical model builder, AutoPMoB, we devised a prototype leveraging a large language model (LLM). This prototype is capable of extracting necessary information, such as variables and equations, standardizing their notations, and generating model candidates. We tested the prototype on a continuous stirred tank reactor and assessed its effectiveness. The prototype successfully extracted all variable symbols and equations and achieved an accuracy of 74% in variable definition extraction. Nonetheless, the process for judging the equivalence of variable definitions was largely ineffective, with over half of the equivalent definitions failing to be identified correctly. However, when the equivalence judgment was accurate and the expressions were standardized, the algorithm could yield the intended model candidates. Future efforts will focus on enhancing the efficacy of each core technology to fulfill the vision of AutoPMoB. Additionally, we plan to develop strategies for sourcing documents essential for model building, leveraging non-literature information, and maintaining the performance of fundamental technologies when dealing with unfamiliar processes.

5. Acknowledgments

This work was supported by JSPS KAKENHI Grant Number JP23K13595 and the Chubei Itoh Foundation.

References

S. Kato and M. Kano, 2022, Towards An Automated Physical Model Builder: CSTR Case Study, Computer Aided Chemical Engineering, Volume 49, Pages 1669–1674.

S. Kato, C. Zhang, and M. Kano, 2023, Simple Algorithm for Judging Equivalence of Differential-Algebraic Equation Systems, Scientific Reports, Volume 13, Page 11534.

S. Kato and M. Kano, 2023, Efficient Physical Model Building Algorithm Using Equations Extracted from Documents, Computer Aided Chemical Engineering, Volume 52, Pages 151–156.

A. Vaswani, N. Shazeer, N. Parmar, J. Uszkoreit, L. Jones, A. N. Gomez, L. Kaiser, and I. Polosukhin, 2017, Attention Is All You Need, Advances in Neural Information Processing Systems, Volume 30.

R. Han, T. Peng, C. Yang, B. Wang, L. Liu, and X. Wan, 2023, Is Information Extraction Solved by ChatGPT? An Analysis of Performance, Evaluation Criteria, Robustness and Errors, arXiv preprint arXiv:2305.14450.

M. Schubotz, L. Krämer, N. Meuschke, F. Hamborg, and B. Gipp, 2017, Evaluating and Improving the Extraction of Mathematical Identifier Definitions, Experimental IR Meets Multilinguality, Multimodality, and Interaction, Pages 82–94.

T. Brown, B. Mann, N. Ryder, M. Subbiah, J. D. Kaplan, P. Dhariwal, A. Neelakantan, P. Shyam, G. Sastry, A. Askell, S. Agarwal, A. Herbert-Voss, G. Krueger, T. Henighan, R. Child, A. Ramesh, D. Ziegler, J. Wu, C. Winter, C. Hesse, M. Chen, E. Sigler, M. Litwin, S. Gray, B. Chess, J. Clark, C. Berner, S. McCandlish, A. Radford, I. Sutskever, and D. Amodei, 2020, Language Models are Few-Shot Learners, Advances in Neural Information Processing Systems, Volume 33, Pages 1877–1901.

M. Suzuki, F. Tamari, R. Fukuda, S. Uchida, T. Kanahori, 2003, INFTY: An Integrated OCR System for Mathematical Documents. Proceedings of DocEng'03, Pages 95–104.

Flavio Manenti, Gintaras V. Reklaitis (Eds.), Proceedings of the 34th European Symposium on Computer Aided Process Engineering / 15th International Symposium on Process Systems Engineering (ESCAPE34/PSE24), June 2-6, 2024, Florence, Italy

A Deep Reinforcement Learning Approach to Slug Flow Control in Oil and Gas Applications

José R. T. Neto [a,*], Bruno D. O. Capron [a], Argimiro R. Secchi [a,b], Antonio Del Rio Chanona [c]

aDepartment of Chemical Engineering/School of Chemistry, Federal University of Rio de Janeiro, 149 Athos da Silveira Ramos Avenue, Rio de Janeiro, RJ, 21941-909, Brazil
bChemical Engineering Program/COPPE, Federal University of Rio de Janeiro, 149 Athos da Silveira Ramos Avenue, Rio de Janeiro, RJ, 21941-972, Brazil
cDepartment of Chemical Engineering, Imperial College London, South Kensington Campus, London, SW7 2AZ, United Kingdom
joseneto@eq.ufrj.br

Abstract

In deep water oil extraction, supervisory control is often challenged by the oscillatory nature of slug flow. This work introduces an adaptive anti-slug control mechanism using the Proximal Policy Optimization (PPO) algorithm, a Deep Reinforcement Learning (DRL) approach that dynamically adjusts to the complexities of slug flow. The proposed strategy involves the control of the Permanent Downhole Gauge (PDG) pressure through two variables: choke valve opening and gas lift flow rate, representing real-world extraction challenges. The methodology was based on a simulation-based learning approach, utilizing the Fast Oil and Water Model (FOWM). The work compares a baseline PPO model (PPO-base) with a modified version that incorporates penalties on control actions and for violations of state constraints (PPO-pen). Results show that PPO-pen surpasses PPO-base in key training metrics, indicating that moderate penalties can enhance control effectiveness and give more adherence to operational constraints. Testing also reveals that policies from PPO-pen are more efficient than PPO-base, indicating a strategy that is resource-efficient and effective in maintaining critical operational parameters. Furthermore, PPO-pen achieves a lower integral time-weighted absolute error (ITAE), highlighting its accuracy in control and error minimization. The findings demonstrate the potential of DRL, particularly PPO with calibrated penalty parameters, in refining control strategies for complex processes like deep water oil extraction.

Keywords: Multiphase Flow Control, Subsea Control Systems, Operational Stability.

1. Introduction

Deep water extraction is increasingly vital for the oil and gas industry as hydrocarbon sources deplete. This process involves extracting hydrocarbons from subsea wells and transporting them to surface platforms via flowlines, manifolds, and risers, followed by export to shore for refining. A primary challenge within the production line is managing slug flow, which can cause significant operational issues, including the overflow of inlet separators in offshore oil fields (Taitel, 1986). For control design, complex process models, like those in the OLGA® simulator (Bendlksen et al., 1991), are computationally expensive. Instead, this work adopts a simplified, yet effective model called Fast Offshore Wells Model (FOWM) (Diehl et al., 2017), effectively capturing the critical dynamics of casing heading and slugging in both terrain and riser. Traditionally, the industry has relied on Proportional-Integral-Derivative (PID) control strategies. Several studies have focused on the effectiveness of PID control in slug flow management, exemplified by works like Di Meglio et al. (2012a), Storkaas and Skogestad (2008), and Jahanshahi (2013). The PID approach, due to its practicality, has been a focal point in research, with significant efforts dedicated to optimizing its tuning for anti-slug control (Pedersen et al., 2014), as seen in the methods proposed by Godhavn et al. (2005). This work introduces a novel approach to slug flow control in oil and gas operations, transitioning from traditional PID controller tuning to the application of Deep Reinforcement Learning (DRL). The primary objective is to explore and establish the effectiveness of DRL as a supervisory control method that can adaptively and dynamically handle the complex, fluctuating conditions characteristic of slug flow. This shift represents a potentially more robust solution for scenarios where traditional control strategies might struggle to maintain stability and efficiency.

2. Methodology

2.1. Slug Flow Model

FOWM is a composite model that divides the production system into three segments: the reservoir and wellbore, the gas lift, and the production line, which includes both the flowline and riser (Figure 1).

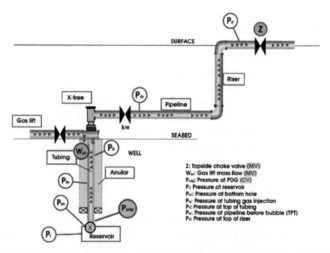

Figure 1: FOWM model for oil and gas production simulation (Adapted from Diehl et al., 2017).

This trisection is articulated through a system of ordinary differential equations (ODEs), based on conservation of mass equations that represent the masses of gas and liquid in different sections of the system. The parameter set from Rodrigues et al. (2018) was selected for characterizing FOWM in this work due to its good alignment with the specific region and initial conditions under consideration, particularly in cases of severe slugging.

2.2. Proximal Policy Optimization

This work employs the Proximal Policy Optimization (PPO) algorithm (Schulman et al., 2017), an on-policy DRL algorithm known for balancing the complexity of policy gradient methods with the stability of trust region methods. PPO restricts policy updates through a clipped surrogate objective function, creating a trust region to ensure stable and moderate changes in the policy. The algorithm uses both a policy network (actor) and a value network (critic), with the latter aiding in stabilizing training by estimating the value function. The advantage function, $A(s, a)$, critical for directing the policy towards more beneficial actions, is calculated using Generalized Advantage Estimation (GAE) (Schulman et al., 2015). The general hyperparameters for the PPO implementation can be found on Table 1.

Table 1: PPO Hyperparameters

Parameter	Value	Definition
dt	200	Simulation time step (seconds)
max_timestep	4320	Max time steps per episode (10 days)
learning_rate	5×10^{-4}	Learning rate for optimization
clip_range	0.2	Range for clipping policy updates
clip_range_vf	0.2	Clipping range for value function updates
total_timesteps	1×10^{7}	Total training time steps
gamma	0.99	Discount factor for future rewards
gae_lambda	0.99	GAE parameter for bias-variance trade-off
ent_coef	5×10^{-3}	Entropy term coefficient in loss calculation
batch_size	240	Batch size for gradient updates
n_steps	480	Steps collected before each update
n_epochs	10	Number of passes over each batch of steps
seed	1990	Seed for random number generation

The neural network architecture for the PPO model was determined through a heuristic exploratory process, similar to Lee (2020). Initially, a range of neural network structures and activation functions were trialed, leading to the selection of the Mish activation function (Misra 2020), defined as $f(x) = x \tanh(softplus(x))$, where $softplus(x)$ is $log(1 + exp(x))$. Mish was selected for its stability and superior performance metrics, trained using the Adam optimizer. The final architecture, featuring two fully connected layers with 16 neurons each for both policy (actor) and value (critic) networks, was chosen for its simplicity and computational efficiency. The architecture's effectiveness was validated in deterministic policy evaluations, prioritizing average reward and episode mean length as key performance metrics.

2.3. Case Study

The study's slugging process control environment was developed using the Gym toolkit (Brockman et al., 2016). The permanent downhole gauge pressure (PDG) was selected as the controlled variable for its precision in capturing well dynamics and its direct impact on production rates. A lower PDG is typically associated with higher production, due to the increased pressure differential with the reservoir. The choke valve position (z) and the gas lift flow rate (W_{gc}) were selected as manipulated variables. The choke valve adjusts the well's output, while the gas lift enhances oil recovery by lightening the fluid column in the well. The observation space consists of a set of variables critical for assessing the well's states (Table 2).

Table 2: Observation Space

Parameter	Definition
P_{rt}	The pressure at the top region of the riser
P_{rb}	The pressure at the flowline before the bubble
P_{pdg}	The controlled pressure at PDG
P_{tt}	The pressure at the top of the tube

P_{tb}	The pressure at the bottom of the tube
P_{bh}	The pressure at the base of the well
W_{lout}	The mass flow rate of the liquid exiting the system
W_{gout}	The mass flow rate of the gas exiting the system

The case study was derived by data from a real-world oil and gas well, referred to as well A (Diehl et al., 2017), illustrated by Figure 2. This well was chosen for its stable limit cycles and controllable gas lift system, providing a rich dataset for DRL training.

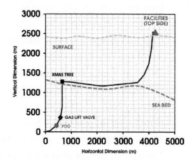

Figure 2: Schematic representation of the case study: well A.

In the control environment, the initial conditions were selected as conditions that could induce slug flow if the system was left uncontrolled. A conservative control strategy, as suggested by Diehl et al. (2018), was adopted, allowing only minor adjustments at each simulation step, of about ±0.048 % for choke valve opening and ±4.762 Sm³/10³ d for gas injection rate. The PDG setpoint was systematically varied over four stages within each episode, aligned with the episode's length. Each stage spanned a quarter of the maximum time steps, with the setpoint starting at 210 bar and gradually decreasing to 203 bar. This approach was specifically designed to test the controller's adaptability to setpoint transitions within the slug flow region, starting at an initial setpoint already within the slug flow conditions. In the PPO model, the reward function aimed to maintain the PDG pressure setpoint and ensure control stability, calculating the error between current and reference pressures with integral time-weighted absolute error (ITAE), to emphasize the duration and magnitude of deviations. The reward bonus scaled according to error proximity to three tolerance zones, with higher rewards for smaller deviations. The reward function also incorporates penalties for variance and mean absolute changes in the control actions, aimed at promoting smoother operations. The cumulative reward at each time step is computed using the following formulation:

$$r = r_{tol} - \zeta_1 \left(var_z + var_{W_{gc}} \right) - \zeta_2 \left(mean\_dif_z + mean\_dif_{W_{gc}} \right) - \omega \qquad (7)$$

In this formula, r_{tol} is determined by the normalized error's alignment with the tolerance zones, var is the variance for each control action, and $mean\_dif$ is the mean absolute change. Furthermore, constraint handling was implemented during training to guide the learning process. This involves terminating a simulation episode and applying a penalty (ω) if state variables exceed the predefined bounds. This mechanism, primarily a training tool, encourages the agent to adhere to operational limits.

3. Results and Discussion

This section compares two simulation tests: PPO-base with no penalties (ζ_1, ζ_2, and ω set to 0) and PPO-pen with penalties ζ_1, ζ_2, and ω set to $(0.5, 0.5, 2.0)$. Key metrics evaluated were Episode Length Mean and Episode Reward Mean, indicating system stability and alignment with operational objectives, respectively. Training progress and performance of both scenarios are detailed in Figure 3, showing that PPO-pen outperformed PPO-base in both episode length and reward means. This suggests that penalties enhanced operational constraints adherence and led to smoother control actions, demonstrating the effectiveness of penalty-based training in control strategies under severe initial conditions.

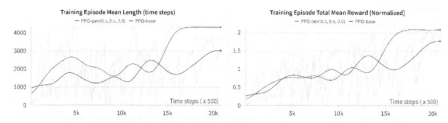

Figure 3: Training performance comparison between PPO-base and PPO-pen.

A detailed performance analysis of both configurations during a test episode (Figure 4) revealed several key findings. In choke valve control, PPO-pen achieved a higher final value, indicating better production efficiency. In gas lift rate control, PPO-pen demonstrated more efficient resource utilization with a systematic reduction in gas lift, contrasting with PPO-base's constant rate. For the PDG pressure control, both scenarios performed similarly, but PPO-pen showed superior consistency and stability, evidenced by a lower ITAE.

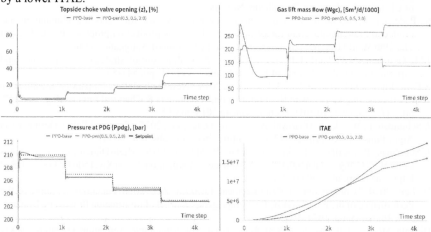

Figure 4: Comparative analysis of control actions and performance metrics in a test episode.

4. Conclusions

This work implemented and evaluated PPO-based control strategy for deep water oil extraction, comparing a baseline model (PPO-base) against a penalty parameter-integrated version (PPO-pen). The results showed that PPO-pen significantly outperformed PPO-base in training metrics, demonstrating the benefits of incorporating moderate penalties in control strategies for balancing operational objectives and constraints adherence. In testing, PPO-pen presented a more resource-efficient control approach, optimizing choke valve position and reducing gas lift usage. Both models effectively were able to maintain the PDG pressure at setpoint and far from slug conditions. Considering the error minimization, PPO-pen achieved lower ITAE, indicating enhanced control performance. These findings highlight the efficacy of DRL, particularly the PPO framework with tailored penalties, in controlling complex systems like deep water oil extraction. They open avenues for further research in applying these methods to varied operational scenarios and integrating more real-world constraints.

References

Y. Taitel, 1986, "Stability of severe slugging," International Journal of Multiphase Flow, Vol. 12, No. 2, pp. 203-217, DOI: 10.1016/0301-9322(86)90026-1.

K.H. Bendlksen, Dag Malnes, Randl Moe, Sven Nuland, 1991, "The Dynamic Two-Fluid Model OLGA: Theory and Application," SPE Production Engineering, Vol. 6, No. 02, pp. 171-180, DOI: 10.2118/19451-pa.

F.C. Diehl, T.K. Anzai, C.S. Almeida, O.F. Von Meien, S. Simões Neto, V.R. Rosa, M.C.M.M. Campos, F. Reolon, G. Gerevini, C. Ranzan, M. Farenzena, J.O. Trierweiler, 2017, "Fast Offshore Wells Model (FOWM): A practical dynamic model for multiphase oil production systems in deep water and ultra-deep water scenarios," Computers & Chemical Engineering, Vol. 99, pp. 304-313, DOI: 10.1016/j.compchemeng.2017.01.036.

F. Di-Meglio, G.O. Kaasa, N. Petit, V. Alstad, 2012, "Model-based control of slugging: Advances and challenges," Proceedings of the 2012 IFAC Workshop on Automatic Control in Offshore Oil and Gas Production, pp. 109–115.

E. Storkaas, S. Skogestad, 2008, "Controllability analysis of two-phase pipeline-riser systems at riser slugging conditions," Control Engineering Practice, Vol. 15, pp. 567–581.

E. Jahanshahi, 2013, "Control Solutions for Multiphase Flow - Linear and nonlinear approaches to anti-slug control," Ph.D. thesis, Norwegian University of Science and Technology, Department of Chemical Engineering, Trondheim, Norway.

S. Pedersen, P. Durdevic, Z. Yang, 2014, "Learning control for riser-slug elimination and production-rate optimization for an offshore oil and gas production process," Proceedings of The 19th World Congress of the International Federation of Automatic Control.

J.M. Godhavn, M.P. Fard, P.H. Fuchs, 2005, "New slug control strategies, tuning rules and experimental results," Journal of Process Control, Vol. 15, pp. 547-557.

R.F. Rodrigues, J.O. Trierweiler, M. Farenzena, 2018, "New methodology for parameter estimation of offshore slug models with Hopf bifurcation," Computers & Chemical Engineering, Vol. 117, pp. 247–255, DOI: 10.1016/j.compchemeng.2018.06.012.

J. Schulman, F. Wolski, P. Dhariwal, A. Radford, O. Klimov, 2017, "Proximal Policy Optimization Algorithms," arXiv:1707.06347, URL: https://arxiv.org/abs/1707.06347.

J. Schulman, P. Moritz, S. Levine, M. Jordan, P. Abbeel, 2015, "High-Dimensional Continuous Control Using Generalized Advantage Estimation," arXiv:1506.02438, URL: https://arxiv.org/abs/1506.02438.

D. Lee, 2020, "Comparison of Reinforcement Learning Activation Functions to Improve the Performance of the Racing Game Learning Agent," Journal of Information Processing Systems, Vol. 16, No. 5, pp. 1074–1082.

Diganta Misra, 2020, "Mish: A Self Regularized Non-Monotonic Activation Function," arXiv preprint arXiv:1908.08681.

G. Brockman, V. Cheung, L. Pettersson, J. Schneider, J. Schulman, J. Tang, W. Zaremba, 2016, "OpenAI Gym," arXiv:1606.01540, URL: https://arxiv.org/abs/1606.01540.

F.C. Diehl, C.S. Almeida, T.K. Anzai, G.Gerevini, S. Simões Neto, O.F. Von Meien, M.C.M.M. Campos, M. Farenzena, J.O. Trierweiler, 2018, "Oil production increase in unstable gas lift systems through nonlinear model predictive control," Journal of Process Control, Vol. 69, pp. 58-69, DOI: 10.1016/j.jprocont.2018.07.009.

Flavio Manenti, Gintaras V. Reklaitis (Eds.), Proceedings of the 34th European Symposium on Computer Aided Process Engineering / 15th International Symposium on Process Systems Engineering (ESCAPE34/PSE24), June 2-6, 2024, Florence, Italy

Bioprocess Control: A Shift in Methodology Towards Reinforcement Learning

Mariana Monteiro,[a*] Cleo Kontoravdi[a*]

[a]*Sargent Centre for Process Systems Engineering, Department of Chemical Engineering, Imperial College London, Exhibition Road, London SW7 2AZ, United Kingdom*
m.monteiro21@imperial.ac.uk, cleo.kontoravdi98@imperial.ac.uk

Abstract

The production of monoclonal antibodies in mammalian cells is a highly complex and nonlinear process. The industry standard for control of this process fails to capture its complex dynamics, leading to high batch-to-batch variability. This inherent complexity makes bioprocesses challenging to model purely mechanistically, while the lack of rich experimental datasets and the need for interpretability in control policies further prevent the use of fully data-driven solutions. We propose a hybrid methodology for optimizing the nutrient feeding strategy that leverages reinforcement learning. We train the controller with an off-policy method due to its data efficiency. This methodology offers the advantage of not needing access to perfect state knowledge, but rather learning from partial observations of the state, which allows for improved generalization. The continuous learning abilities of the proposed method ensure adaptability in response to process changes, while the inclusion of a mechanistic model in the environment aids in the interpretability of the learned control actions.

Keywords: Biomanufacturing, Reinforcement Learning, Control, Mammalian cells

1. Introduction

The global market of biologics reached an annual value of US$359 billion in 2022, with an expected increase to US$1421 billion by 2032 (Precedence Research, 2022). Mammalian cells produce up to 80% of the commercially available therapeutic proteins (e.g., monoclonal antibodies - mAbs), with Chinese Hamster Ovary (CHO) cells being the primary production host (Al-Majmaie et al., 2022). The production of mAbs used in treating cancer and autoimmune diseases is a highly complex and nonlinear process with many correlated variables. The industry standard for control of this process involves PID control of pH, temperature, and dissolved oxygen tension in the production bioreactor. However, these traditional control strategies fail to capture the complex dynamics of the process, leading to high batch-to-batch variability (Aehle et al., 2011).

This is problematic in a highly regulated industry like biopharmaceuticals, which must ensure consistent and safe product quality. The complexity of bioprocesses presents challenges in their mechanistic modelling and simulation. In addition, the absence of sufficient experimental data and the necessity for interpretable control policies restricts the utilization of entirely data-driven methods. Hence, hybrid models encompassing mechanistic and data-driven tools provide a suitable compromise (Narayanan et al., 2020). Yet, it is unclear how best to integrate these two components and how to account for plant-model mismatch that characterizes bioprocesses. To this end, Petsagkourakis et al. (2020) proposed a methodology that leverages a policy gradient algorithm to learn the optimal policy distribution of a 'cheap' simulation model, and then a separate transfer learning algorithm that transfers the optimal policy distribution to the real and more expensive simulation model. Mowbray et al. (2021) proposed a methodology that uses Gaussian processes for the offline simulation, and then uses the posterior uncertainty prediction to account for plant-model mismatch. Andersson et al. (2023) leveraged a Deep Deterministic Policy Gradient-method (TD3) to determine the optimal policies of liquid chromatography columns, and inputs random noise to the control actions. These works lay the foundation for applying reinforcement learning to more complex case studies that are representative of real industrial systems.

In this work, we propose a model-based reinforcement learning methodology to optimize the nutrient feeding strategy of mammalian cell culture producing recombinant therapeutic products. In reinforcement learning, an agent interacts with an environment and learns to act through trial and error. By receiving rewards for its actions, the agent develops a control policy based on the experiences gathered from the environment. We define the environment as a kinetic model of the production bioreactor, simulating CHO cell growth and mAb production dynamics. The agent receives only partial state observations of the reactor. The observations include information on the concentration of amino acids, cell density, and antibody production - measurements commonly available offline during manufacturing and online or at-line during process development. The agent acts on the environment by manipulating the feeding strategy. Our results suggest that the proposed methodology can lead to an optimal control policy. By continuously learning from its environment, without having direct access to it, the controller can adjust to changing conditions in real time, supporting optimal CHO cell growth and antibody production. This adaptability reduces inconsistencies in the production process, leading to more reliable and predictable outcomes.

2. Methodology

Figure 1 depicts the implemented controller. The workflow structure is as follows:
1. Initiate the environment.
2. Simulate the environment for the duration of one step.
3. Provide the state, s_t, to the agent and calculate the reward, r_t.
4. Perform soft policy iteration
5. Provide action a_t to the environment.
6. Redo steps 2-5 until the end of the batch.
7. Reset the environment with new initial conditions and parameters. Redo steps 1-6 until the stop criterion is satisfied.

Figure 1 Controller Steps

The stop criterion is met when the training reaches 15000 steps, where each step is an 8-hour period of a batch operation (which lasts 2 weeks).

2.1. Environment

The simulation model, defined as a gym environment (Brockman et al., 2016), is a kinetic model of a fed-batch reactor describing the material balances of the cells, nutrients, and metabolites. The model, described in detail in Monteiro et al. (2023), was parameterized and validated with experimental data. The state, s_t, corresponds to the measurable variables of the environment, metabolites, and biomass concentrations (in total, 26 variables). The actions, a_t, are the variables the agent can manipulate to reach a specific objective. In this case, they are the volume in and out, which correspond to the typical manipulated variables available during manufacturing. Both the action and the observation spaces are defined as continuous (a 'box') with lower and upper bounds of [-1,1]. It is advised to scale the bounds as the policy algorithm is based on Gaussian processes (see subsection 2.2). To ensure that the controller receives different process conditions at each new batch, the kinetic parameters and initial conditions are varied randomly $\pm 5\%$.

2.2. Agent

The agent is trained according to the Soft Actor-Critic (SAC) (Haarnoja et al., 2018), an off-policy algorithm capable of handling a continuous action space. For that, we consider our system to follow Markov decision process (MDP) defined by (S, A, p, r), where S is the state-space, A, the action space, p the probability of transition between spaces and r the reward from each transition. The policy is defined by π, and the ρ_π the trajectories distributions, with regards to a policy. The RL agent learns the optimal policies by maximizing the expected sum of rewards $\sum_{t=0}^{T} E_{(s_t,a_t) \sim \rho_\pi}[r(s_t, a_t)]$, while also maximising entropy $\alpha H(\pi(.\,|s_t))$ of the policies.

$$J(\pi) = \sum_{t=0}^{T} E_{(s_t,a_t) \sim \rho_\pi}[r(s_t, a_t) + \alpha H(\pi(.\,|s_t))] \qquad (1)$$

α is called the temperature parameter, which tunes the stochasticity of the optimal policy, SAC is composed of an actor who decides which action to take next, and a critic, who estimates how good that action is. The actor performs the *soft-policy improvement* by computing the policy π, according to the maximum entropy (a proxy to randomness and exploration). This policy is modelled as a Gaussian process. The critic performs *soft-policy evaluation*, by computing the soft Q-values for a given policy. In the used algorithm, two independent Q-functions are modelled as neural networks and trained independently to mitigate positive biases. The actor's neural network followed the suggested structure (Raffin et. al, 2021) with two linear layers (256 units each), separated by ReLU activation functions, plus a linear layer that outputs the mean of the action distribution and another layer for the standard deviation. The two critic neural networks have three linear layers; the first two have 256 units each with ReLU activations, while the last one outputs a single Q-value.

2.3. Reward function

The definition of the reward, Rt, is of utter importance. In this context, there are four main incentives:

- i_1: Reach a target mAb concentration. This is defined by a normal distribution of mean 4000 mg/L (the target goal for mAb) and a standard deviation of 500 (the allowed threshold). This format allows the agent to see a smooth improvement in reward when it approximates the target, which helps learning.

- i_2: Reach the target as fast as possible, without harsh changes too suddenly.
- i_3: Maintain the target concentration once achieved.
- i_4: Respect maximum reactor volume.
- i_5: Do not cause any numerical failure in the model of the environment.

Each of the incentives has an associated coefficient term (coef_i_x), which allows their ranking with regards to its importance. Hence, the reward function is written as the sum of the product of the coefficient with the respective incentive:

$$reward = \sum_{x=1}^{4} coef_{i_x} \times i_x \tag{1}$$

The coefficients for each of the incentives were defined as follows:

Table 1 Values of the coefficients associated with the reward function incentives.

Coef. i_1	Coef. i_2	Coef. i_3	Coef. i_4	Coef. i_5
100	20	100	20	1000

Reaching the target mAb concentration (Coef. i_1) provides the maximum reward possible, followed by maintaining that target (Coef. i_3). A very harsh penalty is given for causing any numerical failure in the model. This ensures the agent is rewarded for keeping inside the environment's physical constraints.

3. Results

3.1. Hyperparameter Optimisation

The hyperparameters of the agent model were initially tuned using a variant of Bayesian Optimization (Tree-structured Parzen Estimator) using the Python package Optuna (Akiba et al., 2019). Following the optimization, during the training phase we manually adjusted certain parameters such as the learning rate and the learning start step, as the agent was learning too fast and was returning suboptimal policies without exploring the entire action space.

3.2. Training performance

The following figures (2a and 2b) represent mAb concentration and rewards during training. During the initial phase of the training, the agent explored the allowed action space with regards to both action variables. This led to mAb concentration initially being below the target range, followed by being above the target range for most of the training period.

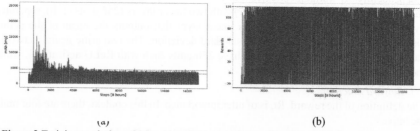

| (a)   (b)

Figure 2 Training evolution of (a) mAb and (b) rewards as a function of training steps. The red dashed lines indicate (a) the target range for mAb and (b) indicate the maximum possible reward (120) for the controller to achieve

The red line in figure 2a indicates the acceptable concentration interval. However, as the reward steadily reduces, mAb concentration increasingly violates the target upper bound. The fed-batch nature of this case study makes it challenging to go back, after violating the upper bound of the target. Hence, the controller had to wait for a batch to end (of simulated duration of 14 days), to try a new policy. A higher production rate is not always desirable given that it might lead to immature mAb glycans, which is undesirable (Jimenez del Val et al., 2016). As such, it is important to train the agent not to violate the target upper bound.

The volume fed to the reactor explored the entire action space in the early stages of the training (figure 3a). As the training progresses, it progressively narrows the window of exploration, settling in the upper region of the action space.

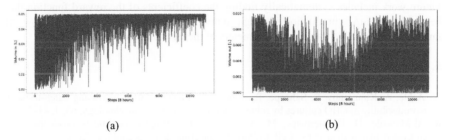

(a) (b)

Figure 3 Training evolution of (a) volume in and (b) volume out as a function of training steps.

The volume removed from the reactor (figure 3b) displays a u-shaped behavior, in which the period when sampling was the lowest matches the highest mAb concentration. The volume constraint was respected throughout the training, while always hitting the upper bound. This means that the agent uses volume out to achieve objectives without violating the volume constraint. The training results also suggest to not feed as a percentage of the reactor volume nor to overfeed, both of which are common industrial practice). The proposed feeding strategy might potentially avoid common overfeeding problems such as increases in osmolality, which may hinder cell growth (Alhuthali et al., 2021).

3.3. Testing performance

The testing consisted of simulating the environment with the control policies of the trained agent and evaluating system performance. To ensure validity, the simulated environment continued to have different kinetic parameters and initial conditions randomly chosen within a ±5% range, similar to training. In figure 4, we can observe that mAb concentration reaches the target interval, initially violating the upper bound, and stabilizing at a lower value close to it. During testing, it is also possible to

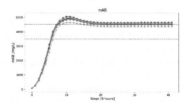

Figure 4 Quantity of mAb produced for different test episodes as a function of batch time

observe an extended stationary phase, which points to a continuous feeding operation.

4. Conclusions

This study introduces a novel methodology to incorporate a complex bioprocess model with a state-of-the-art off-policy reinforcement learning algorithm. Our approach enables the integration of mechanistic knowledge with data to develop more effective control strategies. Furthermore, the proposed control approach offers adaptability, which reduces the need for frequent reparameterization of the controller model when culture conditions change.

Due to the heavily regulated nature of the pharmaceutical industry, it is not only important to maximize the objective, but to consistently achieve the target amount, even if suboptimal. This is because high production rates have been correlated with immature glycans, which can reduce the therapeutic efficiency of mAbs. The proposed methodology can thus be used to ensure consistent process performance.

Future work includes systematically finding the coefficients of the reward function that best achieve mAb production through optimization and increase the window of randomness applied to the kinetic parameters of the environment when training.

5. References

M. Aehle, A. Kuprijanov, S. Schaepe, R. Simutis, A. Lübbert, 2011, Increasing batch-to-batch reproducibility of CHO cultures by robust open-loop control, Cytotechnology, 63, 1, 41-7.

R. Al-Majmaie, D. Kuystermans, M. Al-Rubeai, 2022, Biopharmaceuticals produced from cultivated mammalian cells, Cell Culture Engineering and Technology: In appreciation to Professor Mohamed Al-Rubeai, 3-52, Cham: Springer International Publishing.

D. Andersson, C. Edlund, B. Corbett et al., 2023, Adaptable control policies for variable liquid chromatography columns using deep reinforcement learning, Sci Rep, 13, 11270.

G. Brockman, V. Cheung, L. Pettersson, J. Schneider, J. Schulman, J. Tang, W. Zaremba, 2016, Openai gym, .

T. Haarnoja, A. Zhou, P. Abbeel, S. Levine, 2018, Soft actor-critic: Off-policy maximum entropy deep reinforcement learning with a stochastic actor, International Conference on Machine Learning, PMLR.

I. Jimenez del Val, Y. Fan, D. Weilguny, 2016, Dynamics of immature mAb glycoform secretion during CHO cell culture: An integrated modelling framework, Biotechnology Journal, 11, 610-623.

M. Monteiro, S. Fadda, C. Kontoravdi, 2023, Towards advanced bioprocess optimization: A multiscale modelling approach, Computational and Structural Biotechnology Journal, 21, 3639-3655.

M. Mowbray, P. Petsagkourakis, E.A. Rio-Chanona, R. Smith, D. Zhang, 2021, Safe Chance Constrained Reinforcement Learning for Batch Process Control, Comput. Chem. Eng., 157, 107630.

H. Narayanan, L. Behle, M. F. Luna, M. Sokolov, G. Guillén-Gosálbez, M. Morbidelli, A. Butté, 2020, Hybrid-EKF: Hybrid model coupled with extended Kalman filter for real-time monitoring and control of mammalian cell culture, Biotechnology and bioengineering, 117, 9, 2703–2714.

T. Akiba, S. Sano, T. Yanase, T. Ohta, M. Koyama, 2019, Optuna: A Next-generation Hyperparameter Optimization Framework, KDD.

P. Petsagkourakis, I. O. Sandoval, E. Bradford, D. Zhang, E. A. del Rio-Chanona, 2020, Reinforcement learning for batch bioprocess optimization, Computers & Chemical Engineering, 133, 106649.

A. Raffin, A. Hill, A. Gleave, A. Kanervisto, M. Ernestus, N. Dormann, 2021, Stable-Baselines3: Reliable Reinforcement Learning Implementations, Journal of Machine Learning Research.

S. Alhuthali, P. Kotidis, C. Kontoravdi, 2021, Osmolality Effects on CHO Cell Growth, Cell Volume, Antibody Productivity and Glycosylation, Int J Mol Sci, 2021, Mar 24, 22, 7, 3290.

Flavio Manenti, Gintaras V. Reklaitis (Eds.), Proceedings of the 34th European Symposium on Computer Aided Process Engineering / 15th International Symposium on Process Systems Engineering (ESCAPE34/PSE24), June 2-6, 2024, Florence, Italy

From Data to Alarms: Data-driven Anomaly Detection Techniques in Industrial Settings

Rastislav Fáber[a,*], Martin Mojto[a], Karol Ľubušký[b] and Radoslav Paulen[a]

[a]*Faculty of Chemical and Food Technology, Slovak University of Technology in Bratislava, Bratislava, Slovakia*
[b]*Slovnaft, a.s., Bratislava, Slovakia*
rastislav.faber@stuba.sk

Abstract

This paper introduces a data-driven methodology for anomaly detection in industrial processes. Our focus is on minimizing misclassifications of normal operations and enhancing anomaly and outlier detection. This optimization is based on presumed ground truth (GT) labels associated with a dependent variable (isobutane concentration). Utilizing a moving-horizon approach on an extensive industrial dataset, we perform a comprehensive evaluation of filtering algorithms, and present a representative outlier classification. Secondly, effective anomaly detection, distinct from outlier detection, is achieved by integrating a regression model trained on measurements from independent process variables to fit the dependent variable. Trained regression models consistently achieve effective prediction, staying within an approved process tolerance.

Keywords: Streaming data, Anomaly detection, Outlier detection, Regression

1. Introduction

Ensuring reliable control in any industrial plant necessitates the validation of real-time measurements. Anomaly detection proves effective in identifying subtle signs of malfunctions that could escalate into serious issues. While operators traditionally rely on periodic laboratory samples, there is a growing interest in integrating advanced algorithms to streamline this process and minimize operational burdens. Our focus encompasses the detection of outliers, representing sudden, sharp changes in the monitored signal, as well as distinguishing between the true dynamics of the process and anomalous dynamics caused by measurement disturbances. When anomalous measurements are detected, the operation room should be alarmed.

We employ real-time data analysis to validate incoming online measurements, prioritizing simplicity — an essential factor for implementation on industrial hardware. Various methods, such as threshold or standard deviation filters (Afanasyev and Fedorova, 2019; Blázquez-García et al., 2021), have been explored for detecting outliers in univariate and multivariate time series data. Some papers consider calculating the local mean of a time series using exponentially decreasing weight factors for each prior measurement (Carter and Streilein, 2012; Roberts, 1959). An alternative involves a regression approach that utilizes data-based modeling to identify outliers in a multivariate context, leveraging the autoregressive nature of the model for a nuanced understanding of system dynamics (Yoon et al., 2022). Mathematical models, grounded in fundamental

Acknowledgements: This work is funded by the Slovak Research and Development Agency (project no. APVV-21-0019), by the Scientific Grant Agency of the Slovak Republic (grant no. 1/0691/21), and by the European Commission (grant no. 101079342, Fostering Opportunities Towards Slovak Excellence in Advanced Control for Smart Industries).

laws of nature, offer a deeper grasp of complex process dynamics. For instance, a Kalman filter can be coupled with existing models to estimate the system state (Jin et al., 2022). Another alternative involves deep autoencoders (long short-term memory or convolutional neural network-based models), for enhancing productivity in complex time-series data from the industry (Tziolas et al., 2022).

2. Methodology

Our goal is to generate reliable outcomes of outlier detection in a one-dimensional vector, denoted as $y(t)$. This vector exhibits occasional unexplained behavior and is part of a broader time-series dataset encompassing all process variables over an extended time period, denoted as X. Initially, we enhance the signal clarity by filtering out random fluctuations and noise. As a dynamic model (essential for a Kalman filter) is unavailable, regression techniques offer a viable alternative. We conduct an analysis of the relationships among process variables within X to detect existing trends in the dataset.

2.1. Data Treatment

Visual inspection effectively spots systematic errors, but not all are easily caught. This section explores multivariate data methods to address errors beyond visual detection.

Three-standard-deviations rule. This widely used method assumes a normal data distribution. The 3-sigma interval T is defined based on the sample mean $\hat{y}$ and the standard deviation σ in Eq. (1). Observations outside this interval are considered outliers, with approximately 99.7% of data expected within 3-sigma from the mean. We use:

$$T = \hat{y} \pm 3\sigma, \tag{1}$$

$$T_{t_i} = \hat{x} \pm \chi^2_{n,0.997} S^{1/2} e. \tag{2}$$

Eq. (2) uses the matrix square root $S^{1/2}$ and unit vector e and $\chi^2_{n,0.997}$ is the quantile of the χ^2 distribution with n degrees of freedom and a probability level of 99.7%.

Minimum Covariance Determinant (MCD). This robust method (Rousseeuw and Driessen, 1999) detects outliers in multivariate data using the Mahalanobis distance:

$$d_{MCD,t_i} = \sqrt{(x(t_i) - \hat{x})^T S^{-1}(x(t_i) - \hat{x})}, \tag{3}$$

which shows the dissimilarity between a measurement $x(t_i)$ and the underlying probability distribution using the d_{MCD}. It achieves robustness by iteratively identifying data subsets with the minimum determinant of the sample covariance matrix S, mitigating outlier influence. The process continues until the determinant of S stabilizes. The methods discussed focus on global anomalies and may not effectively capture local deviations. We address this in the following text by taking the temporal dimension into account.

2.2. Outlier Detection using Data Averaging

This method targets unusual values in the local signal behavior within a window of size N, allowing flexibility in focusing on local, temporary, or global deviations based on the chosen N. The confidence interval in this method is computed as:

$$T_{t_i} = \hat{y}(t_i) \pm t_{N,0.997}\sqrt{\sigma^2/N}, \tag{4}$$

where $t_{N,0.997}$ represents the inverse of Student's t distribution (Student, 1908) with N degrees of freedom, and σ^2 corresponds to the variance within the monitored window.

Statistical Mean. This method involves calculating the absolute mean of $y(t)$ over extended periods (N ranges from months to years). The detection criterion is based on (1).

Temporal Mean. By evaluating the mean of consecutive data point differences $\Delta y(t_i) = y(t_i) - y(t_{i-1})$, we detect immediate variations in measurements. Outliers are identified when deviating from the interval in (1).

Simple Moving Average (SIMA). A dynamic average, adapting to dataset changes, uses (5) with a fixed window of past measurements (Oppenheim, 1999). Observations outside the interval (4) are identified as outliers, highlighting inconsistencies in recent history.

$$\hat{y}_{t_i} = \frac{1}{N}\sum_{j=0}^{N-1} y(t_{i-j}). \tag{5}$$

Symmetric Moving Average (SYMA). When dealing with time-series data, our knowledge of future measurements is uncertain. Thus, we use this approach only for evaluating past detection outcomes. We compute the average as:

$$\hat{y}_{t_i} = \frac{1}{N}\sum_{j=-\lfloor (N-1)/2\rfloor}^{\lfloor (N-1)/2\rfloor} y(t_{i-j}). \tag{6}$$

Predictive Moving Average (PMA). We enhance SIMA with additional information from a prediction model to dynamically adjust its value based on other process variables. The predicted difference is added to the filtered value obtained from past measurements:

$$\hat{y}_{t_i} = \frac{1}{N}\sum_{j=0}^{N-1} y(t_{i-j}) + \Delta\hat{y}(x(t_i)). \tag{7}$$

2.3. Anomaly Detection using Regression Methods

We leverage predictive models to identify outliers of the dependent variable based on the positions of measurements relative to the model predictions.

Ordinary Least Squares (OLS). A standard linear regression finds model parameters β by minimizing the squared 2-norm of differences of observed and predicted values:

$$\min_{\beta} \frac{1}{2}\sum_{i=1}^{N}(y(t_i) - \beta^T x(t_i))^2. \tag{8}$$

LASSO. This method extends the regression by incorporating a penalty term based on 1-norm, encouraging model sparsity (Santosa and Symes, 1986). It effectively identifies and reduces the impact of less relevant variables by solving (9), where λ balances model accuracy and overfitting. The ℓ_1-penalization element leads some parameters to become zero, resulting in a less complex, more robust, and interpretable model.

$$\min_{\beta} \frac{1}{2}\sum_{i=1}^{N}(y(t_i) - \beta^T x(t_i))^2 + \lambda\|\beta\|_1. \tag{9}$$

Principal Component Regression (PCR). Principal Component Analysis (PCA) proves valuable in enhancing the interpretability of large, multi-dimensional datasets (Pearson, 1901). By generating new uncorrelated variables, PCA maximizes variance, reducing data dimensionality while minimizing information loss. Subsequently, OLS or LASSO can be employed to learn the model in the latent space. The synergistic application of PCA and LASSO, denoted as PCA+LASSO, harnesses the strengths of both methods.

3. Case Study

The current industrial norm relies heavily on manual processes and lab sampling for anomaly detection. Incorporating an automated algorithm would ease this burden, notifying operators only when an outlier is detected. Our investigation involves a comprehensive industrial dataset (Fáber et al., 2023) with >500 process variables. After preprocessing, we selected 377 entities with 15,907 measurements ($X \in \mathbb{R}^{377 \times 15,907}$). The monitored variable, $y(t)$, represents isobutane concentration, measured every 15 minutes. Within the dataset, we identify three outlier types: level shifts, slow drifts, and additive outliers. Level shifts cause an instant change. The dataset is affected significantly with values potentially returning to the previous level. Drifts gradually deviate, forming challenging-to-detect outliers. Additive anomalies result in unusual values for a single observation, with subsequent points unaffected. The difference between an outlier and anomaly lies in time duration, deviation on short (hours) time scale stands for an outlier; if the deviation lasts longer and requires manual calibration, we classify it as an anomaly.

4. Results

Accurately evaluating anomaly detection methods relies on the presence of anomalies in the dataset. However, even plant operators may struggle to identify anomalies reliably in historical data. To address this, we construct ground truth (GT) labels using a seventh-order SYMA, as shown in (6). This method identified 306 outliers among 15,907 measurements. It is important to note that some outliers in the dataset might not be captured in the GT labels due to missing information from other process variables $X(t)$.

In our evaluation of filter-based approaches, we tested various filter orders and determined that order 7 was the most effective. This choice was validated on a training set of 1,881 measurements, aligning closely with laboratory samples and resulting in the detection of approximately 7.07% of outliers. Subsequent testing on a 750-measurement dataset identified around 7.87% outliers. The inclusion of a higher number of past data points, compared to the SYMA (6), highlights the substantial noise present in the data.

In regression analysis, models were trained to predict both isobutane concentration $\hat{y}(t) = \boldsymbol{\beta}^T \boldsymbol{x}(t)$ and the backward time difference of isobutane concentration $\hat{y}(t) = \boldsymbol{\beta}_\Delta^T \boldsymbol{x}(t)$ using methodology from Section 2.3. Before applying the algorithms, a preprocessing step utilized the MCD method to remove outliers from X (Section 2.1). The dataset was randomly split into training and testing sets (80/20 ratio) for model learning and evaluation. Efficacy was assessed using the Root Mean Square Error (RMSE), with deviations indicating potential outliers:

$$\text{RMSE} = \sqrt{\frac{1}{N}\sum_{i=1}^{N}(y(t_i) - \boldsymbol{\beta}^T \boldsymbol{x}(t_i))^2}, \tag{10}$$

where N is the number of training points. Specifically, we considered the $\pm 2 \times$RMSE confidence interval over $\pm 3 \times$RMSE due to challenges in capturing dataset variability, especially in the presence of outliers among independent variables.

We chose the first seven principal components for PCA-trained models, explaining approximately 62% of the overall variance using the elbow method. Additional components made minimal contributions, indicating saturation in capturing dataset variability. Similarly, for LASSO and the PMA, we applied thresholds of 0.08 and 0.8, respectively, to select relevant coefficients. This ensures that only impactful coefficients are retained, allowing for a more interpretable and effective regression outcome. The prediction model achieved RMSE values ranging from 0.4031 (LASSO) to 0.6655 (PCA+LASSO), all within ±5% of isobutane concentration, meeting the industry-standard confidence region. Variable selection by LASSO, OLS, and PCA provided insights into crucial features. LASSO identified n-butane concentration, olefin feed

Table 1: Confusion matrix entries for implemented outlier detection methods.

Method	TP	TN	FP	FN
Statistical Mean (SM)	15601	0	306	0
Temporal Mean (TM)	15431	61	245	170
Simple Moving Average (SIMA)	14553	122	184	1048
Predictive Moving Average (PMA)	14590	125	181	1011
Regression model	15175	15	291	426

concentration, and pressures of olefin and recycle streams. OLS also demonstrated reasonable variable selection, focusing on pressures at the deisobutanizer accumulator inlet/outlet. However, PCA exhibited less favorable outcomes, selecting compressor discharge, vibrations, and ventilation. Discussions with our industrial partner deemed this variable selection as unsuitable. When analyzing the prediction models, we observe a notable alignment between the fit by LASSO and laboratory measurements, prompting consideration of further investigation in future research.

In predicting output differences, LASSO yielded the lowest RMSE (0.037) among regression methods, closely followed by OLS and PCA+LASSO (RMSE = 0.038). PCR, on the other hand, yielded a higher RMSE = 0.178. Selected variables coincide with those identified by regression models, substituting some with pressure/temperature differences.

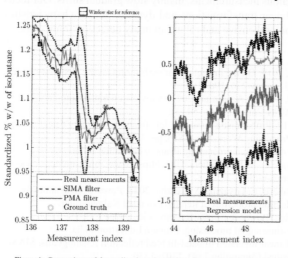

Figure 1: Comparison of the outlier detection (left) and anomaly detection (right).

We analyze the performance of each method using confusion matrices derived from the predefined GT. True positives (TP) and false positives (FP) represent correctly and incorrectly classified non-anomalous measurements, respectively. True negatives (TN) and false negatives (FN) denote correctly and incorrectly identified outliers, respectively. Results are shown in Table 1. The SM approach yielded poor results, detecting no outliers (TN = 0), which was expected given the varying isobutane concentration range across different operation points. TM performed better, correctly identifying 97% of normal operation points (TP = 15,431) yet struggled with over 80% of outliers (TN = 61). SIMA detected 40% of overall outliers (TN = 122), with no foresight into upcoming measurements. PMA improved outlier detection compared to SIMA, reducing false predictions (FP from 1,048 to 1,011; FN from 184 to 181) and enhancing overall accuracy. The TP and TN rates improved as well (TP from 14,553 to 14,590; TN from 122 to 125). These adjustments yielded the best distribution of correctly classified data and reflect the improved use of latent information.

We assessed the regression model (LASSO) using the ±2 × RMSE metric, and identified 15 outliers (TN), showcasing its unique perspective on anomalies beyond the expected range of the dependent variable. These outliers (TN+FN) signify slow, gradual drifts requiring calibration. We illustrate the performance of the SIMA and PMA in Fig. 2 (left graph) using a selected period from testing measurements over multiple days. The fit in the latter approach enhances the mean value to better capture changes in the plant. The comparison reveals differences in outlier detection (red crosses vs. black squares), with the PMA offering additional information for more accurate predictions. While the approach may lead to a higher count of FN (identifying normal instances as outliers) concerning the GT (green circles), it simultaneously emphasizes accurately predicted instances. This method holds the potential to identify outliers that escaped detection by the SYMA, which lacked information about other independent variables X.

5. Conclusions

We studied outlier detection in the process variables. We employ moving-horizon filters and integrate regression-based prediction into our approach. Notably, this method successfully identifies 40% of the outliers while reducing false detections. Conversely, regression models, despite exhibiting lower outlier detection efficacy, provide a means to detect long-term anomalies. The overall fit of the models to the dependent variable, assessed through the computed RMSE criterion, falls within the approved process tolerance. In our future research, we aim to investigate the efficacy of regression approaches for detecting anomalous measurements, mainly slow gradual shifts. Our focus will extend to exploring non-linear transformations and dynamic sensor characteristics and to the development of a comprehensive and robust anomaly detection framework.

References

D. O. Afanasyev, E. A. Fedorova, 2019. On the impact of outlier filtering on the electricity price forecasting accuracy. Applied Energy 236, 196–210.

A. Blázquez-García, A. Conde, U. Mori, J. A. Lozano, 2021. A review on outlier/anomaly detection in time series data. ACM Comput. Surv. 54 (3).

K. M. Carter, W. W. Streilein, 2012. Probabilistic reasoning for streaming anomaly detection. In: 2012 IEEE Statistical Signal Processing Workshop (SSP). pp. 377–380.

A. V. Oppenheim, 1999. Discrete-time signal processing. Pearson Education India.

IBM Corporation, 2021. SPSS Modeler 18.1.0, Outliers. URL https://www.ibm.com/docs/en/s-pss-modeler/18.1.0?topic=series-outliers

Z. Jin, J. Zhao, L. Ding, S. Chakrabarti, E. Gryazina, V. Terzija, 2022. Power system anomaly detection using innovation reduction properties of iterated extended Kalman filter. International Journal of Electrical Power & Energy Systems 136, 107613.

A. V. Oppenheim, 1999. Discrete-time signal processing. Pearson Education India.

F. Santosa, W. W. Symes, 1986. Linear inversion of band-limited reflection seismograms. SIAM Journal on Scientific and Statistical Computing 7 (4), 1307–1330.

T. Tziolas, K. Papageorgiou, T. Theodosiou, E. Papageorgiou, T. Mastos, A. Papadopoulos, 2022. Autoencoders for anomaly detection in an industrial multivariate time series dataset. Engineering Proceedings 18 (1).

Y. S. Yoon, W. Jeong, J. Kim, M. Seok, J. Park, J. Bae, K. Lee, J. H. Lee, 2022. Development of inferential sensor and real-time optimizer for a vacuum distillation unit by recurrent neural network modeling of time series data. Computers & Chemical Engineering 168, 108039

S. W. Roberts, Aug. 1959. Control chart tests based on geometric moving averages. Technometrics 1 (3), 239–250.

K. Pearson, 1901. Liii. on lines and planes of closest fit to systems of points in space. The London, Edinburgh, and Dublin Phil. Magazine and Journal of Science 2 (11), 559–572.

P. Rousseeuw, K. Driessen, 08 1999. A fast algorithm for the minimum covariance determinant estimator. Technometrics 41, 212–223.

R. Fáber, K. Ľubušký, R. Paulen, 2023. Machine Learning-based Classification of Online Industrial Datasets. 2023 24th Int. Conf. on Process Control, 132–137.

Flavio Manenti, Gintaras V. Reklaitis (Eds.), Proceedings of the 34th European Symposium on Computer Aided Process Engineering / 15th International Symposium on Process Systems Engineering (ESCAPE34/PSE24), June 2-6, 2024, Florence, Italy

Machine Learning Models Development for the Optimal Production of Aligned Nanofibers

Francisco Javier López-Flores,[a] Jorge Andres Ornelas-Guillén,[b] Alejandra Pérez-Nava,[c] Janett Betzabe Gonzalez-Campos,[b] José Maria Ponce-Ortega,[a*]

[a] *Chemical Engineering Department, Universidad Michoacana de San Nicolás de Hidalgo, Av. Francisco J. Múgica, S/N, Ciudad Universitaria, Edificio V1, Morelia, Mich., 58060, México*
[b] *Biological and Chemical Research Institute, Universidad Michoacana de San Nicolás de Hidalgo, Av. Francisco J. Múgica, S/N, Ciudad Universitaria, Edificio V1, Morelia, Mich., 58060, México*
[c] *Instituto de Química, Universidad Nacional Autónoma de México, Circuito Exterior S/N, Ciudad Universitaria 04510, CDMX, México*
Corresponding: jose.ponce@umich.mx

Abstract

The generation of electrospun nanofibrous with controlled size, shape, and spatial orientation is crucial for the development of biomedical and electronic devices. Commonly, randomly oriented nanofibers with high porosity and nanoscale morphology are produced using the traditional electrospinning configuration, nonetheless, aligned nanofibers are advantageous over random nanofibers, because the control of spatial orientation can improve electrical and optical properties and play an important role in tissue engineering applications, impacting the mechanical and biological properties of the scaffold. Different machine learning models have been developed to predict the optimal production of electrospun aligned poly (vinyl alcohol) nanofibers. The database was obtained by multiple assays using the air gap electrospinning setup and varying the voltage, flow rate, distance between tip and collector, and polymer concentration. First, binary classification models were developed, which from the electrospinning conditions can predict the production or not of aligned nanofibers; the models used are Artificial Neural Networks, Random Forests, and Logistic Regression. In addition, regression models have been developed to predict the orientation percentage, average angle, and average diameter of the nanofibers when there is production of nanofibers. A convolutional neural network has also been developed using Field Emission Scanning Electron Microscope images of the different assays performed. Through the analysis and comparison of results, it was concluded that for the binary classification, the artificial neural network performs better predictions obtaining an accuracy equal to 0.94 in K-fold cross-validation, and for the validation set an accuracy equal to 0.90 and an F1-score equal to 0.87 were obtained.

Keywords: Aligned Nanofibers, Electrospinning, Machine Learning, Data-driven modeling, Artificial neuron network,.

1. Introduction

Nanofiber structures have become increasingly attractive and gained much interest due to their unique properties; namely highly porous interconnected tridimensional architecture, high surface area to volume ratio, and lightweight, besides the fisicochemical properties inherent to the nature of the components which integrate the nanofibers as such. These features are ideal for use in applications as varied as tissue engineering, sensors development, filtration, energy storage, and functional materials (Thenmozhi et al., 2017).

Electrospinning is the most commonly used technique for the production of nanofiber mats due to it is a simple, low-cost, and versatile methodology to produce controllable nanofiber structures with tunable functional properties. Randomly oriented nanofibers are produced using the traditional electrospinning configuration, nonetheless, aligned nanofibers are advantageous over random nanofibers because it has been demonstrated that the control of spatial orientation can improve electrical and optical properties, and play an important role in tissue engineering applications, impacting the mechanical and biological properties of the scaffold (Pourheydari et al., 2023), besides it can enhance drug delivery by altering release performance (Robinson et al., 2021). Fiber alignment can be achieved by the air gap electrospinning configuration, nonetheless, the production of aligned nanofiber mats involves the control of several parameters which have to be carefully adjusted to achieve a spinnable regime and at the same time, control size, alignment, quality and morphology of nanofiber mats. Therefore, a systematic study on predicting the processing parameters influencing the production and alignments of nanofibers is needed.

Machine learning is a branch of artificial intelligence that focuses on developing algorithms/models that allow computers to learn patterns from data and perform specific tasks without being explicitly programmed (Janiesch et al., 2021). These models, once they have learned the behavior of the data, can be used to predict new data or samples. Due to the good performance of machine learning in various applications (Adekoya et al., 2022; Ugwu et al., 2022) and the need to create materials efficiently at a lower cost, shorter time, and fewer experiments, the development of machine learning models capable of predicting the optimal production of electrospun aligned poly (vinyl alcohol) nanofibers through the synthesis conditions (voltage, flow rate, tip-to-collector distance, and polymer concentration) is proposed. The data required for the development of these models are generated experimentally.

2. Methodology

In this study, the general methodology for developing machine learning models to predict the production of aligned electrospun nanofibers is shown in Figure 1. Initially, data collection was performed by conducting multiple assays using the air gap electrospinning configuration and varying the voltage, flow rate, tip-to-collector distance, and polymer concentration. A total of 48 assays were carried out, and Field Emission Scanning Electron Microscope (FESEM) images, the orientation percentage, average angle, and average diameter were obtained from the electrospun nanofibers produced in each assay. After completing the data collection phase, data analysis revealed that nanofibers were successfully produced in 34 assays, in contrast to 14 assays in which no nanofibers were observed. Furthermore, the complexity of experimental results and the limited availability of data raised the need to implement different tools to model and optimize the production of aligned electrospun nanofibers. Therefore, logistic regression (LR), Random Forests (RF), and artificial neural networks (ANN) have been used to create classification and regression models.

Classification models aim to predict the production or not of electrospun nanofibers from the synthesis conditions (voltage, flow rate, tip-to-collector distance, and polymer concentration). Regression models aim to predict the orientation percentage, average angle, and average diameter of electrospun nanofibers from the processing conditions. In addition, a convolutional neural network (CNN) has been developed to predict the orientation percentage, average angle, and average diameter of electrospun nanofibers from FESEM images.

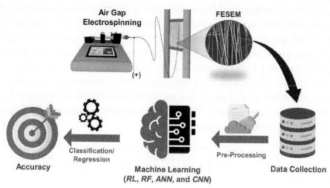

Figure 1. Schematic overview of the methodology.

2.1. Machine Learning

Figure 3 shows in detail the different stages used for the development of machine learning models. Initially, data preprocessing and data normalization are performed. The database is then divided into 80% for a training set and 20% for a validation set. For the training set, oversampling strategies have been used, mainly due to data imbalance; SMOTE (Synthetic minority oversampling technique)(Pears et al., 2014) for the classification models and SMOGN (Synthetic minority over-sampling technique for regression with Gaussian noise) (Branco et al., 2017) for the regression models. Once the training set is oversampled, hyperparameter optimization is performed using Bayesian optimization (Cho et al., 2020) to find highly competitive and accurate models. In ANN the optimized hyperparameters included the hidden layers, the number of neurons in the hidden layers, the type of activation function (hyperbolic tangent, ReLU, and sigmoidal), and the learning rate. In RF, the n estimators, max Depth, max feature, and bootstrap were optimized. In RL, C, solver, and max iter were optimized. After hyperparameter optimization, the model is evaluated by K-fold cross-validation (Jung, 2017), which consists of repeating and calculating the arithmetic mean obtained from the evaluation measures (predicted values versus real values) on different partitions. The final evaluation of the model is done with the validation set which contains pure real data (no oversampled data). Finally, the best models are selected by analyzing the results.

Well-known normalization techniques such as min-max and z-score have been used to build the models. In addition, due to the number of datasets available, k equal to 4 has been used. For the classification models, a stratified K-Folds cross-validation has been implemented, which provides folds with the same percentage of data from each class.

3. Results

3.1. Classification Models

After hyperparameter optimization. The k-fold cross-validation for the classification models has been calculated using the *accuracy* metric and determined for a dataset equal to 52, which contains experimental data and synthetic data labeled in two categories (production of electrospun nanofibers and no production of electrospun nanofibers). The LR, RF, and ANN models obtained a mean accuracy of 0.7833, 0.8972 and 0.9423, respectively. Figure 3 shows the confusion matrix of the k-fold cross-validation of ANN. The evaluation metrics of the classification models (accuracy, precision, recall, and f1-score) are based on the confusion matrix. In essence, the confusion matrix is a graph showing the levels of confusion of the model during classification, portraying the hits and misses made in each category. The confusion matrix is divided into four quadrants: True negative (upper left quadrant), false positive (upper right quadrant), false negative (lower left quadrant), and true positive (lower right quadrant). True means that the values were accurately predicted, and False means that there was an incorrect prediction. It can be seen that the model of 52 datasets only has made three incorrect predictions (see Figure 3). Specifically, the ANN model made two incorrect predictions in category 1 (production of aligned electrospun nanofibers). While one incorrect prediction in category 2 (no production of aligned electrospun nanofibers).

Figure 2. Steps for the development of machine learning models

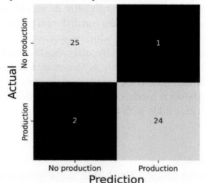

Figure 3. Confusion matrix of the K-fold cross-validation of the ANN

Table 1 shows the results obtained for different metrics during the evaluation of the validation set with the developed models. This data set is equal to 10 and contains only real data. The worst model was logistic regression, and the best is ANN which has only made an incorrect prediction; therefore, the accuracy was equal to 0.90. The random forest, like ANN, only makes an incorrect prediction but in the opposite category, so the F1-score is affected and decreases. F1-score is the metric that combines precision and recall into a single number, providing an overview of the model performance, ANN has achieved the highest F1-score equal to 0.87.

Table 1. Results obtained from the models for the validation set.

Metric	ANN	Random Forest	Regression Logic
Accuracy	0.90	0.90	0.70
Precision	0.84	0.94	0.64
Recall	0.94	0.75	0.60
F1-score	0.87	0.80	0.61

3.2. Regression Models

The ANN model obtained the best results in predicting orientation, angle, and diameter concerning random forests and logistic regression. Table 2 presents the evaluation results of the ANN predictions for the training set and the validation set. The metrics for the training set have been determined by K-fold cross-validation and contain both synthetic and real data. The lower the mean square error (MSE) and the mean absolute error (MAE), the higher the accuracy of the model. The ANN model offers a better performance in predicting the average diameter of nanofibers as it has reached values of (coefficient of determination) R^2 equal to 0.9516 for the training set and 0.8900 for the validation set. The prediction of the orientation percentage is where the model has the most errors as the worst values of the three metrics have been obtained. The model has not performed well in predicting orientation and average angle in the validation set. Overall, the performance of the ANN model has not changed significantly in both datasets, indicating good model training.

Table 2. Results obtained from ANN.

Metric	Training set			Validation set		
	Orientation	Angle	Diameter	Orientation	Angle	Diameter
R^2	0.8127	0.8613	0.9516	0.6740	0.6700	0.8900
MSE	0.0082	0.0036	0.0043	0.0075	0.0047	0.0118
MAE	0.0426	0.0379	0.0349	0.0806	0.0621	0.0966

Table 3 shows the results obtained from the CNN for the training set and the validation set; neither dataset contains synthetic data, and the CNN has been constructed only with the real FESEM images obtained during the different assays. The results obtained with CNN are outstanding (see Table 3), and better than the results achieved with ANN (see Table 2). However, the ANN has been constructed considering as input variables the synthesis conditions, which makes it the most interesting model, but at the same time the one that has to make more complex predictions. CNN has made better predictions for the orientation percentage. The CNN has been able to find correlations in the images, achieving a good performance; only in the validation set the predictions have not been good for the average angle.

Table 3. Results obtained from CNN.

Metric	Training set			Validation set		
	Orientation	Angle	Diameter	Orientation	Angle	Diameter
R^2	0.9360	0.8885	0.9206	0.8959	0.5429	0.8909
MSE	0.0536	0.1158	0.0767	0.1670	0.2640	0.1080
MAE	0.1772	0.2365	0.2043	0.3076	0.3594	0.2538

4. Conclusions

In this study, different machine learning tools have been implemented to develop efficient models that can predict the optimal production of aligned electrospun nanofibers. In general, ANN models have been better compared to random forest and logistic regression. The classification models have achieved very good performances being able to adequately learn the behavior of the data to predict the production or not of aligned electrospun nanofibers from the processing conditions. The results of the ANN model for predicting the orientation percentage, average angle, and average diameter have been interesting and promising since the improvement of this model could reduce the experiment number, costs, and synthesis time. The CNN has been the best model to predict the orientation percentage and average diameter. In future work, it is proposed to increase the database and the number of input variables to improve the performance of the models.

References

S. Thenmozhi, N. Dharmaraj, K. Kadirvelu, H. Y. Kim, 2017, Electrospun nanofibers: New generation materials for advanced applications, Mater. Sci. Eng. B, 217, 36-48.

Z. Pourheydari-Barsari, H. Mirzadeh, M. Farhadi, A. Solouk, M. Jalessi, 2023, Antibacterial aligned nanofibrous chitosan/PVA patch for repairing chronic tympanic membrane perforations, Int. J. Biol. Macromol., 253, 126597.

A.J. Robinson, A. Pérez-Nava, S.C. Ali, J.B. González-Campos, J.L. Holloway, E.M. Cosgriff-Hernandez, 2021, Comparative analysis of fiber alignment methods in electrospinning, Matter 4, 821-844.

C. Janiesch, P. Zschech, K. Heinrich, 2021, Machine learning and deep learning. Electron. Mark, 31(3), 685-695.

O.C. Adekoya, M.E. Yibowei, G.J. Adekoya, E.R. Sadiku, Y. Hamam, S.S. Ray, 2022, A mini-review on the application of machine learning in polymer nanogels for drug delivery, Mater. Today: Proc., 62, S141-S144.

L.I. Ugwu, Y. Morgan, H. Ibrahim, 2022, Application of density functional theory and machine learning in heterogenous-based catalytic reactions for hydrogen production, Int. J. Hydrogen Energy, 47(4), 2245-2267.

R. Pears, J. Finlay, A.M. Connor, 2014, Synthetic Minority Over-sampling TEchnique (SMOTE) for predicting software build outcomes, arXiv preprint arXiv:1407.2330.

P. Branco, L. Torgo, R. Ribeiro, 2017, SMOGN: A pre-processing approach for imbalanced regression, Proceedings of Machine Learning Research, 74,36-50

H. Cho, Y. Kim, E. Lee, D Choi, Y Lee, W Rhee, 2020, Basic enhancement strategies when using Bayesian optimization for hyperparameter tuning of deep neural networks, IEEE Access,8, 52588–608.

Y. Jung, 2018, Multiple predicting K-fold cross-validation for model selection. J. Nonparametric Stat., 30, 197–215.

Flavio Manenti, Gintaras V. Reklaitis (Eds.), Proceedings of the 34th European Symposium on Computer Aided Process Engineering / 15th International Symposium on Process Systems Engineering (ESCAPE34/PSE24), June 2-6, 2024, Florence, Italy

Digital Twins in Operation: The Role of Robust Surrogate Modelling

Isaac Severinsen[a]*, Wei Yu[a], Timothy Gordon Walmsley[b], Brent Young[a]

[a]*Department of Chemical and Materials Engineering, University of Auckland, 5 Grafton Road, Auckland, 1010, New Zealand*
[b]*Ahuora — Centre for Smart Energy Systems, School of Engineering, The University of Waikato, Gate 8, Hillcrest Road, Hamilton, 3240, New Zealand*
*isev820@aucklanduni.ac.nz

Abstract

Digital twins are becoming commonplace in many aspects of the process industry. Despite this, digital twins deployed to assist plant operations in real-time are relatively rare. This work details the unique requirements of an operational digital twin, and what separates them from existing digital twins is explored. Ultimately, this work contributes to the goal of an autonomous plant by analyzing the reliability of models trained. Operational digital twins can have more significant consequences as, in many cases, the output is not interpreted by a human. This is in contrast to other forms of digital twins used for process optimization, fault analysis, or design. This use case means that any underlying model must be extremely robust. This requirement is typically ignored in non-operational applications as modellers strive for accuracy, simplicity, or smooth convex functions. In many cases, dimensionality is reduced, which is antithetical here as the model must reflect the reality of the process and not a specified subset of the feature space. A novel method for surrogate model training is developed to improve the robustness of data driven models. This technique involves splitting the dataset based on the rarity of the datapoint with respect to observed operational conditions. The benefit of a model trained in this way is that accurate results will be given for all operational conditions, helping train a non-human operator. When used to train surrogate models, this can quantify improvements in robustness. This work is developed using a case study of a geothermal power plant. The outcome is to create an operator training simulator. It will be a long time before humans are removed from the loop, and a fully autonomous plant is realized. This work highlights the challenges is reaching this and demonstrates a clear pathway for this progression.

Keywords: Surrogate Modelling, Digital Twin, Operator Training Simulator

1. Introduction

Digital twins are at the forefront of digital chemical engineering. In recent years significant research and development has been devoted to this goal. One definition of a digital twin is presented by Yu *et al.*, (2022) who define a digital twin as a digital representation of system that looks, behaves and connects to the physical system. This work is focusing on the 'behaves-like' aspect where effectively a process model is required.

Surrogate modelling is a technique used to encode information from an existing model. In practice it typically involves training a machine learning model on the outputs of a first-principles model (Forrester et al., 2008). Surrogate models have been presented as a suitable solution for forming part of a digital twin (Bárkányi *et al.*, 2021). While the definitions and use-cases for the digital twin may differ, the consensus is that surrogate modelling provides the best way to encode information from other models into a digital twin. For a digital twin to be used in operation it must be fast to compute, at least as fast as the plant itself. This means that existing accurate but complex models (e.g., CFD) must be encapsulated by faster surrogate models to remain useful within operations.

2. Methodology

2.1. Surrogate modelling

Implementing surrogate modelling typically requires a machine learning approach although many different varieties are used (McBride & Sundmacher, 2019). The approach used depends upon the goal of the work. Most surrogate modelling with process engineering has been with the goal of optimization thus the algorithms used have been focused upon those with smooth convex functions and derivatives. In this work the focus is on accuracy over the feature space of the model. The second objective is to produce a robust model. These requirements mean that methods like kriging and Gaussian process modelling are less appropriate in this context, due to their focus on interpolation.

2.2. Train test split

A significant factor in developing data driven models is the training data supplied. Many focus on the quality of the data supplied, often using data augmentation techniques to improve it. In the case of surrogate modelling the data utilized is typically rich and well distributed over the input feature space. This is in comparison to using standard plant data where the distribution of data is often extremely limited resulting in poor outcomes for modelling.

Typically, the entire data set is split into training and testing sets randomly. This means that when the testing set is evaluated, the ability for the model to interpolate is tested. This is desirable as it helps address the bias-variance tradeoff by ensuring that the fitting function's surface is smooth and not overtrained towards the training data points. There are many other techniques for addressing this overfitting problem, but utilizing the training-testing split is a reliable method of analyzing this.

Here we propose a novel alternative to this training testing split. Instead of splitting the data set randomly we propose splitting the dataset geographically. Specifically, we propose restricting training data to a subset of the feature space and testing on the remainder. This means the model's ability to interpolate is specifically not tested, instead testing extrapolation. We hypothesize that this training testing regime also addresses the bias variance tradeoff, as the response of the model to any unknown data should identify this issue.

This technique is intended to be used in the model discrimination or hyperparameter tuning portion of developing a machine learning model. We will analyze a variety of machine learning techniques for their robustness in extrapolation. Following this we will identify the impacts of changes in hyperparameters or model design that are typically used to address bias-variance tradeoff.

2.3. Case Study

The case study in this work is an industrial binary cycle geothermal power plant in New Zealand. A diagram of the system is given in Figure 1.

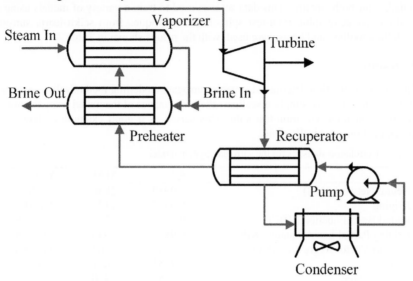

Figure 1. Schematic diagram of the geothermal power plant under study. Blue represents geothermal fluid, red organic fluid.

As seen in Figure 1 the Organic Rankine Cycle (ORC) system largely consists of heat exchangers, which will be the focus of this work. Two years of data was extracted from the data historian in its raw form. This data was preprocessed to form a 1,000,000 point steady state dataset as discussed in Severinsen *et al.*, (2023). This preprocessed data was then used to regress a one-dimensional model built in python for the heat exchanger.

Here we will examine the preheater seen in Figure 1. This unit is typically operated with only single-phase fluids on both sides but in extreme cases the working fluid can be vaporized if conditions allow. The unit can experience temperature cross but there is no chance of the brine being vaporised as at this pressure water boils at ~220°C. This is beyond the scope of brine temperatures in Table 1 where the feature space for input variables is described. Notably the limits on pressure are very tight as loss of pressure during operation is not within scope. Flow rate is varied from 0 to ~150% of nominal operation. This is the main variable of study and truly represents out-of-specification (abnormal) operation.

Table 1. Table describing the input feature space of model.

Variable	Maximum	Minimum	units
brine_T_in	215	100	°C
brine_p_in	25	24	bar
brine_flow	150	0	kg/s
WF_T_in	150	50	°C
WF_P_in	25	15	bar
WF_flow	100	0	kg/s

This feature space was sampled using a Latin hypercube with 10,000 points to ensure uniform exploration of the feature space. This data set was fed to the python-based model of the system with output variables of outlet temperature, pressure drop and change in enthalpy for both streams. This data set was used to train a variety of models using the random and geographic train-test split. Eight techniques from scikit-learn, surrogate modelling toolbox and keras were used, with the results shown in Table 2.

3. Results

The first investigation determined suitable surrogate modelling methods that can be used as a baseline. Here we simply investigate the performance of the model using the normal, interpolation focussed, train-test split. This serves as a good example of how model discrimination is typically done.

Table 2. Correlation statistics for the surrogate python model

	R2	MAE	MSE
Neural Network (NN)	0.9939	2836	1.019E8
Kriging	0.9977	1199	3.487E7
Radial Basis Function (RBF)	0.9774	6785	3.987E8
Kriging Partial Least Squares (KPLS)	0.9882	2943	1.995E8
Support Vector Regression (SVR)	0.9685	9563	4.584E8
Adaboost	0.9954	2081	5.566E7
Decision Tree	0.9852	3470	1.792E8
Random Forest (RF)	0.9958	1910	5.818E7

As seen in Table 2, many of the techniques studied are suitable for surrogate modelling with accurate models produced. These metrics provide a poor measure of model performance and as mentioned only measure interpolation performance. Even when using graphical analysis like QQ plots, model discrimination is difficult. Here we introduce extrapolation as a model discriminator using the aforementioned-technique. The original data is split into training and testing datasets based on Euclidean distance. The threshold Euclidean distance is chosen iteratively so that the training and testing datasets preserve the 80/20 ratio. The two models developed have identical parameters and training times only differing in the geographical feature spaces of the training and testing datasets. To compare this training testing regime, we will compare the predictions of datapoints within both testing datasets directly as seen in Figure 2.

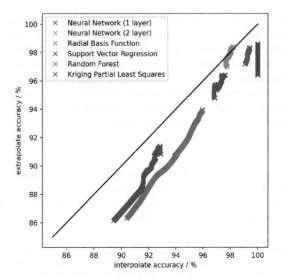

Figure 2. Graph comparing interpolation and extrapolation accuracy for a variety of machine learning techniques.

Figure 2 shows the interpolation and extrapolation accuracy for points within the 'fringe' testing region. Clearly each model has a variety of accuracies which can be analyzed subsequently. Generally, we can see interpolation accuracy is higher than extrapolation which is an expected result. Some techniques have more variation in accuracy both in an absolute sense and relative to extrapolation results. Overall, the robustness of a model can be identified by the proximity of results to the identity line. To examine this further the distance from the identity line has been isolated in Figure 3, where it is plotted against Euclidean distance. Here we examine various hyperparameters and alternatives for the neural network.

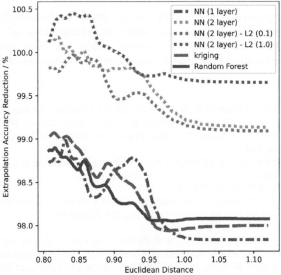

Figure 3. Graph comparing extrapolation ability of different models.

I. Severinsen et al.

Figure 3 shows that extrapolation accuracy relative to interpolation decreases as proximity to training data increases. This is again expected as the model is extrapolating the response into an unknown region. The interesting result from this plot is the performance of each model. Increasing the number of layers in the neural network had a big impact extrapolation accuracy. This is likely because this level of detail was required to fit the shape of the underlying data, indeed it can be seen the interpolation accuracy improved in Figure 2 as well. Most notably we can see that regularisation of the neural network has a significant effect **if** the regularisation parameters are tuned.

4. Discussion

These results do not indicate that the model can be used to extrapolate with this level of accuracy but that in this case extrapolation is only slightly worse outside the training feature space. This result is useful as it provides another tool to analyze the robustness of a model and assess the impact of regularisation.

The challenge with applying this work is that any results are unique to the system. For example, in this system it is known where the phase boundaries are for the fluids in question. If the model were used to extrapolate to a condition where steam could be generated from the working fluid (a condition on which the model is not trained) then it could present accuracy issues. To generalise the issue is that the feature space be known *a-priori* which is certainly a challenge for many newer processes, especially more complex ones. A benefit of the technique is that it is relatively easy to implement but must be manually analyzed.

Future work in this field is likely to focus on understanding multi-dimensional data in a more coherent way. There are also opportunities to use dimensional reduction or non-rectangular feature spaces to enhance this work.

5. Conclusions

This work has proposed a method of analyzing the robustness of models developed. Using a novel training-testing split we can isolate the extrapolation of a model from interpolation. Using this technique, a simple system has been analyzed and the improvement in robustness from using L2 regularisation has been quantified.

References

Bárkányi, Á., Chován, T., Németh, S., & Abonyi, J. (2021). Modelling for Digital Twins—Potential Role of Surrogate Models. *Processes*, *9*(3), Art. 3. https://doi.org/10.3390/pr9030476

Forrester, A., Sobester, A., & Keane, A. (2008). *Engineering Design via Surrogate Modelling*. John Wiley & Sons Ltd.

McBride, K., & Sundmacher, K. (2019). Overview of Surrogate Modeling in Chemical Process Engineering. *Chemie Ingenieur Technik*, *91*(3), 228–239. https://doi.org/10.1002/cite.201800091

Severinsen, I., Yu, W., Walmsley, T., & Young, B. (2023). COVERT: A classless approach to generating balanced datasets for process modelling. *ISA Transactions*. https://doi.org/10.1016/j.isatra.2023.10.031

Yu, W., Patros, P., Young, B., Klinac, E., & Walmsley, T. G. (2022). Energy digital twin technology for industrial energy management: Classification, challenges and future. *Renewable and Sustainable Energy Reviews*, *161*, 112407. https://doi.org/10.1016/j.rser.2022.112407

Flavio Manenti, Gintaras V. Reklaitis (Eds.), Proceedings of the 34th European Symposium on Computer Aided Process Engineering / 15th International Symposium on Process Systems Engineering (ESCAPE34/PSE24), June 2-6, 2024, Florence, Italy

Data-driven diagnostics of variability during changeover in biopharmaceutical freeze-drying

Gianluca Lombardini,[a] Mohamed Rami Gaddem,[a] Stephanie Knueppel,[b] Sara Badr,[a] Hirokazu Sugiyama,[a]*

[a]*Department of Chemical System Engineering, The University of Tokyo, Tokyo 113-8656, Japan*
[b]*Engineering, Science & Technology, F. Hoffmann – La Roche Ltd., Wurmisweg, 4303 Kaiseraugst, Switzerland*
sugiyama@chemsys.t.u-tokyo.ac.jp

Abstract

Changeover processes in biopharmaceutical freeze-drying are crucial to ensure a sterile environment for drug product manufacturing. Leak tests aim to avoid contamination in the freeze-drying chamber using pressure measurements over time. However, process disturbances such as temperature fluctuations can lead to elevated pressure measurements and other process variabilities, which in turn can lead to false alarms. This work investigates the main sources of variability during leak testing by analyzing industrial, noisy batch process data with a relatively low number of batches using principal component analysis and a sparse formulation thereof. It is demonstrated, that for such datasets, adding a sparsity constraint to principal component analysis improves consistency and simplifies interpretability of the results. This work highlights the challenges of using data-driven methodologies with real industrial data and shows the need for developing more tailored solutions to handle noisy, drifting, and imbalanced datasets.

Keywords: Freeze-drying, leak detection, industrial data, data-driven diagnostics, false alarms

1. Introduction

Pharmaceutical freeze-drying is an integral unit operation allowing drug products to be stored over extended time periods. As with all pharmaceutical manufacturing processes, product quality is of paramount importance. Apart from production process and product quality control, changeover processes such as cleaning and sterilization in place (CIP/SIP) or leak testing are essential for assuring high-grade, contaminant-free products. Robust monitoring and control strategies are needed for the safe and efficient operation of pharmaceutical freeze-drying processes, which are already time-, energy-, and cost-intensive with a high potential for quality-impairing faults. However, advanced monitoring strategies for changeover processes are scarce. Leak testing, for example, is performed to measure the amount of external air entering the freeze-dryer, possibly contaminating the sterile environment. Many pharmaceutical companies base leak testing solely on the pressure increase over a specified timeframe. However, pressure increase under vacuum is subject to a multitude of factors, such as temperature fluctuations or evaporation of remaining water in the chamber. These factors lead to so-called internal or virtual leaks, which elevate pressure and potentially cause false alarms (Sahni et al., 2022). Failed tests due to false alarms are often passed through simple repetition without any physical modifications to the equipment. Even so, repetition increases downtime and hence decreases the availability of the machine for production. Virtual leaks are usually characterized by non-linear pressure profiles over time. The only available model to separate virtual from real leaks so far was proposed by Calzavara et al. (2021), which follows a mechanistic approach.

In the last few decades, an extensive amount of data-driven process monitoring, and fault diagnosis systems have been proposed (Yin et al., 2014). Many of these methods, however, are tested and validated on simulated datasets but can be difficult to apply to real industrial datasets (Ji and Sun, 2022). As more data from real pharmaceutical manufacturing plants is being stored, the possibilities to propose and test appropriate monitoring methods are increasing. For that, however, characteristics of industrial data, such as individual machine characteristics, process variabilities, low sample size, non-relevant process variables, and noise must be accounted for. Furthermore, it has been shown that in addition to data drifts, shifts in data baselines can occur over time, especially before and after equipment maintenance (Zürcher et al., 2022), which is an additional source of variability.

This work focuses on identifying the main sources of variability from a low sample size, noisy, and high dimensional dataset of two parallelized, industrial freeze-dryers within the same drug product filling line. Two multivariate methods, namely multiway principal component analysis (PCA) and a sparse formulation thereof (SparsePCA), are compared. It is demonstrated that including multivariate methods in leak test evaluation can reduce false alarms while maintaining leak detection reliability in comparison to currently employed empirical approaches.

2. Methods

2.1. Data Preparation

Data preparation was carried out according to Figure 1. Almost two years of process data were available. First, the sensor measurements were extracted from a data historian, and appropriate sensors were selected based on discussions with process experts and by analyzing the measuring frequency of each sensor. Based on the nature of the data compression algorithm used to store process sensor measurements, sensors with an average of less than one data point per ten minutes during leak testing were considered irrelevant and discarded, resulting in $J = 28$ variables. To obtain variable profiles over time for each batch (interchangeably used with leak test), sensor measurements were interpolated every full minute to obtain $K = 225$ time points. For freeze-dryer 1 (FD 1), $I_1 = 57$ batches were extracted and $I_2 = 48$ for freeze-dryer 2 (FD 2), giving a total of $I = 105$ batches. In the second step, the three-dimensional array $\underline{X}$ was batch-wise unfolded to obtain the data matrix X. Prior to transforming the data by PCA and SparsePCA, X was centered by the mean and scaled by the standard deviation.

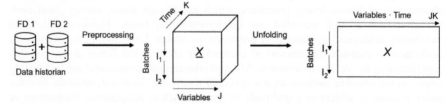

Figure 1: Data preparation workflow was conducted in two main steps. First, process data was extracted from a data historian and preprocessed into an array $\underline{X}$ of size I×J×K, where I = I$_1$ + I$_2$. Then, the array is batch-wise unfolded into a matrix X of size I×JK (or 105×6'300).

2.2. Leak Test Classification

Real leaks were identified based on maintenance records, while virtual leaks were identified as runs that featured failed tests with non-linear pressure profiles that were passed upon simple repetition. In total, six classes of leak tests were defined: FD 1, year 1; FD 1, year 2; FD2, year 1; FD 2, year 2; Virtual leaks; Real leaks.

2.3. PCA and SparsePCA

PCA decomposes a data matrix $X \in \mathbb{R}^{I \times JK}$ into C principal components with score matrix $T \in \mathbb{R}^{I \times C}$ with score vectors $[\ t_1\ \ t_2\ \ ...\ \ t_C\ ]$, a loading matrix $P \in \mathbb{R}^{JK \times C}$ and a residual error $E \in \mathbb{R}^{I \times JK}$:

$$X = TP^T + E. \tag{1}$$

The decomposition can be formulated as an optimization problem according to

$$(\hat{T}, \hat{P}) = \underset{(T,P)}{\text{argmin}}\ \|X - TP^T\|_F^2, \tag{2}$$

where $P^T P = I$ and F refers to the Frobenius norm. The problem can be easily solved by singular value decomposition. For SparsePCA, many formulations are available. The one used in this work is formulated as an optimization problem using the Scikit-learn implementation in Python (Pedregosa et al., 2011) with an l_1 penalty on the components,

$$(\hat{T}, \hat{P}) = \underset{(T,P)}{\text{argmin}}\ \frac{1}{2}\|X - TP^T\|_F^2 + \alpha\|P^T\|_{1,1}, \tag{3}$$

where the sparsity coefficient α equals 0.1 in this work. SparsePCA has been known and previously applied for process monitoring (Luo et al., 2017) and in other fields, e.g., image analysis (Sjöstrand et al., 2007).

From P with elements $p_{c,j,k}$, a sum of loadings value for each variable j for each component c is defined as

$$p_{c,j}^* = \sum_{k=1}^{K} p_{c,j,k}, \tag{4}$$

to simplify extracting dominating variable contributions for each component.

2.4. Silhouette Score

To quantify and compare the ability of PCA and SparsePCA to cluster batches according to freeze-dryer and other factors, the average silhouette score (Rousseeuw, 1987),

$$S = \frac{1}{I}\sum_{i=1}^{I} \frac{b_i - a_i}{\max\{a_i, b_i\}}, \tag{5}$$

is used, where a_i is the mean intra-class distance of sample i and b_i is the mean nearest-class distance of sample i. S ranges from 1 to -1, where 1 is the best value, meaning good clustering, and -1 the worst value.

3. Results and Discussion

3.1. Leak Test Variability

In Figure 2, the first six component scores are shown for PCA and SparsePCA. When the results were compared with each other, two distinct differences were observed:

1. t_1 vs. t_2: The leak tests form four distinct clusters according to FD and year. SparsePCA results in a silhouette score of $S = 0.86$. Ordinary PCA does not achieve such clear separation, with a lower silhouette score of $S = 0.59$.

2. t_5 vs. t_6: SparsePCA separates the failed leak tests due to a real leak from all other leak tests on a single score vector t_5 with $S = 0.89$. Using ordinary PCA, the best separation of the tests during a real leak and all other leak test was found using both t_5 and t_6, where $S = 0.60$. This combination gives a better separation of the real leaks than t_3 and t_4.

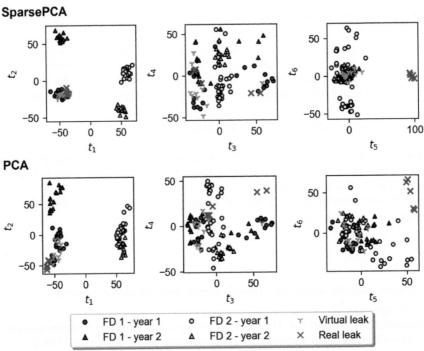

Figure 2: The first six principal components are shown in score plots for SparsePCA and PCA. The leak testing batches are labeled according to freeze-dryer (FD) and year. Failed batches due to virtual or real leaks are labeled individually.

The score plots showed that the SparsePCA results are much more useful for identifying and analyzing variability between leak tests than results from ordinary PCA. Interpretation was simplified due to clustering of the leak tests with higher silhouette scores. The first component scores t_1 divided the leak tests according to machine-to-machine variability. The second component scores t_2 captured year-to-year variability, caused by, e.g., year-end equipment maintenance and sensor recalibration. The fifth component score t_5 separated tests during a real leak, which allowed for determining leak location by investigating the sum of loadings plot in Figure 3. The plot points out five dominating variables of mainly two groups. Variables 10, 11 and 17 represent cooling rod measurements. Variables 23 and 24 are the pressure measurements of two identical capacitance manometers. Closer inspection of the loading plots of variable 24 ($p_{5,24,k}$) revealed that the pressure increase over batch time k was, as expected, higher for the batches during a real leak, as more external air entered the freeze-dryer. Variable 17 is the opening percentage of the control valve for cooling by liquid nitrogen of one of the cooling rods in the condenser. The loading plot over batch time k ($p_{5,17,k}$) shows that the valve opening was higher during leak testing in case of a real leak. Maintenance reports indeed confirmed that a leak was found in the condenser.

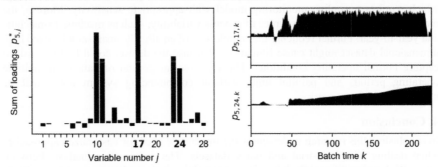

Figure 3: The sum of loadings for each variable for component 5 is shown on the left. On the right, individual loadings of component 5 are shown for variables number 17 (top) and 24 (bottom).

The simplified interpretability of SparsePCA can be explained by the fact that sparsity constraints on loading coefficients are enforced, such that small coefficients are forced to zero. This effect reduces noise introduced by a large number of variables in the dataset with relatively few batches used here. It has been shown that the consistency of PCA, or in simpler terms, the sensitivity to outliers and noise, is improved by including sparsity constraints in a high dimensional and low sample size context (Zou and Xue, 2018).

3.2. Leak Detection

The results above show that in FD 1 in year 1 many leak tests failed due to real and virtual leaks, while FD 2 operated smoothly. The leak rate threshold for the leak test to pass was increased from year 1 to year 2 to the upper limit recommended by Sahni et al. (2022). This led to no false alarms in year 2 for FD 1.

(a) LR_{max} actual			(b) LR_{max} new			(c) SparsePCA		
Total = 41	**Leak Test Result**			**Leak Test Result**			**Leak Test Result**	
	Fail	**Pass**		**Fail**	**Pass**		**Fail**	**Pass**
Leak	TP = 5	FN = 0		TP = 4	FN = 1		TP = 5	FN = 0
No Leak	FP = 11	TN = 25		FP = 2	TN = 34		FP = 2	TN = 34

Figure 4: Confusion matrices are shown for leak tests of FD 1 during year 1 for (a) the actual maximum leak rate LR_{max}, (b) for the upper recommended limit and (c) based on SparsePCA.

However, if the recommended limit were retrospectively applied to leak tests in FD1 during year 1, the false alarms (FP) would have decreased, but one undetected leak would have occurred (FN) (Figure 4(b) compared to 4(a)). Hence, an apparent trade-off between reducing downtimes caused by false alarms and leak detection reliability exists if leak testing is solely based on leak rate thresholds. Here, multivariate statistical process control could offer an additional decision metric for improved pass/fail decisions. The multivariate methods used above were able to distinguish between real and virtual faults. The confusion matrix in Figure 4(c) shows that by applying those results retrospectively, all tests during a real leak are detected (TP) without increasing the false alarm rate (FP). Of course, production operators need to be informed about potential leaks immediately, which requires an online monitoring model with appropriate sensitivity. Moreso, the model should consider other sources of process variability, such as machine-to-machine and year-to-year. Further reducing the sample size of an already small sample-sized high dimensional dataset might cause limitations, because the dataset could be too small to capture normal operating conditions. The effective integration of data from multiple operating periods and parallel units without compounding system noise will be investigated in future work.

4. Conclusion

In conclusion, this research underscores the imperative need for customized approaches when dealing with industrial and noisy datasets. The comparative analysis between SparsePCA and traditional PCA has demonstrated the distinct advantages of SparsePCA, particularly in scenarios characterized by low sample size and high dimensionality. This finding underscores the importance of adapting analytical techniques to the specific challenges posed by datasets common in industrial settings. Finally, the incorporation of multivariate statistics into leak testing has been identified to enhance reliability while managing false alarm rates effectively.

References

E. Sahni, B. Van Meervenne, S. Schneid, M. Dekner, S. Bedi, X. Tang, D. A. Hamilton, O. McGarvey, M. Frei, N. Zinfollino, E. V. Velez, M. Gosmer, D. Hill, 2022, Lyophilizer Leak Rate Testing – An Industry Survey and Best Practice Recommendation, Journal of Pharmaceutical Sciences, 111, 2714-2718.

G. Calzavara, L. Consolini, G. Ferrari, 2021, Leak Detection and Classification in Pharmaceutical Freeze-Dryers: an Identification-Based Approach, 2021 60th IEEE Conference on Decision and Control (CDC), 1568-1573.

S. Yin, S. X. Ding, X. Xie, H. Luo, 2014, A Review on Basic Data-Driven Approaches for Industrial Process Monitoring, IEEE Transaction on Industrial Electronics, 61, 6418-6428.

C. Ji, W. Sun, 2022, A Review on Data-Driven Process Monitoring Methods: Characterization and Mining of Industrial Data, Processes, 10, 335.

P. Zürcher, S. Badr, S. Knüppel, H. Sugiyama, 2022, Data-driven equipment condition monitoring and reliability assessment for sterile product manufacturing: Method and application for an operating facility, Chemical Engineering Research and Design, 188, 301-314.

F. Pedregosa et al., 2011, Scikit-learn: Machine learning in Python, Journal of Machine Learning Research, 12, 2825-2830.

P. J. Rousseeuw, 1987, Silhouettes: A graphical aid to the interpretation and validation of cluster analysis, Journal of Computational and Applied Mathematics, 20, 53-65.

L. Luo, S. Bao, J. Mao, D. Tang, 2017, Fault Detection and Diagnosis Based on Sparse PCA and Two-Level Contribution Plots, Industrial and Engineering Chemistry Research, 56, 225-240.

K. Sjöstrand, E. Rostrup, C. Rydberg, R. Larsen, C. Studholme, H. Baezner, J. Ferro, F. Fazekas, L. Pantoni, D. Inzitari, G. Waldemar, 2007, Sparse decomposition and modeling of anatomical shape variation, IEEE Transactions on Medical Imaging, 26, 1625-1635.

H. Zou, L. Xue, 2018, A Selective Overview of Sparse Principal Component Analysis, Proceedings of the IEEE, 106, 1311-1320.

Flavio Manenti, Gintaras V. Reklaitis (Eds.), Proceedings of the 34th European Symposium on Computer Aided Process Engineering / 15th International Symposium on Process Systems Engineering (ESCAPE34/PSE24), June 2-6, 2024, Florence, Italy

Machine Learning enabled Life Cycle Assessment for Early-stage Sustainable Process Design

Kirti M. Yenkie[a]*, Emmanuel A. Aboagye[a], Austin L. Lehr[a], John Pazik[a], Jared Longo[a], and Robert P. Hesketh[a]

[a]*Department of Chemical Engineering, Rowan University, 201 Mullica Hill Road, Glassboro, New Jersey - 08028, USA*
*yenkie@rowan.edu

Abstract

Holistic assessment during early-stage process design is important for developing environmentally sustainable processes. Life cycle assessment (LCA) is a systematic analysis of potential environmental impacts of raw materials, products, or services during their entire life cycle. LCA requires life cycle inventory (LCI) data for all chemicals and technologies involved within a process, which is not readily available for new alternative chemicals, solvents, and technologies. To this end, this paper presents an innovative method involving machine learning (ML) approaches whereby LCIs can be readily predicted with minimal data collected from the exploratory phase of process design. This dataset consists of physicochemical, and structural properties of known chemicals as well as their LCI labels from databases such as the Ecoinvent. ML regression algorithms such as Artificial Neural Networks (ANN) are used to develop models/correlations for LCI label predictions based on the chemical and structural properties. To illustrate the applicability of these LCI prediction models, a case study on valorization of red wine pomace (acetone basis) through solvent extraction is presented consisting of the complete cradle-to-cradle LCA. The LCIs from ML provide the cradle-to-gate numbers, the red wine pomace valorization process simulation provides the materials and energy consumption in the gate-to-gate phase, and the gate-to-cradle phase is incorporated via the solvent recovery through distillation.

Keywords: Environmental Impacts, Life Cycle Inventories, cradle-to-cradle LCA

1. Introduction

The global chemical market is projected to double between 2017 to 2030, which brings associated concerns for the environment as the chemical waste and releases are bound to increase at an equal or higher rate (US EPA, 2013). A common way to quantify the amount of waste produced is an E-factor (Sheldon 2007), as given by Equation 1. The E-factor values can range between 0.01-100 depending on the type of industry and its products. The pharmaceutical industry is one of the highest waste contributors with E-factor in the range of 25-100.

$$\text{E-factor} = \frac{Total\ mass\ waste\ produced}{Total\ mass\ product\ produced} \tag{1}$$

Furthermore, the growing chemical market is an indication of the development of novel chemicals and processes. New chemicals often lack data needed to accurately quantify their potential environmental impacts, requiring experimentation or computationally intensive simulations to acquire them. These expensive and time-consuming methods can discourage many small-scale production facilities from being able to consider greener or safer alternatives.

Life cycle analysis (LCA) is a systematic analysis of potential environmental impacts of raw materials, products, or services during their entire life cycle (Karka et al., 2019). In previous studies (Narciso and Martins 2020), Machine Learning (ML) has demonstrated its utility in improving energy efficiency and predicting carbon footprints of corporations. On similar lines, this work employs ML for predicting reasonably accurate Life Cycle Inventory (LCI) values for chemicals, especially, for new molecules and process technologies. This innovative method can subsequently lead to safer, more sustainable alternative chemicals and circular process design. Predicting LCI metrics for environmental indicators at the preliminary stages of design can be crucial for advancing greener and sustainable processes. Moreover, ML would allow for this LCI data to be acquired with limited time and computational resources as compared to experimental investigations and high-end molecular scale computations.

2. Methodology: Developing ML Algorithms for LCI Predictions

This section discusses the data collection and preprocessing techniques used in this work. This is followed by the two ML algorithms - Artificial Neural Networks (ANN) and eXtreme Gradient Boosting (XGBoost *not discussed in this paper*), ending with a discussion about the steps involved in the tuning of the hyperparameters for each model. Figure 1 presents the overall workflow, which is organized into two general steps of data preprocessing and model building.

2.1. Data Collection

Developing a fast and reliable method for acquiring the necessary data is integral for ML model development as a

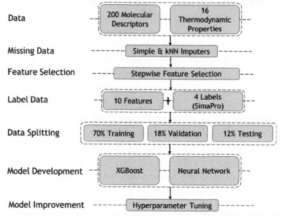

Figure 1. Overview of ML Model workflow

large amount of data is needed to train and test the model. Models trained with larger data sets make better predictions. The model uses an automated data collection process which is divided into two main parts: (i) input feature dataset and (ii) output label dataset. Feature dataset is independent input set from which a prediction is made. Label dataset is what the ML model is trying to predict. In this work, the feature set is comprised of both thermodynamic and molecular descriptor properties of the chemicals, while the label dataset consists of four endpoint impact assessment metrics: human health (HHI), ecosystem quality (EQI), climate change (CCI), and resource utilization (RUI) impacts.

The CAS database comprises of many organic molecules because of their prevalence in chemical industry, thus, they were used in the training set. In total, 16 thermodynamic properties and 200 molecular descriptors were collected, as well as each chemical name, formula, CAS number, and SMILES structure. Priority was placed on properties that directly affected the energy costs of certain processes, such as heat of vaporization, enthalpies of formation, and boiling points. The three main python libraries used in feature extraction of the thermodynamic properties were the "chemicals", "thermo", and "pubchempy" packages. Each package connects to databases such as PubChem, National Institute of Standards and Technology (NIST), and other reputable and publicly available databases. To collect the molecular descriptors for our training set, the python package "rdkit" was used. RDKit is an open-source toolkit developed primarily for cheminformatics. Its core algorithms are in C++ but there are python wrappers that can be used to access the molecular descriptors, provided their SMILEs code is known. A total of 216 features were collected for 502 organic chemicals. The next step was to collect the corresponding LCI metrics for all the 502 chemicals. Multiple methods were used such as the Ecoinvent database and IMPACT 2002+ method to collect the label data - HHI, EQI, CCI, and RUI metrics. Table 1 presents few examples of the type of data extracted for this work.

Table 1. Example of data collected for few chemicals.

Chemical Name	Chemical Formula	CAS #	SMILES	Heat of vaporization (kJ/kg)	Heat Capacity (kJ/kgK)	Number of Hetero-atoms	Climate Change (kgCO$_2$eq)
1-Bromopro-pane	C$_3$H$_7$Br	106-94-5	CCCBr	32200	1.09	1	4.677
1-chloro-1,1-difluoro-ethane	C$_2$H$_3$ClF$_2$	75-68-3	CC(F)(F)Cl	20400	1.31	3	3.979
1,1,1-trichloro-ethane	C$_2$H$_3$Cl$_3$	71-55-6	CC(Cl)(Cl)Cl	29900	1.08	3	2.085
1,1,2,2-tetrachloro-ethane	C$_2$H$_2$Cl$_4$	79-34-5	ClC(Cl)C(Cl)Cl	44400	0.99	4	2.894

2.2. Data Clustering

Once the data was obtained, further work was done to make it optimal for the final ML model. Much of the data was missing and needed to be filled in since the ML model cannot use null values. A K-means clustering algorithm was determined to be the best way to fill in the missing data, and the following flowchart describes the general process for creating a new dataset without any missing values.

In the dataset, rows represent chemicals and columns represent the various thermodynamic properties and molecular descriptors. Columns with missing data were temporarily removed to create a smaller dataset containing all the chemicals and a subset of the properties (with no missing data). This subset was then fed into the algorithm to create different groupings of chemicals that the algorithm determined were

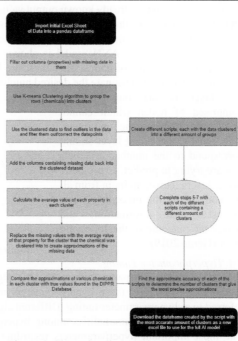

Figure 2 Clustering for missing data prediction

similar. Once clustered, some chemicals appeared as outliers. These chemicals were manually reviewed for error in the data scraping process. The algorithm was then rerun with the new fixed dataset.

After looking at the graph of the accuracy of the clusters compared to the number, the elbow method was used to determine that the optimal number of clusters. Nearly identical scripts were then made for each of the different clustered datasets. For example, when looking at the script where the chemicals were clustered into four groups, the algorithm sorted each of the five hundred chemicals into one of four groups based on the properties. Within each separate dataset, the average for each column is then taken and replaces the missing data in that column. Every column in every separate data set undergoes this process, removing all empty data by replacing it with the column average in that cluster. Once this is complete, the separate datasets then recombine to create a new dataset with no missing values. The average values act as estimates for the missing data. To check the clustered values' accuracy, the estimated density for fifteen different chemicals were chosen and compared to the known density values found in the DIPPR database. Density was chosen because it about half of the chemicals needed it to be estimated and the known densities are readily available in DIPRR to cross compare for accuracy.

2.3. Developing the ML Algorithm - ANN

When training a ML model, the data is split into a testing and training set, and optionally a cross validation set. The training data is used to fit the model; this data is put into the program to create and adjust the variables used in the model to generate predictions. The cross-validation set is then used for the program to compare the model fitted with the training data set. The program then runs the model with the cross validation set and adjusts the weights according to how accurate the predicted outputs are to improve the model. Finally, the testing set is used to run the model and compare the predicted outputs of the testing set to the already known output values to find the accuracy of the ML model. Out of the two models, the ANN model for ML is described in detail. It can be used for a wide variety of applications and is easily accessible for all Python users.

The architecture for an ANN model is shown in Figure 3. There is one input layer comprised of a number of nodes. Then there are hidden layers containing several nodes, of which the user can designate the desired number of layers and nodes in each layer. The last layer is the output layer, comprised of nodes which cannot exceed the number in the input layer. Additionally, the output layer should correspond to the number of labels you are trying to predict. Every node in one layer receives an input from all the nodes from the preceding layer, processes that information, and passes the outcome to the following layer (Géron 2019).

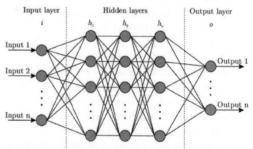

Figure 3 Basic layout of neural network

2.4. Hyperparameter Tuning

Using the default hyperparameters in the ANN algorithm often does not produce the best predictions. Therefore, these hyperparameters must be adjusted to this specific case, referred to as hyperparameter tuning. Different algorithms use different hyperparameters, but there are some commonalities among hyperparameters across multiple algorithms. The most important hyperparameters regarding ANN models are the hidden layers, number of nodes, and step size. Hidden layers are shown in Figure 3 and act as the overall complexity and size of the model. The number of nodes in each hidden layer displays the size and complexity of each layer, and the rate that the model changes is the step size. These hyperparameters help improve the accuracy of the model and help prevent overfitting and underfitting.

3. Results and Discussion

Over 200 features were included in the data set, collected using the code described previously. The main benefits of narrowing down the number of features used in the model are to simplify the input data needed and to minimize the amount of data users would need to input to use the model for finding the LCI of their chemicals. Two feature selection tools were examined from the *sklearn* package: *SequentialFeatureSelector* and *SelectFromModel*. All statistics and accuracy numbers included in this results section use the *SequentialFeatureSelecto*r. Sklearn's *StandardScaler* was used to scale the data, and the data was split into training, cross validation, and testing sets. The percentages for the split can vary, but the numbers included in this section use a 70/18/12 split, respectively.

3.1. Results from the ANN ML Model

In ANN, a model was fitted using the training data and cross validation set. The hyperparameters tuned were learning rate, units, batch size, epochs, activation function, and number of layers. The loss function used was mean squared error. The LCI value of 4 labels were analyzed and shown in Figure 4, which also shows the root mean squared

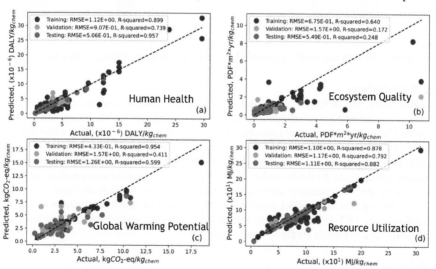

Figure 4 Results from the ANN ML model for the 4 LCI labels

error and R^2 values.

3.3. Results from Case Study: Wine Pomace Valorization

The LCI data from the ML predictions can be used in conjunction with data from case studies in order to conduct a holistic LCA analysis. There are three major life phases within a chemical's lifespan: the production phase, the use phase, and the end-of-life phase. While both the use phase and the end-of-life phase can be modeled using simulation tools such as ASPEN/SuperPro, the LCI for the production phase cannot be easily modeled using traditional methods. As a result, the ML algorithm predicts the cradle-to-gate LCI data, which represents the production phase. By employing a case study, it is possible to incorporate all a chemical's life phases to produce a complete picture of the impact it has throughout its entire lifetime. Selected case study (Vega et al. 2021) describes a process involving recovery of polyphenols from wine pomace. This process involved grinding of wine pomace followed by extraction of polyphenols using a solvent comprised of 67%wt acetone. Following the extraction, spent pomace was pressed and desolventized, with the vapors then entering a condenser. Meanwhile, the liquid stream from the presser entered a distillation column, where acetone was separated from polyphenols dissolved in water and recycled. The water-polyphenol mixture from the distillation column then entered both a nano filter and a spray dryer, with dry polyphenols serving as the final product. It is estimated that 2% of acetone is lost in each cycle, requiring make-up. The overall cradle-to-cradle results are shown in Figure 5.

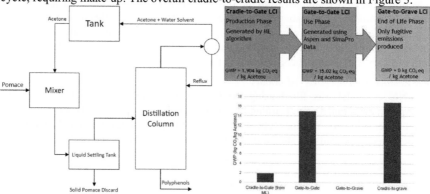

Figure 5 Results for cradle-to-cradle LCA for wine pomace valorization case study

4. Conclusions

In this study, the ANN-ML algorithm, was used to create a program that predicts the environmental impacts of chemicals in the areas of human health, ecosystem quality, global warming potential, and resource utilization with the goal of creating a tool that can be used to predict the effects of novel chemicals and processes. The methodology for data collection, preprocessing, model development and hyperparameter tuning are discussed. Sample results from the ANN model for 4 LCI labels are presented along with a validation case study for wine pomace valorization using acetone as the solvent-basis. This case study showed that ML model predictions can be used to substitute unknown data for cradle-to-gate LCI. Hence, ML was able to fill in the gaps and predict LCI information, allowing for a complete cradle-to-cradle analysis.

References

A. Sheldon, 2007. "The E Factor: Fifteen Years On." *Green Chemistry* 9 (12): 1273–83.
Croxatto Vega, Giovanna, Joshua Sohn, Juliën Voogt, Morten Birkved, Stig Irving Olsen, and Anna Ekman Nilsson. 2021. Combining Techno-Economic and Life Cycle Assessment – a Case Study of Red Wine Pomace. *Resources, Conservation and Recycling* 167 (April): 105318.
Géron, Aurélien. 2019. *Hands-On Machine Learning with Scikit-Learn, Keras, and TensorFlow:* 2nd edition. Beijing China ; Sebastopol, CA: O'Reilly Media.
Karka, Paraskevi, Stavros Papadokonstantakis, and Antonis Kokossis. 2019. Predictive LCA - a Systems Approach to Integrate LCA Decisions Ahead of Design." *Computer Aided Chemical Engineering*, 46:97–102. 29 European Symposium on Computer Aided Process Engineering.
Narciso, Diogo A.C., and F.G. Martins. 2020. Application of Machine Learning Tools for Energy Efficiency in Industry: A Review. *Energy Reports* 6 (November): 1181–99.

Flavio Manenti, Gintaras V. Reklaitis (Eds.), Proceedings of the 34th European Symposium on Computer Aided Process Engineering / 15th International Symposium on Process Systems Engineering (ESCAPE34/PSE24), June 2-6, 2024, Florence, Italy

Personalized Supply Chain Solutions for Sustainable Fashion: Leveraging Social Media Insights and Machine Learning

Sarah Hassaan,[a] Sumaya A. Rahman,[a] Roberto Baldacci,[a] Brenno C. Menezes[a*]

[a]*Division of Engineering Management and Decision Sciences, College of Science and Engineering Hamad Bin Khalifa University, Qatar*
bmenezes@hbku.edu.qa

Abstract

The fast fashion industry's rapid growth in clothing consumption since the 1990s has caused a significant global waste problem. Despite producing 80 billion new garments annually, only 1% is recycled, and 73% ends up in landfills. Before the arrival of fast fashion, the fashion industry typically operated on a two-season model. The shift to a 52-season model disrupted traditional cycles causing an imbalance in sustainable product development which is further increased by the nonconverging consumer needs and the clothing manufacturing. To create uniform symmetry between fashion suppliers and retailers, we must enhance information exchange between retailers and consumers to implement sustainable practices and boost business performance effectively. To achieve this, we propose a framework that analyzes consumer interactions on social media platforms like Instagram and TikTok, which are renowned pioneers of trends. Through this analysis, our framework employs real-time sentiment analysis techniques to identify positive emotional responses with user comments and likes and data image processing methodologies to extract garment types from media content. Subsequently, machine learning algorithms can be employed to select the most matching clothing items available on online markets based on user geographic location to offer consumers personalized recommendations based on their social media activity. Through our application, the data can be aggregated and transmitted to manufacturers who can utilize the advanced image, color, and style analysis techniques to dynamically adjust production and inventory with real-time decision-making techniques, enabling a more precise comprehension and prediction of market trends and reducing waste. This systematic analysis may create deep insights into consumer preferences, feedback, and engagement patterns, facilitating highly tailored product offerings and elevating the overall standard of customer satisfaction.

Keywords: fashion, supply chain, sustainability, artificial intelligence, optimization.

1. Introduction

The fast fashion industry, commanding a substantial global market share, has witnessed exponential growth since the latter half of the 20th century. Its strength lies in promptly meeting consumer demands and producing affordable clothing mirroring the latest fashion trends. These practices enable a continual flow of clothing from production to the consumer's wardrobe, closely following rapidly changing market trends. Although such industries created a booming effect on the development of supply chains, their manufacturing strategies led to a significant build-up of surplus inventory. The industry's extensive reliance on mass production of vast quantities of synthetic and petroleum-based garments in developing countries has resulted in significant textile waste. It forces manufacturers to employ various methods to offload excess garments through secondary distribution channels, deep discount rates to consumers, or disposed of in landfills.

Without a change in current practices in manufacturing and supply chains of any kind of product, emissions will surge by 2.7 billion metric tons by 2030, breaching the IPCC's 1.5°C limit for global temperatures (Wren, 2022). A survey by the Boston Consulting Group underscores the pressing need for action, projecting a potential 62% increase in global textile waste to 148 million tons by 2030 (Ponnambalam et al., 2023). Also, the rapid change in trends causes a mismatch between consumer demand and manufacturer production, which leads to the overproduction of fashionable garments. Most fast fashion industries face an alarming excess inventory, with 80% eventually finding its way to landfills (Goel and Michaelides, 2022).

With the focus on collecting real-time data from the user's social media, retailers and manufacturers alike can benefit from more accurate forecasting to meet the high turnover rates of fast fashion, limiting the need for overproduction. In turn, this limits the environmental impact of the high volume of textile waste turnover generated by the rapidly changing fashion cycles. Furthermore, the user of the application will also benefit from a personalized fashion recommendation. The proposed framework can finally result in an application with a target focus on three stakeholders: consumers, retailers, and the designers/manufacturers, to bridge the gap between production and consumption.

2. Literature review

A fundamental shift toward sustainability and zero-waste practices in the fashion sector is crucial to address these issues. Given the challenges in achieving efficient and on-demand production, extensive research has been conducted to harness the potential of artificial intelligence (AI) and machine learning (ML) technologies to provide comprehensive solutions essential for enhancing sustainability within the sector and engaging all stakeholders in the value chain. By doing so, the fast fashion industry can continue to cater to consumer demands while significantly minimizing its environmental impact.

For example, Wang et al. (2022) and Yang (2022) present an interactive, personalized garment design recommendation system that uses intelligent techniques. Their research offers personalized recommendations, efficient decision-making, and dynamic suggestions to improve user satisfaction by supporting fashion designers as they rapidly generate optimal design solutions. However, the research is limited to the proposed system's market growth and the integration of their proposed model with the existing fashion workflows. Furthermore, no transparency is presented between the manufacturers, retailers, and end-users.

In addition, Papachristou et al. (2021) and Kotouza et al. (2021) focus on utilizing machine learning techniques to enhance the clothing manufacturing process to respond more effectively to brand demands. Their system includes components for data retrieval, user interface, and personalized garment design recommendations for fashion designers, and it primarily extracts meaningful attributes from images and textual data from various sources. Their research can be enhanced by incorporating the extraction of data from videos considering the popularity of short-form videos on social media platforms. These videos often showcase the latest trends, customized trends as well as reviving old trends which can provide insights into user preferences through comments, likes, and dislikes. Another gap in these authors, like the research of Wang et al. (2022) and Yang (2022), is that the primary focus is on the fashion design of the garments, neglecting the supply chain transparency between the retailers and users, leaving the potential of creating a user-centric recommendation which our research aims to address.

Furthermore, Santos et al. (2021) take a more novel approach and propose a digital twin-based system to support operational planning in fast fashion companies. While their work enhances decision-making and resource allocation, it primarily addresses the operational side of the chain. It lacks upstream analysis of consumer trends, preferences, and market behavior. Finally, Wang et al. (2023) create a personalized garment design based on the current market, but access is only limited to the fashion designers. There is also a lack of exploration on the sustainability issues the current supply chains are facing and the mismatch between production and demand leading to overproduction, leaving a gap in the research for the potential comprehensive role of AI to achieve sustainability in the industry.

Even though these studies have made a valuable contribution to the application of AI in fast fashion and supply chains, there are still significant gaps in addressing the challenges of transparency and forecasting. The integration of video data, user-centric recommendations, supply chain personalization, and upstream consumer insights have yet to be incorporated into future research. Bridging these gaps and offering holistic solutions may revolutionize the fast fashion and supply chain landscape. Our proposed framework can inform manufacturers or designers of purchased garments and ensure stores are aligned with their inventory. This can potentially help in the reduction of overproduction and provide valuable insights for fashion designers to understand demand trends, highlighting a crucial gap in exploring further potentials of AI within the fast fashion industry and related logistics and supply chain management.

3. Proposed Framework

To achieve our proposed framework, we suggest the application flow shown in Figure 1. The application represents the artificial intelligence and data analysis occurring, the user represents the consumers using the app, the social media represents the social media platforms that provide video and image content, the retailer represents stores or distributors selling the ready-made garments, and the manufacturer and designers representing those that are creating the garments.

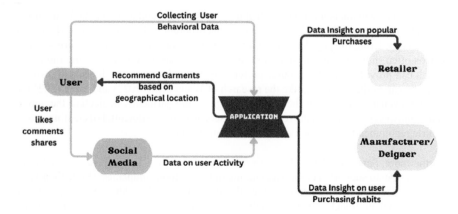

Figure 1: Application flow.

Firstly, the application will be active in the background of the user's cell phone collecting data on their typical spending habits, previous fashion purchases, geographical location etc. These attributes can help in developing the model using content-based or collaborative filtering to update as the user's style or fashion sense develops over time. It can also help with the personalized garment recommendation that the application provides to the user. As the user starts to utilize their social media account, the application can record the positive comments, likes and shares made by the user.

Figure 2 shows the interface view of the consumer, retailer, and manufacturer on the application.

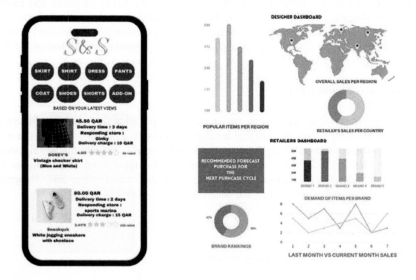

Figure 2: Interfaces shown to the user (left), designers (top right) and retailers (bottom right).

Once the information is collected, data image processing techniques can be applied to the content identifying if any fashion style can be salvaged within a given threshold. Only once the content is above the threshold, we can apply further data image processing methods such as image segmentation to extract the clothing items with other attributes such as color, style, and cut. We can further employ Search Engine Optimization (SEO) to categorize each extracted item. Once this is completed, machine learning algorithms, specifically clustering and regression, can recommend the closest garments (based on fit and geographical location) to the liked content to the user. Only once the user purchases the item does the application record the data for the retailers and designers to use for future forecasting. This can increase the likelihood of the user purchasing due to lesser lead times and refine the variety of options available in the market to achieve an almost or an exact match to the user's choice. In addition, it can also give valuable insight into the ranking of fashion outfits in each state, country, or region.

The proposed framework can result in an application focusing on three stakeholders:

Consumer: Through tracking the consumers' behavior on social media content (their likes, comments, and shares), we can utilize advanced multimedia analysis techniques by utilizing neural networks, like Convolutional Neural Networks (CNNs) for image analysis or Recurrent Neural Networks (RNNs) for sequential data (such as analyzing user interactions over time). This can help to understand complex patterns and relationships within multimedia content to gain insights on everyone's fashion preference, creating a personalized recommendation of garments for each user.

Retailer: Data derived from consumer through pattern recognition and trend analysis can assist retailers in identifying top-selling brands and styles, enabling accurate market predictions, and limiting unsold inventory. Monthly sales comparisons can also aid in informed decision-making for product launches, marketing strategies, and inventory management, reducing overstock issues.

Designers/Manufacturers: From both the retailer and consumer's data, designers, or manufacturers can gain real-time insights into consumer behavior. They may also have access to the sales per region/country to understand which styles and garments are preferred worldwide, curbing excessive garment production. Also, by understanding the market trends in each country, they can forecast which designs to focus on for the upcoming seasons and the expected production for each country.

4. Conclusion

The convergence of personalized supply chain strategies, artificial intelligence applications, and advanced forecasting techniques can hold immense promise for revolutionizing the dynamics of the fashion industry. By tailoring purchasing recommendations to individual preferences, we can enhance consumer engagement and purchasing likelihood, streamlining the vast array of options available. By primarily targeting the fast fashion sector, known for its dynamic and disruptive nature, this innovative concept can resonate strongly within the clothing industry. Its flexibility and inclination toward digital-driven concepts could catalyze the transformation and expansion via data-driven strategies.

Advancements in predictive modeling and deeper data mining techniques can be extremely essential to further enhance the industry's predictive capabilities. Essentially, by combining artificial intelligence with information technologies like ML, data image processing, and natural language processing (NLP), we enable a seamless connection between demand, forecasting, and production. This innovative proposed framework can not only minimize resource wastage but can also addresses critical sustainability concerns, steering the industry towards a more efficient and environmentally conscious future. By mitigating the bullwhip effect and aligning production with evolving consumer preferences, this framework can possibly minimize garment wastage, optimize inventory management for both manufacturers and retailers and grant the flexibility to explore new product offerings while significantly reducing overstock issues.

References

V. Goel, M. Michaelides, 2022, What is the Economic Impact of Fast Fashion?-Economics Research Question, International Journal of Scientific Research in Science and Technology, 9 (5), 571-581.

M. T. Kotouza, A. C. Kyprianidis, S. F. Tsarouchis, A. C. Chrysopoulos, P. A. Mitkas, 2021, Science4Fashion: an end-to-end decision support system for fashion designers. Evolving Systems, 12 (3), 605–624.

E. Papachristou, A. Chrysopoulos, N. Bilalis, 2021, Machine learning for clothing manufacture as a mean to respond quicker and better to the demands of clothing brands: a Greek case study, The International Journal of Advanced Manufacturing Technology, 115, 691–702.

S. G. Ponnambalam, B. Sankaranarayanan, K. Karuppiah, S. Thinakaran, P. Chandravelu, H. L. Lam, 2023, Analysing the Barriers Involved in Recycling the Textile Waste in India Using Fuzzy DEMATEL, Sustainability (Switzerland), 15 (11), 8864.

C. H. Santos, G. T. Gabriel, J. V. S. Amaral, J. A. B. Montevechi, J. A. Queiroz, 2021, Decision-making in a fast fashion company in the Industry 4.0 era: a Digital Twin proposal to support operational planning, The International Journal of Advanced Manufacturing Technology, 116, 1653–1666.

T. Z. T. Ting, J. A. Stagner, 2023, Fast fashion - wearing out the planet. International Journal of Environmental Studies, 80(4), 856–866.

Z. Wang, X. Tao, X. Zeng, Y. Xing, Y. Xu, Z. Xu, P. Bruniaux, J. Wang, 2022, An Interactive personalized garment design recommendation system using intelligent techniques, Applied Sciences, 12(9), 4654.

Z. Wang, X. Tao, X. Zeng, Y. Xing, Z., Xu, P. Bruniaux, 2023, A Machine Learning-enhanced 3D reverse design approach to personalized garments in pursuit of sustainability, Sustainability, 15(7), 6235.

B. Wren, 2022, Sustainable supply chain management in the fast fashion Industry: A comparative study of current efforts and best practices to address the climate crisis, Cleaner Logistics and Supply Chain, 4, 100032.

B. Yang, 2022, Clothing design style recommendation using decision tree algorithm combined with deep learning, Computational Intelligence and Neuroscience, ID 5745457, 10 pages.

Flavio Manenti, Gintaras V. Reklaitis (Eds.), Proceedings of the 34th European Symposium on Computer Aided Process Engineering / 15th International Symposium on Process Systems Engineering (ESCAPE34/PSE24), June 2-6, 2024, Florence, Italy

Integrated energy-water assessment framework for calcium deficiency control in agricultural greenhouses: A data-driven model predictive control approach

Ikhlas Ghiat, Farhat Mahmood, Rajesh Govindan, Tareq Al-Ansari*

College of Science and Engineering, Hamad Bin Khalifa University, Qatar Foundation, Doha P.O. Box 5825, Qatar
Corresponding author: talansari@hbku.edu.qa

Abstract

Widespread calcium deficiency in modern agriculture impacts plant health and crop productivity, as seen in cucumber crops with leaf yellowing, revealing broader nutritional implications. Calcium uptake, crucially linked to transpiration-driven water flow, requires thorough temperature and irrigation management. However, rapid water uptake, driven by high transpiration rates in intense sunlight conditions such as the case in hyper-arid regions, can hinder calcium absorption. In response to this challenge, this study presents an innovative approach using data-driven Model Predictive Control (MPC) to manage calcium deficiency in hyper-arid region greenhouses, integrating two MPC systems for optimal irrigation and temperature control. The irrigation control MPC relies on a comprehensive set of input variables, including microclimate data along with hyperspectral imaging data, processing the latter to calculate vegetation indices for analysing different plant characteristics. This system dynamically regulates irrigation to optimise soil moisture levels and enhance subsequent calcium uptake by plants. Concurrently, the temperature control MPC employs a set of input parameters, including solar radiation, external temperature, humidity, fan speed, and HVAC control. By considering these factors, the MPC system effectively controls temperature within the greenhouse, ensuring an optimal microclimate for calcium uptake. This integrated energy-water assessment framework offers a holistic and technologically advanced approach to calcium deficiency control. It leverages cutting-edge data-driven techniques, microclimate sensors, hyperspectral imaging, and advanced control strategies, exemplifying the use of Agriculture 4.0 and precision agriculture, to create an optimised greenhouse environment that enhances calcium uptake in plants. The findings of this study have significant implications for sustainable agriculture, including improved crop health and yields, decreased resource use, and enhanced food security.

Keywords: Greenhouse, Calcium Deficiency, Model Predictive Control, Precision Agriculture, Agriculture 4.0.

1. Introduction

The use of agricultural greenhouses has become integral for crop cultivation, particularly in regions with unfavourable weather conditions such as hyper-arid regions. Greenhouses offer controlled environments that enhance productivity. However, the inherent challenge of maintaining stable microclimate conditions within these structures often leads to suboptimal crop health (Ghiat et al., 2023a; Mahmood et al., 2020). Unpredictable fluctuations in temperature and inefficient irrigation practices contribute to this issue, creating an environment where the early detection and mitigation of crucial crop stresses and nutritional deficiencies, such as calcium, become challenging (Fahad et al., 2017). Calcium deficiency poses a substantial threat to plant health, influencing nutrient absorption and, consequently, overall crop productivity. Compounding the issue is the difficulty in early detection, as symptoms may manifest late in the growth cycle, hindering timely interventions (Olle and Bender, 2009). Several studies discussed the challenge of calcium deficiency in different plants (Barker and Sonneveld, 1988; Ho and Adams, 1994). Some studies have focused on soil amendment approaches to solve this challenge (Codling and Jaja, 2022). Others have explored advanced irrigation techniques to optimise irrigation water that can ensure a consistent supply of calcium to plants (Kirnak and Demirtas, 2006).

Various control strategies have been employed in agricultural greenhouse environments such as Proportional Integral Derivative (PID), Model Predictive Control (MPC), and fuzzy logic. While the PID method is widely used for its simplicity, it necessitates controller adjustments, resulting in delays. Additionally, it is less adept at handling system disturbances and constraints, assumes linearity in the system, and lacks predictive capabilities. In contrast, MPC can effectively address these limitations, providing a superior control (Mahmood et al., 2021).

This study addresses the challenge of calcium deficiency by proposing an innovative energy-water integrated solution, leveraging advanced data-driven MPC strategies. The goal of this study encompasses understanding fundamental greenhouse operations through the application of data-driven machine learning models capable of discerning intricate relationships among various greenhouse variables. These predictive models are leveraged to evaluate and optimise temperature and irrigation systems. The subsequent step involves integrating these models within a closed-loop MPC framework, employing multi-step tracking and a rolling optimisation to effectively manage temperature and irrigation supply. The ultimate goal is to establish a controlled environment that promotes efficient calcium uptake by the plants through the harmonised interaction of energy and water dynamics.

2. System description

This work was conducted within a closed greenhouse in the State of Qatar, characterised by a Venlo-shaped design and predominantly constructed with 4mm tempered glass, covering a net growing area of 715 m^2. This controlled environment incorporates a microclimate with CO_2 enrichment through propane fed burners inside the greenhouse. Simultaneously, temperature and humidity were regulated by a heating, ventilation, and air conditioning (HVAC) system. The cultivation system within the greenhouse employed hydroponics with coco-peat substrate, specifically for cucumbers.

This work employs a data-driven methodology, emphasising the importance of a substantial dataset in mitigating model bias and overfitting. The data were collected over three crop cycles. For the MPC for temperature control, the measured data include solar radiation, outside and inside temperatures, humidity difference, HVAC control temperature, and ventilation fan speed, with recordings taken at 5-minute intervals. In the case of the MPC for irrigation, the measured data encompasses microclimate parameters such as inside temperature, relative humidity, and CO_2 concentration, as well as solar radiation outside the greenhouse, recorded every 5 minutes. Additionally, short-term transpiration rates at the leaf level (measured every 2 s) and daily hyperspectral image-based vegetation indices were recorded for this control. The data collection involved the use of specific equipment for different types of data. Microclimate data were obtained using the Hoogendoorn aspirator box which utilises electronic sensors. Outside weather data were recorded with Hoogendoorn weather station sensors positioned outside the greenhouse. Transpiration rates were measured using a gas exchange measurement system (CIRAS-3, PP systems) based on infrared gas analysers. Hyperspectral images for vegetation indices were captured with a hyperspectral camera operating within the wavelength range of 400-1000 nm (HSC-2, SENOP).

3. Methodology

Data-driven models play a pivotal role in simplifying the process of building precise system models by reducing the complexity, cost and the overall effort involved. While few studies have utilised data-driven MPC for greenhouse environment control, the novelty of this work lies in the development of an energy-water framework that integrates data-driven MPC systems. This framework is designed to address calcium deficiency in plants by controlling greenhouse temperature and irrigation water. The aim is to establish an efficient microclimate conducive to optimal calcium uptake by the plants.

The Multi-Layer Perceptron (MLP) is a neural network architecture that operates in a feedforward manner, comprising several layers of interconnected nodes. It uses an activation function to introduce non-linearity and undergoes training through a backpropagation algorithm that iteratively adjusts weights to minimise the errors between predicted and actual outputs (Mahmood et al., 2021). In this work, an MLP model with backpropagation was developed for greenhouse temperature prediction, involving an input layer, a hidden layer with 55 nodes, and an output layer. The predictors integrated into this model encompass fan speed, HVAC control temperature, solar radiation, outside temperature, and humidity difference. The Adam optimiser and the Rectified Linear Unit (Relu) activation function are employed optimising and activating the MLP model, respectively.

The Extreme Gradient Boosting (XGBoost) model, introduced by Chen and Guestrin in 2016, is a scalable implementation of Gradient Boosting machines. This model employs an ensemble approach, combining multiple weak learners to create a robust learner through an additive training process. A key feature of XGBoost lies in its ability to minimise a regularised learning objective to mitigate model complexity and prevent overfitting (Chen and Guestrin, 2016). In this study, the XGBoost model was used to predict short-term transpiration rates. This model integrates input variables consisting of microclimate parameters specifically, greenhouse CO_2 concentration, greenhouse relative humidity, greenhouse temperature, and solar radiation. Additionally, it incorporates vegetation indices from hyperspectral images including the normalised difference index (NDVI), the photochemical reflectance index (PRI), and the water band index (WBI). In a prior study, the authors demonstrated that incorporating hyperspectral data enhances the spatial mapping of short-term transpiration prediction. This expansion from a single-point data measurement to a larger sample size significantly improves the model's capability to predict transpiration (Ghiat et al., 2023b).

The datasets for both temperature and transpiration predictions underwent a random split, allocating 20% for model testing and 80% for training. Hyperparameter optimisation was performed for each of the two machine learning models using the GridSearchCV tool, incorporating a five-fold cross-validation. The development of these models was carried out using Python 3.7.

The performance of both predictive models was assessed using two statistical indicators, including the coefficient of determination (R^2), representing the proportion of predictable variance, and the root mean square error (RMSE), measuring the average magnitude of differences between predicted and observed values. Eqs. (1) and (2) detail the calculation of these indicators.

$$R^2 = 1 - \frac{\sum_{i=1}^{n}(Y_{obs,i}-Y_{model,i})^2}{\sum_{i=1}^{n}(Y_{obs,i}-\bar{Y}_{obs,i})^2} \tag{1}$$

$$RMSE = \sqrt{\frac{\sum_{i=1}^{n}(Y_{obs,i}-Y_{model,i})^2}{n}} \tag{2}$$

Moreover, two data-driven MPC systems were implemented using the MLP model for temperature control and the XGboost model for irrigation water control. The MPC algorithm comprises a predictive model, an objective function, and an optimisation algorithm as illustrated in figure 1. The MPC incorporates an optimisation algorithm to identify optimal control values, minimising the sum of squared errors between the reference trajectory or set point (r) and the model-predicted values (ŷ). The MPC anticipates the future behavior of the plant within a specified prediction horizon (H). Equation 3 outlines the objective function, which is constrained by the temperature control conditions specified in Eq. 4 and the irrigation control conditions detailed in Eq. 5. The irrigation water is constrained by a maximum threshold corresponding to the available water for irrigation I_{max}. The temperature control is constrained by both the minimum and maximum range of operation for the fan speed and HVAC control temperature represented by u_{min} and u_{max}.

$$min\, J(k) = \sum_{i=1}^{H}||r(t+i) - \hat{y}(t+1)||^2 \tag{3}$$
$$0 \leq I(t+i) \leq I_{max} \tag{4}$$
$$u_{min} < u(t+i) < u_{max} \tag{5}$$

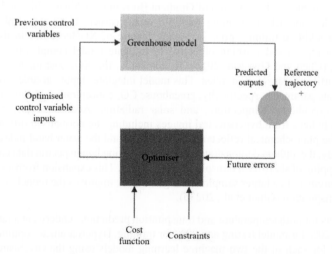

Figure 1: Model predictive control (MPC) framework.

4. Results and Discussion

The implementation of predictive models for temperature and transpiration in the greenhouse, using MLP and the XGBoost, respectively, yielded promising predictive performances. The temperature predictive model, employing MLP, demonstrated a high level of accuracy, with an R^2 of 97.8% and an RMSE of 0.340 °C. Similarly, the transpiration predictive model, utilising XGBoost, exhibited a strong performance, achieving an R^2 of 97.1% and an RMSE of 0.417 mmol/m²/s.

Fig. 2.a illustrates the performance of the developed MPC system for temperature control over a 2-day period. The MPC model, incorporating the MLP predictive model, closely aligns with the desired temperature, demonstrating its ability to adapt to dynamic conditions. Notably, during the first night when ambient temperatures outside the greenhouse dropped to 12 °C, the MPC system effectively maintained the temperature as desired by manipulating the control variables.

In Fig. 2.b, the MPC system for irrigation control is compared to the actual irrigation system in the greenhouse over a 2-day period (daytime only, as irrigation is stopped before sunset). The existing irrigation system, driven solely by solar radiation variations, lacks the precision offered by the XGBoost model. The XGBoost model, incorporating microclimate parameters, crop health indicators represented by hyperspectral image-based vegetation indices, outperforms the conventional system by considering the complex interplay between these factors. The MPC model for irrigation, designed to maintain optimal soil moisture levels (40%), successfully achieved this goal through a mass balance incorporating transpiration rate and irrigation supply. The model surpassed the existing irrigation system by efficiently managing soil moisture, resulting in lower irrigation requirements. This not only indicates improved water-use efficiency but also points to potential issues with the existing system, which tends to overestimate irrigation needs based on solar radiation variations.

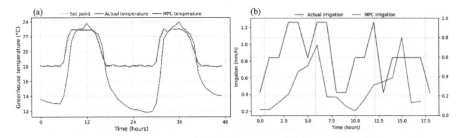

Figure 2: MPC systems for a) temperature and b) irrigation for two days.

The ability of the MPC systems to optimise temperature and irrigation while maintaining optimal soil moisture levels is critical for promoting healthy plant growth and efficient calcium uptake. The observed deficiency in calcium within plants may be attributed to the overestimation of irrigation needs along with unstable temperatures by the existing systems. By leveraging advanced predictive models and MPC, this work demonstrates the potential for enhancing greenhouse control systems and ensuring optimal crop health. The recognition of calcium deficiency's broader impact on nutrient absorption highlights the significance of employing advanced imaging techniques and machine learning methodologies. The incorporation of such technologies not only aids in forecasting optimal greenhouse temperature and water requirements but also serves as a preventive measure against calcium deficiency, contributing to more informed and sustainable approaches to crop management.

5. Conclusion

This study presents an energy-water integrated solution to solve calcium deficiency in agricultural greenhouses, particularly in hyper-arid regions. Leveraging advanced data-driven Model Predictive Control (MPC) strategies for irrigation and temperature management within closed greenhouses, the research demonstrates a holistic approach that incorporates microclimate sensing and hyperspectral imaging. The predictive models employed within the MPC systems exhibit high performances, with the temperature model achieving an R^2 of 97.8% and an RMSE of 0.340°C, while the transpiration model demonstrates a high R^2 of 97.1% and a low RMSE of 0.417 mmol/m²/s. This underscores the accuracy of the models in capturing the complex dynamics of greenhouse microclimate variables, external weather conditions and plant biophysical properties. By dynamically regulating irrigation and optimising the greenhouse microclimate, the proposed framework has the potential to successfully enhance calcium uptake by plants.

Acknowledgment

The authors acknowledge the support provided by Hamad bin Khalifa University, Education, City Doha, Qatar, a member of the Qatar Foundation. The research is funded by the Qatar National Research Fund (MME01-0922-190049).

References

Barker, J.C., Sonneveld, C., 1988. Calcium deficiency of glasshouse cucumber as affected by environmental humidity and mineral nutrition. J. Hortic. Sci. 63, 241–246. https://doi.org/10.1080/14620316.1988.11515854

Chen, T., Guestrin, C., 2016. XGBoost: A Scalable Tree Boosting System, in: Proceedings of the 22nd ACM SIGKDD International Conference on Knowledge Discovery and Data Mining. ACM, New York, NY, USA, pp. 785–794. https://doi.org/10.1145/2939672.2939785

Codling, E.E., Jaja, N., 2022. Effects of amendments on soil chemical properties, alfalfa yield and nutrient uptake. J. Plant Nutr. 45, 33–48. https://doi.org/10.1080/01904167.2021.1943678

Fahad, S., Bajwa, A.A., Nazir, U., Anjum, S.A., Farooq, A., Zohaib, A., Sadia, S., Nasim, W., Adkins, S., Saud, S., Ihsan, M.Z., Alharby, H., Wu, C., Wang, D., Huang, J., 2017. Crop Production under Drought and Heat Stress: Plant Responses and Management Options. Front. Plant Sci. 8. https://doi.org/10.3389/fpls.2017.01147

Ghiat, I., Govindan, R., Al-Ansari, T., 2023a. Evaluation of evapotranspiration models for cucumbers grown under CO2 enriched and HVAC driven greenhouses: A step towards precision irrigation in hyper-arid regions. Front. Sustain. Food Syst. 7. https://doi.org/10.3389/fsufs.2023.1155443

Ghiat, I., Govindan, R., Bermak, A., Yang, Y., Al-Ansari, T., 2023b. Hyperspectral-physiological based predictive model for transpiration in greenhouses under CO2 enrichment. Comput. Electron. Agric. 213, 108255. https://doi.org/10.1016/j.compag.2023.108255

Ho, L.C., Adams, P., 1994. The physiological basis for high fruit yield and susceptibility to calcium deficiency in tomato and cucumber. J. Hortic. Sci. 69, 367–376. https://doi.org/10.1080/14620316.1994.11516466

Kirnak, H., Demirtas, M.N., 2006. Effects of Different Irrigation Regimes and Mulches on Yield and Macronutrition Levels of Drip-Irrigated Cucumber Under Open Field Conditions. J. Plant Nutr. 29, 1675–1690. https://doi.org/10.1080/01904160600851619

Mahmood, F., Ghiat, I., Govindan, R., Al-Ansari, T., 2020. Reduced-order Modelling (ROM) Approach for Optimal Microclimate Control in Agricultural Greenhouses, Computer Aided Chemical Engineering. https://doi.org/10.1016/B978-0-12-823377-1.50314-1

Mahmood, F., Govindan, R., Bermak, A., Yang, D., Khadra, C., Al-Ansari, T., 2021. Energy utilization assessment of a semi-closed greenhouse using data-driven model predictive control. J. Clean. Prod. 324, 129172. https://doi.org/10.1016/j.jclepro.2021.129172

Olle, M., Bender, I., 2009. Causes and control of calcium deficiency disorders in vegetables: a review. J. Hortic. Sci. Biotechnol. 84, 577–584. https://doi.org/10.1080/14620316.2009.11512568

Flavio Manenti, Gintaras V. Reklaitis (Eds.), Proceedings of the 34th European Symposium on Computer Aided Process Engineering / 15th International Symposium on Process Systems Engineering (ESCAPE34/PSE24), June 2-6, 2024, Florence, Italy

Delving into machine learning modeling of catalytic reactor system: a case study of steam methane reforming

Hyeon Yang, Chanhee You, Chanmok Kim, and Jiyong Kim*

School of Chemical Engineering, Sungkyungkwan University, 16419, Republic of Korea
*Corresponding Author's E-mail: jiyongkim@skku.edu

Abstract

Navigating the complexity of reactions is one of the fundamental tasks in the field of chemical engineering. Within this domain, identifying reactions in catalytic systems is one of the challenges due to the intrinsic interplay between process variables and reaction mechanisms. In recent years, an increasing number of researchers have examined the application of machine learning in the development of prediction models for identifying reaction mechanisms. Although, their applications in reaction modeling involving kinetics have remained confined, leading to unreliable predictions and limited insights into reaction systems. To address these challenges, we propose a graph ensemble deep learning approach for multiscale modeling that predicts catalytic reaction systems with process variables (e.g., pressure, temperature, reactor size, and flow rate). Our approach includes a tree-based deep learning model to predict conversion of reaction systems governed by distinct mechanisms. To distinguish the mechanism, our model is ensembled with graphical neural networks for inferring correlation between feature and target, such as chemical distribution and reaction condition profiles. We demonstrated the approach through a case study of Ni-based steam methane reforming under varying conditions using a process simulation dataset derived from kinetic equations. The proposed model has optimized hyperparameters by nested k-fold cross-validation. The prediction result of reaction conversion and selectivity shows that our approach can estimate outcomes and effectively explore undiscovered reaction spaces. Furthermore, our preliminary findings illustrate that the proposed approach is applicable to a wide range of reactions involving complex mechanisms without requiring extended experiments for kinetic study.

Keywords: Machine learning, Deep ensemble learning, Chemical process, Steam methane reforming

1. Introduction

In the chemical industry, modeling of reaction or reactor systems is crucial for designing, scaling up, controlling, and optimizing processes. Modeling has gained significant attention over the past century because it provides a better understanding of the underlying mechanisms, thereby improving the economics and development of chemical process. (Glassey, 2018). Machine learning (ML) approaches are increasingly being utilized in chemical engineering to improve understanding of complex chemical systems. One prominent approach in the development of ML is the Cross-Industry Standard Process for Data Mining (CRISP-DM) (Shearer, 2000). CRISP-DM comprises six distinct phases (i.e., business understanding, data understanding, data preparation, modeling, evaluation, and deployment) and provides a comprehensive and systematic strategy for addressing many challenges inherent in data-driven modeling. CRISP-DM is an inherently iterative process, as insights gained during the modeling process can lead to a redefinition of objectives and approaches, as shown in Figure 1.

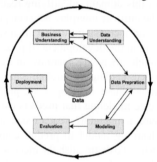

Figure 1 Cross-industry standard process for data mining (CRISP-DM) (Shearer, 2000)

In the deployment of a model, it is crucial to consider generalization, which refers to the ability of the model to accurately predict outcomes using data not previously encountered during development (Kim, 2017). Furthermore, the development of model requires consideration of the risk of overfitting. Overfitting arises when a model becomes too closely tuned to the specific noise or errors in the training dataset, leading to inferior performance on new data (Srivastava et al., 2014). Based on these concepts, developing reliable models in chemical process modeling are requires ensuring consistent performance of the model on both the utilized dataset and the unseen data.

However, while models such as the artificial neural network (ANN), XGBoost (XGB), and ExtraTreesRegressor (ETR) demonstrate high performance in various chemistry-related areas (Wu et al., 2018, Shinya et al., 2021), these studies do not sufficiently address for model capability in aspect of generalization and overfitting. Therefore, our study evaluates model not only in aspect of accuracy but also rigorously examines generalization and resistance to overfitting. By doing so, we aim to provide comprehensive insights into the development and application of ML model in the field of chemical engineering.

2. Methodology

2.1 Data preparation

In this study, we developed model to predict catalytic reaction systems with handling operating conditions (e.g., pressure, temperature, reactor size, and flow rate). Since it is difficult to collect reaction data in the chemical industry, we collected data through simulation which was performed in Aspen Plus V12.0. For case study of Ni-based steam methane reforming, the reaction is simulated with experimentally validated kinetics (Oliveira et al., 2009) and the reforming reactor is assumed as tubular reactor. We reorganized the simulated data with eight input variables and one output variable. The input variables include (1) pressure (P), (2) temperature (T), (3) H_2O ratio in the feedstock, (4) reactor diameter (D), (5) the number of tube ($NTUBE$) in reactors, (6) volumetric flow rate (Q) (7) gas hourly space velocity ($GHSV$) and (8) Linear velocity (LV) driven by Equation 1 and the output variable is CH_4 conversion (X_{CH4}).

$$LV = \frac{Q}{\pi D^2 * NTUBE} \qquad (1)$$

2.2 Data preprocessing

As shown in Equation 1, the variable of reactor size (e.g., D, $NTUBE$) and the flowrate variable of streams (Q, $GHSV$, LV) are highly correlated, and reactor size variables increase exponentially thereby making skewed distribution. To address the skewness of flowrate variables, we first performed a log transformation on the flow variables.

Also, the correlation coefficient within log-transformed flowrate variables is higher than 0.9 in Figure 2. (a), which mean highly intercorrelated features.

To consider these correlations in variables, we applied principal component analysis (PCA). PCA is a technique for dimension reduction, which linearly transform the data into new coordinates system with fewer dimensions, conserving the information about the variation in the data. PCA are used to five variables among the input variables (i.e., D, $NTUBE$, Q, $GHSV$, LV) for make three variables ($PCA1$, $PCA2$, $PCA3$) in new coordinates systems based on the explained variance as shown in Figure 2. (b). For all the cases, 80% of the simulated data were used as the training dataset to optimize the model hyperparameters, while the rest of 20% simulated data were treated as the *test* dataset for evaluation the accuracy of model prediction.

Furthermore, we prepare another *test* dataset called as an *unseen* dataset, which denotes that we regard model performance on not encountered dataset during training as the generalizability and resistance to overfitting. the similar and interpolated boundaries for each variable. An *unseen* dataset is organized similarly with training dataset and has an interpolated boundary. For example, the distribution of X_{CH4} by temperature in *unseen* data are included with in boundary of training data, as shown in Figure 2. (c).

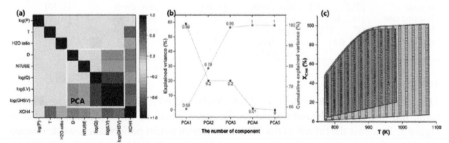

Figure 2. Configuration of dataset about (a) correlation matrix for input and output variables, (b) explained variance ratio of each PCA components, (c) distribution for CH_4 conversion of *test* (blue) and *unseen* (purple) data.

2.3 Model development

After preparing the dataset, we generated three ML models based on different algorithm.

ANN: The ANN model employs a method of correlating input and output variables by multiplying weights, adding biases, and implementing nonlinear functions, known as activation functions (Goodfellow et al., 2016). To prevent overfitting, the model incorporates a dropout method as a regularization technique, which involves randomly omitting a subset of neurons during the training process (Hinton et al., 2012). This approach reduces co-adaptation among neurons, enhancing the model's ability to generalize. The model was developed using the TensorFlow Python package (Abadi et al., 2016).

XGB: The XGB model is based on decision tree algorithms that divide the input variable space and associating specific regions with output variables. In the context of decision trees, overfitting often occurs when the model creates excessive branches in response to outliers or anomalies in the training data. To address this, the XGB model employs the built-in *max_depth* parameter which limits the depth of the trees, reduce model complexity and enhancing generalizability. Additionally, the model employs built-in normalization parameters: *reg_alpha* (L1 lasso regression) and *reg_lambda* (L2 ridge regression). These parameters introduce penalty terms into the loss function, serving to further regularize the model and prevent overfitting. The development of this model was conducted through the XGBoost Python package (Chen et al., 2016)

ETR: The ETR model, while similar to the XGB model in its foundation on decision tree algorithms, extremely randomized algorithm by selecting random subsets of features to split on at each tree node. The parameters (i.e., *max_depth*, *min_samples_leaf* and *min_samples_split*) are used for controlling the complexity of trees, contributing to its resistance to overfitting. This model was created with the ExtraTreesRegressor in scikit-learn(Pedregosa et al., 2011).

By using the nested 5-fold cross validation with Bayesian-optimization, we searched the optimal hyperparameters of each model (Raschka et al., 2018). The search space of hyperparameters is listed in Table 1.

Table 1. Search space of hyperparameters for ANN, XGB, and ETR

ANN		XGB		ETR	
n_layer	[3, 5]	n_estimators	[500, 1000]	n_estimators	[500, 1000]
n_node	$[2^5, 2^6, \ldots, 2^9]$	max_depth	[3, 10]	max_depth	[3, 10]
learning rate	$[1e^{-3}, 3e^{-2}]$	learning rate	$[1e^{-3}, 3e^{-2}]$	min_samples_leaf	[1, 10]
batch size	$[2^6, \ldots, 2^{11}]$	gamma	$[1e^{-9}, 1e^{-6}]$	min_samples_split	[1, 10]
dropout	[0.1, 0.5]	reg_alpha	$[1e^{-5}, 1]$		
		reg_lambda	$[1e^{-5}, 1]$		

3. Result

The performance of each model (i.e., ANN, XGB, and ETR) was evaluated across *train*, *valid*, *test* and *unseen* datasets based on the Mean Absolute Error (MAE), detailed in Figure 3. To assess the impact of the PCA variables on model performance, we developed two cases: Case 1 consists of eight input variables (i.e., *P, T, H₂O ratio, D, NTUBE, Q, LV, GHSV*), Case 2 consists of eight input variables with 3 PCA variables (i.e., *PCA1, PCA2, PCA3).*

In the *train, valid,* and *test* datasets, the XGB model consistently outperformed the other models in both cases both cases, followed closely by the ETR model. The ANN model exhibits the lowest performances among both cases. For instance, the XGB model shows a significantly lower MAE of 0.05% compared to the 3% MAE observed in the ANN model.

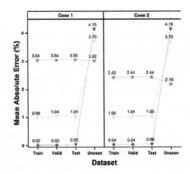

Figure 3. Comparison of model accuracy (MAE (%)) among the datasets

Regarding *train*, *valid*, and *test* datasets, the narrow gap of MAEs across these datasets suggest that all models adequately generalize and resist overfitting. However, the different pattern is exhibited in the *unseen* dataset. A notable shift was observed in the *unseen* dataset, where the performance of the XGB and ETR models was inferior compared to the ANN model. Specifically, the XGB model display a MAE of approximately 4% indicating the highest error, and ETR model follows with a MAE of 3.7%. This reversal in performance for both XGB and ETR model can be attributed to the inherent traits of tree-based algorithm of both models, leading to higher accuracy on familiar *test* data but diminished performance on *unseen* data. Conversely, the ANN model shows the lowest more consistent results, maintaining an MAE range of 2-3% in the *unseen* dataset. The consistent MAE suggests that the ANN model's superior generalization capability, less influenced by the training data. These observations suggest two crucial points in modelling for chemical reaction systems where the reliability and predictability of models are paramount. The first point is the importance of not only high accuracy but also generalizability for deploying of model. The second point is consideration of model's characteristics can be able to improve the model performance.

Table 2. Model accuracy based on R^2 of ANN model by specific range of target.

R^2 gap between Case 2 and Case 1 in R^2 of ANN model								
	Test data				*Unseen* data			
Range of target in data of X_{CH4} (%)	Data density (%)	Case 1	Case 2	ΔR^2	Data density (%)	Case 1	Case 2	ΔR^2
0 ~ 100	100	0.98	0.99	0.01	100	0.98	0.99	0.01
0 ~ 20	19.2	-0.63	-0.40	0.24	12.0	-1.74	-0.87	0.87
20 ~ 40	26.3	0.28	0.77	0.49	31.5	0.39	0.82	0.43
40 ~ 60	19.4	0.79	0.83	0.04	26.0	0.86	0.90	0.05
60 ~ 80	14.9	0.97	0.98	0.02	17.4	0.91	0.90	-0.01
80 ~ 100	20.1	0.98	0.95	-0.03	13.1	0.77	0.72	-0.05

As shown in Figure 3, ANN model exhibits the notable decrease in MAE between case 1 and 2 for both the *test* and *unseen* datasets, while XGB and ETR show similar MAE values. The details of ANN model's accuracy are presented as coefficient of determination (R^2) by various ranges of target (X_{CH4}) and data density in Table 2. The R^2 near 1 indicates high accuracy, whereas R^2 near -1 signifies poor performance. Although the minor increase of R^2 exhibits 0.01 in all range of target, the increase of R^2 by the range of target occurs between 0.02 and over 0.5 excluding the range of 80% to 100%. The improved performance of ANN model is attributed to the use of PCA variables, which are derived from the reactor size and flowrate variables. This result suggests that our approach, which considers the interconnections among process variables in the chemical system, improves model training and emphasizes the importance of in-depth data understanding.

4. Conclusion

In this study, we aim to derive the insights for data mining in chemical process industry. We conducted machine learning based modeling of catalytic reaction, including the prediction of steam methane reforming reaction using operating variables. Based on the understanding about interaction in systems, (i.e., the correlation of operating variables in chemical reactions), we transformed data and introduced new PCA feature using dimension reduction method. Also, we prepare *test* and *unseen* datasets, then develop three model (i.e., ANN, XGB, ETR) and evaluate these models based on MAE. As a results of the validation, resulting models based on tree algorithms such as XGB and ETR may be susceptible to overfitting against *unseen* dataset. Our findings highlight that we consider for model deployment not only based on prediction accuracy, but also generalizability and susceptibility to overfitting. Also, the understanding of the system and data are significant within cycle of data mining process, the need for a balanced approach to modeling, paving the way for the development of more robust and reliable predictive models in the field of chemical engineering.

References

Glassey, J., & Von Stosch, M., 2018. "Hybrid modeling in process industries," CRC Press.

Shearer, C., 2000. "The CRISP-DM model: the new blueprint for data mining," Journal of Data Warehousing, 5(4), 13-22.

Kim, S., 2017. "MATLAB Deep Learning With Machine Learning, Neural Networks and Artificial Intelligence," 1st ed.

Srivastava, N., Hinton, G., Krizhevsky, A., Sutskever, I., Salakhutdinov, R., 2014. "Dropout: a simple way to prevent neural networks from overfitting," J. Mach. Learn. Res., 15, 1929–1958.

Wu, Z., Ramsundar, B., Feinberg, E. N., Gomes, J., Geniesse, C., Pappu, A. S., Leswing, K., Pande, V., 2018. "Chem. Sci.," 9, 513–530.

Mine, S., Takao, M., Yamaguchi, T., Toyao, T., Maeno, Z., Siddiki, S. M. A. H., Takigawa, I., 2021. "nalysis of updated literature data up to 2019 on the oxidative coupling of methane using an extrapolative machine-learning method to identify novel catalysts," ChemCatChem, 13(16)

Oliveira, E. L.G., Grande, C.A., Rodrigues, A.E., 2009. "Steam methane reforming in a Ni/Al2O3 catalyst: kinetics and diffusional limitations in extrudates," The Canadian Journal of Chemical Engineering, 87, 945–956.

Goodfellow, I., Bengio, Y., Courville, A., 2016. "Deep Learning," MIT Press.

Chen, T., Guestrin, C., 2016. "Proceedings of the 22nd ACM SIGKDD International Conference on Knowledge Discovery and Data Mining," 785–794.

Abadi, M., Barham, P., Chen, J., Chen, Z., Davis, A., Dean, J., Devin, M., Ghemawat, S., Irving, G., Isard, M., Kudlur, M., Levenberg, J., Monga, R., Moore, S., Murray, D. G., Steiner, B., Tucker, P., Vasudevan, V., Warden, P., Wicke, M., Yu, Y., Zheng, X., 2016. "12th USENIX Symposium on Operating Systems Design and Implementation (OSDI '16)."

Pedregosa, F., Varoquaux, G., Gramfort, A., Michel, V., Thirion, B., Grisel, O., ... Duchesnay, É., 2011. "Scikit-learn: Machine Learning in Python," Journal of Machine Learning Research, 12,

Raschka, S., 2018. "Model evaluation, model selection, and algorithm selection in machine learning."

Hinton, G. E., Srivastava, N., Krizhevsky, A., Sutskever, I., & Salakhutdinov, R. R. (2012). Improving neural networks by preventing co-adaptation of feature detectors. arXiv preprint arXiv:1207.0580.

Flavio Manenti, Gintaras V. Reklaitis (Eds.), Proceedings of the 34th European Symposium on
Computer Aided Process Engineering / 15th International Symposium on Process Systems
Engineering (ESCAPE34/PSE24), June 2-6, 2024, Florence, Italy

Hierarchical deep reinforcement learning for hydrogen supply chain management

Geunseo Song[a, b], Vahid Khaligh[c], J. Jay Liu[c], Jonggeol Na[a, b,*]

[a]*Department of Chemical Engineering and Materials Science, Ewha Womans
University, Seoul 03760, Republic of Korea*
[b]*Graduate Program in System Health Science and Engineering, Ewha Womans
University, Seoul 03760, Republic of Korea*
[c]*Department of Chemical Engineering, Pukyong National University, Busan 48513,
Republic of Korea*
jgna@ewha.ac.kr

Abstract

For an effective transition from fossil fuel-based energy sources to renewable energy
sources, it is crucial to accompany research on the design and optimization of supply
chain for new energy sources. The traditional tool for optimizing supply chain
management (SCM), the mathematical programming (MP) method, has limitations in
terms of computation time and cost as the scale and complexity of the supply chain
increase. Therefore, we need a new powerful optimization methodology that enables real-
time decision making, considers the interaction among various components within the
supply chain, and accommodates the uncertainties in demand and energy supply. In this
study, we proposed deep reinforcement learning (DRL) as a new tool to overcome the
limitations of MP and satisfy the conditions required for optimizing SCM, as mentioned
earlier. Furthermore, we aim to compare a single-agent reinforcement learning (SARL)
system with a multi-agent reinforcement learning (MARL) system. Our model achieves
successful performance by converging to a value like the optimum of the MP.

Keywords: Hydrogen supply chain, Hierarchical deep reinforcement learning, Multi-
agent, Operation scheduling, Optimization

1. Introduction

As hydrogen receives attention as an energy source that can replace fossil fuels, research
on hydrogen energy is being actively conducted. Fundamental research on hydrogen is
important, but for effective conversion of energy sources, hydrogen supply chain (HSC)
design and optimization must be accompanied.
Some studies have considered the operation scheduling of a small-scale hydrogen supply
chain (HSC) consisting of multiple hydrogen refueling stations (HRSs) and hydrogen
distribution system (HDS) in the retail hydrogen market using a mathematical
programming (MP) approach (Mohammad H. Shames, 2022). Previously, MP approach
was a major tool to optimize the supply chain management (SCM), however, as the scale
and complexity of the supply chain increase, optimizing it with MP leads to an
exponential increase in computation time and cost. Also, there are limitations in
considering fluctuations in demand, energy generation, and other factors within the
supply chain. Therefore, in order to apply the supply chain model to the real-world
scenarios, it is necessary to build a complex model and find a new powerful tool capable
of optimizing it.

In this work, we propose reinforcement learning (RL) as a new methodology to optimize the operation of a comprehensive hydrogen supply chain encompassing production, transportation, storage, and distribution. RL is a category of machine learning algorithms specifically designed for sequential decision-making, offering a promising solution to tackle these challenges (Boute et al. 2022). RL is used in many fields of chemical engineering, such as scheduling (Lee, J.M. 2004) and finding molecular structures (Sanchez-Lengeling, B. 2017), but it has not yet been widely applied in the field of supply chain management. When applying the DRL method for HSC optimization, not only is it advantageous to expand the supply chain, but it can also consider the relationship of each part of the hydrogen supply chain and cope with various fluctuations.

2. Methodology

2.1. RL approach for hydrogen supply chain optimization

We developed a RL model to optimize the operation of a comprehensive hydrogen supply chain, encompassing production, transportation, storage, and distribution of hydrogen. Formally, RL is composed of five elements: agent, environment, state S, action A, and reward R. During the learning process, the agent observes states from the environment, selects actions under a certain policy, and receives corresponding rewards. The goal of RL is to find the optimal policy of actions that maximizes the ultimate cumulative reward. The process is mathematically formalized as a Markov Decision Process (MDP). The MDP functions as a flexible framework for goal-directed learning, defined as a tuple $M = (S, A, P(s_{t+1}, r | s, a), R, \gamma)$.

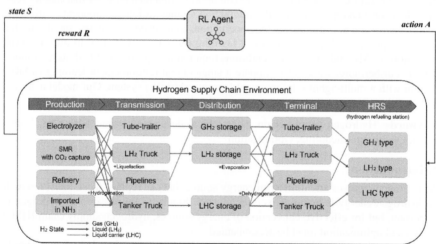

Figure 1. Schematic representation of reinforcement learning (RL) model architecture. The hydrogen supply chain (HSC), which serves as the environment, encompasses production, transportation, storage, and distribution, representing interactions between each part

The schematic diagram of the RL model for optimizing the operation of the hydrogen supply chain is depicted in Figure 1. In production part, hydrogen can be produced from various primary energy sources, such as green domestic hydrogen through the electrolysis process, steam methane reforming (SMR) using natural gas as a feedstock, obtained as a by-product in a refinery, or imported in the form of NH_3. The produced hydrogen is transported and stored through various means depending on the phase and is distributed to different regions according to demand. The RL agent interacts with the environment and determines the time, location, type and capacity of different facilities to minimize the net present value of the overall cost.

2.2. Agent architecture

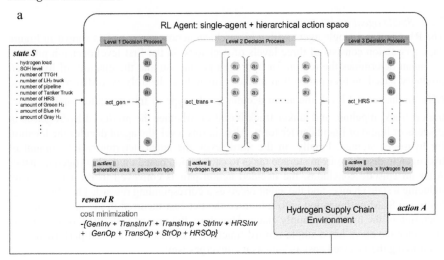

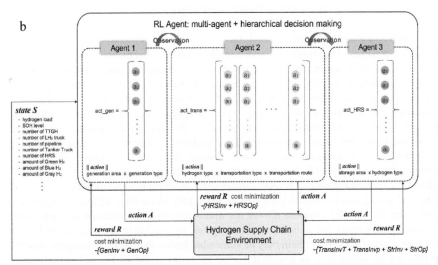

Figure 2. (a) Single agent hierarchical action space architecture. In this system, actions are composed of three levels, and the agent receives a single reward at the end of each episode. (b) Hierarchical multi-agent architecture. This system consists of three agents, and at the end of each episode, the three agents receive different rewards individually.

In this section, we propose two types of agents. A RL model for hydrogen SCM optimization must incorporate a hierarchical decision-making process as it determines the following sequentially: 1) hydrogen production quantity and methods based on demand,

2) transportation means and storage locations based on the type of the produced hydrogen, and 3) distribution according to the hydrogen load in each region. The agent illustrated in Figure 2a is a single agent capable of hierarchical decision-making through hierarchical action space, while the agent represented in Figure 2b satisfies this through multi-agent interactions.

2.2.1. Single agent architecture

The RL agent is a single agent with a hierarchical action space, and as shown in Figure 2a, every action consists of three levels of decisions. In the first level decision process, the agent determines the region for hydrogen production and the quantity of hydrogen produced based on four production methods, including electrolysis, SMR, refinery, and NH₃. In the second level, the agent decides on the type of transportation such as tube-trailer, truck, pipeline, and tanker truck based on whether the produced hydrogen is in gaseous or liquid or liquid carrier form. Also, in this level, the agent decides the location for hydrogen storage. Finally, in the third level, the agent determines the amount of hydrogen to distribute from storage tanks to each region based on the hydrogen demand. After an episode concludes, the decided action pair is conveyed to the environment, inducing a state change, and the agent receives a corresponding reward. The objective of hydrogen SCM optimization is to minimize the net cost incurred in the investment and operation of the hydrogen supply chain. Therefore, the reward is defined as in equation (1). Since the agent has a single reward function, it can exhibit the best performance in minimizing the incurred cost as long as it converges well.

$$Reward = -(GenInv + TransInv + StrInv + HRSInv + GenOp \qquad (1)$$
$$+ TransOP + StrOP + HRSOp)$$

2.2.2. Multi agent architecture

The RL agent depicted in Figure 2b forms a multi-agent system consisting of three agents. In contrast to a single agent, this system involves interactions not only between the agent and the environment but also among the agents themselves. Therefore, each agent not only predicts the value of its individual actions but also learns to take actions by considering the actions of other agents. The first agent determines the quantity of hydrogen based on each production method and, at the end of the episode, receives the corresponding reward, which is formulated in equation (2). The second agent decides on the hydrogen transportation means and storage locations, receiving the reward corresponding to equation (3). Finally, the third agent determines the amount of hydrogen to distribute to each region and receives the reward specified in equation (4).

In the real world, entities within each part of the supply chain have different objectives. Multi-agent RL (MARL) system allows for multi-objective optimization as each agent operates by observing the actions of other agents to maximize its own reward. The operating costs of the supply chain may be somewhat higher than in a single-agent system, but this can be interpreted as a well-reflected outcome of the real-world complexities entwined with relationships among multiple stakeholders.

$$Reward = -(GenInv + GenOp) \qquad (2)$$

$$Reward = -(TransInv + TransOp + StrInv + StrOp) \qquad (3)$$

$$Reward = -(HRSInv + HRSOp) \qquad (4)$$

3. Results

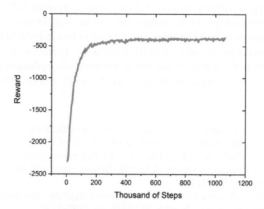

Figure 3. Episode reward mean

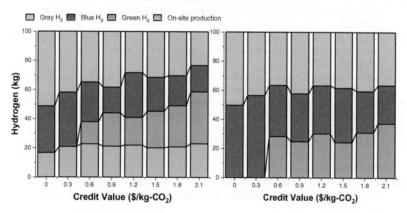

Figure 4. Demand satisfaction of hydrogen refueling stations

To assess the validity of RL methodology compared to conventional mathematical programming (MP) techniques for optimizing the supply chain, we designed a simple hydrogen supply chain model and conducted optimization. Figure 3 shows that the episode reward mean value converges well as the agents are learned. The HSC model consists of a wholesale market that sells three types of hydrogen, a hydrogen distribution system, and two hydrogen refueling stations. The system involves purchasing hydrogen in accordance with demand and selling it to hydrogen vehicles. By satisfying the hydrogen load as depicted in Figure 4, we confirmed the capability of demand-driven decision-making using RL methodology.

3. Conclusion and future works

In this study, we have developed a RL framework to optimize a comprehensive hydrogen supply chain model, including production, transportation, storage, and distribution. RL agents found optimal policies to interact with the supply chain environment to determine the type and location of each facility, and when to minimize the costs incurred. Moreover, RL models overcome the computational limitations of conventional MP methods, enabling real-time decision-making. Furthermore, the performance of the results trained through RL converged with the optimal values obtained through MP, demonstrating the viability of the methodology. In the future, we aim to analyze the differences in agent decision-making results to build and train a single agent hierarchical behavioral space RL framework and a hierarchical multi-agent RL framework. Furthermore, we intend to build a model that considers the unique dynamics of the domestic hydrogen market, conduct a case study, and analyze the trade-off between the economy and the environment.

References

L. Yu, S. Qin, M. Zhang, C. Shen, T. Jiang, 2021. A Review of Deep Reinforcement Learning for Smart Building Energy Managent, IEEE Internet of Things Journal, 8, 9426901

Mohammad H. Shams, Haider Niaz, J.Jay Liu, 2022. Energy management of hydrogen refueling stations in a distribution system: A bilevel chance-constrained approach, Journal of Power Sources, 533, 231400

David Silver, et al. 2018. A general reinforcement learning algorithm that masters chess, shogi, and Go through self-play, Science 362.6419, pp. 1140-1144.

Younghoon Lee and Seunghoon Lee, 2022. Deep reinforcement learning based scheduling within production plan in semiconductor fabrication, Expert Systems with Applications 191, p.116222.

Laura Stops and Roel Leenhouts and Qinghe Gao and Artur. 2022. Flowsheet synthesis through hierarchical reinforcement learning and graph neural networks, eprint arXiv:2207.12051.

Zhou Fan and Rui Su and Weinan Zhang and Yong Yu. 2019. Hybrid Actor-Critic Reinforcement Learning in Parameterized Action Space, arXiv:1903.01344.

Boute, Robert N., Joren Gijsbrechts, Willem van Jaarsveld, and Nathalie Vanvuchelen. 2022. Deep Reinforcement Learning for Inventory Control: A Roadmap. European Journal of Operational Research298 (2): 401–412.

Gang, Z., and S. Ruoying. 2006. Policy Transition of Reinforcement Learning for An Agent Based SCM System. In 2006 IEEE International Conference on Industrial Informatics, INDIN'06, Singapore, 793–798.

Giannoccaro, I., and P. Pontrandolfo. 2002. Inventory Management in Supply Chains: A Reinforcement Learning Approach. International Journal of Production Economics 78 (2): 153–161.

Hirano, M., H. Matsushima, K. Izumi, and T. Mukai. 2021. Simulation of Unintentional Collusion Caused by Auto Pricing in Supply Chain Markets. Lecture Notes in Computer Science (Including Subseries Lecture Notes in Artificial Intelligence and Lecture Notes in Bioinformatics) 12568 LNAI, 352–359. Cham: Springer.

Lee, J. M., Lee, J. H., 2004. Approximate dynamic programming strategies and their applicability for process control: A review and future directions. International Journal of Control, Automation, and Systems, 2(3), 263-278.

Sanchez-Lengeling, B., Outeiral, C., Guimaraes, G.L. and Aspuru-Guzik, A., 2017. Optimizing distributions over molecular space. An objective-reinforced generative adversarial network for inverse-design chemistry (ORGANIC). ChemRxiv, 2017.

Flavio Manenti, Gintaras V. Reklaitis (Eds.), Proceedings of the 34th European Symposium on Computer Aided Process Engineering / 15th International Symposium on Process Systems Engineering (ESCAPE34/PSE24), June 2-6, 2024, Florence, Italy

An Integrated Framework: Inverse Design for Optimal Amine Solvent using Reinforcement Learning and Enhanced CO$_2$ Chemical Absorption Processes

Youhyun Kim[a,b], Haeyeon Choi[a,b], Damdae Park[c], Kyeongsu Kim[c], Jonggeol Na[a,b*]

aDepartment of Chemical Engineering and Materials Science, Ewha Womans University, Seoul 03760, Republic of Korea
bGraduate Program in System Health Science and Engineering, Ewha Womans University, Seoul 03760, Republic of Korea
cClean Energy Research Center, Korea Institute of Science and Technology, Seoul 02792, Republic of Korea
jgna@ewha.ac.kr

Abstract

This study proposes an integrated framework that combines inverse material design via reinforcement learning (RL) and process optimization to determine the optimal solvent for CO$_2$ chemical absorption process (**Figure 1**). The framework addresses the challenges posed by Computer-Aided Molecular and Process Design (CAMPD) and efficiently explores the design space characterized by infeasible subregions and a highly nonlinear relationship between process and molecular structure. The RL model, when combined with combinatorial chemistry, inversely designs amine solvent based on target properties such as CO$_2$ absorption capacity and solubility. Then, conductor-like screening model for real solvents (COSMO-RS) predicts the phase behavior through thermodynamic analysis and evaluates whether the solvent can achieve the desired CO$_2$ removal. This novel approach provides an efficient and systematic way to design an effective solvent and improve the CO$_2$ absorption process.
Keywords: process and product design, Materials discovery, Amine solvent design, CO$_2$ chemical absorption process, Reinforcement learning

1. Introduction

Designing a product that satisfies the desired target properties may not always be optimal from the perspective of the overall process. Process conditions have a considerable influence on solvent performance, and solvent properties directly affect the efficiency and economics of the process. To determine the optimal solvent, it is necessary to consider the interaction between the molecular level and the process level (Lee et al., 2023).

Here we introduce an integrated framework that connects inverse material design through reinforcement learning (RL) and process optimization. The RL model combined with combinatorial chemistry inversely designs molecules for target properties. Our model begins with a randomly chosen initial fragment and proceeds to select the next fragment for combination, considering chemical rules to ensure the generation of valid molecules (H. Kim et al., 2023). Then, the property prediction model such as the conductor-like screening model for real solvents (COSMO-RS) calculates the required features in the

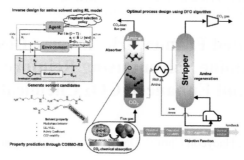

Figure 1. Overall schematic of proposed framework. Simultaneous operation of product design and process optimization

process model. The process system is converted into a surrogate model by nonlinear programming formulation, and DFO algorithm can be used to find the optimal solution in nonconvexity and nonlinearity black-box functions (M. Kim et al., 2023). The results of process optimization are returned to the target properties, which will be reflected in the setting of boundaries and initial values to serve as meaningful feedback. In this research, we will apply the framework to design an effective solvent and CO_2 chemical absorption process.

2. Methodology

2.1. Artificial intelligence-driven combinatorial chemistry

Inverse molecular design is a method to explore molecular structures with desired properties from a starting point. In our previous work, we developed artificial intelligence-driven combinatorial chemistry (AID-CC), which combines RL and combinatorial chemistry for inverse molecular design. Combinatorial chemistry is performed with molecular fragments and fragment combination rules. Since molecular fragments are connected randomly, it is possible to generate molecules with properties that deviate from known data. However, when using combinatorial chemistry to generate molecules, it is very expensive to generate molecules that satisfy the desired properties because the fragments are attached completely randomly rather than according to a learned policy (Furka, 1982). In this regard, RL learns in a way that maximizes the reward among selectable actions, so it was possible to combine the two to generate molecules that don't exist in existing databases. The agent starts with a randomly selected molecular fragment. The policy is learned through the Proximal Policy Optimization (PPO) algorithm(Schulman et al., 2017). PPO is known for its stability, efficiency, scalability, and flexibility in discrete action spaces. Considering constraints such as molecular weight and number of fragments, the policy guides the agent to a more efficient exploration of chemical space by giving higher rewards when the properties of the generated molecules more closely match the target. The action is to select a molecular fragment to combine with the current structure and the state at each step is represented by the molecular structure. To ensure that only valid chemical structures are generated, the agent uses action masking, which prevents the selection of incompatible fragments based on the binding sites of the current molecule.

2.2 COSMO-RS

COSMO-RS is based on the statistical thermodynamics of a simplified model of molecular interactions, in which intermolecular contacts are replaced by contacts that interact independently in pairs between surface segments of the molecular community (Gerlach et al., 2018). The interaction between segments is described by the screening charge density from the COSMO calculation, and the sigma profile is represented by the probability of finding a specific screening charge density at the molecular surface:

$$p_s(\sigma) = \sum_{i \in} x_i \times p_i(\sigma) \tag{1}$$

$$p^{Xi}(\sigma) = \frac{n_i(\sigma)}{n_i} = \frac{A_i(\sigma)}{A_i} \tag{2}$$

where x_i, $p^{Xi}(\sigma)$ and $n_i(\sigma)$ stand for the mole fraction of component "i" in the mixture, the σ profile of any molecule X and the number of distributed segments that has surface charge density σ, respectively. $A_i(\sigma)$ and A_i are the segment surface area that has charge density σ and the area of the whole surface cavity rooted in the medium, respectively.

3. Results

3.1. Application to the discovery of amine solvent for CO₂ absorption

For a promising CO_2 capture solvent, it should (1) absorb a large amount of CO_2 into solution with efficient absorption rate as an ideal capture agent and (2) make captured CO_2 more reactive (Siegel et al., 2023). The descriptors of pKa, ePOS, sphericity, amide bond energy, and NCNN pattern can be used to find amine solvents. We set the CO_2 capture product to methanol and the catalyst to Ru-MACHO. When the amine detaches the hydrogen in the catalyst, its pKa should be larger than the catalyst, otherwise carbamate formation may increase. As the amine intercepts the CO_2 captured in the catalyst, the target properties should have a charge profile complementary to the Ru-MACHO and a small sphericity.

To react with the electronegative part of Ru-MACHO, the target amine must have a wide electropositive area to promote solubility and stability of the catalyst in the solvent. Smaller sphericity is preferred for CO_2 capture solvents. It should also have a low amide bond dissociation energy when the amine bond is broken. Experimental data also suggested that the NCCN pattern could be a key descriptor (Kar et al., 2019). Therefore, the reward is defined as in equation (3). Additionally, synthesizability prediction using AizynthFinder (Genheden et al., 2020) was also considered.

$$Reward = NCCN - BDE + Sphericity + ePos \tag{3}$$

The molecular structures of the generated amine solvents are presented in **Table 1**.

Table1. Three molecular examples that were generated by material design

ID	M1	M2	M3
Molecular Structure			

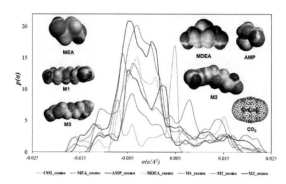

Figure 2. COSMOtherm generated σ profile and σ surface of MEA, MDEA, AMP, CO$_2$ and new amine solvents

3.2. σ profile and σ surface analysis by COSMO-RS model

The interactions between solvents and CO$_2$ significantly contribute to the solubility of CO$_2$. The σ profiles and surfaces of monoethanolamine (MEA), Methyldiethanolamine (MDEA), 2- amino-2-methyl-1-propanol (AMP), CO$_2$ and the generated amine are shown in **Figure 2**. Since the highest peak of CO$_2$ is present in the positive region, and M3 has the highest peak in the negative region, it is predicted to exhibit the best CO$_2$ absorption. The red region of the σ surface is hydrogen-bond acceptor; the blue is hydrogen-bond donor; the green is nonpolar region of the molecule. Since CO$_2$ can act as a hydrogen bond acceptor, in the case of capture solvent, the presence of blue region is advantageous for CO$_2$ capture, and the nonpolar interaction between solvent and CO$_2$ can increase the solubility of CO$_2$.

3.3. Modelling of Amine-H$_2$O-CO$_2$

The solubility of CO$_2$ under a wide range of thermodynamic conditions is a crucial factor in evaluating the potential of a solvent for CO$_2$ capture applications (Pereira & Vega, 2018). To design absorber efficiently, it is necessary to predict the solubility of CO$_2$. In addition, since the regeneration process of the amine solvent occurs in the stripper, the operating conditions should consider CO$_2$ solubility so that the CO$_2$ can be easily separated from the solvent Modelling CO$_2$ absorption in amine aqueous solutions is a fundamental thermodynamic method.

3.3.1. The phase equilibrium

The concentration of CO$_2$ in the liquid phase and the partial pressure of CO$_2$ in the gas phase can be described by Henry's and Raoult's laws (Kim et al., 2022) :

$$\phi_{CO_2} y_{CO_2} P^{tot} = H_{CO_2} \gamma^*_{CO_2} x_{CO_2} \exp\left(\frac{v^\infty_{CO_2}(P - P^0_w)}{RT}\right) \tag{4}$$

where ϕ_{CO_2}, y_{CO_2} and P^{tot} are the fugacity coefficient, the mole fraction of the vapor phase and the total pressure, respectively. The activity coefficient and Henry's law constant are represented by $\gamma^*_{CO_2}$ and H_{CO_2}, respectively. x_{CO_2}, P^0_w and $v^\infty_{CO_2}$ are the mole fraction in the liquid phase, the vapor pressure of water and partial molar volume of CO$_2$ at infinite dilution in water, respectively. The phase equilibrium for the solvent species, amines and water is given by:

$$\phi_w P_w = a_w \phi_w^s P_w^s \exp\left(\frac{v_w(P - P_w^s)}{RT}\right) \tag{5}$$

where subscript W represents water, ϕ_w^s and v_w are the fugacity coefficient of water at its vapor pressure and partial molar volume, respectively.

In this study, the chemical reaction of the H_2O-Amine-CO_2 system was also considered. Chemical reactions were represented as equilibrium constants, and chemical equilibria were modelled by calculating charge balance equation and mass balance equations.

3.3. Discussion the advantages of the proposed method over other established method
Computer-Aided Molecular and Process Design (CAMPD) provides a systematic framework for evaluating a wide range of molecular structures in terms of system metrics when considering desirable physicochemical properties and process performance criteria (Adjiman et al., 2014). In CAMPD, the mathematical models governing the structure-property relationships of molecules and the performance of materials are related to process operating variables and presented as a large mixed-integer nonlinear problem (MINLP) formulation. However, many algorithms face challenges in CAMPD problems. The design space generated by the integrated product-process model is characterized by the presence of infeasible subregions and the relationship between process and molecular structure is highly nonlinear, making it difficult to find a solution (Lee et al., 2023). In addition, integrating machine learning-based material discovery methodology and Derivative-Free Optimization (DFO) algorithms within the CAMPD framework proves challenging, particularly due to the complex nature of MINLP structures. The proposed method can design the capture solvent considering the process conditions by directly applying the optimal amine solvent generated through RL model to the process model and reflecting the results as feedback to the RL model. Instead of solving the MINLP problem, which many algorithms have difficulty solving, the process model is directly designed using the proposed amine solvents, thus avoiding multiple iterations and adjustments. The chemical process is also converted into a surrogate model using the DFO algorithm, which can be optimized more effectively.

4. Conclusion and future works

Consequently, this research can provide remarkable opportunities to effectively design a capture solvent that achieves the optimal performance and economic efficiency. We generated the optimal amine solvent candidates and predicted CO_2 solubility thorough COSMO-RS to connect with CO_2 absorption process. The proposed framework that can adapt to variations in process conditions improve process efficiency and expand domain knowledge of the material discovery. This can reduce the vast solvent design space, providing a clear advantage over sequential optimization which involves multiple iterations and adjustments.
In the future, parameter fitting will be conducted to fit the expected solubility with experimental data to increase accuracy. Therefore, we intend to construct accuracy and efficient VLE modelling of CO_2 absorption applied to new amine solutions. Based on the prediction of CO_2 chemical absorption derived from thermodynamic analysis, we aim to design the optimal process using DFO algorithms. The optimization results will lead to the expansion of domain knowledge and meaningful feedback to the material design framework. It is expected that this framework will be applied to design materials that have superior properties and economic feasibility.

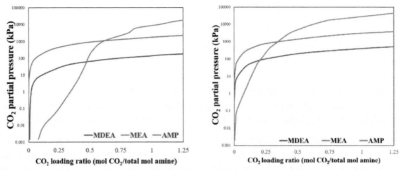

Figure 3. Partial pressure of CO_2 as function of CO_2 loading in aqueous solutions of MDEA, MEA and AMP at different temperatures (a) 313 K (b) 393 K

References

Adjiman, C. S., Galindo, A., & Jackson, G. (2014). Molecules Matter: The Expanding Envelope of Process Design. In M. R. Eden, J. D. Siirola, & G. P. Towler (Eds.), *Computer Aided Chemical Engineering* (Vol. 34, pp. 55-64). Elsevier.

Furka, A. (1982). Study on the possibilities of systematic searching for pharmaceutically useful peptides. *Notarized Report (File number 36237/1982, in Hungarian)*.

Genheden, S., Thakkar, A., Chadimová, V., Reymond, J.-L., Engkvist, O., & Bjerrum, E. (2020). AiZynthFinder: a fast, robust and flexible open-source software for retrosynthetic planning. *Journal of Cheminformatics, 12*(1), 70.

Gerlach, T., Ingram, T., Sieder, G., & Smirnova, I. (2018). Modeling the solubility of CO2 in aqueous methyl diethanolamine solutions with an electrolyte model based on COSMO-RS. *Fluid Phase Equilibria, 461*, 39-50.

Kar, S., Sen, R., Kothandaraman, J., Goeppert, A., Chowdhury, R., Munoz, S. B., Haiges, R., & Prakash, G. K. S. (2019). Mechanistic Insights into Ruthenium-Pincer-Catalyzed Amine-Assisted Homogeneous Hydrogenation of CO2 to Methanol. *Journal of the American Chemical Society, 141*(7), 3160-3170.

Kim, H., Choi, H., Kang, D., Lee, W. B., & Na, J. (2023). Materials Discovery with Extreme Properties via AI-Driven Combinatorial Chemistry. *arXiv preprint arXiv:2303.11833*.

Kim, M., Han, A., Lee, J., Cho, S., Moon, I., & Na, J. (2023). Comparison of Derivative-Free Optimization: Energy Optimization of Steam Methane Reforming Process. *International Journal of Energy Research, 2023*.

Kim, S.-M., Kim, K.-M., Choi, B.-K., Mun, J.-H., Shin, B.-J., Lee, U., Shin, C.-H., Choi, J., Min, B.-M., Lee, U., & Moon, J.-H. (2022). CO2 absorption mechanism in aqueous ternary solutions of alkanolamines: Experimental and thermodynamic modeling approaches. *Chemical Engineering Journal, 428*, 132044.

Lee, Y. S., Galindo, A., Jackson, G., & Adjiman, C. S. (2023). Enabling the direct solution of challenging computer-aided molecular and process design problems: Chemical absorption of carbon dioxide. *Computers & Chemical Engineering, 174*, 108204.

Pereira, L. M., & Vega, L. F. (2018). A systematic approach for the thermodynamic modelling of CO2-amine absorption process using molecular-based models. *Applied Energy, 232*, 273-291.

Schulman, J., Wolski, F., Dhariwal, P., Radford, A., & Klimov, O. (2017). Proximal policy optimization algorithms. *arXiv preprint arXiv:1707.06347*.

Siegel, R. E., Pattanayak, S., & Berben, L. A. (2023). Reactive Capture of CO2: Opportunities and Challenges. *ACS Catalysis, 13*(1), 766-784.

Flavio Manenti, Gintaras V. Reklaitis (Eds.), Proceedings of the 34th European Symposium on Computer Aided Process Engineering / 15th International Symposium on Process Systems Engineering (ESCAPE34/PSE24), June 2-6, 2024, Florence, Italy

ML-based Automated Systems Identification: A Demonstration for Complex Chemical Processes

Robin Hofmann[a], Thomas Grötzner[a], Isuru A. Udugama[b,c], Christoph Bayer[a,*]

[a]*Department of Process Engineering, TH Nuernberg, Nuernberg, Germany*
[b]*Department of Chemical and Materials Engineering, The University of Auckland, Auckland, New Zealand*
[c]*S&D Consulting Inc., Houston, Texas, USA*
christoph.bayer@th-nuernberg.de

Abstract

Chemical processes often exhibit a high degree of complexity and highly nonlinear dynamics. Accurate system identification is essential for optimizing operations and control, resulting in high production rates while ensuring product quality. Machine Learning (ML) has emerged as a transformative technology, offering new possibilities for automating system identification in complex chemical processes. This manuscript provides a demonstration of the application of ML-based automated systems identification techniques. It explores the significance between LSTM neural networks and data preparation through clustering and weighting of timeseries. The central objective of this demonstration is to highlight the potential of ML with control of complex chemical processes in mind.

Keywords: machine learning, LSTM, process engineering, clustering

1. Introduction

Chemical processes often exhibit a high degree of complexity and highly nonlinear dynamics. Accurate system identification is essential for optimizing operations and control. Machine Learning (ML) has emerged as a transformative technology, offering new possibilities for automating system identification. This manuscript provides a demonstration of the application of LSTM neural networks with a particular focus on data preparation through clustering and weighting of data.

2. Data Sources & Preparation

2.1. Process Models

Two simulated processes that vary in size and complexity are used to study the ramifications on the respective neural network and its training. The first model, a simple water mixing tank created by the authors, has three inputs which act on three measured outputs, hence being a 3x3 system. Two streams enter the tank differing in flow and temperature, while a third stream leaves the tank. All streams can be adjusted with valves to control the outflow rate $V3$, the temperature $T3$ and the level h of the liquid in the tank. The second model (4x9) is a conceptual representation of the reactor of the Tennessee Eastman problem (Downs & Vogel, 1993, and Andersen et al., 2022), published by Ricker (1993).

2.2. Data Set

The training timeseries data for the Ricker model are generated on a grid of initial values for each model input (Table 1). Successive input values of an emerging timeseries are generated by a random walk. Any input value changes with a 25 % probability per timestep and any change in value (from the initial value or the value of the prior timestep) is normally distributed with a standard deviation of 1 %-pt. However, a timeseries that exceeds the model's limits, e.g., pressure > 3,000 kPa, is automatically discarded. All resulting timeseries comprise 100 timesteps of data each. Thus, the timeseries are unique while roughly providing an equal distribution of input values. The dataset for training contains approximately 1,500 individual timeseries.

Table 1: Initial input grid for Ricker's training data set for setpoints U1- U4 in percent

	Input	min	step	max
U1	Feed 1 Valve	40 %	5 %-pt	80 %
U2	Feed 2 Valve	10 %	5 %-pt	40 %
U3	Product Valve	20 %	5 %-pt	60 %
U4	Reactor Level Setpoint	40 %	5 %-pt	50 %

Validation data (1,000 timeseries) are generated with identical parameters, though the inputs evolve from random starting points. The protocol for test data generation (10,000 timeseries) is identical with the training data, but 2.5 %-pt grid steps and a standard deviation of 2.5 %-pt were chosen.

The mixing tank's data are generated with a 50 % probability for input change and a standard deviation of 5 %-pt for a change in value of the respective input.

2.3. Clustering & Weighting

The timeseries data are preprocessed by scaling the range of values, then clustering and subsequently weighting of whole timeseries. This shall ensure that the neural network is trained on equally distributed information such that every information represented in the dataset is eventually represented by the neural network.

The temporal dependency of data points renders timeseries more difficult to cluster than individual points. To account for the dependency in time, each series is transformed into a single multidimensional point, which can be clustered. For clustering, three different algorithms are used. k-Means usually serves as a first approach to clustering. DBSCAN (Density-Based Spatial Clustering of Applications with Noise) (Ester et al., 1996) is used to identify outliers within the dataset. SOM (self-organizing map) (Kohonen, 1982) is a generalized AI-driven principle component analysis.

The weighting solver is a gradient-based fixed step algorithm. First, it calculates a mean for each output variable. Then, the current weight for each output variable and each cluster is determined, which is updated based on the difference to the target. This is implemented in such a way that it also works if the number of clusters for each output variable differs, as with DBSCAN. To avoid extremely high or low weights, limits on them are imposed. In case of poorly distributed clusters or an insufficient number of timeseries, the weighting will not equilibrate information density across the full parameter space.

3. Neural Networks

3.1. Neuron and Network Architecture

For this study, the neural network and solvers were implemented in C++/CUDA. This approach targets process control implementations on industrial hardware (Udugama et al., 2020).

Two types of neurons are used: (1) Long Short-Term Memory (LSTM), which structurally supports timeseries prediction through recurrency; (2) Feed Forward (ANN) neurons, which increase and shape the mapping complexity inside the network.

All network structures tested were trained in the form of "Input-LSTM-Output". The input neurons only hold the input information for the network, whereas the output contains sigmoid activations. The LSTM layer is configured as shown by Hochreiter & Schmidhuber (1997). The number of LSTM neurons vary with model complexity. Specifically, mixing tank models are trained with 50 LSTM neurons, while Ricker models are trained with 150 LSTM neurons. Randomized minibatches are used for backpropagation with approximately 1/10 of the whole training set per minibatch.

All data used for training, validation and testing is normalized. Deviating from the usual approach to normalize to a range from 0 to 1, the data are normalized to a range from 0.1 to 0.9, which is due to the sigmoid activation function in the output-layer, which hardly reaches the limits of 0 and 1.

3.2. Solver Algorithm

The widely used ADAM solver, as published by Kingma and Lei Ba (2015), is implemented and used to update the network parameters in the learning process. Deviating from the original publication, the internal parameter β_2 is changed to 0.99 due to estimated higher learning stability. The networks' learning process is further improved by including learning rate decay as given by Eq. (1).

$$\alpha = 2^{-\frac{E \cdot B + M}{H}} \tag{1}$$

α denotes the learning rate, E the current epoch, B the number of minibatches per epoch, and M the current number of calculated minibatches in this epoch. H is a changeable hyperparameter representing the number of iterations that reduces the learning rate by a factor of 2.

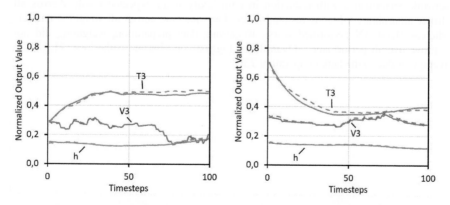

Figure 1: Example of an unweighted mixing tank timeseries; left taken from training set, right from test set; dashed lines represent (true) measurements, whereas solid lines represent network outputs; trained until the loss changed less than 0.002 in 50 epochs.

3.3. Training and Validation

The gradient required for updating a network's weights and biases is based on the objective function as given by Eq. (2).

$$L = \sum_{i=1}^{B} \frac{(y-z)^2}{2 \cdot s} \qquad (2)$$

The loss L is the sum over B minibatches of the squared difference of the true measurements y and the output of the network z, normalized with the batch size s.

The long-range dependencies in time when training on longer timeseries pose difficulties for LSTM neurons. To enhance learning performance, the network is also trained on the previous timestep's measurement as an additional input (lookback). Since this information is not available when using the network for predictions, the lookback variables are substituted with its own generated predictions.

The number of epochs varies throughout this study depending on the process model's complexity. More complex models tend to require more epochs for the same level of feature extraction. Given that real plant operations might also have limitations, the model was not trained to perfection, but rather until most information was learned properly. In any case, it was taken care that the training did not stop prematurely. This is achieved by relating the change in both training and validation losses against additional calculation time. The number of training epochs (for all networks) were set so that a network's loss did improve less than 0.002 over 50 epochs, which equals an improvement of less than 0.005 % compared to the initial loss.

4. Model Identification

4.1. Mixing Tank Model

As shown in Figure 1 (left), the network successfully extracted the features from the training data as to properly mimic the model's underlying behavior. The same can be seen on the right-hand side for data it was not trained on. The loss for all networks trained on mixing tank data are quite low and therefore indicate proper learning. However, counterintuitively at first, all networks performed better on data they have never seen. Since these datasets depict less random input changes (relative to training), an increase in network performance with reduction in complexity is an expected result. Across all cluster algorithms, k-Means resulted in the best outcome across all weighted datasets whereas DBSCAN performed worst. Regarding data preparation, weighting did not improve overall performance. Overall, the biggest contribution to the loss (71.5 % on average) is due to the tank temperature *T3*.

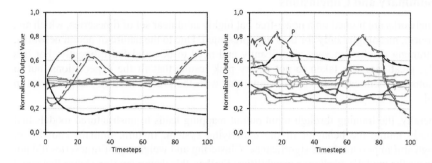

Figure 2: Example of an unweighted Ricker timeseries; left taken from training set, right from test set; dashed lines represent (true) measurements, whereas solid lines represent network outputs; trained until the loss changed less than 0.002 in 50 epochs.

4.2. Ricker Model

As Figure 2 illustrates, the training delivers a neural network that mimics the true behavior with satisfactory precision. Most network outputs follow the measurement values closely. Only output 5, which represents the reactor pressure P, shows a small but visible deviation.

Network loss values are presented in Table 2. Contrary to the mixing tank, the test loss is always higher than the training loss, which is attributable to greater valve dynamics (cp. Figure 2). Most striking are the significantly higher losses of the DBSCAN-weighted datasets in comparison to the others. Nonetheless, weighting of timeseries to adjust for information density in the parameter space does not seem to improve model identification. Further, analysis of individual output variables and their contribution to the network's loss shows that reactor pressure P is on average responsible for 79.5 % of the total. The worst output variable (output variable with the highest contribution to loss) accounts for at least 72 % of the total loss (Table 2). In other words, all other system information is identified far better than the average loss suggests.

Table 2: Summary of results

Model	Set	Loss			Worst Output Variable
		Train	Validation	Test	
Mixing Tank	Raw	0.094	0.088	0.051	69 %
Mixing Tank	k-Means	0.162	0.137	0.108	66 %
Mixing Tank	DBSCAN	0.219	0.188	0.114	72 %
Mixing Tank	SOM	0.141	0.127	0.078	79 %
Ricker	Raw	0.007	0.006	0.036	72 %
Ricker	k-Means	0.010	0.008	0.049	74 %
Ricker	DBSCAN	0.228	0.169	0.405	93 %
Ricker	SOM	0.014	0.013	0.052	79 %

5. Summary and Conclusions

All networks are trained on a noise-free but highly nonlinear set of timeseries, which are, of course, meaningful only for the range presented. Due to the nature of neural networks, the training results can vary significantly and need to be validated diligently. For this study, great care was taken to not cherry pick results that fit the expectations, but to demonstrate both capabilities and limitations with the process industry applications in mind.

Generally, the training through input/output mapping leads to unstructured models that properly mimic the behavior of the underlying system. In turn, domain knowledge, though still important, loses significance. Clustering and weighting of timeseries did not improve the model's predictive capabilities. Further, this demonstration shows that small changes in data can lead to important differences in forecasting precision and network performance. However, these results are sufficiently accurate for further use in model predictive control, the target application.

Acknowledgements

The authors would like to acknowledge the financial support of the AutoKI project by the STAEDTLER foundation.

References

J.J. Downs, E.F. Vogel, (1993). A plant-wide industrial process control problem. *Computers and Chemical Engineering, 17*(3). https://doi.org/10.1016/0098-1354(93)80018-I.

M. Ester, H.-P. Kriegel, J. Sander, X. Xu, (1996). A Density-Based Algorithm for Discovering Clusters in Large Spatial Databases with Noise. *Proceedings of the 2nd International Conference on Knowledge Discovery and Data Mining.*

S. Hochreiter, J. Schmidhuber, (1997). Long Short-Term Memory. *Neural Computation, 9*(8). https://doi.org/10.1162/neco.1997.9.8.1735.

D. P. Kingma, J. Lei Ba, (2015). Adam: A method for stochastic optimization. *3rd International Conference on Learning Representations, ICLR 2015 - Conference Track Proceedings.*

T. Kohonen, (1982). Self-organized formation of topologically correct feature maps. *Biological Cybernetics*, 43, 59-69.

N. L. Ricker, (1993). Model predictive control of a continuous, nonlinear, two-phase reactor. *Journal of Process Control, 3*(2), 109–123.

I. A. Udugama, C. L. Gargalo, Y. Yamashita, M. A. Taube, A. Palazoglu, B. R. Young, K. V. Gernaey, M. Kulahci, C. Bayer, (2020). The role of big data in industrial (bio) chemical process operations. *Industrial Engineering and Chemistry Research, 59*(34), 15283–297.

E.B. Andersen, I.A. Udugama, K. V. Gernaey, A.R. Khan, C. Bayer, M. Kulahci, (2022). An easy to use GUI for simulating big data using Tennessee Eastman process. *Quality and Reliability Engineering International Journal, 38*(1), 264-282.

Flavio Manenti, Gintaras V. Reklaitis (Eds.), Proceedings of the 34th European Symposium on Computer Aided Process Engineering / 15th International Symposium on Process Systems Engineering (ESCAPE34/PSE24), June 2-6, 2024, Florence, Italy

Hyperparameter Optimization of Matheuristics for Hoist Scheduling

Sophie Hildebrandt,[a] Guido Sand[a*]

[a]*Pforzheim University of Applied Science, Tiefenbronner Straße 65, 75175 Pforzheim, Germany*
guido.sand@hs-pforzheim.de

Abstract

Matheuristics combine mathematical programming with heuristic methods to solve real-world decision problems. The construction of a matheuristic requires to optimize a set of hyperparameters which may be continuous, integer, ordinal or categorial in nature. This paper describes a new approach to construct matheuristics based on Bayesian optimization applied to hoist scheduling problems. First numerical studies compare this approach to the state of the art and quantify their pros and cons.

Keywords: hyperparameter optimization, matheuristics, hoist scheduling

1. Introduction

Matheuristics are hybrid algorithms that combine mathematical programming with heuristic methods; they can be used to solve real-world decision problems such as hoist scheduling problems. The construction of a matheuristic is a special type of algorithm selection and tuning problem which requires to optimize a set of hyperparameters. While many hyperparameter optimization methods and applications are described in literature, no application of hyperparameter optimization to matheuristics is known to the authors. This paper describes first insights into hyperparameter optimization of matheuristics using hoist scheduling as an example.

2. Hoist scheduling problem

Hoist scheduling problems are flexible job shop scheduling problems with additional hoists; they are proven to be NP-complete (Lei and Wang, 1989). A hoist transports batches of material in carriers between tanks; a plant may have multiple lines of tanks and multiple hoists which run on the same rail and must not collide. A real-world application of hoist scheduling can be found in electroplating plants where ignoble metal is coated with thin layers of noble metal using electrolysis processes (Reimschüssel et al., 2023).

In hoist scheduling, the processing jobs to be scheduled are given by the batches and their recipes; the number and type of tanks and the number and speed of hoists are given as well. The decisions to be taken comprise the sequencing of the batches, the assignment of processing jobs to the tanks and the assignment of transportation jobs to the hoists. A feasible schedule satisfies constraints imposed by the recipes, the plant capacity, the transportation times, and the collision prevention. A typical objective is the minimization of the makespan or the cycle time in case of cyclic schedules.

Hoist scheduling problems can be classified according to the scheme by Manier and Bloch (2003) with respect to the number of lines, the number of transfer systems between the lines, the need to synchronize hoists and transfer systems, the number of hoists, the number and capacity of tanks, the existence of multifunction tanks, the number of (potentially circulating) carriers, the handling system to return empty carriers, the storage for carriers, cleaning of carriers, a loading/unloading station, the number of batches, the number of recipes, the number of reentrant tanks and the number of processing steps.

3. State of the art

3.1. Construction of Matheuristics

Mathematical programming methods are model based and exact in the sense that they can determine a proven optimal solution of the model in finite computational time. However, if some of the degrees of freedom are subject to integrality constraints, the computational cost often prohibits the practical application to real-world problems. The combination with heuristic methods helps to reduce the computational cost at the price of missing the optimal solution. Research on the combination of mathematical programming methods and heuristics is studied under the headline matheuristics, see e.g. Maniezzo et al. (2009 and 2021). In this context, the term heuristics covers both, population-based metaheuristics like evolutionary algorithms or ant colony optimization, and original heuristics like neighbourhood search and decomposition-based heuristics; the focus of this research is on original heuristics.

The application of matheuristics to hoist scheduling problems was studied in several papers and is still an active research area. Typically, mixed integer programming using general purpose solvers is combined with original heuristics. For instance, Li et al. (2015) combined CPLEX with a zone partition heuristic which limits the range of movement for each of a multitude of hoists. Basán and Méndez (2016) combine GUROBI with a two-phase heuristic combining an incremental construction heuristic with a local improvement heuristic. And Ramin et al. (2023) combined CPLEX with a zone partition and an incremental construction heuristic. The matheuristics are constructed manually or by fully enumerating a predefined grid of potential tuning parameters.

The selection of the heuristic, the tuning of its parameters (e.g. the width of zones in zone partitioning) and the selection of the mathematical programming solver including its parameters are degrees of freedom of the matheuristic construction, but not the only ones: For a given decision problem class like a hoist scheduling problem class multiple mixed-integer programming model formulations exist. For instance, for hoist scheduling problems with one hoist, one line, one recipe, no multi-capacity tanks, and no carrier circulation the models and heuristics described by Basán and Méndez (2016), Chtourou et al. (2013), Feng et al. (2015), Tian et al. (2013), Li et al. (2015), Yan et al. (2018), Zhou and Li (2009) and others are applicable.

3.2. Hyperparameter optimization

The construction of a matheuristic is a special type of algorithm selection and tuning problem. If its degrees of freedom are considered as hyperparameters of the algorithm, its construction can in principle be automated by means of hyperparameter optimization methods. Various methods for the automated configuration of algorithms are studied in the artificial intelligence domain, see e.g. Schede et al. (2022).

The hyperparameters of an algorithm can be continuous, integer, ordinal or categorical in nature. Examples for hyperparameters in the construction of matheuristics for hoist scheduling problems are the maximum CPU-time for mixed-integer programming solver runs (continuous), the number of tanks assigned to each zone in zone partitioning (integer), the model formulation (ordinal), and the selection of the (potentially not state-of-the art) mixed-integer programming solver (categorical).

Feasible values of hyperparameters are not always independent of each other but may be subject to constraints. For instance, for a given model formulation only particular heuristics are applicable, different heuristics may have different tuning parameters, or the tuning parameters of the heuristic depend on each other. The hyperparameter optimization problem has typically two conflicting objectives: minimize the computational cost and maximize the solution quality of the hoist scheduling problem class given by its objective. Since no application of hyperparameter optimization to matheuristics is known to the authors, this research strives for first insights into a potential algorithmic setup, useful software tools, and the numerical performance.

4. Matheuristics construction using Bayesian optimization

The hyperparameter optimization problem is a black-box optimization problem with expensive-to-evaluate objective functions. Both, the computational cost and the solution quality of the matheuristic are functions of the hyperparameters, which can be evaluated pointwise but provide no prior knowledge like gradients. The high computational cost of each sample is mainly caused by the solution of one or a series of mixed-integer programs. Hyperparameter optimization methods can be classified as follows: 1. Grid search methods evaluate all combinations of hyperparameter values on a pre-defined multidimensional grid. They are easy to implement but require all grid points to be evaluated. 2. Random search methods distribute the samples randomly in the hyperparameter space. They are also easy to implement but may search in irrelevant areas of the hyperparameter space. 3. Model based optimization methods like Bayesian optimization fit a probabilistic model of the objective functions to the collected function samples and use this model to guide the optimization by trading off exploration versus exploitation of the search space. Model based methods support an efficient sampling but rely on a robust surrogate model which provides useful approximations of the true objective functions, see Bischl et al. (2023).

Due to its efficient sampling strategy, Bayesian optimization is considered the state-of-the-art hyperparameter optimization method for expensive-to-evaluate objective functions like the one at hand (Hutter et al., 2019). It was originally designed for continuous parameters, but integer, ordinal and categorial parameters can be handled as well. A Bayesian optimization algorithm has two main ingredients: 1. An acquisition function balances the exploration versus exploitation of the search space based on the surrogate model and decides which hyperparameter values to evaluate next. Various types of acquisition functions exist, e.g. expected improvement, probability of improvement, and Thompson sampling. 2. The surrogate model is a probabilistic model that defines a distribution over the objective function value in the hyperparameter space between the sampling points. Various types of surrogate models exist, e.g. a Gaussian process, random forest, Bayesian neural networks.

In each iteration step a Bayesian optimization algorithm proposes the next sampling point, determines the corresponding objective function values, and updates the surrogate model. Here, Bayesian optimization is used as an algorithm to automatically construct another algorithm, namely a matheuristic. The main design parameters of a Bayesian optimization algorithm itself are the selection of the acquisition function and of the surrogate model in addition to the setting of their parameters, see Bischl et al. (2023).

5. Tool selection and settings

Many commercial and non-commercial implementations of Bayesian optimizations algorithms exist, like GPyOpt (https://sheffieldml.github.io/GPyOpt/), Optuna (https://optuna.org/), scikit-optimize (https://scikit-optimize.github.io/stable/), SMAC3 (https://github.com/automl/SMAC3), Spearmint (https://github.com/JasperSnoek

/spearmint) and others. They differ in properties like the programming language (e.g. Python, C++, Julia, R), the spectrum of supported acquisition functions and surrogate models, the ability to handle hyperparameter constraints, extensions (like multi-objective optimization), and the quality of the documentation. For the numerical studies in this paper the non-commercial package SMAC3 was selected, since it supports multiple acquisition functions, surrogate models, all types of parameters (continuous, integer, ordinal, categorial) as well as the handling of hyperparameter constraints.

The entire toolchain was implemented in Python: SMAC3 is a Python-package; it calls the matheuristic (comprising the original heuristics and the mixed-integer programming model of the hoist scheduling problem) which is implemented in Pyomo (www.pyomo.org); the mixed-integer programming problems are solved by CPLEX.

For the SMAC3 design parameters the "black box facade" with expected improvement as acquisition function and Gaussian process as surrogate model was chosen. The standard settings were modified such that multiple evaluations of hyperparameter values are prevented and the initial hyperparameter values are reproducible.

6. Numerical studies

6.1. Hoist scheduling problem classes and matheuristic

Three small hoist scheduling problem instances from three different classes are studied. They are based on the mixed-integer linear programming model described in detail by Basán and Méndez (2016); the model is limited to a single hoist operating on a single line, tanks with a capacity of one carrier and non-circulating carriers. The objective is to minimize the makespan MK for a given set of jobs i, subject to the constraints outlined in section 2 except for the collision prevention. All instances comprise six jobs $i = \{1, ..., 6\}$. Instance 1 (taken from Aguirre et al., 2013), comprises seven tanks $j = \{0, ..., 7\}$ with one reentrant tank and three recipes $Seq_{(i)} \in \{1, 2, 3\}$ with a maximum of eight processing steps $s = \{1, ..., 8\}$, instance 2 comprises seven tanks $j = \{0, ..., 7\}$ with no reentrant tank and three recipes $Seq_{(i)} \in \{1, 2, 3\}$ with a maximum of six processing steps $s = \{1, ..., 6\}$, and instance 3 comprises five tanks $j = \{0, ..., 5\}$ with one reentrant tank and one recipe $Seq_{(i)} \in \{1\}$ with $s = \{1, ..., 6\}$ processing steps.

The heuristic (from the same paper by Basán and Méndez, 2016) combines a constructive with an improvement step. In the constructive step the first NSJ (number of selected jobs) from a list of jobs are scheduled, the first job is fixed, then the next NSJ jobs are scheduled, and so on. In the improvement step the first NRJ (number of released jobs) of the schedule from the construction step are rescheduled. If no better solution is found, jobs two to NRJ+1 are rescheduled, and so on. If a better solution is found, the improvement step starts from job one. With NSJ=1 and NRJ=1, the constructive and the improvement step consist of at least 6 iterations each. Instead of solving the monolithic model for instance 1, 2 and 3 with 11916/6449, 6469/3607 and 8583/4021 constraints/variables, the model is decomposed into smaller problems. During the constructive step the number of constraints/variables range from 451/223, 191/117 and 248/131 in the first iteration to 11916/5810, 6469/3248 and 8583/3662 in the last iteration.

6.2. Grid search versus Bayesian optimization

In the first part of the numerical studies, NSJ and NRJ are the (integer-valued) hyperparameters considered. A grid search method is studied as reference.

The setup of the grid search is as follows: NSJ and NRJ range from one to six resulting in grid covering 36 points; the computational time for the evaluation of one point is limited to 3,600 CPU-s; and the two objectives – makespan of the hoist schedule and total

CPU-time – are combined into one weighted sum using the (a posteriori calculated) inverse mean values over the 36 points as weighting factors.

The setup of the Bayesian optimization is as follows: The limitation of the computational time and the objective function are the same as above. The algorithm terminates after 16 retries of finding new hyperparameter values, which is the standard setting in SMAC3.

The computational results are summarized in Table 1, sub-tables 1.1, 2.1 and 3.1 for instances 1, 2 and 3, respectively. The grid search certainly finds the global optimum while the best solution found by the Bayesian optimization is not necessarily the global optimum. The Bayesian optimization evaluates only 56% (instance 1), 64% (instance 2) and 58% (instance 3) of the points; it finds the global optimum for instances 2 and 3 and a solution with an optimality gap of 10% for instance 1.

For instances 1 and 3 the best value for NRJ is 6. In these cases, the full monolithic scheduling model is solved in step two of the heuristic, indicating that it would have been better not to apply the heuristic.

6.3. Extended hyperparameter space

In the second part of the numerical studies, the dimensionality of the hyperparameter space is extended by the number of fixed jobs (NFJ) in the construction step. While NFJ was one in the previous section, all feasible values are considered now. NFJ must not be larger than NSJ such that the constraint NFJ $\leq$ NSJ applies; consequently, the number of points in the grid search increases to 126.

Due to the results for instance 1 and 3 in the first part (NRJ=6), the studies in the second part are limited to instance 2; the results are summarized in Table 1, sub-table 2.2. Each figure is the best objective value over all NFJ-values. The Bayesian optimization finds the global optimum with only 25% of the points evaluated by the grid search.

Table 1: Objective values of the studied problem instances (points evaluated by Bayesian optimization in bold, optimal value shaded, best value found by Bayesian optimization framed)

1.1

NSJ \ NRJ	1	2	3	4	5	6
1	1.56	**2.07**	2.22	**2.08**	2.08	1.46
2	**1.68**	2.9	**2.34**	2.21	2.20	1.58
3	**1.78**	**1.84**	**2.04**	2.62	2.28	1.66
4	**1.74**	**1.81**	2.00	**2.58**	2.25	1.62
5	2.15	**2.06**	**2.28**	2.14	2.03	**1.72**
6	2.05	**1.95**	2.18	2.03	1.92	**1.61**

2.1

NSJ \ NRJ	1	2	3	4	5	6
1	**1.18**	**1.66**	1.70	2.05	1.98	1.51
2	1.31	**1.48**	1.81	2.30	2.07	**1.60**
3	**1.29**	**1.64**	2.12	**2.50**	2.12	1.65
4	1.73	**2.07**	2.55	**2.77**	**2.56**	2.08
5	**1.61**	1.96	**2.44**	2.77	2.44	1.97
6	**1.60**	**1.94**	2.42	**2.77**	2.43	**1.95**

3.1

NSJ \ NRJ	1	2	3	4	5	6
1	**1.60**	**1.76**	**2.20**	**2.02**	**1.91**	**1.51**
2	**1.53**	1.71	**2.20**	2.01	1.90	**1.50**
3	**1.71**	**1.87**	2.32	**2.14**	**2.02**	1.63
4	1.83	**1.99**	2.44	**2.26**	**2.14**	**1.74**
5	1.98	2.15	**2.60**	2.41	2.30	1.90
6	**1.89**	**2.05**	2.49	**2.31**	2.20	**1.80**

2.2

NSJ \ NRJ	1	2	3	4	5	6
1	1.18	1.66	1.70	2.06	1.98	1.51
2	1.29	1.48	1.81	2.30	2.07	1.59
3	1.26	1.60	2.02	2.46	2.09	1.62
4	1.29	2.05	1.93	2.38	2.09	1.62
5	1.14	1.49	2.02	2.36	1.98	1.51
6	1.60	1.94	2.42	2.77	2.43	1.95

7. Conclusions

In this paper, a new method for the automated construction of matheuristics was described and validated for the application to hoist scheduling problems. First numerical studies indicate that the new approach based on Bayesian optimization is preferrable to grid search in case of hyperparameter spaces with higher dimensions.

Future work will elaborate on limitations of the new method including broader numerical studies (e.g. more problem classes), variation of the design parameters (e.g. other acquisition functions and surrogate models), and other types of hyperparameters (e.g. selection of heuristics). Special attention will be paid to multi-fidelity Bayesian optimization. One idea is to steer the precision of the objective function evaluation by varying the termination criterion of the mixed-integer programming solver.

References

A. Aguirre, C. Méndez, A. García-Sánchez, M. Ortega-Mier, 2013, Applying MILP-based algorithms to automated job-shop scheduling problems in aircraft-part manufacturing, "do SimposioArgentino de Informatica Industrial

N. Basán, C. Méndez, 2016, Hybrid MILP/Simulation/Heuristic Algorithms to Complex Hoist Scheduling Problems, CACE, 38, 1929-1934

B. Bischl, M. Binder, M. Lang, T. Pielok, J. Richter, S. Coors, J. Thomas, T. Ullmann, M. Becker, A. Boulesteix, D.Deng, M. Lindauer, 2022, WIREs Data Mining and Knowledge Discovery, 13, 2

S. Chtourou, M. Manier, T. Loukil, 2013, A hybrid algorithm for the cyclic hoist scheduling problem with two transportation resources, Computers & Industrial Engineering, 65, 426-437

J. Feng, A. Che, C. Chu, 2015, Dynamic hoist scheduling problem with multi-capacity reentrant machines: A mixed integer programming approach, Computers & Industrial Engineering, 87, 611-620

F. Hutter, L. Kotthoff, J. Vanschoren (Ed.s), 2019, Automated Machine Learning – Methods, Systems, Challenges, Springer

L. Lei, T. Wang, 1989, A proof: the cyclic hoist scheduling problem is NP-complete. Graduate School of Management, Rutgers University, Working Paper, 89-0016

X. Li, F. Chan, S. Chung, 2015, Optimal multi-degree cyclic scheduling of multiple robots without overlapping in robotic flowshops with parallel machines, Journal of Manufacturing Systems, 36, 62-57

M. Manier, C. Bloch, 2003, A Classification for Hoist Scheduling Problems, International Journal of Flexible Manufacturing Systems, 15, 37-55

V. Maniezzo, T. Stützle, S. Voß, 2009, Matheuristics – Hybridizing metaheuristics and mathematical programming, Springer

V. Maniezzo, M. Boschetti, T. Stützle, 2021, Matheuristics – Algorithms and Implementations, Springer

D. Ramin, D. Fraizzoli, A. Ballarino, A. Brusaferri, Dynamic hoist scheduling for multi-recipe and multi-stage production lines: A logical framework, 2023, Computers & Industrial Engineering, 182,

S. Reimschüssel, U. Fuchs, G. Sand, 2023, Electroplating scheduling: Closing a research gap from an automation vendor's perspective, CACE, 52, 125-130

E. Schede, J. Brandt, A. Tornede, M. Wever, V. Bengs, E. Hüllermeier, K. Tierney, 2022, A Survey of Methods for Automated Algorithm Configuration, Journal of Artificial Intelligence Research, 75, 425-487

N. Tian, A. Che, J. Feng, 2013, Real-time hoist scheduling for multistage material handling process under uncertainties, AIChE, 59, 1046-1048

P. Yan, S. Liu, T. Sun, K. Ma, 2018, A dynamic scheduling approach for optimizing the material handling operations in a robotic cell, Computers & Operations Research, 99, 166–177

Z. Zhou, L. Li, 2009, A solution for cyclic scheduling of multi-hoists without overlapping, Annals of Operations Research, 168, 5-21

Flavio Manenti, Gintaras V. Reklaitis (Eds.), Proceedings of the 34th European Symposium on Computer Aided Process Engineering / 15th International Symposium on Process Systems Engineering (ESCAPE34/PSE24), June 2-6, 2024, Florence, Italy

TRBO: Transfer Learning Accelerated Bayesian Optimization

Haoyang Hu,[a] Runzhe Liang,[a] Zhihong Yuan[a]*

aThe State Key Laboratory of Chemical Engineering, Department of Chemical Engineering, Tsinghua University, Beijing 100084, China
Corresponding author's E-mail: zhihongyuan@mail.tsinghua.edu.cn

Abstract

Despite its success in delivering high-quality solutions for numerous black-box design problems, Bayesian optimization encounters limitations when experimental resources are strictly constrained, known as the small-sample problem. To overcome this hurdle, we propose a novel optimization method named TRBO (TransfeR learning accelerated Bayesian Optimization). TRBO innovatively replaces the conventional Gaussian process surrogate model in Bayesian optimization with modified TrAdaBoost.R2 algorithm, a variation of AdaBoost.R2 specifically designed for transfer learning, in order to leverage knowledge from historical data. Through comprehensive evaluations and ablation studies, we demonstrate that TRBO significantly elevates optimization performance, particularly when confronted with noisy prior knowledge.

Keywords: Bayesian optimization, surrogate model, machine learning, transfer learning.

1. Introduction

Black-box design problems are pervasive in research and development endeavors, such as the condition design for carrying out chemical reactions and the hyperparameter design for training machine learning models. As the de facto standard solution for gradient-free black-box optimization, Bayesian optimization (BO) attempts to converge within a minimal number of target function evaluations by combining probabilistic surrogate models and acquisition functions (Shahriari et al., 2016).

Despite the high efficiency of BO in utilizing experimental data, the small-sample problem persists in most reaction optimization scenarios, where limited experimental cost constrains the ability of surrogate models to acquire sufficient knowledge within the allowed number of evaluations. On the contrary, in practice, researchers often possess preliminary empirical data from pre-experiments or literature research, which typically follows a different distribution from formal experiments and cannot be directly integrated. Transfer learning presents a promising resolution to alleviate the small-sample problem, thus introducing novel approaches to accelerating BO (Bai et al., 2023). Several BO variations utilizing self-adaptive transfer learning have been proposed for hyperparameter tuning, such as products of Gaussian process (GP) experts (Schilling et al., 2016) and two-stage training strategy (Li et al., 2022). While these methods focus on the adjustment of GP surrogate models, the possibility of other structures remain unexplored.

In this work, we formulate a novel transfer learning accelerated BO variation named TRBO with ensemble learning-powered surrogate model, which self-adaptively extracts the valuable part of historical data that follows similar distribution to improve its performance. By mitigating the small-sample problem through self-adaptive transfer learning, TRBO represents a valuable contribution to accelerating black-box optimization.

2. Transfer learning accelerated Bayesian optimization (TRBO)

The basic idea of TRBO is to adopt modified TrAdaBoost.R2 (Pardoe and Stone, 2010) algorithm instead of popular GP algorithm to construct the surrogate model in BO. TrAdaBoost (Dai et al., 2007), a transfer learning variation of AdaBoost (Freund and Schapire, 1997), concurrently trains a classifier using data from both the source and target domains. TrAdaBoost.R2 is the regressor version of TrAdaBoost. Moreover, since there is some critical difference between general regressors and surrogate models in BO, we modify TrAdaBoost.R2 in TRBO to improve its stability during early iterations. The rest of this section describes the implementation of TRBO.

2.1. Standard Bayesian optimization framework

The standard BO framework comprises two components: the surrogate model and the acquisition function. The surrogate model depicts an estimation of the input-output mapping relationship of the black-box problem, commonly denoted as the target space. The acquisition function determines the sample point to evaluate next, correspondingly. A typical single iteration of BO can be described as:

First, the surrogate model S is built or updated on the currently available dataset D. From a Bayesian perspective, this is equivalent to calculating the posterior distribution of the model parameters s after observing D:

$$p(s|D) = \frac{p(D|s)}{p(D)} p(s) \tag{1}$$

where $p(s|D)$ and $p(s)$ denotes parameter distributions of the updated and the original surrogate model S, and $p(D)$ can be regarded as a normalizing constant.

Then, the acquisition function is calculated with S and optimized to determine the sample next point to evaluate next. For example, the Upper Confidence Bound (UCB) function comprehensively considers the expectation and uncertainty of S. It can be written as:

$$\alpha_{UCB}(x; S) = \mu(x; S) + \kappa\sigma(x; S) \tag{2}$$

where μ and σ denotes prediction and standard deviation, respectively. Hyperparameter κ balances exploration and exploitation. Bigger κ means stronger tendency to exploration. The selected sample point is merged into D after its evaluation on the black-box problem. Such iteration is repeated until the number of iterations reaches a preset value N.

2.2. TrAdaBoost.R2 algorithm

As mentioned above, the surrogate model in BO should estimate both the expectation and uncertainty of a specific sample point in the target space. As an ensemble learning algorithm, TrAdaBoost.R2 implement this through building multiple different weak learners. Mathematically, the training process can be expressed as:

Given the maximum number N of iterations, source domain D_{src} including n samples and target domain D_{tg} including m samples, the initial sample weight vector w^1 is set to:

$$w_i^1 = \begin{cases} 1/n, when\ 0 < i \leq n \\ 1/m, when\ n < i \leq n + m \end{cases} \tag{3}$$

The following steps are repeated until the number of weak learners reaches N:
The sample weight vector w^t is normalized to p^t first. Then, the t-th weak learner h^t is built using p^t on both D_{src} and D_{tg}, but only its prediction error ϵ^t on D_{tg} is calculated:

$$\varepsilon_i^t = \left(\frac{|y_i - h^t(x_i)|}{\max_{j=1}^{n+m}|y_j - h^t(x_j)|}\right)^2 \tag{4}$$

$$\epsilon^t = \frac{\sum_{i=n+1}^{n+m} p_i^t \varepsilon_i^t}{\sum_{i=n+1}^{n+m} p_i^t} \tag{5}$$

The new sample weight vector w^{t+1} is updated according to ϵ^t by:

$$\beta^t = \begin{cases} 1/(1 + \sqrt{2\ln\frac{n}{N}}), when \; 0 < i \le n \\ \epsilon^t/(1 - \epsilon^t), when \; n < i \le n+m \end{cases} \tag{6}$$

$$w_i^{t+1} = \begin{cases} p_i^t(\beta^t)^{\varepsilon_i^t}, when \; 0 < i \le n \\ p_i^t(\beta^t)^{-\varepsilon_i^t}, when \; n < i \le n+m \end{cases} \tag{7}$$

After all weak learners are built, the expectation and uncertainty of the final learner H can be estimated by the weighted median and standard deviation of all weak learners h respectively, where the weight of the t-th weak learner h^t is $-\ln\beta^t$.

During the training process, inaccurately predicted sample points in D_{tg} are treated as the focus of subsequent learning, leading to an increase in their weights. Conversely, inaccurately predicted sample points in D_{src} are treated as interference stemming from different data distributions, prompting a reduction of their weights. In this manner, TRBO identifies the transferable subset in D_{src}, and thus provides valuable knowledge to the surrogate model to expedite exploration in D_{tg}.

2.3. Implementation modification

In application, we observed instability in the behavior of TRBO due to the scarcity of evaluated sample points in the target domain during early iterations. Two reasons were identified, and corresponding modifications were made to the original implementation.

First, an issue arose from the excessively high average weight assigned to sample points in the target domain during early iterations. To rectify this imbalance between the weights of the source and target domains, an additional hyperparameter *target_init_weight_ratio* (TIWR) was introduced into the weight initialization step. Consequently, Eq. (1) was replaced with Eq. (8):

$$w_i^1 = \begin{cases} 1/n, when \; 0 < i \le n \\ TIWR/m, when \; n < i \le n+m \end{cases} \tag{8}$$

Furthermore, we also found that solely factoring in the prediction error on the target domain in Eq. (6) led to an overemphasis on the target domain, and thus hurt the stability due to the inner randomness of acquisition function optimization during early iterations. To give rational weight to prior knowledge, another hyperparameter *target_error_ratio* (TER) was introduced to this step by replacing Eq. (6) with Eq. (9):

$$\epsilon^t = TER \frac{\sum_{i=n+1}^{n+m} p_i^t \varepsilon_i^t}{\sum_{i=n+1}^{n+m} p_i^t} + (1 - TER) \frac{\sum_{i=1}^{n} p_i^t \varepsilon_i^t}{\sum_{i=1}^{n} p_i^t} \tag{9}$$

2.4. Flowchart of TRBO

Figure 1 summarizes the overall flow chart of TRBO.

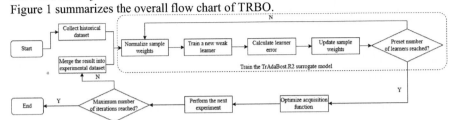

Figure 1 Flowchart of TRBO

3. Case studies

For case study, we conducted detailed evaluations and ablation studies on well-known benchmark black-box functions.

3.1. Benchmark Functions

To comprehensively evaluate the performance of TRBO, we selected three representative benchmark functions: the Rosenbrock function (2 dimensions, 1 global minimum point), the Branin function (2 dimensions, 3 global minimum points), and the Hartman6 function (6 dimensions, 1 global minimum point) All these functions are converted into maximize problems with their global maximum values moved to zero.

3.2. Source training datasets

As mentioned in the Introduction section, unlike the target domain, which is expensive to explore, the source domain is usually derived from related empirical data following a distribution that may differ slightly or even substantially from formal experiments. Hence, source training datasets comprised more samples with strong noise added to their target function values. Specifically, each source training dataset consisted of 200 points randomly sampled from the target space, with their target function values multiplied by a random interference factor ranging from 0.5 to 2.0 as noise.

3.3. Control groups for ablation study

Traditional method to leverage prior knowledge is to directly pretrain the GP model with known sample points. So, standard BO with GP surrogate model pretrained on the source training dataset was used as a control group, hereinafter referred to as pretrained BO.
To evaluate the difference between GP and boosting models, standard BO using normal AdaBoost.R2 algorithm for building surrogate model was also used as a control group, hereinafter simply referred to as AdaBoost.R2. Here, AdaBoost was also pretrained on the source training dataset for fair comparison with TRBO.
Apart from BO, heuristic algorithms are also proved to be powerful solutions for black-box optimization problems, such as genetic algorithm and evolution strategy. We used Covariance Matrix Adaptation Evolution Strategy (CMA-ES) (Hansen, 2006), a popular variation of evolution strategy, as a control group to validate the effectiveness on selected benchmark functions of BO.

3.4. Hyperparameters

For standard BO and pretrained BO, Matern 2.5 kernel with $\alpha=1$ was adopted. For AdaBoost.R2 and TRBO, decision tree regressor with *max_depth*=6 was adopted as the weak learner, and the number of weak learners was set to 25 to avoid overfitting on the source domain. UCB acquisition function with κ decay from $\kappa=10$ to 0.1 was applied to all BO-based algorithms. For CMA-ES, population size was set to 3, the minimum allowed value, to simulate limited parallel evaluation capability in most applications.

Up to 50 target function evaluations, 1/4 of the source training dataset capacity, were allowed for each algorithm to simulate the expensive evaluation cost. To eliminate the influence of randomness, each experiment was repeated 10 times with different random seeds independently. All experiments were performed on an Intel Core i7-8700 CPU.

4. Results and discussion

The means and standard deviations of maximum target function values found by all algorithms on benchmark functions are presented in Table 1.

Table 1 Means and standard deviations of maximum target function values found

	Rosenbrock	Branin	Hartman6
Standard BO	$-(1.98\pm0.227)\times10^{-2}$	$-(1.93\pm1.19)\times10^{-3}$	-0.389 ± 0.0635
Pretrained BO	$-(501\pm1.93)\times10^{-2}$	$-(201\pm8.74)\times10^{-3}$	-0.351 ± 0.0980
CMA-ES	$-(56.5\pm0.228)\times10^{-2}$	$-(329\pm1.37)\times10^{-3}$	-0.615 ± 0.119
AdaBoost.R2	$-(611\pm2.86)\times10^{-2}$	$-(64.9\pm3.87)\times10^{-3}$	-0.637 ± 0.100
TRBO	$\mathbf{-(1.72\pm0.389)\times10^{-2}}$	$\mathbf{-(1.69\pm1.34)\times10^{-3}}$	$\mathbf{-0.345\pm0.0800}$

For clarity, the maximum target function value curve corresponding to each run with the best performance among 10 independent runs is depicted in Figure 2.

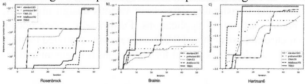

Figure 2 Maximum target function value curves of the best performing runs

Both Table 1 and Figure 2 demonstrate that TRBO consistently outperformed all control groups across various benchmark functions, underscoring its universality in tackling diverse problems. Notably, TRBO exhibited significantly accelerated speed on the Branin function and Hartman6 function, indicating its adept utilization of prior knowledge.

For ablation study, taking the two-dimensional Rosenbrock function as a visible example, detailed optimization processes of the best performing runs are presented in Figure 3.

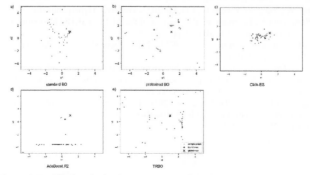

Figure 3 Detailed optimization processes of the best performing runs on the Rosenbrock function

Figure 3 shows that, following the introduction of simulated noisy prior knowledge, pretrained BO was disturbed by differences in data distribution, resulting in diminished performance. In practice, although the quantity of historical data may be substantial, its relevance to formal experiments is often not assured. Therefore, in such cases, the source training dataset cannot be directly employed for target space modeling, and standard BO using GP surrogate model cannot be directly adopted by transfer learning.

Figure 3c shows that, CMA-ES could rapidly identify the approximate orientation of the global maximum, but hardly the precise location. So, under stringent limitations on target function evaluations, the performance of evolution strategy is usually inferior to BO.

Figure 3d shows that, AdaBoost.R2 was also disturbed by differences in data distribution like standard BO, with its performance even worse than that of BO. This implies that, GP indeed outperforms AdaBoost.R2 in normal optimization situations, justifying GP as the default choice for BO. However, Figure 3e underscores that TRBO, bolstered by prior knowledge, not only mitigated the drawbacks of AdaBoost.R2 but also navigated interference from the source domain.

In summary, the above ablation study validates that, the modified TrAdaBoost.R2-based surrogate model is the key of TRBO to enable self-adaptive transfer learning.

5. Conclusion

A transfer learning accelerated black-box optimization algorithm TRBO is proposed under the BO framework to effectively harness historical data with unguaranteed data distribution. The key innovation of TRBO is the modified TrAdaBoost.R2 algorithm which self-adaptively identifies the transferable subset of the historical data to enhance the learning process of surrogate models, thereby elevating overall performance. Given the ubiquity of similar transferable datasets in various design problems, TRBO holds promise for a broad spectrum of applications. Furthermore, since boosting models are open due to their ensemble structure, TRBO can be easily extended to other types of data-driven learners, showcasing its potential for continuous refinement and expansion.

References

Bai, T., Li, Y., Shen, Y., Zhang, X., Zhang, W., Cui, B., 2023. Transfer Learning for Bayesian Optimization: A Survey. arXiv preprint.

Dai, W., Yang, Q., Xue, G.R., Yu, Y., 2007. Boosting for transfer learning, in: ACM International Conference Proceeding Series. pp. 193–200.

Freund, Y., Schapire, R.E., 1997. A Decision-Theoretic Generalization of On-Line Learning and an Application to Boosting. J Comput Syst Sci 55, 119–139.

Hansen, N., 2006. The CMA evolution strategy: A comparing review. Studies in Fuzziness and Soft Computing 192, 75–102.

Li, Y., Shen, Y., Jiang, H., Zhang, W., Yang, Z., Zhang, C., Cui, B., 2022. TransBO: Hyperparameter Optimization via Two-Phase Transfer Learning, in: Proceedings of the ACM SIGKDD International Conference on Knowledge Discovery and Data Mining. pp. 956–966.

Pardoe, D., Stone, P., 2010. Boosting for regression transfer, in: ICML 2010 - Proceedings, 27th International Conference on Machine Learning. pp. 863–870.

Schilling, N., Wistuba, M., Schmidt-Thieme, L., 2016. Scalable hyperparameter optimization with products of gaussian process experts, in: Lecture Notes in Computer Science (Including Subseries Lecture Notes in Artificial Intelligence and Lecture Notes in Bioinformatics). pp. 33–48.

Shahriari, B., Swersky, K., Wang, Z., Adams, R.P., De Freitas, N., 2016. Taking the human out of the loop: A review of Bayesian optimization. Proceedings of the IEEE 104, 148–175. https://doi.org/10.1109/JPROC.2015.2494218

Flavio Manenti, Gintaras V. Reklaitis (Eds.), Proceedings of the 34th European Symposium on Computer Aided Process Engineering / 15th International Symposium on Process Systems Engineering (ESCAPE34/PSE24), June 2-6, 2024, Florence, Italy

Estimation of Long-term Power Demand of Oil and Gas Installations using Hybrid Models

Leif Erik Andersson[a,*], Adriana Reyes-Lúa[a], Heiner Schümann[b], Brage Rugstad Knudsen[a]

[a]*SINTEF Energy Research, Sem Sælandsvei 11, Trondheim, 7034, Norway*
[b]*SINTEF Industry, S.P. Andersens vei 15 B, Trondheim, 7031, Norway*
leif.andersson@sintef.no

Abstract

A methodology to forecast power demand of oil and gas installations which uses publicly production available data, parametric models and data-driven Gaussian regression methods is presented. The methodology also captures the expected fuel gas consumption and energy ratio. The proposed methodology is tested on the Brage field on the Norwegian Continental Shelf. It is shown that the general oil and water production behaviour as well as fuel gas consumption trends can be predicted. However, the forecast inherits a significant uncertainty due to the publicly available dataset lacking metadata and a complete description of the energy sinks.

Keywords: Gaussian Process Regression, Forecast, Oil and Gas, Power demand

1. Introduction

The need for decarbonization and the energy transition will cause a decline in global fossil fuel demand in the years to come (IEA, 2023). Nevertheless, natural gas is expected to play an important role in the path towards decarbonization as a raw material to produce low-carbon hydrogen via steam reforming with carbon capture and storage (Ueckerdt et al, 2024). Extraction of oil and gas is energy intensive and most CO_2 emissions from offshore petroleum activities are related to power generation to sustain offshore operations, with most of the offshore power production using natural gas as fuel (Voldsund et al, 2023). For instance, in 2022, 11.57 mill. ton $CO_{2,eq}$ were emitted in the Norwegian Continental Shelf (NCS), 80.73 % of which were generated by gas turbines and 7.14 % by engines (NDP, 2023). The relation between power demand and oil and gas production varies through the lifetime of a site. Energy intensity and emissions from power generation increase significantly towards the late life of fields due to the need of reservoir pressure support or gas lift to maintain operations. Also, equipment such as gas export compressors may operate far from their design point and thus, at lower efficiencies. There are high-profile studies aiming to predict global oil and gas production trends, which are driven not only by availability but also by economics (Bardi, 2019). At an installation level, it is possible to utilize engineering insights to estimate production and energy intensity (Masnadi and Brandt, 2017). Different machine learning tools have been used to analyze upstream operations (Koroteev et al, 2021), including deep-learning and hybrid models to predict production (Fan et al, 2021; Pan et al, 2023). Here, we analyze the system from the power demand perspective, proposing a methodology to forecast the long-term power demand using public available data for the NCS. Such tools will support operators to plan investment in low-carbon power supply for offshore sites and enable public authorities to monitor energy intensity and thus shape regulations for aging fields.

2. Methodology

2.1. Data set

The data was retrieved from the Norwegian Diskos National Data Repository (DISKOS NDR, 2022). The data set contains monthly production data per field, installation and terminal of oil companies operating on the NCS. A challenge for creating a long-term forecast model is that additional metadata is not available. Therefore, the operational status or events, e.g., downtime, maintenance schedule, installation of new wells, upgrading or installation of new equipment or change of production, is not known. These factors influence the production and are visible as peaks and sudden large changes of trends in the time series data.

2.2. Data pre-processing

A moving average filter is employed for outlier detection. If the data point x in the time series deviates significantly from the moving average value $\hat{x}$ using the standard deviation s over the window, an outlier is detected and the data point x is replaced with its moving average value $\hat{x}$, as in Eq. (1), where δ is the Z-score.

$$\delta = \left| \frac{x - \hat{x}}{\hat{x}} \right| > 2, \tag{1}$$

2.3. Gaussian process regression

Gaussian Process (GP) regression is used for the energy demand and production forecasts. GP is a machine learning method that works well with small data sets (Rasmussen and Williams, 2006), which makes it well suited for the data set used in this article. GPs are non-parametric, probabilistic kernel methods that aim to identify an unknown function f from data. A zero-mean function with automatic relevance squared-exponential covariance is chosen. The log marginal likelihood is used to find the hyperparameters from a training data set.

2.4. Forecast methodology

A hybrid forecast strategy is applied consisting of two parts, a data-driven model and a parametric model that is created based on expected production profiles of oil and gas fields. In case a parametric model is used it can be supplemented by a data-driven model that learns to estimate the difference between real data and parametric model.

2.4.1. Parametric models

Parametric models are included in the forecast framework to allow inclusion of expert knowledge into the forecast. Parametric models for oil, gas, and water production are included. The purpose is to include the knowledge that as oil and gas production declines, water production increases over the lifetime of a field. Exponential decay is used for oil and gas production while logistic growth is used for water production. These models are chosen since they usually fit well with the expected production profiles of and oil and gas field (Holt and Schümann, 2022). The data set is normalized before the parameter estimation step by least squares is employed.

2.4.2. Data-driven models

GP regression is employed for the data-driven model. Alternatively linear regression is also tested to evaluate the advantage of using a nonlinear model. In both cases a (non) linear autoregressive model with exogenous inputs (ARX-type) was chosen for the model structure. All outputs of the previous time step are fed back to the model to predict the next time step.

2.5. Performance parameters

The performance of the forecast models is evaluated calculating normalized root-mean square error (NRMS) on the test data set. We set as boundary the offshore facility and assume that the studied offshore systems are energetically self-sufficient. We use the energy ratio (ER), Eq. (2), to quantify the energy efficiency of the offshore facility:

$$ ER = \frac{E_{gas}^{exp} + E_{oil}^{exp}}{E_{gas}^{pow}} \qquad (2)$$

where E_{gas}^{exp} and E_{oil}^{exp} correspond to the energy in the oil and natural gas exports to the onshore facilities and E_{gas}^{pow} corresponds to the direct energy used to provide the power required for offshore operations, typically for natural gas via gas turbines.

3. Results

Here, we present the results of the proposed forecast methodology for the Brage field on the NCS. The order of the ARX-type model was varied. In addition, forecasts were created with only the parametric model, a hybrid model of parametric and data-driven models, and purely data-driven models, respectively. Figure 1 shows the training and test sets for oil and water production. Both parameters are captured well with the parametric model, and the forecast performance over the test set, to the right of the dashed vertical line, is very good.

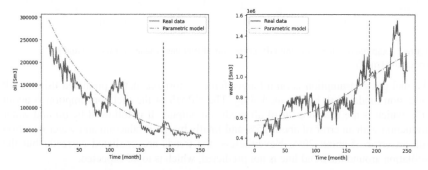

Figure 1 Examples of parametric model fit for the Brage field. The (red) dashed vertical line indicates the split between training and test set.

In a first step, the one-step forecast performance of the forecast methodology is evaluated. Consequently, one month into the future is predicted. For the Brage field the linear regression models usually outperform the GP regression models in accuracy for all outputs. One exception is the hybrid model for oil production where the high order GP regression models perform the best. The GP regression models tend to follow more strongly the parametric models resulting in a smoother and more constant forecast than the linear regression models. This indicates that they rely less on the inputs from the previous time-step (auto-correlation part) to predict the next step. The normalized root-mean square error of all outputs is in the range of 8-15 %, where the oil production is predicted the worst.

In Figure 2, a forecast over about 60 months of the fuel gas consumption (energy consumption of the platform) and oil production for the Brage field is shown. The fuel gas consumption itself is predicted by a data-driven model since no parametric model was developed. However, some of the inputs to the fuel gas consumption model, e.g., the oil production, are forecasted by a parametric model. The variation in the fuel gas consumption is small, which is captured by the model. In fact, the strongest variations are present in the end of the data set (month 35-60), which is likely connected to the change from a primary oil to a primary gas-producing field, information that is not included in the meta-data. All prediction models varying the different parameters and prediction methods show a close to constant fuel gas consumption.

The oil production decreases for the parametric model and hybrid model while it increases for the purely data-driven model. This is not the case for all models, but it is observed that the parametric model alone usually outperforms any data-driven model (hybrid or purely data-driven) for the oil production. In a lesser extent this can also be observed for the water production, which is not shown in Figure 2.

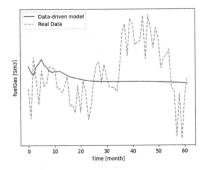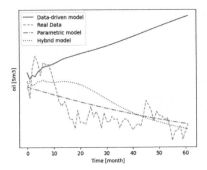

Figure 2 Example of forecast using GP regression of fuel gas consumption (left) and oil production (right).

The fuel gas consumption is on a longer forecast horizons better predicted using a GP regression model with hybrid modelling. The NRMS of the fuel consumption is about 10%, which is the lowest error of all predicted outputs. It is followed by oil and water production with an error of about 15% and finally by gas production and water injection with an error of about 20%. Nevertheless, the trends are predicted correctly but the oscillation around the trend line is not predicted, which is to be expected.

To analyse the data-driven models, step responses of the identified models were tested. It reveals that some internal correlations are not as expected. According to the models, an increase in water injection decreases oil and gas production and decreases fuel gas consumption. On the other hand, a reduction in oil production also reduces gas production, fuel gas consumption and water injection. These two tests contradict each other. A reason is that each output is predicted with a separate model without considering output correlation. Moreover, the public data set is small and metadata is missing making the creation of data-driven models that capture the physics of the system challenging.

A 2030 outlook on the energy ratio of the Brage field is given in Figure 3. Since it is a forecast, this cannot be validated. The best models in the test set using varying input and output lag for the different regression methods are shown. The dashed lines show the best GP regression forecast models and the dash dotted lines the best linear regression forecasts. Moreover, one forecast (solid green line) for the ER is created using the best combination of prediction models for fuel gas, gas, and oil forecast models validated on the test set. It can be noted that the forecasts vary from an efficiency of about 5.5 - 10.0 in 2030. The combination of the best performing models over the test horizon predicts an efficiency of about 7.0 in 2030.

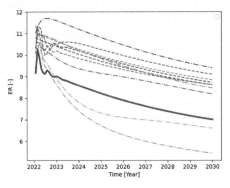

Figure 3 - 2030 forecasts of energy ratio (ER).

4. Discussion

In some tested cases the parametric models' forecasts are the best compared with the data-driven and hybrid models. While the gas, oil, and water production forecasts are improved using parametric models, they do not necessarily have a positive effect on the forecast for other outputs like fuel gas consumption, for which no parametric model was formulated. In fact, a purely auto-regression model of the fuel gas consumption has a similar performance as the model using additional inputs. For the 2030 forecast of the ER, however, the inclusion of the parametric models is essential since the gas and oil production forecast improves significantly, which is part of the ER.

The outputs of the GP regression model are the mean and standard deviation. The standard deviation has not been used in this paper since several models that have also a purely deterministic output were combined. The GP regression models could also be used to create stochastic forecast trajectories. A weakness is that during training it is assumed that the inputs are deterministic and not uncertain while in the long-term forecast uncertain inputs are used. A result is that the uncertainty in the forecast may be underestimated.

When creating the forecast models, physical correlations are not necessarily inferred from the data set, e.g., increase in water injection increases fuel gas consumption. A reason is that a change in one input, e.g., the water injection also influences other variables so the interaction might be more complex. Another reason is that the data set does not account for all consumers on a platform. Furthermore, the data set is small since it has just about 300 data points where just 75% are used for training. It is expected that the forecast methodology improves significantly with a more comprehensive data set. Additionally, the metadata (e.g. installation of new equipment, new well installation, downtime, maintenance time) could be included to avoid wrongly inferred correlations from data.

In this work, just two parametric models were developed, one for oil and gas production and one for the water production. A challenge is to fit a start-up of the production into these models. At the start of a field's lifetime a production ramp-up can usually be observed. Moreover, a few years constant high production is achieved before the decay starts. These periods cannot be represented by the current models. A practical approach could be to exclude the first years of a field's lifetime for the training of parametric models. In addition, parameter estimation is dominated by the first period of production because of the significantly larger production volume and relatively larger error in the model fit compared to production at later periods. However, the goal is to create a model that predicts well the behavior in the future so periods at the end of the training set should be weighted more strongly. A challenge is, however, to find suitable weights. Another challenge that was observed for the Brage field is production increases due to events that are not part of the meta-data, such as installation of new wells or upgrade of equipment. This can increase production for some time, which can lead to an over-prediction of future production by the parametric model.

5. Conclusions

In this paper a forecast methodology was presented that uses publicly available production data from oil and gas fields. It was shown that the general trends can be captured by the forecast models, which helps to estimate future energy consumption on the platform. The parametric models help to support the data-driven models to capture the expected trends for oil and gas productions. In the future, the methodology can be tested on more oil and gas fields. With different types of oil and gas fields, additional parametric models for other production variables may need to be developed.

Acknowlegdment
Support from the Research Council of Norway and partners of PETROSENTER LowEmission (project code 296207) is gratefully acknowledged.

References

C.E. Rasmussen and C.K. Williams , 2006, Gaussian processes for machine learning, MIT Press.

D. Fan, et al., 2021, Well production forecasting based on ARIMA-LSTM model considering manual operations. Energy 220, 119708.

D. Koroteev and Tekic, Z., 2021, Artificial intelligence in oil and gas upstream: Trends, challenges, and scenarios for the future. Energy and AI 3, 100041.

F. Ueckerdt, et al., 2024, On the cost competitiveness of blue and green hydrogen, Joule, 8,1–25.

International Energy Agency (IEA), World Energy Outlook 2023, 2023.
    www.iea.org/reports/world-energy-outlook-2023

M.S. Masnadi, A.R. Brandt, 2017, Climate impacts of oil extraction increase significantly with oil field age, Nature Climate Change, 7, 551-556

M. Voldsund et al., 2023, Low carbon power generation for offshore oil and gas production. Energy Conversion and Management: X 17, 100347.

Norwegian Petroleum Directorate, The DISKOS production database (DISKOS NDR), 2022.
    www.npd.no/en/diskos/production/

Norwegian Petroleum Directorate, Greenhouse gas emissions, 2023.
    www.norskpetroleum.no/en/environment-and-technology/emissions-to-air

Pan, S. et al., 2023, Oil well production prediction based on CNN-LSTM model with self-attention mechanism. Energy 284, 12870.

U. Bardi, 2019. Peak oil, 20 years later: Failed prediction or useful insight? Energy Research & Social Science 48, 257–261.

T. Holt and H. Schümann, 2022, Energy Efficient Operation of Petroleum Production Plants. SPE Norway Subsurface Conference.

Flavio Manenti, Gintaras V. Reklaitis (Eds.), Proceedings of the 34th European Symposium on Computer Aided Process Engineering / 15th International Symposium on Process Systems Engineering (ESCAPE34/PSE24), June 2-6, 2024, Florence, Italy

An Economic Assessment Framework for Intelligent Process Monitoring Systems

Fangyuan Ma[a], Cheng Ji[a], Jingde Wang[a], Nan Zhang[b,*], Wei Sun[a,*]

[a]*College of Chemical Engineering, Beijing University of Chemical Technology, Beijing 100029, China*
[b]*Department of Chemical Engineering, The University of Manchester, Manchester M13 9PL, UK*
Corresponding Author's E-mail: Nan.Zhang@manchester.ac.uk, sunwei@mail.buct.edu.cn

Abstract

In this work, an economic assessment framework for intelligent process monitoring systems is proposed to quantify benefits brought by the application of the systems. To address the issue that the systems do not directly generate economic benefits, a benefit estimation method based on the losses caused by historical faults is described. A stability index is employed to label economically impactful faults in historical data. Then, based on the fault detection results of the systems, the economic losses avoided due to the application of the systems can be calculated, which include those caused by reduced product quality, lower productivity, increased energy consumption, increased labor costs, etc. The framework is then applied to a case study of an ethylene unit.

Keywords: IPDASs, Process Monitoring, Economic Evaluation.

1. Introduction

Maintaining the steady operation of a process is one of the goals of continuous operation in the chemical industry, which requires the timely detection of process upsets. Study on data-driven process monitoring was thus motivated and has attracted extensive attention from both academic and industrial societies, which can be employed to realize fault identification, fault diagnosis, etc. (Ge, 2017). Based on these methods, several Intelligent Process Data Analysis Systems (IPDASs) have been developed and successfully applied to existing industrial processes (Ma et al., 2019; Li et al., 2020). In academia, fault detection rates (FDR), false positive rates (FPR), and alarm time are commonly applied to evaluate these IPDASs (Ma et al., 2023). However, for the industry, whether the economic benefits can be directly accessed due to the application of IPDASs is of great concerned, which has not been specifically studied yet.

The application of economics to industry is not uncommon for similar systems. For example, the economic assessment of advanced process controls (APCs) has been studied for decades (Bauer & Craig, 2008). By analyzing the increased benefits of the process after using APCs, such as improving the process stability and reducing energy consumption, the application benefits of APCs can be calculated. However, unlike APCs, IPDASs do not directly generate economic benefits but rather avoid economic losses from further development of faults by detecting them in advance. Therefore, it is hard to obtain the economic benefits of an IPDASs by direct calculation. To address this problem, the economic losses caused by process deviations that IPDASs can identify are employed to evaluate the economic benefits. In this work, an economic assessment framework for IPDASs is proposed, which can be employed to provide a reference for decision-making in the industry. At first, a stability index (SI) based on the variance of normalized key quality variables is defined to quantify changes in product quality. The control limits of the SI can be calculated using the key quality variable under normal operating conditions. If the SI exceeds the control limit, it means that the process has deviated from the pre-set operating conditions and the product quality has been affected. Process data are entered into IPDAS to obtain fault detection results. Combined with the fault labeled results using SI, the economically impactful fault samples that IPDAS detected will be obtained. Assuming that IPDASs are employed, these fault samples can be identified and eliminated in advance, and the losses caused by the fault can be avoided. Therefore, the losses caused by these identifiable faults are the economic benefits of IPDASs, which can be calculated using data such as product prices, yields, and financial data of enterprises. Data from a refinery enterprise are investigated to validate the proposed economic assessment framework.

The remaining sections of this article are organized as follows: Section 2 contains a detailed introduction to the proposed economic assessment framework for IPDAS. In Section 3, an industrial cracking furnace is investigated as a case study. Finally, a conclusion is present in Section 4.

2. Economic Assessment Framework for IPDASs

The objective of the proposed economic assessment framework in this work is to conduct a systematic and comprehensive economic evaluation of the IPDASs, thereby providing a reference for decision-maker in the industry. To this end, an economic assessment framework as shown in Figure 1 is proposed, and the steps of the proposed framework are explained in detail in the following text.

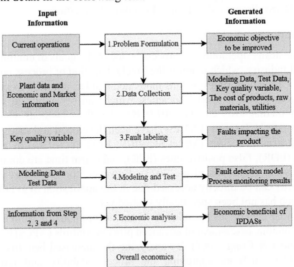

Figure 1. Proposed economic assessment framework for IPDASs.

2.1. Problem Formulation

Process deviations and faults in the chemical industry may threaten the profitability of a company. If these faults can be detected and eliminated in time, the economic losses caused by them can be effectively reduced. For example, the economic losses may be caused by reduced product quality, lower productivity, increased energy consumption, increased labor costs, increased maintenance costs, etc. Therefore, in this work, it is proposed that the economic benefits of IPDASs depend on the economic losses caused by faults that can be detected by IPDASs in historical data.

2.2. Data Collection

In this step, Plant data and economic information need to be collected for calculations in subsequent steps. The content and purpose of the collected data are as follows:

Historical process data: The data collected by DCS are used to develop and test IPDAS.
Key quality variables: Key indicators of production process used to mark process faults.
Internal accounting information: the cost of products, raw materials and utilities for subsequent economic analysis.

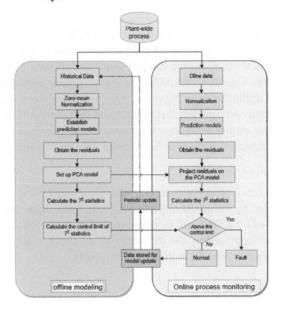

Figure 2. The schematic diagram of adopted fault detection method.

2.3. Fault Labeling

A prerequisite for evaluating the economic benefit of an IPDAS is to identify faults that cause economic losses. In actual production, engineers usually expect key quality variables to be maintained within a pre-set range. When there are abnormal fluctuations in key quality variables, it means that a process fault that impacts economic benefits may have occurred. For this reason, a SI based on the variance of key quality variables is defined to quantify changes in product quality. Given a time series of key quality variable $y(y_1, y_2, \ldots, y_t)$, the SI of the process at time t can be calculated as follows:

$$SI = \frac{1}{t-l} \sum_{i=t-l}^{t} (y_i - \bar{y})^2 \tag{1}$$

$$\bar{y} = \frac{1}{t-l} \sum_{i=t-l}^{t} y_i \tag{2}$$

where *l* represents the window length. The method of selecting the window length l is described in detail in Section 3. Then, the SI of the normal samples (*l-d*) group can be calculated. Based on this, the control limits of SI can be determined as follows:

$$SI_{\lim it} = mean(SI_t, SI_{t+1}, ..., SI_d) \pm std(SI_t, SI_{t+1}, ..., SI_d) \qquad (3)$$

where *mean*() and *std*() represent the average value and standard deviation of the SI. When the SI of a process exceeds the control limits, it means that a fault may have occurred, causing economic losses.

2.4. Modeling and Test

The other prerequisite for evaluating the economic benefit of an IPDAS is to obtain the fault detection performance of its process monitoring method. In this work, an improved fault detection method based on the method from the literature (Ma et al., 2023) is employed as the core algorithm of the IPDAS. The schematic diagram of adopted fault detection method is illustrated in Figure 2. The difference from the method in the literature is the addition of a module that regularly updates the model, making it suitable for monitoring under various conditions of actual industrial processes. More information on the initial fault detection method can be obtained from the literature (Ma et al., 2023).

2.5. Economic Analysis

Based on the fault labelling information obtained in Section 2.3 and the fault detection information provided by the model in Section 2.4, the faults impacting product quality that can be identified by IPDAS will be determined. Then, the economic loss caused by these faults can be expressed by the difference in net profit value between the fault conditions and normal conditions, as illustrated in Eq. (4).

$$\Delta L = \Delta r_{normal} - \Delta r_{fault} \qquad (4)$$

where *ΔL* represents the economic loss, Δr_{normal} and Δr_{fault} represent the net profit under normal conditions and fault conditions, respectively, which can be calculated by Eq. (5).

$$\Delta r_{normal/fault} = p_p \times t_p - p_m \times t_m - p_e \times t_e - s - o \qquad (5)$$

Where p_p, p_m and p_e represent the prices of products, raw materials and energy, respectively; t_p represent the yield of products, t_m and t_e represent the amount of raw materials and energy, respectively. When calculating Δr_{normal}, the average value of normal conditions is used for t_p, t_m and t_e. For calculating Δr_{fault}, the actual operating value during the fault condition is utilized. *s* represents labor cost, and *o* represents other costs, such as environmental costs.

3. Case study

In this work, data from an industrial cracking furnace of an ethylene unit are employed for the economic evaluation of IPDAS. The cracking furnace is the key piece of equipment for the ethylene unit. In the cracking furnace, naphtha and steam are mixed for a cracking reaction to produce olefine, alkanes, and coke. Among them, ethylene and propylene are the target products of primary concern to engineers. Meanwhile,

Propylene/Ethylene (P/E) is commonly used to evaluate the operation of cracking furnaces. Therefore, in this case study, P/E is utilized as a key quality variable to calculate the SI of the process.

Since the value of SI can be affected by the window length, 1000 data samples were utilized to obtain the appropriate window length. As illustrated in Figure 3(a), when the window length is increased to 400 data samples, the SI value does not change significantly with the increase in the window length. Therefore, 400 is determined as the optimal window length in this work. Then, 5000 data samples are used to calculate the SI value and the 6-sigma control limit of the process under normal operating conditions. Data for one complete production cycle are collected for calculating the economic benefits of IPDAS, covering 118,377 samples with a 1-minute interval. The SI values of the production cycle are shown in Figure 3(b). The SI values for six segments of data samples in the production cycle significantly exceed the control limits, indicating that faults affecting product quality occurred during these six periods of time.

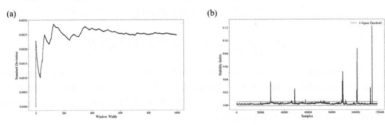

Figure 3. The results of fault labeling. (a) The Standard Deviation calculated with different window widths. (b) The SI values of one complete production cycle.

Following the modelling method described in Section 2.4, a CNN-based fault detection model is established and applied to the process monitoring of the complete production cycle. The process monitoring result for the complete production cycle is illustrated in Figure 4(a). Most faults affecting products can be detected by IPDAS. Taking one of the faults as an example, the fault detection result is shown in Figure 4(b). As can be seen, IPDAS provides an alarm 8 minutes in advance, which can remind operators to detect and eliminate the fault in time. By comparing the fault marking results, fault samples that can be identified by IPDAS and affect the economy can be obtained, as shown by the red scattered in Figure 4(b).

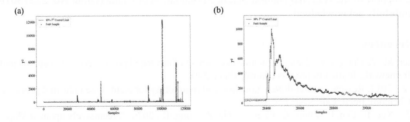

Figure 4. Process monitoring result provided by IPDAS.

However, IPDAS was not used in the actual production process, so the fault could not be detected in advance, and the product yield dropped from 77400 kg/h under normal conditions to 71000 kg/h, with a duration of 3.5 hours. The consumption of naphtha, steam, and fuel oil dropped from 52000 kg/h, 25400 kg/h, and 505 kg/h under normal conditions to 47600 kg/h, 23400 kg/h, and 500 kg/h, respectively. Meanwhile, the mass percentage of ethylene in the product dropped from 30.1% under normal conditions to 28.9%, and the mass percentage of propylene increased from 16.7% under normal conditions to 17.2%. According to internal accounting information, the prices of naphtha, steam, fuel gas, ethylene, and propylene are 3.809 RMB/kg, 0.098 RMB/kg, 2.656 RMB/kg, 7.556 RMB/kg, and 6.944 RMB/kg, respectively. The Δr_{normal} and Δr_{fault} can be calculated by Eq. (6) and Eq. (7). Since the labor cost and other costs are the same for both normal and fault conditions, the economic loss caused by the fault can be calculated using Eq. (8).

$$\Delta r_{normal} = p_{ethylene} \times t_{ethylene}^{normal} + p_{propylene} \times t_{propylene}^{normal} - p_{naphtha} \times t_{naphtha}^{normal} - p_{steam} \times t_{steam}^{normal}$$
$$- p_{fuel} \times t_{fuel}^{normal} - s^{normal} - o^{normal} = 223627.01RMB - s^{normal} - o^{normal} \qquad (6)$$

$$\Delta r_{fault} = p_{ethylene} \times t_{ethylene}^{fault} + p_{propylene} \times t_{propylene}^{fault} - p_{naphtha} \times t_{naphtha}^{fault} - p_{steam} \times t_{steam}^{fault}$$
$$- p_{fuel} \times t_{fuel}^{fault} - s^{fault} - o^{fault} = 192192.32RMB - s^{fault} - o^{fault} \qquad (7)$$

$$\Delta L = \Delta r_{normal} - \Delta r_{fault} = 31434.69RMB \qquad (8)$$

Similarly, the economic losses caused by other faults can be calculated using the proposed framework. By calculating the sum of losses caused by each fault, the application of IPDAS can save economic losses totalling 177,156.48 RMB for one complete production cycle (about 3 months) of the ethylene unit.

4. Conclusions

In this work, an economic assessment framework for IPDASs is proposed to comprehensively calculate the economic benefits brought by the application of IPDASs. The framework addressed the issue that existing evaluation indicators cannot quantify the economic benefits of the systems. The application of the proposed framework to a case study of an ethylene unit illustrated its ease of application and the clear results. As such, it can be concluded that the proposed framework can effectively help enterprises make decisions on whether to apply IPDASs.

Acknowledgements

The support of the National Natural Science Foundation of China (Grant No. 22278018) is gratefully acknowledged.

References

Bauer, M., & Craig, I. K., 2008. Economic assessment of advanced process control–a survey and framework. Journal of process control, 18(1), 2-18.

Ge, Z., 2017. Review on data-driven modeling and monitoring for plant-wide industrial processes. Chemom. Intell. Lab. Syst. 171, 16–25.

Li, X., Xue, F., Qin, L., Zhou, K., Chen, Z., Ge, Z., Song, K., 2020. A recursively updated Map-Reduce based PCA for monitoring the time-varying fluorochemical engineering processes with big data. Chemom. Intell. Lab. Syst. 206, 104167.

Ma, F., Han, C., Han, X., Wang, J., Sun, W., 2019. A web-based industrial process monitoring system for ethylene production. In Foundations of Process/product Analytics and Machine learning (FOPAM) 2019, Raleigh NC.

Ma, F., Ji, C., Wang, J., & Sun, W., 2023. Early identification of process deviation based on convolutional neural network. Chinese Journal of Chemical Engineering, 56, 104-118.

Flavio Manenti, Gintaras V. Reklaitis (Eds.), Proceedings of the 34th European Symposium on Computer Aided Process Engineering / 15th International Symposium on Process Systems Engineering (ESCAPE34/PSE24), June 2-6, 2024, Florence, Italy

Data-driven Discovery of Reaction Kinetic Models in Dynamic Plug Flow Reactors using Symbolic Regression

Ben Cohen,[a,c] Burcu Beykal,[a,b] George M. Bollas[a,c]

[a]*Department of Chemical & Biomolecular Engineering, University of Connecticut, Storrs, CT, USA*
[b]*Center for Clean Energy Engineering, University of Connecticut, Storrs, CT, USA*
[c]*Pratt & Whitney Insitute for Advanced Systems Engineering, University of Connecticut, Storrs, CT, USA*
george.bollas@uconn.edu

Abstract

The method of characteristics is combined with symbolic regression to identify kinetic models of reactions taking place in a dynamic, ideal plug flow reactor (PFR). A change in coordinates facilitates the transformation of time-series measurements collected at a reactor's outlet to data along characteristic curves. The method is applied to three synthetic reactors: one with a nonisothermal, irreversible chemical reaction, one with a reaction described by Hougen-Watson kinetics, and one with measurement noise. The results show that the proposed combination of tools can use time-series data collected at the outlet of a dynamic PFR to discover the Arrhenius expression, rate limited kinetic models, and even analytical solutions to the PFR equation. The toolchain is also flexible enough to allow for discovery of kinetic models even in the presence of measurement noise. Overall, the proposed method offers a simple approach to learn concise kinetic models from dynamic, ideal PFRs and more generally models of source terms in systems described by partial differential equations.

Keywords: Symbolic regression, surrogate modelling, machine learning, genetic algorithms, chemical kinetics

1. Introduction

The surge in available data within the chemical industry has prompted widespread adoption of data-driven modeling tools among process engineers (McBride and Sundmacher, 2019). Many of these methods generate black- or grey-box models and require significantly less oversight than traditional first principles models during development. While these models can offer improved process control (Beykal et al., 2022) and design, a persistent challenge lies in establishing trust due to their poor extrapolative ability beyond the bounds of their training data and limited interpretability.

To improve the extrapolative and interpolative power of data-driven models, Physics-informed Machine Learning (PIML) emerged as an approach to incorporate domain knowledge into the model training process. PIML methods construct models that are consistent with physics, enhancing their ability to extrapolate beyond the training data and making them easier to trust in many applications (Karniadakis et al., 2021). Despite this integration of domain knowledge, interpreting models built using many methods in PIML remains challenging, in part due to the many parameters in data-driven models.

Symbolic regression (SR), as a method in PIML, improves the interpretability of data-driven models while leveraging domain knowledge. It can transform data into concise mathematical representations, resembling and often embodying mechanistic models. In essence, SR provides a data-driven and automated alternative to the traditional expert-driven model ideation process, where a domain expert formulates mechanistic models based on theory, heuristics, and experience. The challenging nature of kinetic model discovery makes SR particularly attractive for this purpose.

The application of SR to discover kinetic models has predominately centered around identifying ordinary differential equation (ODE) models for systems varying in one dimension, typically time (Narayanan et al., 2022). Current SR methods for ODEs often necessitate extensive data sampled across the time domain or involve computationally expensive integration steps (Cornforth and Lipson, 2013). Methods that avoid forward integration approximate derivatives directly from data or rely on surrogate models for determining derivatives analytically.

Despite the progress in SR for discovery of kinetic models in systems described by ODEs, its application to reactors better characterized by partial differential equation (PDE) models – like dynamic plug flow reactors (PFRs) – remains limited. SR methods for PDE discovery encounter similar challenges to their ODE counterparts: dependence on extensive or challenging-to-obtain data (Rudy et al., 2017) or expensive integration (Cohen et al., 2023 under review). Consequently, the endeavor of learning kinetic models using SR from input-output relationships in systems best described using PDEs remains prohibitively expensive.

This work introduces an innovative approach to the discovery of kinetic models specifically tailored for ideal PFRs with constant thermophysical properties. In contrast to prior SR methods for PDE discovery, the proposed approach acknowledges that the PFR equation is already known and directs its focus towards identifying the unknown reaction term. To achieve this, the method of characteristics (MoC) is used to enact a change in coordinates such that the reactor dynamics occur in one dimension. The new coordinates are then leveraged to transform the time-series data collected at the PFR outlet into a dataset sampled across the direction that captures the reactor's dynamics. Subsequently, established methods in ODE model discovery can be applied to reveal the unknown kinetic model without forward integration.

2. Methodology

The ultimate objective of this work is to demonstrate how to automatically discover the unknown reaction term ($\mathbf{R}(\mathbf{x})$) from input-output data of an ideal PFR with constant thermophysical properties governed by Eq. (1). The state variables encompass chemical species concentrations ($\mathbf{c}$) and temperature (T), consolidated as the state vector $\mathbf{x} = [\mathbf{c}, T]$. The variables v, z, and t respectively represent flow velocity through the reactor, space, and time. The reactor's domain is described as $\mathcal{D} = \{z \in \mathbb{R} | 0 \le z \le 1, t \in \mathbb{R} | 0 \le t \le t_f\}$ where t_f is the final time. The subscripts $\mathbf{x}_t = \partial \mathbf{x}/\partial t$ and $\mathbf{x}_z = \partial \mathbf{x}/\partial z$ denote partial derivatives with respect to time and space.

$$\mathbf{x}_t + v(t)\mathbf{x}_z = \mathbf{R}(\mathbf{x}) \tag{1}$$

Automatic discovery of the reaction term using existing SR methods requires either significant data collected across $\mathcal{D}$, or the forward integration of the PFR equation many times. In this work, $\mathcal{D}$ is reparametrized into $s = s(t, z)$ and $r = r(t, z)$ where curves along r are curves of constant $\mathbf{x}$ and curves along s are characteristic curves. This change of coordinates can be leveraged to transform the time-series data collected at the outlet of the PFR into an s-series dataset which captures all the dynamics in the reactor. That s-series dataset can then be used to approximate $d\mathbf{x}/ds$ using either finite differences or taking the analytical derivative of some surrogate model describing $\mathbf{x}$ in s. The derivative can then be used as a target value by SR to discover $\mathbf{R}(\mathbf{x})$.

2.1. Change of Coordinates

The change of coordinates from (t, z) to (s, r) is done using the Method of Characteristics (MoC). The MoC requires Cauchy data collected along a manifold, $\Gamma \in \mathcal{D}$. To discover the kinetic model, the Cauchy data provided is the time-series state measurements collected on Γ, where Γ is defined as the outlet of the reactor ($z = 1$). These measurements are denoted as $\mathbf{f}(t) = \mathbf{x}(t)$ on Γ. Using the MoC and $\mathbf{f}(t)$, the PDE provided in Eq. (1) can be rewritten as the system of ODEs in Eq. (2).

$$\frac{dt}{ds} = 1 \qquad \text{when } s = 0, \qquad t = r$$

$$\frac{dz}{ds} = v(t) \qquad \text{when } s = 0, \qquad z = 1 \tag{2}$$

$$\frac{d\mathbf{x}}{ds} = \mathbf{R}(\mathbf{x}) \qquad \text{when } s = 0, \qquad \mathbf{x} = \mathbf{f}(r)$$

Since the thermophysical properties of the reactor are assumed to be constant, the ODEs which describe t and z are independent of the ODEs which describes $\mathbf{x}$ in Eq. (2). This means given state measurements that span some range of s determined by solving the ODEs for t and z for many values of r, the derivative of $\mathbf{x}$ with respect to s can be approximated and used to discover $\mathbf{R}(\mathbf{x})$ using SR. Care, however, must be taken when selecting a dynamic operating condition that will result in data spanning some range in s. In this work, the flow velocity in Eq. (3), realized by a synthetic control valve that opens at the start of each experiment, helps produce varying values of $\mathbf{x}$ across s.

$$v(t) = 0.25t + 0.5 \tag{3}$$

2.2. Symbolic Regression

Once the time-series data is transformed into an s-series dataset using the MoC, SR via Genetic Programming (GP) can be used to discover the structure and parameter values of $\mathbf{R}(\mathbf{x})$. GP can search a symbol space for an optimal expression by applying genetic operations inspired by biological evolution to expressions represented as expression trees. These genetic operators, crossover and mutation, can be iteratively applied to a population of expression trees to evolve an optimal expression. To search a symbol space, GP needs an argument set, or set of variables that it can include in the expressions, and a primitive set, or set of mathematical operators it can use to create mathematical relations between the arguments. Both sets are selected based on domain expert knowledge of the system of interest. The GP also needs a probability of crossover and a probability of mutation that determine how likely it is that any expression tree within a population will be subjected to the genetic operations crossover and mutation respectively.

To identify an optimal expression, the GP searches for an expression which accomplishes two goals: minimize the mean squared error (MSE) between the expression when evaluated using the measured data and the target value, $d\mathbf{x}/ds$; and be as concise as possible. The Bayesian Information Criterion (BIC) considers both these expectations and thus was used as a fitness criterion for the SR as defined in Eq. (4), where n_c represents the complexity of the expression defined as the number of nodes in the expression tree and n_{data} represents the number of data points used to train the model.

$$\text{BIC} = n_{data}\log(\text{MSE}) + n_c\log(n_{data}) \tag{4}$$

To improve the performance of the GP, a gradient-based parameter estimation scheme was used during the evaluation of each expression. The objective of the parameter estimation step was to minimize the MSE for each expression. This step helps prevent good model structures with bad parameter estimates from being discarded due to poor fitness.

3. Results

To demonstrate the proposed method, the discovery of three kinetic models were explored: Discovery of a nonisothermal kinetic model, discovery of a rate limited kinetic model, and discovery of kinetic models in the presence of noise. Every case study was tested 30 times. Since SR via GP is not deterministic, there are no guarantees that the underlying model will be returned from each trial, but the results demonstrate that the method is robust and can return a wide range of different types of kinetic models.

3.1. Discovery of nonisothermal kinetic models

The first cast study investigates an ideal plug flow reactor with constant thermophysical properties home to the nonisothermal reaction $A \rightarrow B$. Three synthetic experiments were conducted and the time-series data for c_A and T were collected at the outlet of the reactor. The details of the experiments are shown in Table 1 for the Nonisothermal case where the subscript $\cdot_f$ denotes feed, and the subscript $\cdot_c$ denotes coolant. The time-series data collected at the outlet from the three experiments were then transformed into an s-series dataset.

Table 1: Data-generating experiments for each reactor and the genetic programming hyperparameters argument set (Arg. Set), primitive set (Prim. Set), number of individuals in a population (POP), and number of generations of evolution (GEN).

Case	Experiments			Arg. Set	Prim. Set	POP	GEN
	$c_{A,f}$	T_f	T_c				
Nonisothermal	0.25	325	325	$\left\{c_A, \dfrac{1}{T}, \boldsymbol{\theta}\right\}$	$\left\{\begin{array}{c}+,\times,\div,\\ \exp, \text{neg}\end{array}\right\}$	500	50
	1.00	325	350				
	0.25	325	375				
	$c_{A,f}$	$c_{B,f}$	$c_{C,f}$				
Hougen-Watson	0.2	0.8	0.0	$\{c_A, c_B, c_C, \boldsymbol{\theta}\}$	$\{+,\times,\div\}$	500	50
	0.8	0.0	0.2				
Analytical	$c_{A,f}$			$\{s, \boldsymbol{\theta}\}$	$\left\{\begin{array}{c}+,-,\times,\\ \div, \cos,\\ \sin, \exp\end{array}\right\}$	100	10
	1.00						
Isothermal	$c_{A,f}$			$\{c_A, \boldsymbol{\theta}\}$	$\{+,\times,\div\}$	100	10
	1.00						

From the s-series dataset, dc/ds was calculated using finite difference approximations. These approximations served as the target for the GP with the argument set, primitive set, number of individuals in the population, and number of generations shown in Table 1. The unknown parameters were represented by $\boldsymbol{\theta}$. In this work, the parameters were tuned using a gradient-based parameter estimation scheme as described in Section 2.2. The probabilities of crossover and mutation were 60 % and 70 % respectively.

The proposed method was successful in discovering the underlying kinetic model, including the Arrhenius expression, in 93 % of the trails conducted. The small errors, less than 0.5% error, in the parameter estimates shown in Table 2 for the Nonisothermal case are due to numerical errors in the derivative approximations. The average time to return the kinetic model was 218 seconds.

3.2. Discovery of rate limited kinetic models

While many reactions are nonisothermal, few are represented as simply as the monotonic reaction in Section 3.1. To apply the proposed toolchain to a more complicated kinetic model, a reactor with Hougen-Watson kinetics was considered. Two synthetic experiments were run as presented in Table 1. The argument set, primitive set, size of the population, and the number of generations are also shown in Table 1. The probabilities of crossover and mutation were 60 % and 20 % respectively. In 100 % of the trials, the proposed method identified the correct kinetic model with parameter error less than 2%, shown in Table 2, in an average of 104 seconds.

3.3. Discovery of kinetic models in the presence of noise

Although the previous two examples used noiseless data, data collected from physical reactors always exhibit some level of noise. To demonstrate how the proposed method can handle noise, a simple PFR home to an isothermal reaction $2A \rightarrow B$ was considered. One experiment was run with a constant feed concentration of A, $c_{A,f} = 1.0$, as shown in Table 1 for the Analytical and Isothermal cases.

The synthetic time series data, with added Gaussian noise collected at the outlet was transformed into an s-series dataset. SR was then used to discover a function $c_A = g(s)$ using the argument and primitive set shown in Table 1 for the Analytical case. The derivative of $g(s)$ was then taken analytically to build the target for the SR of $R(c_A)$ with the argument and primitive sets shown for the Isothermal case in Table 1. The GP hyperparameters for both cases are shown in Table 1 and the probabilities of crossover and mutation were 60 % and 20 % respectively.

Table 2: Discovered Expressions

Case	Ground Truth	Discovered	Successful Runs	Average Time (s)
Nonisothermal	$-\exp\left(25 - \dfrac{8750}{T}\right) c_A$	$-\exp\left(24.90 - \dfrac{8712.70}{T}\right) c_A$	93 %	218
Hougen-Watson	$-\dfrac{2c_A c_B}{1 + 6c_A}$	$-\dfrac{2.014 c_A c_B}{1 + 6.099 c_A}$	100 %	104
Analytical Model	$\dfrac{1}{1 + s}$	$\dfrac{1.016}{s + 1.024}$	80 %	3.92
Isothermal	$-1.0 c_A^2$	$0.984 c_A^2$	100 %	4.93

The resulting expressions $g(s)$ and $R(c_A)$ are shown in the last two rows of Table 2. 80 % of the trials returned the correct $g(s)$ with less than 3% parameter error and 100 % of the trials returned the correct isothermal kinetic model with less than 2% parameter error. The lower success in discovery of $g(s)$ is due to the simple dynamics in s which can be well represented using many expressions creating using the large primitive and argument sets, and the smaller population than the previous two studies. The average time to complete the search for the analytical model and the isothermal kinetics were 3.92 seconds and 4.93 seconds respectively.

Using the two-stage approach, the proposed method can identify simple reaction models from noisy state measurements collected at the outlet of a PFR. It should be noted that the discovered function, $g(s)$, is the analytical solution to the PFR equation with the chemical reaction model discovered. This is especially convenient when such an analytical solution exists, however even when an analytical solution does not exist, SR can discover simple expressions that describe ODEs well as shown in Tsoulos and Lagaris (2006).

4. Conclusions

Discovery of kinetic models form input-output data of PFRs remains a challenging task. By using the MoC to change coordinates in ideal PFRs, SR becomes a realistic and inexpensive approach to learn kinetic models automatically from data. This chain of methods reliably identified the Arrhenius expression, Hougen-Watson Kinetics, and discovered the analytical solution to the PFR equation.

The demonstrated method is reliable, consistently returning the ground truth model from data. It is also flexible and capable of returning interesting model structures that are not defined a priori. The many methods in SR make the proposed tool chain flexible and adaptable to different reaction schemes and available data so long as the reactor has near constant thermophysical properties.

References

Beykal, B., Diangelakis, N.A., Pistikopoulos, E.N., 2022. Continuous-Time Surrogate Models for Data-Driven Dynamic Optimization, in: Montastruc, L., Negny, S. (Eds.), 32nd European Symposium on Computer Aided Process Engineering, Computer Aided Chemical Engineering. Elsevier, pp. 205–210.

Cohen, B., Beykal, B., Bollas, G., 2023 under review. Physics-informed genetic programming for discovery of partial differential equations from scarce and noisy data.

Cornforth, T.W., Lipson, H., 2013. Inference of hidden variables in systems of differential equations with genetic programming. Genet Program Evolvable Mach 14, 155–190.

Karniadakis, G.E., Kevrekidis, I.G., Lu, L., Perdikaris, P., Wang, S., Yang, L., 2021. Physics-informed machine learning. Nature Reviews Physics 3, 422–440.

McBride, K., Sundmacher, K., 2019. Overview of Surrogate Modeling in Chemical Process Engineering. Chemie Ingenieur Technik 91, 228–239.

Narayanan, H., Cruz Bournazou, M.N., Guillén Gosálbez, G., Butté, A., 2022. Functional-Hybrid modeling through automated adaptive symbolic regression for interpretable mathematical expressions. Chemical Engineering Journal 430, 133032.

Rudy, S.H., Brunton, S.L., Proctor, J.L., Kutz, J.N., 2017. Data-driven discovery of partial differential equations. Sci Adv 3.

Tsoulos, I.G., Lagaris, I.E., 2006. Solving differential equations with genetic programming. Genet Program Evolvable Mach 7, 33–54.

Flavio Manenti, Gintaras V. Reklaitis (Eds.), Proceedings of the 34th European Symposium on Computer Aided Process Engineering / 15th International Symposium on Process Systems Engineering (ESCAPE34/PSE24), June 2-6, 2024, Florence, Italy

Hybrid machine learning for scale-up of biomass production using photobioreactors

Abhishek Sivaram[a], Alireza Mehrdadfar[a], Lara Greco[a], Christian Euler[b], Seyed Soheil Mansouri[a,*]

[a]*Department of Chemical and Biochemical Engineering, Technical University of Denmark, Søltofts Plads, Building 228A, 2800 Kgs. Lyngby, Denmark*
[b]*Department of Chemical Engineering, University of Waterloo, 200 University Avenue West Waterloo, ON, Canada N2L 3G1*
*seso@kt.dtu.dk

Abstract

Artificial intelligence (AI) and machine learning (ML) have found widespread acceptance in the field of chemical engineering for the scale-up of processes. However, the translation of these scale-up strategies to biological processes has been challenging due to the emergence of unexpected phenomenology, including new metabolic pathways, during scale-up. While a key issue is the lack of interpretability and explainability in developed algorithms, the primary challenge lies in the transferability of ML models across different scales. To make these models readily deployable, it is crucial to incorporate comprehensive process information while harnessing the potential of AI. In this work, we present insights into a framework which uses hybrid models combining first-principles knowledge about photobioreactors and AI, validated using experiments at different process scales.

We present this framework in the context of scale-up of biomass production in photobioreactors. Using small-scale experiments with volumes of 500 mL and 3 L; a medium-scale experiment with 30 L experiment is also conducted, which is used to validate our approach. This comprehensive approach not only addresses the challenges of biological process scale-up but also ensures the reliability and adaptability of the developed models for real-world applications.

Keywords: *Artificial Intelligence, Hybrid modeling, Process scale-up, Photobioreactors*

1. Introduction

1.1. Scale-up of processes and artificial intelligence

AI has gained a lot of popularity in quite a few use-cases in biotechnology and bioprocess engineering. The use of AI algorithms is usually driven by specific use-cases/problems of interest, resulting in a significant lack of transferability of results from the various algorithms across scales of operation. This problem is in addition to the lack of sufficient data across scales to train major machine learning models. Dynamical modeling, however, has the potential to minimize the requirement of data for modeling. This is because along with fitting the experimental data, dynamical models must be able to fit the dynamics of the system as well. This additional constraint limits the possible trajectories the system can take (Cuomo et al., 2022; Jin et al., 2021). Another issue with using off-the-shelf algorithms for scale-up is the lack of explainability of why certain solutions are achieved. Various recent works aim to increase global explainability of model forms(Kaiser et al., 2018; Sivaram & Venkatasubramanian, 2022), specifically toward the estimation of process dynamics. These dynamical models aid in the development of efficient control strategies and their reduced order nature also help in identifying fast solutions.

1.2. Photobioreactors as a case-study

A photobioreactor is a high-tech algae incubator. It is a system that uses light to cultivate and grow microorganisms, such as algae or bacteria, to obtain valuable chemical products. The light provides energy for photosynthesis, allowing these microorganisms to thrive and multiply. These photobioreactors have been used in fields like biofuel production, wastewater treatment, and even in some experimental setups for studying and optimizing the growth of microorganisms. Typically, biomass growth models are written in terms of the specific growth rate of the biomass μ,

$$\frac{\mathrm{d}x}{\mathrm{d}t} = \mu x \qquad\qquad\qquad\qquad\qquad\qquad (1)$$

where x is the amount of biomass. The specific growth rate μ (h^{-1}) is a function of the amount of substrate, the amount of intensity of light, etc. Depending on the physics of the process, the biomass growth can be described by kinetics like Monod, Michelis-Menten, Andrews, Droop, Caperon and Meyer, Flynn, Martinez kinetics, etc. (Lee et al., 2015). In these models, specific growth rate are functions of substrate concentrations. In photobioreactors, these models are modified to include the relationship of the specific growth rate on the intensity of the incident light. Using these kinetics and including the transport of the substrates, the models for a photobioreactor take the form of ordinary/partial differential equations that include input and output of biomass, substrates (used for the growth of biomass), and constitutive equations for rate parameters. However, these models are not amenable to tracking biomass concentrations due to observability limitations of the models. In the subsequent section, we show how Eq. (1) can be used across scales, in the process eliminating the observability limitations.

2. Dataset and Methodology

2.1. Dataset description

The literature dataset for this article was collected from (Blanken et al., 2016). The data comes from sources with different operating conditions, operating modes, and process geometry, among other variations across experiments. These include datasets: **70 RPM data, 110 RPM data, 140 RPM exp data, pond M8 data, Pond waste data, A data, B data, C data, D data, E data, F data, G data.** These data come from microorganisms like *Chlorella sorokiniana*, *Chlamydomonas reinhadtii*, and *Phaeodactylum tricornutum*, with geometries of rotating tubular reactor, laboratory-scale pond reactor, torus-shaped reactor, flat panel reactors and bubble columns.

Apart from these experimental data from literature, we also use a separate experiment on our inhouse system of a 30 L bubble column photobioreactor by Synoxis Algae with *Chlorella sorokiniana*. We see that the dataset has considerable variability in operating conditions, choice of the organisms, geometric configurations, and modes of the experiment.

2.2. Model simplification – ignoring substrate concentrations

In this work, we consider this specific model form shown in Eq. (1) with experimental results across various photobioreactors, with the goal of identifying invariants across different reactors to determine unchanged properties across scales. Identifying these invariants would aid in generating scale-agnostic models. Models of reactors conventionally incorporate phenomenology for reaction, transport phenomena etc. Substrate concentrations are not always measured; however, we can estimate a nonlinear dynamical model for just biomass growth.

A different dynamic is given by logistic growth rate, which in turn with the decay of biomass function with death rate parameter k_d, gives rise to the functional form given by the ordinary differential equation, $\frac{dx}{dt} = k_b \left(1 - \frac{x}{K}\right) x - k_d x$, where k_b, K are constants related to birth rate and steady-state value of the biomass, respectively. It is known that the logistic growth model is a specific case of the Monod/Michelis-Menten kinetics, under the condition of proportional substrate usage (Alvarez-Ramirez et al., 2019; Putz et al., 2007). The logistic curve implicitly incorporates the availability of the substrate in the term $(1 - x/K)$ where the greater the biomass the lower the amount of substrate availability. The specific growth rate in this situation can be written as, $\mu = k_b(1 - x/K) - k_d$. However, these dynamics may not encompass all the possibilities of the interaction with higher-order dependence of the specific growth rate on substrate. This can be surpassed by considering the specific growth model can in general be a polynomial function dependent on the biomass concentration. This reduced order representation allows the biomass growth rate to be dependent directly on the biomass concentration.

2.3. Light Intensity as a decision variable for the process

Various light intensity models have been developed to codify the dependence of the specific growth rate with intensity. An example model is from (Blanken et al., 2016) where the microalgae system grows as per Eq. 1, except the specific growth rate is a function of the intensity of incident light. The intensity is a function of the biomass concentration, as an increase in the concentration results in lower light penetration, hence "light resource" availability for the growth of the biomass. In this context, one can see that the light availability for the dynamics, itself is like substrate availability. While we can parametrize substrate availability in terms of biomass concentration, in our work we consider light availability as an extrinsic input to the bioprocess. The intensity is normalized to give u, where u is 0 when no light is given to the system, and 1 when light is given to the system. Any intermediate intensity for growth can also be captured in the gradation of u. We consider this situation where light is continuously provided to the system, i.e., $u = 1$. With this context, our parametric specific growth rate can be assumed to be a polynomial function dependent on the amount of biomass, x (which in turn is a substitute for substrate availability) and light availability u, i.e., $\mu \coloneqq f(x, u)$.

2.3.1. Overall model and estimation of parameters

There are many ways to approximate the functional dependence of specific growth rate on biomass concentration and light availability. A very popular choice in literature for such hybridized models is to incorporate a neural network for this forward function approximation problem (Cuomo et al., 2022; Nielsen et al., 2020). However, this inherently results in reduced explainability and interpretability of the model form. Although linear models have the advantage of increased interpretability, they suffer from low fit to the data. Inspired by earlier work (Kaiser et al., 2018; Sivaram & Venkatasubramanian, 2022), we consider the specific case of using higher-order polynomial features for this approximation. Benefits here are twofold: 1. The model is linear in parameters, hence aids explainability; 2. Polynomial features accommodate nonlinear dynamics and, hence would result in a better fit. We, therefore, use the reduced order model of specific growth given by a second order polynomial, $\mu = c_0 + c_1 x +$

$c_2 u + c_3 x^2 + c_4 xu + c_5 u^2$. Note that this could be in general any higher-order polynomial, but we demonstrate the approach using a second order polynomial function.

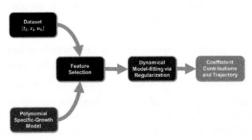

Figure 1: Model simplification and process of coefficient estimation

The general architecture of the methodology is shown in Figure 1. With the reduced order polynomial representation of the specific growth rate, and the dataset corresponding to different sampling points given by $\{t_k, x_k, u_k\}_{k=1}^N$ for each experiment, coefficients corresponding to highly correlated features are systematically set to zero (feature selection). For example, as x and xu are highly correlated, we push c_1 to zero. The model is *integrated* for each experiment, and the objective function of the mean-squared error of the biomass prediction at the time points and the corresponding biomass values is minimized. It is noted that given fewer sample points, the model could overfit the data. Hence, a regularization penalty of the one-norm of the coefficients (LASSO) is utilized to have a simpler model that could explain the dataset, resulting in finally the coefficient contributions and estimated trajectory for each experimental dataset.

3. Results and discussion

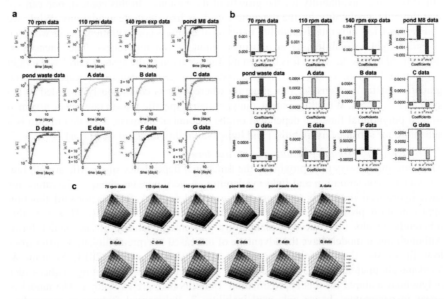

Figure 2: (**a**) Biomass model fit (line) using literature data (marked x) and (**b**) the estimated parameters from the reduced order polynomial model (**c**) Estimated specific growth rate $\hat{\mu}$ as a function of biomass concentration x and incident light u for different experimental data

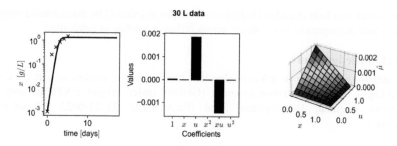

Figure 3: Model fit, parameters, and specific growth rate functional dependence from the in-house experiment on 30 L photobioreactor with *Chlorella sorokiniana*

The estimated model works across scales, geometries, and process conditions of different biomasses (**Errore. L'origine riferimento non è stata trovata.a**), and shows model invariance across scales (**Errore. L'origine riferimento non è stata trovata.b**), demonstrated by similar trends and contributions of relevant features. The specific growth rate functional plots (**Errore. L'origine riferimento non è stata trovata.c**) for each of the individual datasets further enhance our claims of the identified invariance, as the form of the plots remains the same across scales. All the identified characteristics of the model form also fit the in-house 30 L photobioreactor (Figure 3). The estimated steady state value of the biomass concentration was also observed in the 30 L photobioreactor, showing the validity of the estimated model.

This reduced order model for the invariance of the specific growth rate can be written as $\mu = \alpha + \beta u + \gamma x u$. Reasonably, it is seen that the incidence light term and the multiplicative term of the biomass concentration and incident light contribute the most to our predictions. The functional form can be rewritten as $\mu = k_b(1 - x/K)u - k_d$, suggesting logistic dynamics with a multiplicative factor based on the incident light. This functional form is also mechanistically viable in that when there is no incident light, i.e., $u = 0$, the biomass is bound to decay and not grow, an insight that is driven purely from the data-driven approach. In contrast, this constraint must be manually built into mechanistic models. Depending on the estimated parameter values of the dynamics, we see that the specific growth rate has a nonlinear relationship due to the presence of the xu term in the model form. The degree of nonlinearity is dependent on the magnitude of this term. This model form specifically allows us to know when the system reaches a steady state. For this, the specific growth rate should be zero. We see that such a model form would reach steady-state when $x^* = -\frac{1}{\gamma}\left(\frac{\alpha}{u^*} + \beta\right) = \left(1 - \frac{k_d}{k_b u*}\right)K$, where u^* is the steady state light operating input. The maximum value of the steady state is obtained when light is continuously on, i.e., $u^* = 1$.

4. Conclusions

We have obtained a readily transferable, scale-agnostic, and mechanistically plausible biomass growth model, from experimental data across different scales of photobioreactors. The estimated model form maps directly to a logistic growth model, including a dependence on incident light and death rate. The next step based on the invariance of the model form is the development of online control schemes based on different models fit during experimentation. Different model parameters (dependent on scale) would also help in understanding when the process should be discontinued/stopped for efficient management of resources across different batches of cultivation.

5. Acknowledgements

The authors would like to acknowledge that this work was funded in part by Grønt Udviklings- og Demonstrationsprogram (GUDP) under project EXTEND and the European Regional Development Fund (REACT-EU RF-21-0025 "Biosolutions Zealand").

6. References

Alvarez-Ramirez, J., Meraz, M., & Jaime Vernon-Carter, E. (2019). A theoretical derivation of the monod equation with a kinetics sense. *Biochemical Engineering Journal*, *150*. https://doi.org/10.1016/j.bej.2019.107305

Blanken, W., Postma, P. R., de Winter, L., Wijffels, R. H., & Janssen, M. (2016). Predicting microalgae growth. *Algal Research*, *14*, 28–38. https://doi.org/10.1016/j.algal.2015.12.020

Cuomo, S., di Cola, V. S., Giampaolo, F., Rozza, G., Raissi, M., & Piccialli, F. (2022). *Scientific Machine Learning through Physics-Informed Neural Networks: Where we are and What's next*. http://arxiv.org/abs/2201.05624

Jin, X., Cai, S., Li, H., & Em, G. (2021). NSFnets (Navier-Stokes flow nets): Physics-informed neural networks for the incompressible Navier-Stokes equations. *Journal of Computational Physics*, *426*, 109951. https://doi.org/10.1016/j.jcp.2020.109951

Kaiser, E., Kutz, J. N., & Brunton, S. L. (2018). Sparse identification of nonlinear dynamics for model predictive control in the low-data limit. *Proceedings of the Royal Society A: Mathematical, Physical and Engineering Sciences*, *474*(2219). https://doi.org/10.1098/rspa.2018.0335

Lee, E., Jalalizadeh, M., & Zhang, Q. (2015). *Growth kinetic models for microalgae cultivation : A review*. 12, 497–512. https://doi.org/10.1016/j.algal.2015.10.004

Nielsen, R. F., Nazemzadeh, N., Sillesen, L. W., Andersson, M. P., Gernaey, K. V., & Mansouri, S. S. (2020). Hybrid machine learning assisted modelling framework for particle processes. *Computers and Chemical Engineering*, *140*, 106916. https://doi.org/10.1016/j.compchemeng.2020.106916

Putz, M. V, Lacrămă, A.-M., Ostafe, V., Putz, M. V, Lacrămă, A. M., & Ostafe, V. (2007). Introducing logistic enzyme kinetics. In *Article in Journal of Optoelectronics and Advanced Materials* (Vol. 9, Issue 9). https://www.researchgate.net/publication/228470722

Sivaram, A., & Venkatasubramanian, V. (2022). XAI-MEG: Combining symbolic AI and machine learning to generate first-principles models and causal explanations. *AIChE Journal*, *68*(6). https://doi.org/10.1002/aic.17687

Flavio Manenti, Gintaras V. Reklaitis (Eds.), Proceedings of the 34th European Symposium on Computer Aided Process Engineering / 15th International Symposium on Process Systems Engineering (ESCAPE34/PSE24), June 2-6, 2024, Florence, Italy

Correlating the partitioning of organic molecules between water and [MeoeMPyrr]$^+$ [FAP]$^-$ through machine learning

Flora Esposito, [a] Ulderico Di Caprio, [a] Florence Vermeire, [b] Mumin Enis Leblebici[a],*

[a] *Center for Industrial Process Technology, Department of Chemical Engineering, KU Leuven, Agoralaan Building B, 3590 Diepenbeek, Belgium*
[b] *KU Leuven, Department of Chemical Engineering, Celestijnenlaan 200F-bus 2424, Leuven 3001, Belgium*
*muminenis.leblebici@kuleuven.be

Abstract

Lipophilicity is one of many parameters involved in the biological activity of drugs. It is assessed by defining the partitioning of a molecule between an organic (i.e. octanol) and a water phase. Nevertheless, octanol is too simple to encode all of the complicated interactions seen in ionic liquids. Moreover, the experimental determination of logP in specific ionic liquid/water systems (logP$_{IL/W}$) is an arduous and resource-intensive task. Machine learning and hybrid modelling techniques have emerged as essential tools in chemical engineering, providing innovative solutions to complicated physicochemical problems. This study proposes a hybrid model correlating the partitioning of organic molecules in octanol/water with the partitioning in [MeoeMPyrr]$^+$[FAP]$^-$/water systems. The hybrid model is formed by a first principle and a data-driven part. The first is represented by a group contribution model, the latter is represented by an ensemble of 5 Multilayer Perceptron (MLP) models. The model structure with the highest accuracy and generalization properties is searched with 5-fold cross-validation, using hyperparameter optimization.. The prediction capabilities have been evaluated through various metrics, namely the coefficient of determination ($R^2 = 0.93$), the Mean Squared Error (MSE = $1.8 \cdot 10^{-2}$) and the Mean Absolute Percentage Error (MAPE = 25%), showing quite good accuracy.

Keywords: Hybrid Modelling; Octanol/Water Partitioning Coefficient; Artificial Neural Network; Ensembling; Machine Learning

1. Introduction

The octanol/water partition coefficient (logP) plays a pivotal role in drug discovery, environmental chemistry, and industrial processes (Kujawski et al., 2012). It is defined as the partitioning of a molecule between an organic (i.e., octanol) phase and a water phase. As octanol is too simple to encode all of the interactions in more complicated systems, manufactured and natural membranes, such as liposomes and micelles, have lately been exploited as nonaqueous phase alternatives (Loureiro et al., 2018). An ionic liquid (IL) is a salt that is liquid at room temperature. ILs find diverse commercial applications, such as chemical synthesis solvents, gas chromatography stationary phases, liquid matrices for compound isolation, and absorbents (Jiang et al., 2013). Experimental measurements have also shown their potential as solvents for CO_2 absorption. The partitioning mechanism with water is critical for understanding the movement of analytes from the aqueous to the IL phase, which happens during the extraction of hydrocarbons and phenols. However, the available partition data between ILs and water for organic compounds is very limited (Padró et al., 2011). Moreover, the experimental determination of $logP_{IL/w}$ in specific ionic liquid/water systems is an arduous and resource-intensive task. Lipophilicity has traditionally been measured using methods such as water-octanol shake flask and high-performance liquid chromatography. These procedures are time-consuming and can require multistep dilutions (Wenlock et al., 2011).Chemical engineers rely on models for design, research, and day-to-day decision-making. Many recent initiatives have played a role in the spread of machine learning techniques in the research field by creating extensive databases, benchmarks, and representations for chemical applications (Heid et al., 2023). Chemical systems, on the other hand, should adhere to physical principles such as conservation laws and constitutive equations. Hybrid modelling is a methodology that benefits from the synergistic use of first principle and data-driven models, by combining existing process knowledge and information provided by collected data. Such a strategy is especially appropriate for systems and sectors where data creation requires a large amount of resources (Narayanan et al., 2023). This paper proposes a hybrid model structure capable of predicting the $logP_{IL/w}$ in the [MeoeMPyrr]$^+$[FAP]$^-$/water system.

2. Dataset description and preprocessing

The data to train the model were curated from literature (Jiang et al., 2013). The authors provide the experimental partition coefficient of organic molecules in [MeoeMPyrr]$^+$ [FAP]$^-$ ^{1}/Water systems. Simple organic molecules are present in the dataset, such as Acetophenone, Aniline, Benzene and so on. The dataset used consists of 41 experimental points. It contains the names, Chromatographic retention factors (logK) and $logP_{IL/w}$ of organic molecules in [MeoeMPyrr]$^+$ [FAP]$^-$ ^{1}/Water systems. In this work, only the experimental $logP_{IL/w}$ have been employed. Three points were excluded from the dataset since the ratio of logP in the two different solution systems is much lower than one (i.e $\alpha_{1,4-Dioxane} = -2.95$, $\alpha_{Acetic\ Acid} = -15.26$, $\alpha_{Propanoic\ Acid} = -1.75$). Those values are outside the range of expected ones. To robustly evaluate the model performances, a cross-validation strategy is applied. From the original dataset, two sets are randomly extracted: the training and the test sets. The training set contains 30 points and is used to train the network. The test set has 8 points. The MSE on the test set is calculated by k-fold cross-validation. Prior to the model training, the data were normalized in the range [0,1] using a min/max scaler.

3. Model description

The present section provides the main characteristics of the model used in this work. Correspondingly, we here describe the topology of the first principle and the ensemble of data-driven models composing the hybrid model.

3.1. Hybrid Model Structure

Errore. L'origine riferimento non è stata trovata. depicts a brief representation of the model. It requires as input the Simplified Molecular Input Line Entry System (SMILES) of the chemical component and returns the expected value of the $logP_{IL/w}$ in the [MeoeMPyrr]$^+$ [FAP]$^-$ /Water systems system. In the model pipeline, a molecular fragmented description is obtained from the SMILES, through RDKit library in Python. There are 68 fundamental atom types included with one-hot encoding. It includes metals and noble gases as well as the elements usually present in organic compounds (C, H, N, O, S, P, halogens). It is constructed such that each atom in the molecule matches just one type of atom, reducing ambiguity from the typing system (Wildman & Crippen, 1999). The descriptors are then employed as input features for an ensemble of 5 Multi-Layer Perceptron (MLP) models. The ensemble is an estimator that fits a number of regressors and then averages their outcomes to give a final prediction. This technique is used to estimate a proportionality coefficients (α) between logP values in the octanol/water system and those in the [MeoeMPyrr]⁺[FAP]⁻/water system that depends on the molecular structure of the solute.

$$\frac{\log P_{[MeoeMPyrr]^+[FAP]^-/water}}{\log P_{octanol/water}} = \alpha. \tag{1}$$

The logP values in the octanol/water system are found from the molecular structure applying the Crippen method (Wildman & Crippen, 1999). This is done using RDKit library in Python.

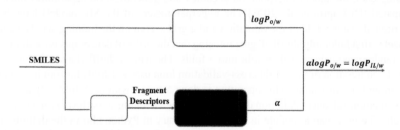

Figure 1: Block diagram of the hybrid model. In the figure, $logP_{o/w}$ is the octanol/water partition coefficient, $logP_{IL/w}$ is the [MeoeMPyrr]⁺[FAP]⁻/water partition coefficient and α is the proportionality coefficient between the two.

3.2. Multilayer perceptron

The ensemble presented in this work is formed by 5 multilayer perceptrons (MLPs). They have been trained through the backpropagation algorithm and with no activation function in the output layer. In the other layers, the activation function used is the rectified linear activation unit (ReLu) The loss function is represented by the squared error. In order to avoid overfitting, an L2 regularization term has been added to the loss function. The strength of the regularization term has been chosen through a k-fold cross-validation. For all the 5 different MLPs, the hyperparameters can be found in Table 1.

3.3. Ensemble of multilayer perceptrons

In machine learning and statistics, ensemble methods are widely used. Ensemble methods provide techniques for combining multiple single predictors to form a committee, resulting in better and more accurate results than a single predictor (Guzman et al., 2016). Training of the ensemble involves independently training multiple MLPs regressors with the same dataset, but not with the same initial model parameters. The expected output is then obtained by averaging all individual single regressors output. In other words, the final prediction of the ensemble for a given data point is the average of the predictions made by each individual model. Table 1 shows the structure of the 5 different MLPs used in the voting ensemble. These structures have been found through a k-fold cross-validation and a grid search, better detailed in Paragraph 4.

Table 1: Structure of the 5 MLPs used in the ensemble.

MLP	Number of hidden layers	Neurons per layer	Regularization term
1	1	6	$1 \cdot 10^{-5}$
2	3	50,50,50	$1 \cdot 10^{-2}$
3	1	38	$1 \cdot 10^{-3}$
4	3	20,20,20	$1 \cdot 10^{-2}$
5	2	20,20	$1 \cdot 10^{-2}$

4. K-fold cross-validation

In statistical modelling, cross-validation is a standard practice. To avoid overfitting the training data, the model interpolation accuracy and generalization capabilities must be estimated (Di Caprio et al., 2023) The hyperparameters of the ML models have been determined using 5-fold cross-validation and a grid search on the training set. The entire dataset is first randomly shuffled, guaranteeing that the order of data points is randomized. The randomized dataset is then split into 5 folds. The data is shuffled again before each split. Each iteration of the k-fold cross-validation loop uses k-1 folds for training and the remaining fold for testing. This operation is done 5 times, with each fold only acting as the validation set once. Additionally, hyperparameter tuning is performed using a grid search. The grid search module in scikit-learn library in Python allows the definition of an estimator (i.e. the ensemble), a grid of parameters (i.e. a grid for the number of hidden layers, neurons per layer and for the strength of the L2 regularization term), and the chosen number of cross-validation folds. The models are trained and evaluated within the cross-validation loop, optimizing the model based on the mean squared error (MSE) on the test set as the evaluation metric. Following that, the model is trained using the whole training set. The model generalization capabilities are determined using the test set, formed by the remaining 8 data points not included in the training set.

5. Model Evaluation

The model accuracy and generalization performances are evaluated using various statistical criteria, namely the coefficient of determination (R^2), Mean squared error (MSE), and mean absolute percentage error (MAPE) for both the training and test sets.

$$R^2 = 1 - \frac{\sum_{i=1}^{N_{dataset}}(y_i - \bar{y}_i)^2}{\sum_{i=1}^{N_{dataset}}(y_i - y_{mean})}, \tag{2}$$

$$MSE = \frac{\sum_{i=1}^{N_{dataset}}(y_i - \bar{y}_i)^2}{N_{test}}, \tag{3}$$

$$MAPE = \frac{1}{N_{dataset}} \sum_{i=1}^{N_{dataset}} \left(\left| \frac{y_i - \bar{y}_i}{y_i} \right| \right) \tag{4}$$

where $N_{dataset}$ is the sum of data points contained in the train and test sets, y_i is the experimental output value of the ith point in the dataset, $\bar{y}_i$ is the output value predicted at the ith point in the dataset, y_{mean} is the average of the output values contained in the dataset.

6. Results

Errore. L'origine riferimento non è stata trovata. shows the prediction capabilities of the model structure with the highest accuracy on the validation set identified by the k-fold cross-validation. In this figure all the points are clustered around the ideal prediction line with a narrow dispersion. With few exceptions, both the predictions on the training and validation points indicate errors of less than 20%.

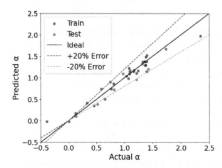
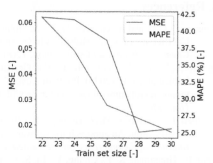

Figure 2: Prediction plot of the model with the highest accuracy on the validation set.

Figure 3: Mean square error (MSE) and mean absolute percentage error (MAPE) on the train and test sets as a function of the train set size.

The most challenging points to model are, as expected, the extreme values of the dataset. As we can see from the plot, the extreme values are indeed the ones with the highest error. Those points represent the partitioning of 1-Butanol and 1-Nitropropane. The R^2 on the train and test sets is 0.93 and the MSE is $1.8 \cdot 10^{-2}$. The metrics on the test set only are, instead: $R^2 = 0.87$, MSE $= 2 \cdot 10^{-2}$ and MAPE $= 15\%$. This highlights accuracy and generalization capabilities of the most performant ensemble identified by the 5-fold cross-validation. The voting ensemble average MSE is $2.29 \cdot 10^{-2}$, slightly higher than the one obtained with the best MLPs structures. Following, the influence of the size of the training set on the model accuracy was investigated. As stated before, experimental measurements for specific ILs/water partitioning can be costly. Therefore, it could be useful to provide a model that can work with a relatively low number of experimental points. **Errore. L'origine riferimento non è stata trovata.** shows the results of the model trained with a decreasing number of points. Both the MSE and the MAPE are calculated on the train and test sets. From this figure, an increasing MSE and MAPE can be appreciated with a decreasing number of points, as expected. On the other hand, the lowest MSE is found with 28 training points with a value of $1.7 \cdot 10^{-2}$. Looking at Figure 3, the MAPE seems to be high. Nevertheless, the values of α range from -0.5 to 2.5. In particular, we can also notice a point for which $\alpha = 0.006$. Looking at (3), in the MAPE formula, the expected value is at the denominator. This usually increases the MAPE, if values close to 0 are taken into account. By excluding the aforementioned point from the metrics evaluation, the MAPE decreases to 15%.

7. Conclusions

A hybrid model for the prediction of $logP_{IL/W}$ in $[MeoeMPyrr]^+[FAP]^-$/water systems has been proposed. The model structure returns accurate predictions with an $R^2 = 0.93$ and good generalization capabilities. The best model structure is found through a k-fold cross-validation. Although the model developed in this paper shows acceptable prediction accuracy, its performance can be further improved. In particular, the first principle part of the model could be improved, providing more physical adherence. Moreover, the model can also be tested with a new set of experimental data in a different kind of organic-aqueous system. However, the hybrid model developed could be used to further analyze the partitioning of organic molecules in ionic liquid/water systems by performing a low amount of experiments.

8. References

Bannan, C. C., Calabró, G., Kyu, D. Y., & Mobley, D. L. (2016). Calculating Partition Coefficients of Small Molecules in Octanol/Water and Cyclohexane/Water. *Journal of Chemical Theory and Computation*, *12*(8), 4015–4024.

Di Caprio, U., Wu, M., Vermeire, F., Van Gerven, T., Hellinckx, P., Waldherr, S., Kayahan, E., & Leblebici, M. E. (2023). Predicting overall mass transfer coefficients of CO2 capture into monoethanolamine in spray columns with hybrid machine learning. *Journal of CO2 Utilization*, *70*.

Guzman, E., El-Haliby, M., & Bruegge, B. (2016). Ensemble methods for app review classification: An approach for software evolution. *Proceedings - 2015 30th IEEE/ACM International Conference on Automated Software Engineering, ASE 2015*, 771–776.

Heid, E., Greenman, K. P., Chung, Y., Li, S.-C., Graff, D. E., Vermeire, F. H., Wu, H., Green, W. H., & McGill, C. J. (2023). *Chemprop: A Machine Learning Package for Chemical Property Prediction*.

Jiang, R., Anderson, J. L., Stephens, T. W., Acree, W. E. (William E., & Abraham, M. H. (Michael H.). (2013). Abraham model correlations for predicting gas-to-liquid partition coefficients and activity coefficients of organic solutes dissolved in 1-(2-methoxyethyl)-1-methylpyrrolidinium tris(pentafluoroethyl) trifluorophosphate. *European Chemical Bulletin, 2013, Hungary: Deuton-X Ltd.*, *2*(10), 741–751.

Kujawski, J., Popielarska, H., Myka, A., Drabińska, B., & Bernard, M. (2012). The log P Parameter as a Molecular Descriptor in the Computer-aided Drug Design – an Overview. *Computational Methods in Science and Technology*, *18*(2), 81–88.

Loureiro, D. R. P., Soares, J. X., Lopes, D., Macedo, T., Yordanova, D., Jakobtorweihen, S., Nunes, C., Reis, S., Pinto, M. M. M., & Afonso, C. M. M. (2018). *Accessing lipophilicity of drugs with biomimetic models: A comparative study using liposomes and micelles*.

Narayanan, H., von Stosch, M., Feidl, F., Sokolov, M., Morbidelli, M., & Butté, A. (2023). Hybrid modeling for biopharmaceutical processes: advantages, opportunities, and implementation. *Frontiers in Chemical Engineering*, *5*, 1157889.

Padró, J. M., Ponzinibbio, A., Mesa, L. B. A., & Reta, M. (2011). Predicting the partitioning of biological compounds between room-temperature ionic liquids and water by means of the solvation-parameter model. *Analytical and Bioanalytical Chemistry*, *399*(8), 2807–2820.

Wenlock, M. C., Potter, T., Barton, P., & Austin, R. P. (2011). A method for measuring the lipophilicity of compounds in mixtures of 10. *Journal of Biomolecular Screening*, *16*(3), 348–355.

Wildman, S. A., & Crippen, G. M. (1999). Prediction of physicochemical parameters by atomic contributions. *Journal of Chemical Information and Computer Sciences*, *39*(5), 868–873.

Flavio Manenti, Gintaras V. Reklaitis (Eds.), Proceedings of the 34th European Symposium on Computer Aided Process Engineering / 15th International Symposium on Process Systems Engineering (ESCAPE34/PSE24), June 2-6, 2024, Florence, Italy

Industrial Data Science for Batch Manufacturing

Mattia Vallerio,[a]* Carlos Perez-Galvan,[a] Francisco J. Navarro-Brull,[b]

a SOLVAY SA, Belgium
b Department of Chemical Engineering, Imperial College London
*mattia.vallerio@solvay.com

Abstract

Batch processes are the main production methodology for a large number of manufacturing industries: e.g., chemicals, food and beverage, pharma, Levenspiel (1998). However, these processes are subject to high variability: raw material composition, initial condition, unit degradation, and their intrinsic nonlinear and dynamic nature. All these reasons make batch processes challenging to analyse, control and optimize, Kourti (2005), Rawlings (2017). Nowadays, data can be considered an additional asset of all manufacturing processes and with the introduction of IoT devices, the economic burden to capture even more data has dropped. This data overload does not help on its own. It generates an added value when it is turned into actionable information (e.g., reduce batch time, increased first-time-right production). This contribution aims at introducing the need to establish the field of industrial data science (Mowbray et al. (2022)), and by doing so it highlights the use of two well-established data analytics methods in the context of batch manufacturing analysis. A well-known industrial example will be used to demonstrate the newly defined workflows to apply these two machine learning methods to convert this high variability and apparent excess of data into valuable information. The first method involves AutoML analysis, Wilson (2017). We will present how to automatically summarize its properties into features and identify the most relevant ones via non-linear correlation analysis (e.g. random forest) for a batch process. Then, trajectory analysis and functional data exploration will be covered. However, before doing so, we will discuss the need to align the data time-wise to effectively use these techniques (Dynamic Time Warping). In this last step, we will use the Functional Data Explorer in JMP Pro to monitor and identify deviations, Silverman (2002). These two novel workflows show how to apply ML method to industrial data successfully.

Keywords: Data Analytics, Machine Learning, Batch Manufacturing, AutoML, FPCA

1. Introduction

Batch processes are widely used in manufacturing, since they allow for minimum capex and maximum flexibility. An inherent characteristic of batch processes is the need to define and follow a recipe. This set of step by step rules guides the production and should ensure that a final product with a specific target quality should be obtained. Given the sometimes quite numerous steps involved in typical industrial recipes, it is quite evident how these processes will exhibit large variability between different batches with the same recipe. In recent years this drawback has been mitigated by the introduction of advanced automation and control methods specifically developed for batch processes (e.g., trajectory control, MPC). Kourti (2005); Rawlings et al. (2017). More recently the process industry has seen a sharp increase in interest and investments in Machine Learning (ML) and Artificial Intelligence (AI) Beck et al. (2016); Chiang et al. (2022); Sansana et al. (2021). It is now clear that methods and best practices used in other fields do not translate well to industrial data analysis in the process industry Mowbray et al. (2022). This is mainly due to three reasons: (i) the necessity to ensure safe operation, (ii) the lack of large and relevant industrial datasets and (iii) presence of legacy, outdated or underperforming automation and operational technology infrastructure. Clarke (2016); Shang and You (2019); Schweidtmann et al. (2021). In this work, we review the challenges in analyzing industrial batch data and present two novel workflows to obtain valuable insights using ML: Feature screening with AutoML (supervised learning) and anomaly detection with Functional Principal Component Analysis (FPCA) (unsupervised learning). The novelty of this work is in the methodology to apply ML on industrial data successfully. Additionally, we also introduce the use of noise as a feature to assess factor importance.

2. Batch data analytics: drying process use case

Analysing batch data is challenging due to varied model inputs (e.g., raw material properties, evolving conditions). This study explores two data-driven workflows for (i) screening for root causes and (ii) batch monitoring for anomalous events. The two workflow will be shown on an industrial batch drying process. The batch dataset is openly available and includes three phases: (i) Deagglomeration, (ii) Heating, and (iii) Cooling (see Fig.1). Structural and chemical reactions occur during drying. The batch begins with a variable cake amount and unknown solvent (Z). The operator adjusts dryer temperature and agitation speed and measures 10 variables (Xs). At the end, a sample determines the remaining solvent (Y) for quality control. (Garcıa-Munoz et al., 2003, 2004).

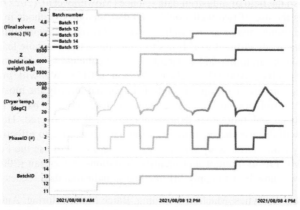

Fig.1 - Example of different type of variables shown in a trend over a sequence of five different batches.

3. Feature screening with AutoML

Batch data of varying time lengths is often analysed by summarizing each batch through statistics and process knowledge, such as peak temperature or its average rate of change during the reaction phase. These are referred to in the literature as landmark points or fingerprints. This approach assumes that subject matter experts (SMEs) know in advance the essential features to generate. Extending this method, one can compute statistics (e.g., max, min, average, range, std, quantiles) for every sensor, during each phase, for every batch, and grade. In ML, this process is known as feature engineering, often coupled with algorithms for optimal predictor selection.

3.1. Auto ML for batch processes

AutoML aims to streamline machine learning problems by automating traditionally manual, complex analytical tasks that are often performed by data analysts. It operates under the assumption that there is an excess of data for fitting multiple models (training dataset), selecting model parameters to avoid overfitting (validation dataset), and finally assessing with unseen data (test dataset). In industrial applications, this assumption may not always hold, making AutoML mainly suited to screen for relevant sensors effortlessly.

3.2. Feature engineering & selection

Automatic calculation of summary statistics for a batch process is possible. Once feature sets are generated per product, batch, and phase, these can serve as model inputs (X's). These features can be as granular as needed, summarizing statistics per automation step). They can also leverage all available process knowledge (e.g., pressure compensated temperature). ALAMO (Wilson and Sahinidis, 2017) is a well-known software package for this task. After generating the desired features, the next step is feature selection, achievable with any ML method capable of efficiently handling challenges like non-linear relationships, high co-linearity, and noise. Fig. 2 illustrates the results of this approach. Multiple statistics (mean, max, min, standard deviation, coefficient of variance) for every sensor, phase, and batch are calculated. A random forest model (termed Predictor Screening in JMP [SAS Inst.]) is used to list the contribution of each predictor. We introduce the use of an artificial noise signal as a cut-off to distinguish important factors.

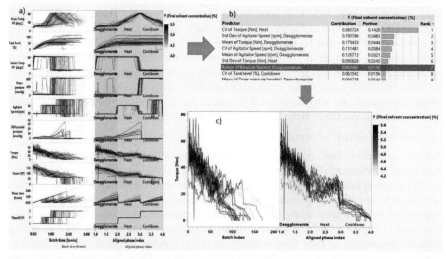

Figure 2 - AutoML approach for batch process data. a) Statistics of all sensors per phase and batch are calculated, b) then a random forest model identifies the fingerprints with the strongest correlation to the target and c) exemplified by the torque sensor showing a correlation to the target.

4. Anomaly detection with FPCA

The variability in the drying process exemplifies the diverse durations encountered in batch processes (see Fig. 2a). In the dryer dataset, the primary source of variability arises from batch-to-batch differences in the loaded product amount and its solvent content. Typically, phases can extend due to various perturbations, catalyst deactivation, variations in raw material quality or quantity, reduced heating/cooling capacity, or simply from maintenance issues or scheduling decisions. This complexity introduces variability in the expected progression of a batch manufacturing process, whether executed through automated or manual procedures. Various techniques exist to align batch data with differing durations. The simplest and most efficient approach involves using automation triggers or, alternatively, a monotonously increasing or decreasing variable along the batch duration (e.g., conversion of the reaction or amount of water evaporated instead of time). When information for batch alignment is neither measured nor known, or real-time alignment is necessary, Dynamic Time Warping (DTW) prove useful. These methods statistically align batch trajectories and can be employed for classifying anomalous batches or identifying correlating parameters (Spooner et al., 2017; Zuecco et al., 2020).

4.1. Functional or shape analysis (FPCA)

When batch-to-batch variability is minimal or exploring specific subsets of sensors is crucial, summary statistics might not be detailed enough and detailed trajectory analysis methods should be used. Functional Principal Components Analysis (FPCA) is an extension of PCA that analysis curves or trajectories. In batch processes, FPCA captures the primary sources of variation among multiple trends (see Fig.3) as a "function of batch time". FPCA applications extend to various domains: HPLC data (function of analysis time), spectroscopy data (function of wavelength), vibration (function of frequency), and battery degradation. Using FPCA, these trends or trajectories are summarized with a mean curve and a series of "shape functions" (eigenfunctions). These shapes have associated weights (loadings or eigenvalues). Each shape encapsulates the variability observed in latent trajectories (Silverman and Ramsay, 2002; Srivastava and Klassen, 2016). If the batch data is pivoted, FPCA insights might seem analogous to standard PCA. FPCA excels in identifying a set of component shapes that explain the maximum variation in the observed data. These can be interpreted as distinctive features seen in the process for certain batches, such as a different level rate in the deagglomeration phase or a temperature "shoulder" in the heating phase. Each batch trend can be reconstructed with the mean trajectory and a linear combination of these weighted shapes. The weights are called FPCs score and vary from batch to batch. As not all shape functions have equal contribution or importance, their weight must be considered when examining score plots.

4.2. Functional statistical process control

Process engineers face constraints in creating, monitoring, and modifying Key Performance Indicators (KPIs) for their processes. Functional Statistical Process Control (FSPC) offers a crucial advantage by alleviating them of this task. The core concept analysis is to compare batch trajectories instead of relying on pre-selected KPIs. This process can be automated using FPCA to identify intrinsic trajectories for each sensor. Illustrated in Fig.4 a, a multivariate control chart can quantify the anomaly level in drying batches, irrespective of their time duration. Initially, batches undergo pre-alignment to eliminate any anomaly directly related to batch duration. Then, functional components serve as fingerprints for both tank level and drying temperature (Fig.4b & c). The Hotelling-T2 score indicates batch trajectories that shows anomalous behaviour. Examining the aligned batches in Fig. 4d reveals anomalous patterns in both temperature and tank level. Using FPCA, the only input required from process engineers is specifying which tags (sensors) to monitor closely. However, if a specific KPI, such as quality or production, is a priority, an AutoML screening analysis using correlation can be conducted first (refer to the previous example examining solvent content). This step can reduce the number of monitored tags improving focus on quality and production.

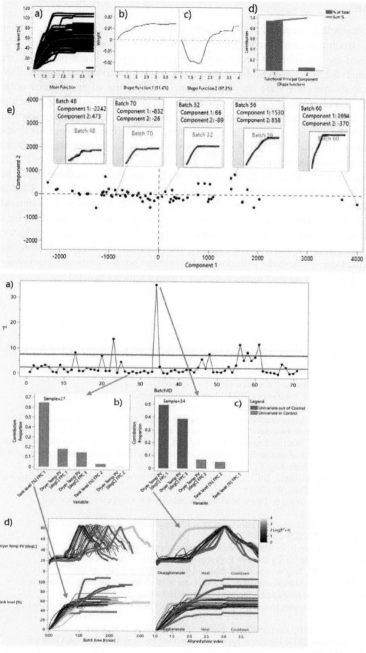

Figure 3 (top) & 4 (bottom) – Top: FPCA analysis of the tank level. This illustrates the description of the tank level a) using the average trajectory and a combination shape functions b) & c) with varying importance d), enabling the detection of anomalous batches e). Bottom: FSPC: A Hotelling-T2 control chart (a) is monitoring FPCA scores. Individual contributions for tank level and dryer temperature are depicted for an in-control (b) and an out-of-control batch (c). Colored batch trajectories for these sensors are shown d, not aligned left & aligned right.

5. Conclusions

In conclusion, this article emphasizes the growing importance of Industrial Data Science for analyzing, troubleshooting, and monitoring batch manufacturing processes. The challenges posed by the inherent variability and complexity of batch processes are addressed through the integration of data science and machine learning techniques. Two novel data analysis workflows are introduced along with the use of an artificial noise signal as a way to automatically discriminate import factors. The AutoML approach is introduced for feature screening, summarizing batch properties, and identifying relevant features through non-linear correlation analysis. The second method involves Functional Principal Component Analysis (FPCA) for anomaly detection, leveraging the entire trajectory of batch data. The alignment of batch data in terms of time and the use of FPCA shape functions are highlighted as essential steps in this data-driven methodology. The application of these methods is illustrated through a case study on an industrial batch drying/reaction process, showcasing the potential for actionable insights and continuous improvement in process control and optimization. The article underscores the need for a nuanced approach in applying machine learning methods to the process industry, considering safety, data limitations, and existing infrastructure challenges. Overall, the integration of data-driven methods with domain knowledge holds significant promise for advancing the efficiency and effectiveness of batch manufacturing processes.

References

D. A. C. Beck, et al. , 2016. Data science: Acc-elerating innovation and discovery in chemical engineering. AIChE Journal 62,1402–1416.

L. H. Chiang, et al., 2022. Towards artificial intelligence at scale in the chemical industry. AIChE Journal 68 (6).

S. Garcia-Munoz, et al., 2003. Troubleshooting of an industrial batch process using multivariate methods. Industrial & Engineering Chemistry Research 42 (15), 3592–3601.

S. Garcia-Munoz, T. Kourti, J. F. MacGregor, 2004. Model predictive monitoring for batch processes. Industrial & Engineering Chemistry Research 43 (18), 5929–5941.

T. Kourti, 2005. Application of latent variable methods to process control and multivariate statistical process control in industry. International Journal of Adaptive Control and Signal Processing 19 (4), 213–246.

O. Levenspiel, 1998. Chemical Reaction Engineering, 3rd Edition. John Wiley & Sons, Nashville, Tennessee.

M. Mowbray et al., 2022. Industrial data science – a review of machine learning applications for chemical and process industries. React. Chem. Eng. 7 (7),1471–1509.

J. B. Rawlings, D. Q. Mayne, M. Diehl, 2017. Model predictive control: theory, computation, and design. Vol. 2. Nob Hill Publishing Madison, Wisconsin.

J. Sansana, et al., 2021. Recent trends on hybrid modeling for industry 4.0. Computers & Chemical Engineering 151, 107365.

A. M. Schweidtmann, et al., 2021. Machine learning in chemical engineering: A perspective. Chemie Ingenieur Technik 93 (12), 2029–2039.

C. Shang, F. You, 2019. Data analytics and machine learning for smart process manufacturing: Recent advances and perspectives in the big data era. Engineering 5 (6), 1010 – 1016.

B. Silverman, J. Ramsay, 2002. Applied functional data analysis: methods and case studies.

M. Spooner et al., 2017. Selecting local constraint for alignment of batch process data with dynamictime warping. Chemometrics and Intelligent Laboratory Systems 167, 161–170.

M. Spooner et al., 2018. Harvest time prediction for batch processes. Computers & Chemical Engineering 117, 32–41.

A. Srivastava, E. P. Klassen, 2016. Functional and shape data analysis. Vol. 1. Springer.

Z. T. Wilson, N. V. Sahinidis, 2017. The alamo approach to machine learning. Computers & Chemical Engineering 106, 785–795.

F. Zuecco et al., 2020. Troubleshooting an industrial batch process for the manufacturing of specialty chemicals using data analytics. 30th ESCAPE. Vol. 48 of CACE. Elsevier, pp. 1129–1134.

Flavio Manenti, Gintaras V. Reklaitis (Eds.), Proceedings of the 34th European Symposium on Computer Aided Process Engineering / 15th International Symposium on Process Systems Engineering (ESCAPE34/PSE24), June 2-6, 2024, Florence, Italy

Automation of Experimental Workflows for High Throughput Robotic Cultivations

Lucas Kaspersetz,[a] Fabian Schröder-Kleeberg,[a] Federico M. Mione,[b] Ernesto C. Martinez,[b] Peter Neubauer,[a] Mariano Nicolas Cruz-Bournazou[a*]

[a] *Technische Universität Berlin, Bioprocess Engineering, Ackerstraße 76, 13355 Berlin, Germany*
[b] *Ingar (CONICET-UTN), Avellaneda 3657, S3002GJC Santa Fe, Argentina*
Mariano.n.cruzbournazou@tu-berlin.de

Abstract

Robotic cultivation platforms optimally operated with computational tools can serve as generators of high-information content data. However, the generated data should be accompanied with the executed workflows to enable reproducibility of experiments. Workflow management systems support data provenance and enable traceability of experimental workflows. In contrast to production environments with highly standardized structures and strict operating regimes, integration of workflows in robotic experimental facilities is often challenging. The challenges are due to proprietary interfaces, rapidly changing objectives, and lack of adequate representation of the implemented workflows which prevents their interoperability and automated metadata capture. In this work, we present the design and implementation of a digital infrastructure with a workflow management system as the top layer. The execution of experimental workflows is automated using Apache Airflow enabling to manage all necessary steps for fed-batch cultivations, including sampling, sample transport by a mobile robot, feed additions, data collection, storage in a SQL database and model fitting. Thus, the generated experimental data can be accompanied with the executed workflows, facilitating transparency, and sharing of experimental protocols.

Keywords: directed acyclic graphs, workflow automation, reproducibility

1. Introduction

The lack of high quality, reproducible experimental data for biological systems is still the main obstacle to achieve (Rogers et al., 2022) scientific breakthroughs in bioengineering. To tackle this issue, robotic cultivation platforms optimally operated with computational tools can serve as generators of Findable, Accessible, Interoperable and Re-usable (FAIR) data with high information content. To this aim, the generated data should be accompanied by the executed workflows, which are necessary for increasing reuse and reproducibility (Mitchell et al., 2022). Particularly in bioprocess development, where scale-up decisions are based on small-scale experimental data, transparency and interoperability in experimental and computational workflows are essential and currently missing. A workflow management system (WMS) for automatically scheduling and executing the experimental and computational tasks not only increases the degree of automation but also contributes to implementing FAIR data principles. The implementation of a WMS is often challenging due to missing standardized device interfaces or lack of adequate data management infrastructure for handling the different data sources (Maffettone et al., 2023). Current approaches for the management and scheduling of workflows in laboratories are often limited to subtasks such as analytical workflows, using mobile robots for automated sample transport (Neubert et al., 2019) or specific scheduling tasks of parallel cultivations (Bromig et al., 2022). In such cases, not all tasks, constraints, or data processing steps that are necessary for the effective operation of robotic cultivations can be automated or digitally handled for reproducibility and provenance. The open-source platform Apache Airflow (AA) provides the possibility of developing, scheduling, and monitoring workflows via directed acyclic graphs (DAG) (Harenslak and Ruiter, 2021). The applicability of DAGs for enforcing FAIR principles by design in high throughput cultivation facilities has been recently addressed for computational workflows (Mione et al., 2022). Still, without a similar approach for the experimental tasks, FAIRness cannot be achieved. In this work, we present the design and implementation of a WMS based on DAGs in a robotic cultivation facility. We show that the WMS not only increases the degree of automation but also contributes to FAIRizing experimental workflows. We demonstrate the feasibility and added value of our tool with *E. coli* BL21 (DE3) scale-down experiments for the production of elastin like proteins (Huber et al., 2014).

2. Material and Methods

2.1. BioXplorer cultivation platform

The BioXplorer 100 (H.E.L group, London, United Kingdom) composed of eight parallel cultivations in glass STRs, equipped with off-gas analyzers (BlueVary, BlueSens, Herten, Germany) was used for the cultivation workflows. The system is integrated into a liquid handling station (Tecan Group, Männedorf, Switzerland). A mobile robotic lab assistant (Astechproject Ltd., Runcorn, United Kingdom) was used for automated sample transport. The reader is referred to (Kaspersetz et al., 2022) for a detailed description of the platform and sampling procedures and at-line measurement procedures.

2.2. Strain

All experiments were carried out with *E. coli* BL21 (DE3) strains, carrying the pET28-NMBL-mEGFP-TEVrec-(V2Y)15-His expressing a recombinant fusion protein of an elastin like protein and eGFP, under the IPTG inducible *lac*UV5-promoter.

2.3. Cultivation

The preculture was set to an OD600 of 0.25 and cultured in 50 mL EnPresso B medium (Enpresso GmbH, Berlin, Germany) with 6 U L^{-1} Reagent A in 500 mL shake flask overnight at 37°C and 220 rpm in an orbital shaker (25 mm amplitude, Adolf Kühner AG, Birsfelden, Switzerland). Main-cultures were run in four parallel glass stirred tank reactors (STR) each equipped with one Rushton type impeller at 37°C and pH was controlled at 7.0 with 7.5 % ($NH_{3(aq)}$). The main cultures were started as 90 mL batch cultures with an initial glucose concentration of 5 g L^{-1}. Two substrate addition strategies were used in the scale-down experiment: continuous feeding and bolus feeding profiles. The pulse-based feed followed a 10~min interval. Aeration and stirring were increased following a pre-defined scheme.

2.4. Apache Airflow

Apache Airflow 2.2.4 and Python 3.7 were used to programmatically describe, schedule and monitor the experimental cultivation workflows. The official Docker Image for Apache Airflow is hosted on DockerHub (apache/airflow:2.2.4). The workflows were authored as DAGs. All necessary for running an experimental workflow were included in docker-compose.yml. All containerized applications were run via Docker Desktop 4.4.4

(73704) for Windows and a Windows Subsystem Linux 2 based back engine. The code is publicly available under: https://git.tu-berlin.de/bvt-htbd/airflow_workflow/-/tree/escape?ref_type=heads.

2.5. E. coli growth model

The model is based on a mechanistic *E. coli* model with glucose partitioning, overflow metabolism, and acetate re-cycling. The mathematical model was formulated as an ODE system describing the changes in state variables for glucose, acetate, biomass, product and dissolved oxygen tension (DOT). The parameters of the model were obtained by fitting the model to the experimental data. A more detailed description of the underlying model and the functioning of the framework can be found in (Kim et al., 2023).

3. Device integration and workflow automation

In bioprocess development, the implementation of automated cultivation workflows requires the integration of different devices, including mobile robots. Such robotic cultivation platforms usually consist of parallel bioreactor systems embedded in liquid handling stations (LHS) and analytical devices such as high-throughput analysers or additional LHS. In Fig. 1 a hierarchical infrastructure for the robotic cultivation platform is presented. All devices were integrated following a client-server architecture based on google Remote Procedure Call (gRPC) or Standardization in Lab Automation (SiLA2). The WMS in AA was implemented as the top layer. This digital infrastructure aims to provide a comprehensive tracking of the complete experimental workflow and to support transparency and reproducibility (Mitchell et al., 2022). All process data were stored in a SQL-database, while a shared file system was used to exchange data between containerized applications. The Apache Airflow web-service served as a user-interface for the experimental operator, allowing to trigger and monitor all experimental workflow steps.

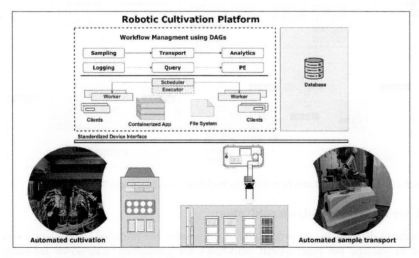

Figure 1: Schematic representation of the robotic cultivation platform with a workflow management system as the top layer.

3.1. Implementation of experimental workflows

All experimental workflows for managing fed-batch cultivations were represented through DAGs. The Airflow scheduler executed the respective tasks on an array of workers (fig. 1) while following the pre-defined dependencies. The automated sampling DAG manages the sampling event of the LHS, the transportation of the microtiter plate by the mobile robot and the corresponding analytics. All nodes which are associated to a device, used the PythonOperator and the corresponding client for communication. The DAG starts with a node that triggers the sampling procedure of the LHS. If the sampling event is successfully completed, the transportation node is carried out. After completion of the sample transport the corresponding analytics device is started, while in parallel the LHS can perform an additional task. Once the at-line analytics has been completed, the database is accessed to retrieve the corresponding results. The logging and monitoring DAG manages the data needed by the cultivation system as well as queries data from the database for monitoring and updating the parameter estimation procedures. For the cultivation system and the off-gas analysis the implementation followed the same approach, using the PythonOperator and a client-server architecture. As soon as both devices are requested to send their online measurements to the database, the TriggerDagRunOperator starts the parameter estimation DAG. The computational pipeline for parameter estimation is executed inside a docker container. Containerized applications reduce integration effort, whilst increasing interoperability and reproducibility of computational workflows (Boettiger, 2015).

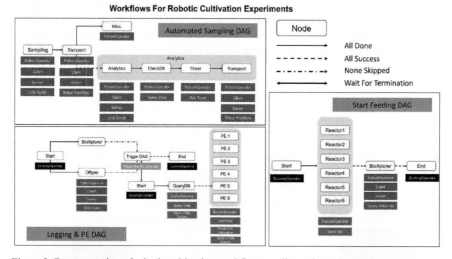

Figure 2: Representation of robotic cultivation workflows as directed acyclic graphs.

4. Case study – Scale-down cultivation

In order to demonstrate the practicality of the system, the proposed infrastructure was used to manage the experimental workflows for conducting scale-down fed-batch cultivations. Process performance parameters such as yields and titres of biotechnological process are often faltered when scaled-up to industrial scale. This limitation occurs due to lack of robustness of the microbial host to perturbations in large-scale conditions (Olsson et al., 2022). As cells move through the industrial-scale reactor, they are steadily exposed to changing environments. Hence, investigating the microbial response to such perturbations in usually homogenous and well-mixed small-scale reactors is necessary for a robust bioprocess development. Two different feeding regimes were applied, following a continuous feeding or a pulse-based feeding regime to investigate the robustness of *E. coli* BL21 (DE3) to glucose oscillations. In Fig. 3 the cultivation data for parallel fed-batch cultivations with continuous feeding (R1 & R2) and pulse-based feeding (R3 & R4) are shown. The WMS successfully collected and stored all online process measurements in the database. The sampling DAG allowed for seamless acquisition of at-line measurements, while controlling the mobile robot for automated sample transport. The pulse-based feeding was scheduled over a 10-min cycle interval which leads to an oscillating pattern in the measured O_2-concentration. For the assessed feeding strategies, no influence on the max. specific substrate uptake rate ($q_{Smax} = 1.5$ g g h^{-1}) and specific product (fig. 3) parameters were observed. However, an increased maintenance coefficient ($q_m = 0.09$ g g h^{-1}) for the pulse-based feeding strategy was observed.

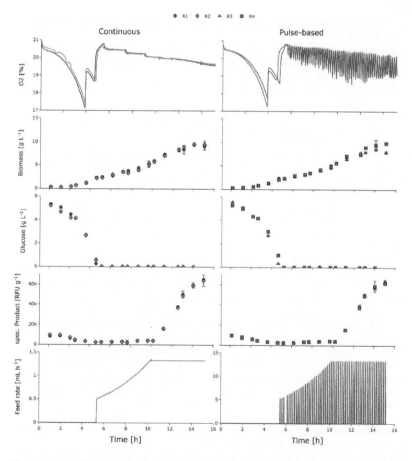

Figure 3: Parallel *E. coli* fed-batch cultivations, producing elastin like proteins, with continuous feeding (R1 & R2) in comparison to pulse-based feeding (R3 & R4).

5. Conclusions

We present the successful implementation of a WMS, based on DAGs, in a robotic cultivation facility. The proposed digital infrastructure is capable of scheduling and managing all necessary workflows for scale-down fed-batch cultivations. In the scale-down experiment, *E. coli* BL21 showed to be robust with no adverse measurable physiological responses to glucose oscillations under the tested conditions. The generated experimental data can be accompanied with the executed DAGs, which facilitates sharing of the conducted workflows, while increasing reproducibility and FAIRness of complex high-throughput experiments.

Acknowledgements
We gratefully acknowledge the financial support of the German Federal Ministry of Education and Research (01DD20002A – KIWI biolab).

References

Boettiger, C., 2015. An introduction to Docker for reproducible research. ACM SIGOPS Oper. Syst. Rev. 49, 71–79.

Bromig, L., von den Eichen, N., Weuster-Botz, D., 2022. Control of parallelized bioreactors I: dynamic scheduling software for efficient bioprocess management in high-throughput systems. Bioprocess Biosyst. Eng. 45, 1927–1937.

Harenslak, B., Ruiter, J. de, 2021. Data pipelines with Apache Airflow. Manning Publications Co, Shelter Island, NY.

Huber, M.C., Schreiber, A., Wild, W., Benz, K., Schiller, S.M., 2014. Introducing a combinatorial DNA-toolbox platform constituting defined protein-based biohybrid-materials. Biomaterials 35, 8767–8779.

Kaspersetz, L., Waldburger, S., Schermeyer, M.-T., Riedel, S.L., Groß, S., Neubauer, P., Cruz-Bournazou, M.-N., 2022. Automated Bioprocess Feedback Operation in a High-Throughput Facility via the Integration of a Mobile Robotic Lab Assistant. Front. Chem. Eng. 4.

Kim, J.W., Krausch, N., Aizpuru, J., Barz, T., Lucia, S., Neubauer, P., Cruz Bournazou, M.N., 2023. Model predictive control and moving horizon estimation for adaptive optimal bolus feeding in high-throughput cultivation of E. coli. Comput. Chem. Eng. 172, 108158.

Mione, F.M., Silva, A.N., Luna, M.F., Cruz B., M.N., Martinez, E.C., 2022. Managing Experimental-Computational Workflows in Robotic Platforms using Directed Acyclic Graphs. In: Yamashita, Y., Kano, M. (Eds.), Computer Aided Chemical Engineering, 14 International Symposium on Process Systems Engineering. Elsevier, pp. 1495–1500.

Mitchell, S.N., Lahiff, A., Cummings, N., Hollocombe, J., Boskamp, B., Field, R., Reddyhoff, D., Zarebski, K., Wilson, A., Viola, B., Burke, M., Archibald, B., Bessell, P., Blackwell, R., Boden, L.A., Brett, A., Brett, S., Dundas, R., Enright, J., Gonzalez-Beltran, A.N., Harris, C., Hinder, I., David Hughes, C., Knight, M., Mano, V., McMonagle, C., Mellor, D., Mohr, S., Marion, G., Matthews, L., McKendrick, I.J., Mark Pooley, C., Porphyre, T., Reeves, A., Townsend, E., Turner, R., Walton, J., Reeve, R., 2022. FAIR data pipeline: provenance-driven data management for traceable scientific workflows. Philos. Trans. R. Soc. Math. Phys. Eng. Sci. 380, 20210300.

Neubert, S., Gu, X., Göde, B., Roddelkopf, T., Fleischer, H., Stoll, N., Thurow, K., 2019. Workflow Management System for the Integration of Mobile Robots in Future Labs of Life Sciences. Chem. Ing. Tech. 91, 294–304.

Rogers, A.W., Vega-Ramon, F., Yan, J., Río-Chanona, E.A., Jing, K., Zhang, D., 2022. A transfer learning approach for predictive modeling of bioprocesses using small data. Biotechnol. Bioeng. 119, 411–422.

Flavio Manenti, Gintaras V. Reklaitis (Eds.), Proceedings of the 34th European Symposium on Computer Aided Process Engineering / 15th International Symposium on Process Systems Engineering (ESCAPE34/PSE24), June 2-6, 2024, Florence, Italy

Optimisation of a Production Chain for Active Corrosion Protection via Digitalisation

Peter Klein,[a*] Heinz A. Preisig,[b] Thomas F. Hagelien, [c] Natalia Konchakova [d]

[a]*Fraunhofer Institute for Industrial Mathematics, Fraunhofer-Platz 1, 67663 Kaiserslautern, Germany*
[b]*Norwegian University of Science and Technology, 7491 Trondheim, Norway*
[c]*SINTEF, Otto Nielsens veg 10, 7052 Trondheim, Norway*
[d]*Helmholtz-Zentrum Hereon, Max-Planck-Straße 1, 21502 Geesthacht, Germany*
peter.klein@itwm.fraunhofer.de

Abstract

Product optimisation is commonly done within a company, even though a product may result from a production chain involving several companies. Exchanging information related to the local optimisation between the involved companies allows for adjusting the local optimisation towards achieving a global optimal product. Making the Pareto fronts of the company-local compromise available to the related partners enables the global optimisation of a B2B2B (Business-to-Business-to-Business). We introduce this technology to manufacturing active corrosion protection coating systems involving nanoparticles, paint producers, and consumers.

Keywords: materials and product digitalisation, optimally distributed production, innovation environment, product design.

1. Introduction

The H2020-funded research and innovation project VIPCOAT [VIPCOAT, 2021] implements a Multi-Criteria Optimization (MCO) technology in an Open Innovation Platform (OIP). The optimisation requires product performance information, which in parts is obtained from the users, from (standardised) experiments and simulations, thus digital twins.

One of the platform's main challenges is bringing together all information in a form that computing devices can process, thus realise the digitalisation of all information [Ekaputra et al, 2022]. It starts with giving things "names" and associating each of these names with a global identifier. Data models that use these global identifiers must be generated for each data stream. The data models can then be shared, allowing for a smooth transfer, thereby guaranteeing *data interoperability* between all software components. It also enables automating data management and streamlining interaction with (external) databases and data sources [Klein et al, 2023].

Centralising the data also allows for the documentation of the production and the product, which opens the possibility of issuing digital product passports for intermediate and final products. Using IT technologies that build a knowledge graph makes data processing efficient and enables the use of AI technologies for searching, comparison, reasoning, automation, and optimisation.

This paper also discusses the need to digitalise industrial product data and their use for optimisation and documentation to issue digital product passports. The application area is the active protection of metal surfaces in aggressive environmental conditions on the background of having to replace chromates as the main corrosion-protection ingredient. The project involves three industrial partners: an SME that produces nanoparticles containing the active anti-corrosion component, an international paint producer, and a consumer which is an aeroplane manufacturer.

2. Overall workflow

The design process starts with defining an over-arching objective. A common one is a replacement request, such as a poisonous active component on a material/product, which is augmented with the request of having an equivalent or better or acceptable performance but not being toxic and satisfying a list of constraints associated with operation, application and environment, which leads to the definition of the first task, namely the search for a suitable replacement, which in our demo case is chromates.

The workflow starts with exploring the space where one hopes to find a replacement based on the defined specifications. An AI-based model is trained on this initial information generating an initial set of candidates (feasible component exploration). It is the beginning of an iteration process (experiment, simulations, exploration), which uses experiments and simulations to narrow down the candidate set.

In each iteration step, the candidates' suitability must be verified, defining the next set of performance experiments on probes of the final product, namely the primed metal sheet. Modelling & simulation augment experimental work. A tight dependency exists between those two efforts, as models require data that can only be obtained from experiments. Figure 1 shows a rough picture of the different components and their interactions.

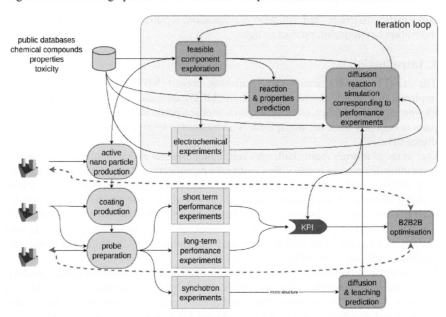

Figure 1: A rough workflow for the chromate-replacement innovation process

Once a set of promising candidates is identified, the iteration loop is extended with coating tests (short & long term). The companies produce a test coating product, and its structure is explored in synchrotron experiments (material's microstructure), which in turn is utilised to obtain improved estimates on diffusivity. Advanced synchrotron in-situ experiments also lead to the estimation of the leaching kinetics.

Modelling focuses on different aspects of the product with the objective of assessing the performance. It will encompass models for different scales and physical aspects, including the molecular scale, lower granular scale, like particles, agglomerates, and energy dissipation processes driving the macroscopic behaviour.

All these models require input, some of which are generated by experiments, and again, data that are to be connected with the digital environment are being generated.

In each iteration, the candidate set is expected to shrink. Once a reasonable small set is identified, test panels are produced by the coating-producing and the application company, both testing independently the suggested primer for its performance.

In parallel, the obtained information on the product's behaviour is used to define simulations of the panel tests to predict the experimental result and the primer's performance on the application surface.

Key Performance Indicators (KPIs) provide a performance measure and are the main ingredient for the optimisation task spanning the complete production and application sequence and their associated companies.

3. The VIPCOAT Open Innovation Platform

The platform operates with workflows. Some are predefined; others can be built and tailored to the user's needs online.

Data uploading workflow: The various external data streams, mainly experimental and simulation data, are connected to the platform. Each experimental data set is furnished with three metadata sets.

1. Cataloguing data resources: Providing high-level information about data resources to enhance the findability and reuse of information. The proper data documentation in a catalogue offers a standardised way of describing and indexing data resources, making it easier for users to locate and utilise the data they need.
2. Metadata extraction: Documenting the data's contents in terms of data points. The objective of metadata extraction is to provide a more detailed and accurate description of the data.
3. Mapping metadata to standard vocabularies: Often represented as ontological concepts. This step allows semantic interoperability to be achieved, ensuring that external systems can understand the information, which means that the data can be interpreted consistently, regardless of the specific software system or application being used.

The result is a data catalogue and the interoperability of the connected sources. The data are automatically linked to the platform's data exchange space. The connecting operation is done via a semantic service, which takes the metadata and generates a data model. The data model operates like a port definition and is stored in a knowledge graph for application. The port can be accessed over a data pipeline service by any of the platform's processes [Konchakova et al, 2022] giving direct access to the stored data.

Simulation workflows for Inhibitor efficiency prediction: It considers a user case on a prediction of corrosion inhibitors` properties and supports selecting the best inhibitors. The final goal is to assess three relevant KPIs: Inhibition efficiency, Toxicity, and Price. VIPCOAT OIP connects the different simulations via the platform's data space using the APIs generated by the semantic service. For example, information is extracted from the

PubChem database. PubChem is a public database that merges more than 750 important international chemical sources such as ECHA, OSHA, etc. Each chemical can be searched and presented at the OIP in the form of the name, CAS number, molecule symbol, or SMILES formula.

Coating Microstructure and Leaching prediction workflow: The second use case deals with the effective medium description (Pseudophase) of the coating and its leaching properties. The detailed morphology of the coat resolving geometrical details at microscales is based on dedicated stochastic geometrical models trained with experimental data from the Synchrotron images. The input parameters for the simulation are collected by the interactive dialogue with the OIP user fixed by the user's active confirmation. The leaching prediction based on generated synthetic morphologies and coating microstructure. The results represent the leaching front and the individual pigment flux that changes over time. This outcome is used for the prediction of the material's behaviour in a coating defect area and simulates the accelerated corrosion test.

Accelerated corrosion test workflow: The corrosion test and respective simulations are done for dynamic and static environmental conditions. Different anti-corrosion pigments are considered, and their influence on coating defects over a metallic substrate is assessed via experiment and multi-ion simulation.

Innovation facilitation workflow: Our aim is to implement an open innovation process using B2B2B digital environment. We focus on automatic knowledge and data exchange thought the OIP by providing efficient operation and giving the owner complete control over accessibility to all (meta-) data. The VIPCOAT project revealed that companies are ready to share their data under these conditions and participate in the co-development and co-creation process in the frame of an innovation project.

VIPCOAT OIP supports innovation processes consisting of 4 steps: Ideas, Project Proposal, Partnerships and Projects (see Figure 2).

Figure 2: VIPCOAT OIP landing page, https://vipcoat-oip.com/welcome

The platform will serve as a digital environment for an interactive cooperation and co-design of new products – protective coatings. The information generated by the simulations and experiments is utilised to generate Key Performance Indicators (KPI), which, in turn, are the information used in the B2B2B optimisation.

4. Optimisation along a production chain via Digitalisation

A Multi-Criteria Optimisation (MCO) approach and a decision-making methodology have been used for the business decision support system (BDSS) based on Pareto fronts and implemented on the VIPCOAT platform. The method guidelines the construction of suitable initial and boundary conditions of modelling workflow related to the VIPCOAT use cases and their integration into collaborative industrial decision-making methodologies using MCO in a B2B2B environment, as realised by VIPCOAT industrial partners along a production chain. This optimisation technique allows us to find a set of tuneable design variables satisfying constraints and simultaneously optimise the KPIs. The MCO leads to non-unique solutions. Pareto fronts represent the best possible and feasible compromises among conflicting objectives, for example, quality versus cost (Figure 3)

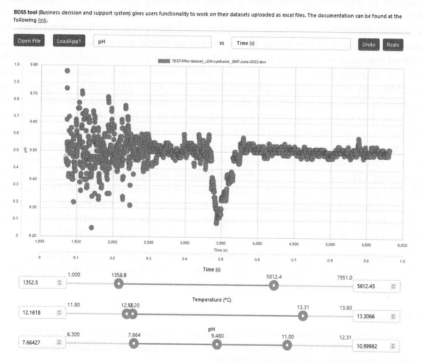

Figure 3: Pareto front explorer applied to the reactor producing LDH structures.

In the VIPCOAT digital B2B2B environment, the optimisation workflow is guided by a BPMN diagram. A business decision support system integrated into the OIP allows users to find an optimal solution based on identified KPIs. Users can apply their datasets to the system. The platform reads the set and prepares it properly for the interactive graph application. The user can consider different KPIs to select the optimal frame of the product parameters. The analysis could be an iterative one. The optimisation process could be focused on the challenges of only one industrial player or support collaborative decision-making for two (B2B) or more innovation partners (B2B2B). The collaborative MCO has been implemented at VIPCOAT OIP, providing the Pareto front of supplier variants (B2B) for downstream usage in an MCO design space (B2B). The approach allows the execution of a fast technological iteration in case of surprise specifications or requirements:

> downstream: technological as quality KPIs;
>
> upstream: technological design options and business KPIs (pricing).

5. Conclusion

Collaborative optimisation and decision-making process unlock hereto hidden product innovation potentials. Following this idea, VIPCOAT consortium successfully works under implementation of the digital environment to support the innovation facilitation and optimization along the production chain for active corrosion protection for airspace. Leading European industry and academia apply modelling and multi-criteria optimization technique to accelerate development a protective coating with best possible corrosion inhibitor replaced hexavalent chromium-based compounds. VIPCOAT platform supports the optimal materials design process based on modelling prediction from describing the materials properties and available data provided by distributed manufacturing, and the involved materials components to new product development. This approach necessarily calls for interoperability along the value-added chain, which requests proper data documentation and ontological representation. VIPCOAT platform is equipped with Application Programmer Interfaces that provide automatic connection to REACH and PubChem data bases. Later provides the end-users with different important information regarding toxicity of investigated chemicals, properties of new inhibitors, list of potential restrictions or other parameters to support the decision making on a production use of potential coating components. It makes VIPCOAT OIP an attractive digital environment for creating a Digital Materials and Product Passport as requested by the EC for different industrial areas. The passport will support co-innovation processes and will be developed based according to industrial needs. The discussed in this paper approach of the optimization along a production chain via Digitalisation is a step forward to implement Circular Economy transition and Safe and Sustainable by Design paradigm[1].

Acknowledgements: VIPCOAT H2020-NMBP-TO-IND-2020, Grant Agreement No. 952903; MEDIATE European net project; DigiPass HORIZON-CL4-2023-RESILIENCE-01-39, Grant Agreement No. 101138510.

References

Virtual Open Innovation Platform for Active Protective Coatings Guided by Modelling and Optimization (VIPCOAT, Grant Agreement No 952903), https://ms.hereon.de/vipcoat/ , https://cordis.europa.eu/project/id/952903/de

P. Klein, H.A. Preisig, N. Konchakova, 2023, Translation Ontology of optimal Decision Making along a Distributed Production Chain by Example, Computer Aided Chemical Engineering, 52, https://doi.org/10.1016/B978-0-443-15274-0.50333-4

N. Konchakova, H.A. Preisig, C. Kavka, M.T. Horsch, P. Klein, S. Belouettar, 2022, Bringing Together Materials and Business Ontologies for Protective Coatings, CEUR Workshop Proceedings, http://ceur-ws.org/Vol-3240/ .

F.J. Ekaputra, F. Piroi, M. Noeske, J. Friis, Jesper, A. Calvio, N. Konchakova, R. Foidl, W.L. Cavalcanti, L. Foschini, T.F. Hagelien, A. More, C.W. Andersen, B. Andreon, 2022, Towards an Open Translation Environment for Supporting Translators in the Materials Domain, CEUR Workshop Proceedings, http://ceur-ws.org/Vol-3240/ .

---

[1] https://publications.jrc.ec.europa.eu/repository/handle/JRC128591

Flavio Manenti, Gintaras V. Reklaitis (Eds.), Proceedings of the 34th European Symposium on Computer Aided Process Engineering / 15th International Symposium on Process Systems Engineering (ESCAPE34/PSE24), June 2-6, 2024, Florence, Italy

Fault Detection and Analysis via Latent Space Differences Between the Plant and the Model Representing Normal Operation

Enrique Luna Villagomez[a], Hamidreza Mahyar[b], Vladimir Mahalec[a*]

[a]*Dept. of Chemical Engineering,* [b]*WBooth School of Eng. Practice and Technology*
McMaster University, Hamilton, ON L8S 4LS, Canada
*mahalec@mcmaster.ca

Abstract

Abnormal plant operations (faults) occur when equipment or an instrument no longer functions well. Detection of such faults is made more difficult by process control applications, which attempt to ameliorate the impact of faults by keeping the production on target. Closed loop controls cause the plant to operate in a narrow region, which in turn limits the validity of data-driven fault detection methods to such a limited scope. This work introduces a fault detection architecture that employs data generated from steady-state simulation models to build a latent space model (e.g., Principal Component Analysis, PCA) of the normal operation, thereby overcoming limitations inherent in the plant's historical data. In real-time, variables from the model and the plant are processed by identical copies of PCA. The pattern of the differences indicates the fault occurrence and gives insight into possible causes.

Keywords: fault detection, abnormal operation, differences between normal and abnormal operation, latent space differences

1. Introduction

Fault detection (FD) based on plant data usually proceeds by identifying a model representing normal operation from plant data. This model could be a first principles model or a data-driven model that is then deployed in real-time to detect the occurrence of faults. The methodology of parity equations (Iserman, 2005) compares the model variables with their corresponding plant measurements to identify the occurrence of faults. Conversely, a data-driven model, usually a reduced dimensionality space model (e.g., PCA or kernel PCA) measures the deviation from the normal operating region using statistical techniques to detect the occurrence of abnormal operation, i.e., faults (Yoon et al., 2001). The recurrent neural network data-driven model, introduced by Sun et al., (2020), characterizes dynamic behavior during normal operation, offering the possibility to detect and identify the faults based on comparing the measured process variables and the likely values of these variables in a normal operation.

Continuously operating plants operate in relatively narrow regions due to closed-loop controls. When disturbances enter the process, the resulting deviations from desired operating process outputs are rapidly corrected by the control actions. Data representing such plant operations is confined to a relatively narrow region. Consequently, fault detection and identification methods based on data-driven models built from the narrow normal operating region data cannot discern whether a fault (e.g., catalyst poisoning or heat transfer rate decrease due to fouling) forces the control system to move the plant outside the normal operating window in multimodal operations.

Over the last four decades, many first principles process models have been built for design and plant improvement applications. These models represent the behavior of the real plants reasonably well, but they are not perfect. Model parameters (e.g., heat transfer coefficients or reaction rates) are estimated from correlations or first principles equations, resulting in process models that may have considerable error (in the order of 5%) in heat transfer coefficients, reaction rates, or a similar relative error in predicting the concentration of product impurities. Nevertheless, these models adequately represent process behavior over various operating conditions, even if nonlinearity exists.

2. Fault Detection via latent space differences

This work relies on the ability of the process models to generate data over a wide operating region (wider than the data available from normal plant operation). Even if such data are generated from the models with incorrect model parameters, these data can be used to train unsupervised learning models (e.g., PCA or Autoencoder) representing (somewhat inaccurately) the normal operating conditions, NOCs. In the proposed FD approach, a trained unsupervised learning model, e.g., PCA, is deployed in real-time to have data from the plant as its inputs, while another instance of the same PCA model has the variables from the simulation model as its inputs. The simulation model takes feed, disturbances, and operating targets as inputs, enabling it to determine the values of the manipulated (control loop) variables. Differences between the latent space variables of these two instances of the latent space model are zero in normal operation if the model matches the plant perfectly. When a fault occurs, these differences are non-zero. Figure 1 depicts this fault detection architecture.

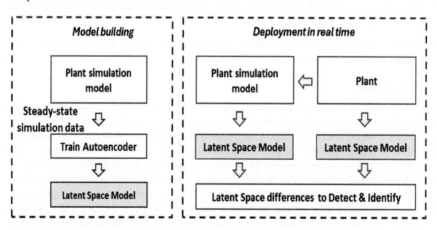

Figure 1. Fault detection and analysis via latent space differences.

This architecture has the potential to enable PCA in multimodal operations as an alternative to cluster-based techniques. For example, in the event of a setpoint change, this can be incorporated into the plant reference model, thereby ensuring that the latent space spanned by the PCA adjusts accordingly to maintain the differences close to zero. Notice that if plant/model mismatch is present, the differences in normal operation have a bias (i.e., they are not zero). Therefore, the bias needs to be corrected before proceeding with the fault detection task.

3. Experiments in fault detection

The proposed fault detection architecture has been tested on the CSTR example studied by Yoon et al. (2001). Steady-state data from a model of that CSTR has been used to train a PCA model. The PCA model explains 98% of the variance in the original dataset with two components. A mismatch between the plant and the model has been considered by creating another copy of the original CSTR model. This duplicate represents the plant under conditions where the reaction rate is either overestimated ($r_{plant} = 0.85 \cdot r_{model}$) or underestimated ($r_{plant} = 1.1 \cdot r_{model}$). To further explore these scenarios, we conducted experiments simulating two specific events: a sudden catalyst poisoning (where the reaction rate reduces from 100% to 90%) and a drift (ramp) in the readings from the analyzer measuring the concentration of reactant A in the reactor. Figure 2 depicts the two latent variables and their differences when catalyst poisoning occurs at time = 1,000 min.

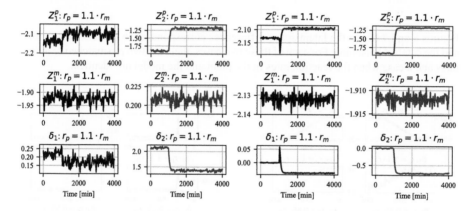

Figure 2. Catalyst poisoning at t=1,000;   Figure 3. Filtering and bias adjustment of
$r_{plant} = 1.1 \cdot r_{model}$.   the latent space differences

Since process noise makes it difficult to discern the shape of the difference plots, the data have been filtered (arithmetic moving average filter, 40 observations), and the differences $\delta_i = Z_i^{model} - Z_i^{plant}$ have been offset by their biases that occur in normal operation (time up to 1,000 min), as shown in Fig. 3. Filtering and bias adjustment of the differences (to correct for the plant-model mismatch) opens a possibility that the plant operators could use the difference plots to detect visually occurrence of the faults ("difference is not zero = fault is in place").

Figure 5 shows the two filtered latent variables and their bias-adjusted differences when the concentration sensor drift starts at t = 1,000 min until t = 3,000 min, after which the error remains constant. The difference plot's slope depends on the analyzer drift's slope. As long as the analyzer error keeps increasing, the difference also increases. Figure 4 depicts the unfiltered and unadjusted data of the same case for reference purposes.

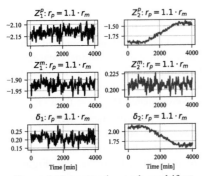

Figure 3. Concentration analyzer drift at
t=1,000; $r_{plant} = 1.1 \cdot r_{model}$.

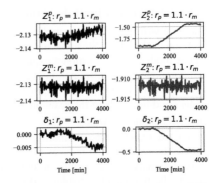

Figure 4. Concentration analyzer drift:
filtered latent variables and their differences.

Figures 6 and 7 depict the latent space differences corresponding to the analyzer failure
and the catalyst poisoning. For each of these two cases, there are two mismatched reaction
rates and a case when the reaction rates in the plant and the model are identical.

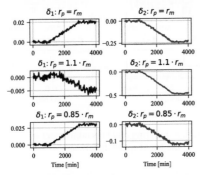

Figure 5. Analyzer drift starting at t=1,000
until t=3,000; latent space differences at
different levels of reaction rates mismatch.

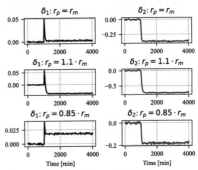

Figure 6. Catalyst poisoning occurs at
t=1,000; latent space differences at different
levels of reaction rates mismatch.

As seen from Fig. 6, when reaction rates in the model and the plant are the same, the δ_1
difference becomes positive while the δ_2 difference becomes negative. The same pattern
is observed when the reaction rate in the plant is less than the rate in the model.
Conversely, if the reaction rate in the plant is greater than the rate in the model, both δ_1
and δ_2 become negative.

If catalyst poisoning occurs (Fig. 7), a similar pattern is observed, i.e., if the reaction rate
in the plant is greater than the reaction rate in the model, when a fault occurs, both (bias
adjusted) differences have the same sign. In contrast, in all other cases, the first difference
assumes the values that have the opposite sign of the second difference sign. Further
research is needed to verify that this is the case when the mismatch is due to reaction rate.

4. Fault detection performance

To evaluate the performance of the proposed FD approach, we conducted comparative tests using classic PCA. PCA models were developed using data exclusively from normal operating conditions to ensure each plant-mismatch level scenario was paired with a corresponding PCA model. In this case, the PCA models were created to explain at least 98% of the variance in the training datasets. Notably, this level of explanation was achieved with just two principal components in all cases. The Square Prediction error (SPE) was selected as the metric to perform the fault detection via classic PCA:

$$SPE_i = x_i^T x_i - x_i^T P P^T x_i.$$

To ensure a fair comparison, the PCA training datasets were filtered (arithmetic moving average filter, 40 observations) before z-scaling. In our proposed FD framework, we have introduced an anomaly score termed 'Square Sum of Differences' (SSD). This score quantifies all the differences in the latent space between the plant and its simulation model. The SSD is defined as follows:

$$SSD_j = \sum_j z_j^m(i) - z_j^p(i).$$

In both methodologies, we employed Kernel Density Estimation (KDE) to fit a distribution to the metric. Subsequently, we established the control limit for each metric at the 99.99th percentile of its respective distribution.

Table 1. Fault detection times and F1 scores

Case	Fault	t_d (SPE) [min]	F1 score (SPE)	t_d (SSD) [min]	F1 score (SSD)
		Classic PCA		This method	
No Mismatch	Sensor drift	310.5	0.9719	191.5	0.9811
No Mismatch	Catalyst poisoning	7.5	0.9996	16	0.9990
$r_p = 1.1 \cdot r_m$	Sensor drift	322.5	0.9712	136.5	0.9878
$r_p = 1.1 \cdot r_m$	Catalyst poisoning	7.5	0.9996	15	0.9991
$r_p = 0.85 \cdot r_m$	Sensor drift	310.5	0.9722	426.5	0.9566
$r_p = 0.85 \cdot r_m$	Catalyst poisoning	7.5	0.9997	18.5	0.9987

The filtering techniques employed in this research were critical in mitigating process noise interference during the fault detection process. Moreover, to reduce the incidence of false alarms, it was determined that a fault alarm should only be activated following 15 consecutive observations exceeding the established threshold for normal operation. The results, presented in Table 1, detail the detection times (**t_d**) and F1 scores for both metrics.

5. Discussion

Latent space difference plots enable visual observation of the faults as they occur and of their progress through time.

Table 1 shows that in cases with no plant/model mismatch, or when the reaction rate is underestimated, the proposed parallel configuration excels in detecting slowly increasing faults (ramp). It also performs satisfactorily in detecting abrupt faults (step), as indicated by a high F1-score. The difference in detection time w.r.t. classic PCA is about 8 to 10 minutes, while at the same time the difference plots offer the insight in the nature of the fault (ramp or step change). We attribute this time difference to the filtering process, which averages down the values in the latent space during the occurrence of step behavior. Further experimentation with different filter types and filter is in progress.

Since plant model reproduces nonlinear behavior of the plant, and the plant model runs in parallel with the plant, it is expected that the proposed methodology will perform better than the classic PCA if a plant behaves nonlinearly, and it moves from one operating region to another.

6. Conclusions

The proposed fault detection architecture makes it possible to use the vast number of already existing process equipment simulation models to be used for fault detection. The models need not match the plant perfectly since the method performs well in case of the plant-model mismatch.

When a fault occurs in plant operation, the number of alarms sent to the operator console increases very quickly, which leads to an alarm overload and operators ignoring alarms. Graphical display of the latent space difference plots will allow operators to visually detect occurrence of a fault and eliminate broadcasting of numerous textual alarms for the same fault, which will significantly improve human-machine interface.

In addition to detecting the faults, the latent space differences open a possibility to diagnose the source of the fault by analyzing the pattern of the differences in addition to differences in the process variables between the plant and the model.

References

R. Iserman, 2005, Model-based fault-detection and diagnosis – status and applications. Annual Reviews in Control, 29 (1), 71-85

W. Sun, A.R.C. Paive, P. Xu, A. Sundaram, R.D. Braatz, 2020, Fault detection and identification using Bayesian recurent neural networks, Computers and Chemical Engineering, 141, 106991

Yoon, S., MacGregor, J.F. (2001) Fault diagnosis with multivariate statistical models. part i: using steady state fault signatures. Journal of Process Control, 11, 387–400

Flavio Manenti, Gintaras V. Reklaitis (Eds.), Proceedings of the 34th European Symposium on Computer Aided Process Engineering / 15th International Symposium on Process Systems Engineering (ESCAPE34/PSE24), June 2-6, 2024, Florence, Italy

Dynamic Scheduling of Ethylene Cracking Furnaces System Leveraging Deep Reinforcement Learning

Haoran Li,[a,b] Yixin Wei, [a,b] Tong Qiu[a,b*]

[a] *Department of Chemical Engineering, Tsinghua University, Beijing 100084, China*
[b] *Beijing Key Laboratory of Industrial Big Data System and Application, Tsinghua University, Beijing 100084, China*
qiutong@tsinghua.edu.cn

Abstract

The profitability and resilience of traditional scheduling algorithms for ethylene steam cracking systems in the face of supply chain fluctuations are comparatively weak. To address this issue, a dynamic ethylene scheduling framework based on deep reinforcement learning is proposed in this study. Through a comparative analysis with literature cases, this framework demonstrates a notable enhancement of 5.7 % in daily revenue, showcasing strong resilience to supply chain fluctuations.

Keywords: deep reinforcement learning, ethylene, dynamic scheduling

1. Introduction

Ethylene stands as one of the most prolifically produced chemicals globally, with the prevailing method of production being steam cracking(Bi et al., 2021). Owing to the inherent volatility in the supply and demand dynamics along the value chain, the profitability of ethylene cracking furnace systems (ECFS) is susceptible to perturbations. While traditional static mixed-integer nonlinear optimization (MINLP) models effectively optimize the scheduling of various feedstocks across multiple cracking furnaces to maximize economic benefits(Li et al., 2022), their resilience to fluctuations is limited. Consequently, dynamic scheduling tailored to conditions of supply chain volatility has emerged as a pivotal strategy for enhancing the profitability of ethylene cracking furnace systems(Li et al., 2023).

In recent years, deep reinforcement learning has garnered attention from researchers in the field of process systems engineering, owing to its robust handling of stochastic scenarios. In this study, we have developed a deep reinforcement learning framework specifically tailored for the ethylene scheduling system, comprising an ethylene scheduling Markov Decision Process (MDP) environment and a Deep Q-Network (DQN) decision network to address the dynamic scheduling challenges under supply chain fluctuations. The subsequent sections are organized as follows: Part 2 outlines the definition of the ethylene scheduling problem, Part 3 provides the methodology, Part 4 presents the results of a case study, and the final conclusions are provided in Part 5.

2. Problem statement

The steam cracking production of ethylene is a semi-continuous process with slow dynamic shifts during the batch because of coking inside the furnace tube. The cracking furnace will be switched out and decoked once the coke accumulates to a certain extent to ensure safety. An ethylene cracking furnaces system usually consists of *NC* types of

feed, *NF* cracking furnaces and *NP* products. The scheduling of ECFS on each day is to decide:
1) whether to end the current batch and perform decoking
2) the next feed type after decoking
The objective of the scheduling problem is to maximize the net profits while satisfying the constraints including non-simultaneous decoking, feed inventory, and batch length lower and upper bounds, etc.

3. Method

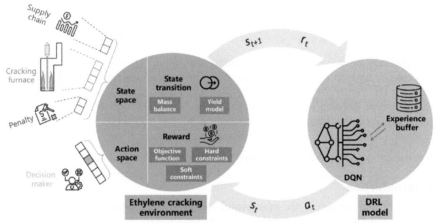

Figure 1. Framework of Dynamic Ethylene Scheduling Environment and DRL-based Decision Model.

3.1. Ethylene Scheduling System Environment Formulation
We considered the scheduling problem of an ECFS with 3 types of feeds, 5 cracking furnaces, and 3 types of products. Then we formulated it as an MDP with state (s_t), action (a_t), reward (r_t), and probability transition function ($P(s'|s, a)$).

3.1.1. State space
The state is a 27-dimensional vector consisting of the furnace states, historical supply chain parameters, and penalty terms.

$$s_t = [Fd_{j,t}, Blen_{j,t}, Invent_{j,t}, Prod_{p,t}, Sp_{i,t}^{his}, Pr_{i,t}^{his}, Pr_{p,t}^{his}, Penalty_{1,t}, Penalty_{2,t} \tag{1}$$

Where i, j, p are the indexes for feeds, furnaces, and products. $Fd_{j,t}$ and $Blen_{j,t}$ are the current inlet feed type and batch length of furnace j, $Invent_{i,t}$ is the current feed inventory level of feed i, and $Prod_{p,t}$ is the flowrate of product p. $Sp_{i,t}^{his}, Pr_{i,t}^{his}, Pr_{p,t}^{his}$ are historical value of the supply amount of feed i, price of feed i, and price of product p.

3.1.2. Action space
The action is designed as an integer variable from [0,15] indicating the decision on whether to perform decoking and the next inlet feed type after decoking. If $a=0$, no furnaces will perform decoking. Otherwise, the decoking furnace and next feed type will be determined as Eqs. (2) and (3).

$$Decoke\ No._t = (a_t - 1)//3 + 1 \tag{2}$$

$$Next\ feed_t = (a_t - 1)\%3 + 1 \tag{3}$$

For example, if $a_t = 8$, then decoking will be performed on Furnace 3 on that day ($Decoke\ No._t = 3$) and Feed B will be processed afterwards ($Next\ feed_t = 2$).

3.1.3. Reward function design

The reward function is designed as net profit minus the penalty terms which are used to account for the violation of constraints, as shown in Eq. (4). The net profit is calculated by the product revenue minus the feed cost, operation cost, and the decoking cost.

$$R_t = \sum_{j}^{NC} \sum_{p}^{NP} [\sum Pr_{p,t} F_{i,j,t} - \sum_{i}^{NF} (Pr_{i,t} + Cv_{i,j}) F_{i,j} y_{i,j,t} - \sum_{i}^{NF} Cs_{i,j} x_{i,j,t}]$$
$$- Penalty_{1,t} - Penalty_{2,t} \tag{4}$$

Where $y_{i,j,t}$ and $x_{i,j,t}$ are auxiliary binary variables. If furnace j is processing feed i and is not under decoking then $y_{i,j,t} = 1$. If furnace j was processing feed i and is under decoking then $x_{i,j,t} = 1$. $F_{i,j,t}$ is the feed processing flowrate, $Cv_{i,j}$ is the operation unit cost, and $Cs_{i,j}$ is the decoking unit cost.

$Penalty_{1,t}$ and $Penalty_{2,t}$ correspond to penalties for violating hard constraints and soft constraints, respectively. The distinction lies in the fact that hard constraints are inviolable—if violated, action a_t will be rewritten, whereas soft constraints are not. In this case, the hard constraint is the batch length lower and upper bounds. If violated, the furnaces will be forced to be decoked or not to be decoked, as shown in Eqs.(5) and (6).

$$Penalty_{1,t} += M, if\ Blen_{j,t} > tup_{i,j}\ and\ Decoke\ No._t$$
$$\neq j, Forced\ decoking \tag{5}$$

$$Penalty_{1,t} += M, if\ Blen_{j,t} < tlo_{i,j}\ and\ Decoke\ No._t$$
$$= j, Forced\ no\ decoking \tag{6}$$

The soft constraint is the feed inventory level. If the inventory is negative, the usage of the feed will pay a price surplus α.

$$Penalty_{2,t} += \alpha(invent_{i,t-1} - invent_{i,t}), if\ invent_{i,t}$$
$$< 0\ and\ invent_{i,t} < invent_{i,t-1} \tag{7}$$

3.1.4. Probability transition function

The uncertainties originate from the fluctuating daily feed supply amount $Sp_{i,t}$, feed prices $Pr_{i,t}$, and product prices $Pr_{p,t}$. On each day, once the state s_t and action a_t are given, the next state s_{t+1} will be updated by the probability transition function.

If furnace is not decoked, then the $Fd_{j,t+1}$ will the same as $Fd_{j,t}$ and $Blen_{j,t+1}$ will be incremented by 1. Otherwise, $Fd_{j,t+1}$ will be set as $Next\ feed_t$ and $Blen_{j,t+1}$ will be set as 0.

The inventory level of feed i will be updated by the supply amount and consumption on that day, as in Eq. (8). $Comsup_{i,t}$ is the total processing amount of feed i on day t, and is determined by the $Fd_{j,t}$.

$$Invent_{i,t+1} = Invent_{i,t} + Sp_{i,t} - Comsup_{i,t} \tag{8}$$

The product yield model is in the exponential form, as shown in Eq. (9). And the flowrate of products will be calculated by the yields and feed flowrate processed by each furnace.

$$Yield_{i,j,p,t+1} = kc_{i,j,p} + ka_{i,j,p} \, exp(kb_{i,j,p} Blen_{j,t+1}) \qquad (9)$$

Where $kc_{i,j,p}, ka_{i,j,p}, kb_{i,j,p}$ are the reaction dynamics parameters.
The supply chain parameters will be updated by the newly observed values.

$$Sp_{i,t+1}^{his}, Pr_{i,t+1}^{his}, Pr_{p,t+1}^{his} = Sp_{i,t}, Pr_{i,t}, Pr_{p,t} \qquad (10)$$

3.2. Deep Reinforcement Learning-based Model
A version of DQN algorithm(Mnih et al., 2013) is applied to train the deep reinforcement learning model. The Q-network (ϕ) is the used the predict the future rewards of the given combination of s_t and a_t. The action is chosen using the ε-greedy strategy. With a probability of ε, a random action is selected; otherwise, the action with the highest prediction is chosen.

$$a_t = \begin{cases} random \ action, Prob = \epsilon \\ argmax_a \phi(s_t, a), Prob = 1 - \epsilon \end{cases} \qquad (11)$$

The target network (ϕ') is used to predict the future rewards of (s_{t+1}, a_{t+1}). The loss function is the mean squared error between the prediction value and the target value, and the network is updated by the calculation of the loss on a minibatch of N samples from the experience replay buffer.

$$L = \frac{1}{N} \sum_{i}^{N} [R_t + \gamma \phi'(s_{t+1}, a_{t+1}) - \phi(s_t, a_t)^2 \qquad (12)$$

4. Case study

We utilized a case study in the literature (Liu et al., 2010). Firstly, the MINLP model in the original literature was formulated into an MDP environment following the method in Section 3.1. Then, the DQN model was trained by interacting with this environment. Finally, the scheduling decisions generated by the original MINLP and DQN models are both validated to compare the performances.

4.1. Model training
Figure 2 shows the loss function curve and the episode reward curve during model training. The loss function value decreased drastically in the beginning and converged after around 1 million environment steps. At the same time, the episode reward increased from negative values to positive values and also stabilized after 1 million steps. The negative value was caused by the penalty terms.

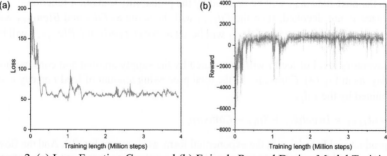

Figure 2. (a) Loss Function Curve and (b) Episode Reward During Model Training.

4.2. Scheduling performance validation

After training, the original MINLP model and the trained DQN model are tested on a 1000-day case in which the daily feed supply, feed price and product price parameters fluctuate from day to day, as shown in Figure 3. The fluctuations in these parameters bring the necessity of dynamic scheduling of ECFS because once the parameter changes, the original optimal solution will become sub-optimal or even infeasible.

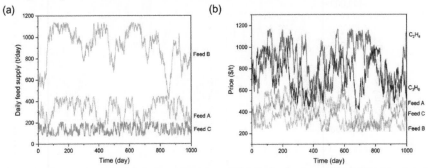

Figure 3. Fluctuating supply chain parameters of (a) Daily feed supply and (b) Feed and Product Price.

Figure 4 is the Gantt chart which demonstrates the feed allocation among the five cracking furnaces using the decision results generated by the two models. Figure 4(a) is the result from the original MINLP which did not consider the parameter fluctuations in the optimization model. Thus, the Gantt chart shows a repeated pattern. On the contrast, the DQN model was trained to tackle the fluctuations and did not show the repeated pattern.

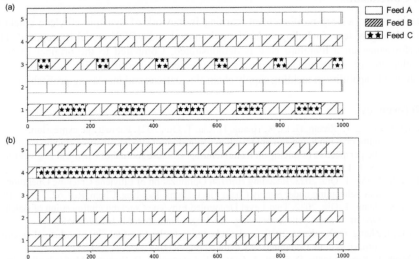

Figure 4. Scheduling Gantt Chart of (a) MINLP Model and (b) DQN Model.

Figure 5 shows the daily net profit under these two solutions. The solid line represents DQN solution and dash line represents MINLP solution. On most of the days during the testing length, the daily net profit from DQN solution is higher than MINLP solution. The profit gaps between the two solutions are especially significant at around day 400 and 550, where large net profit losses appear extensively because of the penalty from the inventory constraint violations. Overall, the average daily net profits from the MINLP and DQN solutions are 103,227 \$/day and 161,703\$/day. An improvement of 5.7 % is achieved by the DQN model in this case, showing the strong capability of the DQN model to handle the supply chain parameter fluctuations during ethylene cracking scheduling.

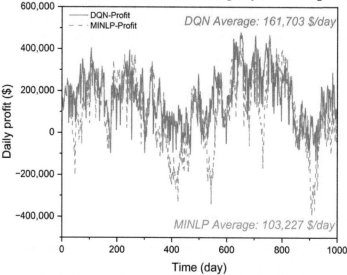

Figure 5. Daily Net Profit During the Testing Length.

5. Conclusions

In this work, a deep reinforcement learning framework of dynamic ethylene cracking scheduling systems including an MDP environment and a DQN model is proposed. The performance on a literature case is demonstrated. Compared to the original MINLP model, the proposed model improves the average net profit by 5.7 %, showing its enhanced capability of tackling supply chain fluctuations and increasing profitability.

References

K. Bi, S. Zhang, C. Zhang, H. Li, X. Huang, H. Liu, T. Qiu, 2021. Knowledge expression, numerical modeling and optimization application of ethylene thermal cracking: From the perspective of intelligent manufacturing. Chinese Journal of Chemical Engineering 38, 1–17.

H. Li, S. Zhang, T. Qiu, 2023. Receding Horizon Optimization of Ethylene Cracking Operation and Scheduling under Supply Chain Fluctuations. Ind. Eng. Chem. Res. 62, 5125–5140.

H. Li, S. Zhang, T. Qiu, 2022. Two-Level Decoupled Ethylene Cracking Optimization of Batch Operation and Cyclic Scheduling. Ind. Eng. Chem. Res. 61, 16539–16551.

C. Liu, J. Zhang, Q. Xu, K. Li, 2010. Cyclic scheduling for best profitability of industrial cracking furnace system. Computers & Chemical Engineering 34, 544–554.

V. Mnih, K. Kavukcuoglu, D. Silver, A. Graves, I. Antonoglou, D. Wierstra, M. Riedmiller, 2013. Playing Atari with Deep Reinforcement Learning.

Flavio Manenti, Gintaras V. Reklaitis (Eds.), Proceedings of the 34th European Symposium on Computer Aided Process Engineering / 15th International Symposium on Process Systems Engineering (ESCAPE34/PSE24), June 2-6, 2024, Florence, Italy

Towards Intelligent Wastewater Treatment: Prediction of Biodegradation Processes Through the Application of Machine Learning

Jiayuan Ji[a,*], Xinwu Zhou[b], Yuichiro Kanematsu[c], Yasunori Kikuchi[a,c,d]

[a]Institute for Future Initiatives, The University of Tokyo, 7-3-1 Hongo, Bunkyo-ku, Tokyo 113-8654, Japan
[b]Institute of Fluid Science, Tohoku University, 2-1-1 Katahira, Aoba-ku, Sendai 980-8577, Japan
[c]Presidential Endowed Chair for "Platinum Society", the University of Tokyo, 7-3-1 Hongo, Bunkyo-ku, Tokyo 113-8656, Japan
[d]Department of Chemical System Engineering, the University of Tokyo, 7-3-1 Hongo, Bunkyo-ku, Tokyo 113-8656, Japan
*Corresponding: kikaen@ifi.u-tokyo.ac.jp

Abstract

With the rapid growth of global population and the change of human living habits, the treatment of municipal wastewater is facing serious challenges. To solve the problems of high energy consumption, big amount of greenhouse gases emission, and huge volume of waste sludge production of the current process, a series of innovations and developments based on anaerobic process are being focused on. However, the processes generally require long experimental cycles because of the biodegradation reaction. If the microbial degradation in anaerobic process is modelled, the experimental period will be drastically reduced, but the traditional modeling methods are less generalizable and thus difficult to be applied. In recent years, artificial intelligence tools have been applied to dealing with complicated situations. This led our research team to the idea of using machine learning approach to model and predict microbial degradation processes. The prediction performance was obtained with good results. Afterwards, the authors recognized that the research work on the construction of dataset is of great importance in the future work.
Keywords: wastewater treatment, machine learning, prediction modeling.

1. Introduction

The contemporary landscape of municipal wastewater treatment grapples with formidable challenges, accentuated by the rapid global population surge and dynamic shifts in human living habits. Central to these challenges is the widely employed activated sludge process, a key process used in the wastewater treatment. Despite its prevalence, this method contends with significant drawbacks, manifesting in heightened energy consumption, substantial greenhouse gas emissions, and the generation of vast volumes of waste sludge. Among the avant-garde approaches gaining prominence is the strategic application of anaerobic digestion in treating low-strength municipal wastewater. This pioneering process, as previously reported in a review paper (Hu et al., 2020), transcends traditional treatment methodologies. It not only facilitates the recovery of energy and valuable resources from wastewater but also demonstrates promising reductions in greenhouse gas emissions and the generation of waste sludge. However, the efficacy of such technologies is hampered by their inherent reliance on microbial communities for degradation. This reliance, in turn, imposes prolonged experimental cycles, a bottleneck facing the real application emphasized in the previous research work (Ji et al., 2021).

Recognizing the urgency of addressing these challenges, our research team has embarked on a multifaceted exploration of the complex field of modeling microbial degradation processes within anaerobic treatment systems. This scientific work was motivated by the enormous potential to revolutionize wastewater treatment. Traditional modeling methods, although fundamental, have their limitations in terms of generalizability, especially when applied to realistic scenarios (Brdjanovic et al., 2013). The emergence of artificial intelligence, especially in the field of machine learning, provides unprecedented opportunities to overcome these challenges. The seminal work of Bengio et al. (Bengio et al., 2013) revealed the transformative power of these tools in navigating complex situations, prompting our team to utilize the power of machine learning to accurately model and predict microbial degradation processes.

Additionally, our research agenda extends to the field of neural network modeling to include a variety of approaches to further improve the efficiency of microbial degradation prediction. Through this comprehensive exploration, we are harnessing the power of artificial intelligence to model wastewater treatment to provide effective, efficient, and sustainable solutions. In this paper, we briefly describe our recent study (G. Li et al., 2022) in this field and further explore the problems and possibilities.

2. Methodology

2.1. Wastewater Treatment System

The experimental system was applied anaerobic digestion into municipal wastewater treatment. This is not only aimed at recovering energy and resources, but also at reducing greenhouse gas emissions and sludge generation. Based on the experimental results operation situation, we first meticulously organized and confirmed the operating parameters of the wastewater treatment system, including influent (inf.) characteristics (for example, chemical oxygen demand (COD)), temperature, hydraulic retention time (HRT), pH, and oxidation-reduction reaction potential (ORP) (Ji et al., 2021).

2.2. Dataset Construction

The core of our approach consists of modeling the microbial degradation processes within an anaerobic treatment system. Therefore, the dataset is a key component. Recognizing the critical importance of datasets in machine learning applications, we began working to optimize the construction of the dataset (Fig. 1). Operation temperature (R-T), temperature of the environment (T-env), temperature of the influent (T-in), influent pH (pH-in), influent COD concentration (COD-in), and flux were selected as the input, and effluent COD concentration (COD-eff), and COD removal efficiency (COD-re) were selected as the predicted outputs (Table 1).

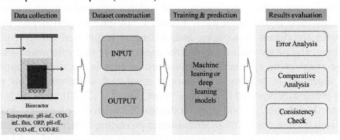

Fig. 1 Dataset Construction and Machine Learning Processes.

Table 1. Characteristics of the dataset.

	Mean	Standard Error	Minimum	Maximum
T-R	25.49	1	20.8	30
T-in	17.83	5.49	8	26.4
T-env	17.41	6.4	6.8	27.9
pH-in	7.17	0.16	6.89	7.62
COD-in	376.2	88.85	202.88	740.33
Flux	0.2	0.06	0.07	0.35
COD-eff	44.78	9.82	19.49	87.3
COD-re	87.57	3.6	75.82	94.86

2.3. Machine Learning Algorithms and Evaluation Metrics

Our research adopts deep neural networks of Basic Machine Leaning Network, Convolutional Neural Network, and DenseNet to discern patterns and predict the degradation process of wastewater treatment. For specific information on neural networks, refer to the printed paper (G. Li et al., 2022). To rigorously assess the performance of models, we employ a range of evaluation metrics. The mean square error (MSE) was selected as the loss function, as shown in Eq. (1).

$$MSE(y, \hat{y}) = \frac{\sum_{a=1}^{b}(y_a - \hat{y}_a)^2}{b} \tag{1}$$

In addition, the following metrics were applied for evaluation: the mean absolute error (MAE), root mean square error (RMSE), mean relative error (MRE), and Coefficient of determination (R^2). The equation for calculate those metrics is shown in Eq. (2), (3), (4), and (5).

$$MAE(y, \hat{y}) = \frac{\sum_{i=1}^{N}|y_i - \hat{y}_i|}{N} \tag{2}$$

$$RMSE(y, \hat{y}) = \sqrt{\frac{\sum_{i=1}^{N}(y_i - \hat{y}_i)^2}{N}} \tag{3}$$

$$MRE(y, \hat{y}) = \frac{\sum_{i=1}^{N}\frac{|y_i - \hat{y}_i|}{|y_i|}}{N} \tag{4}$$

$$R^2(y, \hat{y}) = 1 - \frac{\sum_{i=1}^{N}(y_i - \hat{y}_i)^2}{\sum_{i=1}^{N}(y_i - \bar{y})^2} \tag{5}$$

Where y represents the real experimental value, $\hat{y}$ represents the DL predicted value, and $\bar{y}$ is the average value of the experimental values.

2.4. Iterative Learning Process

Recognizing the dynamic nature of our research domain, we institute an iterative learning process. This involves continuous refinement of our models based on real-time feedback, allowing for adaptability to evolving conditions and insights gained during the course of the study. The number of training epochs (number of training iterations) was set with a number of 1000 for all the above-mentioned evaluation parameters.

3. Results and Discussion

3.1. Overview of Prediction Results

After completing the machine learning task, a comprehensive assessment of the model performance became the focus of our results. Preliminary observations indicate that these deep learning models we applied are feasible for predicting microbial degradation processes in anaerobic treatment systems. The prediction results are show in Fig. 2. From this figure, it can be seen that the prediction of COD removal efficiency is better that the effluent concentration. However, since this presentation is not clear enough, further analysis becomes especially important.

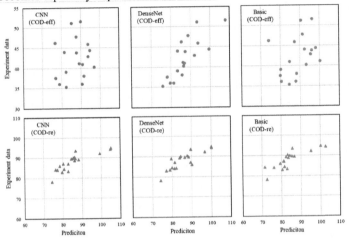

Fig. 2 Prediction results and experiment data shown in yy-plot.

Table 2. The prediction result of applied machine learning.

DL models	Items	COD-eff	COD-re
Basic Machine Leaning Network	MAE	4.73 ± 2.53	5.71 ± 2.73
	RMSE	5.34 ± 5.11	6.29 ± 6.07
	MRE	$11.78 \pm 6.82\%$	$6.49 \pm 3.17\%$
	R^2	0.76	1.94 (0.89*)
Convolutional Neural Network	MAE	5.26 ± 3.90	5.34 ± 2.77
	RMSE	6.48 ± 7.91	5.98 ± 5.69
	MRE	$13.52 \pm 12.67\%$	$6.02 \pm 3.00\%$
	R^2	0.31	2.28 (0.89*)
DenseNet	MAE	3.65 ± 3.33	4.34 ± 1.83
	RMSE	4.88 ± 7.69	4.69 ± 4.32
	MRE	$9.70 \pm 11.82\%$	$4.93 \pm 2.05\%$
	R^2	0.78	2.52 (0.93*)

*The values modified by removed error data.

The evaluation metrics provide quantitative insights into the efficacy of the models in order to compare the accuracy of their predictions (Table 2). From these results, the possibility that neural networks can be applied to wastewater treatment processes using microbial degradation was further demonstrated. Moreover, it makes the evaluation of different models quantifiable. Based on the analysis and evaluation by MAE, RMSE,

MRE, and R^2, it can be concluded that DenseNet performs the best among the three network models. However, it is necessary to mention that for the prediction of COD removal rate, the R^2 values were beyond 1. This indicates the occurrence of overfitting or error. After checking the predicted values, it was found that there were some values that exceeded 100%, which could not be present in the removal rate values. The optimization for this phenomenon needs to be considered in the following.

Overall, deep neural networks demonstrated successful predictive capabilities for wastewater treatment processes in this study. This exploration reveals the potential benefits of machine learning, especially neural network architectures in interpreting microbial degradation processes.

3.2. Comparison with other Predictive Models

The evolution from prior predictions, informed by deep networks, to the current study showcases the advancements achieved through dataset optimization and the incorporation of diverse machine learning methodologies. Previous research applied machine learning to the aerobic wastewater treatment process and obtained an sMAPE (Symmetric mean absolute percentage error) result of 5.63% (Zaghloul et al., 2021). Anther research reported that they have obtained the MAE of 4.8~9.6 with algorithms of stacked denoising auto-encoders, traditional backpropagation neural network, support vector regression, extreme learning machine, gradient boosting decision tree, and stacked auto-encoders (Shi & Xu, 2018). However, the data processing in these studies used feature extraction to expand the dataset.

The anaerobic biochemical treatment process of wastewater is characterized by complex mechanisms, high nonlinearity, and instability. To address these characteristics, a recent study has developed an automatic optimization-seeking water quality prediction model based on deep learning, which realizes high-precision prediction of COD and gas production of effluent from anaerobic wastewater treatment systems (J. Li et al., 2022). Not only for modeling and predicting the removal of organic pollutants from wastewater by anaerobic digestion, but machine learning also obtained high prediction outcomes for the process of anaerobic ammonia oxidation for the removal of ammonia nitrogen from wastewater (Ji, 2023). Insights gleaned from this comparative analysis contribute to the broader understanding of predictive modeling in this domain.

3.3. Practical Implications and Future Directions

The results obtained have a direct impact on the practical advancement of prediction of wastewater treatment processes. Based on our findings, the integration of machine learning approach is expected to optimize the treatment process, minimize environmental impacts, and facilitate the transition to smart wastewater management. In addition, our study paves the way for future research directions, including exploring advanced neural network for biodegradation and integrated real-time monitoring systems for the process.

3.4. Limitations of the Study

Although we achieved good prediction results and gained some insights into the optimization of the dataset, the future remains challenging. Specifically, first of all, the process flow varies from different wastewater treatment plant or experimental operation. Although with data training and parameter tuning, machine learning can be applied to different process flows, the preliminary preparations, such as the construction and optimization of the dataset, without a unified solution is a problem. Secondly, in some cases the dataset is small or insufficient for training, how to apply the network model already trained by other treatment processes directly to the new prediction is a challenging task. In addition, there are many network models that have been developed to relative sophistication, and it is therefore important to consider how to choose the proper model.

4. Conclusions

In summary, this study demonstrates that machine learning is feasible for prediction in wastewater treatment. Further enhancement of the prediction results is achievable by optimizing the dataset construction and exploring various machine learning algorithms. The results of this research have practical implications for optimizing wastewater treatment methods and promoting sustainable development and environmental management. It not only contributes to the current understanding of predictive modeling, but also helps pioneer the way for future innovations in intelligent and adaptive wastewater treatment strategies.

Acknowledgements

This study was supported by JSPS KAKENHI JP19J12023, JST COI-NEXT JPMJPF2003, NEDO Moonshot R&D Program Grant Number JPNP18016, and the Hirose Foundation. Activities of the Presidential Endowed Chair for "Platinum Society" at the University of Tokyo are supported by Mitsui Fudosan Corporation, Sekisui House, Ltd., the East Japan Railway Company, and Toyota Tsusho Corporation.

References

D. Brdjanovic, S. C. Meijer, C. M. Lopez-Vazquez, C. M. Hooijmans, M. C. van Loosdrecht, 2015, Applications of activated sludge models, IWA publishing, London, United Kingdom.

G. Li, J. Ji, J. Ni, S.Wang, Y. Guo, Y. Hu, S. Liu, S. F. Huang, Y. Li, 2022, Application of deep learning for predicting the treatment performance of real municipal wastewater based on one-year operation of two anaerobic membrane bioreactors, Science of the Total Environment, 813, 151920.

J. Ji, Y. Chen, Y. Hu, A. Ohtsu, J. Ni, Y. Li, S. Sakuma, T. Hojo, R. Chen, Y. Li, 2021, One-year operation of a 20-L submerged anaerobic membrane bioreactor for real domestic wastewater treatment at room temperature: pursuing the optimal HRT and sustainable flux, Science of the Total Environment, 775, 145799.

J. Ji, 2023, Introduction of deep learning networks to predict anammox-based low-carbon biological nitrogen removal processes, The 14th HOPE Meeting with Nobel Laureates, Tsukuba, Japan.

J. Li, Z. Chen, X. Li, X. Yi, Y. Zhao, X. He, Z. Huang, M. A. Hassaan, A. El Nemr, M. Huang, 2022, Water quality soft-sensor prediction in anaerobic process using deep neural network optimized by Tree-structured Parzen Estimator, Frontiers of Environmental Science & Engineering, 17, 6, 67.

M. S. Zaghloul, O. T. Iorhemen, R. A. Hamza, J. H. Tay, G. Achari, 2021, Development of an ensemble of machine learning algorithms to model aerobic granular sludge reactors, Water Research, 189, 116657.

S. Shi, & G. Xu, 2018, Novel performance prediction model of a biofilm system treating domestic wastewater based on stacked denoising auto-encoders deep learning network, Chemical Engineering Journal, 347, 4, 280–290.

Y. Bengio, A. Courville, P. Vincent, 2013, Representation learning: A review and new perspectives, IEEE Transactions on Pattern Analysis and Machine Intelligence, 35, 8, 1798–1828.

Y. Hu, H. Cheng, J. Ji, Y. Li, 2020, A review of anaerobic membrane bioreactors for municipal wastewater treatment with a focus on multicomponent biogas and membrane fouling control, Environmental Science: Water Research & Technology, 6, 10, 2641–2663.

Flavio Manenti, Gintaras V. Reklaitis (Eds.), Proceedings of the 34th European Symposium on Computer Aided Process Engineering / 15th International Symposium on Process Systems Engineering (ESCAPE34/PSE24), June 2-6, 2024, Florence, Italy

An Efficient Approach for Droplet Coalescence Videos Processing based on Instance Segmentation and Multi-Object Tracking Algorithms

Wenle Xu,[a,b] Shuyuan Zhang,[a,b] Kai Wang,[a,c] Tong Qiu[a,b*]

[a]Department of Chemical Engineering, Tsinghua University, Beijing, 100084, CHINA
[b]Beijing Key Laboratory of Industrial Big Data System and Application, Tsinghua University, Beijing, 100084, CHINA
[c]The State Key Laboratory of Chemical Engineering, Department of Chemical Engineering, Tsinghua University, Beijing 100084, CHINA
qiutong@tsinghua.edu.cn

Abstract

Controlled coalescence of droplets is a crucial method of performing reactions and synthesises within droplets. Among all methods employed for droplet characterization within microchannels, microscopic imaging stands out for its capacity to capture ample information. However, the processing of images and videos still predominantly relied on massive manual works, which falls short of meeting the demands for high-throughput analysis. To address this problem, this paper proposes an efficient approach based on instance segmentation and multi-object tracking algorithms to analyse the droplet coalescence videos in microchannels. This approach initially segments droplets in microscopic images and consequently associate the identical droplets and recognize the coalescence processes across consecutive frames. Finally, further analysis of these data can yield critical statistics of the droplet coalescence process, such as coalescence probability and coalescence time. This approach enables automated and efficient analysis of videos to decipher the droplet coalescence process, thereby accelerating the discovery and exploration of droplet coalescence patterns in microfluidics.

Keywords: Microfluidics, Droplet Coalescence, Instance Segmentation, Multi-Object Tracking.

1. Introduction

Droplet coalescence is considered as a pivotal technique in microfluidics, with significant potential applications in versatile chemical such as the formation of particles, kinetics studies, and chemical synthesis (Teh et al., 2008). Conducting droplet coalescence experiments on microfluidic platforms equipped with microscope and high-speed cameras offers distinct advantages, including high throughput, precise control, and minimal resource consumption. However, researchers often grapple with the manual processing of large volumes of microscopic photos and videos, a task that consumes several weeks to accumulate sufficient data and obtain related statistics. This manual approach results in a substantial gap between the speed of data generation and analysis. Although several commercial tools can assist in automatically identifying droplets in photos, these tools are struggled to handle droplets with irregular shapes, not to mention that the extraction of coalescence time and coalescence probability requires analyzing videos frame by frame.

Some researchers have made attempts to apply deep learning based computer vision algorithms to process microchannel microscopic photos and videos (Rutkowski et al., 2022; S. Zhang et al., 2022). Notably, up to this point, no deep learning model has been proposed to process videos recorded coalescence process, the models aforementioned lack the ability to identify droplets before and after the coalescence occurs.

This paper proposes an efficient approach based on instance segmentation and multi-object tracking algorithms. This approach begins by employing a convolutional neural network-based instance segmentation model to detect and segment droplets in microscopic images. Subsequently, the droplet tracking and coalescence judging algorithm can associate identical droplets and recognize coalescence processes across consecutive frames. Finally, further analysis of these data can yield critical statistics of the droplet coalescence processes such as coalescence probability, the distribution of coalescence numbers and coalescence time. Compared to manual analysis, this approach can automatically and intelligently analyze the droplet coalescence videos, achieving human-level accuracy and significantly faster video processing speed.

2. Method

The approach to process droplet coalescence videos involves three main stages: data pre-processing, instance segmentation, and droplet tracking and coalescence judging.

2.1. Data pre-processing

The videos analyzed in our paper are derived from a droplet coalescence experiment in microchannels with a sudden expansion chamber (Wang et al., 2016).

The data pre-processing stage involves two main steps: video splitting and image annotation. Since the subsequent instance segmentation and droplet tracking and coalescence judging algorithms operate on images as the basic unit rather than videos, it is necessary to split the video into individual images. To capture the complete coalescence process, the videos are split at a frequency of once per frame. Following this, image annotation is performed. Once considered a laborious task, it requires the outlining of thousands of droplets to train an instance segmentation model. Each droplet necessitated more than 30 precise clicks around its contour. Fortunately, leveraging state-of-the-art pretrained models such as Segment Anything Model (Kirillov et al., 2023), the outlining task can now be achieved with a single click anywhere on the droplets' bodies. It significantly accelerates the annotation by more than 30x.

A total of approximately 1500 droplets in 473 images are annotated. Subsequent to annotation, the images are divided into training and testing sets, with detailed information shown in Table 1.

Table 1. The characteristics of training set and testing set.

	Training Set	Testing Set
Total number of images	372	101
Average number of droplets per image	3.2	3.3
Average projection area (pixels)	11450	12190

2.2. Instance segmentation

Instance segmentation models based on convolution neural networks (CNNs) can be categorized into 2 types: mask-based models and contour-based models. While both types leverage CNNs to extract features, the former processes the mask of each instance, and the latter focuses on contours. In common objects dataset, mask-based models usually outperform in accuracy but tend to be slower compared to contour-based models.

However, the most notable distinction of the droplets and background lies in their contours, contour-based models may achieve a higher accuracy. Consequently, unlike the mask-based model Mask R-CNN utilized in previous work, a contour-based model, E2EC, is employed to extract the contours of droplets in our paper, potentially achieving better accuracy and faster inference speed (He et al., 2017; T. Zhang et al., 2022).

Transfer learning is particularly useful in downstream applications where there is a lack of sufficient and high-quality data. In this paper, transfer learning is implemented by transferring the weights of E2EC pretrained on COCO dataset (Lin et al., 2014). Furthermore, a series of reductions are applied to the training set to simulate the common dilemma of lacking sufficient annotated images, the sizes of training sets are shown in Table 2. The performances of the models (E2EC, E2EC with transferred weights, and Mask R-CNN) trained on these reduced training sets are compared.

Table 2. Total number of the training sets.

	Training Set 1	Training Set 2	Training Set 3	Training Set 4	Training Set 5
Total number of images	372	186	93	37	18

The confusion matrix depending on Intersection over Union (IoU) is depicted in Figure 1. The mean Average Precision (mAP) across a series of IoU is used to evaluate the instance segmentation results, as defined in Eq. (1).

$$mAP = \sum_{IoU=0.50,0.55,...,0.95} \frac{TP_{IoU}}{TP_{IoU} + FP_{IoU}} \tag{1}$$

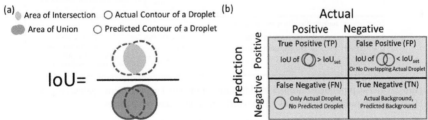

Figure 1. (a) A computation example of intersection over union. (b) Confusion matrix of droplet instance segmentation.

2.3. Droplet tracking and coalescence judging

This paper proposes a droplet tracking and coalescence judging algorithm (shown in Figure 2.), which consists of a droplet tracking part and a coalescence part. The droplet tracking part adopts the idea of performing assignments based on a distance matrix in SORT (Bewley et al., 2016), and the coalescence judging part is designed based on three fundamental assumptions that (1). No droplet will disappear unless it flows out of the microchannel, (2). The droplet's area does not increase suddenly, and (3). Coalescence is based on contacting. The workflow of the algorithm can be summarized as follows:

I. Estimate: Current positions of tracks (referring to the historical droplets in frame T-1) are estimated based on their historical speeds and positions.

II. Associate: An association refers to link detections (meaning the instance segmentation results in frame T) to their tracks. An association cost matrix between all tracks and detections is computed by Eq. (2). Then, the association problem is converted to an assignment problem which is solved by using the Hungarian algorithm. Additionally, any association with an association cost exceeding a predetermined threshold is rejected.

$$\text{Association cost(track, detection)} = 1 - \frac{\text{intersection area}^{1.5}(\text{track, detection})}{\text{area}^{1.5}(\text{detection})} \quad (2)$$

After assignment, the tracks and detections are divided into three sets: the unassociated tracks set (UT), the unassociated detections set (UD), and the associations set (AS).

III. Coalescence judging: Figure 2(b) illustrates two different coalescence scenarios. (1). Two droplets (A and B) with similar area coalesce and produce a droplet (C) in Frame T. The association cost of (A, C) and (B, C) are high, and consequently A and B are distributed to UT and C is distributed to UD. (2). A small droplet and a large droplet (A and B) coalesce and produce a droplet. (B, C) has a low enough cost to be associated.

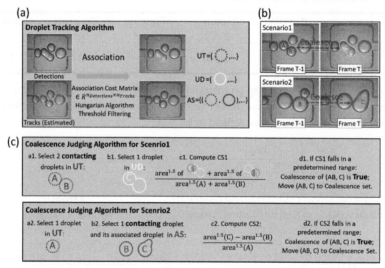

Figure 2. (a) The pipeline of droplet tracking algorithm. (b) Two different coalescence scenarios. (c) Coalescence judging algorithm for two different coalescence scenarios.

IV. Two coalescence judging algorithms are designed for these two scenarios. For the first coalescence scenario, the algorithm work as bellows:

a1. Select two contacting droplets from UT, denoted as A and B. b1. Select a droplet from UD, denoted as C. c1. Compute the coalescence score 1 (CS1) of A, B, and C by Eq. (3). d1. If CS1(AB, C) falls in a predetermined range, the coalescence event (AB, C) is considered to have occurred and (AB, C) is moved to coalescence set.

$$\text{CS1 (AB, C)} = \frac{\text{intersection area}^{1.5}(\text{A, C}) + \text{intersection area}^{1.5}(\text{B, C})}{\text{area}^{1.5}(\text{A}) + \text{area}^{1.5}(\text{B})} \quad (3)$$

For the second coalescence scenario, the algorithm work as bellows:

a2. Select a droplet from UT, denoted as A. b2. Select one contacting droplet of A and its associated droplet from AS, denoted as B and C. c2. Compute the coalescence score 2 (CS2) of A, B, and C by Eq. (4). d2. If CS2(AB, C) falls in a predetermined range, the coalescence event (AB, C) is considered to have occurred and (AB, C) is moved to coalescence set.

$$CS2 \, (AB, C) = \frac{\text{area}^{1.5}(C) - \text{area}^{1.5}(B)}{\text{area}^{1.5}(A)} \tag{4}$$

V. After coalescence judging, the aforementioned three sets are further subdivided into four sets: individual droplets set, new detections set, leaving tracks set, and coalescence droplets set. The coalescence time, coalescence probability, and other critical statistics can be figured out directly based on this subdivision.

Multiple Object Tracking Accuracy (MOTA) serves as an evaluation metric for assessing the performance of tracking algorithms. It is calculated using Eq (5), which incorporates false positives (FP), false negatives (FN), and identity switches (IDSW), normalized over ground-truth (GT) tracks. FP represents the number of incorrect assignments of detections to tracks when the droplets have flowed out or coalesced. FN represents to the number of missed assignments of detections to tracks. IDSW represents the number of wrong assignments of detections to track. GT represents the total number of droplets. Precision rate and recall rate are employed to evaluate the results of coalescence judging.

$$MOTA = 1 - \frac{FP + FN + IDSW}{GT} \tag{5}$$

3. Results and discussions

3.1. Instance segmentation

The mAP of three models (E2EC, E2EC with transferred weights, and Mask R-CNN) trained on the reduced training sets are shown in Figure 3(a). Notably, E2EC outperforms than Mask R-CNN in the droplet segmentation task, and this superiority becomes more pronounced as the training set size decreases. Figure 3(b) presents a comparative example between E2EC and Mask R-CNN, both trained with a dataset consisting of 37 annotated images. E2EC demonstrates precise segmentation even for droplets with irregular shapes, while Mask R-CNN has a rough segmentation at the droplets' contours, with large areas of missed detection. Additionally, E2EC achieves an inference speed of 22.24 images per second, while Mask R-CNN only infers 11.91 images per second, tested on a RTX 3070Ti GPU. Figure 3(c) compares E2EC and E2EC with transferred weights trained with 18 annotated images. The E2EC trained from scratch struggles to maintain its performance under the limitation of a small training set. Conversely, E2EC with transferred weights performs well, showcasing the efficacy of transfer learning for downstream tasks with sparse data.

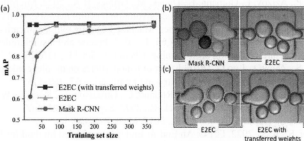

Figure 3. (a) The mAP of E2EC, E2EC with transferred weights, and Mask R-CNN trained on the training sets. (b) A comparison of E2EC and Mask R-CNN trained with 37 annotated images. (c) A comparison of E2EC and E2EC with transferred weights trained with 18 annotated images.

3.2. Droplet tracking and coalescence judging

We select 12 videos to evaluate the algorithm. Manual analysis shows the presence of 415 droplets totally, of which 158 coalesce. The testing results for droplet tracking shows no FN or FP, and IDSW is 1, resulting in a high MOTA of 0.998. For coalescence judging, both FN and FP are zero, resulting in high precision and recall rate of coalescence judging of 1. Based on it, coalescence time and coalescence number can be precisely determined. Take coalescence time as an example, it can be directly figured out by counting the frames from when two droplets come into contact to the moment of coalescence.

3.3. Analysis speed comparison

The only stage requiring researchers' participation is image annotation. However, this step demands only a few minutes to annotate sufficient images for training an instance segmentation model, with the assistance of pretrained models and transfer learning technology. In comparison to manual analysis, our approach demonstrates a significantly superior processing speed. For instance, the analysis of a video consisting of 1000 frames, involving the determination of droplet sizes, coalescence numbers, and coalescence time, could consume researchers dozens of hours. In contrast, our approach completes this task in approximately 50 seconds, showcasing a huge superiority.

4. Conclusions

In general, this paper proposes an approach based on instance segmentation and multi-object tracking algorithms to analyze droplet coalescence videos automatically and intelligently. This approach is able to precisely identify droplets and coalescence events in the video. Compared to manual analysis, this approach presents a human-level accuracy and a much faster video processing speed. Our work exhibits a possibility of applying deep learning-based computer vision technology for analyzing the critical interphase of multiphase systems in chemical engineering.

Acknowledgements

The authors gratefully acknowledge the National Natural Science Foundation of China for its financial support (Grant No. 21991100, 21991104).

References

Teh, S.-Y., Lin, R., Hung, L.-H., Lee, A.P., 2008. Droplet microfluidics. Lab Chip 8(2), 198-220.

Rutkowski, G.P., Azizov, I., Unmann, E., Dudek, M., Grimes, B.A., 2022. Microfluidic droplet detection via region-based and single-pass convolutional neural networks with comparison to conventional image analysis methodologies. Machine Learning with Applications 7, 100222.

Zhang, S., Liang, X., Huang, X., Wang, K., Qiu, T., 2022. Precise and fast microdroplet size distribution measurement using deep learning. Chem Eng Sci 247, 116926.

Wang, K., Yi, S., Zhou Q., Luo G., 2016. Effect of nanoparticles on droplet coalescence in microchannel. Journal of Chemical Industry and Engineering 67, 469-475.

Kirillov, A., Mintun, E., Ravi, N., Mao, H., Rolland, C., Gustafson, L., Xiao, T., Whitehead, S., Berg, A.C., Lo, W.-Y., Dollár, P., Girshick, R., 2023. Segment Anything.

He, K., Gkioxari, G., Dollar, P., Girshick, R., 2017. Mask R-CNN.

Zhang, T., Wei, S., Ji, S., 2022. E2EC: An End-to-End Contour-based Method for High-Quality High-Speed Instance Segmentation.

Lin, T.-Y., Maire, M., Belongie, S., Hays, J., Perona, P., Ramanan, D., Dollár, P., & Zitnick, C. L., 2014. Microsoft COCO: Common Objects in Context.

Bewley, A.; Ge, Z.; Ott, L.; Ramos, F.; Upcroft, B., 2016. Simple Online and Realtime Tracking.

Flavio Manenti, Gintaras V. Reklaitis (Eds.), Proceedings of the 34th European Symposium on Computer Aided Process Engineering / 15th International Symposium on Process Systems Engineering (ESCAPE34/PSE24), June 2-6, 2024, Florence, Italy

Comparison of different data and information fusion methods to improve the performance of machine learning models

Pál P. Hanzelik*[a,b], Alex Kummer[b], Márton Mócz[c], Szilveszter Gergely[c], Dorián L. Galata[d], János Abonyi[b]

[a]*Group Enterprise Data, MOL ITD GBS Hungary Ltd., Dombóvári út 28., H-1117 Budapest, Hungary*
[b]*HUN-REN Complex Systems Monitoring Research Group, University of Pannonia, Egyetem u. 10., H-8200 Veszprém, Hungary*
[c] *Dept. of Applied Biotechnology and Food Science, Faculty of Chemical Technology and Biotechnology, Budapest University of Technology and Economics, Műegyetem rkp. 3., H-1111 Budapest, Hungary*
[d] *Dept. of Organic Chemistry and Technology, Faculty of Chemical Technology and Biotechnology, Budapest University of Technology and Economics, Műegyetem rkp. 3., H-1111 Budapest, Hungary*
*pphanzelik@molitdgbs.com

Abstract

The combined handling of information from fast and non-destructive spectroscopic measurement techniques enables more accurate and robust models. Machine learning algorithms that estimate qualities are sometimes not accurate enough for a given quality, so to improve the models' accuracy, we need to provide additional information from different analytical measurements. This research compares five data and information fusion techniques tested on spectroscopic results from various oil industry samples. We aim to show examples of which fusion technique should be used and how to build models in this way. We used the boosting technique to compare which approach provides the most information from the measurements. We used mid-infrared and Raman spectral data from the same samples in this study and applied low, medium, high, and complex data fusion techniques. Our motivation is to combine and compare the treatment of different measurement techniques that can provide additional information. The difference between the five methods is the level at which the fusion takes place. The variables come from spectral data at a low level, but at a medium level, we used individually created model results. Furthermore, at the complex level, we used the data of the models built together with the ensemble learning technique for the spectral data.

Considering our achievements in the oil industry, data fusion techniques can significantly improve the accuracy of machine learning models. In our case study, the best results were obtained by the fifth-level data fusion technique, where half of the developed model can predict the hydrocarbon/imide ratio of the additive with an error as if data fusion had not been applied.

Keywords: model development, data fusion, ensemble learning, spectroscopy, quality control

1. Introduction

By storing and using the data from different measurements in a shared database, we can provide data faster and more efficiently. We can obtain more accurate models with machine learning (ML) algorithms built on fused data. Based on increasingly essential quality criteria and environmental protection regulations, data fusion techniques built on laboratory data represent a vast potential for digitizing laboratory activities. The quality of a material can be determined from the results of several laboratory measurements. However, to reduce the turnaround time of the laboratories, fast measurements with much information are preferred. According to the literature review, the data fusion techniques began to spread in the second half of 2017, after which they gained more and more emphasis in the work of quality assurance laboratories. Most scientific literature on data fusion techniques was published in the food and pharmaceutical industries. The growing number of multi-dimensional analytical instruments and chemical measuring devices that produce data sets of different dimensions provide a considerable amount of analytical information about complex samples and, at the same time, pose a challenge during data evaluation. The use of ML tools helps the efficient use of these data volumes. Furthermore, the development of chemometrics revolutionized the steps in the interpretation of analytical processes and contributed to the solution of more complicated analytical problems.

Data fusion techniques are necessary to examine the complexity of an analysis problem from several different perspectives. The goal is to create the most comprehensive and complex picture possible of the reviewed materials, and it is also essential for us to obtain as much information as possible from the point of view of qualification quickly and non-destructively using a small number of samples. Many questions and challenges in food chemistry or the pharmaceutical industry can only be solved by combining the results of different instruments with a broader characterization of the given samples. Data fusion enables the simultaneous extraction of meaningful and valuable information from various analytical sources. It can be seen from the literature that in recent years, data fusion has produced better results for the investigated systems than the evaluation of individual data sets [1]. Spectroscopic measurements result in multiple data points whose historical storage and use in modelling provide an opportunity to improve the quality assurance of production processes with an Industry 4.0 approach. Data fusion techniques were applied to modern process analytical technology (PAT) data for non-destructive prediction of drug tablet dissolution. They could directly model the dissolution of the tablets from the near-infrared (NIR) and Raman spectra of the tablets. Data fusion techniques have greatly improved the accuracy of the models. During the research, partial least squares (PLS) models were built on the data of the NIR and Raman devices separately or in combination, and artificial neural network models were constructed on their output to predict better dissolution by Nagy et al. [2]. In the food industry, for example, research indicating the caprolactam content of sauce-based foods is also an excellent example of applying data fusion techniques. The measurements were performed using near-infrared (NIR) and mid-infrared (MIR) spectroscopy, and models were built using the data fusion technique (PLS) and support vector machine (SVM) based on the measurement results. The results of each method were combined into different weighted coefficients according to their contribution by the work of Zhu et al. The high-level fusion model provided the best performance, followed by the MIR model, then the low, and medium-level fusion models, and finally, the NIR model proved to be the weakest [3]. In our research, we tested different data fusion approaches on the infrared and Raman spectroscopic measurement spectra on oil industry samples to build models with sufficient accuracy for quality parameters that are difficult to predict. In the case study, we present an additive's hydrocarbon/imide ratio, where the model built on the Raman and MIR models needed sufficient accuracy in terms of proper classification.

2. Methodology

We performed the IR and Raman spectroscopy measurements of the same samples. Then, we built ML models to predict the sample quality using different data fusion techniques to predict the hydrocarbon/imide ratio of the additive. Our goal is to demonstrate that using and properly producing quality data from other analytical measurements can result in more accurate ML models.

Figure 1 presents the five investigated model development techniques with no or different data fusion techniques. In mode *A*, we built a model separately for the IR and Raman data. In this case, we did not apply data fusion. We did this for reference, to which we can compare the results of different methodologies, and the other four modes are distinguished depending on the implementation level of data fusion techniques. In the low-level data fusion (*B*) route, the raw datasets were fused and analyzed as a single dataset. In this case, feature selection was applied to the entire data set, and then a regression ML model was built. The middle-level data fusion path (*C*) fuses important actual or latent variables extracted from feature selection on each data set. We combined the essential properties of infra and Raman and built a model. The high-level data fusion path (*D*) builds a separate model for all available data sets, combines the model prediction results, and then merges them to create a standard model using the ensemble technique. The complex-level data fusion path (*E*) is an ensemble model built on the latent variables of the models based on the pre-processed and fused data set and the model prediction results.

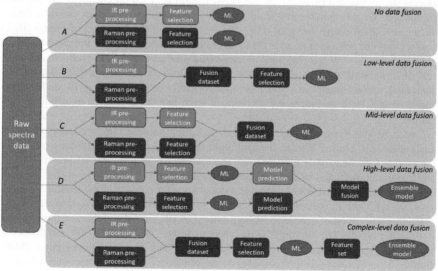

Figure 1: Five different techniques of data fusion.

The essence of the ensemble model used in ways *D* and *E* is that it performs the prediction by combining the results of the previously built ML model or models and considering its prediction. Ensemble learning has become one of the practical and popular techniques for increasing the accuracy of ML models in data science. By applying the methodology, we aim to emphasize the strength of individual ML models and achieve more accurate and robust results.

The feature selection in Figure 1 modes *A*, *B*, *D* and *E* refers to the Genetic Algorithm (GA). This technique automatically selects the variables that result in models with lower root-mean-square error (RMSE) values. GA runs were performed with a window width of 20 and a population size of 64.5 replicate runs, as each time, the initially included variables are selected randomly. Therefore, the results can vary each time.

In the case of mode *C*, feature selection was the Principal Component Analysis. The value of the first ten principal components was used to represent the spectra. These principal components describe more than 90% of the total variance for both Raman and infrared.

The ML model in Figure 1 refers to PLS models combined with GA. The modes *D* and *E* in the ensemble learning technique have different versions depending on the method used for learning, but in this study, we dealt in detail with the boosting technique. We chose the eXtream Gradient Boost (XGBoost) technique in this research because the algorithm can dynamically determine the depth of the decision trees used as weak learners, adding penalty parameters to the high-depth prevention trees, which can prevent the model from overfitting or improving its performance [4].

3. Case studies

Our goal is to predict the quality of additives accurately. For this, we need fast, easy-to-use and accurate forecasting. We preferred fast, non-destructive techniques based on spectral data, but if only IR or Raman techniques were used, the accuracy of the models needed to be improved. Therefore, we need to use data fusion to improve quantitative forecasting. In our case, this is the hydrocarbon/imide ratio of the selected additive. During the production of additives, the classification is based on chemical and physical parameters. Quality parameters are difficult to predict, so we have to use data fusion techniques. In the future, our goal is to integrate inline Industrial Internet of Things (IIoT) sensors into our processes in addition to laboratory measurements, which can be used to predict the quality of raw materials, intermediate products, and final products online in real-time, as well as the different effects of quality on production [5]. Our chosen analytical measurements are spectroscopic measurements, including IR and Raman spectroscopy. Both measurement techniques have industrial sensors available on the market.

We used IR and Raman spectroscopy in the research because they are complementary analytical tools. During Raman inelastic light scattering, the monochromatic excitation laser beam hits the sample material, and the scattered light provides information about molecular vibrations and chemical structure. Raman detects vibrations along the covalent bonds, the advantage of which is that the possible water content of the sample does not interfere with the measurement, in contrast to IR spectroscopy. IR is based on the molecular absorption of irradiated IR light caused by vibrational and rotational transitions in covalent bonds. The IR range is the spectral section between 12,800 and 10 cm-1, within which we distinguish three different regions, and the mid-infrared range (MIR: 4000-650 cm-1) was used in this study. At the same time, infrared detects the vibration of polar covalent bonds, while Raman detects the vibration of non-polar covalent bonds. The advantage of infrared spectroscopy is that it is not disturbed by fluorescence compared to the Raman technique [6]. Our target variable is the hydrocarbon/imide ratio, an essential parameter when qualifying the additive sample. Our goal was to build an accurate model for this parameter when building the model, so we compared the five modes based on these.

4. Results

The number of additive samples was 99, whose IR and Raman spectra were measured. The dependent variable X of the spectrum of the samples was preprocessed with Autoscale and Mean center settings in the PLS toolbox of MATLAB 2020a.

The results were summarized based on the methodology presented in Section 2; the models were compared based on RMSE and Pearson R2 key performance indicators. The models were checked using both calibrations, where all samples were used for model development and the Venetian blinds cross-validation techniques. In the case of the Venetian blinds cross-validation, each test set is determined by selecting every s-th object in the data set, starting at objects numbered 1 through s, which in our case was s=10 (Figure 2, 3).

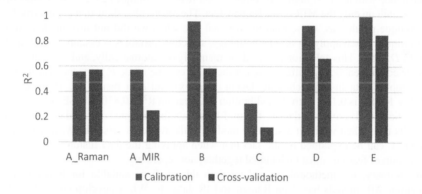

Figure 2: The square of Pearson correlation coefficient of the five modes: *A*, *B*, *C*, *D* and *E*.

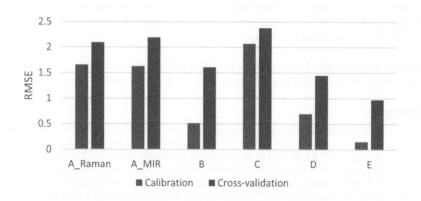

Figure 3: RMSE of the five modes: *A*, *B*, *C*, *D* and *E*.

The results show that modes *B*, *D* and *E* gave better results than mode *A*. Among the five methods, *E* gives the best results. Venetian blinds Cross-validation reduces the model error (RMSE) by more than half, doubling the square of Pearson correlation (R^2). In mode *E*, we processed the input spectra separately for IR and separately for Raman, then pooled the entire spectral data set and ran PLS regression. After the PLS model, we built an ensemble model, which was an XGBoost regression model. The latent variables of the first model served as input, which were selected by the generative algorithm. The weakest results were given by mode *C*, with medium-level data fusion. The results were even lower than in mode *A*, where we did not use data fusion. Mid-level data fusion (mode *C*) performs feature selection on infrared and Raman data sets. After selecting the function, we compiled the reduced data set produced by the PCA analysis of the IR and the Raman data set separately. We then built a PLS regression model for the 10-10 main components. The results of modes *B*, *C*, *D*, and *E* prove that selecting variables is essential when using data fusion techniques..

5. Conclusion

The results show that the models based on the hydrocarbon/imide ratio of the investigated substance with the low, high and complex data fusion techniques gave better results than those built on only the MIR or the Raman data. The results also show that the intermediate technique result was worse than the original one when we did not use the data fusion technique. When applying the methodology, selecting variables is essential in all modes *B*, *C*, *D* and *E*. This selection can be done manually or automatically, and in our use case, we used the genetic algorithm to select the features. The mode *E* gives the best result as a complex data fusion technique. Using complex-level data fusion (*E*), Pearson R^2 is 0.996, RMSE is 0.154 from the calibration set, Pearson R^2 is 0.850, RMSE is 0.975 from Venetian blinds cross-validation. The mid-level data fusion tested on *C* did not give better results than when we built a separate model for the two data sets. The weaker result of mode *C* can be explained by the fact that when applying the data fusion technique, the selection of features must be handled together, not separately.

In summary, the methodology presented in this study is suitable for building more accurate ML models based on Raman and IR datasets. When developing models, it is essential to be careful and to filter out noisy spectral ranges. In connection with the development of the model, we can extract and combine information from other sources to improve the performance of the models. We can further enhance the performance of the ML models by directly using sensor data from industrial plants (e.g. temperature, pressure) to estimate product quality.

Acknowledgements: The research was funded by the National Research, Development and Innovation Fund in the frame of the 2019-1.3.1-KK-2019-00004 project.

References

[1]   A. Biancolillo, F. Marini, C. Ruckebusch, R. Vitale, 2020, Chemometric strategies for spectroscopy-based food authentication, Applied Sciences, 10, 18, 6544.

[2]   B. Nagy, D. Petra, D. Galata, B. Démuth, E. Borbás, G. Marosi, A. Farkas, 2019, Application of artificial neural networks for Process Analytical Technology-based dissolution testing, International Journal of Pharmaceutics, 567, 118464.

[3]   J. Zhu, X. Fan, L. Han, C. Zhang, J. Wang, L. Pan, M. Zhang, 2021, Quantitative analysis of caprolactam in sauce-based food using infrared spectroscopy combined with data fusion strategies, Journal of Food Composition and Analysis, 104, 104130.

[4]   A. Kumar, J. Mayank, 2020, Ensemble learning for AI developers, BApress: Berkeley, CA, USA, 2-56.

[5]   P. P. Hanzelik, A. Kummer, J. Abonyi, 2022, Edge-Computing and Machine-Learning-Based Framework for Software Sensor Development, Sensors, 22, 11, 4268.

[6]   Monograph. NIR Spectroscopy, 2014, A guide to near-infrared spectroscopic analysis of industrial manufacturing processes, Metrohm AG, CH-9101 Herisau, Switzerland.

Flavio Manenti, Gintaras V. Reklaitis (Eds.), Proceedings of the 34th European Symposium on Computer Aided Process Engineering / 15th International Symposium on Process Systems Engineering (ESCAPE34/PSE24), June 2-6, 2024, Florence, Italy

Reliable Data-Driven Soft Sensor Modeling with the Aid of Stable Loss Function and Sample Graph

Ruikun Zhai,[a] Jinchuan Qian,[a] Xiaoyu Jiang,[a] Xinmin Zhang,[a,*] Zhihuan Song,[a] Manabu Kano[b]

[a]The State Key Laboratory of Industrial Control Technology, College of Control Science and Engineering, Zhejiang University, Hangzhou, 310027, China
[b]Department of Systems Science, Kyoto University, Kyoto 606-8501, Japan
xinminzhang@zju.edu.cn

Abstract

Data-driven soft sensors, as a replacement or complement of physical sensors, have been prevalent in predicting hard-to-measure key quality indicators of industrial chemical processes. However, with the existence of noise, outliers, and process drifts in process data, data-driven soft sensors suffer from poor reliability. Based on the manifold regularization framework, this paper proposes two new soft sensor models, namely Laplacian Huber regression and Laplacian piecewise-linear regression, in which new loss functions that are more stable in the face of noise and outliers are proposed, and the prior knowledge of the target process is injected into the learning objectives in the form of a graph Laplacian. The graph Laplacian is derived from an undirected graph obtained by combining prior knowledge and historical data, which embeds the relationships between process samples and helps form an intrinsic regularization term. The new loss functions together with the intrinsic regularizer can guide the learning process of the model in the correct direction, keeping the model from overfitting and being misled by noise or outliers. New optimization methods have also been developed to efficiently solve the learning objectives of the proposed models. The improved reliability performance of the newly proposed models has been validated by a simulation study and a case study of the real-world high-low transformer unit process.

Keywords: Data-driven Modelling, Reliable Soft Sensors, Manifold Regularization, Graph Laplacian

1. Introduction

In modern industry, fast and accurate measurement and analysis of key quality indicators (KQIs) are of great significance to improve process safety and product quality (Kano and Fujiwara, 2013). Unfortunately, many of the process KQIs are impossible, difficult, or costly to measure in real time (Luo et al., 2023). To tackle this problem, soft sensing technology has been rapidly developed in the last decades (Zhang et al., 2023). To build a soft sensor, either a first principle-based approach or a data-driven approach can be typically used (Sun and Ge, 2021). As modern processes become increasingly complicated, it becomes increasingly difficult to build accurate first principle-based models. On the other hand, with the development of distributed control systems and computer technology, data-driven soft sensor modeling is becoming increasingly popular. However, data-driven models are prone to overfitting or are sensitive to noise and outliers. Therefore, it is very meaningful to build reliable soft sensor models.

To improve the reliability of data-driven models, there are some studies in the literature that inject prior knowledge of the process into data-driven modeling process (Westerhuis et al., 2007). They sought to add knowledge-specific regularization terms to the learning objective of data-driven models. As a common form of knowledge, graph structures can be found in many aspects of the process industry, e.g., process diagrams. Such knowledge can be abstracted into undirected graphs, whose graph Laplacian can then be used to form a regularization term. In the manifold regularization framework (Belkin et al., 2006), the graph Laplacian of training samples served as a discrete approximation of the Laplace-Beltrami operator on the data manifold. The quadratic form of model predictions and the graph Laplacian (called the *intrinsic* regularization term) is added to the learning objective of the function estimation framework in the reproducing kernel Hilbert space (RKHS) (Pillonetto *et al.*, 2022) and the Laplacian support vector regression (LapSVR) model is proposed. Some models have also been proposed based on the manifold regularization framework, e.g., semi-supervised hierarchical extreme learning machine (Yao and Ge, 2018). However, most contributions under the manifold regularization framework have been focused on the semi-supervised setting. Nevertheless, it is argued that manifold regularization can also prevent data-driven models from overfitting and being affected by data noise and outliers, which is an enjoyable merit for both supervised and semi-supervised learning scenarios.

To further improve the reliability of soft sensors, this study proposes two new reliable soft sensor models under the manifold regularization framework, namely Laplacian Huber regression (LapHBR) and Laplacian pointwise-linear regression (LapPLR). In LapHBR and LapPLR, efficient optimization methods are proposed to solve the learning objectives of the two models. In addition, a general approach for extracting graph information based on the historical time series of process variables is proposed, which is a method to obtain the graph Laplacian operator in the model. The effectiveness of the proposed LapHBR and LapPLR models was verified through a simulation experiment and a real-world industrial process. Application results demonstrate that the proposed two models exhibit higher reliability compared to other conventional soft sensor models.

2. Reliable Soft Sensing in Manifold Regularization Framework

2.1. Graph Laplacian

Assume that the curve of the KQI variable y with time is smooth. Then, construct the graph G with N vertices, and then perform the following operations on all the samples to construct the weight matrix $\mathbf{W}$:

- Given a sample i and a pre-determined positive integer w, only the samples whose timestamps fall within the time window $[i - w, i + w]$ (excluding sample i) may have an edge with sample i.

- Only the k samples ($1 \leq k \leq 2w$, and in this paper k is set to 5) inside the window that have the smallest Euclidean distances from sample i are connected to the i-th sample with the connection weight $W_{i,j} = \exp\left(-\left\|x_i - x_j\right\|^2 / 2\sigma^2\right)$.

Update $\mathbf{W}$ by $\mathbf{W} \leftarrow (\mathbf{W} + \mathbf{W}^T)/2$ to guarantee that the graph is undirected. Finally, the graph Laplacian $\mathbf{L}$ can be obtained by $\mathbf{L} = \mathbf{I} - \mathbf{D}^{-1/2}\mathbf{W}\mathbf{D}^{-1/2}$, where $\mathbf{D}$ is diagonal with diagonal entries $D_{i,i} = \sum_{j=1}^{N} W_{i,j}, i = 1, \ldots, N$.

The proposed approach is a hybrid approach combining prior knowledge and process data. It is also a general approach that can be applied to all time-series modeling scenarios.

2.2. Manifold Regularization Framework

Assume that each sample has p process variables, which are drawn from the marginal distribution P_X, where $X \in \mathrm{R}^p$ is the underlying data manifold. Further, it is assumed that conditional distributions $P(y|x_1)$ and $P(y|x_2)$ are similar, if two data points x_1 and x_2 are close in P_X. Belkin et al. (2006) claimed that the graph can serve as a discrete approximation of P_X, and proposed the manifold regularizer $f^T \mathbf{L} f$, where $f = [f(x_1), \dots, f(x_N)]^T$, resulting in the *manifold regularization framework*:

$$\min_{\alpha \in \mathrm{R}^N} C \sum_{i=1}^N l\big(y_i - (\mathbf{K}\alpha)_i\big) + \frac{1}{2}\alpha^T \mathbf{K}\alpha + \frac{1}{2}\mu\alpha^T \mathbf{KLK}\alpha, \tag{1}$$

where α is the coefficients of the function f in RKHS induced by a Mercer kernel $\mathbf{K}$ with $f = \sum_{i=1}^N \alpha_i K_{x_i}$, and $\mathbf{K}$ is the kernel matrix whose i,j-th entry is $K(x_i, x_j)$.

2.3. Reliable Soft Sensor Models: LapHBR and LapPLR

2.3.1. Laplacian Huber Regression

The Huber loss is defined as

$$l_{Huber,\epsilon}(e) = \begin{cases} e^2, & |e| \le \epsilon \\ 2\epsilon|e| - \epsilon^2, & |e| > \epsilon \end{cases} \tag{2}$$

where ϵ is a hyper-parameter and e is the error. The advantage of Huber loss is that it is less sensitive to outliers, since it grows linearly for errors $|e| > \epsilon$. Therefore, this study proposes LapHBR, where the data loss l in Eq. (1) is instantiated as the Huber loss in Eq. (2), and an additional bias parameter b is added. With the help of Lagrange multipliers $\lambda \in \mathrm{R}^N$, we can calculate the dual problem of the proposed LapHBR model as follows:

$$\begin{aligned} \max_{\lambda} \quad & -\frac{1}{2}\lambda^T \left(\frac{1}{2C}\mathbf{I} + \mathbf{K}(\mathbf{I} + \mu\mathbf{LK})^{-1}\right)\lambda + \lambda^T y \\ \mathrm{s.t.} \quad & -2C\epsilon\mathbf{1} \le \lambda \le 2C\epsilon\mathbf{1} \\ & \mathbf{1}^T\lambda = 0. \end{aligned} \tag{3}$$

This dual problem is a quadratic programming (QP) problem with linear and box constraints that can be solved more efficiently than the primal problem by convex optimization algorithms, such as the interior-point methods (Boyd and Vandenberghe, 2004). After solving the dual problem, the values of α and b can be obtained in sequence and thereby obtaining the optimal LapHBR model.

2.3.2. Laplacian Piecewise-Linear Regression

The LapSVR model under the manifold regularization framework uses the ϵ-insensitive loss, which completely ignores errors less than or equal to ϵ, and consequently may cause the model to underfit. On the other hand, the Huber loss uses the squared error on small e, which may cause the model to overfit. Based on the above thoughts, a new loss called pointwise-linear (PL) loss is proposed as follows:

$$l_{\mathrm{PL},k,\epsilon}(e) = \begin{cases} k|e|, & |e| \le \epsilon, \\ |e| + (k-1)\epsilon, & |e| > \epsilon, \end{cases} \tag{4}$$

where $k \in [0,1]$. The PL loss also takes the small errors into account, and overfitting and underfitting w.r.t. small errors can be balanced by tuning the k parameter. Note that the ϵ-insensitive loss and the absolute error loss $l_{\mathrm{abs}}(e) = |e|$ are two extreme cases of the newly proposed PL loss. Based on this, the LapPLR model is proposed, whose objective function is Eq. (1) with the loss function instantiated by the PL loss in Eq. (4) and bias b. Likewise, the dual problem of LapPLR can be obtained,

$$\min_{\xi^*,\xi,\lambda} \quad \epsilon \mathbf{1}^T(\xi^* + \xi) + \frac{1}{2}\lambda^T \mathbf{K}(\mathbf{I} + \mu \mathbf{LK})^{-1}\lambda - \lambda^T y$$

$$\text{s.t.} \quad -C \le \lambda \le C, \lambda \le Ck + \xi^*, -\lambda \le Ck + \xi, \mathbf{1}^T \lambda = 0 \tag{5}$$

$$\xi^*, \xi \ge 0,$$

where $\xi^*, \xi \in \mathbb{R}^N$ are slack variables. This dual form is also a QP problem with linear equality and linear inequality constraints that can be solved efficiently by QP solvers.

3. Case Study

3.1. Simulation Example

The simulation experiment was implemented based on 3 components, $c_1(k) = \sin(k)$, $c_2(k) = \cos(k/10)$ and $c_3(k) = \sin(k/2)$. The data were generated by

$$x_1 = \frac{1}{1+\exp(-(c_1+c_2+c_3))} + \epsilon$$

$$x_2 = \max(c_1, c_2) + \epsilon$$

$$x_3 = \tanh(c_1 - c_2 - c_3) + \epsilon$$

$$x_4 = c_1 + c_2^2 + c_3^3 + \epsilon \tag{6}$$

$$x_5 = \sinh(c_1 + c_2 + c_3) + \epsilon$$

$$y = \frac{1}{1+\exp(x_1+x_2+x_3)} + \tanh(x_4 + x_5) + \delta$$

where $\epsilon \sim N(0,1)$ is random additive noise and δ represents the outlier component in the generation of y. Given a predefined hyperparameter p_o, δ have a probability p_o of being 10 (the outlier value), and probability $1 - p_o$ of being 0.

Different sets of data were generated with different values of p_o, ranging from 0 % to 40 %. Each set of the data comprises 2000 training data points and 2000 test ones. The mean squared error (MSE), mean absolute error (MAE), and the coefficient of determination (R^2) were used to evaluate the models.

When $p_o = 25$ %, the best performances of LR, MLP, LapPLR, LapHBR, and LapSVR with different μ values are shown in Table 1.

Table 1. Best performance of the models in comparison under outlier ratio $p_o = 25$ %. The second column indicates the μ value of the models.

Model	μ	Test R^2	Test MSE	Test MAE
LR	N/A	-7.5650	5.8144	2.3641
MLP	N/A	-8.6069	6.5217	2.4342
LapSVR	0.01	0.7334	0.1810	0.3694
LapHBR	**0.01**	**0.9070**	**0.0632**	**0.1968**
LapPLR	**1.0**	**0.9385**	**0.0418**	**0.1330**

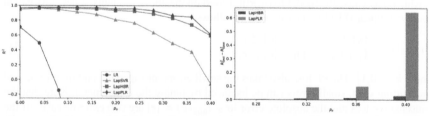

Figure 1. Performance of different models under different p_o values. Left: the test R^2 of different models. Right: The relative improvements $R_{best}^2 - R_{base}^2$ of LapHBR and LapPLR, where R_{base}^2 is the R^2 value with $\mu = 0$ and R_{best}^2 is the R^2 value with $\mu > 0$.

The MLP and LR fail to capture the real relationship between the process variables and the KQI variable. The LapSVR model struggled to give moderate-level predictions, but its performance is far behind those of LapHBR and LapPLR. In this scenario, the poor performance of LR and MLP results from their squared loss function, which focuses too much on the small losses, thus being overly affected by the outliers. Moreover, all three models LapSVR, LapHBR and LapPLR achieved the best performance with a positive μ, which implies that the incorporation of the proposed graph Laplacian can also improve the reliability of soft sensor models.

The test R^2 of the LR, LapSVR, LapHBR and LapPLR models under different values of p_o is shown in the left part of Figure 1. As p_o grows, the performance of LapSVR starts to drop. Contrastively, LapHBR and LapPLR perform stably with the increase of outliers. The effect of *a priori* sample graph is illustrated by recording the relative improvements of the test R^2 of LapPLR and LapHBR when the graph Laplacian is added. As shown in the right part of Figure 1, the graph has a positive effect on the performance of the models under different values of p_o, which also increases with the proportion of outliers. In a situation where there are 40 % outliers in the training data, the graph even helps the test R^2 of LapPLR increase by over 0.6. This once again validates the claim of this study that through the introduction of graph Laplacian, data-driven models can learn in the correct direction when faced with polluted training data.

3.2. Real-World High-Low Transformer Unit

The high-low transformer unit is a critical device in the real-world ammonia synthesis process, and its schematic diagram is shown in Figure 2. Within this unit, 26 process variables can be gathered, and the KQI variable is the residual content of CO at the outlet. To build the prediction model, 5000 training samples and 1500 testing samples were collected. The performance of different models is shown in Table 2.

Table 2. Best performance of models for the high-low transformer unit. The second column indicates the μ value of the models.

Model	μ	Training R^2	Test R^2	Test MSE
LR	N/A	0.8960	0.7889	1.39×10^{-5}
MLP	N/A	0.9547	0.4424	3.68×10^{-5}
LapSVR	1.0	0.8408	0.7970	1.34×10^{-5}
LapHBR	0.0	0.8954	0.7784	1.46×10^{-5}
LapPLR	**10.0**	**0.8589**	**0.8073**	$\mathbf{1.27 \times 10^{-5}}$

Both LapHBR and LapPLR exhibited better generalizability, with LapPLR performing the best. In addition, the relationship between the test R^2 and the graph Laplacian regularizer coefficient μ for LapHBR and LapPLR is also shown in Figure 3. Within the appropriate range, the test R^2 of the two models generally increases with μ.

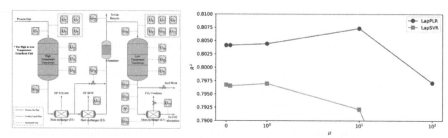

Figure 3. The schematic diagram of the high-low transformer process.

Figure 2. Test R^2 values of LapHBR and LapPLR with the change of model hyper-parameter μ.

4. Conclusions

To improve the robustness of the soft sensor model, two new soft sensor models LapHBR and LapPLR are proposed in this study, where Huber loss and piecewise linear loss are designed in the learning objective under the manifold regularization framework. In addition, dual problems for two new model objectives have been derived, which can be solved more efficiently by the quadratic programming solvers utilizing the interior-point methods compared to the primal model objectives. Besides, a general approach to obtain sample graph structure and the graph Laplacian used in the intrinsic regularizer has been proposed in this work. Such graph information can aid data-driven models, guiding them in the correct direction and at the same time keeping them from being misled by the noise or outliers inside the training data. Experiments have been conducted in both a simulation study and a real-world high-low transformer unit process, which demonstrated the excellent reliability of the proposed soft sensing model as well as the graph Laplacian constructed by the sample graph construction method.

References

Belkin, M., Niyogi, P. and Sindhwani, V., 2006. Manifold regularization: A geometric framework for learning from labeled and unlabeled examples. Journal of machine learning research, 7(11), 2399-2434.

Boyd, S. and Vandenberghe, L., 2004. Convex Optimization. Cambridge University Press, Cambridge, England.

Kano, M. and Fujiwara, K., 2013. Virtual sensing technology in process industries: trends and challenges revealed by recent industrial applications. Journal of chemical engineering of Japan, 46(1), 1-17.

Luo, Y., Zhang, X., Kano, M., Deng, L., Yang, C. and Song, Z., 2023. Data-driven soft sensors in blast furnace ironmaking: a survey. Frontiers of Information Technology & Electronic Engineering, 24(3), 327-354.

Pillonetto, G., Chen, T., Chiuso, A., De Nicolao, G. and Ljung, L., 2022. Regularized system identification: Learning dynamic models from data. Springer Nature, Cham, Switzerland.

Sun, Q. and Ge, Z., 2021. A survey on deep learning for data-driven soft sensors. IEEE Transactions on Industrial Informatics, 17(9), 5853-5866.

Westerhuis, J.A., Derks, E.P., Hoefsloot, H.C. and Smilde, A.K., 2007. Grey component analysis. Journal of Chemometrics: A Journal of the Chemometrics Society, 21(10-11), 474-485.

Yao, L. and Ge, Z., 2017. Deep learning of semisupervised process data with hierarchical extreme learning machine and soft sensor application. IEEE Transactions on Industrial Electronics, 65(2), 1490-1498.

Zhang, X., Kano, M. and Tani, M., 2023. Stacked supervised Poisson autoencoders-based soft-sensor for defects prediction in steelmaking process. Computers & Chemical Engineering, 172, 108182.

Flavio Manenti, Gintaras V. Reklaitis (Eds.), Proceedings of the 34th European Symposium on Computer Aided Process Engineering / 15th International Symposium on Process Systems Engineering (ESCAPE34/PSE24), June 2-6, 2024, Florence, Italy

Industrial Edge MLOps: Overview and Challenges

Fatima Rani[a,*], Nicolas Chollet[b], Lucas Vogt[a], Leon Urbas[a]

[a]*Faculty of Electrical and Computer Engineering, Chair of Process Control Systems & Process Systems Engineering Group, Technische Universität Dresden, 01069 Dresden, Germany*

[b]*LyRIDS (Laboratory of Research in Interdisciplinary Digital engineering & Sciences) ECE Paris engineering school, 75015, Paris, France*

* fatima.rani@tu-dresden.de

Abstract

Machine Learning Operations (MLOps) is not a buzzword anymore. In the last few years, there has been a lot of booms in different MLOps tools and frameworks. Basically, it's a paradigm that focuses on the automation and operationalization of AI development, including model packaging, monitoring, and deployment. While there have been advancements in MLOps tools and frameworks, there are still challenges and research gaps when it comes to deploying MLOps pipelines on edge devices. This paper provides an overview of the Edge MLOps area. Our aim is also to define the basic architecture and components needed for the industrial MLOps deployment. In this context, we also highlight some tools and frameworks. Moreover, we address some limitations and research gaps in the Industrial edge MLOps area.

Keywords: MLOps, Edge Computing, IIoT, Industry 4.0, Process Industry.

1. Introduction

Presently, Machine Learning (ML) and Artificial Intelligence (AI) are inevitable, and there is a bloom in Industrial Internet of Things (IIoT) devices, resulting in substantial growth in real-time series industrial plant data. Besides this, ML models are booming in the process industry, and to compensate for the hidden technical debts in ML systems, MLOps is the way to go. In the last few years, MLOps has been an emerging paradigm that aims to operationalize the machine learning models into production (Rani et al., 2023). Kreuzberger et al. (2023) emphasize the need to automate and operationalize ML products and provide an aggregated overview of the principles, components, roles, architecture, and workflows of MLOps. However, there are still some challenges presents in deploying the ML models on the cloud (Paleyes et al., 2020). Hence, in the ever-evolving data-driven landscape of industrial plants, the convergence of edge computing (Barakat et al., 2023) and MLOps, or edge MLOps, is essential. As a result, Edge Computing enables us to make decisions at the data sources rather than send the data to the cloud and centralized database, which allows us to reduce the issues of latency, bandwidth, economics, and privacy (especially to meet regulations of countries like GDPR in Europe), and reliability and energy consumption as transmitting large data file is usually a power-hungry process for IoT devices running on battery. In addition, consumers need low latency for real-time experiences, and businesses require local processing to operate securely and reliably while complying with government privacy regulations (Ahmed et al., 2017). Thus, in this contribution, we ask the research question:

RQ: *What is the industrial edge MLOps? What are the best practices that can be implemented in Industrial Edge MLOps? "What are the key challenges in it?*

To answer this question, we conducted a literature survey to (a) identify the core principles of Edge MLOps and (b) its challenges, which contribute to an understanding of Industrial Edge MLOps concepts. In this article, we provide a comprehensive and aggregated overview of the architecture components that facilitate the MLOps on edge devices. We also highlight the open challenges and research gaps for deploying the MLOps pipelines on edge devices. Finally, this work points out some use cases to deploy the MLOps on Edge and its tools and framework.

2. Methodology

To derive the main insights for Industrial Edge MLOps, we conduct (a) a structured literature review and (b) tool review (details of these are out of the scope of this article due to page limitation). On the basis of this methodology, we elaborate on our finding of core components required for Edge MLOps architecture, its challenges, use cases, tools, and framework in the next sections.

3. Edge MLOps Architecture

The architecture of the typical Industrial Edge MLOps involves the following components:

3.1. Data Collection and Preprocessing

3.1.1. Edge Devices

This stage involves collecting data from various devices located at the edge of the industrial network sources, such as sensors, machines, actuators, different databases, and control systems, where the data is either generated or already stored (Raj et al., 2021).

3.1.2. Data preprocessing

Then, the different lightweight preprocessing techniques (like cleaning, transformation etc.) are applied to make data suitable for ML model training at the edge device (Raj et al., 2021).

3.2. Model Training and Development

3.2.1. Machine Learning Models

In this stage, ML models are developed and trained using preprocessed data. This may involve selecting appropriate algorithms, optimizing hyperparameters, and evaluating model performance. Basically, these are predictive models developed by utilizing ML algorithms to analyze and take actions based on the data collected from industrial processes. In many cases, a hybrid approach is employed, for the deployment of ML models (Rani et al., 2023; Paleyes et al., 2020).

3.2.2. Edge Compute

This is the computational infrastructure located close to the edge devices, where machine learning models could be deployed and executed. It could include edge servers or gateway devices (Raj et al., 2021).

3.3. Model Deployment and Orchestration

This is the crucial stage in which trained ML models are deployed to edge devices, which may be microcontrollers, embedded systems, or specialized AI accelerators. Furthermore, tools for deploying ML models onto edge devices and orchestrating their execution (Kreuzberger et al., 2023). This step may involve containerization technologies like Docker and orchestration tools like Kubernetes.

3.4. Model Monitoring and Management

After the deployment of the ML model, there is a continuous need either centralized or decentralized retraining for the deployed models to be continuously monitored for performance, accuracy, and potential issues. This may involve real-time data analysis, anomaly detection, and model retraining. A key issue of Edge ML is its sensitivity to model drift. Model Drift is the inevitable degradation of a model's performance due to the ever-changing nature of data (Rajapakse at el., 2023). This means that the model, once deployed, needs to be updated over time with new and local data. Also, systems are used to monitor the performance of deployed models, collect logs, and provide insights into the behavior of the models in real-time.

3.5. Model Versioning and Governance

ML models are versioned and managed to ensure reproducibility, traceability, and compliance with regulatory requirements by tools like DVC, MLflow, TensorBoard etc.

3.6. Security and Compliance

Ensuring the security by means of data encryption, access control, containerization etc., of the deployed models and compliance with industry regulations and standards.

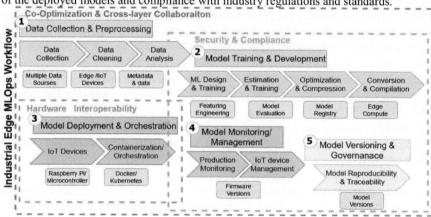

Figure 1- The main components of the Industrial Edge MLOps Architecture (Adopted from Hymel et al., 2022).

4. Edge MLOps Challenges

There are several challenges that need to be addressed while implementing the industrial edge MLOps.

4.1. Resource Constraints

The biggest challenge is that edge devices often have limited computing, memory, and storage resources, which can constrain the complexity and performance of ML models. Most of the time, due to these limited computational resources, deploying and running complex machine learning models becomes complicated, and hardware must be carefully selected to fit the application requirements. Another issue with resource-constrained hardware is their inability to train the Edge ML model, a process that usually requires significant computation power and that is required to avoid the model drift issue (Rajapakse et al., 2023). Another important resource constraint is energy consumption. IoT devices usually run on battery, and therefore, the implementation of the MLOps procedure should keep power usage to a minimum.

4.2. Data Availability and Quality

Industrial edge environments may have limited or noisy data, which can impact ML model accuracy and reliability (Raj et al., 2021). Generic application models should always be refined through additional training with locally collected data from a device to cover for device drift.

4.3. Connectivity and Latency

Edge devices may operate in remote or offline scenarios, requiring reliable communication and low-latency data processing. Achieving low-latency processing is crucial for real-time decision-making, which may be challenging in resource-constrained edge environments (Shafique et al., 2021). Another issue is the usage of wireless communication for sensors running on batteries, as it is usually an energy-hungry procedure. Low Power Wide Area Networks are often used by such sensors to allow communication at minimal power cost but only offer low data rates that can be insufficient for MLOps procedures (Hymel et al., 2022).

4.4. Data Security and Privacy

Industrial edge systems handle sensitive data and control critical processes, requiring robust security and privacy measures. Ensuring the security of sensitive industrial data when processing it at the edge is a critical concern. Moreover, governments tend to enforce needed but constraining regulations to avoid the over usage of private data.

4.5. Continuous Integration and Continuous Delivery (CI/CD)

Integrating and deploying ML models to edge devices in a continuous and automated manner can be challenging. Especially, when updating edge devices over the air after their deployment.

4.6. Model Versioning and Updates

Managing the versions of deployed models and updating them seamlessly without disrupting operations.

4.7. Interoperability & Scalability

Integrating different edge devices, protocols, and ML models from various vendors can be challenging. ML can be performed at the edge through numerous software, hardware, or hybrid methods. Ensuring that the MLOps infrastructure can scale to accommodate the growing number of edge devices and the increasing complexity of ML models.

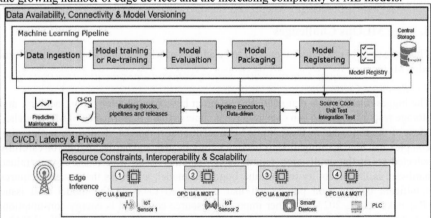

Figure 2- The cloud and edge network challenges of the Industrial Edge MLOps Architecture (Adopted from Raj at el., 2021).

5. IIoT Use Cases

MLOps can be applied to various domains by streamlining and automating the lifecycle of machine learning models, ensuring their efficient development, deployment, and maintenance across diverse applications such as the one presented in Fig. 3:

- Industry and Factory operations: Edge ML can be used in automation, predictive maintenance, and quality control processes (Kreuzberger et al., 2023).
- Healthcare: Wearable edge devices can be used in patient diagnosis, treatment personalization, and healthcare data analysis (Khattak at al., 2023).
- ADAS: Car manufacturers can apply MLOps for Advanced Driver-Assistance Systems (ADAS) to manage and maintain Edge AI applications across the vast fleet of vehicles (Gupta et al., 2021).

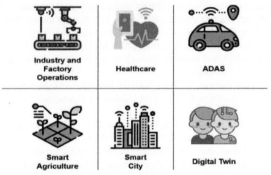

Figure 3– Edge MLOps domains of application in a nutshell.

- Agriculture: MLOps can help manage sensors in energy-efficient Low Power Wide Area Networks (LPWAN) and, in doing so, keep the sensors fleet running on battery for multiple seasons (Chollet et al., 2022).
- Smart city: Sensors in a smart city can perform tasks like real-time traffic management, environmental monitoring, and public safety surveillance, enhancing urban living and operational efficiency (Goethals et al., 2021).
- Digital twin: Overall, MLOps can be used in all domains of applications to implement the digital twin paradigm (Fujii et al., 2021).

6. Tools and Frameworks

Numerous tools exist to answer the different needs of each step of the MLOps process. In regard to the complete MLOps framework (Rani et al., 2023), good practices and a few options have already been proposed, and they are gathered by the authors (Kreuzberger et al., 2023). Research conducted by our team has intensively used Edge Impulse (Chollet et al., 2022). It is a SaaS proposed by Google that enables efficient data collection, model training, and validation at the edge, facilitating real-time analytics and decision-making in various applications, and it integrates seamlessly with MLOps workflows for continuous improvement and deployment of these models. For all of these reasons, we can recommend this tool for managing edge AI device operations.

7. Conclusion

Despite these challenges, Industrial Edge MLOps are becoming increasingly important as ML becomes more pervasive in industrial applications. By addressing these challenges, organizations can reap the benefits of ML in edge environments, such as improved decision-making, real-time optimization, and predictive maintenance. In a nutshell, Industrial Edge MLOps represents the intersection of edge computing and machine learning operations, addressing the unique challenges and requirements of deploying and managing machine learning models in industrial environments.

References

A. Paleyes, R.G. Urma, N.D. Lawrence, 2022, Challenges in deploying machine learning: a survey of case studies, ACM Computing Surveys (CSUR).

D. Kreuzberger, N. Kühl, S. Hirschl, 2023, Machine learning operations (mlops): Overview, definition, and architecture, IEEE Access.

E. Ahmed, A. Ahmed, I. Yaqoob, J. Shuja, 2017, Bringing computation closer toward the user network: Is edge computing the solution?, IEEE Communications Magazine, 55(11), 138-144.

E. Raj, D. Buffoni, M. Westerlund, K. Ahola, 2021, Edge MLOps: An automation framework for aiot applications, IEEE International Conference on Cloud Engineering (IC2E).

F. Rani, V. Khaydarov, D. Bode, I. Hasan, L. Urbas, 2023, MLOps Practice: Overcoming the Energy Efficiency Gap, Empirical Support Through ecoKI Platform in the Case of German SMEs, PAC World Global Conference.

F.K. Khattak, V. Subasri, A. Krishnan, E. Dolatabadi, D. Pandya, L. Seyyed-Kalantari, F. Rudzicz, 2023, MLHOps: Machine Learning for Healthcare Operations, arXiv preprint, arXiv:2305.02474.

G. Symeonidis, E. Nerantzis, A. Kazakis, G.A. Papakostas, 2022, Mlops-definitions, tools and challenges, In 2022 IEEE 12th Annual CCW, pp. 0453-0460.

M. Barakat, R.A. Saeed, S. Edam, 2023, A Comparative Study on Cloud and Edge Computing: A Survey on Current Research Activities and Applications, IEEE 3rd International Maghreb Meeting of the Conference on Sciences and Techniques of Automatic Control and Computer Engineering (MI-STA).

M. Shafique, A. Marchisio, RV.W. Putra, M.A. Hanif, 2021, Towards energy-efficient and secure edge AI: A cross-layer framework, In 2021 IEEE/ACM ICCAD, pp. 1-9.

N. Chollet, B. Naila, R. Amar, 2022, TinyML Smart Sensor for Energy Saving in Internet of Things Precision Agriculture platform, In 2022 Thirteenth ICUFN, pp. 256-259.

S. Gupta, B. Amaba, M. McMahon, K.Gupta, 2021, May, The evolution of artificial intelligence in the automotive industry, In 2021 Annual RAMS, pp. 1-7.

S. Hymel, C. Banbury, D. Situnayake, A. Elium, C. Ward, M. Kelcey, M. Baaijens, M. Majchrzycki, J. Plunkett, D. Tischler, A. Grande, L. Moreau, D. Maslov, A. Beavis, J. Jongboom, V.J. Reddi, 2022, Edge Impulse: An MLOps Platform for Tiny Machine Learning, arXiv preprint, arXiv:2212.03332.

T. Goethals, B. Volckaert, F.D. Turck, 2021, Enabling and Leveraging AI in the Intelligent Edge: A Review of Current Trends and Future Directions, IEEE Open Journal of the Communications Society, 2, 2311-2341.

T.Y. Fujii, V.T. Hayashi, R Arakaki, W.V. Ruggiero, 2021, A digital twin architecture model applied with MLOps techniques to improve short-term energy consumption prediction. Machines, 10(1), 23.

V. Rajapakse, I. Karunanayake, N. Ahmed, 2023, Intelligence at the extreme edge: A survey on reformable tinyml, ACM Computing Surveys, 55(13s), 1-30.

Acknowledgments: This work was Funded by the German Federal Ministry for Economic Affairs and Climate Action (BMWK) under the grant number 03EN2047C.

Declaration of AI-assisted technologies: While preparing this manuscript, the authors employed the AI-tools for enhancing the manuscript's language and readability. The authors carefully reviewed and revised the contents and took the responsibility for the research work and idea for this article content. publication

Flavio Manenti, Gintaras V. Reklaitis (Eds.), Proceedings of the 34th European Symposium on Computer Aided Process Engineering / 15th International Symposium on Process Systems Engineering (ESCAPE34/PSE24), June 2-6, 2024, Florence, Italy

Operationalization Management: Enhancing Life Cycle Management of Digital Twins

Balázs Palotai,[ab]* Ágnes Bárkányi,[b] Gábor Kis,[a] János Abonyi[b]

[a]*MOL Group Plc., Dombóvári Street 28, Budapest, H-1117, Hungary*

[b]*University of Pannonia, Egyetem Street 10, Veszprém, H-8200, Hungary*
bpalotai@mol.hu

Abstract

The recent progress in development of Information Technology (IT) gave rise to a new wave of industrial transformation marked by cloud computing, the Industrial Internet of Things (IIoT), Big Data analytics, Industry 4.0 principles, and autonomous systems. Digital Twins are at the core of this revolution, by bridging physical world with its digital representation to optimize Cyber-Physical Production Systems (CPPS) in order to create more value. However, it is quite challenging to validate that of the anyway obvious theoretical advantages even in the case of a pilot project not to mention a full production unit size Digital Twin. Another aspect of challenges is the need for model life-cycle management emerges to preserve the benefit captured by the new Digital Twin based technologies. This paper introduces a novel methodology inspired by Operations-based frameworks and Model Engineering, addressing these bottlenecks. It offers a unique solution for managing simulation models monitoring and maintenance in Digital Twins applications. The paper shows the benefit of surrogate-based automated flowsheet model fitting solution for a simplified refinery case-study to reduce the expensive simulation use for model fitting, and reduced the time required compared with the direct simulation fitting without losing accuracy.

Keywords: Digital Twin, Life cycle, SimOps, Surrogate

1. Introduction

Industrial processes, encompassing from chemical manufacturing to power generation, have long relied on simulation and optimization to enhance efficiency, cost-effectiveness, and safety. Traditional manual process simulation models, built with precise attention to detail, have been fundamental in achieving these goals. These models, based on the governing physical and thermodynamic principles, have provided critical insights, enabling informed decision-making. This widespread use of flowsheet process simulation models made them perfect constituents of Digital Twin solutions which naturally brings the need for standardization and automation of model creation, maintenance, and utilization. The emergence of Machine Learning Operations (MLOps) offers a promising solution for this purpose as showed by D. Kreuzberger et al. Initially designed for machine learning models, MLOps is now expanding to encompass first-principal process simulation models (SimOps) as demonstrated by the work of I. Pan et al.

In this paper, we present an evolution of process simulation, transitioning from labor-intensive manual methods to MLOps-driven automation and efficiency. We highlight the most critical challenges in traditional simulation model maintenance and propose an automated solution. This solution combines the precision of first-principal models with the agility of modern data-driven and surrogate approaches. In this paper we show the benefit of proposed surrogate-based automated flowsheet model fitting solution through a simplified refinery case-study to reduce the expensive simulation use for model fitting.

2. General introduction of Digital Twin life cycle management

Digital Twins represent an innovative paradigm where digital counterparts of physical systems bridge the gap between production processes, enabling dynamic data collection for real-time monitoring, asset health analysis, performance evaluation, and informed decision-making as it is presented by the work of Singh et al. This seamless synchronization between digital and physical systems, whether in an online or offline context, is the key to continuous optimization and monitoring within production systems.

In the refining sector, and in the broader process industry, flowsheet simulation historically takes a pivotal role. These tools are instrumental in the detailed examination of process technologies, the execution of "what if" scenario analyses, process optimization, and equipment health monitoring. Based on these capabilities they can provide an acceptable foundation for Digital Twin applications.

The literature highlights a critical challenge in Digital Twin (DT) adoption: a lack of trust among stakeholders, hindering effective implementation as it is described in the work of Müller et al. To resolve this problem, it's essential to select sufficiently simple and understandable project(s) for demonstration of DT benefits which can facilitate, building trust and acceptance from the future users. Once benefits are confirmed, the focus shifts to seamless DT integration with existing processes, supporting business decisions. Maintaining transparency and credibility is key for value creation (Figure 1). To achieve this, proper life cycle management is a prerequisite.

Given the intricate nature of DT frameworks, leveraging methodologies such as DevOps, MLOps, DataOps, and SimOps are instrumental for their life cycle management. DevOps offers a comprehensive framework for overseeing the entire DT life cycle, ensuring quality and continuous improvement. MLOps facilitates the development and performance management of machine learning models within DTs. DataOps, a process-driven methodology, provides data-focused analytics and sustains data quality throughout the life cycle. Similarly, SimOps, which has the same function as MLOps, supports the life cycle management of simulation models as proposed by I. Pan et al. MLOps can serve as a robust guideline to introduce SimOps for maintaining flowsheet process simulation models within the Digital Twin framework, as the model data requirements and building steps align closely with ML model development methodologies (Figure 2).

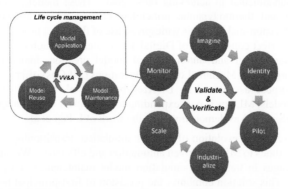

Figure 1. Digital Twin steps and AI readiness combined with model life cycle management

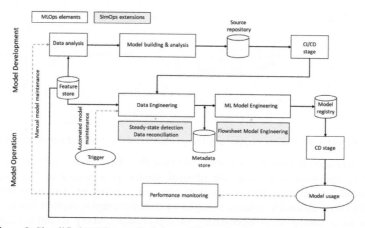

Figure 2. Simplified MLOps methodology with proposed SimOps connection points

The key steps in MLOps and SimOps for flowsheet simulation models (FSMs):

- **Data Pipeline**: Digital Twin frameworks employing steady-state flowsheet models require, additional steps become necessary like steady-state detection and data reconciliation as showed by B. Farsang et al.
- **Simulation Model Building**: Creating, fine-tuning, and evaluating simulation models often necessitates manual modeling expertise. While research into automated flowsheet identification is ongoing as showed by M. Barth et al., manual input most probably will remain essential.
- **Model Monitoring**: Various approaches exist for detecting concept/model drift during the operation as summarized by F. Bayram et al.
- **Model Maintenance**: As FSMs are primarily manually generated, therefore development and maintenance of industrial applications based on these models can be laborious and costly as highlighted by G. S. Martínez et al. While data-driven approaches can be maintained with less engineering effort by applying MLOps methodology.

From our literature review, it becomes evident that addressing flowsheet model drift is a pivotal component of FSM life cycle management. If concept drift arises from operational degradations like fouling in heat exchangers, separation efficiency reduction, or catalyst deactivation, the model maintenance process could be automated by adopting MLOps methodology. To address this, we introduce a novel solution for the automated re-training of flowsheet process simulation models.

3. Proposed automated model re-training solution

Model retraining practically an optimization challenge, focusing on minimizing the residual error between the model's estimated and observed parameters. However, using optimization algorithms with flowsheet models the complexity increases significantly. Some of these models can demand extensive CPU computational resources. Even when computational time is not excessive, accurately estimating derivatives for gradient-based algorithms becomes problematic due to the noise introduced by these black box models. This noise can originate from factors like small variable sensitivities, algorithm termination criteria or model stability.

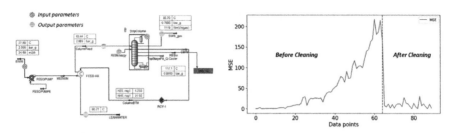

Figure 3. Sour-water stripper unit Hysys model and the observed fouling effect

When practicality dictates that not practical to use flowsheet models for optimization, an alternative approach is to treat the original model as a source of "computational experiments," generating data points as if physical experiments had been conducted. These data are then used to construct simpler models that employ explicit functions, often referred to as surrogate, reduced-order, or metamodels. Many research efforts have utilized this surrogate approach for the optimization of flowsheet-based operations as it is showed by J. A. Caballero et al. Despite the advantages, so far just limited research has been carried out on the use of surrogate approaches for model fitting type of optimization.

To illustrate the advantages of using surrogate models for model fitting as a partial inverse model, we employed Aspen Hysys steady-state simulation for sour-water stripper unit model (Figure 3), wherein a frequently occurring heat exchanger fouling phenomenon was investigated. Historical data indicated a decrease in column inlet temperature and an increase in lean water temperature which caused by the increasing fouling in feed heat-exchanger. To simplify the problem and focus now solely on surrogate-based model fitting, we used the historical steady-state daily average operational data after model-based data reconciliation as a fitting dataset and tried to identify the fouling parameter for each day by minimizing the residual error between the validation and model estimated temperatures. The applied process workflow summarized on Figure 4.

3.1. Data Generation and Surrogate Training
Utilizing the base Hysys model, we generated 500 simulation data points for training an Artificial Neural Network (ANN) surrogate within the operational envelope, using Latin Hypercube Sampling (LHS). The ANN was designed with input parameters, including boundary conditions (such as feed quality and mass-flow), manipulated parameters (e.g., reflux rate), and the fitting factors, such as the Fouling factor. The ANN output parameters included independent variables like column inlet temperature and lean water outlet temperature, steam consumption, etc. The trained surrogate model consistently achieved an impressive average R-squared value of 0.935 on test data (30%). For clarity and accessibility, we stored both the Hysys and surrogate models, as well as the associated training data, in a model registry and model datastore, respectively.

3.2. Optimization Process
The optimization phase involved the utilization of the Particle Swarm Optimization (PSO) algorithm. The cost function, the Mean Square Error (MSE), quantified the difference between measured and predicted key parameters (in this scenario, column inlet and lean water temperature were used) and the acceptance limit was defined based on practical modelling considerations. The optimization started with the surrogate model (full operation envelope & 20 particles), which proposed optimal fitting parameters for the daily fitting data (90 data points). These proposed parameters were subsequently cross verified against the original Hysys model.

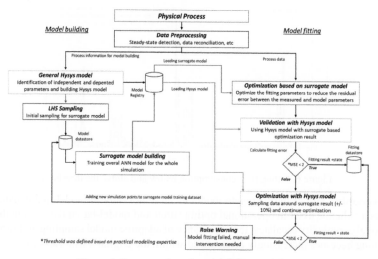

Figure 4. Surrogate-based model fitting workflow

If the simulation MSE fell below the predefined threshold, the outcome, along with state conditions, was stored in the fitting datastore. Conversely, if the threshold was not met, the optimization continued with employing the simulation model within a narrow parameter range (+/- 10% & 5 particles). If this secondary simulation result met the threshold, it was added to the fitting datastore, and the corresponding simulation data was incorporated into the surrogate training dataset, enhancing model accuracy. In cases where the threshold proved elusive, a warning raised the need for manual intervention to investigate the anomaly.

3.3. Results and discussion

Leveraging the surrogate model's exceptional accuracy, the optimization process mostly proposed optimal fitting parameters (Figure 5). Additional simulation optimization was only required when the surrogate model's accuracy fell under the desired threshold. In summary, the surrogate model not just contributed to cost reduction by minimizing the need for expensive simulations in model fitting but also reduced the overall time required for the process (Figure 6), without compromising the accuracy of the results. Utilizing additional simulation-based optimization results, the overall accuracy of surrogate model can be further improved and consequently the expensive simulation-based optimization usage can be reduced. It's important to emphasize that the primary role of the surrogate model was not to estimate fouling factors but to replace the simulation model.

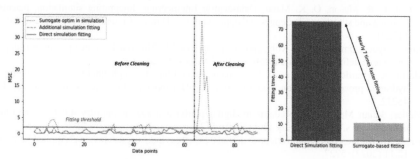

Figure 5. Fitting results by datapoints and fitting steps

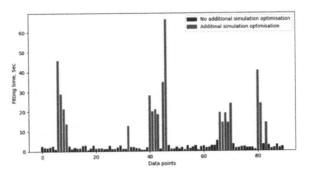

Figure 6. Fitting time consumption below and above the threshold

This versatility allows the surrogate model to serve not only in model maintenance but also as a valuable asset in operational optimization and model-based data reconciliation. As model complexity escalates, the importance of adaptive model sampling and surrogate retraining becomes increasingly pronounced within the Digital Twin framework.

4. Conclusions

Based on the literature review, the flowsheet model drift handling is the most critical part of life cycle management of flowsheet models based Digital Twin framework. If the concept drift caused by operational degradations like fouling in heat-exchangers, reduced separation efficiency or catalyst deactivation, the model maintenance can be automated. The introduced novel hybrid surrogate-based automated flowsheet model fitting solution yielded promising results for a simplified refinery case-study and demonstrated the benefits of using surrogate models in the Digital Twin framework. Applying this method, the use of expensive simulation can be significantly reduced in comparison to the time required by the direct simulation fitting without losing accuracy.

References

Barth, Mike, and Alexander Fay. "Automated generation of simulation models for control code tests." Control Engineering Practice 21.2 (2013): 218-230.

Bayram, Firas, Bestoun S. Ahmed, and Andreas Kassler. "From concept drift to model degradation: An overview on performance-aware drift detectors." Knowledge-Based Systems 245 (2022): 108632.

Caballero, José A., and Ignacio E. Grossmann. "An algorithm for the use of surrogate models in modular flowsheet optimization." AIChE journal 54.10 (2008): 2633-2650.

Farsang, Barbara, Sándor Németh, and János Abonyi. "Role of steady state data reconciliation in process model development." Hungarian Journal of Industry and Chemistry 41.1 (2013): 65-75.

I. Pan, L. R. Mason, O. K. Matar, Data-centric Engineering: Integrating simulation, machine learning and statistics. Challenges and opportunities, Chemical Engineering Science 249 (2022) 117271

Kreuzberger, Dominik, Niklas Kühl, and Sebastian Hirschl. "Machine learning operations (mlops): Overview, definition, and architecture." IEEE Access (2023).

Martínez, Gerardo Santillán, et al. "Automatic generation of a high-fidelity dynamic thermal-hydraulic process simulation model from a 3D plant model." IEEE Access 6 (2018): 45217-45232.

Müller, Julian Marius. "Antecedents to digital platform usage in Industry 4.0 by established manufacturers." Sustainability 11.4 (2019): 1121.

Singh, Maulshree, et al. "Applications of digital twin across industries: A review." Applied Sciences 12.11 (2022): 5727.

Flavio Manenti, Gintaras V. Reklaitis (Eds.), Proceedings of the 34th European Symposium on Computer Aided Process Engineering / 15th International Symposium on Process Systems Engineering (ESCAPE34/PSE24), June 2-6, 2024, Florence, Italy

Multi-objective reinforcement learning for self-optimization of flow chemistry

Ashish Yewale[a], Yihui Yang[b], Neda Nazemifard[b], Charles D. Papageorgiou[b], Chris D. Rielly[a], Brahim Benyahia[a]*

[a] Department of Chemical Engineering, Loughborough University, LE11 3TU Leicestershire, UK
[b] Process Chemistry and Development, Takeda Pharmaceuticals International Company, 40 Landsdowne Street, Cambridge, Massachusetts 02139, United States
b.benyahia@lboro.ac.uk

Abstract

The pharmaceutical industry is undergoing a paradigm shift with the increased adoption of digitalization leading to more effective process design and operating strategies. The identification of more selective, robust, and cost-effective synthetic pathways for active pharmaceutical ingredients is crucial during early development stages. In addition, more sustainable process designs and production strategies are increasingly being adopted, which require multi-objective optimization strategies to find the best decision compromises and feasible operating windows. Hence, this work proposes a Multi-Objective Deep Deterministic Policy Gradient (MODDPG) method to handle conflicting objectives and find Pareto optimal solutions for complex continuous-flow reaction schemes. The method is validated using Claisen-Schmidt reactions in a tubular reactor and compared against benchmark methods such as Genetic Algorithms, and Bayesian Optimization.

Keywords: Reaction Optimization, Multi-objective Reinforcement Learning, Flow Chemistry, Multi-Objective Deep Deterministic Policy Gradient (MODDPG).

1. Introduction and background

The synthesis of the Active Pharmaceutical Ingredient (API) is a crucial step in the production of all pharmaceuticals. The growing demand for safer and more effective medications has led to significant changes in the manufacturing technologies, requiring accelerated development and integration strategies. This has led to an increased demand for more flexible, cost-effective, and advanced technologies to deliver high quality medicines, while achieving stringent regulatory and environmental considerations. Achieving some of these critical objectives requires more effective process design and optimization of the synthetic pathways to meet urgent healthcare requirements by significantly reducing production time, while upholding the greatest standards of quality and safety.

The complex chemical reactions involved in API manufacturing require specialists to evaluate a wide range of reaction parameters, including discrete and continuous decision variables. This problem is commonly addressed based on single objective experiment intensive methodologies or even on trial and error, which can be time-consuming and may lead to poor or suboptimal solutions. To address these limitations and speed up the development process, computer-aided optimization algorithms combined with continuous flow chemistry and advanced process analysis techniques (PAT) have become the focus of scientists and engineers in recent years. These methods minimize human intervention and inherent bias, ensuring enhanced key performance indicators such as high productivity, reduced reaction time, and improved risk management. Integrating these technologies allows real-time self-optimization of reaction processes, enhancing efficiency and adaptability. It also prevents suboptimal solutions commonly associated with off-line model-based strategies due to model uncertainties or/and operational bias.

Single-objective algorithms such as Nelder-Mead Simplex (Fath et al., 2020), and SNOBFit (Clayton et al., 2020) have been extensively used to optimize single objectives of chemical reactions. However, for API and high value chemical manufacturing, it is highly critical to consider multiple performance criteria. Often, multi-objective optimization problems are converted into single objective optimization problems using a weighted sum. However, this approach requires prior knowledge of the relative importance of each objective, which is commonly highly uncertain in most real-world problems.

In this research, an artificial intelligence-based multi-objective reinforcement learning (MORL) technique is used to self-optimize the operating conditions of a multistep continuous reaction process. The proposed RL, which is a sequential decision-making process, is combined with the first principle knowledge of the chemistry and the reaction process to quickly identify the optimal reaction conditions under multiple objective optimization settings (Yewale et al 2023, Benyahia et al., 2021). In recent years, RL methods have increasingly been implemented to identify optimal reaction conditions or to improve process control (Zhou et al., 2017, and Neumann and Palkovits 2020). However, most of these studies were designed for single objective optimization. Hence, this will be the first attempt to apply a multi-objective reinforcement learning approach to address self-optimization of flow chemistry, where conflicting objectives can be considered simultaneously.

2. Problem statement or Methodology

Multi-objective optimization problems (MOPs) which are characterized by several competing or conflicting objectives are encountered in most real-world problems (Benyahia, et al., 2010; Liu et al., 2023). Instead of a single optimal solution, these problems have a set of Pareto-optimal solutions (PS), which represent the best trade-offs between the objectives. In this work, a MORL methodology was developed to address a flow chemistry problem in a dynamic environment where the agents can interact, learn and adapt in real-time. The optimization process involves finding a policy that achieves the best compromises amongst multiple objectives. The MORL's adaptable structure and transfer learning capabilities allow the agents to quickly adapt to new process conditions, unlike the traditional multi-objective optimization strategies which are set at fixed conditions leading to poor flexibility and very limited transferability.

2.1. Introduction of the MODDPG

RL uses a Markov decision process to guide successive agent-environment interactions to maximize the long-term rewards. In this procedure, the agent begins with a set of specific environment conditions (i.e., reaction conditions represented in the state space). The agent then implements the chosen actions to the environment, and as a result it receives rewards or penalties which help evaluate the overall quality of the executed actions. Based on this recurring interaction between the environment and the agent through the states, actions, and rewards, the agent learns to identify the best possible actions that maximize the cumulative rewards.

The proposed MORL approach is a generalized version of the standard RL, which involves the extension of scalar reward to a multiple reward vector. In essence, the MORL evaluates a vector of rewards associated with the selected objectives based on the proposed actions. An algorithm based a combination of Deep learning and RL (DRP), allows the agent to learn and gain knowledge about the complex reaction environment based on repetitive interactions and adjustments of the actions. A Deep Deterministic Policy Gradient (DDPG) method, which extends the Deterministic Policy Gradient (DRL) based framework, is proposed to solve the current MOP. DRL uses a neural network (NN) to map out the set of inputs onto a set of outputs. This complete framework will be defined as a Multi-Objective Deep Deterministic Policy Gradient (MODDPG) as described by the architecture shown in Figure 1 (a). To extract temporal information from sequential acts and Q-values, NNs are employed as the actor and the critic approximator networks.

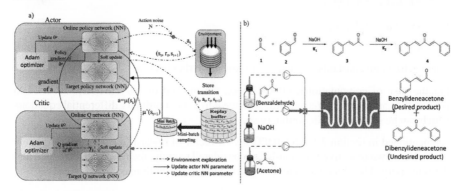

Fig.1 a) Framework of the MODDPG RL agent b) Reaction set up for the proposed Claisen-Schmidt condensation reaction.

2.2. Process Model/ Environment

The MODDPG is implemented and tested using a multistep continuous Claisen-Schmidt condensation reaction between acetone and benzaldehyde where the objective is to maximize benzalacetone yield over dibenzalacetone (Fig 1(b)). It is worth noting that it is difficult to produce benzalacetone because the two α-Hs in acetone reacts with benzaldehyde quickly, often resulting in dibenzalacetone which is the undesired product. As a result, identifying and continuously monitoring the optimal reaction conditions is necessary to maximize the yield and selectivity of benzalacetone.

Before deploying the RL agent in a real system, it is important to train, test and refine it using a mathematical model. This study uses a mechanistic model for the training/optimization framework. The model was constructed based on several assumptions including: (i) the reaction is homogeneous, (ii) the reactor is plug-flow (i.e., no axial diffusion), and (iii) the heat transfer coefficient is constant.

The mass balances of the reactants and products in the tubular reactor are presented by Eq(1) below.

$$\frac{\partial c_{iz}}{\partial t} = -v_z(z)\frac{\partial c_{iz}}{\partial z} \pm r_i \tag{1}$$

where c_{iz} represents the concentration of reactant or product i, v_z is the velocity in the z direction, and r_i is the rate of reaction.

The energy equation accounts for the heat of reaction, diffusive flux, and heat exchange between the reaction side and the jacket. The energy balance equation is given by Eq (2).

$$\sum C_p \frac{\partial T_z}{\partial t} = -v_z(z)C_p \frac{\partial T_z}{\partial z} \pm \sum r_i * \Delta H_{react} + UA(T_c - T_z) \tag{2}$$

where C_p refers to the specific heat capacity, T_z and T_c represent the temperature of the tubular reactor and coolant respectively, UA is the overall heat transfer coefficient, and ΔH_{react} is the reaction enthalpy.

The reaction rates of the different species are given by

$$r_A = -k_1 C_A C_B \tag{3}$$
$$r_B = -k_1 C_A C_B - k_2 C_B C_D \tag{4}$$
$$r_D = k_1 C_A C_B - k_2 C_B C_D \tag{5}$$
$$r_U = k_2 C_B C_D \tag{6}$$

The reaction rate constants (k_1 and k_2) follow an Arrhenius law.

For the sake of computational effectiveness, the method of lines (MOL) was used to convert the partial differential equations above into a set of ordinary differential equations which can be solved by using ordinary solvers.

As mentioned in section 2.1, MODDPG uses a vector of reward functions to address the MOP. Here, two objective functions were considered namely: the reaction conversion and the selectivity. The objective functions given below were both maximized.

$$\text{Conversion } (X_B) = \frac{C_{B,0} - C_B}{C_{B,0}} \tag{7}$$
$$\text{Selectivity } (S_D) = \frac{C_D}{C_{B,0} - C_B} \tag{8}$$

3. Results and discussion

It is important to accurately simulate the reactor behavior and use the simulations as an environment to train the agent. The mechanistic model introduced in the previous section can be used as an environment to perform the intended MODDPG optimization. Firstly, a comprehensive sensitivity analysis was carried out to rank all possible inputs or manipulated variables according to their impact on the outputs. The results suggest that 4 inputs are enough to generate optimal impact on the objective functions and effectively deliver a good trade-off between exploration and exploitation.

The training performance of the MODDPG agent is shown in Fig. 2. Each of the colored stripes in Fig. 2 represents 10 training episodes, where each circle represents the reward obtained at the end of each episode. In each episode, at least 10 e-greedy actions must be undertaken in order to get rewards based on the performance associated with the selectivity and conversion. Fig. 2 also suggests that the range of variation or exploration associated with the conversion is narrower compared to selectivity. This may be attributed to the inherently fast kinetics which in this case result in fast and nearly complete conversion of the limiting reactants.

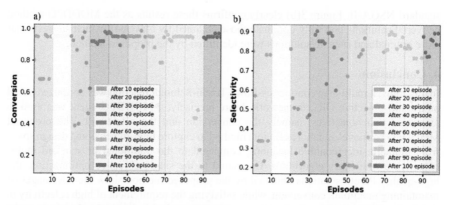

Fig.2. Training performance of the MODDPG agent for: a) conversion, and b) selectivity.

Figure 3 (a) shows the evolution of the Pareto front identified by the MODDPG agent over the training episodes. Clearly, the Pareto front undergoes significant improvement compared to the initial Pareto, which was identified at earlier training episodes. Based on Figure 3(b), the conversion, considered here as the first objective function, spans a range of variation of 9%, whereas the selectivity (i.e., second objective function) spans a range of variation of 29%. These observations are overall consistent with the discussions associated with figure 2 above and confirm that all Pareto solutions exhibit relatively high conversions. Nevertheless, the range of variation of the selectivity is still broad enough which highlights the inherent conflicting nature of the selected objectives and the need for a set of compromises to help achieve well-informed decision making.

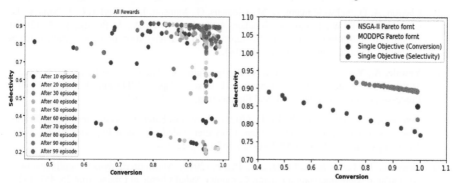

Fig.3. a) Pareto solutions generated by the MODDPG agent over the training episodes, and b) Final Pareto front obtained by MODDPG agent vs. genetic algorithm.

The results obtained based on the MODDPG agent were compared against those obtained based on a popular non-dominated sorting genetic algorithm (NSGA-II). A hypervolume (HV) evaluation metric, also called the Lebesgue measure, is used to compare the quality of the Pareto solutions. The Lebesgue measure evaluates the quality of the approximated solutions and distribution of the nondominated solution along the Pareto front based on an HV indicator score. Higher HV values indicate better Pareto results and suggest that the obtained solutions are closer to the true Pareto front. The proposed method produces HV indicator values of 0.78 and 0.53 for MODDPG and NSGA-II, respectively. These scores clearly demonstrate that the at the proposed MODDPG method outperforms the standard NSGA-II. Figure 3(b) clearly confirms these results as the MODDPG method delivered solutions that fully dominate those obtained by NSGA-II, which suggests that more optimal and reliable solutions were identified by the proposed method.

4. Conclusion

In this study, a multi-step continuous-flow Claisen-Schmidt reaction was optimized based on a multi-objective DRL framework. More precisely, a MODDPG agent was used to maximize two objectives, namely the conversion and the selectivity. The proposed MODDPG is a novel and more efficient method to explore high-dimensional design space from mutually incompatible locations, compared to the traditional or standard multi-objective evolutionary algorithms. Compared to the single objective optimization, the high-quality Pareto solutions obtained by the proposed method show the advantages of maintaining maximum conversion, while satisfying the requirement of high selectivity in the synthesis of API. This research may prove very valuable and highlights the benefits of RL in real-time self-optimization of real-world problems which inevitably involve multiple objectives that must be optimized simultaneously.

Acknowledgements:

This research work is sponsored by Takeda pharmaceutical international company, USA.

References

1) Fath, V., Kockmann, N., Otto, J., & Röder, T. (2020). Self-optimising processes and real-time-optimisation of organic syntheses in a microreactor system using Nelder-Mead and design of experiments. Reaction Chemistry and Engineering, 5(7), 1281–1299.

2) Clayton, A. D., Schweidtmann, A. M., Clemens, G., Manson, J. A., Taylor, C. J., Niño, C. G., Chamberlain, T. W., Kapur, N., Blacker, A. J., Lapkin, A. A., & Bourne, R. A. (2020). Automated self-optimisation of multi-step reaction and separation processes using machine learning. Chemical Engineering Journal, 384.

3) Yewale, A., Yang, Y., Nazemifard, N., Papageorgiou, C., Rielly, C., & Benyahia, B. (2023). Multi-Agent Reinforcement Learning and RL-Based Adaptive PID Control of Crystallization Processes. Computer Aided Chemical Engineering, 52, 1667–1672.

4) Benyahia, B., Anandan, P., Rielly, C. (2021). Control of batch and continuous crystallization processes using reinforcement learning. Computer Aided Chemical Engineering, 67, 1371–1376. https://doi.org/10.1016/B978-0-323-88506-5.50211-4.

5) Benyahia, B., Latifi, M.A., Fonteix, C., Pla, F. (2010). Multicriteria dynamic optimization of an emulsion copolymerization reactor. Computer Aided Chemical Engineering 28, 457-462.

6) Zhou, Z., Li, X., & Zare, R. N. (2017). Optimizing Chemical Reactions with Deep Reinforcement Learning. ACS Central Science, 3(12), 1337–1344.

7) Neumann, M., & Palkovits, D. S. (2022). Reinforcement Learning Approaches for the Optimization of the Partial Oxidation Reaction of Methane. Industrial and Engineering Chemistry Research, 61(11), 3910–3916.

8) Liu, J., & Benyahia, B. (2023). Single and multi-objective superstructure optimization of an integrated continuous multistage reaction-crystallization-filtration process with recycles. Computer Aided Chemical Engineering, 52, 667–672.

Flavio Manenti, Gintaras V. Reklaitis (Eds.), Proceedings of the 34th European Symposium on Computer Aided Process Engineering / 15th International Symposium on Process Systems Engineering (ESCAPE34/PSE24), June 2-6, 2024, Florence, Italy

Combining Predictive Models and Reinforcement Learning for Tailored Molecule Generation

Miriam Nnadili[a], Andrew N Okafor[a], David Akinpelu[b], Teslim Olayiwola[a], Jose Romagnoli[a]

[a]Cain Department of Chemical Engineering, Louisiana State University, Baton Rouge, Louisiana 70803, United States.
[b]Department of Mechanical & Industrial Engineering, Louisiana State University, Baton Rouge, Louisiana 70803, United States.

Correspondence to: *jose@lsu.edu*

Abstract

This study introduces a three-fold methodology that harnesses the capabilities of generative artificial intelligence (AI), predictive modelling, and reinforcement learning to craft customized molecules with desired properties. The model seamlessly integrates deep learning techniques with Self-Referencing Embedded Strings (SELFIES) molecular representation, constructing a generative model for producing valid molecules. In the framework, a graph neural network model was used to predict molecular properties and a combined Variational Autoencoder and reinforcement learning model to generate new molecules with specific attributes. Experimental data from a surfactant study validates the effectiveness of the framework. This innovative approach not only streamlines molecular design for surfactant systems but also anticipates transformative advancements in diverse scientific and industrial domains.

Keywords: Molecular design, Predictive modelling, Reinforcement learning

1. Introduction

Contemporary science and industry are deeply dependent on understanding the complex relationship between a molecule's structure and its function. Traditional methods frequently face difficulties in dealing with complicated molecular systems. However, the need to create molecules with specific properties offers both significant challenges and promising opportunities. In critical domains such as medicine and materials science, the significance of innovative and intelligent molecule design methods cannot be overstated. The spotlight has recently intensified on molecule generation and property prediction due to breakthroughs in deep generative model (Walters and Barzilay 2020). The pursuit of predicting and customizing molecular properties forms the crux of advanced research, propelling innovations and discoveries across diverse scientific domains (Zhang and Chen 2022). Accurately predicting molecular properties and generating molecules that meet specific criteria demand not only advanced computational models but also a profound understanding of molecule chemistry.

This study proposes a Reinforcement Learning (RL) methodology for inverse molecule design, where forward modeling predicts properties given a molecule, and inverse modeling infers molecules from given properties. The methodology integrates generative artificial intelligence (AI), predictive graph neural networks (GNN) modeling, and RL. The initial phase incorporates the Self-Referencing Embedded Strings (SELFIES) molecular representation, coupled with a deep generative model (Variational Autoencoder (VAE)). For property prediction, GNN approach is employed due to its superior performance, eliminating the need for informative descriptors typically found in quantitative structure-property relationships. RL serves as the pivotal guiding mechanism in our approach for molecule generation, using the Variational Autoencoder (VAE). A tailor-made RL learning algorithm is proposed to steer the VAE's latent representations to generate molecules with specific desired properties. Tanimoto similarity (or the Jaccard coefficient) was used to quantify the similarity and diversity between the original and generated molecular structures. To understand the features of the generated surfactant molecules that explain the Critical Micelle Concentration (CMC) values, saliency maps were generated for the selected surfactants. The feasibility of this approach is demonstrated in a case study focused on non-ionic surfactant molecules. Specifically, it targets the generation of new molecules with low CMC, a crucial surfactant characteristic.

2. Methodology

Figure 1 illustrates the graphical representation of the proposed architecture towards tailored molecules generation. The initial phase of the proposed architecture utilizes the Self-Referencing Embedded Strings (SELFIES) (Krenn, Häse et al. 2020) molecular representation, paired with deep generative model. Here, the VAE model encoded molecules into low-dimensional vectors in latent space as continuous and smooth probability distributions, and the decoder of VAEs converted these continuous vectors back to discrete molecular representations (Doersch 2016). The continuous representations of molecules allow sampling of the chemical space stepwise, leading to the successful optimization of molecules with desired properties. A GNN for property prediction is used to estimate the fitness of the generated molecules to the actual property. Lastly, RL (Wiering and Van Otterlo 2012), is finally used as a tool for optimizing an objective, in this case, RL is applied as a technique for fine-tuning target properties.

2.1 SELFIES

SELFIES is a string-based representation of a molecular graph, is one hundred percent robust because each SELFIES corresponds to a valid molecule, even entirely random strings. It is important to note, however, that validity is defined with respect to valency rules. As a result, molecules that are valid may not necessarily be stable. SELFIES are independent of the machine learning model and can be used as a direct input without any adaptations of the models.

2.2 Variational Autoencoder (VAE)

The Variational Autoencoder (VAE) (Xue, Gong et al. 2019) architecture used in this work is a neural network comprising two main components: an encoder and a decoder. The encoder processes the input data, which is represented as a one-hot encoding (OHE) of SELFIES and maps it to a lower-dimensional latent space (An and Cho 2015). This latent space is characterized by a set of continuous variables that represent the essence of the input data in a compact and meaningful way. Each point in the latent space corresponds to a potential molecular structure. The latent space is typically assumed to follow a multivariate Gaussian prior distribution. The decoder, on the other hand, reconstructs the original SELFIES representation of the molecule from the latent variables generated by the encoder. The decoder predicts the parameters (atom types, connectivity, and coordinates) of the reconstructed molecule. Simplified Molecular-Input Line-Entry System (SMILES) (Weininger 1988) is a notation that encodes molecular structures as strings to text. To perform unconstrained optimization for specific properties, the decoder is responsible for reconstructing from the latent vector to the

SMILES with chemical validity. This allows VAEs to generate new samples while capturing the underlying structure of the input data.

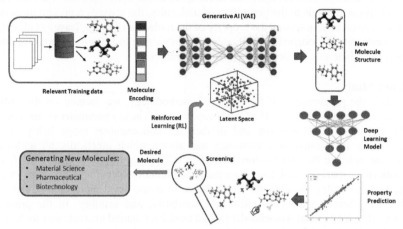

Figure 1: Schematic representation of methodology.

2.3 Predictive Model

In this study, the property prediction model adopted the GNN approach due to their superior performance and to avoid the need for informative descriptors as in quantitative structure-property relationships (QSPRs). The underlying structure of the adopted GNN model closely mirrors that proposed by Qin et. al. (Qin, Jin et al. 2021). At the outset, the GNN model integrates a sequence of graph network layers which adapt node features in a molecular graph based on those of interconnected atoms. For this study, an extensive set of atoms was considered. Consequently, the atom type was one-hot encoded (OHE) into 43 distinct features, grounded on a predetermined list of chemical elements. Although edge features (like bond type) weren't directly incorporated, they were represented indirectly through atom-specific attributes like hybridization and aromaticity. The overall representation hence consisted of 74 atom-based features. These encompass OHE atom type, OHE atom degree, OHE implicit Hydrogen count, formal charge, radical electron count, OHE atom hybridization categories (SP, SP2, SP3, SP3D, SP3D2), aromaticity indicators, and OHE total Hydrogen count. The final predictive model contains two (2) GNN layers, each having 256 hidden units, employed a ReLU activation function, and 3 fully connected layers to map the pre-processed input matrix to predict the critical micellar concentration.

2.4 Reinforcement learning (RL)

For molecule generation, we integrated RL with a VAE. The core objective is to harness the potential of RL in steering the VAE's latent representations to generate molecules possessing specific desired properties. The architecture of the RL component encompasses three fundamental elements: a policy network, a reward computation mechanism, and an optimization strategy. The policy network, referred to as 'Policy', stands as the keystone in modifying the latent representations of the VAE to guide the molecule generation process. Essentially, the policy network takes a latent vector 'z' and transforms it into decoded molecules through the VAE's decoder. The policy network operates as a neural network with the responsibility of determining actions in a given state. In the context of molecule generation, these actions correspond to modifications in the latent space that influence the VAE's output. We formulated our algorithm to follow the Markov decision process where the latent space of the VAE represents the states, and the actions corresponds to the generation of molecules, the rewards represent numerical values received after assessing the property of the molecule (Popova, Isayev et al. 2018). The architecture is designed to facilitate the policy's role in learning to produce latent vectors that align with the desired molecular properties.

3. Case Study

To verify the performance of the proposed methodology, we focused on the critical micelle concentration (CMC). The CMC property serves as key parameter to characterize surfactant behavior in solution and defines the concentration range below which surfactant is in solution as a monomer and above which practically all additional surfactant added to the solution forms micelles (Cifuentes, Bernal et al. 1997). Herein, we collected experimental dataset from published literature detailing CMC data for 285 surfactant molecules. Onward, this study hopes to create novel molecules exhibiting a low CMC, thereby enhancing efficiency, solubility, and stability. In the proposed framework, a Variational Autoencoder (VAE) model is required to create new molecules. To train a VAE model, a large database containing molecules of interest is required. Owing to small dataset, a transfer learning approach is proposed to leverage the knowledge acquired from the pretrained VAE model trained initially on a comprehensive dataset comprising over 20,000 polymer structures. This strategy demonstrates its effectiveness in generating meaningful representations for a wide range of molecular structures.

4. Result and Discussion

The fine-tuning process on a pretrained VAE using a smaller dataset expands the distribution in the latent space, surpassing the outcomes of training solely on the smaller dataset. Figure 2 visually illustrates the scatter plot that directly compares the predicted CMC values generated by the model with the experimental CMC values and the latent space inhabited by RL-generated molecules in the unconstrained space. Notably, VAE + RL-generated molecules form a distinct cluster (depicted in green), indicating the successful influence of the reinforcement learning strategy in steering the VAE to generate molecules meeting the specified property threshold of a CMC below 0.1mM.

The structural integrity of molecules generated by a model was rigorously validated to ensure adherence to fundamental chemical principles, including proper atomic coordination and avoidance of unusual valences. The process included an in-depth analysis of ring structures, assessing both cyclic structures and branched rings for the correct number of rings and their chemical plausibility in terms of size. Additionally, the practicality of these synthesized molecules for surfactant design was evaluated using Tanimoto similarity coefficients. This involved a quantitative comparison with surfactants from the training dataset, aiding in the selection of molecules with close resemblance to established surfactants. Saliency maps, used in deep learning to identify crucial image features for classification, were employed to discern key features of surfactant molecules affecting their CMC values. By calculating the input atom feature gradients and multiplying them with the input, the relative significance of each feature, particularly for atom presence or absence, was determined. This method helped identify the importance of various atom types on CMC predictions. Figure 3 showcases the saliency maps for selected surfactants, both original and newly generated, ensuring that the original ones met the CMC threshold for a valid comparison. Atoms in these maps are color-coded: red indicates a positive influence on CMC, while blue signifies a negative one. The maps reveal that polar atoms like O and N raise the CMC values, while nonpolar atoms like C lower them. Furthermore, the maps illustrate that surfactants with more branches tend to have smaller CMC values, especially when compared to those with long, unbranched tails, aligning with the understanding that increased polarity leads to higher CMC values.

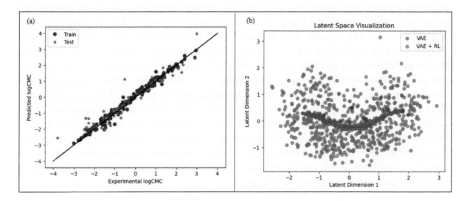

Figure 2: a) Cross plot of predicted and experimental CMC for the GNN model at best cross validation; b) Latent space visualization of the RL generated molecules in the unconstrained space. RL generated molecules are in a region within diverse space. The VAE + RL-generated molecules exhibited a distinctive cluster (green) implying that the reinforcement learning strategy successfully influenced the VAE to generate molecules meeting the desired property threshold of CMC below 0.1mM.

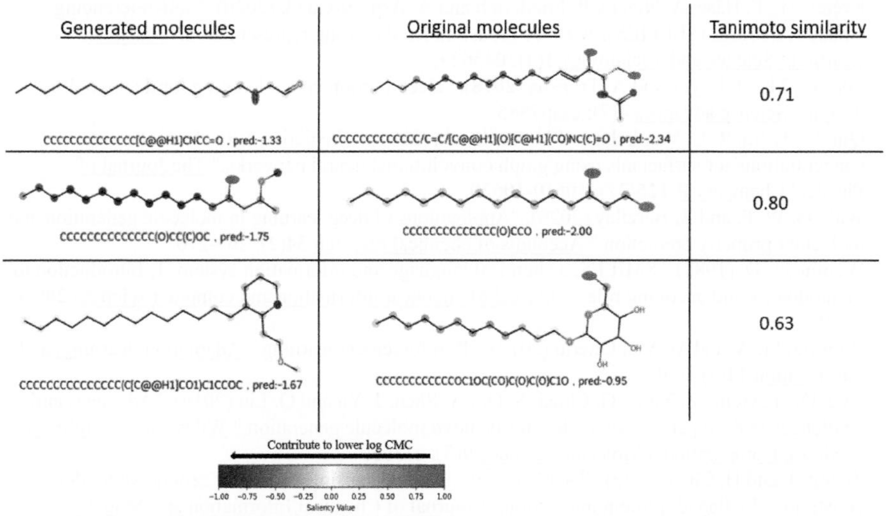

Generated molecules	Original molecules	Tanimoto similarity
CCCCCCCCCCCCCC[C@@H1]CNCC=O , pred:-1.33	CCCCCCCCCCCCC/C=C/[C@@H1](O)[C@H1](CO)NC(C)=O , pred:-2.34	0.71
CCCCCCCCCCCCCC(O)CC(C)OC , pred:-1.75	CCCCCCCCCCCCC(O)CCO , pred:-2.00	0.80
CCCCCCCCCCCCCC(C[C@@H1]CO1)C1CCOC , pred:-1.67	CCCCCCCCCCCCOC1OC(CO)C(O)C(O)C1O , pred:-0.95	0.63

Contribute to lower log CMC

-1.00 -0.75 -0.50 -0.25 0.00 0.25 0.50 0.75 1.00
Saliency Value

Figure 3: Molecular saliency maps of selected generated surfactants with the corresponding original surfactant molecule and their Tanimoto similarity values. The higher the value (darker red), the more a node contributes to a higher log CMC and vice versa. Herein, the gradients are computed for each node followed by normalization between −1 and 1.

4. Conclusions

In this article, we delved into an advanced machine learning approach, harnessing the power of Graph Neural Networks (GNN) for predictive modelling, and combining Variational Autoencoders (VAE) with policy-based Reinforcement Learning (RL) for the purpose of generating molecules with specific desired properties. Our focus cantered on surfactants, with a particular emphasis on achieving low Critical Micelle Concentration (CMC) values. The results demonstrated that the proposed framework effectively generates valid molecules within the specified property threshold values. Tanimoto similarity was used to quantify the similarity and diversity between the training datasets and generated molecular structures. Furthermore, in our endeavour to gain insights into the characteristics of the generated surfactant molecules, we generated saliency maps that shed light on the critical factors influencing the Critical Micelle Concentration (CMC) values. These observations align with our intuitive understanding, as surfactants tend to exhibit lower CMC values when characterized by extended, unbranched tail groups and higher values in cases of heightened polarity. This validation reinforces the framework's capacity to tailor molecules to desired specifications and enhances our understanding of molecular behaviour in surfactant systems.

References

An, J. and S. Cho (2015). "Variational autoencoder based anomaly detection using reconstruction probability." Special lecture on IE **2**(1): 1-18.

Cifuentes, A., J. L. Bernal and J. C. Diez-Masa (1997). "Determination of critical micelle concentration values using capillary electrophoresis instrumentation." Analytical Chemistry **69**(20): 4271-4274.

Doersch, C. (2016). "Tutorial on variational autoencoders." arXiv preprint arXiv:1606.05908.

Krenn, M., F. Häse, A. Nigam, P. Friederich and A. Aspuru-Guzik (2020). "Self-referencing embedded strings (SELFIES): A 100% robust molecular string representation." Machine Learning: Science and Technology **1**(4): 045024.

Popova, M., O. Isayev and A. Tropsha (2018). "Deep reinforcement learning for de novo drug design." Science advances **4**(7): eaap7885.

Qin, S., T. Jin, R. C. Van Lehn and V. M. Zavala (2021). "Predicting critical micelle concentrations for surfactants using graph convolutional neural networks." The Journal of Physical Chemistry B **125**(37): 10610-10620.

Walters, W. P. and R. Barzilay (2020). "Applications of deep learning in molecule generation and molecular property prediction." Accounts of chemical research **54**(2): 263-270.

Weininger, D. (1988). "SMILES, a chemical language and information system. 1. Introduction to methodology and encoding rules." Journal of chemical information and computer sciences **28**(1): 31-36.

Wiering, M. A. and M. Van Otterlo (2012). "Reinforcement learning." Adaptation, learning, and optimization **12**(3): 729.

Xue, D., Y. Gong, Z. Yang, G. Chuai, S. Qu, A. Shen, J. Yu and Q. Liu (2019). "Advances and challenges in deep generative models for de novo molecule generation." Wiley Interdisciplinary Reviews: Computational Molecular Science **9**(3): e1395.

Zhang, J. and H. Chen (2022). "De novo molecule design using molecular generative models constrained by ligand–protein interactions." Journal of Chemical Information and Modeling **62**(14): 3291-3306.

Flavio Manenti, Gintaras V. Reklaitis (Eds.), Proceedings of the 34th European Symposium on Computer Aided Process Engineering / 15th International Symposium on Process Systems Engineering (ESCAPE34/PSE24), June 2-6, 2024, Florence, Italy

Deep Learning for Fast Inference of Mechanistic Models' Parameters

Maxim Borisyak*[a] Stefan Born[a] Peter Neubauer[a] Mariano Nicolás Cruz-Bournazou[a]

a Technische Universität Berlin, Straße 17 des Juni 135, 10623 Berlin, Germany
maxim.borisyak@tu-berlin.de

Abstract

Inferring parameters of macro-kinetic growth models, typically represented by Ordinary Differential Equations (ODE), from the experimental data is a crucial step in bioprocess engineering. Conventionally, estimates of the parameters are obtained by fitting the mechanistic model to observations. Fitting, however, requires a significant computational power.

Specifically, during the development of new bioprocesses that use previously unknown organisms or strains, efficient, robust, and computationally cheap methods for parameter estimation are of great value. In this work, we propose using Deep Neural Networks (NN) for directly predicting parameters of mechanistic models given observations. The approach requires spending computational resources for training a NN, nonetheless, once trained, such a network can provide parameter estimates orders of magnitude faster than conventional methods.

We consider a training procedure that combines Neural Networks and mechanistic models. We demonstrate the performance of the proposed algorithms on data sampled from several mechanistic models used in bioengineering describing a typical industrial batch process and compare the proposed method, a typical gradient-based fitting procedure, and the combination of the two. We find that, while Neural Network estimates are slightly improved by further fitting, these estimates are measurably better than the fitting procedure alone.

Keywords: mechanistic models, inference, deep learning

1. Introduction

Mechanistic growth models play an important role in bioprocess development. These models are derived from the first principles and their parameters are readily interpretable. Such models also enable computer-aided design and control of bioprocesses. Most of the models are expressed as systems of Ordinary Differential Equations (ODE). Examples include models by Lin et al. (2001), Neubauer et al. (2003) and Anane et al. (2017). Typically, such ODE systems do not admit analytical solutions and, therefore, one has to rely on dedicated ODE solvers. Since the systems tend to be highly non-linear, a solver needs to perform a large number of integration steps. This is especially the case, when models contain both, fast and slow dynamics (Anane et al., 2017).

Estimation of mechanistic models' parameters is conventionally done by fitting the model to observations following the Maximum Likelihood principle:

$$L(\theta) = -\log P(x \mid \theta) = -\sum_i \log P(x_i \mid \theta) \rightarrow \min_\theta; \qquad (1)$$

where x, θ are observations and parameters of the model.

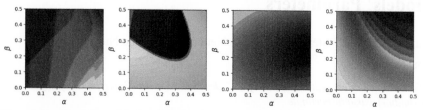

Figure 1: Random slices of the loss function for an E. coli cultivation. For each of the slices, three random parameter vectors are drawn from within the corresponding ranges, the loss function is evaluated on linear combinations of these parameters with coefficients α and β. For illustration purposes, levels are set such that each level contains roughly the same area.

The optimisation is typically carried out by gradient or quasi-Newton methods such as the BFGS algorithm (see, for example, Fletcher, 2000). Firstly, gradient of an ODE solution tends to take noticeably more computational time than just obtaining the forward solution. Secondly, the non-linear nature of the models tends to induce a highly complex landscape of the loss function, Figure 1 illustrates this effect. This might lead to a significant increase in the number of steps an optimiser needs to perform for convergence. Moreover, the loss function seems to have a significant number of local minima, which is typically addressed by the multi-start algorithm (see, for example, Fletcher, 2000), deterministic (Lin et al., 2006) or nondeterministic (Da Ros et al., 2013) global optimisation methods. Multiple shooting also proved to reduce this problem in this context (Peifer at al., 2007). In this paper, we consider multi-start as our baseline as it offers a more direct comparison with the proposed method.

All of the features of mechanistic models described above generally lead to a high demand for computational resources when performing fitting. Bayesian methods, like Monte-Carlo Markov chains, are fairly similar to Maximum Likelihood fitting procedures in terms of computational resources, although they might require substantially more computational power. Additionally, please, notice that the mentioned algorithms display a limited degree of parallelism: both gradient optimisation and ODE solver are inherently sequential, albeit methods like multiple shooting partially alleviate the problem (Gander et al., 2007).

High usage of resources might limit online applications such as monitoring, control and, especially, online design of experiments. Currently, modern hardware seems to provide enough computational power for such applications assuming a small number of unknown parameters and good initial estimates (for instance, see Kemmer et al. 2022, Krausch et al., 2022), nonetheless, more complex mechanistic models or a need for a more frequent response might prove difficult.

In this work, we propose a novel inference method that dramatically reduces the computational burden: training a Neural Network to directly predict parameters of a mechanistic model given observations. To the best knowledge of the authors, there is no prior literature describing such an approach.

2.   Deep Learning for inference

All of the fitting algorithms mentioned above are general-purpose methods, they place weak assumptions on the loss function and work practically with any reasonable model, treating the latter as a black box that provides trajectories, values of the loss function, gradients at arbitrary points etc.

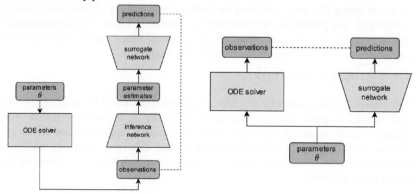

Figure 2: Schematic representation of the proposed method. Arrows represent flow of the data, "inference network" and "surrogate network" are represented by neural networks. Dashed lines indicate which quantities are used for the loss computation. (Left) Inference network training procedure, surrogate network is frozen during training. (Right) "Surrogate network" training.

If one, however, considers a particular model, then the inference task, Eq. (1), can be viewed as a mapping from observations x to the optimal parameters $\theta^*(x)$:

$$\theta^*(x) = \arg\min_{\theta}[-\log P(x \mid \theta)];\tag{2}$$

and, therefore, can be cast as a regression problem with the loss function:

$$L(\psi) = -\sum_i \log P\big(x_i \mid f(x_i \mid \psi)\big) \to \min_{\psi};\tag{3}$$

where f denotes the regressor parametrised by ψ. The regressor f can be represented by a neural network, which we call the inference network. Please, notice that, unlike typical regression problems, Eq. (3) defines a loss function that closely resembles that of an auto-encoder (Kramer, 1991): the inference network provides parameter estimates $\theta(x) = f(x \mid \psi)$, which are then passed into the mechanistic model M to make predictions $\mu = M(f(x \mid \psi))$, and, in a sense, are "decoded into" predictions, and the latter are compared against observations using the noise model $P_n(x \mid \mu)$:

$$-\log P\big(x \mid \theta = f(x \mid \psi)\big) = -\log P_n\big(x \mid \mu = M(f(x \mid \psi))\big).\tag{4}$$

2.1.   Surrogate network

The major downside of the proposed algorithm is that networks typically require a large number of steps for training which greatly exceeds the number of training samples, and each step the algorithm requires evaluation of the mechanistic model and its gradient, which cannot be precomputed as they depend on network's predictions. In order to circumvent the need for the mechanistic model during NN training, we propose replacing the model with a surrogate network which is trained to approximate the output of the mechanistic model.

To train the surrogate network we sample a large dataset of model's parameters: parameters are drawn randomly within the ranges that cover biologically feasible values. It is worth noting that more advanced methods such as Kriging (Press, 2007) could also be employed. The parameters are then used for generating a dataset of observations. The surrogate network $g(t, \theta)$ is trained to map observations' timestamps t_i and parameters θ_i to observations x_i by minimizing the negative log likelihood:

$$\mathcal{L} = - \sum_i \log P_n \left(x_i \mid g(t_i, \theta_i) \right). \tag{5}$$

Once trained, the surrogate network offers a fast approximation of the mechanistic model, which is used to guide the inference network (Figure 2). In our experiments, such a procedure results in decent inference networks, however, approximation errors of the surrogate network prevent it from reaching precise solutions. Thus, we additionally retrain the inference network trained with a surrogate network with the mechanistic model when it is not too costly.

3.   Numerical experiment

To evaluate the performance of the proposed method, we simulate data from two mechanistic models: Michaelis–Menten kinetics (MMK) and the E. coli growth model by Anane et al. (2017), both expressed as ODE systems. For each model we sample parameters from a wide prior distribution that covers biologically feasible values, obtain trajectories and from each trajectory we generate a small number of observations for each of the observed channels, overall, 14 observations for MMK, 30 observations for the E. coli model. Observations' timestamps are randomly distributed within the corresponding range: 2 hours for MMK, 6 hours for E. coli. For emulating realistic conditions, channel observations are not aligned, i.e., only one channel is measured per sample. Initial conditions are assumed to be unknown and inferred along with models' parameters. For each of the models, we draw just above a million training samples. As shown below, conventional fitting procedures take a significant amount of time, thus, we use only around a thousand of test samples, any significantly larger number of test sample would make experiments unfeasibly long. Nonetheless, the test sample is sufficiently large to keep the estimation errors small (Table 1).

For the inference networks we utilise Deep Set architecture (Zaheer et al., 2017) and employ triplet encoding (Yalavarthi et al. 2022) for processing asynchronous observations. To improve training, we apply an invertible transformation that maps prior distribution of parameters and initial conditions into the standard normal distribution, thus, bringing all parameters to the same scale.

As a baseline we employ the BFGS optimisation algorithm (see, for example, Fletcher, 1987). We set a limit of 1024 iterations per sample to reflect the real-world time constraints of an online application. Additionally, we perform a multi-start procedure with a varying number of initial guesses. To assess the improvement potential for the proposed method, we also fine-tune predictions of the networks by running a fitting algorithm starting from the networks' estimates.

Table 1 Results of the numerical experiments. R^2 is computed based on squared errors normalised by variances of the noise in each individual channel. "MM" denotes fine-tuning with the corresponding mechanistic model, "Deep Inference + BFGS" denotes the fitting procedure (a single start) with initial guess produced by the network. When applicable, time measurements are given for GPU / CPU evaluations, CPU only otherwise.

Method	MMK		E. coli	
	R^2	time per samp.	R^2	time per samp.
BFGS, 1 start	0.928 ± 0.010	50 msec	0.442 ± 0.108	2.04 sec
BFGS, 2 starts	0.957 ± 0.001	93 msec	0.930 ± 0.016	3.59 sec
BFGS, 4 starts	0.958 ± 0.001	180 msec	0.984 ± 0.002	8.15 sec
BFGS, 8 starts	0.958 ± 0.001	344 msec	0.989 ± 0.001	16.5 sec
Deep Inference	0.949 ± 0.001	10 μsec / 37 μsec	0.945 ± 0.007	18 μsec / 260 μsec
Deep Inference + MM	0.954 ± 0.001	10 μsec / 37 μsec	-	-
Deep Inference + BFGS	0.958 ± 0.001	41 msec	0.990 ± 0.001	1.3 sec

We evaluate performance of the algorithms on 1024 independently drawn test samples. We also measure inference speed: BFGS-based methods are evaluated on a CPU (AMD Ryzen 5 5600X), all networks – also on a GPU (NVIDIA GeForce RTX 3070).

Results of our experiments are summarised in Table 1. Results show that even for simple models, such as Michaelis–Menten kinetics, optimisation algorithms are sometimes stuck in local minima (as shown by the gains of the multi-start). The proposed method achieves a lower average loss than a single fitting run and performance comparable to the multi-start procedure. Fine-tuned predictions are on par with the best multi-start results. Importantly, please, note the difference in the inference speed: the network is faster by 3 orders of magnitude for the simplest of the models, and by 6 orders for the E. coli model. Additionally, we observe that the fitting procedure aided by the inference network tend to converge faster.

The time measurements in Table 1 represent a lower bound on response time of online algorithms that use parameter estimation as their first step. Please, note that the computational time of conventional fitting algorithms approaches measurement frequency of some devices (for example, 30 seconds for pH and DOT measurements, Hans et al., 2020). Moreover, in an online application, parameter estimation is often followed by other computationally demanding algorithms such as Model Predictive Control (see, for example, Krausch et al., 2022), potentially making the parameter estimation step a bottleneck in the data processing pipeline.

4. Conclusion

We present an alternative framework for quickly and reliably estimating models' parameters given observations. Based on Deep Learning techniques, it speeds up Maximum Likelihood estimations by several orders of magnitude while preserving accuracy of optimisation-based techniques. Additionally, our experiments indicate that the proposed method does not suffer from the local minima problem. The proposed method has a potential to significantly improve online applications, such as monitoring, control of bioprocesses and design of experiments by providing nearly instantaneous parameter estimations. Moreover, fast inference enables the use of much more complex and precise models, potentially leading to overall improvement of bioprocess development.

Acknowledgements

We gratefully acknowledge the financial support of the German Federal Ministry of Education and Research (01DD20002A – KIWI biolab).

References

Anane E, Neubauer P, Bournazou MN. 2017 Modelling overflow metabolism in Escherichia coli by acetate cycling. Biochemical Engineering Journal. 15;125:23-30.

H.Y. Lin, B. Mathiszik, B. Xu, S.O. Enfors, P. Neubauer, 2001, Determination of the maximum specific uptake capacities for glucose and oxygen in glucose-limited fed-batch cultivations of Escherichia coli, Biotechnol. Bioeng. 73 347–357

P. Neubauer, H.Y. Lin, B. Mathiszik, 2003, Metabolic load of recombinant protein production: inhibition of cellular capacities for glucose uptake and respiration after induction of a heterologous gene in Escherichia coli, Biotechnol. Bioeng. 83

Fletcher, R., 2000. *Practical methods of optimization*. John Wiley & Sons.

Peifer, M., and Timmer, J. (2007). Parameter estimation in ordinary differential equations for biochemical processes using the method of multiple shooting. IET Systems Biology 1, 78–88. 10.1049/iet-syb:20060067.

Da Ros, S., Colusso, G., Weschenfelder, T.A., de Marsillac Terra, L., de Castilhos, F., Corazza, M.L., and Schwaab, M. (2013). A comparison among stochastic optimization algorithms for parameter estimation of biochemical kinetic models. Applied Soft Computing 13, 2205–2214. 10.1016/j.asoc.2013.01.019.

Gander, M.J. and Vandewalle, S., 2007. Analysis of the parareal time-parallel time-integration method. *SIAM Journal on Scientific Computing*, 29(2), pp.556-578.

Kemmer, A., Fischer, N., Wilms, T., Cai, L., Groß, S., King, R., Neubauer, P. and Cruz-Bournazou, M.N., 2022. Nonlinear state estimation as tool for online monitoring and adaptive feed in high-throughput cultivations.

Krausch, N., Kim, J.W., Barz, T., Lucia, S., Groß, S., Huber, M.C., Schiller, S.M., Neubauer, P. and Cruz Bournazou, M.N., 2022. High-throughput screening of optimal process conditions using model predictive control. *Biotechnology and Bioengineering*, 119(12), pp.3584-3595.

Kramer, M.A., 1991. Nonlinear principal component analysis using autoassociative neural networks. *AIChE journal*, 37(2), pp.233-243.

Fletcher, R., 1987, Practical Methods of Optimization (2nd ed.), New York: John Wiley & Sons, ISBN 978-0-471-91547-8

Zaheer, M., Kottur, S., Ravanbakhsh, S., Poczos, B., Salakhutdinov, R.R. and Smola, A.J., 2017. Deep sets. *Advances in neural information processing systems*, 30.

Yalavarthi, V.K., Burchert, J. and Schmidt-Thieme, L., 2022, October. DCSF: Deep Convolutional Set Functions for Classification of Asynchronous Time Series. In *2022 IEEE 9th International Conference on Data Science and Advanced Analytics (DSAA)* (pp. 1-10). IEEE.

Lin, Y. and Stadtherr, M.A., 2006. Deterministic global optimization for parameter estimation of dynamic systems. *Industrial & engineering chemistry research*, 45(25), pp.8438-8448.

Press, W.H., 2007. Numerical recipes 3rd edition: The art of scientific computing. Cambridge university press.

Hans, S., Ulmer, C., Narayanan, H., Brautaset, T., Krausch, N., Neubauer, P., Schäffl, I., Sokolov, M. and Cruz Bournazou, M.N., 2020. Monitoring parallel robotic cultivations with online multivariate analysis. Processes, 8(5), p.582.

Flavio Manenti, Gintaras V. Reklaitis (Eds.), Proceedings of the 34th European Symposium on
Computer Aided Process Engineering / 15th International Symposium on Process Systems
Engineering (ESCAPE34/PSE24), June 2-6, 2024, Florence, Italy

Automation in Port Areas and Industry for Safe and Effective Management of Dangerous Goods

Tomaso Vairo, Margherita Pettinato, Evgeniia Taubert, Ahmad M. Tahir, Bruno Fabiano*

DICCA- Civil Chemical and Environmental Engineering Deprtment, University of Genova, Via Opera Pia 15, 16145, Italy
*brown@unige.it

Abstract

In the present era, the spread of cyber-physical systems within the framework Industry 4.0, is leading towards a complete automation of industrial processes, which are increasingly decentralized, smart, and require fewer and fewer frontline personnel. The storage, transportation, and handling of dangerous goods in port areas pose significant challenges due to the potential risks involved. The risk assessment process is certainly not excluded from the revolution and in perspective needs to be automatic, dynamic, and linked with the actual emerging conditions of complex systems. This paper focuses on designing an operational management system suitable to predict and reduce operational errors, improving the learning and education patterns, thus decreasing personnel vulnerability to hazardous substances. The system, based on ML algorithms and Bayesian reasoning, is constantly "learning" with the data provided by the physical system.

Keywords: Automation, Digitalization, Hazardous materials, Industrial ports, Safety 4.0

1. Introduction

The fourth industrial revolution is characterized by the appearance of cyber-physical systems, Internet of Things (IoT), smart factories, and generalized decentralized processes [1], providing new design principles and higher level of automation in the operations. The higher level of communication and autonomous systems require a risk assessment process that can keep up with dynamic and rapid information flows, moving towards RA process automatization. Emerging risks are connected to the combined action of energy transition, climate change, and digitalization [2], while control systems adopted in industry (Operational Technologies OT) need ad-hoc approaches to mitigate cyber risk [3]. Within the bustling domains of ports, hazardous materials introduce inherent risks, demanding a trade-off between efficiency and caution [4]. Italy's strategic Mediterranean location is supported by a vital network of seaports, including the Ports of Genoa, Livorno and Naples, which proactively embraced advanced technologies to enhance operational reliability [5]. A pivotal role in managing safety in complex systems, is represented by the Safety Management System (SMS) [6] representing a challenge and an up-to-date research topic. The commitment extends to the adherence on EU regulations, prioritizing safety and reliability in handling dangerous goods through integration of advanced technologies [7]. Vairo et al. [8] outlined a framework for dealing with those networks as complex systems aiming at identifying intervention priorities. The bow-tie method is a well-established risk assessment tool, widely used within the broad context of complex systems [9,10]. However, it suffers several recognized limitations, mainly connected to the actual assessment of likelihood and interdependencies in the fault and event trees.

Bow ties can be easily translated into Bayesian Networks, a robust probability reasoning method under uncertainty, providing a tool for incorporating evidence during the ongoing operations [11]. This facet can be automatized, modifying the structure, to derive from operational experience evidence updated risk parameters related to the failure probabilities and accidental scenarios occurrence [12]. Empirical results highlight the relevant contribution of human error, which is estimated 10^{-4} and 10^{-3}, respectively for routine operations and non-routine actions, as reported in IOGP [13]. This paper is focused on building an operational management system, starting from field experience, for automatically design a predictive model, suitable to intercept and avoid common operational errors. To verify the actual capability of the approach combining data- and experience-driven concepts to anticipate system deviations, the pilot application is tested in a port terminal handling petro-chemical products by a complex pipeline network.

2. Methods

2.1. Bow Tie analysis
The bow-tie analysis logically combines the fault-tree analysis (FTA) and the event-tree analysis (ETA). From a top event, the fault tree extends to the left-hand side and the event tree to the right-hand side, so that it is possible connecting causes (or threats) and consequences (or outcomes) with relevant preventive or mitigating barriers.

2.2. Hierarchical Bayesian Nets
Bayesian hierarchical modelling is a statistical model written in multiple levels (hierarchical form) that estimates the parameters of the posterior distribution using the Bayesian method. The sub-models combine to form the hierarchical model, and Bayes' theorem is used to integrate them with the observed data and account for all the uncertainty that is present. The result of this integration is the posterior distribution as additional evidence on the prior distribution is acquired. Hierarchical modelling is used when information is available on several different levels of observational units. In the outlined framework, we consider Fault and Event Trees prior probabilities, boolean failures, and predictions on critical variables values as relevant information sources. In deriving the posterior distribution. Y is a random variable following a normal distribution with expected value θ and variance 1:

$$Y \mid \theta \sim N(\theta, 1) \tag{1}$$

The expected value θ has a normal distribution with expected value μ and variance 1:

$$\theta \mid \mu \sim N(\mu, 1) \tag{2}$$

The expected value of (2), μ, follows, for example, a standard normal distribution, $N(0, 1)$. The parameter μ is called the hyperparameter, while its distribution given by $N(0, 1)$ is an example of a hyperprior distribution. The notation of the distribution of Y changes as another parameter is added, i.e.:

$$Y \mid \theta, \mu \sim N(\theta, 1) \tag{3}$$

So, in the following stage, μ, is characterized by normal distribution with expected value β and variance ε, meaning:

$$\mu \sim N(\beta, \varepsilon) \tag{4}$$

β and ε can be defined hyperparameters characterized by their hyperprior distributions as well. For a 3-stage hierarchical model, the posterior distribution is by:

$$(\theta,\varphi, X \,|Y) = ((Y \mid \theta) \, (\theta \mid \varphi) \, P(\varphi \mid X) \, P(X)) \, / \, P(Y) \tag{5}$$

In the present framework, each hierarchical level of the Bayes net, represents a stage of the Bow Tie. The transposition from the operational safety assessment to the Bayesian nets is performed by a customized tool, using the Python library PyBNBowTie.

3. Pilot application: loading of petrochemical products from the terminal

The logical flowchart of the critical assessment allowing transfer starting are depicted in Fig. 1. Product transfer takes place according to the sequence summarized in Fig. 2.

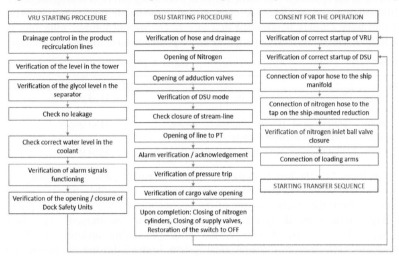

Figure 1: Flowchart for operating consent to HC transfer sequence starting.

The operation involves a series of steps to be carried out sequentially, with step-by-step conditional operational and safety verifications. Each operation may be subjected to error, either from a technological perspective (e.g., valve opening/closing failure, plant component feedback), or from a human viewpoint (incorrect, untimely, or missed actions). Each of the stages in the two flowcharts is associated with a given failure probability, used for training the model, as a priori probability. The history of failures, aggregated for the main steps, obtained by the Boolean chaining of elementary failures of each sub-steps, is represented in Table 1.

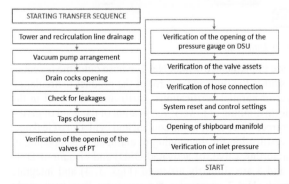

Figure 2: Flowchart for critical element checking and start of hydrocarbon transfer.

Table 1: Prior probabilities for the failures of the main sequential operative steps.

Main Step	Prior probability of failure (order of magnitude)
VRU starting procedure	1E-5 occ./y
DSU starting procedure	1E-4 occ./y
Consent for the operation	1E-4 occ./y
Start of the operation	1E-3 occ./y

The event analysis was extended over 5-years field observation and showed that the main cause of failure in the operation was human error in overriding valves or failing sequence of the different transfer pipelines. A conservative estimate of operational failures, classified into three clusters is provided in Table 2. The overall transfer reliability is estimated at 90%, with errors implying transfer interruption and no or low-severe damage.

Table 2: Human error evidence in transfer operation (occurrence probability for each step).

Error type	Occurrence probability, occ./op.
Analysis phase: Observation (observation missed; false observation; wrong identification)	1E-4 occ./y
Analysis phase: Interpretation (faulty diagnosis; wrong reasoning; decision error; delayed or incorrect prediction)	1E-3 occ./y
Synthesis phase: Planning (inadequate plan; priority error)	1E-3 occ./y

The system is trained on the historical data of failures of each equipment operating for the product transfer facility (as a prior probabilities) and incorporates the signals collected on site. Starting from the safety analysis of the operation, for each operational phase different Bayesian nets are designed, where each node is "pre-trained" on failure historical data. The subsequent step is the prior probability updating by field measurements for each element of the physical system. In the following, we provide an outline of the whole process, structured into sequential nets.

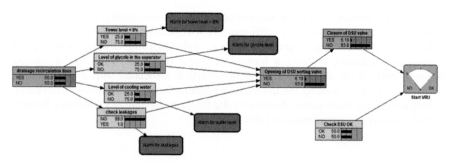

Figure 2: Start of the Vapour Recovery Unit - Net 1.

Following checks and feedback are implemented within Net 1, whose outcome is sent to Net 3. The input node of Net 1 start is the drainage control of the product recirculation lines. This is followed by a layer of parallel verifications: verification the level in the tower is less than 8% (if not, perform draining of tower); verification of the level of glycol in the separator; verification of correct water level in the coolant and evidence of leakage. Additionally following steps of verification for functioning of alarm signals, opening of Dock Safety Unit (DSU) vapour sorting valve (of activated DSU) and closure of DSU valve of standby DSU. Nets 2 and 3 are similarly arranged (Figs. 3, 4) and integrate relevant verifications and feedback. Net 3 aggregates the outcomes from previously outlined steps and includes a number of critical and final checks, before allowing the starting of hose connected (HC) transfer operations (Fig. 5).

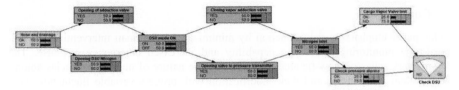

Figure 3: Start of the Dock Safety Unit – Net 2.

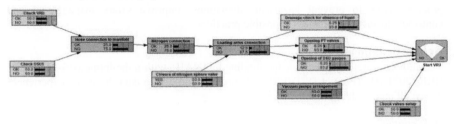

Figure 4: Consent for the safe operation – Net 3.

The checks linked into a single network are continuously updated during the transmission process, providing a dynamic alert on possible emerging operative risk.

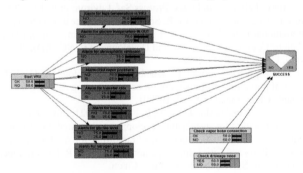

Figure 5: Starting the HC transfer under safe conditions.

Fig. 6 depicts the design of the whole safety operational control system, defined by the interconnection of the previously described operative nets. It should be underlined that OT systems are exposed to cyber threats imposing an in-depth defence strategy to be developed in accordance with the ANSI/ISA99 standard, by network segmentation into different layers with well-monitored connections and the most sensitive part at the centre.

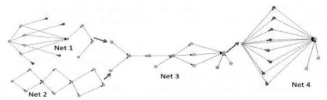

Figure 6: Schematic drawing of the predictive system addressing safety operational control.

The OT management system was tested in the pilot port terminal application, allowing to perform an operative reliability higher than 99.5 % over yearly field observations.

4. Conclusion

This paper emphasizes risk reduction by minimization of human intervention through real-time monitoring, predictive capability and increased emergency response. The framework relies on bow-tie analysis exploring the nature of interdependencies among the system components and their modification with process variable fluctuation, thus capturing the changes in operational conditions and improving the dynamic facet of risk. The approach, under current refinement with implementation of cyber vulnerability evaluation for each critical architecture element (Hw and SW), can be applied in different process plants to prevent hazardous deviations, improve safety management and contribute to sustainable and responsible practices.

Acknowledgment

The authors gratefully acknowledge funding by INAIL, within the framework of the call BRIC/2021/ID3 (Project DRIVERS - Approccio combinato data-driven ed experience-driven all'analisi del rischio sistemico).

References

[1] M. Hermann, T. Pentek, B. Otto, 2016, Design principles for industrie 4.0 scenarios, in: 2016 49th Hawaii international conference on system sciences (HICSS), IEEE. pp. 3928–3937.

[2] H. Pasman, E. Sripaul, F. Khan, B. Fabiano, 2023, Energy transition technology comes with new process safety challenges and risks, Process Saf. Environ. Prot. 177, 765-794.

[3] G. Assenza, L. Faramondi, G. Oliva, R. Setola, 2020, Cyber threats for operational technologies. International Journal of System of Systems Engineering, 10(2), 128-142.

[4] United Nations Conferences on Trade and Development (UNCTAD), 2022, Review of Maritime Transport, UNCTAD/RMT/2022.

[5] D'Amico, G., Szopik-Depczyńska, K., Dembińska, I., and Ioppolo, G., 2021, Smart and sustainable logistics of port cities: A framework for comprehending enabling factors, domains, and goals, Sustainable Cities and Society 69, 102801.

[6] A.S.Markowski, A. Krasławski, T. Vairo, B. Fabiano, 2021, Process safety management quality in industrial corporation for sustainable development, Sustainability 13, 9001.

[7] A. Carpenter, R. Lozano, 2020, Proposing a Framework for Anchoring Sustainability Relationships Between Ports and Cities. In: Carpenter, A., Lozano, R. (eds) European Port Cities in Transition. Strategies for Sustainability. Springer, Cham.

[8] T.Vairo, A. Bruzzone, S. Magrì, A.P.Reverberi, B. Fabiano, 2023, Understanding the vulnerability of complex systems. An integrated approach, Chemical Engineering Transactions 99, 277-282.

[9] L. Ding, F. Khan, J. Ji, 2020, Risk-based safety measure allocation to prevent and mitigate storage fire hazards. Process Saf. Environ. Prot., 135, 282-293.

[10] K.R. Brown, P. VanBerkel, F.I. Khan, P.R. Amyotte, 2021, Application of bow-tie analysis and inherently safer design to the novel coronavirus hazard, Process Saf. Environ. Prot., 152, 701-718.

[11] T. Vairo, M. Pettinato, A.P. Reverberi, M.F. Milazzo, B. Fabiano, 2023, An approach towards the implementation of a reliable resilience model based on machine learning, Process Saf. Environ. Prot., 172, 2023, Pages 632-641.

[12] T. Vairo, A.C. Benvenuto, A. Tedeschi, A.P. Reverberi, B. Fabiano, 2022, Make bow-tie dynamic by rethinking it as a hierarchical bayesian network. Dynamic risk assessment of an Lng bunkering operation, Chemical Engineering Transactions, 91, 277-282.

[13] IOGP International Association of Oil and Gas Producers, 2010, No. 434–5 Human factors in QRA. IOGP ed. London, UK.

Flavio Manenti, Gintaras V. Reklaitis (Eds.), Proceedings of the 34th European Symposium on Computer Aided Process Engineering / 15th International Symposium on Process Systems Engineering (ESCAPE34/PSE24), June 2-6, 2024, Florence, Italy

Data Augmentation Scheme for Raman Spectra with Highly Correlated Annotations

Christoph Lange[1], Isabel Thiele[2], Lara Santolin[2], Sebastian L. Riedel[2,3], Maxim Borisyak[1], Peter Neubauer[1,2], Mariano Nicolas Cruz-Bournazou[1]

1) KIWI biolab, Technische Universität Berlin, Ackerstr. 76, Berlin 13355, Germany
2) Technische Universität Berlin, Institute of Biotechnology, Chair of Bioprocess Engineering, Berlin, Germany
3) Berliner Hochschule für Technik, Department VIII – Mechanical Engineering, Event Technology and Process Engineering, Laboratory of Environmental and Bioprocess Engineering, Berlin, Germany
Correspondence: christoph.lange@tu-berlin.de

Abstract

In biotechnology Raman Spectroscopy is rapidly gaining popularity as a process analytical technology (PAT) that measures cell densities, substrate- and product concentrations. As it records vibrational modes of molecules it provides that information non-invasively in a single spectrum. Typically, partial least squares (PLS) is the model of choice to infer information about variables of interest from the spectra. However, biological processes are known for their complexity where convolutional neural networks (CNN) present a powerful alternative. They can handle non-Gaussian noise and account for beam misalignment, pixel malfunctions or the presence of additional substances. However, they require a lot of data during model training, and they pick up non-linear dependencies in the process variables. In this work, we exploit the additive nature of spectra in order to generate additional data points from a given dataset that have statistically independent labels so that a network trained on such data exhibits low correlations between the model predictions. We show that training a CNN on these generated data points improves the performance on datasets where the annotations do not bear the same correlation as the dataset that was used for model training. This data augmentation technique enables us to reuse spectra as training data for new contexts that exhibit different correlations. The additional data allows for building a better and more robust model. This is of interest in scenarios where large amounts of historical data are available but are currently not used for model training. We demonstrate the capabilities of the proposed method using synthetic spectra of *Ralstonia eutropha* batch cultivations to monitor substrate, biomass and polyhydroxyalkanoate (PHA) biopolymer concentrations during of the experiments.

Keywords: Raman Spectroscopy, Convolutional Neural Network, Data Augmentation

1. Introduction

Raman spectroscopy gained popularity in biotechnology as it enables measuring process parameter *online* in a non-invasive manner. It tracks vibrational modes of molecules that reveal information about the cultivation all in one spectrum. While partial least squares is the model of choice to predict concentrations from spectra, convolutional neural networks are used more often (Qi *et al.,* 2023). CNNs are able to handle non-Gaussian noise and account for beam misalignment, pixel malfunctions or the presence of additional substances. Still, due to their immense predictive power, CNNs require large amounts of training data. Hence, data augmentation is common training a CNN (Yun *et al.,* 2019). It prevents the model from overfitting on characteristics of single observations and promotes learning underlying patterns. This additional data improves the generalization of the neural network and has a regularizing effect on the model.

Data obtained from a cultivation process typically has strong dependencies. For example, for a batch cultivation, substrate is inversely related to biomass. Machine Learning models are able to learn these dependencies, which allows them to improve biomass predictions using spectral lines of substrate. While this improvement is desirable for making predictions for similar cultivations, quality quickly degrades when the model is applied to a different process. Continuing the example, a fed-batch cultivation would not have such strong dependencies between biomass and substrate, thus, applying a model trained on a batch cultivation to data from a fed-batch cultivation would, most likely, result in biased predictions.

In this paper, we propose a method for "erasing" these dependencies from training data, thus, making the resulting model suitable for a much wider range of processes. We evaluate our approach with multiple synthetic datasets, where the scheme of the synthesis was learned from real Raman spectra recorded during cultivations of *Ralstonia eutropha,* which produced the biodegradable polyhydroxyalkanoate (PHA) copolymer poly(hydroxybutyrate-*co*-hydroxyhexanoate) [P(HB-*co*-HHx)], with changing monomer compositions, depending e.g. on the substrates used (Santolin and Thiele *et al.,* 2023). As Alcântara *et al.* (2023) showed this is a challenging task that CNNs can provide additional benefit for.

2. Material and Methods

In this setup m-dimensional Raman spectra $X \in R^{n \times m}$ are recorded during fermentation experiments like Alcântara *et al.* (2023). To use Raman spectroscopy as a PAT tool we use spectra to predict the concentrations of process parameters $Y \in R^{n \times k}$ that will be called labels using a CNN.

2.1. Data Augmentation Scheme

Neural networks are almost exclusively trained on mini batches. The following algorithm is applied to each batch, hence n is the batch size. We want to remove the correlations from our annotations Y, so we just sample new uncorrelated annotations $U \in R^{n \times k}$ from uniform distributions,

$$u_{ij} \sim U\left(0, max\left(\{Y_{lj}, 1 \leqslant l \leqslant n\}\right)\right) \tag{1}$$

in the range of the correlated annotations Y. Now we are looking for coefficients $\Lambda \in R^{n \times n}$ that yield the sampled annotations.

$$\Lambda Y = U \tag{2}$$

We need these coefficients for combining the given spectra X to newly generated spectra ΛX that correspond to the uncorrelated annotations U. For solving Eq. (2) we use a singular value decomposition (SVD) of the original annotation matrix Y.

$$Y = U \Sigma V^T \tag{3}$$

Using a right inverse Σ^R of Σ we obtain the coefficients Λ via:

$$\Lambda = UV\Sigma^R U^T \tag{4}$$

The mixing procedure changes the measurement noise in a non-linear fashion. Assuming that measurement noise is homoscedastic and Gaussian with known variance σ_l^2, the variance of the noise for the i-th synthetic sample in the l-th component is:

$$VAR\left(\sum_{j=1}^{N}\lambda_{ij}x_{jl}\right) = \sum_{j=1}^{N}\lambda_{ij}^2\sigma_l^2 = \left(\sum_{j=1}^{N}\lambda_{ij}^2\right)\sigma_l^2 \tag{5}$$

Analogous expressions can be derived for different kinds of noise. To match the noise of the generated samples to the original ones, we add artificial noise with variance $1 - \sum_{j=1}^{N}\lambda_{ij}^2$. Unfortunately, that is not possible when $\sum_{j=1}^{N}\lambda_{ij}^2 > 1$. In this case, we simply reject the sample. In the following we refer to this process as filtering.

2.2. Data Synthesis

For generating synthetic Raman spectra from *R. eutropha* cultivations, we first use real spectra $X \in R^{n \times m}$ and *offline* measurements $Y \in R^{n \times k}$ from two cultivations and decompose them with non-negative matrix factorization (NMF).

$$X \approx YH \tag{6}$$

Using least squares yields the spectra components H that belong to the respective substance, and we generate new spectra via $c^T H$ with concentrations $c \in R^k$.

The concentrations are obtained from synthetic cultivations that are generated with the help of mechanistic models for *R. eutropha* producing PHA by Khanna and Srivastava (2006). We infer parameters θ of the model by least squares fit to the *offline* measurements from our *R. eutropha* cultivations (Figure 1). To diversify the set of cultivation parameters we perturb the estimated parameters θ using a gamma distribution. We set $\alpha = \beta = 5$ to ensure an expected value $E(w_i) = 1$ and preserve similar cultivation dynamics as in the original model.

$$\theta = w^T \theta, w_i \sim \Gamma(\alpha, \beta) \tag{7}$$

We use the same mechanism to perturb the initial conditions y_1.

2.3. Evaluation Setup

We use synthetic spectra of *R. eutropha* batch cultivations that produce the copolymer [P(HB-*co*-HHx)] with varying monomer composition depending on the available substrates. Canola oil is used for HB and HHx synthesis, whereas fructose only leads to the incorporation of HB monomers into the copolymer (Santolin and Thiele *et al.* (2023)). With such a procedure we model realistic changes in statistical dependencies between various substances and measure the performance under novel conditions.

2.3.1. Datasets

We use the mechanistic model described in 2.2 to generate cultivations over a period of 72 h. We use real data from two different cultivations to infer the parameters of the mechanistic model from the *offline* measurements of cell dry weight (CDW), residual cell dry weight (CDW without PHA), fructose, urea, HB and HHx monomer content .

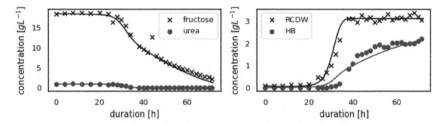

Figure 1: The fit of ODE model to the observations of one cultivation. Left: Substrates. Right products. RCDW = residual cell dry weight, HB = hydroxybutyrate content of the copolymer.

For the training and validation sets we use two different cultivations. Generally, the training set and the validation sets differ in two aspects. On one hand the underlying mechanistic models have different parameters and on the other hand for some validation datasets the fraction of the two carbon substrates differs from the training set ratios according to Table 1 which leads to different ratios of HB and HHx. For comparing our algorithm against uncorrelated data, we add the dataset no_corr, where all concentrations are randomly sampled from a uniform distribution without any structure from a mechanistic model.

Table 1: An overview of the datasets used for the model evaluation. For the training dataset, the percentage is either the first number or the second within one cultivation. The validation datasets are named according to their oil content and "no_corr" refers to no correlation present. HB, HHx = hydroxybutyrate, hydroxyhexanoate content of the PHA copolymer and all % refer to wt.%.

dataset	train	val_0	val_2	val_4	val_6	val_8	val_10	no_corr
canola oil [%]	0 / 100	0	20	40	60	80	100	any
fructose [%]	100 / 0	100	80	60	40	20	0	any
samples	50,000	10,000	10,000	10,000	10,000	10,000	10,000	50,000
HB [%]	100 / 80	100	96	92	88	84	80	any
HHx [%]	0 / 20	0	4	8	12	16	20	any

One cultivation and the mechanistic model are depicted in Figure 1. All generated cultivations contain all five labels every 3 h with the corresponding spectra. For the training set we use 2,000 cultivations and for the validation sets 400 cultivations respectively. As canola oil is difficult to measure with both Raman spectra and assays, we ignore them for parameter inference and the spectra components.

2.3.2. Model Architecture

For all evaluation procedures we use the exact same neural network structure. It is a ReZero architecture by Bachlechner *et al.* (2021) with minor adaptations for one spatial dimension and depthwise separable convolutions from Chollet (2017) to reduce the number of parameters. The network consists of 8 residual blocks followed by 3 fully connected layers with dropout of 0.2 to make sure the model is properly regularized.

3. Results

3.1. Characteristics of the Decorrelation Algorithm

Comparing the spectra from the training set obtained by the algorithm to the original spectra from the validation set in figure 2, we observe that some of the spectra look similar to the ones from the validation set.

Some spectra, however, look different, in particular, as if they were inverted. This occurs when some of the mixing coefficient are negative. While such spectra are unrealistic, they do not harm the overall performance, moreover, they might potentially have a regularizing effect on the model.

Due to the phenomenon of noise amplification according to Eq. (5) we filter samples. Looking at figure 3 we observe that a high ratio of random samples is filtered out for a batch size of 32.

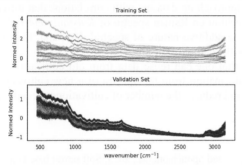

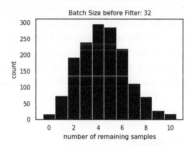

Figure 2: Normalized spectra generated from the decorrelation algorithm in the training set and unchanged spectra from the validation set.

Figure 3: When filtering out samples with coefficients which norm is greater than 1, we observe this distribution for batch size 32.

3.2. Impact on Model Performance

We use six different validation datasets that were generated as described in 2.3.1. We train four models in different training setting. For illustration purposes, we include the ideal scenario: one of the models is trained on a dataset with a priori uncorrelated labels (referred to as "no_corr"). We trained the others on correlated data for 100 epochs.

According to Table 2 the model trained on the uniform dataset is most successful at transferring its prediction capabilities to different experimental conditions. Among the models trained on the correlated experiments the decorrelation algorithm with filtering performs best. We also highlight the consistency of the proposed method across different validation sets. Not filtering the spectra with excessive noise causes the model to perform even worse than the model only trained on correlated data despite the decorrelation algorithm being in place.

4. Conclusions

We propose a data augmentation procedure that allows training robust Machine Learning models on Raman spectra. We show that the procedure "erases" unwanted dependencies in training data, and removes the corresponding biases from the models. The procedure ensures a similar performance of the models across a wide range of cultivation conditions, which dramatically simplified further analysis.

Table 2: The results of the evaluation procedure. The first three columns describe the training setup of the model. The next six columns depict the mean squared error on the normalized labels of the validation sets described in Table 1. The last column shows the mean of all validation sets.

Training Set	decorrelate	filter	val_0	val_2	val_4	val_6	val_8	val_10	mean
no_corr	no	no	0.27	0.18	0.11	0.1	0.05	0.09	0.13
train	no	no	0.42	0.50	0.41	0.47	0.42	0.48	0.45
train	yes	no	0.54	0.58	0.52	0.55	0.53	0.58	0.55
train	yes	yes	0.23	0.25	0.20	0.23	0.20	0.23	0.22

We demonstrated performance of our approach on datasets with correlations that differ from the training set. We used the algorithm on Raman spectra of *Ralstonia eutropha*, however, the algorithm exploits only the additive nature of spectral data, and, thus, is agnostic to the spectroscopy methods or the nature of the substances.

In practice with the help of our algorithm one can reuse data from old cultivation as training data for a model that infers information from the spectra of a new cultivation setup. This makes models more robust and reduces the number of cultivations needed for new experimental settings.

References

Alcântara, J.M.G., Iannacci, F., Morbidelli, M. and Sponchioni, M., 2023. Soft sensor based on Raman spectroscopy for the in-line monitoring of metabolites and polymer quality in the biomanufacturing of polyhydroxyalkanoates. *Journal of Biotechnology*, *377*, pp.23-33.

Bachlechner, T., Majumder, B.P., Mao, H., Cottrell, G. and McAuley, J., 2021, December. Rezero is all you need: Fast convergence at large depth. In *Uncertainty in Artificial Intelligence* (pp. 1352-1361). PMLR.

Chollet, F., 2017. Xception: Deep learning with depthwise separable convolutions. In *Proceedings of the IEEE conference on computer vision and pattern recognition* (pp. 1251-1258).

He, K., Zhang, X., Ren, S. and Sun, J., 2016. Deep residual learning for image recognition. In *Proceedings of the IEEE conference on computer vision and pattern recognition* (pp. 770-778).

Khanna, S. and Srivastava, A.K., 2006. Computer simulated fed-batch cultivation for over production of PHB: a comparison of simultaneous and alternate feeding of carbon and nitrogen. *Biochemical engineering journal*, *27*(3), pp.197-203.

Qi, Y., Hu, D., Jiang, Y., Wu, Z., Zheng, M., Chen, E.X., Liang, Y., Sadi, M.A., Zhang, K. and Chen, Y.P., 2023. Recent Progresses in Machine Learning Assisted Raman Spectroscopy. *Advanced Optical Materials*, p.2203104.

Santolin, L., Thiele, I., Neubauer, P. and Riedel, S.L., 2023. Tailoring the HHx monomer content of P (HB-co-HHx) by flexible substrate compositions: scale-up from deep-well-plates to laboratory bioreactor cultivations. *Frontiers in Bioengineering and Biotechnology*, *11*, p.1081072.

Yun, S., Han, D., Oh, S.J., Chun, S., Choe, J. and Yoo, Y., 2019. Cutmix: Regularization strategy to train strong classifiers with localizable features. In *Proceedings of the IEEE/CVF international conference on computer vision* (pp. 6023-6032).

Flavio Manenti, Gintaras V. Reklaitis (Eds.), Proceedings of the 34th European Symposium on Computer Aided Process Engineering / 15th International Symposium on Process Systems Engineering (ESCAPE34/PSE24), June 2-6, 2024, Florence, Italy

DL based real-time prediction of product formation in biopharmaceutical manufacturing

Md Nasre Alam,[a] Sami Ullah Bhat,[a] Hariprasad Kodamana,[a,b,*] Anurag S. Rathore[a,b,*]

[a]Department of Chemical Engineering, Indian Institute of Technology Delhi, New Delhi, 110016, India
[b]Yardi School of Artificial Intelligence, Indian Institute of Technology Delhi, New Delhi, 110016, India
asrathore@biotechcmz.com, kodamana@iitd.ac.in

Abstract

The extraordinary growth in the use of sensors, as well as in our computational abilities, has resulted in a massive amount of data generated in biopharmaceutical manufacturing plants. This, in turn has fuelled researchers to explore the applications of Machine Learning (ML) and Deep Learning (DL) as superior alternatives to the traditional Multivariate Data Analysis (MVDA) methods. For manufacturers of biotherapeutic products, achieving a consistent product titer is paramount. This study explores the application of DL techniques for real-time prediction of growth and product formation in aerobic microbial fermentation in a bioreactor. Process parameters, including dissolved oxygen, airflow rate, revolution per minute, pH, and temperature, were considered input features, and their impact on product formation has been explored, with optical density and protein titer being output variables. Three different DL regression algorithms: U-shaped Network (UNET), Convolutional Neural Network (CNN), and Multilayer Perceptron (MLP), have been incorporated in this study to measure the prediction performance. Their performance is measured in terms of R^2, MSE, RMSE, MAE, and MAPE. UNET consistently performed better than CNN and MLP methods. R^2 was 0.9094 and 0.8872 for optical density and protein titer prediction, respectively, in the UNET model, followed by 0.8948 and 0.8766 in the CNN model, and 0.8590 and 0.8548 in the MLP model. The study demonstrates how DL techniques can assist in the manufacturing of safe and efficacious biotherapeutic products.

Keywords: Deep learning, Multivariate data analysis, Microbial fermentation, Regression

1. Introduction

A typical bioprocess consists of multiple unit operations, each intended to perform a specific function. The bioreactor aims to offer a controlled environment to the cells with respect to physical and chemical attributes so that the cells can multiply at the desired rate. However, controlling a fermentation process is non-trivial due to the fact that most biological processes are non-linear in nature (Rathore et al., 2021). Hence, process parameters such as temperature, pH, oxygen transfer, mixing, and substrate concentration need to be controlled to their desired setpoints to ensure optimal performance (Wang & Zhong, 2007).

Over the past decade, modeling of fermentation processes has seen advancements through the application of data-driven models (DDMs), leveraging Artificial Intelligence (AI), particularly machine learning (ML), and deep learning (DL) techniques. For instance, the relationship between inputs and outputs in mammalian cell cultures secreting monoclonal antibodies (mAbs) has been scrutinized using diverse ML methods (Schinn et al., 2021). Several machine learning algorithms based soft sensors have been successfully implemented for correlating input parameters during fermentation with the target variables (Escalante-Sánchez et al., 2018; Wang et al., 2023). These have been applied depending on the online data of different bioprocess parameters. This study tries to further explore the utility and advantage of online data obtained from microbial fermentation process using deep learning frameworks. It is essential to recognize that no single DDM can serve as a universal strategy in output prediction for such datasets. This limitation arises because model performance is intricately tied to factors such as model structure, specific elements of the process, datasets available, and data volume, among other considerations (Von Stosch et al., 2021).

In this study, we introduce a structured framework designed to assess different DL model which utilizes and leverages more deeper understanding of algorithms in capturing intricate pattern of dynamic process data. The proposed framework has been demonstrated to be suitable for real-time monitoring of a microbial fermentation process.

2. Materials and methods

2.1. Bioreactor cultivation

Recombinant Escherichia coli expressing the protein therapeutics of interest were cultured in Sartorius Biostat Bplus bioreactors (Sartorius, Germany) with a total capacity of 5 liters, employing both batch and fed-batch processes. The initial volume of the medium was set at 1.5 liters. The batch medium was a defined media containing carbon sources, nitrogen sources, and trace metals. Glucose ($C_6H_{12}O_6$), glycerol ($C_3H_8O_3$), magnesium sulphate ($MgSO_4$), thiamine HCl, trace elements, and antibiotics were added separately, with all components dissolved in Milli-Q water obtained from the Milli-Q® water purification system. The pH was regulated before the transfer to the bioreactor for sterilization. Batch medium inoculation was performed with an overnight-grown primary culture of quantity 200 ml. To provide optimal growth conditions, a thermal mass flowmeter was used to control the airflow rate. pH probe (Hamilton®, USA) was used to monitor pH levels. 2 N HCl and 12.5% liquid ammonia were used to maintain pH. D.O. probe (Hamilton®, USA) was used to monitor dissolved oxygen levels. Further, D.O. levels were controlled by adjusting the stirrer speed, air flow rate, and pure oxygen in a cascading manner.

During the cultivation in batch phase, glucose and glycerol concentrations of 10 g/L and 2 g/L, respectively, were kept initially for each bioreactor operation. Upon depletion of glucose, cells transitioned to glycerol as the carbon source after a brief period of adaptation. Exhaustion of the carbon source leads to the dissolved oxygen (D.O.) spike, which signifies the end of batch phase. Glycerol and $MgSO_4.7H_2O$ concentrations of 400 g/L and 20 g/L, respectively, were added through a peristaltic pump during the fed-batch phase for feeding. Lactose served as an inducer to achieve a working concentration of 5 g/L lactose inside the bioreactor in three pulses.

2.2. Methodology

Three different models: U-shaped Network (UNET), Convolutional Neural Network (CNN), and Multilayer Perceptron (MLP), were implemented in Python 3.11.4 to model the microbial cell culture data. Data consists of 28 batches each for 5 inputs: (i) dissolved oxygen, DO (%), (ii) air flow rate, F (lph), (iii) revolution per minute, RPM, (iv) temperature, T (°C), (v) pH; and 2 outputs: (i) optical density, OD, (ii) protein titer, PT (g/l). 20 batches were used for training and 8 batches for testing. Training and testing split ratio were 70:30. The statistical study of data is shown in Table 1.

Different model architectures and their workings have been explained below, and implementation details are mentioned in Table 2.

Table 1. Statistical analysis of cell culture data

Parameters		#Samples per batch	Minimum value	Maximum value
Inputs	DO (%)	900	0	112.59
	F (lph)	900	18.48	143.97
	RPM	900	401	905.4
	T (°C)	900	33.41	39.02
	pH	900	6.87	7.71
Outputs	OD	1	26.6	118
	PT (g/l)	1	0.09	7.8

2.2.1. U-shaped Network (UNET)

UNET, characterized by its encoder-decoder structure, is a convolutional neural network (CNN) designed to optimize data efficiency without compromising accuracy and speed. Its architecture features a distinctive contracting and expansive path. The contracted pathway of UNET is designed to identify relevant features within the input image. Spatial sharpness of feature maps is reduced by encoder layer through the convolutional processes. In contrast, the expanding path decodes the encoded data while preserving the spatial sharpness of the image. The decoder layers in the expanding path employ upsampling and convolutional operations, with skip connections aiding in retaining spatial information lost during the contraction, enabling more precise feature localization (Ronneberger et al., 2015). Flattening layer is followed by dense layers are employed after the decoder layers to get the final output.

2.2.2. Convolutional Neural Network (CNN)

CNNs are one of the most widely utilized types of deep neural networks (DNNs), employing layers that facilitate comprehension and interpretation of image or visual data. Serving as a regularized feed-forward neural network, CNN autonomously learns features through the optimization of filters or kernels. A standard CNN comprises three types of layers: input layer, hidden layer, and output layer. The input layer is responsible for supplying model input. The hidden layer gets input from the input layer. Multiple hidden layers may be present depending on the applied model and quantity of data. The number of features increases as the number of neurons increase in each hidden layer. Matrix multiplication over the preceding layer's output including learnable weights, biases and an activation function of layer contribute to the output of the next layer (Alzubaidi et al., 2021). The output of hidden layers is flattened to feed the dense layer. Finally, the dense layer is sent to the output layer.

2.2.3. Multilayer Perceptron (MLP)

MLP denotes a type of neural network that is extensively employed in ML for classification and regression tasks. Its nomenclature stems from the incorporation of multiple layers of nodes, also known as artificial neurons, interconnected with each other.

The framework of an MLP consists of three principal elements: input layer, hidden layers, and output layer. The input layer receives input data and transmits it to the hidden layers, comprising nodes representing features in the incoming data. The number of input data features align with the count of nodes in the input layer. Transformation of input data into an appropriate form for the output layer is performed by hidden layers. Performance for specific tasks can be optimized by adjusting the count of hidden layers and number of nodes in each layer. Hidden layer provides the transformed representation to output layer for getting the output (Popescu et al., 2009).

Table 2. Different models and details of the parameters used

Models	Training parameters	Values
UNET	Input shape	[900×5×1]
	Contracting path	#Convolutional layers = 4
		#Pooling layers = 4
	Bottleneck	#Convolutional layers = 1
	Expansive path	#Upsampling layers = 4
		#Concatenation = 4
		#Convolutional layers = 4
	#Learning rate	0.001
	Optimizer	Adam
	Loss function	MSE
CNN	Input shape	[900×5×1]
	#Convolutional layers	4
	#Pooling layers	4
	Learning rate	0.001
	Optimizer	Adam
	Loss function	MSE
MLP	#Input layer	1
	#Hidden layer	5
	#Output layer	1
	Optimizer	Adam
	Loss function	MSE

3. Results and discussions

The process parameters were recorded by the Supervisory Control and Data Acquisition (SCADA) system of the bioreactor and stored in an Excel file. The offline data included the target variables: OD and PT for multiple batches of input parameters. Based on the preprocessing of SCADA and offline data, regression results were obtained, and five evaluation metrics: R^2, MSE, RMSE, MAE, and MAPE computed for each prediction of outputs (Table 3). The UNET model performed better than CNN and MLP for OD and PT predictions.

Table 3. Different models performance comparison for output variable

Output variables	Models	R^2	MSE	RMSE	MAE	MAPE
OD	UNET	0.9094	38.8750	6.2350	6.1250	12.0721
	CNN	0.8948	45.1250	6.7175	6.6250	13.2219
	MLP	0.8590	60.5000	7.7782	7.7500	15.4234
PT (g/l)	UNET	0.8872	0.1906	0.4365	0.4075	63.3211
	CNN	0.8766	0.2084	0.4565	0.4250	64.9737
	MLP	0.8548	0.2452	0.4952	0.4113	48.8736

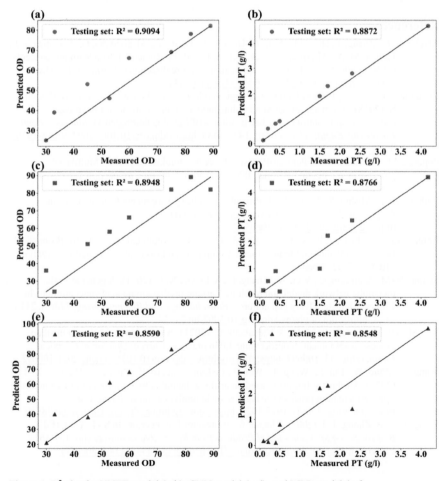

Figure 1. R^2 plot for UNET model (a-b), CNN model (c-d), and MLP model (e-f)

The robustness of the implemented model has been demonstrated by the R^2 plot for each output variable (Figure 1). R^2 plot is shown for 8 batches of OD and PT under testing case for their measured vs predicted values. Higher R^2 is consistently obtained for the UNET model for OD and PT predictions followed by the CNN and the MLP models.

4. Conclusions

Bioprocessing encompasses vast amounts of data that are collected but seldom analyzed. Process data from all these operations can provide valuable information regarding the process and the product itself. This study explores the application of DL techniques for real-time prediction of product formation in microbial fermentation. Three different models have been applied and compared based on performance. Multiple evaluation metrics were computed to assess model performance, and it was concluded that UNET performed better than CNN and MLP algorithms. In the future study, other ML based algorithms such as gradient boosting model, random forest, etc. can be applied to measure the adaptability and performance. Use of DL models to analyze bioreactor data and predict product formation will facilitate real-time decisions by the operator.

References

Alzubaidi, L., Zhang, J., Humaidi, A. J., Al-Dujaili, A., Duan, Y., Al-Shamma, O., Santamaría, J., Fadhel, M. A., Al-Amidie, M., & Farhan, L. (2021). Review of deep learning: concepts, CNN architectures, challenges, applications, future directions. *Journal of Big Data*, *8*(1), 53. https://doi.org/10.1186/s40537-021-00444-8

Escalante-Sánchez, A., Barrera-Cortés, J., Poggi-Varaldo, H. M., Ponce-Noyola, T., & Baruch, I. S. (2018). A soft sensor based on online biomass measurements for the glucose estimation and control of fed-batch cultures of Bacillus thuringiensis. *Bioprocess and Biosystems Engineering*, *41*(10), 1471-1484. https://doi.org/10.1007/s00449-018-1975-3

Popescu, M.-C., Balas, V. E., Perescu-Popescu, L., & Mastorakis, N. (2009). Multilayer perceptron and neural networks. *WSEAS Transactions on Circuits and Systems*, *8*(7), 579-588.

Rathore, A. S., Mishra, S., Nikita, S., & Priyanka, P. (2021). Bioprocess Control: Current Progress and Future Perspectives. *Life (Basel)*, *11*(6). https://doi.org/10.3390/life11060557

Ronneberger, O., Fischer, P., & Brox, T. (2015). U-Net: Convolutional Networks for Biomedical Image Segmentation. Medical Image Computing and Computer-Assisted Intervention – MICCAI 2015, Cham.

Schinn, S.-M., Morrison, C., Wei, W., Zhang, L., & Lewis, N. E. (2021). A genome-scale metabolic network model and machine learning predict amino acid concentrations in Chinese Hamster Ovary cell cultures. *Biotechnology and Bioengineering*, *118*(5), 2118-2123. https://doi.org/https://doi.org/10.1002/bit.27714

Von Stosch, M., Portela, R. M. C., & Varsakelis, C. (2021). A roadmap to AI-driven in silico process development: bioprocessing 4.0 in practice. *Current Opinion in Chemical Engineering*, *33*, 100692. https://doi.org/https://doi.org/10.1016/j.coche.2021.100692

Wang, K., Zhao, W., Lin, L., Wang, T., Wei, P., Ledesma-Amaro, R., Zhang, A.-H., & Ji, X.-J. (2023). A robust soft sensor based on artificial neural network for monitoring microbial lipid fermentation processes using Yarrowia lipolytica. *Biotechnology and Bioengineering*, *120*(4), 1015-1025. https://doi.org/https://doi.org/10.1002/bit.28310

Wang, S.-J., & Zhong, J.-J. (2007). Chapter 6 - Bioreactor Engineering. In S.-T. Yang (Ed.), *Bioprocessing for Value-Added Products from Renewable Resources* (pp. 131-161). Elsevier. https://doi.org/https://doi.org/10.1016/B978-044452114-9/50007-4

Flavio Manenti, Gintaras V. Reklaitis (Eds.), Proceedings of the 34th European Symposium on Computer Aided Process Engineering / 15th International Symposium on Process Systems Engineering (ESCAPE34/PSE24), June 2-6, 2024, Florence, Italy

Adaptive Physics-Informed Neural Network for Prediction with Evolving Process Parameters

Devavrat Thosar,[a,*] Abhijit Bhakte,[b] Zukui Li,[a] Arvind Rajendran,[a] Rajagopalan Srinivasan,[b] Vinay Prasad[a]

[a]Department of Chemical and Materials Engineering, Donadeo Innovation Centre for Engineering (ICE), University of Alberta, Edmonton, Alberta T6G 1H9, Canada
[b]Department of Chemical Engineering, Indian Institute of Technology Madras, Chennai 600036, India
*thosar@ualberta.ca

Abstract

Deep learning models are widely favored for their ability to model complex processes. These models are data-driven and lack physics-based knowledge. To address this limitation, Physics-Informed Neural Networks (PINNs) have emerged as a promising solution to integrate first principles knowledge, particularly in complex processes like Pressure Swing Adsorption (PSA). Presently, PINNs are predominantly employed for processes with constant process parameters. However, real-world processes may face variation in parameters due to exogenous factors, such as adsorbent degradation. Such changes can compromise performance of the model. This motivates a need to update the PINN model dynamically. In this work, an adaptive PINN framework is developed, that monitors changes in process parameters, using residual loss function of the PINN. Once a significant process change is detected, the PINN model is re-trained. The efficacy and capability of the proposed method is demonstrated on a PSA process.

Keywords: Physics-Informed Neural Network, Process Monitoring, Pressure Swing Adsorption, Deep Learning, Hybrid Modelling

1. Introduction

With increasing digitalization driven by Industry 4.0, big data has become abundantly available in chemical industry. This has led to the widespread adoption of data-driven models, with specific attention being paid to artificial neural networks, known for their ability of 'universal approximation' to model complex process data. However, these are black-box models that lack an inherent understanding of the underlying physics. To address this limitation and incorporate essential physics-based knowledge into such models, Physics-Informed Neural Networks (PINNs) (Raissi et al., 2019) have emerged as a compelling solution to model complex chemical processes such as Pressure Swing Adsorption (PSA) (Subraveti et al., 2022).

To incorporate physics knowledge, PINNs leverage residual errors obtained from the governing equations through automatic differentiation and add them to the loss function as a soft constraint during model training. Despite their significant advantages in terms of greater generalizability and ability to work with limited data, PINNs require prior knowledge of the process's governing equations, including structural details and parameters, such as activation energy, heat transfer coefficients etc. Presently, PINNs are primarily utilized for processes with constant process parameters. In our previous work, we successfully demonstrated the application of PINNs in modeling each individual step of a PSA process, assuming a constant set of process parameters, such as adsorption isotherms, kinetic parameters etc., (Subraveti et al., 2022). However, PSA processes may experience variations in one or more of these parameters due to evolving environmental conditions. These changes may result from physical transformations in equipment or materials, such as the degradation of adsorbents or reduction in bed voidage due to attrition. Such changes can lead to a decline in the performance of the predictive model, necessitating the need for model updating and parameter identification.

The term Adaptive PINN is used in the field of computational physics, where the adaptation refers to the selection of domain to sample collocation points for training a PINN (McLenny and Braga-Neto, 2022, Subramanian et al., 2022), and has not been used in the field of Chemical Engineering. To address the need for model updates due to changes in process parameters, several approaches have been published in the process control literature. For instance, Darsha Kumar et al. (2018) developed a framework for re-identification of process model in reactor systems to accommodate changes in reaction parameters. Similarly, Oshima et al. (2022) proposed a method for re-identification of process model in an MPC framework. However, most methods use simple system identification models which may not be applicable to complex nonlinear and cyclic processes. Additionally, parameter identification utilizes process data to deduce the values that yield the optimal fit to the observed data. Various methodologies, as documented in the literature use PINNs to estimate the updated process parameters. Raissi et al. (2019) demonstrated the inverse problem of parameter identification using PINN to estimate parameters of PDE equations from observed data. To the best of our knowledge, a framework combining process monitoring, model updating and parameter estimation using residuals in PINN has not been addressed previously in chemical engineering.

This study proposes an adaptive PINN approach to dynamically monitor and integrate real-time changes in a set of process parameters during the changing environmental conditions. Section 2 provides a detailed description of the proposed methodology. Section 3 outlines the PSA process, reports original PINN performance results, subsequent monitoring, and adaptation. The concluding Section 4 offers a brief discussion on takeaways and future research directions.

2. Adaptive PINN

Consider a process represented by a set of partial differential equations $F = \{f_1, f_2, \ldots, f_m\}$ as given in Eq. (1) describing dynamics of m output variables,

$$\dot{y}_i = f_i(x, y, \theta) \qquad \forall\, i = 1, 2, \ldots, m \tag{1}$$

where $x \in \mathbb{R}^d$, $y \in \mathbb{R}^m$ and θ represent the sets of the input vector, output vector and process parameters, respectively. The system thus consists of d input variables and m process outputs. A PINN model, g, is employed to predict the output variables, such that, $\hat{y} = g(x, \theta_{NN})$, where θ_{NN} are the neural network parameters (weights and biases). PINN integrates physics-based knowledge by penalizing model outputs inconsistent with underlying physics of the process. This is accomplished by introducing a physics term to the training loss function ($\mathcal{L}$) as given in Eq. (2),

$$\mathcal{L} = \mathcal{L}_{LD} + \lambda \mathcal{L}_{PDE} \tag{2}$$

where $\mathcal{L}_{LD}$ is the mean-squared error between the PINN model prediction and the labelled data, $\mathcal{L}_{PDE}$ is the loss associated with the residuals of differential equations. The parameter λ is the weighting hyper-parameter, imparting significance to the residual loss values. The terms in the overall loss function can be as given in Eqs. (3) and (4),

$$\mathcal{L}_{LD} = \frac{1}{n}\sum_{j=1}^{n}\left(y_j - \hat{y}_j\right)^2, \tag{3}$$

$$\mathcal{L}_{PDE} = \sum_{i=1}^{m}\frac{1}{n_{res}}\sum_{j=1}^{n_{res}}(\dot{\hat{y}}_{ij} - f_i(x_j, \hat{y}_j, \theta))^2 \tag{4}$$

where, n indicates the number of labelled data points, n_{res} indicates the number of internal collocation points sampled to incorporate physics-based constraints in PINN, $\dot{\hat{y}}_{ij}$ is the gradient of predicted output y_i for sample j obtained using automatic differentiation. The PINN is trained by minimizing the loss function in Eq. (2) using an appropriate optimizer to obtain the optimal values of θ_{NN}. Once trained, the PINN model g is deployed online to predict $\hat{y}$. As discussed previously, one or more parameters in θ may change over time, due to changing process conditions, leading to variations in the true values of θ. As the PINN model deployed online is trained on the original set of parameters, it fails to capture the evolving parameters, resulting in a degradation of model performance. To address this challenge, we propose a two-step methodology:

Step 1: Monitoring using residual loss

As the process undergoes a change in parameters, performance of the PINN model is expected to gradually deviate from its original state. To monitor this shift in PINN predictions, residual losses are computed by utilizing measurements from the process, along with the corresponding gradients ($\dot{\hat{y}}$) calculated through automatic differentiation. Considering $y_c \subseteq y$ as the set of measured output variables and y'_c as the set of unmeasured variables, the residual loss $\hat{\mathcal{L}}_k$, intended for monitoring purposes for the kth sampling instance, can be calculated using Eq. (5).

$$\hat{\mathcal{L}}_k = \sum_{i=1}^{m}\left(\dot{\hat{y}}_{ik} - f_i\left(x_k, \begin{bmatrix} y_c \\ \hat{y}'_c \end{bmatrix}_k, \theta\right)\right)^2 \tag{5}$$

To monitor this deviation, a threshold value δ is introduced. δ can be considered as a tuning parameter, signifying a tolerance on the degrading performance of the PINN model. This strategic use of the residual loss enables the direct identification of deviations that may not be entirely captured by the current PINN model. In the course of real-time operation, if the computed residual loss surpasses this predefined threshold ($\hat{\mathcal{L}}_k > \delta$), a significant process change is detected. This, in turn, triggers the updating of the model.

Step 2: Re-training PINN model and parameter estimation

Since performance of PINN model g, trained using the set of original process parameters θ, starts degrading, there is a need to systematically re-train the PINN model to effectively adapt to the evolving process conditions. This adaptation is achieved by first collecting historical data X^h and then re-training the model using X^h as labelled data. Data is collected over a window of samples from either the start of the process or the time instance of the previous threshold breach, until the current time instant. The re-training is achieved by initializing the weights of the neural network with the existing PINN model and minimizing the loss function given in Eq. (2), as discussed previously. To facilitate parameter estimation concurrently with model training, the process parameters θ are treated as trainable entities in Eq. (4). The resulting updated PINN model, g_{new}, incorporates the knowledge of the evolving process conditions and the set of estimated process parameters obtained during re-training is denoted as θ_{new}. The new model is deployed if $\hat{\mathcal{L}}_k(g_{new}, \theta_{new}) \le \hat{\mathcal{L}}_k(g, \theta)$. The proposed methodology is demonstrated through a case study on a PSA process.

3. Case Study: Pressure Swing Adsorption

Pressure Swing Adsorption (PSA) is a nonlinear cyclic process for gas mixture separation utilizing a selective adsorbent material. Its potential for enhanced energy efficiency compared to traditional methods makes PSA an attractive choice for researchers to pursue. The PSA process involves a bed filled with adsorbent material undergoing cyclic stages of adsorption and desorption. In this work, an axially dispersed, isothermal PSA for separation of a gas mixture of CO_2+N_2 with IISER MOF 2 as an adsorbent is considered. The steps in a single bed- four step PSA cycle for post-combustion carbon capture consists of Pressurization, Adsorption, Blowdown and Evacuation in that order. The governing PDEs for axially dispersed, isothermal PSA, the corresponding boundary conditions for each step and values of the process parameters are as given in (Subraveti et al., 2022). The output variables are gas phase composition of CO_2 (y_1), pressure ($\bar{P}$), solid loading for CO_2 ($\bar{q}_1$) and solid loading for N_2 ($\bar{q}_2$). Non-dimensionalized variables are indicated by a bar above their symbol.

Table 1: Operating conditions to get training data

v_{feed}	0.7	0.27	0.1	0.75	0.5
t_{ads}	35	25	35	25	45

To generate simulation data, the spatial coordinates are discretized using a Total Variation Diminishing scheme with a Van-Leer Flux Limiter, dividing the bed into fifty grid points. Resulting ODEs are solved using 'ode23s' in MATLAB. The parameter ε, representing bed voidage, is assumed to be changing over time, to emulate the degradation of bed particles caused by attrition. The initial value of parameter $\varepsilon = 0.37$. Comparing with Eqs. (1) and (5), $\theta = \varepsilon$, $y = [y_1 \quad \bar{P} \quad \bar{q}_1 \quad \bar{q}_2]^T$ and $y_c = y$, assuming that all variables are measured at inlet ($z = 0$) and outlet ($z = L$) of the bed. The initial condition for a step of PSA is the state of the bed at the previous step. These conditions, therefore, act as inputs to the system. Therefore, $x = [y_{1,1}^0 \quad \cdots \quad y_{1,50}^0]^T$. Ideally, initial conditions of other three output variables should also be added as inputs. These are excluded in this work to reduce the complexity of the neural network and are included as labelled data instead. The residual equations for PSA process can be given as:

$$f_1 = \frac{\partial(y_1\bar{P})}{\partial \bar{t}} + c1\left(\bar{v}\bar{P}\frac{\partial y_1}{\partial \bar{z}} + y_1\bar{P}\frac{\partial \bar{v}}{\partial \bar{z}} + y_1\bar{v}\frac{\partial \bar{P}}{\partial \bar{z}}\right) - c2\frac{\partial^2(y_1\bar{P})}{\partial \bar{z}^2} + c3\frac{\partial \bar{q}_1}{\partial \bar{t}},$$

$$f_2 = \frac{\partial \bar{P}}{\partial \bar{t}} + c1\left(\frac{\partial(\bar{P}\bar{v})}{\partial \bar{z}}\right) - c3(\frac{\partial \bar{q}_1}{\partial \bar{t}} + \frac{\partial \bar{q}_2}{\partial \bar{t}}),$$ where $c1 = \frac{v_0 t_0}{L}$, $c2 = \frac{D_L t_0}{L^2}$, $c3 = \frac{RT_0 q_{s0}}{P_0}\frac{1-\varepsilon}{\varepsilon}$, are the

constants as given in (Subraveti et al., 2022). It is also shown in (Subraveti et al., 2022) that the PINN for a PSA can be trained without using the adsorption isotherm information. Therefore, the equations for $\bar{q}_1$ and $\bar{q}_2$ are not used as residual equations for PINN training and subsequent process monitoring assuming that isotherm information is not known.

3.1. Training PINN for PSA

In this study, particular emphasis is placed on the adsorption step, which serves as the focal point for demonstrating the proposed methodology. The detailed model simulation was carried out for five sets of operating conditions given in Table (1), with an empty bed simulated until cyclic steady state for each operating condition, with corresponding initial

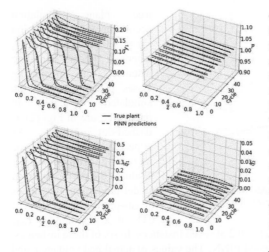

Figure 1: PINN prediction performance

condition profiles collected for subsequent analysis. v_{feed} is the feed velocity, in m/s, at bed inlet and t_{ads} is the adsorption time in seconds. Next, the adsorption step is simulated independently for each initial condition, for 50 cycles each, with $t_{ads} = 25\ s$ and $v_{feed} = 0.5\ m/s$, which are the operating conditions of interest. To emulate an actual experimental setup, the non-dimensionalized data for output variables at the feed and outlet boundaries and at initial conditions inside the bed are used for training the PINN. For every cycle, 250 random spatiotemporal collocation points are sampled within the bed using Latin Hypercube sampling to incorporate physics-based residual constraints in the PINN. The PINN architecture consists of 1 input layer with 52 neurons ($\bar{z}$, $\bar{t}$ and initial gas phase composition values at fifty grid points), 8 hidden layers with 100 neurons and one output layer with 4 neurons. Activation function for all hidden layers, except the last hidden layer, are set to "Tanh". The model is trained using L-BFGS optimizer. A test data set is created by simulating the process again from an empty bed until cyclic steady state at $t_{ads} = 25\ s$ and $v_{feed} = 0.5\ m/s$. The testing results for each cycle at $t = t_{ads}$, for first 50 cycles are given in Fig. (1). It can be seen from the figure that the spatiotemporal profiles are predicted to a good extent using the trained PINN, even at the points within the bed where labelled data is not used. The trained model is deployed to monitor the PSA process.

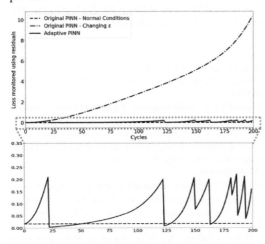

Figure 2: Loss monitoring using residuals

3.2. Process monitoring using PINN and model re-training

The process is simulated using the procedure discussed previously. It is assumed that the process has reached cyclic steady state and is operating under normal operating conditions with bed voidage $\varepsilon = 0.37$. Cycle time for PSA is considered as sampling time for monitoring. The residual loss for monitoring is calculated according to Eq. (5) at every sampling instance by using values of y_1 and $\bar{P}$ at outlet of the bed as measurements. The loss at normal operating conditions are denoted by dashed line in Fig. (2). To emulate changes in values of process parameters, a ramp change is introduced in bed voidage in

D. Thosar et al.

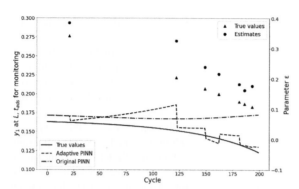

Figure 3: Parameter estimation during model re-training and comparison of adaptive PINN predictions

true plant simulation according to the equation $\varepsilon = -0.001357k + 0.37$, where k is the sampling instance. The monitoring losses calculated with the simulated change in parameter, are in Fig. (2) as dashed-dot line. As expected, the value keeps increasing with time. To evaluate the performance of model prediction, the values of gas-phase composition of CO_2 at $z = L$ and $t = t_{ads}$ are plotted in Fig. (3). Loss value reaches 0.2 at seven instances. In six of these instances, prediction improves compared to original PINN. The values of actual bed voidage ε and parameter estimates obtained during re-training are also given in Fig. (3). Parameter estimation captures the trend of the changing parameter and generates values with a bias. These results demonstrate the ability of the proposed methodology in identifying parameters that cause a change in model predictions.

4. Conclusions

This study introduces an adaptive PINN framework for dynamic processes, demonstrated through a case study on PSA. The proposed method successfully detects and adapts to the changes in process parameters ensuring the model's resilience in real-world scenarios. By integrating physics-based knowledge with machine learning, the adaptive PINN methodology offers a promising solution for industries seeking robust models capable of monitoring and adapting to the evolving environmental conditions. In the future, our proposed methodology will be applied across all the four steps of the PSA process. We will also focus on multiple process parameters evolving simultaneously.

References

Darsha Kumar, D.M., Narasimhan, S., Bhatt, N., 2018. Detection of model-plant mismatch and model update for reaction systems using concept of extents. Journal of Process Control. 72, 17-29 https://doi.org/10.1016/j.jprocont.2018.08.005

McLenny, L., Braga-Neto, U., 2022. HyperPINN: Self-Adaptive Physics-Informed Neural Networks using a Soft Attention Mechanism. arXiv:2009.04544

Oshima, M., Kim, S., Shardt, Y.A.W., Sotowa, K., 2022. Effective Re-Identification of a Multivariate Process under Model Predictive Control Using Information from Plant-Model Mismatch Detection. Computer Aided Chemical Engineering. 49, 361–366. https://doi.org/10.1016/B978-0-323-85159-6.50060-9

Raissi, M., Perdikaris, P., Karniadakis, G.E., 2019. Physics-informed neural networks: A deep learning framework for solving forward and inverse problems involving nonlinear partial differential equations. Journal of Computational Physics 378, 686–707. https://doi.org/10.1016/j.jcp.2018.10.045

Subramanian, S., Kirby, R.M., Mahoney M.W., Gholami A., 2022. Adaptive Self-supervision Algorithms for Physics-informed Neural Networks. arXiv:2207.04084.

Subraveti, S.G., Li, Z., Prasad, V., Rajendran, A., 2022. Physics-Based Neural Networks for Simulation and Synthesis of Cyclic Adsorption Processes. Ind. Eng. Chem. Res. 61, 4095–4113. https://doi.org/10.1021/acs.iecr.1c04731

Flavio Manenti, Gintaras V. Reklaitis (Eds.), Proceedings of the 34th European Symposium on Computer Aided Process Engineering / 15th International Symposium on Process Systems Engineering (ESCAPE34/PSE24), June 2-6, 2024, Florence, Italy

Potential for Counterfactual Explanations to Support Digitalized Plant Operations

Abhijit Bhakte,[a] Rajagopalan Srinivasan,[a,b,*]

[a]*Department of Chemical Engineering, Indian Institute of Technology Madras, Chennai 600036, India*
[b]*American Express Lab for Data Analytics, Risk & Technology, Indian Institute of Technology Madras, Chennai 600036, India*
*raj@iitm.ac.in

Abstract

The advent of digitalization in the chemical industry has begun a new era of technological advancements, where artificial intelligence (AI) methods play a pivotal role in diverse applications, from process optimization to product development. However, a major challenge persists – operators and stakeholders often find it challenging to comprehend the outputs provided by AI models due to their inherent complexity. Counterfactual explanations (CFs) are emerging as a promising approach to demystify AI predictions. A counterfactual explanation tells you what changes could have been made in a situation to get a diverse outcome. CF is rooted in causal inference and thus has the potential to provide insights, especially related to operations in complex chemical processes. Using process monitoring as an example application, this paper demonstrates that CF can be used for various use cases – aiding model developers during the training phase of AI applications, empowering plant operators to better interpret AI predictions, and training new personnel effectively.

Keywords: Explainable Artificial Intelligence, Deep Learning, Chemical Industry, Process Operations

1. Introduction

The advent of Industry 4.0, improved instrumentation, and ubiquitous sensor data play a pivotal role in the development of AI. However, despite the better performance, these algorithms often lack interpretability in their decision-making processes. Therefore, domain experts in the chemical industry may find it hard to understand or trust the outputs and recommendations provided by AI-based models. This poses a significant barrier to the adoption of AI in real-world plant operations, where safety and reliability are paramount. In response to the broad interpretability challenge of AI models, there is a recent emergence of Explainable Artificial Intelligence (XAI).

XAI offers tools and techniques to generate high-quality, interpretable, intuitive, human-understandable explanations for AI prediction. The common ways to enable humans to interpret any situation are visual explanation, explanation-by-simplification, rule-based explanation, feature relevance explanation, and explanation-by-examples (Arrieta et al., 2020). In the chemical industry, where sensor data is predominant, the major utilization of feature relevance and explanation-by-simplification is observed. For example, Bhakte et al. (2022) proposed an attribution-based XAI method that identifies key variables responsible for fault occurrence as a feature relevance method. Bhakte et al. (2023)

proposed the Limit-based Explanations for Monitoring (LEMON) method, emphasizing model simplification with the process knowledge. Explanation-by-example is a method that involves the extraction of data examples closely tied to the results generated by a specific model. These techniques include: 1) Prototype explanations that involves "instances other than predefined inputs that effectively represent the model predictions." 2) Counterfactual explanations involve the "smallest change to the feature value that changes the prediction to a predefined output" (Molnar, 2022).

Counterfactual explanations, rooted in casual inference, enable stakeholders to comprehend why an AI model generated a particular output, what factors contributed to it, and how changes to these factors can affect the results. CF has been applied in various domains, from finance to healthcare, yet its potential remains underexplored in chemical engineering. Specifically, within process operations, the application of CFs enables us to envision what would occur in various scenarios. While factual explanations aid in logical reasoning for a process operator, counterfactuals offer additional insights beyond the known facts. Hence, they are more informative and facilitate creative problem-solving. Thus, CFs can be used for numerous applications, such as predicting the remaining useful life and dynamic planning of operations. This work describes a methodology to generate CF explanations and explores its potential to help decision-making during process monitoring.

2. Methodology

Consider a chemical process that is being monitored by a DNN model F. The DNN F is trained on a dataset XH of historic samples with labels YH. Here, XH_t is the tth training samples with N measurement variables. Given an online process sample X_t, the model F outputs the probability of C process states, i.e., $P_t = [p_t^1, p_t^2, ..., p_t^c, ..., p_t^C]$. The end-user is provided with the most probable state $Y_t = \underset{c \in [1,...,C]}{armax}[p_t^1, p_t^2, ..., p_t^c, ..., p_t^C]$. To enable the operator to understand the output Y_t, we propose a two-step methodology that generates the explanation-by-example.

Step 1: Variable Selection

The trained DNN F is deployed for online process monitoring. Now, understanding the AI prediction Y_t in time, given N process variables, becomes challenging. Hence, if an operator has given the subset of n variables responsible for the model output, this makes his job easier and aids in fast process recovery in abnormal situations. To address this, Integrated Gradient methodology in (Bhakte et al., 2022) is used for feature selection. The IG is a gradient-based attribution motivated by the concept of Shapley value, a technique to explain DNNs predictions Y_t by attributing them to the neural network's inputs X_t. Now, to select the top n highly attributed variables, we use the concept of inseparability ($\pi_j = \frac{A_j}{A_{j+1}}$) defined as the "ratio of the attribution of the variable to that of the next highest attributed variable." Here, A represents variable attribution wheras index j represents the ranking of variables' attribution value sorted in descending order; a low value ($\pi_j \approx 1$) represents that both variables at position j and $j + 1$ are important, whereas ($\pi_j \gg 1$) represents only the variable at position j is important. Therefore, a threshold value (π_{min}) must be chosen to display the key variables to the operator. Here, we have only key variables selected, but more insights can be obtained if distinct 'if-else' scenarios are provided to the operator.

Step 2: Counterfactual Generation

The process state $Y_t = \underset{c\in[1,...,C]}{armax}[p_t^1, p_t^2, ..., p_t^c, ..., p_t^C]$ and the c subsequent classes with the highest probabilities obtained from DNN output are stored. Next, the k nearest neighbors are searched from historic data XH that belongs to class Y_t. This nearest neighbor is called prototype X_t^P and calculated using the loss function $\mathcal{L}_P$.

$$\mathcal{L}_P = \underset{X_t^P \in XH}{armin}[\, d(X_t^P, X_t) \mid F(XH_t) = Y_t \,] \tag{1}$$

The training dataset XH is utilized to select the nearest neighbors as it automatically incorporates complex causal relationships amongst the process variables. Here, prototypes X_t^P help the operator to see how the real-time sample X_t best fits the predicted state Y_t. In contrast, CFs for the c subsequent classes with the higher probabilities after Y_t are obtained using the loss function $\mathcal{L}_{CF}$.

$$\mathcal{L}_{CF} = \underset{X_t^{CF} \in XH}{armin}[\, d(X_t^{CF}, X_t) \mid F(XH_t) \neq Y_t \,] \tag{2}$$

These CFs help the operator understand what distinguishes the real-time sample from the other classes. Next, the prototypes and CFs for the key variables selected during Step 1 are presented to the operator. This helps the operator to understand the DNN output by focusing on key variables responsible for process state prediction. The proposed methodology is demonstrated through a CSTR case study.

3. Case Study: Continuous Stirred Tank Reactor

This section illustrates the proposed methodology using a jacketed CSTR process featuring the irreversible liquid-phase decomposition of reactant A into B, driven by first-order kinetics. The reaction is exothermic; therefore, a cooling jacket is employed to maintain the reactor temperature at T_R. The process consists of five measurement variables: reactor inflow (Q_i), reactor outflow (Q_o), outlet concentration (C_A), reactor temperature (T_R), Reactor height (H), and Coolant temperature (T_c). The process consists of two steady states, NS-1 and NS-2. It is susceptible to five faults, i.e., Catalyst deactivation (F-1), Heat exchanger fouling (F-2), Ramp decrease in T_c (F-3), Ramp increase in T_c (F-4), and Step increase in the inlet (F-5). A DNN model is trained for monitoring using the aforementioned six variables. The training dataset consists of 120 samples from six simulation runs where faults were introduced at sample $t = 41$. In the testing dataset, each fault test simulation run consisted of 100 samples where faults were introduced at sample $t = 31$. In this work, we seek to provide an explanation-by-example for the outputs generated by DNN. To achieve this, a DNN model (6–50–25–12–7) is trained using the training dataset, and the resultant model is subsequently deployed for real-time monitoring. The proposed methodology is then employed to explain the DNN's predictions.

In this study, we consider test run 1 as an illustrative example. During test run 1, a fault occurred at sample $t = 31$, causing a decrease in coolant temperature T_c. This increases the heat removal rate, resulting in a decrease in reactor temperature T_R. The decrease in the reactor temperature causes a drop in the reaction rate, leading to an increase in the concentration of unreacted A (C_A). The DNN correctly flags F-3 (Ramp decrease in T_c) with a diagnosis delay of 11 samples. To interpret the DNN predictions, Prototypes and CFs are generated through the proposed methodology. Figure 1 provides a visual representation of this analyses, specifically focusing on key variables, i.e., (T_c, T_R, C_A) identified through variable selection. Each plot in Figure 1 represents a real-time sample,

10 preceding samples (depicted as lines), 10 prototype samples (depicted as triangles), and 10 CF samples from two subsequent classes with the highest prediction probabilities (represented by squares). Our analysis yields several insights, offering valuable information for operators to interpret and act upon the DNN predictions:

Steady-state insights: These insights involve understanding DNN when the process operates within the normal operating range. During test run 1, all process variables remained within normal operating range until $t = 30$, and the DNN model classifies these samples correctly. To understand the DNN predictions, Prototypes and CF generated through the proposed methodology are analyzed at sample $t = 25$. At $t = 25$, the model predicted the given sample as normal with a probability of 0.97; it also flags the class F-1 with 0.01 probability as the next likely candidate. These probabilities clearly indicate that the current state as normal. This is evident in Figure 1 (a) & (b), where the present samples align within the normal class cluster (prototypes). In contrast, clusters corresponding to abnormal samples, i.e., F-1 and F-4 (CF w.r.t. current samples) are far away.

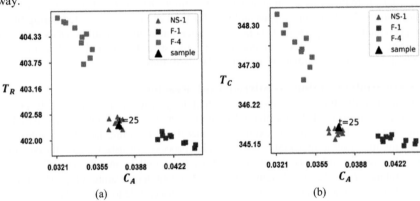

(a)   (b)

Figure 1 Counterfactuals and prototypes for test run 1 at t=25

Target-based insights: These refer to actionable information provided to operators for returning the system to a desired normal state. In the case study, the emergence of a fault initiates a gradual escalation at $t = 31$, resulting in the misclassification of the initial five samples as normal by the DNN. Subsequently, at $t = 36$, the DNN identifies the fault as F-1. Analysis of the sample at $t = 38$, the DNN predicted the given sample as F-1 with a probability of 0.42; it also flags the class F-3 and NS-1 with 0.34 and 0.24 probability as the next likely candidate. The corresponding prototypes and CFs plotted in Figure 2 (a) & (b) demonstrate the sample's proximity to the decision boundaries of F-3 and NS-1, representing diagnostic uncertainty. In such a situation, target-based insights suggest that to restore normal steady state-1 (NS-1), T_c and T_R need to be increased to 345.20°C and 402.10°C, respectively. These insights provide actionable guidance for operators to rectify deviations from the desired state.

Pattern-based insights: These involve the analysis of observed patterns in data, particularly focusing on the historical behavior of variables within a system. In the case study, examining the 10 prototypes of fault class F-1 and counterfactuals of class F-3 at $t = 38$ (see Figure 2), if C_A alone changes with time, it confirms the F-1 state. In contrast, if a $1°\ C$ change in T_R changes 0.0015 mol/L of C_A, it confirms the F-3 state. This knowledge is not explicitly given to the DNN but extracted from the training data in the vicinity of the real-time sample. Utilizing these counterfactuals and prototype explanations proves instrumental for operators navigating diagnostic uncertainties. Utilizing these explanations enhances operators' ability to interpret evolving states more comprehensively.

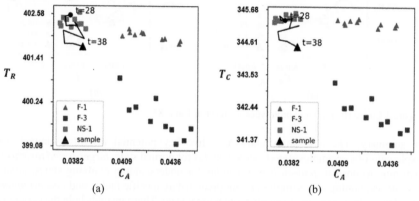

(a)   (b)

Figure 2. Counterfactuals and prototypes for test run 1 at t=38

Counter Insights: It explains instances where a model deviates from an expected outcome. In the case study, the fault state F-3 is detected by DNN at sample $t = 42$. One such sample at $t = 85$ predicted as F-3 by DNN with a probability of 0.78; it also flags the class NS-2 with 0.2 probability as the next likely candidate. The CF and prototypes are generated to explain the DNN prediction at $t = 85$, as shown in Figures 3 (a) & (b). At $t = 85$, why the current sample is not predicted as F-1, even though C_A is within the fault range? The counter insight reveals that the significant drop in T_c and T_R indicates a different fault F-3. Understanding these counter insights is essential for operators navigating diagnostic uncertainties and refining their understanding of the fault detection process.

Nearest Optimal Insights: These insights guide the operator towards the most feasible steady state when returning the desired normal steady state is unattainable. In the case study, if the operator aims to return to normal steady state-1 (NS-1) at $t = 85$ (see Figure 3), he can follow the distinct control moves to reach that state. However, if returning to NS-1 is impossible, the operator is provided with the nearest normal that can be operated, i.e., normal steady state-2 (NS-2) in the current scenario. Operating the system under NS-2 ensures stability and minimizes potential risks.

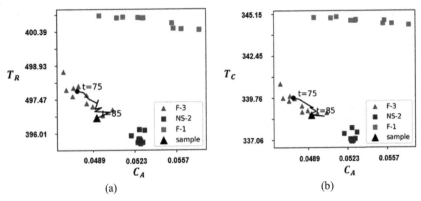

Figure 3.Counterfactuals and prototypes for test run 1 at t=85

In summary, The case study showcases five key potential insights obtained from explanation-by-examples: *steady-state insights* for normal state, *target-based insights* for returning to normal, *pattern-based insights* for understanding evolving states, *counter insights* explaining why samples are not predicted as specific faults, and *nearest optimal insights* guiding operators to an operable normal state. These insights help the operator to understand AI decisions more intuitively and aid the process recovery.

4. Conclusions

This work introduces the potential of explanations-by-example in the chemical industry, addressing the interpretability challenges associated with AI model results. The proposed methodology combines variable selection and counterfactual generation to enhance the understanding of AI predictions for the operator. Using counterfactuals in the CSTR Case study, we presented the distinct potential of prototype and counterfactual to provide insights, i.e., steady-state, target-based, pattern-based, counter, and nearest optimal insights. This aids in decision-making, process recovery, and effective training of plant personnel. This innovative use of CFs holds significant potential for developing trust and facilitating the adoption of AI in real-world chemical industries. In the future, we will focus on providing insights as well as systematic mitigation strategies to the operator for process recovery.

References

Arrieta, A.B., Díaz-Rodríguez, N., Ser, J.D., Bennetot, A., Tabik, S., Barbado, A., Garcia, S., Gil-Lopez, S., Molina, D., Benjamins, R., Chatila, R., Herrera, F., 2020. Explainable Artificial Intelligence (XAI): Concepts, taxonomies, opportunities and challenges toward responsible AI. Information Fusion 58, 82–115. https://doi.org/10.1016/j.inffus.2019.12.012

Bhakte, A., Chakane, M., Srinivasan, R., 2023. Alarm-based Explanations of Process Monitoring Results from Deep Neural Networks. Computers & Chemical Engineering 179, 108442. https://doi.org/10.1016/j.compchemeng.2023.108442

Bhakte, A., Pakkiriswamy, V., Srinivasan, R., 2022. An explainable artificial intelligence-based approach for interpretation of fault classification results from deep neural networks. Chemical Engineering Science 250, 117373. https://doi.org/10.1016/j.ces.2021.117373

Molnar, C., 2022. Interpretable Machine Learning: A Guide for Making Black Box Models Explainable.

Flavio Manenti, Gintaras V. Reklaitis (Eds.), Proceedings of the 34th European Symposium on Computer Aided Process Engineering / 15th International Symposium on Process Systems Engineering (ESCAPE34/PSE24), June 2-6, 2024, Florence, Italy

Understanding Cognitive Behavior in Collaborative Control Rooms through Eye Tracking

Haider Altaf[a], Jhareswar Maiti[b], Babji Srinivasan[a,d], Rajagopalan Srinivasan[c,d,*]

[a]Department of Applied Mechanics and Biomedical Engineering, Indian Institute of Technology Madras, Chennai, 600036, India

[b]Department of Industrial and Systems Engineering, Indian Institute of Technology, Kharagpur 721302, India

[c]Department of Chemical Engineering, Indian Institute of Technology Madras, Chennai, 600036, India

[d]American Express Lab for Data Analytics, Risk and Technology, Indian Institute of Technology Madras, Chennai, 600036, India

* Corresponding Authors' Email: raj@iitm.ac.in, babji.srinivasan@iitm.ac.in,

Abstract

In the digital era, industrial control rooms have transformed into collaborative workstations. This shift, while technologically advanced, introduces challenges to operators, such as information overload, testing the limits of human cognitive processing. Consequently, understanding operators' cognitive behavior in these collaborative environments has become essential to enhance operational efficiency and safety. Studies have shown that eye tracking is a valuable tool for understanding operator behavior. However, its application faces limitations in collaborative control room settings due to the presence of multiple and overview displays at varying heights. This work addresses this gap by introducing a novel methodology that integrates eye-tracking data with a three-dimensional (3D) model of a control room, enabling a comprehensive visualization of operator gaze patterns and cognitive behavior. The accuracy and precision of the recorded gaze were tested by studies involving human subjects. Additionally, we conducted a case study using a simulated control room environment, demonstrating the practical applicability of our methodology. This case study provided valuable insights into how operators interact with and respond to different elements in a collaborative control room, underscoring the potential of our method in capturing and analyzing cognitive behavior in real-world scenarios.

Keywords: Cognitive behavior, Collaborative control rooms, Eye-tracking, Operator performance, Safety.

1. Introduction

Control rooms are evolving into collaborative spaces in today's digitized process industries. Examples such as ABB's Extended Operation Workstations and BAW Architecture's Integrated Operation Center highlight this trend toward centralizing operations in a unified space (Borås & Sverige, 2021; BAW Architecture, 2018). These advanced environments combine individual operator panels with overview displays, essential for team-based access and decision-making. However, with the influx of data facilitated by automation and AI, operators face the challenge of information overload. This can impair judgment and decision-making, increasing cognitive workload and the likelihood of errors. Understanding operator behavior, especially under high cognitive demands, is crucial. Operators need to effectively switch focus between individual and overview displays, requiring a mix of individual task comprehension and efficient teamwork.

Recently, eye tracking has been used to understand human cognitive behavior in various safety-critical domains. For instance, an eye-tracking study reported that novices frequently shifted their gaze across multiple information sources, indicating a potential unfamiliarity with the ongoing abnormality of the process (Wu et al., 2020). Our findings from previous work revealed that operators well-versed in process dynamics predominantly focused on key process variables related to the situation at hand (Bhavsar et al., 2017). We have also developed a mathematical framework to decode operators' mental representations of process dynamics (Shahab et al., 2022).

The above studies are limited to cognitive behavior studies within conventional control room settings like single-screen setups. This narrow focus has restricted our understanding of operator behavior in the collaborative environment of modern control rooms, which often feature an array of multiple and overview displays. Such multi-screen settings introduce unique challenges, particularly when operators collaboratively navigate and respond to abnormal scenarios. More recently, we have shown the application of eye-tracking to encompass multi-screen, multi-user control room environments, revealing considerable variations in attention and gaze patterns among operators (Shajahan et al., 2023). Building on this foundation, our current work extends the scope even further. We aim to provide a more comprehensive understanding of operator cognitive behavior, considering the additional complexity introduced by the overview display. This approach not only enriches our understanding of the operator's cognitive behavior and decision-making strategies but also paves the way for more effective training and operational strategies tailored to the realities of modern control rooms.

2. Proposed Methodology

We propose a methodology to analyze operators' cognitive behavior in collaborative control rooms by visualizing their gaze patterns and obtaining eye-tracking metrics. Traditional eye trackers can capture gaze data on calibrated displays within a predefined range. However, they fall short in capturing gaze data on large overview displays, primarily due to their substantial size, and relying solely on a single-eye tracking system is insufficient. In our approach, the key to extending gaze tracking to overview displays lies in using gaze vector data, a fundamental output of standard eye-tracking systems. The gaze vector represents the direction in which the user is looking. In our methodology, we repurpose this gaze vector, applying it to visualize eye movements on the overview display found in collaborative control rooms. We utilize this data without physically altering the eye-tracking apparatus or its orientation. Instead, we project the gaze vector onto the overview displays. This is technically achieved by integrating the gaze vector with a 3D model of the control room.

The 3D model is constructed using photogrammetry, a technique that employs multiple photographs taken from various angles. Once we have the 3D model, we employ ray casting. This technique, common in computer graphics, involves projecting rays from a point—in our case, from the origin of the gaze vector—into the 3D space and determining where these rays intersect with the 3D model. We used PyVista visualization toolkit available in the Python programming language. Subsequently, the intersection of the gaze vector with the 3D environment is visualized by representing them as small spheres within the 3D model. This allows us to accurately trace the paths of the operators' gaze as it moves across different control room displays, including the overview displays.

The methodology was validated in an experimental setup emulating a collaborative control room with multi-screen displays. This setup included three 22-inch monitors in a triple-monitor setup (which are calibrated to the eye tracker) and a 170-inch projector screen as the overview display (uncalibrated) placed at a 52 cm distance from the center display (fig. 1). an eye tracker with three infrared cameras was used to track the eye movement in this setup. Human-subject studies were conducted to validate the proposed methodology's accuracy and precision and show its potential application in a collaborative control room. Next, we discuss the protocol of the human subject studies.

2.1. Human Subject Studies

Our first series of experiments aimed to assess the accuracy and precision of our methodology by employing a technique similar to that used for traditional eye-tracking studies (Tobii, 2020; Feit et al., 2017). Accuracy, the average angular offset between the target and recorded gaze vectors, and precision, the gaze data's standard deviation from its mean value, are crucial metrics for evaluating the reliability of our method, especially given the challenges of adapting eye tracking to large, uncalibrated displays. We conducted controlled experiments in the

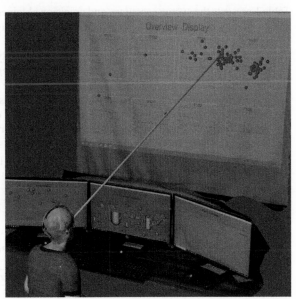

Figure 1: 3D model of the collaborative control room, with small spheres are gaze fixation points for a specific task performed by a participant, and the 3D line (gaze direction vector) connecting eye to the fixation point.

previously discussed setup with participants focusing on nine calibration points. These points were strategically placed at 7, 21, and 31 degrees of angular height, spanning the entire size of the overview display.

Beyond technical validation, our methodology underwent real-world testing in a study involving four postgraduate students from IIT Madras who played the roles of control room operators. They were instructed through video and PDF handouts to understand chemical processes and utilize valves to rectify abnormalities and restore normal operation. They interacted with a four-screen chemical process simulator in a typical collaborative control room setup, as discussed previously (Fig. 1). This setup included various displays: a central screen showing the plant's schematic interface, a screen for process trend analysis, a screen for alarm summaries, and an overview display for monitoring key process variables trends of the chemical plant. Time-based information such as trends aids operators in understanding the past and present states of the process, thereby boosting their capabilities to make a prognosis (Bennett et al., 2005).

3. Results

This section presents the results of our experiments, focusing on the accuracy and precision of our methodology. Using a case study, we also demonstrate the potential of the proposed methodology for understanding the operator's cognitive behavior in a collaborative control room setting.

3.1. Accuracy and precision

Table 1 presents the average accuracy and precision obtained from ten participants, giving a detailed view of the performance at different viewing heights on the overview display.

For the overview display, central to our study and not typically covered by standard calibration, we observed an average accuracy of 2.4 degrees and a precision of 5.8 cm(horizontal) and 2.8 cm(vertical) across all heights. We further analyzed the accuracy and precision at individual angular heights relative to the user's horizontal visual lines on the overview display. Table 1 shows that at the height of 7 degrees, the average accuracy was recorded as 2.5 degrees with a precision of 3.9 cm (horizontal) and 3.1 cm (vertical). At greater angular heights of 21 and 31 degrees, we found similar levels of accuracy (2.7 and 2.2 degrees). However, the precision in the horizontal plane decreases as the angular height increases, indicating degradation in eye gaze data quality.

Table 1: Accuracy and precision of the methodology at three angular heights of the overview display.

Angular height (degrees)	Accuracy (degrees)	Precision (centimeter)	
		Horizontal	Vertical
7	2.5	3.9	3.1
21	2.7	6.0	2.0
31	2.2	7.6	3.3

Despite challenges of large size and beyond the range of calibrated displays, the overview display maintains good precision and accuracy. The results are comparable to those of accuracy and precision in a controlled environment (Feit et al., 2017). Notably, the overview display in collaborative control rooms typically features less dense information with larger areas of interest. Our results indicate that the eye gaze on the overview display can provide valuable insights into operators' attention patterns.

Next, we will demonstrate the effectiveness of the proposed methodology in capturing cognitive behavior in a collaborative control room setting.

3.2. Case study

The case study involves a simulated chemical process simulator, as discussed previously. Participants played the role of operators. They were asked to monitor and intervene during abnormalities. During the task, participants encountered a disturbance in the reflux ratio of the distillation column, which triggered alarms at tray temperatures. This required them to adjust the reflux valve to bring the process to the operating limit. Therefore, the tray temperatures and the reflux valve are the relevant sources of information for this task, and all other variables are irrelevant.

Table 2 shows the percentage of time spent by the participants on the relevant and irrelevant information sources on each display, as captured by fixation duration. This was obtained by ray casting of the participant's gaze on the 3D model of the experimental setup.

Table 2: Percentage of time the participants spent on various displays' information sources.

Participant	Overview display		Schematic display		Trend panel	Alarm summary
	Relevant	Irrelevant	Relevant	Irrelevant		
1	32.0	2.8	27.0	25.4	12.4	0.0
2	39.9	1.0	20.0	22.0	16.6	0.6
3	14.6	0.7	18.2	46.8	6.4	13.1
4	4.9	1.3	24.4	47.0	22.5	0.0

Consider participant 4, who spent 48.3% of the total time on irrelevant information sources, indicating a lack of awareness about the disturbance's root cause (Table 2). Additionally, they allocated 6.2% of their time to the overview display, suggesting a limited understanding of using time-based information to anticipate control action effects.

In addition, participants three and four devoted almost half of the time (47.5% and 48.3%, respectively) to irrelevant information sources, indicating a lack of understanding of the process dynamics. As a result, participants three and four took more time (127 s and 130 s) to complete the task. In contrast, participants one and two are more attentive to relevant information sources related to a disturbance in reflux ratio (71.4% and 77.1%, respectively). They dedicated nearly one-third of their time to the overview display, efficiently monitoring the impact of their actions on the process. The process trend indicates a proactive monitoring strategy of these participants, a characteristic of experts. The relatively lower attention of participants three and four indicates that they were unaware of the effect of their control action and adopted a reactive strategy (a characteristic of a novice) to deal with the abnormal situation. Thus, the proposed methodology effectively captures the participant's understanding of the process dynamics in a collaborative control room setting. The results align with the previous studies in a controlled control room environment with participants interacting with the process via a screen display (Sharma et al., 2016).

Our proposed methodology effectively captured 254 fixations on the uncalibrated overview display, showcasing its excellence in capturing operator focus. In contrast, the traditional eye-tracking techniques failed to register any fixations on the uncalibrated overview despite having 254 fixations captured by our approach. Both methodologies adeptly capture attention on the three calibrated displays. This absence of fixation on overview display, evident in the traditional eye-tracking techniques, highlights the crucial role our proposed approach plays in revealing nuanced attention patterns that would otherwise go unnoticed.

4. Conclusions

In this paper, we proposed a methodology to understand the operator's cognitive behavior using eye tracking within modern collaborative control rooms. This is achieved by integrating eye gaze data with a 3D model of the control room, providing a detailed visualization of gaze patterns and eye-tracking metrics to understand the operators' cognitive behavior and attention dynamics. The technical validity of our methodology was demonstrated through conventional accuracy and precision metrics for eye gaze data validation. The potential of the proposed methodology in capturing the operator's cognitive behavior is demonstrated using a case study on a chemical process simulator. The findings revealed that operators, when completing a disturbance rejection task efficiently, consistently focused on process trends displayed in the overview display. This nuanced observation underscores the significance of our methodology, as traditional eye-tracking methods might overlook operators' attention to the overview display, providing an incomplete depiction of cognitive behavior. The insights gained from this work could significantly improve human performance, particularly in understanding cognitive behavior in modern control rooms. Our future work will develop additional eye-tracking metrics tailored to comprehend individual and team cognitive behavior in collaborative control rooms.

Acknowledgment: This work is partially funded by American Express lab for Data Analytics, Risk and Technology, IIT Madras.

References

BAW Architecture.(2018).Integrated Operation Centers. https://bawarchitecture.com/project/integrated-operations-center/

Bennett, K. B., Payne, M., & Walters, B. (2005). An evaluation of a" time tunnel" display format for the presentation of temporal information. *Human factors*, *47*(2), 342-359.

Bhavsar, P., Srinivasan, B., & Srinivasan, R. (2017). Quantifying situation awareness of control room operators using eye-gaze behavior. Computers & chemical engineering, 106, 191-201.

Borås & Sverige.(2021, May 07).Tarkett enhances operator wellbeing - with advanced ABB control room desks.ABB.https://new.abb.com/news/detail/75697/tarkett-enhances-operator-wellbeing-with-advanced-abb-control-room-desks.

Feit, A. M., Williams, S., Toledo, A., Paradiso, A., Kulkarni, H., Kane, S., & Morris, M. R. (2017, May). Toward everyday gaze input: Accuracy and precision of eye tracking and implications for design. In *Proceedings of the 2017 Chi conference on human factors in computing systems* (pp. 1118-1130).

Shahab, M. A., Iqbal, M. U., Srinivasan, B., & Srinivasan, R. (2022). HMM-based models of control room operator's cognition during process abnormalities. 1. Formalism and model identification. Journal of Loss Prevention in the Process Industries, 76, 104748.

Shajahan, T. V., Madbhavi, R., Shahab, M. A., Srinivasan, B., & Srinivasan, R. (2023). Dhrushti-AI: A multi-screen multi-user eye-tracking system to understand the cognitive behavior of humans in process industries. In Computer Aided Chemical Engineering (Vol. 52, pp. 2043-2048). Elsevier.

Sharma, C., Bhavsar, P., Srinivasan, B., & Srinivasan, R. (2016). Eye gaze movement studies of control room operators: A novel approach to improve process safety. *Computers & Chemical Engineering*, *85*, 43-57.

Tobii, A. B.(2020). Eye Tracker Data Quality Test Report: Accuracy, Precision and Detected Gaze under Optimal Conditions—Controlled Environment.

Wu, Y., Liu, Z., Jia, M., Tran, C. C., & Yan, S. (2020). Using artificial neural networks for predicting mental workload in nuclear power plants based on eye tracking. Nuclear Technology, 206(1), 94-106.

Flavio Manenti, Gintaras V. Reklaitis (Eds.), Proceedings of the 34th European Symposium on Computer Aided Process Engineering / 15th International Symposium on Process Systems Engineering (ESCAPE34/PSE24), June 2-6, 2024, Florence, Italy

A data-driven approach for constructing the prediction bounds on the output variables using a modified loss function and analysing information retained during development of the model

Waqar Muhammad Ashraf, Vivek Dua*

The Sargent Centre for Process Systems Engineering, Department of Chemical Engineering, University College London, Torrington Place, London WC1E 7JE, UK.

E-mail: v.dua@ucl.ac.uk

Abstract

The model-based simulated responses are plagued by prediction errors for models obtained by using machine learning (ML) techniques, thereby leading to the need to estimate the prediction bounds around the model-simulated responses. Here in this work, we propose a novel method utilizing the iterative values of the model parameters obtained during model development to construct the prediction bounds around the model-simulated responses using artificial neural network (ANN) model. The loss function of the ANN model includes the least-mean squared error and is also augmented with the standard deviation between the true and model-simulated responses. During the training and development of ANN model, the values of connection weights and the biases associated with the working layers of the ANN model are stored and at the end of the training these values are deployed to construct the prediction bounds around the model-simulated responses. The proposed methodology is applied to energy efficiency cooling and energy efficiency heating (bench-mark dataset from University of California – Irvine database for ML). The developed ANN model showed superior modelling performance having following predictive errors: energy efficiency cooling (RMSE_test = 1.40%) and energy efficiency heating (RMSE_test = 0.46%) compared with those of feedforward neural network reported in literature (RMSE_test = 1.63% and RMSE_test = 0.63% respectively). The width of prediction bounds made by the proposed technique is found to be comparable to those of input perturbation method. The proposed SWARM approach for drawing the prediction bounds can be applied to different real-life applications, facilitating the decision makers to incorporate these bounds for optimal decision making.

Keywords: Data-driven prediction bounds; Machine Learning; Uncertainty Quantification.

1. Introduction

With the explosion in utilizing machine learning (ML) models for different applications, it has become imperative to estimate the range of variability or the prediction bounds around the model predicted responses to account for the uncertainty. Computer vision, object detection and natural language processing are some of the popular application domains of ML [1]. However, regression-based applications for industrial applications are reported less in literature. Furthermore, the techniques developed for drawing the prediction bounds for regression-based modelling algorithms are also different than those of classification-based ML models.

Bayesian method and ensemble approach are the probabilistic techniques for drawing the prediction bounds. Gaussian process regression models work well in conjunction with the Bayesian method and can include the domain knowledge of the system to improve the prior estimate for the characterization of the underlying distribution in the data [2]. However, the modelling performance of the Bayesian method deteriorates when the modelling assumptions are violated. On the other hand, ensemble method can be considered as an approximate of the Bayesian method where each model can be understood as a point in the hyperparameter space. However, ensembles may not explicitly model the uncertainty in a probabilistic sense and lack the formal probabilistic interpretation of the uncertainty.

Conformal prediction is another class of prediction bound construction methods and it draws the prediction bounds for the dataset using the non-conformity measure [3]. The method is computationally intensive since the model is to be trained for each datapoint. The variant of conformal prediction method called inductive conformal prediction offers reduced computational efforts [3]. However, there is a trade-off between the accuracy of the prediction bounds drawn by the two techniques considering the computational resource utilization. Direct interval estimation method [3] modifies the loss function and incorporates a fixed confidence level for drawing the prediction bounds. However, the change in the confidence-level requires retraining the model thus limiting the flexible utilization of the technique for drawing the prediction bounds for any confidence level.

In this work, we propose a novel data-driven approach called Storage of Weights And Retrieval Method (SWARM) to construct the prediction bounds around the model predicted responses for artificial neural network (ANN) model. The SWARM approach for drawing the prediction bounds is implemented on the energy efficiency cooling and energy efficiency heating performance of the buildings, and the dataset is taken from the University of California Irvine open-source datasets for ML [4]. The SWARM method offers a flexible approach to compute the prediction bounds using the parameters information stored during the ANN model development and thus eliminating the need to carry out extensive post-model computational experimentation to estimate the prediction bounds.

2. Data-driven approach to construct the prediction bounds using ANN

ANN is a universal function approximator and can model the nonlinear function space with a reasonable accuracy. The weight connections in the different layers of ANN are processed with the feeding information to simulate a response [5]. Our SWARM approach is inspired by the working of direct interval estimation method, and we have modified the loss function to include the least mean square error and standard deviation between the actual and model predicted response. The loss function customized in this work for the development of ANN model is given as:

$$\mathcal{L} = \frac{(D-Z)^2}{2} + \frac{|D-Z|}{\sqrt{2}} \tag{1}$$

Here, D and Z represent the true and model simulated observations. The first term in the loss function in the least mean squared error while the second term measures the standard deviation between D and Z. The online training mode of development for ANN model is implemented [6] where one input vector is fed from the training dataset for the parameters update and the whole dataset is passed-on in the sequential approach for the extensive parameters update. The standard deviation is minimized between D and Z for each observation that also contributes to the parameters update in the iterative training of ANN model. The parameters update across the hidden and output layers of ANN by gradient descent with momentum algorithm is given as follows [7]:

$$W_1^{new} = W_1 - \eta \, Vw_1 \tag{2}$$

$$V_{w1} = \beta Vw_1 - (1-\beta)\frac{\partial L}{\partial W_1} \tag{3}$$

A data-driven approach for constructing the prediction bounds on the output variables   3087
using a modified loss function and analysing information retained during development
of the model

$$W_2^{new} = W_2 - \eta((1-\beta)\frac{\partial L}{\partial W_2}) \tag{4}$$

$$b_1^{new} = b_1 - \eta((1-\beta)\frac{\partial L}{\partial b_1}) \tag{5}$$

$$b_2^{new} = b_2 - \eta((1-\beta)\frac{\partial L}{\partial b_2}) \tag{6}$$

here, W_1, W_2, b_1 and b_2 are the matrices containing the weight connection and bias values from input to hidden and hidden to output layer of ANN respectively. η and β are the learning rate and momentum parameter respectively. V_{w1} is the velocity matrix having the same dimensions as that of W_1 and initialized as zero.

The iterative training of the ANN model updates the parameters and upon completion of the model training, the model predicted response is computed which is represented as Z^*. The prediction bound around the model predicted responses can be calculated as follows:

$$Prediction\ bound = Z^* \pm CL \times \sigma(Z)_\zeta \tag{7}$$

here, CL represents the confidence level that is taken as 3 corresponding to 99% confidence interval for this work, and it can be specified by the user for the desired level of confidence interval (e.g., 95% or some other value) to construct the prediction bounds; ζ refers to the fraction of the parameters extracted for drawing the prediction bounds and $\sigma(Z)$ is the standard deviation in the model simulated responses (Z). As the ANN model's training starts, the value of the weights fluctuate a lot and possess large variance. However, as the iterative training proceeds, the weights' update tends to be smooth. Thus, the fraction of weights, that starts from Z^*,

can be extracted from the stored parameters space to compute the model-simulated responses for Z and the prediction bounds around each observation of Z can be constructed using equation (7).

The predictive performance of the ANN models is computed by coefficient of determination (R^2) and root-mean-squared-error (RMSE). Mathematically, the terms are expressed as follows:

$$R^2 = 1 - \frac{\sum_i^N (Z_i - D_i)^2}{\sum_i^N (D_i - \bar{D}_i)^2} \tag{8}$$

$$RMSE = \sqrt{\frac{1}{N}\sum_{i=1}^N (Z_i - D_i)^2} \tag{9}$$

where R^2 is a measure of modelling accuracy and varies from zero to one and RMSE indicates the mean deviation between the true and model-predictive responses.

3. Results and Discussion

3.1. Modelling performance of the ANN models for the case study

The energy efficiency cooling (ENC) and energy efficiency heating (ENH) dataset consists of 768 observations associated with the variables. A feedforward neural network (FFNN) is reported in literature having 10 hidden layer neurons for ENC and ENH dataset. Thus, we also deploy the same number of hidden layer neurons for building the ANN models for ENC and ENH; η and β are taken as 0.01 and 0.9 respectively. The stopping conditions to terminate the model development include: loss function value on testing dataset is equal to 0.01 or the maximum number of epochs are achieved. The modelling algorithm of ANN is implemented in MATLAB 2019 b version.

Figure 1 shows the predictive performance of the trained ANN models for ENC and ENH for training and testing dataset. Overall, a good match between the actual and model predicted responses for the output variables is observed. The ANN models achieved R^2 and RMSE values of 0.98 and 1.28 % & 0.29% for ENC and ENH respectively on the training dataset. Whereas, the performance metrics on the test datasets are as follows: $[R^2\_test = 0.98, RMSE\_test = 1.40\%]_{ENC}$ and $[R^2\_test = 0.98, RMSE\_test = 0.46\%]_{ENH}$. The R^2 values for the trained ANN models are reasonably high along with marginal error values both for training and testing datasets for ENC and ENH that demonstrates the good predictive performance of the models.

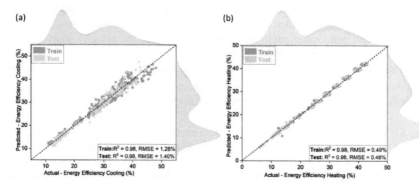

Figure 1. Predictive performance of the developed ANN models for energy efficiency cooling and energy efficiency heating on training and testing dataset.

3.2. Performance comparison of the trained ANN models with those of FFNN

The predictive performance of the trained ANN models for ENC and ENH is compared with those of a FFNN reported in literature [8]. RMSE is computed on the testing dataset for the two output variables and shown on Figure 2. It is noted that RMSE_test computed on the FFNN for ENC and ENH are 1.63% and 0.63% which are higher than those of ANN models developed in this work. This demonstrates the better generalization performance of the ANN models trained in this work to predict the profiles of ENC and ENH than that reported in the literature.

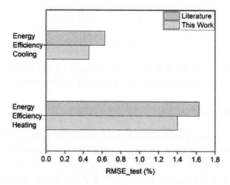

Figure 2. Comparison of the modelling performance of the ANN models trained in this work with those of FFNN model reported in literature [8].

3.3. Comparison of the prediction bound by the SWARM and input perturbation method

The model-based prediction bounds are constructed by the SWARM on $\zeta = 95\%$. Whereas, different values of the noise levels are tried to find the comparable width of prediction bounds by the input perturbation method. Thus, 0.05% of minimum value of the input variables is found as the noise level for the design of 10000 simulated experiments for each input vector by input perturbation technique. The procedure is applied for the two output variables and the prediction bounds around for the training and testing datasets with 99% confidence for ENC and ENH are presented on Figure 3 and Figure 4 respectively. The true and model simulated responses are also presented along with the prediction bounds. It is noted that prediction bounds seem to cover the true as well as model predicted responses within its shaded region not only for training but also for the testing dataset. This shows the reasonable accuracy of the SWARM method to draw the prediction bounds. Furthermore, the width of the prediction bounds method to

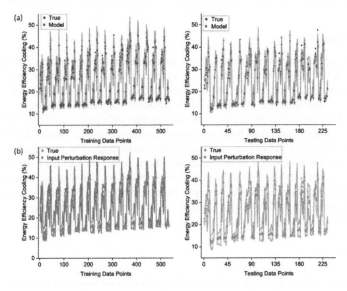

Figure 3. Construction of prediction bounds around the model predicted responses for training and testing datasets for energy efficiency cooling by a) SWARM and b) input perturbation method.

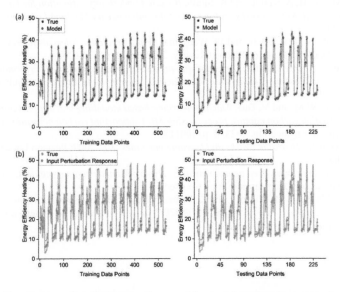

Figure 4. Construction of prediction bounds around the model predicted responses for training and testing datasets for energy efficiency heating by a) SWARM and b) input perturbation method.

draw the prediction bounds. Furthermore, the width of the prediction bounds made by the SWARM is compared with those of input perturbation technique that shows that the SWARM can produce the similar results as those of input perturbation method when the noise level is taken as 0.05% of the minimum value. Thus, the parameters information stored during the ANN model development can be readily deployed for the construction of prediction bounds without further computational analysis to draw the prediction bounds.

4. Conclusions

In this work, we proposed a novel data-driven approach to construct the prediction bounds around the ANN model based simulated responses using the parameters information stored during model development. The loss function is modified to include the least mean squared error and standard deviation term between the true and model simulated responses. The algorithm is applied on the energy efficiency cooling and energy efficiency heating dataset taken from an open-source database. The results show not only the superior modelling performance of the ANN models trained in this work compared with those of FFNN reported in literature, but the comparable width of the prediction bounds is observed with those of input perturbation technique when noise level was taken as 0.05% of the minimum values of the input variables. This work presents the utilization of the parameters information stored during the ANN model development for drawing the prediction bounds and can be applied for different real-life applications.

References

1. Ou, X., et al., *A Hyperspectral Image Change Detection Framework With Self-Supervised Contrastive Learning Pretrained Model.* IEEE Journal of Selected Topics in Applied Earth Observations and Remote Sensing, 2022. **15**: p. 7724-7740.
2. Teye, M., H. Azizpour, and K. Smith. *Bayesian uncertainty estimation for batch normalized deep networks.* in International Conference on Machine Learning. 2018. PMLR.
3. Dewolf, N., B.D. Baets, and W. Waegeman, *Valid prediction intervals for regression problems.* Artificial Intelligence Review, 2023. **56**(1): p. 577-613.
4. Tsanas, A. and A. Xifara, *Accurate quantitative estimation of energy performance of residential buildings using statistical machine learning tools.* Energy and buildings, 2012. **49**: p. 560-567.
5. Ashraf, W.M. and V. Dua, *Machine learning based modelling and optimization of post-combustion carbon capture process using MEA supporting carbon neutrality.* Digital Chemical Engineering, 2023. **8**: p. 100115.
6. Haykin, S., *Neural networks and learning machines, 3/E.* 2009: Pearson Education India.
7. Ng, A., *Improving deep neural networks: Hyperparameter tuning, regularization and optimization.* Deeplearning. ai on Coursera, 2017.
8. Arnaldo, I., U.-M. O'Reilly, and K. Veeramachaneni. *Building predictive models via feature synthesis.* in Proceedings of the 2015 annual conference on genetic and evolutionary computation. 2015.

Flavio Manenti, Gintaras V. Reklaitis (Eds.), Proceedings of the 34th European Symposium on Computer Aided Process Engineering / 15th International Symposium on Process Systems Engineering (ESCAPE34/PSE24), June 2-6, 2024, Florence, Italy

Enhancing cell culture understanding in the development of biopharmaceuticals by integrated first-principle modelling and machine-learning

Edoardo Tamiazzo,[a] Gianmarco Barberi,[a] Paloma Diaz-Fernandez,[b] Gary Finka,[b] Pierantonio Facco [a,*]

[a]CAPE-Lab – Computer-Aided Process Engineering Laboratory, Department of Industrial Engineering, University of Padova, via Marzolo, 9 – 35131 Padova PD, Italy

[b]Biopharm Process Research, Drug Substance Development, GSK, Gunnels Wood Rd, SG1 2NY Stevenage, UK

*pierantonio.facco@unipd.it

Abstract

Monoclonal antibodies (mAbs) are biopharmaceuticals which are used to treat a variety of diseases, including cancer and autoimmune disorders. These products are typically produced in mammalian Chinese Hamster Ovary (CHO) cell cultures whose complex and variable nature poses a significant challenge to product and process development. This study aims at understanding the phenomena occurring in mammalian cell cultures and relating the dynamics of cell metabolism to the macroscopic chemical, physical and biological phenomena occurring in the cell cultures through first-principle modelling and machine learning. In particular, we propose a novel approach in which an improved cell kinetic model is used to describe the macroscopic behavior of the cell cultures. Then, metabolomics data, which provide information on the metabolic dynamics of the cells along the culture, are used to relate the cell metabolism to the phenomena described by the kinetic model through supervised machine learning. The approach is applied to an industrial case study for the mAbs development in AMBR15® miniature bioreactors. A strong relationship of chemical-physical and biological phenomena with the dynamics of cell metabolism is found (average determination coefficients in cross-validation in the range of ~46-90%). Furthermore, the proposed approach allows understanding the effect of cell metabolism on the macroscopic phenomena occurring in the system.

Keywords: monoclonal antibody, mechanistic modelling, parameter estimation, metabolomics, machine learning.

1. Introduction

Biopharmaceuticals are drugs and treatments derived from genetically engineered living organisms and designed to produce specific biological substances with therapeutic properties. At the forefront of the biopharmaceutical market monoclonal antibodies (mAbs) (Walsh & Walsh, 2022) have gained significant popularity due to their critical role in treating a wide range of diseases. Monoclonal antibodies are typically cultured in CHO mammalian cells in fed-batch bioreactors which contain media with all the essential macro- and micronutrients required for cells optimal growth and viability. Fed-batch cultures are also provided with daily boluses of nutrients, containing the primary sources of carbon such as Glucose, Glutamate and Glutamine, and amino acids.

The characterization of this type of system requires the use of all the information obtained from the analysis of the cell cultures (Barberi et al., 2022). The types of information which may be available in CHO cell culture are: *i)* process data, which describe the macroscopic behavior of cell cultures, and *ii)* metabolomics data, which provide valuable insights into the microscopic metabolic reactions occurring in the system.

State-of-the-art first-principle models for CHO cell cultures rely on kinetic models (Kyriakopoulos et al., 2018), whose parameters are estimated from process data by fitting experimental data. Model parameters embed a strong physical meaning as they are associated with chemical, physical and biological phenomena occurring in the system (Kontoravdi et al., 2010). However, this model does not take into account the vast amount of information on cell metabolism. This is mainly due to the challenge of dealing with the large number of metabolites measured as ions during an experimental batch.

Some models attempts to integrate -omics data in model's equations adding metabolites as intermediates in equilibrium and using them to fit new parameters (Ahn and Antoniewicz, 2012). However, this increases model complexity and makes the parameters estimation a challenge. Overcoming these issues and exploiting the potential of metabolomics information promises to unlock new knowledge and optimize mAb development and production.

The aim of this work is to integrate the metabolic information on CHO cell cultures (obtained from metabolomics data) and the chemical, physical and biological phenomena occurring in the system (available in first-principle models of the culture built from process data) in an industrial case study for the development of mAbs in AMBR15® miniature bioreactors. This is achieved by linking the metabolomics data to a kinetic model using data-driven methods to determine the relationships between the most important model parameters for the underlying chemical, physical and biological phenomena, and cell metabolism.

2. Materials and methods

2.1. Proposed methodology

In order to relate the information on metabolic dynamics to the macroscopic culture phenomena occurring in CHO cell cultures, a novel methodology is proposed that consists of the following steps (Figure 1):

1. first-principle model building: a state-of-the-art model for CHO cell lines (Kontoravdi et al., 2010) is improved to better describe the contributions of Glutamate and Lactate in order to be representative for the case study considered. The structural identifiability of the model (Villaverde et al., 2016) is verified to determine whether parameter values are unique and meaningful, allowing for reliable model analysis, validation, and prediction;

2. sensitivity analysis: due to limited number of measurements per cell line (namely, $T = 7$ time points) of the V_P process variables, a maximum of $P = 7$ parameters can be estimated for each cell line. Sensitivity analysis is performed to rank the parameters and identify those which are the most important in describing the specificity of the cell lines behavior. These 7 parameters are referred to as the *most influent* parameters, while the rest of the parameters are referred to as *fixed* parameters;

3. first-principle model parameters estimation: the proposed model is fitted to the process data to estimate the model parameters:
   a. most influent parameter estimation: the set **y** of the most important parameters is estimated with maximum likelihood estimation (Myung, 2003) from process data for each cell line, while the values of the remaining parameters is fixed;

     b. fixed parameters: cell lines are divided into three groups based on their productivity performances and the fixed parameters are set to a constant value for all the cell lines within a group;

4. machine-learning correlative modelling: the relationships between the cell metabolism dynamics and culture phenomena is studied building a multivariate latent-variable regression model relating the dynamics of the metabolomics data with the most influent parameters;

5. biological understanding: results from machine-learning models are examined to determine which metabolites are the most important in predicting a particular parameter (i.e., highly correlated to a particular phenomenon).

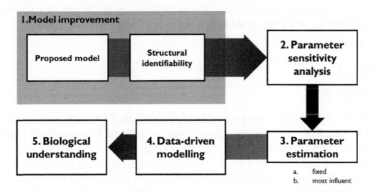

Figure 1. *Schematic of the proposed modelling strategy for relating the information on metabolic dynamics to the macroscopic culture phenomena occurring in CHO cell cultures.*

2.2. Available data and preprocessing

Data from the industrial development of mAb are available for two runs performed in the AMBR15® miniature bioreactor using GSK (Stevenage, UK) proprietary platform process. Both process data and metabolomics data are available.

In particular, a set of $V_P = 7$ process variables are measured in $T = 7$ time instants during an experimental batch for $N = 96$ CHO cell lines: viable cell concentration (VCC), concentration of mAb, Glucose, Glutamate, Glutamine, Lactate and Ammonium. These are arranged in a three-dimensional process dataset $\underline{\mathbf{X}}_P [N \times V_P \times T]$.

For each cell line, intracellular metabolites are analyzed using liquid chromatography-mass spectrometry performed in negative ionization mode. Metabolomics profiles consisting of $V_I = 4587$ ions intensities are sampled in two replicates $R = 2$ and arranged in a four-dimensional array $\underline{\mathbf{X}}_I [N \times V_I \times (T - 1) \times R]$. Raw metabolic data is pre-processed for peak detection, global scan alignment, and metabolite annotation (Barberi et al., 2022). Additionally, ions with more than 20% missing intensities are removed from the data set, while missing data imputation (Troyanskaya et al., 2001) is used to impute the remaining missing data. Metabolomics data are then: *i)* variable-wise unfolded in order to account for replications $\underline{\mathbf{X}}'_I [N \cdot R \times V_I \times (T - 1)]$; *ii)* batch-wise unfolded in order to account for data dynamics $\mathbf{X}_I [N \cdot R \times V_I \cdot (T - 1)]$; *iii)* Pareto scaled.

2.3. State-of-the-art kinetic model for CHO cell cultures

The considered state-of-the-art model (Kontoravdi et al., 2010) represents the CHO cell culture behavior through a set of differential equation with 20 parameters and 7 process variables: Volume, Viable Cell Concertation (VCC), Glucose, product titer, Lactate,

Glutamine and Ammonia. Unfortunately, this kinetic model does not fully capture the complexity of the system under study and should be improved (see Subsection 3.1).

2.4. Multivariate statistical analysis

Multiway Partial Least-Square (MPLS) (Nomikos & MacGregor, 1995) consists of a Partial Least-Squares (PLS) model built on a batch-wise unfolded matrix used to consider variables dynamic trajectories. PLS (Wise & Gallagher, 1996) is a linear multivariate regression method which captures the relationship between a matrix of predictors and a matrix of responses. In our case seven models are built, each one using the unfolded metabolomics dataset $\mathbf{X}_I$ as a predictor matrix, and a response vector $\mathbf{y} = [N \times 1]$ which collects the values of one of the most influent model parameters for all the cell lines. PLS identifies the direction of maximum covariance between predictors and responses by projecting both $\mathbf{X}_I$ and $\mathbf{y}$ into a reduced space of A Latent Variables (LVs):

$$\mathbf{X}_I = \mathbf{T}\mathbf{P}^T + \mathbf{E} \ , \tag{1}$$

$$\mathbf{y} = \mathbf{T}\mathbf{q} + \mathbf{f} \ , \tag{2}$$

$$\mathbf{T} = \mathbf{X}\mathbf{W}(\mathbf{P}^T\mathbf{W})^{-1} \ , \tag{3}$$

where $\mathbf{P}\ [A \times V_I]$ and $\mathbf{q}\ [A \times 1]$ are the loading matrices, $\mathbf{T}\ [N \times A]$ is the score matrix, $\mathbf{E}\ [N \times V_I]$ and $\mathbf{f}\ [N \times 1]$ are the residual matrices of $\mathbf{X}$ and $\mathbf{Y}$, respectively (minimized in a least-square sense) and $\mathbf{W}\ [N \times A]$ is the weight.

The appropriate number A of LVs is selected by cross-validation (Geladi & Kowalski, 1986). The validation performance of the PLS models is improved through an iterative ion selection procedure retaining only the most informative ions for the prediction (Fernández Pierna et al., 2009).

PLS is used to predict the response $\hat{\mathbf{y}}$ (i.e., the relevant model parameter) from a set of new predictors $\mathbf{x}_{NEW}\ [1 \times V_I]$:

$$\hat{\mathbf{y}} = \mathbf{x}_{NEW}\mathbf{B} \tag{4}$$

where $\mathbf{B} = \mathbf{W}(\mathbf{P}^T\mathbf{W})^{-1}\mathbf{Q}^T$ are the regression coefficients of the PLS model. The PLS model is validated through a Monte-Carlo leave-5-out procedure on $I = 10^5$ iterations, partitioning the N available samples in 91 cell lines used for calibration and $M = 5$ randomly selected for validation. The prediction performance is evaluated through: *i)* determination coefficient in validation $\overline{Q^2}$ averaged throughout the M validation samples and the I iterations; *ii)* index $MMAE/\sigma$ defined as the median value of MAE/σ (mean absolute error of prediction) throughout the I Monte-Carlo iterations, where at each iteration:

$$MAE/\sigma = \frac{\sum_{m=1}^{M}|y_m - \hat{y}_m|/M}{\sigma} \ , \tag{4}$$

where M is the number of samples in validation, y_m is the m-th sample model parameter, $\hat{y}_m$ is the first-principle model parameter predicted by the PLS model for the same validation samples, and σ is the standard deviation of the considered model parameter used for PLS model calibration.

3. Results

3.1. Proposed CHO cell model and structural identifiability

Since the complexity of the system under study is not captured by state-of-art kinetic model of CHO cell cultures (Kontoravdi et al., 2010), the model representativeness is improved for what concerns Glutamate and Lactate consumption (Barberi et al., 2022). In particular, the role of the Glutamate in the culture is added through Equation:

$$\frac{dC_{GLU}}{dt} = \frac{F_{IN}}{V}\left(C_{in,glu} - C_{GLU}\right) - \left(\frac{\mu}{Y_{x,glu}} + m_{GLU}\right)X_V + \frac{\mu}{Y_{glu,X}} + k_1 C_{GLN} - k_2 C_{GLU} C_{AMM} \qquad (5)$$

where $C_{in,glu}$ is the concentration of Glutamate in a feeding bolus, k_1 and k_2 are the kinetic constant regulating conversion of Glutamate to Glutamine and Y_{gluX} and $Y_{X,glu}$ are the Glutamate production constant. Additionally, Lactate consumption is described a:

$$\frac{dC_{LAT}}{dt} = -\frac{F_{IN}}{V}C_{LAT} + Q_{lat,glc}X_V + \left(Q_{GLU}Y_{lat,glu}\right)X_V - \left(\frac{1}{Y_{x,lat}}\left(\frac{C_{lat}}{K_{c,lat}+C_{lat}}\right)\left(\frac{K_{c,glc}}{K_{c,glc}+C_{GLC}}\right)\right)X_V \qquad (6)$$

where novel addends regard the last two terms of (6). $Y_{lat,glu}$ represents the yield of Lactate with respect to Glutamate, Y_{xlat} is the yield of Lactate consumption, $K_{c,lat}$ and $K_{c,glc}$ regulate the Lactate consumption to Glucose. The proposed model is composed of 8 process variables and 25 parameters, and is structurally identifiable, as verified through the generalized Observability-Identifiability condition (Villaverde et al., 2016).

3.2. Parameter sensitivity analysis
Parameters sensitivity analysis is performed to identify the parameters that have the largest impact on the first-principle model responses. Sensitivity of each parameter is evaluated by Elementary Effect Test (Saltelli et al., 2008). The most influent parameters that control the phenomena occurring into the culture are: Y_{Xglc} and Y_{Xglu} linked to nutrients consumption, μ_{max} linked to cell growth, KI_{amm} and Y_{latglc} related to Ammonia and Lactate inhibition and Y_{mAbglc} that regulates antibody formation.
The remaining parameters are fixed according to the method described in Subsection 2.1.

3.3. Biological understanding through PLS modelling
The prediction performance the PLS models predicting the most influential first-principle model parameters from metabolomic dynamics are shown in Table 1 and are reported in term of $\overline{Q^2}$ and $MMAE/\sigma$. The resulting average determination coefficients for all cell lines range from 45% to 90% showing that a strong relationship between cell metabolism and culture phenomena is found. Additionally, the value of $MMAE/\sigma$ shows that median absolute errors of prediction are lower than the standard deviation of the parameters used for model calibration.

Table 1. *PLS model validation average results for the predicted first-principle kinetic model parameters of all the cell lines.*

Parameter	MMAE/σ	$\overline{Q^2}$
μ_{max}	8.64%	75.20%
Y_{mAbglc}	7.10%	50.00%
Y_{xglc}	6.67%	45.80%
Y_{xglu}	16.30%	90.40%
KI_{amm}	34.70%	76.40%
Y_{latglc}	41.30%	80.90%
Y_{glux}	32.90%	82.20%

Furthermore, the PLS models allows the investigation of metabolites associated with the cell culture behaviors. This analysis is performed through the VIP index (Chong & Jun,

2005) and the regression coefficients **B** of the PLS models. For example, we found that the cell growth and viability is correlated to the metabolism of Arginine and Taurine.

4. Conclusions

This work proposed a hybrid approach to relate the microscopic information on the metabolism dynamics of the cell lines with the macroscopic chemical, physical and biological phenomena occurring in CHO cell cultures to produce monoclonal antibodies in the biopharmaceutical industry. This was done through first-principle modelling and machine learning. In particular, process data were used to estimate the model parameters of a kinetic model describing the cell behavior. First-principle model parameters, which represent the most important phenomena occurring in the culture, were then linked to metabolic dynamics using data driven approaches. For this purpose, an improved version of a state-of-the-art CHO cell model (Kontoravdi, 2010) was proposed to better represent Glutamate and Lactate consumption. Metabolomics data were then linked to kinetic model parameters using multivariate latent-variable regression models. These highlighted a strong relationship between chemical-physical-biological phenomena and the dynamic evolution of cell metabolism, which allowed understanding the effect of the metabolites on peculiar culture phenomena. For example, cell growth resulted to be related to the metabolism of Arginine and Taurine.

References

Ahn, W. S., & Antoniewicz, M. R. (2012). Towards dynamic metabolic flux analysis in CHO cell cultures. Biotechnology Journal, 7(1), 61–74.

Barberi, G., Benedetti, A., Diaz-Fernandez, P., Sévin, D. C., Vappiani, J., Finka, G., Bezzo, F., Barolo, M., & Facco, P. (2022). Integrating metabolome dynamics and process data to guide cell line selection in biopharmaceutical process development. Metabolic Engineering, 72, 353–364.

Chong, I. G., & Jun, C. H. (2005). Performance of some variable selection methods when multicollinearity is present. Chemometrics and Intelligent Laboratory Systems, 78(1–2), 103–112.

Geladi, P., & Kowalski, B. R. (1986). Partial least-squares regression: a tutorial. Analytica Chimica Acta, 185(C), 1–17.

Kontoravdi, C., Pistikopoulos, E. N., & Mantalaris, A. (2010). Systematic development of predictive mathematical models for animal cell cultures. Computers & Chemical Engineering, 34(8), 1192–1198.

Kyriakopoulos, S., Ang, K. S., Lakshmanan, M., Huang, Z., Yoon, S., Gunawan, R., & Lee, D. Y. (2018). Kinetic Modeling of Mammalian Cell Culture Bioprocessing: The Quest to Advance Biomanufacturing. Biotechnology Journal, 13(3).

Myung, I. J. (2003). Tutorial on maximum likelihood estimation. Journal of Mathematical Psychology, 47(1), 90–100.

Nomikos, P., & MacGregor, J. F. (1995). Multi-way partial least squares in monitoring batch processes. Chemometrics and Intelligent Laboratory Systems, 30(1), 97–108.

Saltelli, A., Ratto, M., Andres, T., Campolongo, F., Cariboni, J., Gatelli, D., Saisana, M., & Tarantola, S. (2008). Introduction to Sensitivity Analysis. Global Sensitivity Analysis. The Primer.

Troyanskaya, O., Cantor, M., Sherlock, G., Brown, P., Hastie, T., Tibshirani, R., Botstein, D., & Altman, R. B. (2001). Missing value estimation methods for DNA microarrays. BIOINFORMATICS, 17(6), 520–525.

Villaverde, A. F., Barreiro, A., & Papachristodoulou, A. (2016). Structural Identifiability of Dynamic Systems Biology Models. PLOS Computational Biology, 12(10), e1005153.

Walsh, G., & Walsh, E. (2022). Biopharmaceutical benchmarks 2022. Nature Biotechnology 2022 40:12, 40(12), 1722–1760.

Wise, B. M., & Gallagher, N. B. (1996). The process chemometrics approach to process monitoring and fault detection. Journal of Process Control, 6(6), 329–348.

Flavio Manenti, Gintaras V. Reklaitis (Eds.), Proceedings of the 34th European Symposium on Computer Aided Process Engineering / 15th International Symposium on Process Systems Engineering (ESCAPE34/PSE24), June 2-6, 2024, Florence, Italy

Towards Cognitive Engineering-Driven knowledge graphs for Chemical Processes: Serialization of Abstraction Decomposition Hierarchy Using OntoCAPE

Nazanin Hamedi[a*], Anselm Klose[b], Leon Urbas[c]

[a]DFG RTG Conducive Design of Cyber Physical Systems, TU Dresden, Germany
[b]Chair of Process Control Systems, Process-to-Order Lab, TU Dresden, Germany
[c]Process Control Systems & Process Systems Engineering, TU Dresden, Germany
naznin.hamedi@tu-dresden.de

Abstract

Inspired by principles of cognitive engineering, this study explores the formalization of the results of an Abstraction Decomposition Hierarchy (ADH) towards a Digital Twin for supporting the design of interactive information systems for chemical processes. ADH is a two-dimensional hierarchical space, comprising a functional abstraction hierarchy and a physical decomposition hierarchy. While the decomposition dimension deals with the process sectioning from a superficial organizational perspective, the functional dimension analyzes the actual phenomena occurring in the process. This framework offers a formalism for presenting information in a way to enhance the decision-making and fault diagnosis abilities of human operators.

In this research, we leverage OntoCAPE, a widely recognized ontology for semantically describing Computer-Aided Process Engineering (CAPE), to create a knowledge graph of the ADH. To investigate the merits and limits of the suggested formalization, we applied it to the Tennessee Eastman Process (TEP). Our model is capable of answering competency questions not only regarding the structural aspects of the process, including the configuration of process units and the connectivity between various pieces of equipment, but also the actual physico-chemical phenomena happening in the process and their influence on process parameters.

This work presents promising results for further development of software tools based on an ADH-driven knowledge graph for the design of decision support systems. These tools have the potential to significantly advance decision support and fault diagnosis in complex processes.

Keywords: Abstraction Decomposition Hierarchy, OntoCAPE, Knowledge graph, Information querying

1. Introduction

As the complexity of production plants continues to grow, the demand for decision support systems for operators becomes increasingly imperative. One of the major problems arises from different level of novelty of events from the viewpoints of the operators and designers of systems representing the process (e.g., expert systems, or human-machine interface). To deal with this problem a formalism is needed to be considered for knowledge representation that covers different aspects of the process (Jamieson and Vicente, 2001). This knowledge representation, often referred to as a

Knowledge Graph (KG), serves as a pivotal component within the developed software tools, playing a crucial role in enhancing the efficiency and effectiveness of decision-making processes (Eibeck, Lim and Kraft, 2019).

Rooted in cognitive engineering, the Abstraction-Decomposition Hierarchy (ADH) serves as an effective tool for representing the task related knowledge in complex work domains. This two-dimensional hierarchical framework comprises two distinct hierarchies, as illustrated on the right side of Figure 1: the abstraction hierarchy (AH) along the vertical axis and the decomposition hierarchy along the horizontal axis. The decomposition hierarchy involves the sectionalization of the process from a surface-level perspective (e.g., plant → units → equipment). Conversely, the vertical aspect encapsulates the AH, delving into the actual phenomena occurring in the process. In fact, the solution to the question of how to achieve the objectives of this layer lies at a lower level in the hierarchy (Rasmussen and Vicente, 1989; Jamieson, Ma and St-Cyr, 2020).

The ADH has previously been employed to describe chemical processes (Jamieson and Vicente, 2001 Son *et al.*, 2019). However, the crucial area requiring investigation lies in the utilization of an established standard for formally (in a computer-understandable manner) describing processes using ADH. Indeed, two crucial facts should be taken into account: Firstly, the serialization of the ADH-based KG; secondly, and perhaps of equal or greater significance, a standardized way for serialization. The latter not only provides a foundational framework for collaborative developing of ADH-based KGs but also enables seamless interaction among different individuals with each other's KGs and empowers computational tools to engage with diverse KGs crafted by various contributors.

In this study, OntoCAPE has been utilized for developing the KG of Tennessee Eastman Process (TEP) based on ADH. In the remainder of this paper, the general hypothesis will be initially presented, followed by an outline of the requirements analysis. Subsequently, the modelling approach will be detailed, concluding with an evaluation of the model.

2. Research Approach

Based on previous studies (Jamieson and Vicente, 2001; Son *et al.*, 2019), the hypothesis of this contribution is that the ADH can provide a robust structure for constructing a KG with the capability to address diverse inquiries posed by operators across various facets of the process. To investigate this research hypothesis, we chose the TEP (Downs and Vogel, 1993) for an use case study, given its extensive utilization in process control and specifically in exploring fault diagnosis methodologies (Reinartz *et al.*, 2019; Suresh, Sivaram and Venkatasubramanian, 2019). The major input to our study was the detailed description of the TEP given by (Vosloo *et al.*, 2020).

3. Case Study

3.1. Requirement Analysis

Left side of Figure 1 outlines the general structure of ADH. As mentioned, the horizontal direction of this two-dimensional framework deals with structural decomposition of a chemical plant; while the vertical hierarchy describes the functional aspects of the process. Its topmost level; Functional Purpose, encapsulates the purpose of the process in the most abstract form. Progressing to the second tier, the Abstract Function, endeavours to analyse the function of each component within the process. Subsequently, the Generalized Function links the abstract functional perspective with the physical functional layers. The final level, Physical Function, is the closest to the tangible reality, offering detailed insights into each equipment constituting the process (Jamieson and Vicente, 2001; Son *et al.*, 2019).

3.2. Phenomena-oriented Analysis of the Generalized Function Level

An analysis of the ADH literature reveals that the most problematic layer seems to be the generalized functions layer as the different studies are not coherent on how to fill this layer. Jamieson & Vicente (2001), for instance suggest to provide information about heat transfer and material flow on this layer, as well as chemical reactions. Son et. al. (2019) described on this layer the general processes that are involved in accomplishing the defined functional purposes. Both approaches are cumbersome: The approach of Jamieson & Vicente lacks of a clear distinction to the abstract function layer, while the approach of Son has too many degrees of freedom and does not provide the necessary guidance. We, therefore, suggest to follow the approach proposed by (Lutze, 2011), which introduces phenomena as a set of eight classes that serve as the (physico-chemical) building blocks for processes, such as mixing, stream dividing, phase contact, phase transition, phase change, phase separation, reaction and energy transfer (Lutze, 2011). This approach makes it possible to describe the generalized function layer with a fixed set of classes, a prerequisite for proper modelling and comparison of different analyses.

3.3. Selection of Information Model

As highlighted previously, the principal objective of this study is to develop not only a computer readable, but also standard compatible KG for the ADH of TEP. Hence, it was important to identify an existing standard which is capable of describing different layers of information considered in ADH. To this end, some of the notable existing standards such as Data Exchange in the Process Industry (DEXPI) (Wiedau *et al.*, 2019), Computer Aided Engineering Exchange (CAEX) (IEC 62424, 2016), and OntoCAPE (Marquardt *et al.*, 2010) has been considered. In fact, the bottleneck for choosing the right information modelling standard for the purpose of describing an ADH of a process is the Generalized Function layer which involves the description of the behavior of the process. This fact made OntoCAPE the only suitable information representation standard for the aim of developing an ADH-based KG.

3.4. Modeling in OntoCAPE

OntoCAPE is a formal ontology that has been implemented in the OWL notation. It describes diverse aspects of CAPE. It has an extensible architecture that makes it possible to cover very many tasks of CAPE, such as mathematical modelling, or data integration and management with sub-models. OntoCAPE is organized through different layers of abstraction, spanning from the most generic abstract layer, the Meta Layer, to the most detailed application specific layer. OntoCAPE models a process as a composite system (Morbach, Wiesner and Marquardt, 2008) and tries to capture systems from different composition aspects, such as its function, realization, and behaviour.

As shown in Figure 1, the Abstract Function, Generalized Function, and Physical Function layers of ADH, are respectively modeled by the CPS_function, CPS_behavior, and CPS_realization partial models of OntoCAPE. Moreover, it models each aspect of a system as a network of connected Devices and Connections. This pattern is identical in all of the process aspects of interest in this paper. As noted earlier, the most challenging part of serializing ADH was to define the Generalized Function; therefore, this section will be explained in more detail in the next sub section.

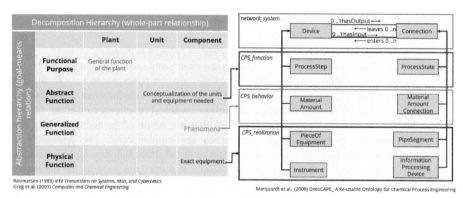

Figure 1: Compatibility of OntoCAPE and ADH

3.4.1. Description of Generalized Function in OntoCAPE

In previous publications regarding ADH (Jamieson and Vicente, 2001; Son *et al.*, 2019), Generalized Function level was developed in different formats, thereby introducing considerable complexity and diminishing its practical utility. Establishing a standardized format for Generalized Function level development not only expedites the developer's workflow by providing a pre-defined structure but also fosters collaborative development and software interoperability. OntoCAPE behavioral model (from partial model CPS_behavior) arises as an appropriate candidate due to its alignment with our criteria for the Generalized Function level. Indeed, it tries to qualitatively model the behavior of chemical processes. Figure 2 depicts this model for the reactor. As can be seen, at first, the Material Amount or Material Amount Connection should be defined which reflects the material content of a physical piece of equipment, on which a physico-chemical phenomenon happens, and governs its behavior (Marquardt *et al.*, 2010). Afterwards, we have the physical properties that are influenced by the phenomenon.

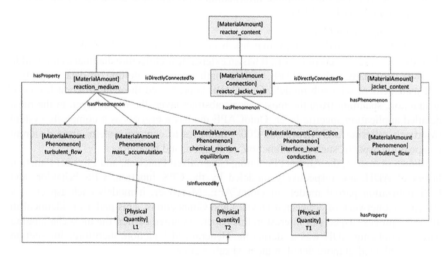

Figure 2: Behavioral model of TEP reactor based on OntoCAPE

Towards Cognitive Engineering-Driven knowledge graphs for Chemical
Processes: Serialization of Abstraction Decomposition Hierarchy Using OntoCAPE

3101

3.5. Querying information in the developed KG

As OntoCAPE is an OWL based ontology, the construction of our KG was smoothly done utilizing the software Protégé. Subsequently, to query in the developed graph-based space, it was imported to Python using Owlready2 library (Lamy, 2017), where series of formulated queries were executed.

4. Evaluation

To evaluate our developed KG, some competency questions are shaped, which then formulated as queries, and answered by our KG. One of the competency questions is: How is pipe segment 14 (pipe entering the reactor) connected to condenser? This question should be converted to a computer algorithm as shown in Figure 3.. The result of this algorithm would be an array named connectivity which is equal to [PS14, reactor vessel, PS20, PI01, PS21, condenser1] (PS 20 and PS21 respectively show the pipe segment between reactor and PI01, and PI01 and condenser 1). Some more competency questions, their query format, and the obtained result are tabulated in Table 1. It should mention that in both Table 1 and Figure 1 entities defined in OntoCAPE are illustrated by ***italic bold*** style.

Table 1: Competency questions as a means for evaluating the KG (query format is based on owlready2 library in Python, where the imported ontology is named ADH).

Competency question	Query format of the competency question	Result of the query
What process units exist in TEP?	ADH. ***ProcessUnit.*** instances ()	[reactor, condenser, V-L separator, stripper, compressor]
What are the components of the control loop for controlling flow A?	ADH. controlling_flow_A ***hasSubsystem***	[FI01, valve01, FC01]
What phenomena happens in the boiler's shell-tube wall?	ADH. boiler_shell_tube_wall. ***hasPhenomenon***	[interface_heat_conduction]
What phenomena influences temperature of the reactor?	ADH. T2. ***isInfluencedBy***	[interface_heat_conduction, chemical_reaction_equilibrium, turbulent_flow]

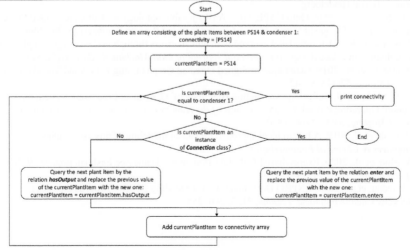

Figure 3: Algorithm for finding the plant items between PS14 (reactor entering pipe segment) to condenser.

5. Conclusions

In summary, this study highlights the potential of the ADH as a robust framework for the development of a KG that appropriately represents chemical processes. An inherent strength of the ADH lies in its ability to explain both the superficial, and functional aspects of a complex system, here a chemical plant. To model the ADH in a computer understandable way, OntoCAPE, as a well-know ontology was used. A significant contribution of this work is to offer a formalism for developing the Generalized Function layer of the ADH, which provide a qualitative modelling approach to explain the behaviour of the process. To evaluate our KG, several competency questions were formulated and queried in the KG. Our result indicates the capability of the model in different aspects of the process.

Acknowledgments: This work was Funded by the Deutsche Forschungsgemeinschaft (DFG, German Research Foundation) – 319919706 /RTG2323.

References

J. J. Downs, E. F. Vogel, 1993, A plant-wide industrial process control problem, *Computers & Chemical Engineering*, 17, 3, 245–255.

A. Eibeck, et. al., 2019, J-Park Simulator: An ontology-based platform for cross-domain scenarios in process industry, *Computers & Chemical Engineering*, 131, 106586.

IEC 62424, 2016, *Representation of process control engineering - Requests in P&I diagrams and data exchange between P&ID tools and PCE-CAE tools.*

G. A. Jamieson, 2020, Benefits of Ecological Interfaces Under Equivalent Sensor Sets, *IEEE International Conference on Systems, Man, and Cybernetics (SMC)*, 2232–2236.

G. A.Jamieson, K. J. Vicente, 2001, Ecological interface design for petrochemical applications: supporting operator adaptation, continuous learning, and distributed, collaborative work, *Computers & Chemical Engineering*, 25, 7, 1055–1074.

J. B. Lamy, 2017, Owlready: Ontology-oriented programming in Python with automatic classification and high level constructs for biomedical ontologies, *Artificial Intelligence in Medicine*, 80, 11–28.

Lutze, P., 2011, *An Innovative Synthesis Methodology for Process Intensification*. PhD thesis, DTU.

W. Marquardt, et al., 2010, *OntoCAPE A Re-Usable Ontology for Chemical Process Engineering*. Springer Berlin Heidelberg.

J. Morbach, et. al., 2008, Onto CAPE 2.0 —A (Re-)usable ontology for Computer-Aided Process Engineering, *18 European Symposium on Computer Aided Process Engineering*. 991–996.

J. Rasmussen, K. J. Vicente, 1989, Coping with human errors through system design: implications for ecological interface design, *International Journal of Man-Machine Studies*, 31(5), 517–534.

Reinartz, C. et al., 2019, Generation of Signed Directed Graphs Using Functional Models, *IFAC-PapersOnLine*, 52(11), 37–42.

Son, C. et al., 2019, Reflecting Abstraction Hierarchy of a Chemical Processing System on Standard Operating Procedures, *Proceedings of the Human Factors and Ergonomics Society Annual Meeting*, 63(1), 1806–1810.

R. Suresh, et al, 2019, A hierarchical approach for causal modeling of process systems, *Computers & Chemical Engineering*, 123, 170–183.

J. Vosloo, et al., 2020, Exergy-based fault detection on the Tennessee Eastman process, *IFAC-PapersOnLine*, 53, 2, 13713–13720.

M. Wiedau, et al., 2019, ENPRO Data Integration: Extending DEXPI Towards the Asset Lifecycle, *Chemie Ingenieur Technik*, 91, 3, 240–255.

Flavio Manenti, Gintaras V. Reklaitis (Eds.), Proceedings of the 34th European Symposium on Computer Aided Process Engineering / 15th International Symposium on Process Systems Engineering (ESCAPE34/PSE24), June 2-6, 2024, Florence, Italy

Surrogate-Based Optimization of the OPEX of a Modular Plant for Biogas Conversion to Methanol Using the MADS Algorithm

Luis Felipe Sánchez Martínez[a], Andrea Galeazzi[a], Flavio Manenti[a,*]

[a]CMIC Department "Giulio Natta", Politecnico di Milano, Piazza Leonardo da Vinci 32, Milano, 20133, Italy

flavio.manenti@polimi.it

Abstract

The present work studies the potential of surrogate models for the global optimization of complex chemical processes. In particular, a modular plant for the conversion of biogas to methanol is considered. The Aspen HYSYS simulation of this plant was run 480 times, which ensured the even distribution of points in the input space. The evenness of this design of experiments was evaluated using a discrepancy measurement called the Mixture Discrepancy. With the simulation data, some of the most widely used surrogate models such as regression models and the Kriging Gaussian process were trained. The most accurate model for the prediction of each output variable was selected and used for the optimization of the OPEX. The optimization complemented the trained surrogate models with the Mesh Adaptive Direct Search (MADS) algorithm. For this purpose, the open-access computational implementation of the MADS algorithm called NOMAD was used. With the surrogate-based optimization, the computational times were reduced an 88% with respect to the simulation-based optimization. In addition, the accuracy of the surrogate model was paramount, as an average 0.75% prediction error was found. Consequently, the models proved sufficient for optimizing the studied process, resulting in a 22.2% reduction in the OPEX.

Keywords: surrogate model, optimization, MADS, NOMAD

1. Introduction

The mathematical complexity of a chemical process increases rapidly with the number of involved unit operations or the presence of intricate thermodynamics or kinetics (McBride and Sundmacher, 2019). To tackle these complexities while maintaining computational accuracy, surrogate models, a form of supervised machine learning, have gained relevance (Alizadeh et al., 2020). These mathematically simpler models require data from the process to be trained. Consequently, the quality of the surrogate is related to the quality of the extracted data (McBride and Sundmacher, 2019).

Considering the high accuracy presented by surrogate models in several applications (Alizadeh et al., 2020; Pishkari et al., 2023), this study presents the development of a surrogate model for a modular plant for the production of methanol from biogas. A one-shot space-filling design using the maximin-optimized LHS complemented with discrepancy measurements is adopted to guarantee uniform distribution and unbiased representation of the domain. The surrogate models trained were selected considering the most commonly used in chemical engineering. These models include polynomial regressions, regression trees and support vector machines, previously used by Galeazzi et al. (2023) for surrogate modeling of an amine-washing section of a plant. Additionally, the Kriging Gaussian process, known for its effectiveness in managing complex mathematical systems, was incorporated. The most accurate surrogate model was then used to optimize the Operational Expenditures (OPEX) through a black-box derivative-free optimization powered by the NOMAD open-access software (Le Digabel, 2011).

2. Problem statement and process description

The objective of the present work is to optimize the OPEX of a modular plant which produces methanol from biogas. This module has been installed in a heat and power plant in Italy, and corresponds to the industrial validation of the BIGSQUID process, an innovative technology licensed by the Politecnico di Milano (Fedeli and Manenti, 2022; Negri et al., 2022). The BIGSQUID (BIoGaS to liQUID) process comprises five main steps: biogas upgrading to remove H_2S, biogas reforming to produce syngas, syngas purification to reach the synthesis requirements, methanol synthesis from syngas, and methanol purification (See Figure 1).

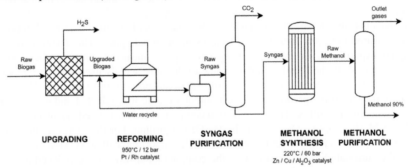

Figure 1: Overview of the BIGSQUID process to produce methanol from raw biogas.

For this process, a rigorous Aspen HYSYS simulation was developed by Fedeli and Manenti (2022) for the SuPER team of the Politecnico di Milano. Even if the number of unit operations shown in Figure 1 seems small and manageable, the presence of two recycle streams in the simulation, which involve critical process variables, considerably increased its complexity. The average simulation time was found to be around 2.77 seconds, while the convergence rate obtained from preliminary experiments was 60%. In a first attempt to optimize the process, the Aspen HYSYS optimizer failed. This failure condition was maintained even when different initial points were tested. This lack of convergence may be correlated to the low convergence rate of the simulation, the high correlation of the variables and their complex interactions. For the mentioned reasons, a different optimization approach should be considered. To avoid increasing the complexity of the problem through complex optimization software such as GAMS, the surrogate approach for the optimization presented an interesting alternative. The surrogate models were trained from real data extracted from the simulation using a computer with a processor 11th Gen Intel® Core™ i9-11900 @ 2.50GHz and 32 GB of RAM.

3. Data generation

The input variables for the rigorous simulation and the surrogate model were selected and delimited considering their physical, chemical, and process-related constraints. The variables are shown in Figure 1, and their boundaries are presented in Table 1.

Surrogate-Based Optimization of the OPEX of a Modular Plant for Biogas
Conversion to Methanol Using the MADS Algorithm

3105

Table 1: Input variables to the black-box model of the BIGSQUID process.

Stream	Description	Variable	Nominal value	Minimum value	Maximum value
		F (kg/h)	600.0	500.0	700.0
BIOGAS	Raw biogas	x_{CO2}	0.46	0,4	0,5
		x_{CH4}	0.53	0,45	0,7
DEMIWATER	Make-up in reforming recycle	F	10	9	25
2cc	Compressed BIOGAS	P (bar)	16.0	12.0	20.0
BRProduct	Reformer outlet	T (C)	950.0	800.0	1000.0
5b	BRPRoduct after cooling	T (C)	5.0	5.0	25.0
CompressedSyngas	Purified syngas	P (bar)	60.0	50.0	70.0
WATER	Water for syngas purification	F (kg/h)	5000.0	4500.0	6000.0
CLEANWATER	Make-up for syngas purification recycle	T (C)	10.0	5.0	25.0
TOREACTOR	Synthesis reactor inlet syngas	T (C)	250.0	220.0	270.0
7	Synthesis reactor outlet	T (C)	10.0	5.0	25.0

Data from Table 1 was used in a Design of Experiments (DoE) based on the maximin-optimized LHS, one of the most widely implemented DoE methods in the chemical industry (McBride and Sundmacher, 2019). The number of samples was set on 480, which was the lowest number of samples to minimize the Mixture Discrepancy, an accurate metric for the evaluation of the space-filling characteristics of a DoE (Zhou et al., 2013). These samples were introduced to the Aspen HYSYS simulation of the BIGSQUID. With the simulation data, the dataset for the training of the surrogate models was obtained.

4. Surrogate modeling

The input/output relation of the variables was determined by training 10 regression models, previously considered by Galeazzi et al. (2023), plus the Kriging Gaussian process. All the models were trained once for each output variable. The accuracy of the models was determined using the average Mean Absolute Error (MAE) of a 5 k-fold cross-validation. As the MAE was calculated over normalized data, the reported MAE is a representation of the relative error of the models. Equations 1 and 2 show the data normalization process and the MAE calculation, respectively. The output variables, their description inside the process and the best surrogate model for its prediction using the MAE as evaluation metric is presented in Table 2. In addition, Figure 2 presents the parity plots of the output variables, which confront the simulated (real) and predicted values for each variable.

$$x_{new} = \frac{|x - x_{min}|}{|x_{max} - x_{min}|} \tag{1}$$

$$MAE = \frac{\sum_i |y_i^{real} - y_i^{predicted}|}{n} \tag{2}$$

Table 2. Best Surrogate Models

Stream	Description	Variable	Best model	MAE (%)
METHANOL	Outlet methanol stream	F (kg/h)	Kriging	1,00%
		xMeOH	Kriging	1,37%
Qreactor	Reformer heat requirement	Q (kW)	Kriging	1,59%
QP100	Reformer make-up recycle pump	Q (kW)	Linear Regression	0,00%
Qk2	Syngas compressor before purirfication	Q (kW)	Kriging	0,57%
Duty	Synthesis reactor cooling requirement	Q (kW)	Kriging	1,00%
Q104	Cooling of refrigerant	Q (kW)	Kriging	1,61%
Q107	Cooling of refrigerant	Q (kW)	Kriging	1,33%
K100	First stage compressor of raw biogas	Q (kW)	Third Order Polynomial Regression	0,01%
K100-1	Second stage compressor of raw biogas	Q (kW)	Third Order Polynomial Regression	0,03%
QP-02	Reformer recycle pump	Q (kW)	Kriging	1,17%
P101	Syngas purification recycle pump	Q (kW)	Second Order Polynomial Regression	0,00%
Q03	Syngas cooling during purification	Q (kW)	Kriging	0,27%
			Average	0,77%

5. Optimization

The objective function for optimization is the OPEX of the system described as:

$$\min OPEX = \sum_{i=1}^{11} C_i Q_i$$

$$s.t.: l_j \leq x_j \leq u_j \forall j \in \{1, \dots, 12\}$$

$$10.0 - METHANOL.F \leq 0$$

$$0.90 - METHANOL.x_{MeOH} \leq 0$$

(3)

Where i represents each of the 11 output energetic streams of Table 2, C_i represents the cost of each energetic stream and Q_i its heat flow. The cost of each energetic stream depends on the utility required and was extracted from Turton et al. (2012). Moreover, j represents each of the 12 input variables of Table 1 delimited by its lower l_j and upper u_j boundaries. Streams BIOGAS and CLEANWATER have not been considered for optimization as they are disturbances of the process and not optimization variables. Finally, the required flowrate and purity of methanol in the plant, which correspond to 10 kg/h and 90% respectively, were set as the constraints for the METHANOL stream.

By implementing the trained surrogate models and the derivative-free open-access black-box optimizer NOMAD, the optimization process was repeated. In this case the optimization time was 86 seconds, which represents a reduction of 88% in the computational time with respect to the original optimization with the simulator, which required around 700 seconds. The results were validated by introducing the found optimal values to the Aspen HYSYS simulation. Nevertheless, the objective function and the constraints were not respected. To determine the cause of the mismatch, a sensitivity analysis with the surrogated model was proposed. The results of the sensitivity analysis showed a high sensitivity of the variable DEMIWATER, which monotonically (and almost linearly) increased the total OPEX. Considering this behavior, the upper boundary of the variable was re-set to 15 kg/h in Table 1.

With the new boundaries for DEMIWATER, the surrogate modelling methodology presented in this work was repeated. In this case, the validated results were satisfactory, and reduced the OPEX 22.2% compared to the base case. Table 3 presents a summary of the results from both optimizations, before and after the sensitivity analysis compared to the nominal case. As an important remark, Figure 2 and Table 2 present the results of the surrogate model trained after the sensitivity analysis.

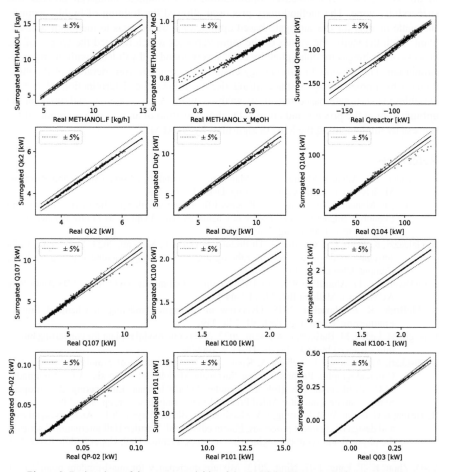

Figure 2. Parity plots of the output variable of the BIGSQUID process after the surrogate modeling process. Dotted lines delimit the zone with a prediction error below ± 5%.

Table 3. Results for the optimization of the BIGSQUID process.

Variable	UoM	Original	Before Sensitivity	After Sensitivity
BRProduct.T	°C	950.0	849.8	800.0
DEMIWater.F	kg/h	10.0	9.0	9.0
CompressedSyngas.P	bar	60.0	66.9	59.0
TOREACTOR.T	°C	250.0	265.0	255.9
7.T	°C	10.0	5.1	20.3
5b.T	°C	5.0	5.2	25.0
2cc.P	bar	16.0	12.0	12.0
WATER.F	kg/h	5000.0	4664.0	4500.0
OPEX Surrogate	$/y	22195	14929	17286
OPEX HYSYS	$/y	23569	20195	18329
OPEX reduction	%	0.0%	14.3%	22.2%

6. Conclusions

In this work, the surrogate-based optimization of a complete industrial process was successfully done. The methodology proposed allowed the training of highly accurate surrogate models for the surrogate-based optimization of a biogas to methanol modular plant. With the study, the values of the input variables which reduced the OPEX of the process of the biogas modular plant by 22.2% were found and validated with the rigorous simulation. The presented methodology ensures the complete consideration of the input domain by implementing a space-filling design, allows the determination of critical variables via surrogate-based sensitivity analysis, reduces the computational times for the optimization of the process and ensures the determination of an accurate optimum of the process by implementing the MADS algorithm by NOMAD.

References

R. Alizadeh, J.K. Allen, F. Mistree, 2020. Managing Computational Complexity Using Surrogate Models: A Critical Review. Res. Eng. Des. 31, 275–298.

M. Fedeli, F. Manenti, 2022. Assessing Process Effectiveness with Specific Environmental and Economic Impact of Heat, Power & Chemicals (HPC) Option as Future Perspective in Biogas. Clean. Chem. Eng. 2, 100016.

A. Galeazzi, K. Prifti, C. Cortellini, A. Di Pretoro, F. Gallo, F. Manenti, 2023. Development of a surrogate model of an amine scrubbing digital twin using machine learning methods. Comput. Chem. Eng. 174, 108252.

S. Le Digabel, 2011. Algorithm 909: NOMAD: Nonlinear Optimization with the MADS Algorithm. ACM Trans. Math. Softw. 37, 44:1-44:15.

K. McBride, K. Sundmacher, 2019. Overview of Surrogate Modeling in Chemical Process Engineering. Chem. Ing. Tech. 91, 228–239.

F. Negri, M. Fedeli, M. Barbieri, F. Manenti, 2022. A versatile modular plant for converting biogas into advanced biofuels. Invent. Discl. 2, 100008.

R. Pishkari, M. Fechtner, T. Keßler, A. Kienle, 2023. Optimization of Simulated Moving Bed Chromatographic Processes using Surrogate Models, in: Kokossis, A.C., Georgiadis, M.C., Pistikopoulos, E. (Eds.), Computer Aided Chemical Engineering, 33 European Symposium on Computer Aided Process Engineering. Elsevier, pp. 343–348.

R. Turton, R.C. Bailie, W.B. Whiting, J.A. Shaeiwitz, D. Bhattacharyya, 2012. Analysis, synthesis, and design of chemical processes, Fourth edition. ed, Prentice Hall international series in the physical and chemical engineering sciences. Prentice Hall, Upper Saddle River, N.J. Munich.

Y.-D. Zhou, K.-T. Fang, J.-H. Ning, 2013. Mixture discrepancy for quasi-random point sets. J. Complex. 29, 283–301.

Flavio Manenti, Gintaras V. Reklaitis (Eds.), Proceedings of the 34th European Symposium on Computer Aided Process Engineering / 15th International Symposium on Process Systems Engineering (ESCAPE34/PSE24), June 2-6, 2024, Florence, Italy

Toward autocorrection of chemical process flowsheets using large language models

Lukas Schulze Balhorn,[a] Marc Caballero,[b] and Artur M. Schweidtmann[a]

[a]*Process Intelligence Research Group, Department of Chemical Engineering, Delft University of Technology, Van der Maasweg 9, Delft 2629 HZ, The Netherlands*
[b]*Department of Chemical Engineering, Delft University of Technology, Van der Maasweg 9, Delft 2629 HZ, The Netherlands*
a.schweidtmann@tudelft.nl

Abstract

The process engineering domain widely uses Process Flow Diagrams (PFDs) and Process and Instrumentation Diagrams (P&IDs) to represent process flows and equipment configurations. However, the P&IDs and PFDs, hereafter called flowsheets, can contain errors causing safety hazards, inefficient operation, and unnecessary expenses. Correcting and verifying flowsheets is a tedious, manual process. We propose a novel generative AI methodology for automatically identifying errors in flowsheets and suggesting corrections to the user, i.e., autocorrecting flowsheets. Inspired by the breakthrough of Large Language Models (LLMs) for grammatical autocorrection of human language, we investigate LLMs for the autocorrection of flowsheets. The input to the model is a potentially erroneous flowsheet and the output of the model are suggestions for a corrected flowsheet. We train our autocorrection model on a synthetic dataset in a supervised manner. The model achieves a top-1 accuracy of 80% and a top-5 accuracy of 84% on an independent test dataset of synthetically generated flowsheets. The results suggest that the model can learn to autocorrect the synthetic flowsheets. We envision that flowsheet autocorrection will become a useful tool for chemical engineers.

Keywords: autocorrection, SFILES 2.0, Large Language Models (LLM), Process and instrumentation diagram (P&ID), generative AI

1. Introduction

The process engineering domain widely uses Process Flow Diagrams (PFDs) and Process and Instrumentation Diagrams (P&IDs) to represent process flows and equipment configurations. However, the P&IDs and PFDs, hereafter called flowsheets, can contain errors like missing or misplaced components, incorrect signal or stream connections, or even missing or misplaced subsystems. These errors can cause significant safety hazards, delays in development, inefficient operation, and unnecessary expenses. Hence, identifying and correcting errors in flowsheets is important but currently a tedious, manual process.

In the scientific literature, there are a few initial publications on the error detection and corrections of process flowsheets. These works are based on two main concepts: (i) rule-based approaches and (ii) machine learning-based (ML) approaches. Rule-based approaches encode engineering rules for common errors, e.g., as graph patterns, and then detect and correct the errors, e.g., through graph manipulations. For example, Bayer and Sinha (2019) and Bayer et al. (2022) define and apply graph patterns that contain erroneous patterns and their corrections. Similarly, Shin et al. (2023) encode graph manipulations to correct the setup of compression devices. The definition of graph patterns and manipulations makes the approach understandable for users. However, this approach relies on graph isomorphism to find the graph patterns in the P&ID graph which is computationally expensive. In addition, rule-based approaches are limited to hard-coded rules which are difficult to develop, maintain, and extend.

Besides rule-based approaches, a few initial ML-based approaches have recently been proposed for error correction. Dzhusupova et al. (2022) detect four engineering error patterns directly on P&ID images using object detection. For instance, they detect configurations where the symbol of a spectacle blind is placed right next to the symbol of a butterfly valve which might cause the blind and the disk to clash if the butterfly valve is opened. A drawback of this approach is its low generalizability to new drawing styles and that it can only detect errors involving items with close visual proximity. Using an ML-based method, Rica et al. (2022) detect anomalies in process graphs. In particular, they create a simple graph embedding by counting neighboring unit operations. This embedding is the input to a multi-layer perceptron (MLP) that predicts the component type of the component of interest. In case there is a mismatch between the predicted and the actual component type, an anomaly is indicated. Furthermore, Shin et al. (2023) train a support vector machine to classify common subgraphs from process graphs as correct or anomaly. Mizanur Rahman et al. (2021) utilize a node degree comparison and a graph convolutional network (GCN) to detect anomalies on a process graph via binary node classification. Recently, Oeing et al. (2022, 2023) also use a GCN to detect inconsistencies in the process design. For each node in a process graph, they predict the component type and compare it with the actual component type (similar to Rica et al., 2022). The first works on ML for autocorrections are promising but there are still a few conceptual limitations. Most ML approaches only check one component individually at a time. Therefore, they cannot detect missing components, incorrect connections, or engineering mistakes involving two or more components. In addition, the computational costs of analyzing one component at a time scales linearly with the number of components in the P&ID which could result in long runtimes for large P&IDs.

For grammatical error correction in human language, large language models (LLMs) proved to be successful (Alikaniotis et al., 2019). In the context of chemical engineering flowsheets, we recently demonstrated that LLMs can autocomplete flowsheets (Vogel et al., 2023). This technology represents flowsheets as strings using the SFILES 2.0 notation (d'Anterroches, 2005; Vogel et al., 2023a) and uses transformer language models to autocomplete flowsheets. Furthermore, we recently formulated the development of P&IDs as a machine translation problem where flowsheets without a control structure are translated to flowsheets with a control structure (Hirtreiter et al., 2023).

In this study, we propose to formulate the autocorrection of flowsheets as a machine translation problem where potentially erroneous flowsheets are translated to correct flowsheets. In particular, we train a transformer language model with flowsheet pairs where the input is a potentially erroneous flowsheet and the output is a corrected flowsheet. Thereby, the model can learn complex error patterns from data and errors in the context of complete flowsheets. For training, we generate synthetic flowsheet pairs with predefined error patterns.

2. Autocorrection methodology using transformer models

Our proposed autocorrection model is based on the sequence-to-sequence transformer model using the T5-small transformer model (Raffel et al., 2020). The input to the model is a flowsheet encoded as a string in the SFILES 2.0 notation (Vogel et al., 2023a). The model then generates a new flowsheet which is a corrected version of the input. We can derive suggestions for correction from the new flowsheet by comparing the model input with the model output. As the model generates complete flowsheets, our approach is not limited to modifications of single components.

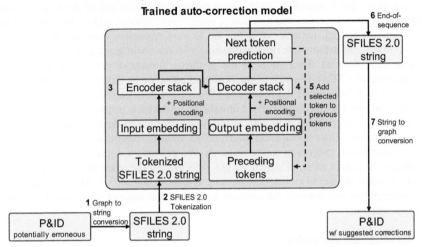

Figure 1. Overview of the autocorrection methodology with the transformer model.

Figure 1 provides an overview of the methodology. The methodology starts with a potentially erroneous flowsheet graph. In Step 1, the flowsheet graph is serialized to a string using the SFILES 2.0 notation (Vogel et al., 2023a). No topological information is lost in this conversion. Then, the SFILES is broken into tokens (Step 2). A token is a small text piece defined in the SFILES vocabulary that represents, for instance, unit operations, raw materials, products, a start-of-sequence (SOS) token, or an end-of-sequence (EOS) token (c.f. Vogel et al., 2023). The SFILES 2.0 vocabulary contains 53 tokens in total. In Step 3, the tokens are mapped to a vector space and their position is encoded. For all vectors, the encoder stack calculates a numerical representation, i.e., the embedding, of the flowsheet using the attention mechanism (Vaswani et al., 2017). The attention mechanism processes all token vectors in parallel which is an advantage over previous recurrent network architectures. Then, Steps 4 and 5 iteratively predict the output tokens. In Step 4, the decoder stack takes two different inputs. One is the numerical embedding from the encoder stack. The other one is the embedding of the preceding output tokens. In Step 5, the decoder stack predicts a likelihood for every token in the vocabulary. The next token is selected using beam search based on the maximum likelihood. For example, in the first iteration, the preceding token is only the SOS token. The decoder stack then predicts the raw material token <raw> as the next token. In the second iteration, the preceding tokens are SOS and <raw>. Steps 4 and 5 are repeated until the EOS token is selected. In Step 6, the sequence of tokens is translated back into an SFILES string. Finally, the SFILES string is converted to a graph in Step 7, thereby generating the corrected flowsheet suggestions.

3. Dataset

The autocorrection model is a supervised machine-learning approach. Therefore, it requires source-target data. In our case, the training data contains pairs of flowsheets where one flowsheet is erroneous, the source flowsheet, and the other one is the corresponding correct flowsheet, the target flowsheet. In this proof of concept, we generate such pairs synthetically by using common error patterns in flowsheets. In the future, we plan to train our algorithm on industrial flowsheets.

We define 27 patterns commonly occuring in flowsheets (Towler and Sinnott, 2021; Svrcek et al., 2014; Shinskey, 1979). Each pattern focuses on one of the following unit operations: Mixer, heat exchanger, pump, compressor, storage, adding reactant, reactor, or column. For each pattern, we define up to nine erroneous versions. We aggregate different patterns to complete flowsheets using a Monte Carlo graph generation approach. For a more detailed description of the synthetic flowsheet generation, we refer to Hirtreiter et al. (2023). For 40% of the flowsheet pairs, we include erroneous patterns for the input flowsheet, while the remaining 60% contain only correct flowsheet pairs (i.e., source and target are the same correct flowsheet). This idea is inspired by error correction of human language (Yang et al., 2022) and avoids that the model expects all flowsheets to be erroneous. The optimal ratio of erroneous input flowsheets depends on the model application and is subject to future research. We generate a dataset of 500,000 unique synthetic flowsheet pairs, of which we use 80% to train the autocorrection model, 10% as a validation dataset to monitor the training and detect potential overfitting, and 10% as an independent test dataset. All datasets have a similar ratio of correct and erroneous flowsheet pairs.

4. Results and discussion

To optimize the hyperparameters of the model, we perform a grid search. The grid search includes the following hyperparameter ranges with the optimum highlighted in bold: (i) The dimension of a vector that embeds a token (**128**, 256, 512), (ii) the number of layers in the encoder and decoder stack (2, **4**, 6), (iii) the learning rate (1e-4, **5e-4**, 1e-3), and (iv) the batch size (8, 16, **32**). The final model has 7.9 million trainable parameters.

The (top-1) accuracy for predicting the target flowsheet is 80.1% on the independent test dataset. If we consider the five beams with the highest maximum likelihood in the beam search instead of only one, we get five different predictions from the autocorrection model. Considering these five predictions the autocorrection model reaches a (top-5) accuracy of 83.6%. In our test dataset, we assume that a unique correct solution exists which is not a general case. There might exist other correct solutions.

Figure 2 shows the model predictions for an illustrative case study from the independent test set. Note that the test data consist of synthetic flowsheets that do not represent an existing process. However, they fulfill the purpose of illustrating the model's potential. The case study process includes a reaction with a gaseous product which is separated with a distillation column into two product streams. The input flowsheet of the case study contains two potential design errors. Firstly, a pressure controller is missing for the reactor. Pressure can build up in the reactor from the gaseous product of the reaction. The pressure controller is crucial to regulate the mass flow to the downstream system. Secondly, a temperature controller is missing for the heat exchanger before the column. Therefore, the flow controller of the service stream valve does not get feedback from the product stream temperature. The autocorrection model detects both errors and corrects them in the output flowsheet as illustrated in Figure 2. The model adds a temperature controller to the heat exchange and connects it to the product stream and the flow controller. In addition, the model adds a pressure controller to the reactor to control the pressure relief. The suggested corrections from the model correspond to the target flowsheet (i.e., the corrected flowsheet) and is thus considered a correct model prediction. Notably, other feasible corrections of the input flowsheet may exist.

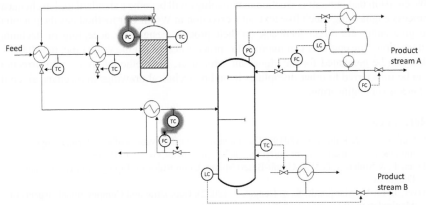

Figure 2. Illustrative case study generated from flowsheet patterns. In the erroneous flowsheet, the pressure and temperature controller highlighted in green are missing. The autocorrection model correctly suggests adding the missing controllers.

While the majority of the model predictions are correct, there are also several false predictions. In case the output flowsheet from the model is incorrect, we observe two common mistakes. Firstly, the model does not or only partially corrects the existing error in the flowsheet. Secondly, the model introduces new errors in the flowsheet. In some cases, the model also alters the SFILES such that the SFILES 2.0 notation is violated and the flowsheet cannot be processed.

Overall, our results suggest that our proposed autocorrection model can learn to autocorrect flowsheets. In particular, the model can add missing components/connections, remove components/connections, and even rearrange components which is a significant advantage over previous works. Also, the LLM has a high learning capacity which has already proven to be effective for autocorrection of human text. While our initial proof of concept shows promising results, there are still several shortcomings and scientific challenges that should be addressed in future research. First, the current model is limited to the topology information of the flowsheet. In the future, further information should be added to the model. For example, (knowledge or hyper) graph representations of flowsheets and graph neural networks are a promising avenue for future research. The graph representation would also allow to increase the complexity of the diagrams (e.g., considering complex industry P&IDs). Second, our current model is trained on synthetic data limiting its industrial application and relevance. In the future, we envision to establish an industry-relevant training dataset. Also, further rules could improve the quality of the synthetic data. Third, various other model architectures such as other LLMs, diffusion models, (variational) autoencoders, or graph-to-sequence could be explored. Finally, the current approach lacks physical/engineering knowledge. We envision to integrate such knowledge into future autocorrection models. For instance, rule-based methods can be integrated with data-driven approaches.

5. Conclusions

We present a novel methodology for the autocorrection of flowsheets. Our methodology uses SFILES to represent flowsheets as strings and implements LLMs to automatically correct errors in chemical process flowsheets. Our results show that the proposed autocorrection model can successfully correct flowsheet topologies based on a synthetic dataset with a (top-1) accuracy of 80.1%.

We envision that our autocorrection methodology will become a standard tool in chemical process engineering much like text autocorrection in Word. Our method has the potential to give engineers direct feedback on their process design. By accepting or declining suggestions, the engineer can improve the process design. At the same time, new training data can be generated for the algorithm. Moreover, the methodology of autocorrection can be transferred to other disciplines including technical drawings in mechanical, civil, or electrical engineering.

References

Alikaniotis, D., & Raheja, V. (2019). The unreasonable effectiveness of transformer language models in grammatical error correction. arXiv preprint arXiv:1906.01733.

Bayer, J., & Sinha, A. (2019). Graph-Based Manipulation Rules for Piping and Instrumentation Diagrams.

Bayer, J., Li, Y., Marquardt, S., & Dengel, A. (2022). Geometric and Computational Aspects of Manipulation Rules for Graph-Based.

d'Anterroches, L. (2005). Process Flowsheet Generation & Design through a Group Contribution Approach. [CAPEC], Department of Chemical Engineering, Technical University of Denmark.

Dzhusupova, R., Banotra, R., Bosch, J., & Olsson, H. H. (2022). Pattern Recognition Method for Detecting Engineering Errors on Technical Drawings. 2022 IEEE World AI IoT Congress (AIIoT) (pp. 642–648). IEEE.

Hirtreiter, E., Schulze Balhorn, L., & Schweidtmann, A. M. (2023). Toward automatic generation of control structures for process flow diagrams with large language models. AIChE Journal.

Mizanur Rahman, S., Bayer, J., & Dengel, A. (2021). Graph-Based Object Detection Enhancement for Symbolic Engineering Drawings. 74–90.

Oeing, J., Brandt, K., Wiedau, M., Tolksdorf, G., Welscher, W., & Kockmann, N. (2023). Graph Learning in Machine-Readable Plant Topology Data. Chemie Ingenieur Technik, 95, 1049–1060.

Oeing, J., Welscher, W., Krink, N., Jansen, L., Henke, F., & Kockmann, N. (2022). Using artificial intelligence to support the drawing of piping and instrumentation diagrams using DEXPI standard. Digital Chemical Engineering, 4, 100038.

Raffel, C., Shazeer, N., Roberts, A., Lee, K., Narang, S., Matena, M., . . . Liu, P. J. (2020). Exploring the limits of transfer learning with a unified text-to-text transformer. The Journal of Machine Learning Research, 21, 5485–5551.

Rica, E., Alvarez, S., Moreno-Garcia, C. F., & Serratosa, F. (2022). Zero-error digitisation and contextualisation of piping and instrumentation diagrams using node classification and sub-graph search. 274–282.

Shin, H.-J., Lee, G.-Y., & Lee, C.-J. (2023). Automatic anomaly detection in engineering diagrams using machine learning.

Shinskey, F. G. (1979). Process control systems. McGraw-Hill, Inc.

Svrcek, W. Y., Mahoney, D. P., & Young, B. R. (2014). A real-time approach to process control. John Wiley & Sons.

Towler, G., & Sinnott, R. (2021). Chemical engineering design: principles, practice and economics of plant and process design. Butterworth-Heinemann.

Vaswani, A., Brain, G., Shazeer, N., Parmar, N., Uszkoreit, J., Jones, L., . . . Kaiser, Ł. (2017). Attention Is All You Need.

Vogel, G., Balhorn, L. S., & Schweidtmann, A. M. (2023). Learning from flowsheets: A generative transformer model for autocompletion of flowsheets. Computers & Chemical Engineering, 171, 108162. doi:10.1016/j.compchemeng.2023.108162

Vogel, G., Hirtreiter, E., Balhorn, L. S., & Schweidtmann, A. M. (2023a). SFILES 2.0: an extended text-based flowsheet representation. Optimization and Engineering.

Yang, L., Wang, C., Chen, Y., Du, Y., & Yang, E. (2022). Controllable data synthesis method for grammatical error correction. Frontiers of Computer Science, 16, 1–10.

Flavio Manenti, Gintaras V. Reklaitis (Eds.), Proceedings of the 34th European Symposium on Computer Aided Process Engineering / 15th International Symposium on Process Systems Engineering (ESCAPE34/PSE24), June 2-6, 2024, Florence, Italy
© 2024 Elsevier B.V. All rights reserved. http://dx.doi.org/10.1016/B978-0-443-28824-1.50520-2

Transfer Learning of Hydroprocessing Model from Fossil Feedstocks to Waste Plastic Pyrolysis Oil

Warumporn PEJPICHESTAKUL*, Per Julian BECKER, Benoit CELSE

IFP Energies nouvelles, Rond-point de l'échangeur de Solaize, BP 3, 69360 Solaize, France
warumporn.pejpichestakul@ifpen.fr

Abstract

Hydroprocessing of waste plastic pyrolysis oil (WPPO) is a promising technology for upgrading low-quality pyrolysis oil in order to send it to a steam cracker. This unit operation is the first step to the chemical plastic recycle. However, developing predictive models for this process is challenging due to limited data availability. The aim of this paper is to show that the knowledge from fossil feedstocks can be transferred to plastic recycle. This study shows an application of transfer learning application to develop a naphtha density model for WPPO using data from fossil fuels. The Bayesian transfer learning approach effectively transferred knowledge from the source data to the target data. The cross validation at different g-prior was applied to obtain the optimal g value. The transfer model with optimal g value results in an accurate predicted naphtha density on the testing and unseen datasets. It outperforms the model trained solely on the target data while delivering comparable performance on the training dataset. This confirms the robustness and predictive capability of the transfer model.

Keywords: Transfer Learning, Hydrocracking, Pyrolysis Oil, Bayesian Statistics

1. Background

The need to address plastic waste management and reduce reliance on fossil feedstocks in the petrochemical industry requires sustainable solutions. One such solution is the upgrade of waste plastic pyrolysis oil (WPPO) through hydroprocessing. This approach has the advantage of using existing facilities in refineries. It furthermore provides a means to transform the low-quality and impure pyrolysis oil into more valuable products that can be used as chemical feedstocks for a steam cracker to produce precursors for new plastics.

The understanding of the hydroprocessing of this novel feedstock remains elusive, in contrast to the extensive knowledge accumulated over decades in the hydroprocessing of fossil feedstocks. To accelerate the industrialization of this process, there is a critical need for predictive models to support process development.

This work aims to develop a product property model for the hydroprocessing of WPPO by applying transfer learning based on the Bayesian approach from the fossil fuel data. The criteria of accuracy and robustness are used to evaluate the model.

1.1. Process description

Hydroprocessing is a crucial process in petroleum refining, which converts the heavy fractions into more valuable products. Typically, it consists of one or more fixed bed reactor(s), where feedstock is fed over a catalyst with the presence of hydrogen. The classic hydroprocessing of fossil fuels includes the hydrotreatment (HDT) section, which removes impurities i.e., sulfur and nitrogen, followed by the hydrocracking (HCK) section, which breaks down heavy hydrocarbons into lighter, more valuable products. It is a flexible unit which can operate in different modes such as the maxi-middle distillate mode which aims to maximize diesel and jet yields and maxi-naphtha mode which aims to maximize naphtha yield. Further information on the maxi-naphtha mode is discussed elsewhere (Becker et al., 2023). The feedstocks for the maxi naphtha mode can be vacuum gas oil (VGO) or middle distillate.

The WPPO upgrade via hydroprocessing aims at transforming the impure WPPO into the steam cracker feed, which must adhere to strict feedstock specifications. Therefore, it requires several steps of impurities removal and hydrotreatment to produce naphtha. The products from hydrotreatment of WPPO might contain the diesel fraction that requires further conversion i.e., via hydrocracking to maximize naphtha.

This work focuses on the hydrocracking reactor, which is typically a single reactor in the pilot plant study as shown in Figure 1. The HCK reactor feed is first hydrotreated to remove impurities, particularly organic nitrogen that is a poison to zeolitic HCK catalyst. The catalysts are commercial bifunctional zeolite-base hydrocracking catalysts.

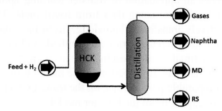

Figure 1 Schematic representation of hydrocracking reactor used in the pilot plant study.

1.2. Product and Feedstock properties

1.2.1. Fossil fuels

Petroleum feedstocks and products are complex mixtures of long-chained hydrocarbons. The detailed characterization of gas oil (GO) or heavier cuts remains currently impossible, as they are composed of thousands of individual species. Petroleum cuts are characterized by Simulated Distillation SimDist (ASTM D2887), and density (ISO 12185), as well as the concentration of nitrogen and sulfur. Thanks to its extensive knowledge in petroleum feedstocks, some properties such as aromatic carbon (CA), naphthenic carbon (CN) and paraffinic carbon (CP) can be estimated using the ndM method (ASTM D3238).

1.2.2. Waste Plastic Pyrolysis Oil

WPPO is produced from the pyrolysis process of plastic waste. Its composition is different from that of fossil fuels as it contains unsaturated compounds and contaminants that are derived from the additives of the plastic. Its lower heating value is comparable to diesel. Hydrotreated WPPO is used as a feedstock in this study. Therefore, olefins are saturated and contaminants i.e., silicon, chlorine and metals have been removed. The macroscopic properties such as SimDist, density, sulfur, and nitrogen are characterized using the same standards as for fossil fuels. However, the CA content is evaluated using ^{13}C NMR analysis, as the ndM method is not adapted to this new feedstock.

1.2.3. Naphtha product

Full range naphtha is a mixture of C_5-C_{12} hydrocarbon with a boiling range between 30-200 °C. The liquid composition is characterized using gas chromatography with flame-ionization detection (GC/FID). It provides the concentration of each family (n-paraffins, iso-paraffins, olefins, naphthenes and aromatics). and carbon number. These measurements are combined with the analysis of the gas produced from the reaction. This recombined data allows for the calculation of the density and distillation curve of the cuts. It also allows for the creation of naphtha cuts with different cut points i.e., C_5-150 or C_5-175 °C. In this work, the product property of interest is naphtha density.

2. Methodology

The product property models are typically linear models as they are simple, robust, and interpretable. The models have been developed for the hydrocracking of fossil fuels, which are used as the source model. The source model is developed using an ordinary linear square (OLS) method. The features are selected using exhaustive feature selection (Section 2.1). Then it is transferred to the target data, the hydrocracking of WPPO, while maintaining identical features, using a Bayesian transfer learning (Section 2.2). The data is scaled according to the median for centering and interquartile range for reducing. The cross validation at different g-priors (Section 2.3) was performed to estimate the optimal value to be used for the transfer model. This transfer learning method is applied to different feedstocks (fossil to WPPO) having distinct matrices. Additionally, the g-value cross-validation is applied to guarantee the transfer model's predictability and robustness.

2.1. Feature Selection
Exhaustive feature selection was performed using all available macroscopic descriptors (feed properties, operating conditions and SimDist of the naphtha cut) discussed in Section 1.2. The retained parameters are SimDist of the naphtha cuts at 30 % and 70 %, CA content of feed, and conversion.

2.2. Bayesian Transfer Learning
The methodology has been discussed in detail elsewhere (Iapteff et al., 2021), a brief overview is provided here. The linear model for the target data is $y = \beta_t X + \epsilon$, where β_t is model parameters of size n_p, X is the design matrix, and y is the target variable. In the transfer approach (Bouveyron and Jacques, 2010), β_t is treated as a random variable with a prior density $\pi(\beta_t)$. The Bayes' theorem is then applied to derive the posterior of β_t with respect to target observations.

An improvement of Zellner's prior (Zellner, 1986), also known as g-prior, was proposed by (Iapteff, 2022). Only the mean of the prior distribution is affected by the source data when using such a prior. The target data determines the structure of the prior covariance of βt. The impact of the prior distribution can be adjusted using a scalar parameter g. The posterior mean (Eq. 1) tends to the maximum likelihood estimator learned on only the source data ($\hat{\beta}_s$) for large values of g and to the prior mean ($\hat{\beta}_t$) for small values. Iapteff (2022) proposed a heuristic method for estimating for optimal g value in Eq. 3, which was tested for diesel density prediction. It is the inverse of the diagonal elements of Σ_s as given in Eq. 2. The parameters with subscription s correspond to the source data.

$$\hat{\beta}_t = (X_t^T X_t + \sigma_t^2 g^{-1}\Sigma_s^{-1})^{-1}(X_t^T y_t + \sigma_t^2 g^{-1}\Sigma_s^{-1}\hat{\beta}_s) \tag{1}$$

$$\Sigma_s = \sigma_s^2 (X_s^T X_s)^{-1} \tag{2}$$

$$g = \left(\frac{1}{n_p} \sum_{j=1}^{n_p} (\Sigma_s)_{j,j} \right)^{-1} \tag{3}$$

2.3. Cross Validation at Various g-prior

As discussed in Section 2.2, the g-prior is crucial for the transfer. The sensitivity analysis on the g-prior was carried out by varying the g values at different orders of magnitude with respect to the suggested value by Iapteff (2022). The cross validation (CV) of the target data with 5-fold cross validation was carried out. The optimal g value is then chosen based on the lowest mean RMSE on the testing dataset of the cross validation.

3. Datasets

3.1. Source Data

The source data is from the hydrocracking of VGO and GO in maxi-naphtha mode. The VGO data comprises two sets: stage 1 (the hydrocracking of hydrotreated VGO) and stage 2 (hydrocracking of the middle distillate and residue fractions of stage 1 effluent). The detailed composition of naphtha cuts makes it possible to create different virtual cuts, which are C_5-150 °C and C_5-175 °C. By using these two virtual cuts, twice the number of data points are obtained which can be used for the development of a generic model for naphtha cuts. 263 observations were retained after the outlier removal using local outlier detection (LOF). The data is split into training and testing datasets using the Kennard-Stone algorithm. The features were then selected as discussed in Section 2.1. Table 1 summarizes the performance of the training and testing datasets of the source data. The model performances are well below the acceptance criteria of ± 0.005 g/cm^3.

Table 1 Statistical indicators for source model.

Dataset	Nb. points	MAE	RMSE	± 0.01 (%)	± 0.005 (%)	± 0.0025 (%)
Train	194	0.0031	0.0039	97.9	82.5	49
Test	69	0.0023	0.0031	98.6	94.2	66.7

3.2. Target Data

The target data for WPPO hydrocracking contains 6 experimental points from one feedstock and two liquid hourly space velocities (LHSV). The compositions of the total liquid were analyzed using GC/FID and two-dimensional gas chromatography (GCxGC). This makes it possible to construct virtual cuts beyond 175 °C. Due to the limited information, the training and testing datasets were split by LHSVs. Table 2 summarizes the datasets of the target data. The training and testing datasets are the naphtha cuts with the same as the source data (C_5-150 °C and C_5-175 °C). The WPPO data at other cut points, i.e., C_5-160, C_5-200, C_5-225, and C_5-250 °C are then used to validate the models and considered an unseen dataset.

Table 2 Summary of the target data.

Datasets	Nb. points	Cuts	LHSV (h^{-1})
Train	8	C_5-150, C_5-175 °C	A
Test	4	C_5-150, C_5-175 °C	B
Unseen	24	C_5-160, C_5-200, C_5-225, C_5-250 °C	A & B

4. Results and Discussion

The application of transfer learning to the naphtha density model, transferring knowledge from fossil data to WPPO, is examined and compared with a model trained solely on the target data (without transfer). Different g values in the transfer models are evaluated against an estimation by Iapteff (2022) , which is 0.05. In Figure 2a, the mean RMSE from cross validation is compared across various g values, indicating an optimal g value of 0.0005. A small g value indicates that the posterior mean tends to the prior mean. With the optimal g value, the signs of all normalized coefficients from the source model are conserved, as depicted in Figure 2b.

A smaller g value of 5E-05 results in a higher mean RMSE than the optimal value (0.05), indicating a similarity to the model without transfer (Target model). Notably, the model without transfer results in a negative coefficient for SimDist at 30 %, unlike the source model, contradicting the expectation that higher boiling point generally correspond to higher density. This contradiction of the model without transfer results from the insufficient training data and implies that without transfer learning the model suffers from significant overfitting.

The models with and without transfer are first applied to the training and testing datasets of the target data, the WPPO data. Then, they are applied to predict the unseen dataset, naphtha at other cut points. This challenges the model as it is an extrapolation to cut points higher than the ones used in the training dataset. Figure 3 shows the parity plot of the model predictions using the model with transfer (blue) and the model without transfer (orange) on the unseen dataset.

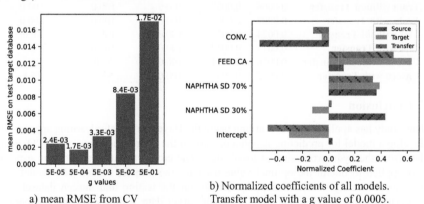

a) mean RMSE from CV

b) Normalized coefficients of all models.
Transfer model with a g value of 0.0005.

Figure 2 Panel a: mean RMSE from cross validation at different g values. Panel b: the comparison of the normalized coefficients of different models.

Table 3 presents a summary of the statistical indicators for models applied to the training, testing, and the unseen datasets of the target data. The model without transfer, calibrated solely on the target data, marginally outperforms the transfer model using a g value obtained from cross validation (0.0005). However, the transfer model provides better performance overall on the testing and unseen datasets, surpassing the model developed solely on the target data (without transfer) while delivering comparable performance on the training dataset. This confirms the robustness and predictive capability of the transfer model.

Transfer learning is a powerful tool that can facilitate model development for new conditions and feedstocks. Cross validation at various g values is used to selecting the optimal value for g-prior. Due to limited experimental data, assessing its robustness across different WPPO feedstocks poses a challenge.

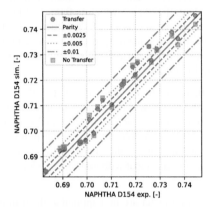

Figure 3 Parity plot comparing the model with (blue) and without transfer (orange) on the unseen dataset.

Table 3 Statistical indicators of models for target data.

Dataset/ model	MAE	RMSE	± 0.01 (%)	± 0.005 (%)	± 0.0025 (%)
Train without Transfer	0.0006	0.0007	100.0	100.0	100.0
Train with Transfer	0.0007	0.0009	100.0	100.0	100.0
Test without Transfer	0.0024	0.0027	100.0	100.0	50.0
Test with Transfer	0.0013	0.0017	100.0	100.0	75.0
Unseen without Transfer	0.0036	0.0041	100.0	75.0	29.2
Unseen with Transfer	0.0032	0.0037	100.0	83.3	45.8

5. Conclusion

This study has applied transfer learning using the Bayesian transfer learning approach to develop a model for predicting naphtha density of the hydroprocessing of WPPO, using data from the hydroprocessing of fossil fuels. The cross validation at different g-priors was applied to obtain the optimal value used for the transfer model. The model with transfer accurately predicted naphtha density on the testing and unseen datasets and outperforms the model trained solely on the target data while delivering comparable performance on the training dataset. This confirms the robustness and predictive capability of the transfer model.

References

P.J. Becker, L. Iapteff, B. Celse, Improving Model Robustness with Transfer Learning for Product Property Models, 33rd European Symposium on Computer Aided Process Engineering, 52, p. 1053–1058 (2023)

C. Bouveyron, J. Jacques, Pattern Recognition Letters ,31, 2237–2247 (2010)

L. Iapteff, Transfer Learning for Smart Predictive Analytics. PhD Thesis (2022)

L. Iapteff, J. Jacques, M. Rolland, B. Celse, J. R. Stat. Soc. Ser. C. Appl. Stat. ,70, 1344–1364 (2021)

A. Zellner, Bayesian Inference and Decision techniques, 233–243 (1986)

Flavio Manenti, Gintaras V. Reklaitis (Eds.), Proceedings of the 34th European Symposium on Computer Aided Process Engineering / 15th International Symposium on Process Systems Engineering (ESCAPE34/PSE24), June 2-6, 2024, Florence, Italy

Data-Driven Forecasting for Anomaly Detection in a Compressor Unit

Aycan Sapmaz,[a*] Aslı Yasmal,[a] Gizem Kuşoğlu Kaya,[a] Yasin Utar,[b] Barış Akgün[c]

a Turkish Petroleum Refinery, Körfez, Kocaeli, 41780, Türkiye
b Turkish Petroleum Refinery, Hacılar, Kırıkkale, 7180, Türkiye
c Dept. of Computer Engineering, Koç University, Sarıyer, Istanbul, 34450, Türkiye
aycan.sapmaz@tupras.com.tr

Abstract

Equipment reliability is crucial for refineries and timely anomaly (equipment failures, sensor faults, wear and tear, unexpected inputs etc.) detection is essential to keep equipment running safely, improve performance, and have an effective maintenance strategy. Modern refineries generate large amounts of data. Combined with machine learning, models that can monitor the operation of complex processes and equipment in real-time can be learned. These models can guide operators, and engineers in identifying faults. This study proposes a data-driven approach to detect anomalies of a reciprocating compressor in a petrochemical refinery. The idea is to capture the regular operating behavior of the compressor with a learned model and compare its predictions with measurements. As such, a model that forecasts future sensor outputs given past measurements is trained from real-world historical data. Deep neural networks with recurrent layers are utilized. After training, the forecasted measurements are compared with the observed measurements and any large deviations are flagged as potential anomalies. The approach is evaluated both on historical and real-time data. The results demonstrate that the approach can be used as an anomaly detection decision-aid for operators and engineers. The approach has the potential to facilitate rapid actions, to help avoid major faults, and for reducing operator fatigue and cognitive load, letting them focus on higher level tasks such as monitoring entire processes versus single equipment.

Keywords: Reciprocating Compressor, Predictive Maintenance, Anomaly Detection, Fault Detection, Condition Monitoring.

1. Introduction

The petroleum industry has strict monitoring requirements, with operational security and safety serving as guiding values. Damaged equipment compromises safety leads to energy shortages and causes financial losses. Anomalous equipment or process behavior often signals such issues beforehand which motivates the development and deployment anomaly detection systems. We highlight that many chemical processes have normal/acceptable within a range and that these behaviors can be learned from historical data. This learned model can be deployed online and its predictions can be compared with observations, raising a warning when the two do not agree.

Due to the availability data, prevalence of machine learning and importance of anomaly detection, multiple data-driven approaches have been created. Recurrent Neural Network (RNN) models are popular in the literature due to their ability to model sequences (Rivas et al. 2020). For example, Canizo et al. (2019) used RNNs in industrial elevator systems for predictive maintenance. Koprinkova-Hristova et al. (2011) used RNNs for predictive maintenance on power plant mill-fans and to perform online monitoring. These methods use the deviations between observations and predictions to detect anomalies.

As a use case, we focus on reciprocating compressors which are an important part of any refinery. They are prone to performance degradation during extended operation due to the dynamic nature of oil refining. It is crucial to promptly identify any anomalies in their operation and warn operators to avoid hazardous situations and costly shutdowns. We use Long-Short Term Memory (LSTM) and Gated recurrent units (GRUs), both types of RNNs, to capture the typical behavior of a compressor and use it for anomaly detection.

2. Methodology

2.1. Process Description

The process where the reciprocating compressor located is producing high octane reformate, a main component of gasoline, obtained from low octane heavy naphtha. High purity hydrogen gas (Net gas) is also produced with this process, making it a main hydrogen producer on top of its octanizing feature. Unit feed enters reactors to produce high octane aromatic compounds from paraffins and naphthene. After this reaction, liquid and gas phase products are separated. The gas phase is further separated to two, for the recycle gas compressor and the net gas compressor. After the compression section, liquid and gas phases are again separated and the produced hydrogen is distributed to whole process unit from the effluent of these net gas compressors and the separator. The remaining liquid phase goes to stabilizer section to split reformate from low hydrocarbon product which is the result of the cracking side reactions in the reactors. Within this process, high octane reformate and high purity hydrogen gas are obtained.

Net gas compressors are reciprocating type compressors and use pistons (Mobley, R. K. 2001). They consist of 3 stages and the first stage consists of 2 cylinders. They have high maintenance costs comparted to the centrifugal compressors (Brown, R. N.1997). Since they supply hydrogen, they are crucial for other units as well.

2.2. Data Description

We posit that the compressor discharge temperature and cylinder vibration can be used to detect anomalies. Based on our expertise and discussions with process engineers, we selected 18 sensor measurements involving stage suction temperatures (°C), cylinder and crank case vibration values (rpm), gas flow rate (m^3/h), stage suction pressure (kg/cm^2) and stage outlet pressure (kg/cm^2). Our idea is to predict the near-future (15 minutes) discharge temperature based on a temporally local history of these measurements.

2.3. Computational Details and Proposed Methodology

As mentioned in Section 1, we utilize Long Short-Term Memory (LSTM) and Gated Recurrent Unit (GRU) layers to build deep neural networks and to model the normal behavior of our compressor. These layers are selected as they are good at modelling sequences. To avoid overfitting, a drop-out layer is added after the recurrent layer. These layers drop random unit outputs based on a given probability which enhances robustness and forces generalization. Then a feed-forward layer is added with Rectified Linear Unit (ReLU) activations, followed by the prediction layer.

The resulting models take a window of past observations, including the most recent one, as input to make a prediction. This window slides over the sequence one step at a time. This is called the sliding window technique and is usually employed with a fixed window size denoted as 'W' which we set to 10.

We first train this model with substantial amount of data from a timeframe that we know to not include anomalies. Then we deploy it and compare its predictions with new observations. However, due to the dynamic nature of refineries, the measurement time-series are non-stationary, i.e., even their regular behavior changes over time. As such, a learned model will lose its predictive power and result in erroneous detection. Re-training the models with the recently observed data is a way to alleviate this issue. We use a retraining frequency of 100 and use the last 1000 data points to fine-tune the current model. This is called moving window re-training and helps the model to adapt to changing patterns in the data over time. Such an approach has been shown to be effective for tasks such as stock price prediction, weather forecasting, and many others (Hota et al., 2017).

2.4. Performance Analysis

We use the Mean Absolute Error (MAE) and Root mean squared error (RMSE) metrics for model selection. In addition to performance metrics, model results are also examined visually. Exponentially Weighted Moving Average (EWMA) control charts are used for this. The chart consists of upper and lower control lines notated as UCL and LCL, respectively. Calculations of UCL and LCL are shown below where σ is the standard deviation of data, μ_0 is the target value, λ is weighting factor and L is the number of standard deviations.

$$LCL_i = \mu_0 - L\sigma \sqrt{\frac{\lambda}{(2-\lambda)}[1 - (1 - \lambda)^{2i}]} \tag{1}$$

$$UCL_i = \mu_0 + L\sigma \sqrt{\frac{\lambda}{(2-\lambda)}[1 - (1 - \lambda)^{2i}]} \tag{2}$$

3. Experiments, Results and Discussion

3.1. Modelling Regular Behavior

We first make use of a dataset that we know to be devoid of significant anomalies, since the measurements come after a maintenance period. The dataset is sampled with 15 minutes intervals and contains a total of 4375 data points. We divide this dataset into training set – used to learn the model, test set – used to evaluate the model. The idea is to make sure the natural behaviour of the process is captured. We trained multiple models with GRU and LSTM layers, composed of 64 and 128 hidden units with this data. The dropout ratio was fixed at 0.5 for each model. The MAE and RMSE values of this first data set is given in Table 1. Similarly, the residuals are provided in Figure 1. We can see that the GRU-based model with 128 hidden units has the best performance, with the same sized LSTM-based model close behind. Based on this, the GRU-128 model was selected to be the basis of the anomaly detection approach.

3.2. Anomaly Detection Dataset

For evaluating anomaly detection, a larger dataset spanning 2 years of operation has been selected. This dataset gas 64,875 data points, sampled with 15 mins frequency. It includes anomalies, shutdowns, interventions, times where the compressor works alone and other operational changes. From the perspective of the model, these are outside the regular behaviour and should be flagged as anomalies. A total of 7 anomalies were observed in 2-years dataset. Anomalies 1 and 3 are operational changes, anomalies 2 and 6 involve vibration problems, anomalies 4 and 5 belong to date when compressor works alone and anomaly 7 is due to a change of vibration sensor. Not all of these are actual anomalies (1,3,4,5 and 7).

Table 1. Model performance metrics for the first dataset

	Train				Test			
	GRU(64)	GRU(128)	LSTM(64)	LSTM(128)	GRU(64)	GRU(128)	LSTM(64)	LSTM(128)
MAE	0.49	0.25	0.41	0.28	1.03	0.52	0.78	0.63
RMSE	0.66	0.38	0.54	0.37	1.39	0.85	1.09	0.90

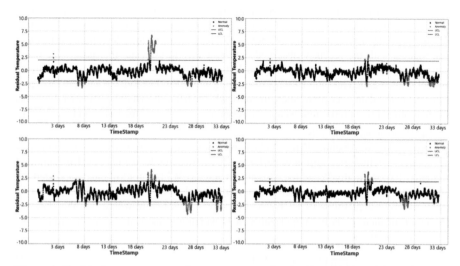

Figure 1. Residual compressor outlet temperatures for the first dataset with models: (a) GRU(64), (b) GRU(128), (c) LSTM(64), (d) LSTM(128)

3.3. Anomaly Detection without Retraining

We first evaluate the model learned with the first dataset on the second dataset. We use control charts for visual inspection, Figure 2 for this case. The y-axis shows the difference between the actual and model-predicted values, and the x-axis the time. Horizontal lines represent the LCL and UCL which are set to ±2. This decision was based on Equations. 1 and 2, and discussions with process engineers. The part between the limits (control zone) is taken as normal operation and the outside grey points are labelled as anomalies.

Figure 2 shows that the residuals of the model fluctuate wildly and have large magnitudes most of the time. This leads to labelling most measurements as anomalies. Furthermore, such large magnitudes signal learning issues and non-stationary behaviour.

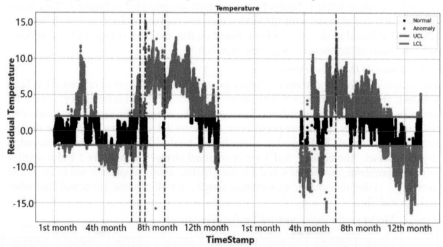

Figure 2. Compressor outlet temperature residuals for the second data without re-training.

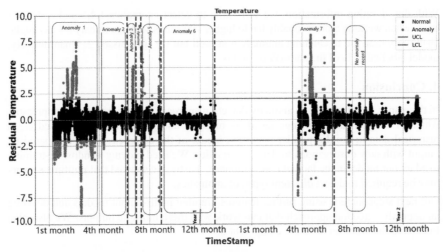

Figure 3. Compressor outlet temperature residuals for the second data with re-training.

3.4. Anomaly Detection with Moving Window Re-Training

For this part of the study, we start with the model learned with the first dataset but fine-tune it every 100-time steps with the last 1000 data points. We only perform 2 epochs so that the model does not overfit. Figure 3 depicts the results. We can see that anomalies 1,3 and 7 were detected. There were signals for anomalies 3 and 5 as well but not as strong. These correspond to compressor working alone and perhaps do not need to be labelled as anomalies. A clean set of measurements by the second 8th month were wrongly labelled as anomalies. Quantitatively, our method was able to detect 71% of the anomaly points. Lastly, anomalies 2 and 6 went unnoticed which were due to vibrations issues.

3.5. Anomaly Detection with Vibration Target

Based on our last observation, we decided to utilize vibration information for anomaly detection instead of temperature with the same model architecture and re-training strategy. The results are depicted in Figure 4.

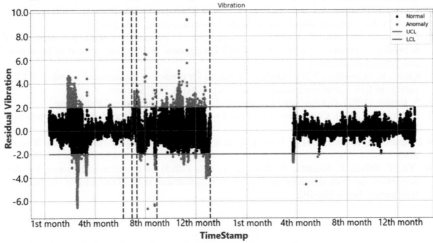

Figure 4. Residual of compressor vibration for 2 years (with mw)

With the vibration information, we were able to detect anomalies 1,4,5 and 6. Higher loads when working alone probably led to higher vibrations so that anomaly 5 was caught. Using vibration led to catching anomaly 6 as well but we still missed 2. Quantitatively, model labelled 57% of the anomalous points.

4. Conclusion

In this paper, we presented an anomaly detection approach for reciprocating compressors which is a significant challenge faced by most oil and gas refineries. We used clean historical data to build a regular operation model of the compressor and compared its output with new observations to detect anomalies. We used moving window re-training to adapt our model in the face of non-stationary. Lastly, we showed that multiple sensors may be required to detect different types of anomalies.

Our next steps include using further features, training multi-output models and devising an anomaly detection approach that can work with these multiple outputs. We also plan to expand our work on different equipment's.

References

A. Bao, E. Gildin, J. Huang, E. J. Coutinho, (2020, July). Data-driven end-to-end production prediction of oil reservoirs by enkf-enhanced recurrent neural networks. In SPE latin american and caribbean petroleum engineering conference. OnePetro.

A. Rivas, J. M Fraile, P. Chamoso, A. González-Briones, I. Sittón, J. M. Corchado, (2020). A predictive maintenance model using recurrent neural networks. In 14th International Conference on Soft Computing Models in Industrial and Environmental Applications (SOCO 2019) Seville, Spain, May 13–15, 2019, Proceedings 14 (pp. 261-270). Springer International Publishing.

G. Qi, W. T. Tsai, Y. Hong, W. Wang, G. Hou, Z. Zhu, (2016, March). Fault-diagnosis for reciprocating compressors using big data. In 2016 IEEE Second International Conference on Big Data Computing Service and Applications (BigDataService) (pp. 72-81). IEEE.

H. S. Hota, R. Handa, A. K. Shrivas, (2017). Time series data prediction using sliding window based RBF neural network. International Journal of Computational Intelligence Research, 13(5), 1145-1156.

H. Purohit, K. Phogat, P. S. V. Nataraj, Performance Monitoring of Centrifugal Compressor System using LSTM based Deep RNN.

M. Canizo, I. Triguero, A. Conde, E. Onieva, (2019). Multi-head CNN–RNN for multi-time series anomaly detection: An industrial case study. *Neurocomputing*, *363*, 246-260.

P. Koprinkova-Hristova, M. Hadjiski, L. Doukovska, S. Beloreshki, (2011). Recurrent neural networks for predictive maintenance of mill fan systems. International Journal of Electronics and Telecommunications.

P. Kamat, R. Sugandhi, (2020). Anomaly detection for predictive maintenance in industry 4.0-A survey. In E3S web of conferences (Vol. 170, p. 02007). EDP Sciences.

R. N. Brown, (1997). Compressors: Selection and sizing. Gulf Professional Publishing.

R. K. Mobley, (2001). Compressors. In Plant Engineer's Handbook (pp. 601-614). Butterworth-Heinemann.

S. Bisgaard, M. Kulahci, (2011). Time series analysis and forecasting by example. John Wiley & Sons.

W. Yu, T. Dillon, F. Mostafa, W. Rahayu, Y. Liu, (2019). A global manufacturing big data ecosystem for fault detection in predictive maintenance. IEEE Transactions on Industrial Informatics, 16(1), 183-192.

Flavio Manenti, Gintaras V. Reklaitis (Eds.), Proceedings of the 34th European Symposium on Computer Aided Process Engineering / 15th International Symposium on Process Systems Engineering (ESCAPE34/PSE24), June 2-6, 2024, Florence, Italy

Policy Explanation of Reinforcement Learning Agent in Chemical Process Safety

Kinga Szatmári,[a,*] Sándor Németh,[b] Alex Kummer[a,b]

[a]*Department of Process Engineering, University of Pannonia, Egyetem st. 10, H-8200 Veszprém, Hungary*
[b]*ELKH-PE Complex Systems Monitoring Research Group, University of Pannonia, Egyetem st. 10, H-8200 Veszprém, Hungary*
**szatmari.kinga@mk.uni-pannon.hu*

Abstract

A well-designed intervention action is required to avoid non-desired events for exothermic reactions in batch reactors, otherwise, thermal runaway may occur. We apply resilience-based explainable reinforcement learning to prevent the runaway, where explainability helps to gain trust in the decisions of the agent, so the policy can be presented in a transparent way. Our case study is a styrene polymerization batch reactor, where the artificial agent can decide whether to intervene or not based on the present state of the system. The state variables are the reactor temperature and the monomer concentration, and the actions are injecting cold diluent or not. Since the states are continuous variables and the actions are discrete events, we use Deep Q-learning as a reinforcement learning algorithm, where resilience metric is a reward function for the learning process. To explain the decisions of the artificial agent, we propose to train a decision tree classifier to predict the discrete actions using the reactor's state representation for the agent as features. The results show that the trained classification tree can help to understand the learned policy by the agent, which policy can be visualized in a concentration-temperature phase plane for better understanding.

Keywords: process safety, styrene polymerization, Deep Q-learning, classification tree

1. Introduction

Reinforcement learning (RL) has been applied in chemical processes, mainly for control purposes (R. Nian, 2020), for example, to control a semi-batch reactor (A. Sass, 2022). In reinforcement learning, the agent interacts with the environment, where due to the agent's action, the system drives to a new state and the agent gets a reward for the action. The goal of reinforcement learning is for the agent to learn an optimal policy (H. Dong, 2020). However, to develop a trustworthy and reliable agent, it is essential to explain its actions (Vouros, 2022).

In explainable reinforcement learning (XRL), two core elements are identified, namely interpretability and explainability (A. B. Arrieta, 2020). Interpretability means that the decision making and inner logic of the agent are transparent and understandable during the process. In contrast, explainability is a post-hoc property that represents the extent to which the agent takes the input state into account to make a decision (Y. Qing, 2022). Explainability can be used to gain trust between reinforcement learning algorithms and humans. This allows users to understand the outputs of the model (A. Krajna, 2022).

A taxonomy for categorizing explainable reinforcement learning is based on the different parts of the reinforcement learning process. Therefore, the actions of the RL agent can be made understandable by model-explaining, reward-explaining, state-explaining, and task-explaining models as well. During model-explaining methods, the agent is trained to be explainable by having an understandable explanation of its structure. Reward-explaining methods explain the weights of the reward function and can occur by reward decomposition or reward shaping. State-explaining methods provide explanations based on the observation and can be historical trajectory, current observation explanations, and future predictions. Finally, task-explaining methods are used in hierarchical reinforcement learning (Y. Qing, 2022).

A model-explaining method is self-explainable if its structure is explained by itself or by limiting its complexity, and a model is explanation-generating if it learns an explicit explanation logic during training to generate an explanation (Y. Qing, 2022). Self-explainable models can be a decision tree, for example, a linear model U-tree is applied as an RL algorithm, and the transparent tree structure instantly explains the decisions of the agent (G. Liu, 2018). This method learns to represent the Q-value, but the policy can also be represented by a self-explainable method, for example in (A. Verma, 2018), where a Programmatically Interpretable Reinforcement Learning framework is presented, which represents the policy by a domain-specific high-level programming language.

During the operation of chemical reactors, the temperature may increase due to insufficient conditions, and reactor runaway may occur. The most used method to reduce the effect of the runaway is to add a cold diluent to the system. Reinforcement learning (RL) can be applied to prevent the development of reactor runaway by intervention action. We designed a mitigation system by adding cold diluent to a styrene polymerization reactor activated by a reinforcement learning-trained agent in a simulation environment. The RL agent decides if intervention is required in the system after a disruption based on the current state, and the resilience metric is used as a reward function. With this agent, we propose an explainable reinforcement learning method by a decision tree. In Section 2, the Deep Q-network is introduced and the explainable reinforcement learning method is proposed, and Section 3 presents the results of the policy explanation.

2. Policy representation in a decision tree

Deep Q-network (DQN) is applied as an RL algorithm in our work because in chemical reactors the state space is large and continuous, and the actions are discrete values. DQN combines Q-learning with a neural network, where the Q function is approximated with a neural network because learning efficiency increases with it (T. H. Oh, 2021).

The structure of the investigated system is shown in Figure 1, where based on the state the RL agent learns which action to take (whether to inject the cold diluent or not) by the reward received. Reinforcement learning helps to optimize the intervention time to prevent the runaway.

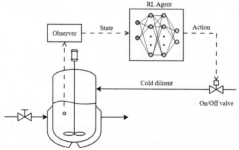

Figure 1: Structure of a chemical reactor with RL agent

The considered states are the reactor temperature and the monomer concentration, as presented in Eq. (1), and the actions are described in Eq. (2), it is 0 when the cold diluent is not injected, and it is 1 when the diluent is injected.

$$S = \langle T, c_M \rangle \tag{1}$$

$$A = \langle 0, 1 \rangle \tag{2}$$

The reward is the system's resilience, which is shown in Eq. (3). The system's maximum resilience is 1, therefore the maximum reward is also 1. The baseline resilience (R_b) is the resilience of the system without any intervention, when the diluent is not injected, and it helps to determine the rewards. If R_b is close to 1, so no runaway occurs, but the agent still decides to inject the diluent, the agent gets negative rewards, else the reward is the resilience (R). The negative rewards are lesser if the agent chooses to inject the diluent at a later time, so if it makes a bad decision later.

$$r_t = \begin{cases} 5/t_{inj} & \text{if } R_b > 0,99 \text{ and action} = 1 \\ R & \text{otherwise} \end{cases} \tag{3}$$

Decision trees can be applied to explain the interpretability of the reinforcement learning agent, since actions in DQN are discrete variables, the policy can be classified into a decision tree. After the agent has learned the optimal policy, a binary decision tree algorithm is applied to make the agent explainable.

During the training of the decision tree, the data is split according to the Gini impurity, which is the measure of the diversity of the tree and is described in Eq. (4), where $p(D,I)$ is the proportion of elements that belong to the *I*th class in the case D. Gini index helps to decide at which attribute to split, and the index is minimized at each split, so the best split is the one that decreases the Gini index the best. When the Gini impurity is zero at a node, it means that the data are completely classified (Sundhari, 2011), (G. Dorgo, 2021).

$$Info_{Gini}(D) = \sum_{I=1} p(D,I)(1 - p(D,I)) \tag{4}$$

The decision tree algorithm divides the data by a decision threshold that results the highest information gain. Eq. (5) shows the information gained in the parent set (D_p) by splitting into right and left sets, according to the test Te, where $|D_{left}|$ and $|D_{right}|$ are the number of individual elements of sets D_{left} and D_{right}, and $Info$ is the Gini index (G. Dorgo, 2021).

$$Gain(D_P, Te) = Info(D_p) - \frac{|D_{left}|}{|D_p|} Info(D_{left}) - \frac{|D_{right}|}{|D_p|} Info(D_{right}) \tag{5}$$

The depth and complexity of a decision tree are determined by using cost-complexity pruning to avoid overfitting. Cost-complexity is defined in Eq. (6), where N is the case in the training set, E is the cases incorrectly classified, N_t is the number of leaves and α is the cost of one extra leaf (D. D. Patil, 2010).

$$\text{Cost - complexity} = \left(\frac{E}{N} \right) + \alpha \cdot N_t \tag{6}$$

When a tree is pruned, the new tree contains N_{t-1} fewer leaves and incorrectly classifies *M* more cases. Eq. (7) shows the determination of α (D. D. Patil, 2010).

$$\alpha = \left(\frac{M}{N \cdot (N_t - 1)} \right) \tag{7}$$

With each subtree, α is calculated and the pruned subtree is selected when α has the smallest value. In each case, a standard error (SE) of the misclassification is determined, which is shown in Eq. (8), where *A* is the misclassification rate of the pruned tree and the smallest decision tree that does not reach the value *A+SE* in the test set will be selected (D. D. Patil, 2010).

$$SE = \left(\frac{A \cdot (100 - A)}{N} \right) \tag{8}$$

3. Results

The agent first learned when to intervene and when not to intervene using the DQN algorithm. This uses a feedforward linear neural network is used to predict the Q-function. The activation function is ReLU function, and we used layer normalization on all layers of the networks. Also, the inputs of the network, so the states are normalized between 0 and 1. The weights of the Q-network are updated with soft update, and ε-greedy method is used for the action selection during the learning. The agent can decide about the cold diluent injection every one minute, and when the diluent is injected, it cannot be injected again.

Sensitivity analysis is applied to the structure of the neural network to determine the number of neurons in the hidden layer and the number of hidden layers. Figure 2 shows the average reward with one hidden layer, where the average reward is determined in every 50 episodes. The best number of neurons in the hidden layer is 128, where the maximum average reward is reached. The maximum average reward cannot be approached with fewer neurons or two hidden layers. The other hyperparameters of the agent are manually tuned, the discount factor is γ=0,99, the learning rate is α_r=0,001, the size of the memory is N=2000, the size of the minibatches is M=32, and the parameter for the soft update is τ=0,0001.

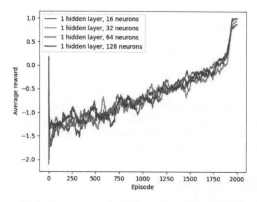

Figure 2: Average reward of the agent with one hidden layer

The behaviour of this agent is explained in our work with a decision tree. At first, the actions of the agent at given temperatures and concentrations with 100 episodes are determined, where two initial parameters are uncertain, the initial reactor temperature is between 324-330 K, and the initial monomer concentration is between 4-5 mol/L. When the action is zero, the agent does not intervene, and when it is 1, the cold diluent is injected. Since zero is in the vast majority of the actions due to the decision of the agent every minute, we used SMOTEENN for oversampling for a true representation of the agent's actions. Then a decision tree is trained, and with cost-complexity pruning, the depth of the decision tree is determined, where $\alpha=0,001$, and the depth of the decision tree is 7. The decision boundaries of the final decision tree are presented in Figure 3, where the class with no action, where the agent does not intervene is shown with blue, and the classes with synthetic action and original action, where the agent intervenes are shown with red and brown, respectively. The original actions are the actions taken by the agent, and the synthetic actions are the oversampled actions. The separation between the two classes is the splits in the decision tree.

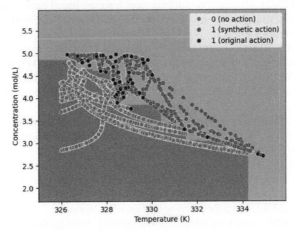

Figure 3: The discovered decision boundaries and the performed actions by the agent at specific concentration-temperature states

4. Conclusions

Explainable reinforcement learning has been investigated in a styrene polymerization batch reactor, where the actions of the agent were made interpretable. With a well-functioning DQN algorithm, where the considered states are the reactor temperature and the monomer concentration, and the reward is the resilience, reactor runaway can be prevented. A decision tree is applied as an explainable reinforcement learning method to explain the decisions of the agent. Since the agent can decide about the injection every minute, we have an imbalanced dataset, where the agent does not intervene in most cases. Therefore, SMOTEENN method is applied to oversampling, so the zero and one data are equal, and for the determination of the depth of the decision tree, cost-complexity pruning is used. The decision tree can classify the actions of the agent, and makes the behaviour of the agent transparent. Following future research directions can be using another explainable reinforcement learning method, for example, Shapley value or fuzzy controller.

Acknowledgements

Supported by the ÚNKP-23-4 New National Excellence Program of the Ministry for Culture and Innovation from the Source of the National Research, Development and Innovation Fund. This work has been implemented by the TKP2021-NVA-10 project with the support provided by the Ministry of Culture and Innovation of Hungary from the National Research, Development and Innovation Fund, financed under the 2021 Thematic Excellence Programme funding scheme.

References

A. B. Arrieta, N. D.-R.-L. (2020). Explainable artificial intelligence (xai): Concepts, taxonomies, opportunities and challenges toward responsible ai. *Information fusion 58*, 82-115.

A. Krajna, M. B. (2022). Explainability in reinforcement learning: perspective and position. *arXiv preprint*.

A. Sass, A. K. (2022). Multi-agent reinforcement learning-based exploration of optimal operation strategies of semi-batch reactors. *Computers & Chemical Engineering 162*.

A. Verma, V. M. (2018). Programmatically interpretable reinforcement learning. *International Conference on Machine Learning, PMLR*, 5045-5054.

D. D. Patil, V. W. (2010). Evaluation of decision tree pruning algorithms for complexity and classification accuracy. *International Journal of Computer Applications 11*, 23-30.

G. Dorgo, A. P. (2021). Decision trees for informative process alarm definition and alarm-based fault classification. *Process Safety and Environmental Protection 149*, 312-324.

G. Liu, O. S. (2018). Toward interpretable deep reinforcement learning with linear model u-trees. *Machine Learning and Knowledge Discovery in Databases: European Conference, ECML PKDD*.

H. Dong, H. D. (2020). *Deep Reinforcement Learning*. Springer.

R. Nian, J. L. (2020). review on reinforcement learning: Introduction and applications in industrial process control. *Computers & Chemical Engineering 139*.

Sundhari, S. S. (2011). A knowledge discovery using decision tree by gini coefficient. *2011 International Conference on Business, Engineering and Industrial Applications, IEEE*, 232-235.

T. H. Oh, J. W. (2021). Automatic control of simulated moving bed process with deep q-network. *Journal of Chromatography A 1647*.

Vouros, G. A. (2022). Explainable deep reinforcement learning: state of the art and challenges. *ACM Computing Surveys 55*, 1-39.

Y. Qing, S. L. (2022). A survey on explainable reinforcement learning: Concepts, algorithms, challenges. *arXiv preprint*.

Flavio Manenti, Gintaras V. Reklaitis (Eds.), Proceedings of the 34th European Symposium on
Computer Aided Process Engineering / 15th International Symposium on Process Systems
Engineering (ESCAPE34/PSE24), June 2-6, 2024, Florence, Italy

Machine Learning Based Modeling and Optimization of an Industrial Thermal Cracking Furnace

Melike Duvanoğlu,[a,b,*] Gizem Kuşoğlu Kaya,[a] Onur Savran,[a] Erdal Aydın [b,c]

[a] Turkish Petroelum Refinery, Körfez, Kocaeli, 41790, Turkey
[b]Department of Chemical and Biological Engineering, Koç University, Rumelifeneri,
İstanbul, 34450, Turkey
[c]Koç University, TUPRAS Energy Center (KUTEM), Rumelifeneri, İstanbul, 34450,
Turkey
mduvanoglu22@ku.edu.tr, melike.duvanoglu@tupras.com.tr

Abstract

Machine learning methods can capture the distinctive characteristics of a system without
any prior knowledge of the process given enough actual data. In addition, they are well
suited to represent systems that are complicated for first principles modeling and have
many unmeasured disturbances. Accordingly, data-based modeling for the thermal
cracking furnace is a promising study using actual process data set and various machine
learning methods. The study's focus is on the machine learning prediction of time-series
Controlled Variables (CV), which is a prerequisite for using an Advanced Process Control
(APC) system in a petrochemical plant. The most crucial component of an APC system
is the prediction of the controlled variables and the adjustment of those anticipated values
to bring them within the user's chosen range (Lee et al., 2023). Predicting the controlled
variables is our main goal in this investigation. We specifically used a variety of machine
learning approaches to forecast future controlled variables by utilizing historical
controlled variables.

In this study, the cycle time of the furnace of a visbreaker unit and the temperature of the
hottest zone of the furnace are modeled using different machine learning methods such
as Support Vector Machines, Multiple Linear Regression, Decision Tree, Random Forest,
and Artificial Neural Networks. Although the Random Forest model is good at predicting
temperature and remaining day for the shut-down time, ANN model is used for process
optimization purposes, by incorporating it in the fitness function of the genetic algorithm.
When using a genetic algorithm (GA) to optimize a model for a specific task, the choice
of the model as the fitness function is crucial. The fitness function evaluates how well a
particular solution (set of model parameters or hyperparameters) performs the task at
hand. The reason for using an Artificial Neural Network (ANN) as a fitness function in a
genetic algorithm instead of a Random Forest (RF) is search space and differentiable
nature of the ANN structure. Having estimated the cycle time by training the machine
learning models, the inverse problem is attempted to solve such as calculating the optimal
values of the features (controlled variables) for maximizing the operation time of the
process within certain limits. This optimization problem is solved by sampling-based
optimization methods formulating the trained machine learning models as fitness
function. In this way, the necessary manipulated variables will be adjusted by the
controller so that the unit can operate in the most efficient way.

Keywords: Visbreaker unit, thermal cracking furnace modelling, genetic algorithm, time-series prediction, controlled variables for advanced process control.

1. Introduction

Please use the SI set of units as much as possible. Wherever the application domain uses Thermal cracking process of heavy residue hydrocarbons occurs under severe thermal conditions. Visbreaking is a mild cracking in which mild heating is used to crack the residue, thereby reducing the viscosity while producing lighter products. While vacuum or atmospheric residue feedstock is heated and mildly cracked in the visbreaker furnace, soaker favors visbreaking between the furnace and the quenching step. Most of the limits faced by visbreaking units are caused by fouling. Thermal cracking of highly unstable and crucial asphaltenes causes fouling. When the temperature is reduced below thermal cracking by quenching after the furnace and soaker, this causes the production of coke particles at thermal cracking temperatures above 400–410°C (in the furnace) and subsequent precipitation. The coke is deposited on the walls of the furnace, which in turn leads to an increase in the tube wall temperatures and reduces the overall heat transfer coefficient. Determination of furnace fouling/coking tendency can help refiners boost visbreaker economics. (Speight, 1991).

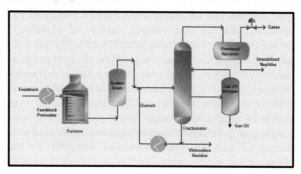

Figure 1. Simplified process flow diagram of Visbreaker process

The unit must be shut-down, and coke cleaning and maintenance must be carried out before the wall temperatures reach 600-650°C. Since many different types of crude oil-based residues are processed in the unit, the severity of the operation varies and this is the main reason for the coke formation process, which has already nonlinear nature. It is crucial to predict the degree of fouling or coking from the tube wall temperatures in different zones of the furnace and to optimize operation conditions while meeting product demand amount and desired quality.

In this study, various machine learning models are studied to predict the temperatures of the hottest part of the furnace and remaining day to shut down. ANN model is used as a fitness function, and the decision variables required to increase the time to shut down (extend the cycle time) and minimize the coil temperatures in the hottest region are determined by using genetic algorithm. Then these optimized controlled variables are set as a set point in the controller and the required action is taken in the controller by using manipulated variables.

2. Methodology

2.1. Artificial Neural Network

An artificial neural network (ANN) is a mathematical model that attempts to simulate the structure and function of biological neural networks. The basic elements of all artificial neural networks are artificial neurons or simple mathematical models (functions). These patterns have three simple sets of rules: multiplication, addition, and activation. The inputs to the artificial neurons are weighted. That is, each input value is multiplied by its individual weight. At the heart of the artificial neuron is a summation function that adds all the weighted inputs and biases. At the output of an artificial neuron, the sum of the previously measured inputs and biases is passed through an activation function called a transfer function. (Van Laerhoven, 2000)

A feedforward ANN model is generally expressed as:

$$y = f_1 (A \cdot f_2(B \cdot u + C) + D) \tag{1}$$

where *f1* and *f2* are output and hidden layer activation functions respectively. *A* and *B* are weight matrices; *C* and *D* are bias vectors; *u* is the input vector and *y* are the output vector. The dimensions of related ANN parameters are dependent on the number of inputs, outputs, and neurons, which are manually chosen prior to training.

2.2. Genetic Algorithm

A genetic algorithm is defined as an optimization technique that is based on the principles of natural selection and is used to both constrained and unconstrained optimization situations. The idea of repeatedly changing the set of distinct answers forms the foundation of the algorithm. To create the next iteration and eventually arrive at an optimal solution, the algorithm randomly selects individuals at each stage. Genetic algorithms have been employed to forecast time series in the literature. One such example is the work of Khashei and Bijari, who demonstrated through examples how effective genetic algorithms can be for "time series modelling and forecasting. (Sohail, 2021)

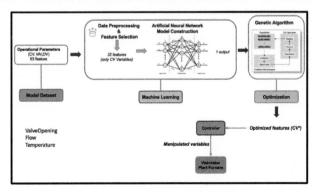

Figure 2. Schematic of the solution architecture

3. Results and Discussions

There are about 63 operational parameters of the visbreaker unit. Firstly, feature selection studies are carried out. Although the model is built using all features, modeling studies are developed by selecting only the most relevant features to reduce model complexity. From these data, 32 control parameters are selected that are related to the thermal cracking process specifications and provided information about the furnace operation and status. These inputs can be classified as heater outlet temperature, feed flow valve openings, flow temperature differences, coil flow differences, fuel gas pressure and temperature.

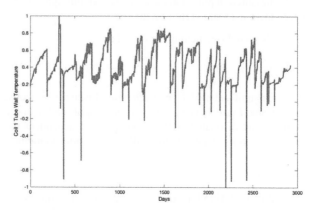

Figure 3. Target variable changes during the 10 years operation

These input and output variables are normalized between -1 and 1 values. Then, the ANN model is constructed by separating the 10-years of daily average data, that includes 2927 operation days and various cycles, 70% of training, 15% validation and 15% test data. The number of hidden layers is 16 and the *trainlm* function trains a feedforward neural network using the Levenberg-Marquardt optimization algorithm. The output of the ANN model is the coil 1 temperature of the hottest zone of the furnace.

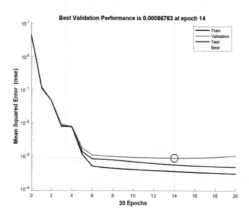

Figure 4. Learning Curve for ANN

Table 1. ANN model results

Performance	Mean Squared Error (MSE)
Best training	3.43e-04
Best validation	8.68e-04
Best test	5.40e-04

Best validation performance observed in epoch number 14 as can be seen in Figure 4. It can be concluded that ANN model is successful for predicting the coil tube wall temperatures of the furnace from the performance metrics table. After the ANN model is built, this model is called by genetic algorithm as a fitness function that aims to minimize the temperature of the coil 1. The optimal decision variables that minimize the temperature of coil 1 is calculated. Although the 32 decision variable results exist, only 4 of them is shown in there.

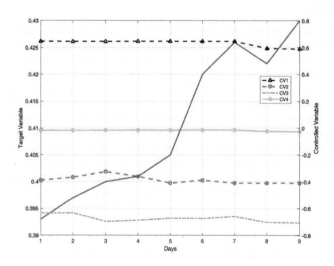

Figure 5. Target variable and controlled variable changes 10 consecutive days.

Table 2. Some of the optimal solution results of ANN-GA hybrid model *(from 32 input variables only 4 are shown. Variables are normalized for proprietary reasons)*

Controlled Variable	Feature	Optimal Value
CV1	Heater outlet temperature	-0.6066
CV2	Fuel gas pressure	-0.8045
CV3	Coil 1 valve opening	-0.8641
CV4	Coil 1 out temperature	-0.9146

Upon analyzing the optimum decision variables, the optimal decision is to reduce the 4 variables which are heater outlet temperature, fuel gas pressure, coil 1 valve opening, and coil 1 out temperature. From process perspective, it is logical to keep these variables to a minimum to reduce the coil 1tube wall temperature. To reduce the temperature in the furnace tube, it is required to reduce the heater outlet temperature, to reduce the pressure of the fuel gas, to send less feed to heater by reducing the valve opening of the flow of that tube, and to reduce the exit temperature of this coil at the end of the furnace.

For process, operation, and control engineers, changing these optimal control values with slower rates might be critical in terms of process safety and product specification and plant limits. Thus, it is planned to include rate change constraints into the formulation for hierarchical optimal operation and control. There are 32 control variables, and after they are sent as set points to the controller, the manipulated variables must be tracked by the DCS controllers. These control variables must be validated by working with safer and more accurate constraints so that the controller can take appropriate action.

4. Conclusions

In this study, we examined an industrial Visbreaker unit, which contains a thermal cracking furnace and has frequent shutdowns due to coking-related reasons. Since the coking and thermal cracking processes are quite complex, building physical models is challenging and time-consuming. Therefore, data-based modeling and optimization could be promising. It is concluded that the ANN model is successful in predicting the tube wall temperatures inside the furnace. Then, optimum decision variables, which will be sent to lower-level regulatory controllers, are computed to minimize the temperature. When the trends of these optimum (control) variables are examined, it is seen that they give reasonable and interpretable results. In the future stages, these control variables will be given as set points to the control system and the manipulated variable behavior will be examined and validated. By setting the control variables correctly and adjusting the appropriate manipulated variables of the controller, the cycle time of the furnace will be increased.

References

A. Sohail, 2021, Genetic Algorithms in the Fields of Artificial Intelligence and Data Sciences. Annals of Data Science, 10(4), 1007–1018.

J. Speight, 1991, The Chemistry and Technology of Petroleum, 2nd ed., Marcel Dekker, New York.

K. Van Laerhoven, 2000, Introduction to artificial neural networks. Proceedings Electronic Technology Directions.

M. Lee, Y. Yu, Y. Cheon, S. Baek, Y. Kim, K. Kim, H. Jung, D. Lim, H. Byun, C. Lee & J. Jeong, 2023, Machine Learning-Based Prediction of Controlled Variables of APC Systems Using Time-Series Data in the Petrochemical Industry. Processes, 11(7), 2091.

Flavio Manenti, Gintaras V. Reklaitis (Eds.), Proceedings of the 34th European Symposium on Computer Aided Process Engineering / 15th International Symposium on Process Systems Engineering (ESCAPE34/PSE24), June 2-6, 2024, Florence, Italy

Completing Partial Reaction Equations with Rule and Language Model-based Methods

Matthijs van Wijngaarden[a], Gabriel Vogel[a], Jana Marie Weber[a,*]

[a]*Delft Bioinformatics Lab, Department of Intelligent Systems, Delft University of Technology, Van der Maasweg 9, Delft 2629 HZ, The Netherlands*
j.m.weber@tudelft.nl

Abstract

Large chemical reaction data sets often suffer from incompleteness, such as missing molecules or stoichiometric information. Incomplete chemical reaction equations currently hinder us to perform automated mass balances across large sets of chemical reactions. In this work, we integrate two approaches for computational completion of partial reaction equations. Specifically, we combine a rule-based method and a machine learning model, a tailored version of the pre-trained Molecular Transformer, to complete reactions. The rule-based method takes sets of helper species into a linear solver and therewith balances some incomplete reactions. The machine learning model is trained to take partial reactions as inputs and predicts missing molecules and stoichiometries. We apply our methodology to the USPTO STEREO chemical reaction data set. The rule-based method completes about 50 % of the reactions. The language model shows a top 1 accuracy of 88.3 % on our test set and high validity (> 99 % of outputs are valid SMILES).

Keywords: Molecular transformer, Chemical reaction completion, rule-based methods, reaction SMILES, Language models

1. Introduction

The digitalisation of patents and publications in chemical science has led to a substantial body of electronically accessible chemical reactions (Lowe, 2012). This body of reactions is a valuable data source in predictive chemistry, e.g. for reaction prediction, retrosynthesis, reaction yield prediction, or reaction condition prediction (Schwaller et al., 2019; Liu et al., 2017; Schwaller et al., 2021; Gao et al., 2018). Recently, there has also been a growing interest in using this data for automated reaction pathways selection and early-stage sustainability analysis (Ulonska et al., 2016; Weber et al., 2022). Yet, most chemical reaction databases are incomplete. For instance, one can find recorded reactions without temperature and pressure, without yield, or without information about solvents or catalysts (Jacob et al., 2017a). Also, fundamental information such as reaction equations are incomplete. They often lack co-reactants, by-products, and the stoichiometric coefficients. The lack of this knowledge currently limits automated mass balances across the large body of reaction alternatives. This is particularly relevant for mass-based assessment strategies, e.g. sustainability focused assessment, of chemical reactions (Jacob et al., 2017b; Weber et al., 2021).

To address this problem, recent works aim to curate incomplete chemical reaction equations. Vaucher et al. (2020) proposed to complete chemical reactions through a transformer-based language model (LM). Note that their definition of completeness does not correspond to mass balance complete reactions; it corresponds to predicting the original atom-wise incomplete database entry. Arun et al. (2023) developed an algorithm that balances chemical reactions by adding small "helper" molecules. This procedure is one of eight data processing steps for impurity prediction where the balancing step is used for filtering purposes. Zhang et al. (2023) used a similar algorithm, but also included a transformer-based encoder-only LM, based on RoBERTa (Yinhan et al., 2019), that predicts missing molecules. Their hybrid approach is a prominent step towards solving the reaction completion problem and works in an iterative fashion between the rule-based and the language model-based part. We also propose a hybrid approach. Our approach works sequentially, first through a rule-based approach like the work of Zhang et al. (2023), and then through an autoregressive transformer-based encoder-decoder LM, based on the original transformer architecture (Vaswani et al., 2017).

2. Methods

Two methods are combined for completing incomplete chemical reactions in this work. We define an incomplete reaction equation as an equation in which the number of atoms and charges on the left-hand side (LHS) and right-hand-side (RHS) of an equation are not balanced with one another.

2.1. Dataset

The dataset used for this work is the publicly available patent-mined dataset known as the USPTO STEREO (https://ibm.ent.box.com/v/ReactionSeq2SeqDataset) of which 3.5 % are balanced reactions and 96.5 % are imbalanced.

2.2. Rule-based reaction completion

The rule-based method uses a set of hard-coded mathematical and chemical rules to identify missing molecules, i.e. small helper species, necessary for a balanced reaction. Additionally, stoichiometric ratios are determined. The rule-based reaction completion is solved through a linear solver.

2.2.1 Helper species selection

Different sets of helper species considered in this work are depicted in Figure 1. Set A is the strict uncharged set, set B and C make up the strict charged helper species, and set D is taken from literature (Arun et al., 2023) illustrating a more lenient selection of helper species. Here, we test the usage of single helper species first and only if the algorithm is unsuccessful, combinations of two helper species (sets A+A, A+B, A+C, A+D).

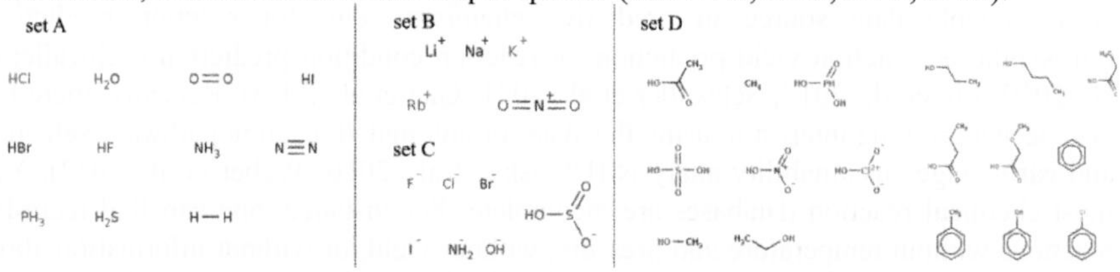

Figure 1. Helper species sets. Set A is the strict uncharged set, set B and C make up the strict charged based helper species, and set D (lenient set) is based on Arun et al. (2023).

2.2.2 Rule-based algorithm with linear solver

The rule-based algorithm can be subdivided into four parts. Firstly, atom and charge-level balances are calculated for a reaction equation, identifying the surplus or lack of atoms/charges from the left-hand-side (LHS) to the right-hand-side (RHS). Secondly, helper species are selected when their atom types coincide with the in step one identified imbalanced atom types. In the first iteration, only one helper species (single-type) is selected to complete the equation and in the second iteration of this step, a combination of two helper species (pairwise-type) is selected. Thirdly, the linear solver identifies the stoichiometry of the added helper species. For single-typed solutions, the linear solver checks if the number of missing atoms can be divided by the number of atoms of the helper molecule. For pairwise solutions, the less ambiguous helper species is selected first: in the case of a charge imbalance, a charged helper species; without a charge imbalance, a helper species with unique atom type. The stoichiometric value of the selected molecule is then set to balance the charge or unique atom type. The atom/charge balance is updated, and the secondary helper species is selected as in the single-type solution. Lastly, if a reaction cannot be completed through the previous steps, we check if the atom imbalance exactly coincides with one of the reactants or products. If this is the case, we assume that that molecule was incorrectly added to the reactant or product side, while it should have been recorded as a reagent and thus remove it.

2.3. Language-model based reaction completion

The second method is a transformer-based encoder-decoder LM that is trained on pairs of partial and complete reactions and predicts missing molecules and stoichiometries. Molecules are presented as string-formatted words with their atoms as tokens using SMILES (simplified molecular input line entry system) notation. Reactions are a sequence of words: a sentence, see Figure 2 (a). We fine-tune the Molecular Transformer (Schwaller et al., 2019) on a reaction completion task. The averaged 20 checkpoint Molecular Transformer (https://ibm.ent.box.com/v/MolecularTransformerModels) from the USPTO STEREO dataset with separated solvents is used for initialisation. To generate fine-tuning data, we partialised the data set of complete reactions obtained from the rule-based model. We then subsequently train the model to predict the complete reaction equation from a partialised equation, see Figure 2 (b). Each reaction was first assigned to the train, test, or validate data set with a data split of 90/5/5 and then partialised. Reactions from the test set were partialised only once, while reactions belonging to training and validation set are partialised up to ten times depending on the number of possible combinations, keeping at least 50 % of the atoms from the complete reaction equation. In some cases, two different reactions produce the same partialised reaction. Then, both correct answers are recorded for each partial reaction. During testing, the prediction of either one is considered correct.

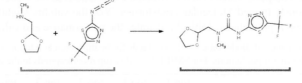

(a)   CNCC1OCCO1.O=C=Nc1nnc(C(F)(F)F)s1 >> CN(CC1OCCO1)C(=O)Nc1nnc(C(F)(F)F)s1

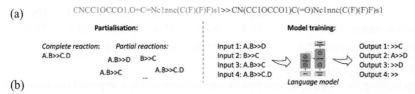

(b)

Figure 2. Illustration of a reaction SMILES as input for the LM (a) and the partialisation strategy (b). In (a), tokens before ">>" correspond to reactant molecules and tokens afterwards to product molecules. In (b), partial reactions are used for model training.

2.3 Model evaluation

We propose three evaluation scenarios. Solutions from the rule-based model are considered complete if they fulfil the atom and charge balance as also proposed by Zhang et al., (2023). Note that this is an approximation with false positives, and that for example chemical template matching and expert judgments would be beneficial. With the previous assumption, we can consider the data completed through the rule-based approach as ground truth for the LM and can thus record the prediction accuracy. Lastly, we test the LM on the reactions that could not be completed by the rule-based approach. There, we evaluate if the model predicts atom- and charge-balanced reactions and perform an additional consistency check through the round-trip accuracy, inspired by retrosynthesis prediction tasks (Schwaller et al., 2019). We define a round-trip accurate prediction as one whose output, if newly partialised (50 - 80 % of atoms remain) and fed into the LM, leads to the same complete chemical reaction.

3. Results and discussion

3.1. Rule-based completion
Using the rule-based reaction completion algorithm increases the fraction of complete reactions from 3.5 to 49.37 % (strict helper species set) and 55.57 % (lenient helper species set). We outline the completion rate per algorithm stage for the strict species set in Table 1. Notably, the helper species-based completion algorithm contributes to most of the completed data while the erroneous reactant step only identifies very few mislabelled reaction records. Our cumulative results are in line with our reimplementation of the rule-based method ChemBalancer (Zhang et al., 2023) that resulted in a curation rate of 54 % on a sample set of incomplete reactions.

Table 1. Data completion rate at each step in the rule-based algorithm using the strict set of helper species and the cumulative value also for the strict species set.

	initial data	strict	err. reactants	cumulative
Completion rate [%]	3.5	45.53	0.37	49.37

3.2. Language-based completion with ground truth assumption
The fine-tuned Molecular Transformer shows a top five accuracy of 95.6 % on the test set of the by the rule-based method completed dataset. 99.78 % of top 1 predictions are valid SMILES outputs, which is in line with our expectations as the model was initialised on the previously trained Molecular Transformer. Yet, the validity slightly decreases in respective next n predictions. Table 2 illustrates the performance and validity.

Table 2. Performance of model on test set. BS stands for beam search and top n considers the accuracy of the first n predictions. For SMILES validity top n corresponds to the nth prediction.

	top 1 BS 1	top 1 BS 5	top 2 BS 5	top 3 BS 5	top 4 BS 1	top 5 BS 1
Top-n accuracy [%]	88.3	88.8	93.6	94.8	95.3	95.6
Valid SMILES output [%]	99.78	99.88	88.07	94.23	93.27	91.94

3.2.1. Degree of partialisation
When limiting the scope of the reaction incompleteness problem to partial reactions with exactly one molecule missing, our LM achieved a top 1 accuracy of 96.3 %. In Figure 3 (a), we outline the model's performance for remaining combinations of reaction partialisation scenarios. Note that for zero missing molecules, the model always predicts that no additional molecule is needed, thus that the reaction is already complete. Furthermore, we observe a gradient from left to right highlighting the increasing complexity with more missing molecules.

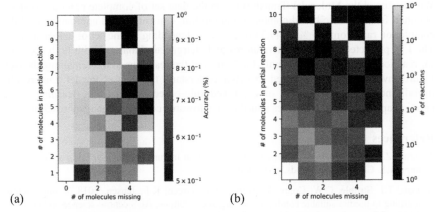

Figure 3. Model accuracy with degree of partialisation. In (a), we show the model accuracy across degrees of partialisation and in (b) we illustrate the corresponding amount of data across the degrees of partialisation.

3.2.2. Length of missing molecules

We also analyse the impact of the length of the missing molecules on the prediction accuracy and compare our results to reported results of the previously suggested encoder-only architecture, ChemMLM, (Zhang et al., 2023). Both models show a drop in accuracy when the length of the model output increases, see Table 3, yet the accuracy of the encoder-decoder architecture of this work decreases less. The autoregressive prediction of the encoder-decoder model takes previously predicted tokens into account, which helps the prediction of longer outputs, while the encoder-only RoBERTa architecture only considers non-masked information (incomplete reaction) for each mask prediction.

Table 3. Model accuracy rates per output length. Due to different tokenisation strategies, we translate our output length to their categories through the following: "short" corresponds to two atom tokens, "medium" to up to 20 atom tokens, and "long" to more than 21 atom tokens. ChemMLM results are not reimplemented, but taken from their work (Zhang et al., 2023).

Model type	"short" accuracy	"medium" accuracy	"long" accuracy
ChemMLM	99.9 %	78.3 %	16.4 %
Encoder-decoder	99.9 %	91.8 %	82.8 %

3.2.3. Language-based assumption without ground truth assumption

Considering the top five predictions, our LM predicts a reaction that is atom and charged balanced for 5.36 % of the reactions from the dataset without ground truth assumption. This is a drop from the high accuracy of the previous test set predictions based on the data with ground truth assumption and indicates larger differences between the data sets. Additionally, we tested the consistency of the model predictions as a basic sanity check through the round-trip accuracy. Here, at a partialisation where 70 % of the atoms are given, the model is relatively consistent in predicting the original reaction again (in 80 % of the cases considering top five).

4. Conclusions

In this work, we present a sequential hybrid approach for the completion of incomplete chemical reaction equations. We used a rule-based method to curate the bulk of incomplete reactions by applying mathematical rules based on atom and charge balances.

We fine-tuned the Molecular Transformer on the data set of complete reactions that we obtained from the rule-based completion algorithm. Our rule-based approach raised the completion rate from 3,5 % to 49.37 or 55.57 % depending on the set of helper species. The LM predicted reactions where atoms and charges are balanced with high accuracy for reactions in the test set, yet only for 5.36 % of the reactions in the remaining dataset. Future investigations are needed to better understand the dataset impact. Our results overall indicate the suitability of combined rule-based and machine learning based curation approaches and provides a further step towards complete chemical reaction data.

References

A. Arun, Z. Guo, S. Sung, A.A. Lapkin, 2023, Reaction impurity prediction using a data mining approach, Chemistry-Methods, e202200062

H. Gao, T.J. Struble, C.W. Coley, Y. Wang, W.H. Green, K.F. Jensen, 2018, Using machine learning to predict suitable conditions for organic reactions, ACS central science, 4(11), 1465-1476

B. Liu, B. Ramsundar, P. Kawthekar, J. Shi, J. Gomes, Q. Luu Nguyen, S. Ho, J. Sloane, P.Wender, V. Pande, Retrosynthetic reaction prediction using neural sequence-to-sequence models, ACS central science, 3(10), 1103-1113

P.M. Jacob, T. Lan, J. M. Goodman, A. A. Lapkin, 2017a, A possible extension to the RInChI as a means of providing machine readable process data, Journal of Cheminformatics, 9, 1-12

P.M. Jacob, P. Yamin, C. Perez-Storey, M. Hopgood, A. A. Lapkin, 2017b, Towards automation of chemical process route selection based on data mining, Green Chemistry, 19(1), 140-152

D.M. Lowe, 2012, Extraction of chemical structures and reactions from the literature. Diss. University of Cambridge

P. Schwaller, T. Laino, T. Gaudin, P. Bolgar, C.A. Hunter, C. Bekas, A.A. Lee, 2019, Molecular transformer: a model for uncertainty-calibrated chemical reaction prediction, ACS central science, 5(9), 1572-1583

P. Schwaller, A.C. Vaucher, T. Laino, J.L. Reymond, 2021, Prediction of chemical reaction yields using deep learning, Machine learning: science and technology, 2(1), 015016

K. Ulonska, M. Skiborowski, A. Mitsos, J. Viell, 2016, Early-stage evaluation of biorefinery processing pathways using process network flux analysis, AIChE Journal, 62(9), 3096-3108

A.Vaswani, N. Shazeer, N. Parmar, J. Uszkoreit, L. Jones, A. N. Gomez, Ł. Kaiser, I. Polosukhin, 2017, Attention is all you need, Advances in neural information processing systems 30

A.C. Vaucher, P. Schwaller, T. Laino, 2020, Completion of partial reaction equations, Chemrxiv

J.M. Weber, Z. Guo, C. Zhang, A.M. Schweidtmann, A.A. Lapkin, 2021. Chemical data intelligence for sustainable chemistry, Chemical Society Reviews, 50(21), 12013-12036

J.M. Weber, Z. Guo, A.A. Lapkin, 2022, Discovering Circular Process Solutions through Automated Reaction Network Optimization, ACS Engineering Au, 2(4), 333-349

L. Yinhan, M. Ott, N. Goyal, J. Du, M. Joshi, D. Chen, O. Levy, M. Lewis, L. Zettlemoyer, V. Stoyanov, 2019, Roberta: A robustly optimized bert pretraining approach, arXiv preprint arXiv:1907.11692

C. Zhang, A. Arun, A.A. Lapkin, 2023, Completing and balancing database excerpted chemical reactions with a hybrid mechanistic-machine learning approach. Chemrxiv

Flavio Manenti, Gintaras V. Reklaitis (Eds.), Proceedings of the 34th European Symposium on Computer Aided Process Engineering / 15th International Symposium on Process Systems Engineering (ESCAPE34/PSE24), June 2-6, 2024, Florence, Italy

LSTM-based soft sensor for the prediction of microalgae growth

Tehreem Syed,[a]* Shyam Kalliadan,[b,c] Jonathan Mädler,[d] Kris Laukens,[c] Luc Roef,[b] Leon Urbas[d]

[a]*Faculty of Electrical and Computer Engineering, Technische Universität Dresden, 01069 Dresden, Germany*
[b]*Proviron Holding NV, 2620 Hemiksem, Belgium*
[c]*Faculty Department of Computer Science, University of Antwerp, 2020 Antwerpen, Belgium*
[d]*Process Systems Engineering Group, Technische Universität Dresden, 01069 Dresden, Germany*
tehreem.syed@tu-dresden.de

Abstract

In biotechnological processes, biological process parameters such as biomass concentration, nutrient concentration, chlorophyll content, and product quality can be challenging to measure online. Typically, these parameters are measured in laboratory settings employing offline sample analyzers. Yet, offline measurements cannot be used as quick feedback signals for process control because of the significant delay between sampling and result generation. Moreover, though generally very accurate, they are equally expensive and often come with high maintenance costs. Therefore, soft sensors are widely utilized to address this problem, allowing reliable online estimations of these essential biological process parameters. Deep learning-based soft sensors are prevalent these days due to higher prediction performance. This work describes the use of Long Short-Term Memory (LSTM), a deep-learning architecture specifically designed for time series data, to predict microalgal growth. LSTM has the advantage of predicting future values based on history. The LSTM-based soft sensor developed for predicting microalgae biomass shows higher prediction performance than the support vector regression (SVR) based soft sensor. An LSTM was trained on the indoor cultivation data of *Nannochloropsis* cultivated in a vertical flat panel photobioreactor. The dataset consists of 28,741 samples, with 20,280 used for training and 8461 used for evaluation. Our LSTM-based soft sensor performed better than the SVR-based sensor and achieved an R^2 score of 0.91, which was higher than the R^2 score of 0.781 achieved using the SVR-based soft sensor.

Keywords: Microalgae cultivation, Soft sensor, Support vector regression, Long short-term memory

1. Introduction

Process parameters in microalgal cultivations that are often challenging to measure online are evaluated using offline laboratory analyzers. Although offline laboratory analyzers can provide accurate measurements, the sampling cycle is often very long, and it usually leads to small sampling rates and significant measurement delays. On the other hand, online-quality instruments tend to be costly and require complex maintenance. The real-time process monitoring, control, and optimization requirements are not sufficiently satisfied by either offline tests or online sensors. Soft sensors are increasingly being used to quickly estimate process parameters in real-time due to their rapid reactivity, maintenance-cost effectiveness, and accurate prediction results. Soft sensors can forecast difficult-to-measure quality metrics by developing mathematical models based on secondary process parameters that are straightforward to monitor, such as temperatures, pressures, and flow rates (Shao and Tian, 2015).

Artificial neural networks (ANNs) or advanced multiple regression techniques provide an alternative approach for acquiring values of process variables that are not directly measurable. These estimators are typically called "software sensors", emphasizing their significance in providing process variable values as if they were generated by physical sensors intended for monitoring and control applications. Researchers have recently employed data-driven-based soft sensor approaches such as nonlinear regression and Artificial Neural Networks (ANNs) to estimate the biomass.

However, they have some limitations such as limited applicability for highly nonlinear systems, inefficient utilization of unlabeled data, inability to predict multiple outputs concurrently, and demand for extensive computational resources to handle substantial data (Havlik et al., 2022). Deep neural networks (DNN) proposed by Hinton et al. (2007) can successfully overcome the challenges associated with network training by employing a combination of layer-wise unsupervised pretraining and supervised fine-tuning. Deep architectures exhibit superior generalization when dealing with highly different nonlinear functions since they comprise several layers of parameterized nonlinear features (Bengio et al., 2005).

Rao et al. (2023) proposed extreme gradient boosting (XGBoost) soft sensors, utilizing surrogate indicators to emulate algal cell density (ACD). This study chose seven crucial elements from indicators associated with water quality, meteorology, and temporal factors and then developed the model using the XGBoost algorithm. Nevertheless, the study attained a predictive performance of 0.76, as XGBoost is not specifically designed for handling time series data. Wang et al. (2023) proposed a soft sensor utilizing a four-input (ANN) model, with input parameters such as fermentation time, dissolved oxygen concentration, initial glucose concentration, and added quantities of sodium hydroxide. The ANN-based soft sensor enabled accurate online monitoring of dry cell weight, glucose concentration, and lipid production with high accuracy. Nevertheless, shallow ANNs have a limited capacity to represent complicated functions, and their generalization capability is constrained to larger systems. Multilayer networks are susceptible to issues related to gradient vanishing and exploding, which can impact their stability and performance. Deep learning-based architecture, such as Long short-term memory, remains unexplored in biotechnological processes.

This paper investigates and compares the efficiency and effectiveness of support vector regression (SVR) and Long Short-Term Memory (LSTM) techniques to predict the growth of microalgae *Nannochloropsis sp.*, in a closed indoor vertical photobioreactor system focusing on a combination of process parameters and optical monitoring features. We propose an LSTM-based soft sensor to estimate the biomass concentration in comparison with SVR based on the evaluation of the model performance using R^2 and RSME performance metrics. LSTMs are best suited for time series data because of their ability to capture complex patterns and adapt to changing sequences. The inherent flexibility and adaptability of LSTM contribute to enhanced generalization and the handling of temporal data dynamics. We hypothesize that the LSTM model, leveraging its enhanced capability to capture temporal dependencies, will demonstrate superior performance in predicting microalgae growth compared to the SVR model.

2. Methodology

2.1. Data Collection and Preprocessing

The dataset employed in this research pertains to a 21 day production campaign of *Nannochloropsis* sp. in a 6 L capacity ProviAPT vertical flat panel array reactor (Roef et al., 2012), within a fully automated lab unit integrating Arduino and Raspberry Pi modules, and controlled by the OpenSCADA system developed by Roman Savochenko (Merchán et al., 2017). Data from the photobioreactor were extracted from August 18, 2023, to September 7, 2023, at 5-second intervals. The campaign followed a semi-batch cultivation strategy involving one daily harvest and concurrent feeding session. The microalgae production operates in a range of 2.00 to 3.00 dry weight grams of algae per liter. The major growth parameters that have undergone experimental changes during the cultivation period include intensity and spectrometrical composition of photosynthetically active radiation, CO_2 concentration, and the respective duration of day-night cycles. Our target variable 'algae dry weight' is measured offline on four samples per day, with samples being taken at the beginning and at the end of the night cycle, and just prior to and after the harvest/feeding routine. Later, the offline dry-weight data samples in four data points per day are resampled to five-second intervals using linear interpolation. The final cumulative data set comprises 13 input features and algae dry weight measurement as one target variable with datetime as an index (Table 1). After filling in missing values by spline interpolation, the data was separated into training and testing sets before undergoing additional preprocessing steps. The training set comprises 70% of the data, while the remaining 30% is allocated for evaluation. The input sequence for both SVM and LSTM is generated following a sequence of preprocessing steps. The data, initially captured in five-second intervals, is transformed into one-minute intervals by averaging over 12-time windows after applying an exponentially weighted moving average for smoothening (Yu et al., 2020). Input features are further simplified, and the multicollinearity problem is addressed by applying Principal Component Analysis (PCA) and selecting the first five significant components as input features (Sulaiman et al., 2021).

Table 1- The description of the inputs and outputs employed in this study

Description of the variables used	Unit
Unix time point in date time format	Date time
Cumulative absorption rate	%
Absorption rate of blue light	%
Absorption rate of red light	%
Absorption rate of green light	%
CO_2 concentration set point	%
Percentage of the intensity of blue light (quality)	%
Percentage of the intensity of red light (quality)	%
Percentage of the intensity of white light (quality)	%
Max CO_2 into the system	%
Reactor temperature	°C
pH value	
Photosynthetic active radiation	$\mu mol * m^{-2} * s^{-1}$
Algae dry weight	g

2.2. Overview of Support vector regression and Long short-term memory

This paper compared the SVR with the LSTM to predict the biomass concentration in an indoor laboratory-scale reactor. SVR can handle linear and non-linear models by determining the best fitting line (hyperplane) in linear cases, which gathers most data points inside a specified epsilon tube (Cristianini and Scholkopf, 2002). SVR employs various kernels, such as Gaussian and radial basis kernels, to transform the data into a higher-dimensional space for nonlinear problems. This procedure makes it easier to understand the relationships between inputs and outputs. On the other hand, an LSTM, categorized as a type of recurrent neural network (RNN), is particularly good for handling time series (Reddy and Prasad, 2018). The input gate controls the addition of new information to the memory, the forget gate decides whether to keep or discard past data, and the output gate determines the appropriate information for producing the output. As a result, sigmoid functions are employed to regulate the gates for reading, writing, and clearing the memory.

2.3. Implementation details

The details of the hyperparameters used in this study for training SVR and LSTM models are listed in Table 2.

Table 2- The list of the hyperparameters employed in this study

Hyperparameters	Values
LSTM hidden units	50
Number of layers	3
SVR radial basis function	1
Batch size	100
Number of epochs	100
Window size	3
Learning rate	0.0001
Optimizer	Adam
Library	Python (PyTorch)

3. Results and Discussions

The results in Table 3 reveal that the LSTM model outperforms the SVR model in biomass prediction for the testing set, demonstrating a better fit evidenced by a higher R2 score and lower RMSE as shown in Figure 1. However, the SVR model shows signs of overfitting, as indicated by its superior performance on the training dataset compared to the testing dataset as shown in Figure 1. The disparity in performance between the LSTM and SVR models can be attributed to their inherent algorithmic characteristics. LSTM, a type of RNN, excels at capturing temporal dependencies through its memory cells, making it particularly adept at handling time series data. It can express complex patterns and adapt to different sequences, thus offering better generalization, which is reflected in its superior R2 value. In contrast, nonlinear SVR is a kernel-based technique that transforms an input into a higher-dimensional space using fixed-width kernels. This approach often struggles with capturing complex temporal relationships in time series data, leading to overfitting when the model tries to fit noise instead of meaningful patterns.

The findings of this study indicate that the LSTM model demonstrated remarkable accuracy in predicting biomass dry weights ranging from 0 to 3 grams per liter, aligning with the Proviron production strategy's operational range. As illustrated in Figure 1, the predictive accuracy diminishes for higher dry weight measurements, particularly within the 2.5 g/L to 3 g/L biomass dry weight range. Further validation is required, and addressing this issue may involve training the model on a broader range of biomass concentrations. The LSTM model, trained on Nannochloropsis cultivation data, surpasses the performance of the SVR model, attaining a higher R2 score of 0.91 compared to R2 score of SVR 0.781. Despite its overall efficacy, the LSTM model sometimes encounters difficulties with certain instances or patterns, resulting in occasional large offsets as shown in Figure 1. This could be due to its sensitivity to specific data properties, outliers, or challenges in generalizing certain patterns, especially in learning from feed and harvest instances. While LSTM generally provides more accurate predictions, these occasional large offsets can be significant in practical applications. SVRs, effective at handling linear separations, captured the influence of feed and harvest instances represented in Boolean format. In contrast, LSTM, though superior to sequential data, sometimes fails to capture underlying patterns associated with these instances. Further validation is needed to overcome the large offset encountered in the LSTM.

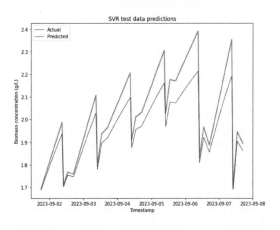

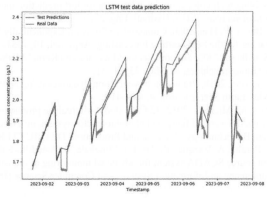

Figure 1 – Prediction performance of SVR and LSTM model on the test data

Table 3- R^2 and RMSE of LSTM and the SVR for the predictions of the biomass concentration

Dataset	Criterion	LSTM	SVR
Train	R^2	0.991	0.929
	RMSE	0.042	0.088
Test	R^2	0.91	0.781
	RMSE	0.061	0.723

4. Conclusion

The results of this study confirm that the use of machine learning models such as SVR and LSTM can predict microalgae growth by incorporating biomass concentration or optical density and time series input features. Specifically, the LSTM model demonstrates a remarkable capability in capturing the inherent complex behavior of the process better than the SVR model. In summary, this study introduces a soft sensor utilizing LSTM for predicting microalgae growth, overcoming issues in the online measurement of essential biological process parameters. This enhancement is significant for real-time monitoring and optimizing microalgal biomass concentration.

References

W. Shao, X. Tian, 2015, Adaptive soft sensor for quality prediction of chemical processes based on selective ensemble of local partial least squares models, Chem. Eng. Res. Des. 95,113-132.

W. Rao, X. Qian, Y. Fan, T. Liu, 2023, A soft sensor for simulating algal cell density based on dynamic response to environmental changes in a eutrophic shallow lake, Sci. Total Environ. 868, 161543.

K. Wang, W. Zhao, L. Lin, T. Wang, P. Wei, R. Ledesma-Amaro, A. Zhang, X.Ji, 2023, A robust soft sensor based on artificial neural network for monitoring microbial lipid fermentation processes using Yarrowia lipolytica, Biotechnol. Bioeng, 120, 1015–1025.

G.E. Hinton, 2007, Learning multiple layers of representation, Trends Cogn. Sci. 11, 428–434.

Y. Bengio, O. Delalleau, N. Roux, 2005, The Curse of Highly Variable Functions for Local Kernel Machines, in: Advances in Neural Information Processing Systems, MIT Press.

I. Havlik, S. Beutel, T. Scheper, K.F. Reardon, 2022, On-Line Monitoring of Biological Parameters in Microalgal Bioprocesses Using Optical Methods, Energies 15, 875.

M.S. Sulaiman, M.M. Abood, S.K. Sinnakaudan, M.R. Shukor, G.Q. You, X.Z. Chung, 2021, Assessing and solving multicollinearity in sediment transport prediction models using principal component analysis, ISH J. Hydraul. Eng. 27, 343–353.

J. Yu, S.B. Kim, J. Bai, S.W. Han, 2020, Comparative Study on Exponentially Weighted Moving Average Approaches for the Self-Starting Forecasting, Appl. Sci. 10, 7351.

N. Cristianini, B. Scholkopf. 2002, Support Vector Machines and Kernel Methods: The New Generation of Learning Machines, AI Mag. 23, 31–31.

D.S. Reddy, P.R.C. Prasad, 2018, Prediction of vegetation dynamics using NDVI time series data and LSTM, Model. Earth Syst. Environ. 4, 409–419.

L. Roef, M, Jacqmain, M. Michiels, 2012, 13 Case study: Microalgae production in the selfsupported ProviAPT vertical flat-panel photobioreactor system, in: Posten, C., Walter, C. (Eds.), Microalgal Biotechnology: Potential and Production, DE GRUYTER, pp. 243–246.

D.F. Merchan, J.A. Peralta, A. Vazquez-Rodas, L.I. Minchala, D. Astudillo-Salinas, 2017, November, Open source SCADA system for advanced monitoring of industrial processesIEEE International Conference on Information Systems and Computer Science (INCISCOS), pp. 160-165.

Flavio Manenti, Gintaras V. Reklaitis (Eds.), Proceedings of the 34th European Symposium on
Computer Aided Process Engineering / 15th International Symposium on Process Systems
Engineering (ESCAPE34/PSE24), June 2-6, 2024, Florence, Italy

Adaptive Data-driven Modelling and Forecasting of Effluent Treatment Plants

Rihab Abdul Razak,[a*] Arvind Ravi,[a] Resmi Suresh,[a] Koen de Leeuw,[b] Jose M Gonzalez[b]

aShell India Markets Pvt Ltd, Bengaluru, India
bShell Global Solutions International B.V., Amsterdam, The Netherlands
Rihab.AbdulRazak@shell.com

Abstract

Contaminants from industrial wastewater can be removed by biological treatment which is a slow process (residence time of the order of days) with non-linear dynamics. Modelling of its key performance indicators (KPIs) is challenging due to multiple factors such as uncertainties in the upstream processes, environmental conditions and reliability of process and lab measurements. In this paper, we propose a reliable dynamic model that can be used for forecasting the biotreater KPIs. Since developing a physics-based model is challenging in an industrial setup, we propose a data-driven adaptive linear model which can capture the correlations and delays between different variables of interest accurately. We use forecasting methods from time-series analysis to forecast the exogenous inputs. Uncertainties associated with the predictions are also computed.

Keywords: Data-driven dynamic model, Forecasting, Biotreater, Effluent treatment

1. Introduction

Effluent from industrial processes often contains high quantities of organic chemical compounds with potential harmful effects on the environment (Sunita et al., 2020). The generated effluent stream can be biologically treated and the process water recovered for reuse or discharge. The effluent treatment plant (ETP) consists of large basins or biotreaters where the continuous flow of effluent is brought into contact with microorganisms (biomass). The biotreater is aerated from the bottom to provide dissolved oxygen (DO) for the aerobic microbes to consume the complex organic compounds (Eckenfelder and Musterman, 1998). The microbial activity follows a non-linear dynamics with relatively slow reaction rates (Newhart et al., 2019). Hence, long residence time is established in these biotreaters to reach the desired degradation of organic compounds.

In chemical plants, the effluent streams are collected from multiple process units. Therefore, modelling and prediction of the performance of the biotreaters are strongly influenced by the uncertainties in the upstream processes (plant disturbances / shutdowns). Under such circumstances, even highly non-linear models, such as

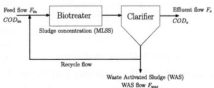

Figure 1: Schematic diagram

artificial neural networks (ANN), show reduced predictive performance due to sudden abnormal changes in the effluent quality (Sung et al., 2002). Other factors include reliability of process and lab measurements (Puig et al., 2008), and environmental conditions like temperature and humidity (Sayigh and Malina, 1978). The process is in a continuous non-steady state and the ability to accurately predict these input variables will directly impact the predictive capabilities of the biotreater forecasting models. Consequently, the availability of reliable forecasts and automated control strategies are expected to enhance the performance of the biotreater (Sarna et al., 2023). Though it is impossible to model unplanned shutdowns or plant disturbances in the upstream units, one can still model the progressive effect of these events. Time-series forecasting (Kotu and Deshpande, 2019) can offer a robust alternative to model the effect of environmental factors on the process.

The objective of this work is to develop a reliable adaptive dynamic model that can be used for forecasting the biotreater KPIs and thus, can help in making informed decisions. Since developing a physics-based model is challenging in an industrial setup (Sung et al., 2002), the aim is to develop a data-driven model which captures the correct correlations and incorporates appropriate process delays between different variables of interest. We use forecasting methods from timeseries analysis to forecast the exogenous inputs that are required to forecast the KPIs. Along with the forecasts, uncertainties associated with the predictions are also computed.

2. System Description

A simplified schematic of the system is given in Figure 1. The feed flow containing contaminants (mainly hydrocarbons) enter the biotreater and the biomass (measured as Mixed Liquor Suspended Solids or MLSS) inside biotreater feeds on the contaminants in the feed. The amount of contaminants in the water are measured in terms of the Chemical Oxygen Demand (COD). As the feed flows through the biotreater basins, biomass reduces the COD level and produces more biomass. The job of the clarifier is to settle the solid biomass so that pure water with low COD levels comes out of the clarifier in the effluent flow. A part of the settled biomass (sludge blanket) taken out from the bottom of the clarifier; is recycled back into the biotreater (Recycle Activated Sludge or RAS) and the remaining part is removed from the system (Waste Activated Sludge or WAS). Since COD conversion takes place in the biotreater and the chemical content is not changed in the clarifier, COD levels in the outlet of biotreater and clarifier are assumed to be the same in our analysis. The list of measured variables used for system identification are given in Table 1. Some measurements are available real-time through online sensors, while some are intermittent measurements obtained from lab analysis. In addition, the measurements of COD and MLSS tend to have high variance.

3. Data-driven Modelling

In this section, we discuss the proposed data-driven modelling framework for ETP. In

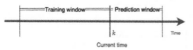

Figure 2: Online modelling

addition to modelling the biotreater and clarifier operation, we also need to forecast the input variables to the system if we are to use the model for forecasting the desired output features. Additionally, quantifying the uncertainties associated with the predictions of the model and the forecasted inputs can be valuable in taking operational decisions based on the predictions.

3.1. Dynamic Model for Biotreater & Clarifier

One of the challenges in constructing data-driven models for the biotreater system, as with many other dynamical systems is the fact that the system behavior changes with time, and the parameters estimated from historical data obtained historically may not be applicable to describe the system now. This means that a single model developed using a single set of historical data may not work well. To address this, we update the model whenever a new batch of data is made available leading to an adaptive model framework. In this paper, we assume that the process is linear for the short duration we consider in one batch of data. As the dynamics of the biotreater process are quite slow, the assumption of linearity for a short duration is reasonable. Moreover, linear models are preferred since they are simpler to handle and can be used to design efficient algorithms for control and optimization. Hence, we look at linear models which can describe the output features of both main reactor and clarifier accurately. The residence time of the biotreater is usually of the order of a few weeks, and the delays have to be properly encoded into the model for accurate predictions. We implemented Ordinary Least Squares (OLS) in an online modelling framework by using a window-based training and prediction scheme as shown in Figure 2.

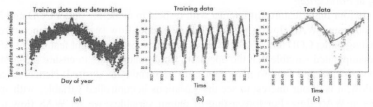

Figure 3: Temperature forecasting. (a) Model (b) Forecast on training set (c) Forecast on test set

Table 1: List of variables

Variable	Data Source	Symbol	Units
Inlet COD	Online Analyzer	COD_{in}	ppm
Inlet flow	Online sensor	F_{in}	tons/hr
Biomass in biotreater	Lab analysis	$MLSS_b$	ppmW
Outlet COD	Online analyzer	COD_o	ppm
Outlet flow	Online sensor	F_o	tons/hr
WAS flow	Online sensor	F_{WAS}	tons/hr
Sludge blanket level in clarifier	Manual	SBL	ft
Ambient temperature	Online sensor	T_{amb}	°C

The proposed linear model is given as:

$$x_b[k] = A_b x_b[k-1] + B_b u[k - l_{bu}] + \sum_i G_i v_i[k - l_{bi}] \tag{1}$$

$$x_c[k] = A_c x_c[k-1] + A_{cb} x_b[k] + B_c u[k - l_{cu}] + \sum_i H_i v_i[k - l_{ci}] \tag{2}$$

where $x_b = [COD_o, MLSS_b]^T$ is the state vector related to the biotreater, $x_c = [SBL]$ is the state vector related to the clarifier, $u = F_{was}$ is the independent variable, and v_i represent various disturbance variables. Here, $v_1 = COD_{in}, v_2 = F_{in}, v_3 = T_{amb}$. $A_b, A_c, A_{cb}, B_b, B_c, G_i, H_i$ are constant matrices of appropriate sizes, $l_{bu}, l_{cu}, l_{bi}, l_{ci}$ are integers representing the time delays between the states and the corresponding input or disturbance variables. The above model is essentially an ARX (auto-regressive exogenous) model with fixed lags for exogenous inputs. The objective of the modelling exercise is to estimate $A_b, A_c, A_{cb}, B_b, B_c, G_i, H_i, l_{bu}, l_{cu}, l_{bi}, l_{ci}$ from data. The modelling proceeds by first determining the lags $l_{bu}, l_{cu}, l_{bi}, l_{ci}$ using process knowledge. If we have a good estimate for the lag from process understanding, we can use these lags. If not, we follow the steps below to determine the lags:

1. From process knowledge, determine the directional sensitivity s_i of the given disturbance v_i w.r.t $MLSS_b$, i.e., determine the direction of change of $MLSS_b$

when a positive step change in v_i is given. Thus, $s_i = +1$ if direction of change is positive, and $s_i = -1$ if the direction of change is negative. Similarly, find the directional sensitivity s_u of the input u w.r.t $MLSS_b$.

2. Determine l_{bi} and l_{bu} using $l_{bi} = \arg\max_l s_i \rho_{b,i}(l)$ and $l_{bu} = \arg\max_l s_u \rho_{b,u}(l)$ where $\rho_{b,i}(.)$ is the cross-correlation between v_i and $MLSS_b$ and $\rho_{b,u}(.)$ is the cross-correlation between u and $MLSS_b$.

3. We repeat the same procedure for the clarifier to determine l_{ci} and l_{cu}, by choosing cross-correlation of input variables with SBL instead of $MLSS_b$.

Once the lags are determined, the parameter matrices $A_b, A_c, A_{cb}, B_b, B_c, G_i, H_i$ are then determined by using ordinary least squares (OLS).

3.2. Input Forecasting

There are four input features of interest with respect to modeling outlet COD and MLSS in the biotreater: WAS flow (u), inlet COD (v_1), inlet flow (v_2), and temperature (v_3). Forecasting outlet COD and MLSS requires forecasts for these input features. WAS flow is the manipulated variable that the operators would manipulate to ensure the controlled variables (MLSS and food to mass ratio) are performing as desired. Hence, in case of WAS flow, it is of our interest to see the variations in controlled variables with specific changes in WAS flow. For forecasting of output variables, we set WAS flow to be a specific constant value of interest.

Inlet flow (F_{in}) and inlet COD (COD_{in}) are dependent on the upstream processes. We forecast these input variables using an auto-regressive (AR) model of order 1:

$$v_i[k] = a_{v_i} v_i[k-1] + e_{v_i}[k] \tag{3}$$

where $e_{v_i}[k]$ represents the error in v_i for sample k. Temperature is modelled as a combination of linear trend and a cubic model (which models the periodic behaviour throughout the year). This model is trained using the historical data available for 8-9 years. One can also estimate the variance in temperature prediction for every day of the year from this training set. Figure 3a shows the plots for temperature forecasting and 3b shows the forecasting results. Note that the model is able to capture the seasonality as well as the increasing trend in time.

3.3. Uncertainty Quantification

To quantify the uncertainty associated with model predictions (or forecast), we estimate the variance σ^2 of each prediction. For a fixed lag ARX model of the form

$$x[k] = Ax[k-1] + \sum_i D_i w_i[k - l_{w_i}] + e_x[k] \tag{4}$$

where w_i for all i are inputs and e_x is the error in x. After re-writing $x[k]$ as a function of $x[0]$ and assuming that variance in $x[0]$ is zero (since $x[0]$ is known), the covariance matrix of $x[k]$ $(\Sigma_{x[k]})$ can be derived as follows:

$$\Sigma_{x[k]} = \sum_i \sum_{j=1}^{k} A^{(k-j)} D_i \Sigma_{w_i[j-l_{w_i}]} D_i^T A^{(k-j)^T} + \sum_{j=1}^{k} A^{(k-j)} \Sigma_{e_x[j]} A^{(k-j)^T} \tag{5}$$

Assuming 95% confidence interval, uncertainty in k^{th} sample prediction of ith variable $(x_i[k])$ can be quantified as $\pm 2\sigma_{x_i}[k]$ where $\sigma_{x_i}[k]$ is the standard deviation of $x_i[k]$ obtained from the ith diagonal element in $\Sigma_{x[k]}$. This approach can be used to quantify uncertainty in both x_b and x_c. To evaluate this, we require the covariance matrix for error and all inputs (u and v). The error covariance matrix (Σ_{e_x}) can be estimated from the training set. Since WAS flow (u) is a manipulated variable (value set by the user), standard deviation for the same can be set to zero for all time. Since the input variables v_1 and v_2 are modelled using AR model, their variances can be computed as explained for the ARX model.

$$\sigma_{v_i[k]} = \sum_{j=1}^{k} a_{v_i}^{k-j} \sigma_{e_{v_i}} a_{v_i}^{k-j^T}, \quad \forall i = 1,2. \tag{6}$$

For modeling uncertainty in temperature, the variance can be estimated from the training data for each day of the year during model building process. By mapping k with the corresponding day of the year, $\sigma_{v_3}[k]$ can be computed. Using the variances obtained for all input features and error, variance in x can be computed and then used to obtain prediction uncertainty interval of $\pm 2\sigma$.

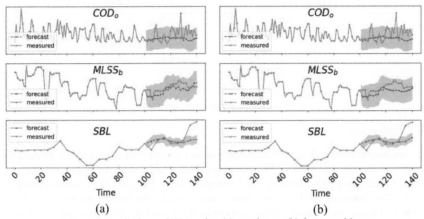

Figure 4: Predictions of KPIs using (a) true inputs (b) forecasted inputs

4. Results

In this section, we discuss the modelling results on an industrial biotreater and compare the predictions obtained from model simulation with the actual measurements. A training window of 100 days and a model update window of 21 days are used in the simulations. The modelling parameters used in this study are given in Table 2. The model presented in this paper is obtained using OLS and the model is updated at regular intervals so that it adapts to the changing conditions in the plant. The training window refers to the number of samples used for training a model, and the update window refers to the time after which the model is updated. Thus, each model is used to predict for 14 days after which an updated model based on the more recent data is generated.

Table 2: RMSE for predictions

RMSE (R^2 score)	COD_{in}	$MLSS_b$	SBL
True inputs	3.88 (0.54)	113.75 (0.94)	0.27 (0.79)
Forecasted inputs	3.99 (0.52)	134.65 (0.92)	0.28 (0.78)

We compare the results for two cases: (1) when the true input variables (inlet flow, inlet COD, ambient temperature) are used for predicting the states, (2) when the forecasted inputs are used for predicting the states. The predictions for the true input case are show in Figure 4a. As can be seen, the model starts predicting after about 100 days, the data prior to that being used for training the first model. The actual measured values are also plotted along with the predicted values for comparison. Once the model is built, it will be used for prediction for the next 21 days. Then a new model is built and used for prediction for the next 21 days. The total time of predictions shown in the plot is 40 days. The predictions for the forecasted input case are shown in Figure 4b. The corresponding forecasts for the inputs are given in Figure 5. The forecasts try to capture the mean trend in the variables based on the immediate past. This is effective if the upstream processes are in a steady state. We can also see a jump in the predictions after 21 days due to model update. The Root Mean Squared Error (RMSE) and R^2 scores for the predictions are shown in Table 2.

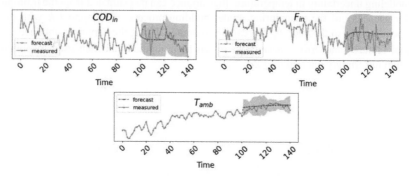

Figure 5: Forecast of input variables

5. Conclusion

In conclusion, this work aims at building data-driven dynamical models for an industrial biotreater and clarifier system. The model is expected to be used for forecasting the states and for model predictive control. For forecasting KPIs, forecasts of exogenous inputs are used. The proposed models can capture the correct correlations between inputs and outputs. Future work incudes improvement of the model by attempting recursive linear models or nonlinear models. Implementation of control algorithm for ensuring required food to mass ratio is part of the future work.

References

Sayigh, B.A., Malina, J.F., 1978. Temperature effects on the activated sludge process. Journal (Water Pollution Control Federation), 678-687.
Eckenfelder, W., Musterman, J., 1998. Activated sludge: Treatment of industrial wastewater. Technology and Engineering, CRC Press.
Ioannou, P., Fidan, B., 2006. Adaptive Control Tutorial. Advances in Design and Control, Society for Industrial and Applied Mathematics.
Kotu, V., Deshpande, B., 2019. Time series forecasting. Data Science.
Newhart, K.B., Holloway, R.W., Hering, A.S., Cath, T.Y., 2019. Data-driven performance analyses of wastewater treatment plants: A review. Water Research, 157, 498–513.
Puig, S., M.C.M, V.L., J, C., S.C.F, M., 2008. Data evaluation of full-scale wastewater treatment plants by mass balance. Water research, 42, 4645–4655.
Sarna, S., Patel, N., Corbett, B., McCready, C., Mhaskar, P., 2023. Process-aware data-driven modelling and model predictive control of bioreactor for the production of monoclonal antibodies. The Canadian Journal of Chemical Engineering, 101, 2677–2692.
Sung, L.D., Jeon, C.O., Park, J.M., Chang, K.S., 2002. Hybrid neural network modelling of a full-scale industrial wastewater treatment process, Biotechnology and Bioengineering, 78, 670-682.
Sunita, V., Joshi, R., Srivastava, V.K., Ngo, H.H., Guo, W., 2020. Treatment of wastewater from petroleum industry: current practices and perspectives, Environmental Science and Pollution Research, 27, 27172-27180.

Flavio Manenti, Gintaras V. Reklaitis (Eds.), Proceedings of the 34th European Symposium on Computer Aided Process Engineering / 15th International Symposium on Process Systems Engineering (ESCAPE34/PSE24), June 2-6, 2024, Florence, Italy

A Comparative Study of Data-driven Offline Reinforcement Learning for Fed-batch Process Control

Omid Sobhani[a,*], Furkan Elmaz[a], Michiel Robeyn[b], Johan Van den Hauwe[c], Shahab Pormoradi Gerdposhteh[c], Benedict Carius[c], Kevin Mets[a], Siegfried Mercelis[a]

[a]University of Antwerp – imec, IDLab - Faculty of Applied Engineering, Sint-Pietersvliet 7, 2000 Antwerp, Belgium

[b]University of Antwerp – imec, IDLab - Department of Computer Science, Sint-Pietersvliet 7, 2000 Antwerp, Belgium

[c]allnex R&D, allnex, Anderlechtstraat 33, 1620 Drogenbos, Belgium

* seyedomid.sobhani@uantwerpen.be

Abstract

Reinforcement Learning has gained traction in optimizing industrial processes; however, its application is hindered by safety concerns and the challenge of accurately simulating complex real-world scenarios. In response, Offline RL emerges as a promising approach, enabling agents to learn from historical data. This study investigates the use of Offline RL in a fed-batch chemical process, where the reward function is customized to train the agent to replicate optimal batches based on a reward function. Four state-of-the-art RL algorithms, including Conservative Q-Learning (CQL), and Batch Constrained Q-Learning (BCQ), Implicit Q-Learning (IQL), and Behavior Cloning (BC) are compared. This research examines the impact of dataset quality on RL agent performance, highlighting the importance of designing data collection experiments. Our results show that CQL outperforms other algorithms. Combining different recipe datasets reduces agent performance, while focusing solely on golden-batch experiments improves it at the expense of generalization. Overall, this study demonstrates the potential of Offline RL in controlling chemical processes.

Keywords: Offline-Reinforcement Learning, Data-driven control, Fed-batch process

1. Introduction

Reinforcement learning (RL) is a machine learning technique to learn an optimal policy to solve a sequential decision-making problem based on a reward function. The use of RL has received significant attention due to its impressive performance. This attention has spurred an increasing interest in implementing RL-based control and optimization algorithms in chemical processes (Ma, et al. 2019, Elmaz, et al. 2023). RL algorithms learn optimal policies by engaging in numerous interactions between agents and their environment (Sutton and Barto 2018). However, such interactions might not always be practical in industrial settings due to safety concerns and the lengthy nature of these processes. On the other hand, training within a simulation often suffers from the discrepancies between real-world scenarios and the simulation, due to the complexity of the process and potential inaccuracies. This can result in total failures when implementing the trained agent on-site.

To address these challenges, Offline RL has been introduced, allowing the agent to determine the best strategy based solely on logged data. While utilizing logged data helps minimize the simulation-to-reality (sim-to-real) gap, risks such as overfitting or bias in the dataset persist.

Additionally, such data may lack sufficient exploration, indicating the importance of data quality. In this study, we explore the utilization of offline RL techniques in a fed-batch industrial process scenario. The main objective of the designed agent is to control the process to follow predefined set-points by the human expert. We investigate the applicability of four state-of-the-art RL algorithms for optimizing the control policy of the process. Moreover, the study highlights how data quality impacts the performance of the trained agent. The remainder of this article is organized as follows: the experimental setup and data acquisition process is presented in section 2. The offline RL methodology is discussed in section 3. The results and conclusion are presented in section 4 and 5, respectively.

2. Reaction System and Data Collection

The process of interest includes a semi-batch (fed-batch) operating mode with a risk of uncontrolled side reactions causing failure. It's an exothermic reaction, demanding precise temperature control. The bath temperature and feed rate of one of the reagents are manipulated variables, while the inside temperature and the residual molar equivalents of the main reactants are the main controlled variables. Reactant molar equivalents are estimated via online near infra-red (NIR) spectroscopy. The impurities in the reagents and the reaction conditions, including the total feed length and mixture temperature affect the product quality. It is important to prevent the accumulation of side reactions during the reaction, as they can lead to the formation of a highly viscous product, which is undesired. The process involves a feeding phase and a post-feeding phase.

In this study, 44 lab-scale experiments were conducted with two recipes (recipe 1 and recipe 2) under different initial conditions and strategies, and measurements were taken each minute. The feeding time is the main difference between these two recipes. Among these, 4 are 'golden batch' experiments, optimized by human experts. Additionally, a simulation environment based on mass and heat balance equations was developed. Using this, and incorporating the control actions from the experiments, 44 simulated datasets were created, with the main difference being that observations are outputs from the simulation model. The agent is trained offline using experimental control strategies but observes outputs from the simulation. Validation occurs within the simulation environment, aiming to minimize observation discrepancies between training data and the validation environment.

It is important to note that due to the confidentiality of the reaction system, all chemical names have been masked, and the presented variables and graphs are normalized.

3. Offline Reinforcement Learning

Offline RL is a method where an agent learns exclusively from a fixed dataset without interacting with the environment (Levine, et al. 2020). The dataset comprises a set of transitions previously gathered, and no new data is collected during training. This can lead to the agent encountering states during deployment that it hasn't seen in training, causing extrapolation errors. This can cause the policy to overestimate the value of out-of-distribution states, leading to sub optimal actions with low rewards. While distributional shift can also occur in off-policy RL, the agent can mitigate and correct those over-estimations through environment interaction and learning from real-time experiences.

Conservative Q-Learning (CQL) (Kumar, Zhou, et al. 2020), Batch Constrained Q-Learning (BCQ) (Fujimoto, Meger and Precup, 2019), Implicit Q-Learning (IQL) (Kostrikov, Nair and Levine 2021), and Behavior Cloning (BC) (Fujimoto and Gu. 2021) are offline algorithms designed for static datasets, each with its approach to optimize policy learning. CQL and BCQ focus on constraining their learning to avoid overestimation and overfitting, with CQL being more conservative and BCQ focusing on actions' distribution. IQL introduces robustness by considering a distribution of Q-values. In contrast, BC takes a more direct approach by simply replicating expert behaviors without long-term vision. For training the agent, the data is structured into a Markov Decision Process (MDP) with states including time step, component concentration, and reactor temperature, alongside their desired future values. The action space includes two continuous variables to manipulate the flow rate of component A and set point temperature. The reward at time step t is defined as follows:

$$r_t = -\omega_1 \left| C_A^t - C_{A-ref}^t \right| - \omega_2 \left| T^t - T_{ref}^t \right|,$$

where ω_1 and ω_2 are weight factors to emphasize the importance of the elements in the reward functions. To investigate the performance of the trained agent, we used the simulation environment described in the previous section. The simulation model is wrapped as OpenAI Gym (Brockman, et al. 2016) environment and python library d3rlpy (Seno and Ima 2022) is utilized for training.

4. Results

In this section, first, we compare the convergence of different RL algorithms for this specific problem. Then using the best algorithm, we investigate how the different subsets of the data sets can affect the performance of RL agent. Finally, we compare the action and observations of one golden-batch experiment with the optimal RL agent.

4.1. Offline RL Algorithms Comparison

Figure 1.a illustrates the training curves for BCQ, CQL, IQL and BC algorithms. For the training procedure we used the same data set (recipe 1, see sec 4.2) for different algorithms and the training procedures were performed for 18k training steps. This figure indicates that CQL outperforms the other algorithm both in performance and stability during the learning step. It also indicates that BCQ converges to a suboptimal policy, while IQL and BC didn't converge to a certain policy. Moreover, Figure 1.a indicates that CQL converges to the optimal policy after 6k training steps and starts to overfits the data after 7k training steps, indicating a sign to stop the training procedure.

4.2. Dataset Effect on Agent's Performance

CQL does not impose any specific assumption on the data sets. Some studies suggest that by combining datasets of different simple tasks, the trained agent can aggregate those simple tasks and perform more complex tasks (Kumar, Agarwal, et al. 2022). In this section we test the hypothesis that the quality of the logged episodes can affect the performance of an RL agent design to perform a simple control task in a chemical reaction. For a fixed reward function, Figure 2 illustrates the reward distribution for different subsets of experiments, and the average reward for full episodes is summarized in Table 1. As it is shown in this figure, the distribution of the reward for the full data sets and the subset with only recipe 1 is almost the same and the difference in average reward for these data sets is about 8.1%.

Figure 1.b represents the learning curve for CQL with the same hyperparameters using different subsets of training data. As it is shown in this figure, using the full data set, the performance of the agent increases during first few steps of the training (training step less than 2k). Afterwards, the performance of the agent decreases by continuing the learning steps. This figure shows by removing recipe 2 (with longer feed time) from the data sets, the training procedure became stable and converge to optimal policies. Training using only golden batch can easily over fits the policy leading to sub optimal policy, while using a data set consisting of only recipe 1 illustrates a robust learning procedure.

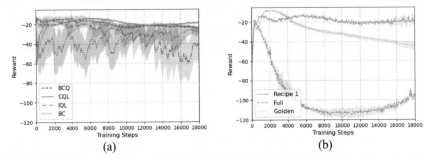

(a)   (b)

Figure 1. returned reward of the agent during the training procedure, (a) comparing different algorithm using recipe 1 and (b) comparing performance of CQL using different subset of data

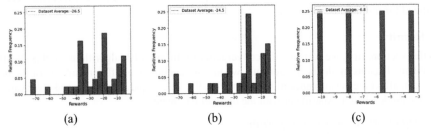

(a)   (b)   (c)

Figure 2. distribution of reward for (a) full experimental data set, (b) only experiments with recipe 1, and (c) for only golden-batch experiments.

Table 1. Summary of average reward of different datasets and the best performance of RL agent during training.

	Full data set	Recipe 1	Golden batches
Data set average reward	-26.5	-24.5	-6.8
CQL best reward (training step)	-13.4 (1k)	-9.9 (18k)	-7.5 (2.6k)

4.3. Performance Analysis of the agent

To analyze the performance of the trained agent, we initialize the simulation model based on one of the golden-baches experiments, let the agent interact with the environment, and compare the actions and observations of RL agent with experimental data as baseline. As shown in Figure 3, the actions of the RL agent have good agreement with the actions in the data set, indicating that the agent learnt the optimal policy from the experiments.

Figure 4 compares the states during the experiments. The solid lines are the experimental values (for one golden-batch experiment), and dash lines represent the simulation values controlled by RL agent. Table 2 summarized the correlation and errors between the golden-batch experiment and RL agent. As it is represented in this table, the main deviation is related to the temperature. It is mainly due to gap between simulation and real world (the accuracy off heat transfer equations is not as good as mass balance) and the fact that in experiments the temperature are changed discretely but the action space for the agent is continuous. Additionally, we analysed how measurement noise affects the agent's performance. We used a random Gaussian noise model added to only measurement values as a percentage of the original value. Experiments show that increasing noise levels to 8% reduces mean reward by approximately 3.25%, while 10% noise can lead to a 15.3% reduction.

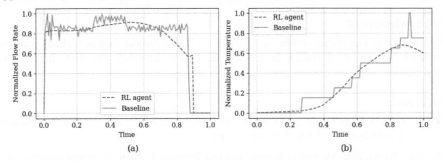

Figure 3. comparison of actions: (a) flow rate of the feed, and (b) setpoint temperature of the heat bath.

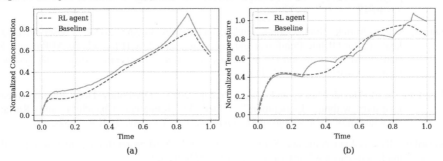

Figure 4. comparison of observations: (a) concentration of component A, and (b) the mixture temperature.

Table 2. correlation coefficient and mean squared error (MSE) of main state elements compared to one of golden-batch experiments.

	C_A	C_B	Temperature
R^2	0.894	0.999	0.705
MSE	0.004	0.003	5.711

5. Conclusions

This research demonstrates the application of offline RL algorithms to control a chemical reaction and reproduce the optimal batches. A dataset of 44 experiments, utilizing two recipes and various strategies, was used to train the RL agent through algorithms like BCQ, IQL, CQL, and BC. To investigate the performance of RL agent an ideal simulation model based on first principal heat and mass balance equations is developed to mimic the experimental setup. Using the same data set, CQL has the better performance in converging to the optimal policy while BC has the worth performance as there is no long-term index in this algorithm. Moreover, the data quality's impact was assessed by segmenting the datasets. Our investigations indicate that combining two recipes can reduce the performance of RL agent, significantly, while training on only golden-batch experiments can slightly improve the final performance of the agent but affects generalization. This paper showed the performance of offline RL algorithm in chemical industry. The future work will compare the performance offline RL agent with classical online methods. The reward function employed in this study was a simple function to follow predefined setpoints. The future work will design more complex reward function to optimize the process based on different objectives.

Acknowledgment

This work was performed within the CHAI imec ICON project. It was realized with the financial support of Flanders Innovation & Entrepreneurship (VLAIO, project no. HBC.2021.0671)

References

Sutton, Richard S, and Andrew G Barto. 2018. *Reinforcement Learning: An Introduction.* Cambridge, MA, USA: A Bradford Book.

Ma, Yan, Wenbo Zhu, Michael G Benton, and José Romagnoli. 2019. "Continuous control of a polymerization system with deep reinforcement learning." *Journal of Process Control* 75: 40-47.

Kumar, Aviral, Aurick Zhou, George Tucker, and Sergey Levine. 2020. "Conservative Q-Learning for Offline Reinforcement Learning." Edited by H Larochelle, M Ranzato, R Hadsell, M F Balcan and H Lin. *Advances in Neural Information Processing Systems* (Curran Associates, Inc.) 33: 1179-1191.

Fujimoto, Scott, David Meger, and Doina Precup. 2019. "Off-Policy Deep Reinforcement Learning without Exploration." Edited by Kamalika Chaudhuri and Ruslan Salakhutdinov. *Proceedings of Machine Learning Research.* PMLR. 2052-2062.

Kostrikov, Ilya, Ashvin Nair, and Sergey Levine. 2021. "Offline reinforcement learning with implicit q-learning." *arXiv preprint arXiv:2110.06169.*

Fujimoto, Scott, and Shixiang (Shane) Gu. 2021. "A Minimalist Approach to Offline Reinforcement Learning." *Advances in Neural Information Processing Systems.* Curran Associates, Inc. 34.

Brockman, Greg, Vicki Cheung, Ludwig Pettersson, Jonas Schneider, John Schulman, Jie Tang, and Wojciech Zaremba. 2016. *OpenAI Gym.*

Seno, Takuma, and Michita Ima. 2022. "d3rlpy: An Offline Deep Reinforcement Learning Library." *Journal of Machine Learning Research* 23: 1-20.

Levine, Sergey, Aviral Kumar, George Tucker, and Justin Fu. 2020. "Offline reinforcement learning: Tutorial, review, and perspectives on open problems." *arXiv preprint arXiv:2005.01643.*

Elmaz, Furkan, Ulderico Di Caprio, Min Wu, Yentl Wouters, Geert Van Der Vorst, Niels Vandervoort, Ali Anwar, M. Enis Leblebici, Peter Hellinckx, and Siegfried Mercelis. 2023. "Reinforcement learning-based approach for optimizing solvent-switch processes,." *Computers & Chemical Engineering* 176: 108310.

Kumar, Aviral, Rishabh Agarwal, Xinyang Geng, George Tucker, and Sergey Levine. 2022. "Offline q-learning on diverse multi-task data both scales and generalizes." *arXiv preprint arXiv:2211.15144.*

Flavio Manenti, Gintaras V. Reklaitis (Eds.), Proceedings of the 34th European Symposium on Computer Aided Process Engineering / 15th International Symposium on Process Systems Engineering (ESCAPE34/PSE24), June 2-6, 2024, Florence, Italy

Supporting Carbon Capture, Utilization, and Storage Supply Chains (CCUS) with Blockchain Technology: A Sustainable Solution for Climate Change Mitigation

Manar Y. Oqbi[a,*], Dhabia M. Al-Mohannadi[b]

[a]Artie McFerrin Department of Chemical Engineering, Texas A&M University, College Station, TX, 77843, USA
[b]Department of Chemical Engineering, Texas A&M University at Qatar, P.O Box 23874, Education City, Doha, Qatar
manar.oqbi@tamu.edu

Abstract

The urgency for adopting emission reduction mitigation strategies is growing as the consequences of climate change become more threatening. Carbon Capture, Utilization, and Storage (CCUS) emerges as a pivotal solution, facilitating substantial carbon dioxide abatement in high-emission industries. However, CCUS encounters challenges related to supply chain transparency, as well as emission accounting and reduction verification. This study introduces a framework, proposing the integration of blockchain technology into the optimization models of CCUS supply chains. Emissions data from various elements of the optimal CCUS supply chain are securely stored in blocks within the proposed blockchain system, ensuring the integrity and tamper-proof nature of the recorded data. This innovative approach empowers decision-makers to optimize the design of CCUS supply chains, improve computational efficiency, transparently trace emissions from CCUS elements, and verify emission reductions. Anticipated to play a pivotal role in climate change mitigation and sustainable practices, the developed blockchain-based approach is poised to contribute significantly to ongoing efforts in designing and enhancing the effectiveness of the optimal CCUS supply chains.

Keywords: Carbon Capture Utilization and Storage (CCUS), Optimization, Emissions Reduction Verification, Blockchain technology.

1. Introduction

Climate change is one of the most significant challenges nowadays, necessitating innovative approaches to mitigate the impact of greenhouse gases (GHG) and facilitate the transition towards a net zero economy. The global surface temperature has increased by 1.1 °C in the last decade compared to 1850 - 1900 temperatures. In 2019, the global net anthropogenic GHG emissions were about 54 % higher than 1990 levels (IPCC, 2023). Carbon capture, utilization, and storage (CCUS) is a promising decarbonization technology, especially for hard-to-abate industries including iron, steel, refineries, and chemical production plants (Azadnia et al., 2023). Approximately 40 operational commercial capture facilities globally currently have an annual capture capacity exceeding 45 million tons (Mt) of CO_2. However, this falls significantly short, constituting roughly a third of the 1.2 Gt CO_2 per year needed to align with the Net Zero Emissions by 2050 (NZE) Scenario (IEA, 2023).

The effectiveness of CCUS is influenced by various factors, including technological maturity, policy and regulatory frameworks, stakeholders' acceptance, economic viability, and robust emission reduction verification (Luo et al., 2023). Ensuring emission reduction reliability is crucial for the transparency and effectiveness of CCUS systems, fostering stakeholder trust and contributing significantly to climate change mitigation. However, the intricate nature of CCUS networks, combined with challenges in data accuracy, poses transparency obstacles. Reliable emission reduction verification is essential for policymakers to comprehend the true potential of CCUS networks, gain stakeholder approval, and ensure project success (GAO, 2022). The verification process typically involves monitoring through emission factors or sensors, self-reporting, and third-party verification, which can be time-consuming, resource-intensive, and costly.

A promising avenue for achieving optimal and transparent design of CCUS supply chains is through the integration of blockchain technology. Blockchain technology, initially conceived as the underlying framework for Bitcoin proposed by Satoshi Nakamoto (Nakamoto, 2008). Blockchain serves as a decentralized, distributed ledger that records transactions across a network of computers in a tamper-proof manner. Blockchain comprises a sequential linkage of data blocks, fostering an indelible ledger. Integral cryptographic techniques bolster data security and integrity (Thakur et al., 2023). This work introduces a novel method for integrating blockchain technology into CCUS supply chains optimization models. The next sections review relevant literature, detail the proposed approach and current challenges followed by conclusions.

2. Literature Review

Research in the modeling and optimization of carbon capture, utilization, and storage (CCUS) has garnered significant attention, particularly in the pursuit of improving cost-effectiveness and environmental performance. Zhang et al. (2020) contributed to this field by developing an optimization-based framework that integrates CO_2 storage and utilization, exploring various paths within the CCUS supply chain, with a primary focus on economic performance. Rakhiemah and Xu (2022) conducted an in-depth analysis of the economic viability of CCUS with Enhanced Oil Recovery (EOR) in Indonesia, placing emphasis on cost-benefit considerations and the potential for additional oil recovery. Simultaneously, environmental aspects have been scrutinized by various researchers, including Leonzio et al. (2023) and Facchino et al. (2022), who utilized life cycle assessments to systematically evaluate the impact of large-scale CCUS supply chains on carbon emissions reduction in Germany, Italy, and Poland.

Blockchain technology is increasingly recognized as a solution to enhance transparency in emissions reduction, although its application has primarily been in carbon trading markets. Shu et al. (2022) proposed a blockchain-enhanced trading system for the construction industry, incorporating smart contracts to improve efficiency and reliability. Sadawi et al. (2021) presented a hierarchical blockchain framework for carbon emission trading, leveraging Blockchain of Things (BoT) and smart contracts. Muzumdar et al. (2022) focused on a permissioned blockchain system for emission trading, addressing issues like scams and poor monitoring. A comprehensive blockchain-based platform for carbon accounting and trading in the UK construction industry for increased transparency was introduced by Blumberg and Sibilla (2023). In parallel, Lu et al. (2022) proposed STRICTs, a blockchain-enabled system for curbing carbon emissions in road transport, showcasing practical performance through a Hyperledger Fabric-based prototype.

Commercial initiatives by Mitsubishi Heavy Industries and IBM Japan, such as "CO2NNEX," demonstrate the integration of blockchain and IoT devices in CCS infrastructures to streamline the CO_2 supply chain (MHI, 2021). CarbonKerma, in 2023, introduced a blockchain-based marketplace for carbon credits from CCUS, symbolized as digital tokens, ensuring traceability and legitimacy in a transparent distributed ledger system (CarbonKerma, 2023). These initiatives highlight the practical applications of blockchain technology in enhancing transparency and reliability in the CCUS sector.

The literature review highlights a notable research gap in emission reduction verification within the framework of Carbon Capture, Utilization, and Storage (CCUS). Previous studies have explored the intricacies of modeling and optimizing the CCUS supply chain infrastructure. The emergence of blockchain technology presents a promising avenue to address the need for transparency in emission tracing within CCUS supply chains. Although prior applications of blockchain in emission reduction have predominantly focused on creating transparent markets for carbon trading, this study introduces an innovative approach. It proposes an integrated decision-making framework that combines blockchain technology with an optimization-based model, offering a strategic and transparent approach to carbon planning within the CCUS context.

3. Proposed Approach

CCUS supply chains include emissions reduction data from source-sink matching besides emissions data from different elements such as capturing units, compression, transportation, utilization, and geological storage. The proposed approach advocates the enhancement of transparency in designing CCUS supply chains through the integration of blockchain technology. This integration involves incorporating the blockchain network into the CCUS optimization model, aiming to achieve an optimal design for the CCUS network that facilitates improved transparency in emissions tracking and reduction. Emissions from sources, and different stages of the CCUS supply chains are considered during the optimization. By integrating the blockchain network into the optimization model, the recording of emissions data and emission reduction verification becomes transparent. The developed framework advocates the optimization of the CCUS network and the establishment of a distributed ledger encompassing CCUS emissions data related to various source-sink matches and elements using the blockchain network.

The CCUS-blockchain system is initiated as follows: when new emissions data is available from the CCUS supply chain, a new block is generated. This block undergoes a secure and decentralized sharing process with authorizing and validating nodes, in accordance with the chosen consensus mechanism. This approach assumes that only participating plants have authorized access as validating nodes to maintain the data privacy of the CCUS sources and sinks. Once validated, the new emissions data block is seamlessly appended to the existing sequence of blocks by the nodes within the network. The block is safeguarded by its unique hash and the hash of the preceding block. Emissions data originating from each stage is recorded in a block that is validated, encrypted, and added to the sequence of preceding blocks.

Emissions data are recorded in blocks in an order that is equivalent to the elements sequence in the CCUS supply chain. The recorded data undergoes meticulous processing through smart contracts, culminating in the creation of comprehensive CCUS performance reports and emissions profiles. These reports function as invaluable tools for stakeholders, providing a systematic evaluation of CCUS performance and identifying specific areas for potential improvement. The generated reports serve as a transparent monitoring, reporting and verification mechanism for ensuring regulatory compliance, thereby obviating the necessity for third-party verification. Figure 1 illustrates the developed framework for integrating blockchain technology to design optimal CCUS supply chains with enhanced transparency of emissions tracking and verification.

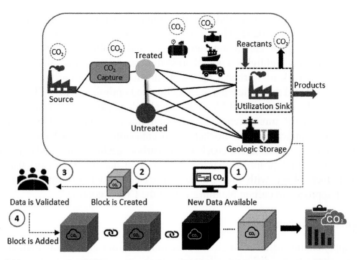

Figure 1: Integration of blockchain technology for designing CCUS supply chains with enhanced emissions tracking.

The proposed methodology presents opportunities to significantly enhance computational efficiency by leveraging decentralization and distributed computing, enabling parallel processing across a network of nodes. The approach enables streamlining verification processes and reduces the need for redundant computations. Overall, these advancements contribute to a more streamlined and efficient CCUS optimization framework. However, integrating blockchain technology into the CCUS framework presents several challenges that merit careful consideration such as regulatory compliance, stakeholder acceptance, and scalability (Uddin et al., 2023). Gaining approval and active participation from all stakeholders in the CCUS network is a key success element of the proposed framework. Resistance or hesitancy from stakeholders may impede the successful implementation. The limited scalability of blockchain technology may be a concern as CCUS projects expand and involve an increasing number of participants. Finally, non-compliance with regulatory frameworks may lead to legal issues and undermine the credibility of the proposed system. Addressing these challenges requires a concerted effort from stakeholders, technology developers, and policymakers to ensure the seamless integration of blockchain technology into CCUS supply chains, maximizing its potential benefits for transparent and effective emission reduction strategies.

4. Case Study

This example illustrates the proposed approach that integrates blockchain network into CCUS optimization models. Blockchain technology was integrated into a previously developed mixed-integer nonlinear optimization model (MINLP) by Al-mohannadi and Linke (2016) aiming to minimize the total cost considering capturing, transportation, sink utilization and storage as expressed in Eq. (1). The model incorporates constraints to ensure carbon balance around carbon sources and sinks, as indicated by Eq. (2) and Eq. (3), respectively. Detailed data, including carbon compositions and flows from sources, as well as required carbon quality and flows for sinks, are presented in Table 1.

Total Cost = Capture cost + Transportation cost + Sink cost   (1)

$$\text{Carbon Source i} = \text{Sum of treated flows} + \text{Sum of untreated flows} \tag{2}$$

$$\text{Carbon sink j} = \text{Treated flows to sink j} + \text{Untreated flows to sink j} \tag{3}$$

Cost elements were considered as illustrated by Al-mohannadi and Linke (2016). The net capture emission was constrained to 80% of total emissions. Employing a Python implementation on a desktop with an Intel® Core™ i7-10700 CPU @ 2.90GHz, 2904 Mhz, 32 GB memory and 64-bit operating system, the optimal design was identified. The total cost was 142 MM \$/yr, and the source to sink carbon connections are determined. The emissions data within the blockchain-based network are visualized by Figure 2. Each block provides specific information, enhancing transparency in the CCUS process. The initial block sets the baseline emissions from carbon sources. The second block focuses on capturing unit emissions, while the third block represents emissions due to transportation. Block 4 showcases carbon flows from sources to sinks, emphasizing matching emissions with sinks and the last block outlines sink emissions. The proposed blockchain-based optimization model enables a transparent tracking and verification of each stage's emissions and environmental impact for the optimal CCUS design.

Table 1: Data of carbon dioxide sources and sinks.

industry	Y_{CO2} (wt%)	CO_2 Flow (t/d)
Power plant 1 (S1)	6	3843
Power plant 2 (S2)	5.6	4654
Urea (J1)	99	1488
Saline storage (J2)	94	7500

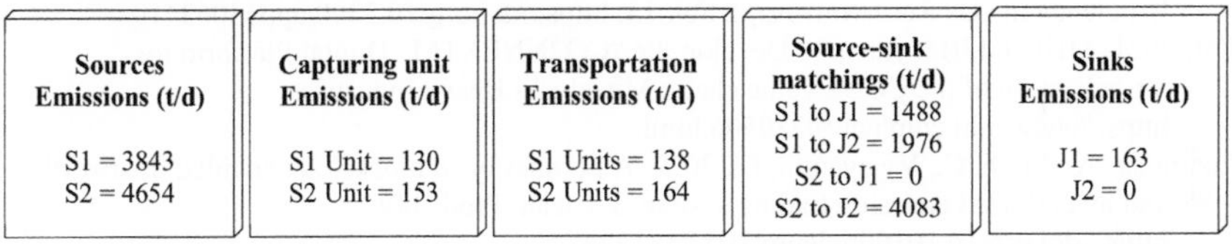

Sources Emissions (t/d)	Capturing unit Emissions (t/d)	Transportation Emissions (t/d)	Source-sink matchings (t/d)	Sinks Emissions (t/d)
S1 = 3843	S1 Unit = 130	S1 Units = 138	S1 to J1 = 1488	J1 = 163
S2 = 4654	S2 Unit = 153	S2 Units = 164	S1 to J2 = 1976	J2 = 0
			S2 to J1 = 0	
			S2 to J2 = 4083	

Figure 2: Blockchain visualization of emissions data in the optimal blockchain-based CCUS network.

5. Conclusions

The devised approach harnesses the capabilities of blockchain technology in conjunction with CCUS supply chains optimization models, elevating the transparency of emission reductions and improving computational efficiency. Comprehensive emissions data, encompassing CO_2 utilization, storage, and various CCUS processes, is systematically recorded in discrete blocks which undergo a rigorous validation process and are seamlessly integrated into the blocks sequence. This blockchain-integrated CCUS framework restricts data validation exclusively to authorized nodes, safeguarding data privacy and security. The cryptographic foundation of the blockchain ensures the utmost reliability and immutability of the recorded data. Despite the potency of the proposed system, potential obstacles such as scalability, stakeholder acceptance, and regulatory compliance need to be addressed to fully unlock its capabilities.

References

Al-mohannadi, D.M., Linke, P., 2016. On the systematic carbon integration of industrial parks for climate footprint reduction. J. Clean. Prod. 112, 4053–4064. https://doi.org/10.1016/j.jclepro.2015.05.094

Azadnia, A.H., McDaid, C., Andwari, A.M., Hosseini, S.E., 2023. Green hydrogen supply chain risk analysis: A european hard-to-abate sectors perspective. Renew. Sustain. Energy Rev. 182. https://doi.org/10.1016/j.rser.2023.113371

Blumberg, G., Sibilla, M., 2023. A Carbon Accounting and Trading Platform for the uk Construction Industry. Energies 16. https://doi.org/10.3390/en16041566

CarbonKerma, 2023. The global marketplace for CCUS-derived carbon credits. https://carbonkerma.com.

Facchino, M., Popielak, P., Panowski, M., Wawrzyńczak, D., Majchrzak-Kucęba, I., De Falco, M., 2022. The Environmental Impacts of Carbon Capture Utilization and Storage on the Electricity Sector: A Life Cycle Assessment Comparison between Italy and Poland. Energies 15. https://doi.org/10.3390/en15186809

GAO, 2022. Decarbonization: Status, Challenges, and Policy Options for Carbon Capture, Utilization, and Storage. United States Government Accountability Office. https://www.gao.gov.

IEA, 2023. Carbon Capture, Utilisation and Storage. International Energy Agency. https://www.iea.org/energy-system/carbon-capture-utilisation-and-storage.

IPCC, 2023. Climate Change 2023: Synthesis Report. Contribution of Working Groups I, II and III to the Sixth Assessment Report of the Intergovernmental Panel on Climate Change. Geneva, Switzerland. https://doi.org/10.59327/IPCC/AR6-9789291691647

Leonzio, G., Bogle, I.D.L., Ugo Foscolo, P., 2023. Life cycle assessment of a carbon capture utilization and storage supply chain in Italy and Germany: Comparison between carbon dioxide storage and utilization systems. Sustain. Energy Technol. Assessments 55. https://doi.org/10.1016/j.seta.2022.102743

Lu, Y., Li, Y., Tang, X., Cai, B., Wang, H., Liu, L., Wan, S., Yu, K., 2022. STRICTs: A Blockchain-enabled Smart Emission Cap Restrictive and Carbon Permit Trading System. Appl. Energy 313, 118787. https://doi.org/10.1016/j.apenergy.2022.118787

Luo, Y., Qin, J., Cai, J., Tang, Y., 2023. The Influencing Factors of CO2 Utilization and Storage Efficiency in Gas Reservoir. Appl. Sci. 13. https://doi.org/10.3390/app13063419

MHI, 2021. MHI and IBM Japan to Develop the "CO2NNEXTM" Digital Platform for Visualization of the CCUS value chain. Mitsubishi Heavy Industries. https://www.mhi.com/news/210506.html.

Muzumdar, A., Modi, C., Vyjayanthi, C., 2022. A permissioned blockchain enabled trustworthy and incentivized emission trading system. J. Clean. Prod. 349. https://doi.org/10.1016/j.jclepro.2022.131274

Nakamoto, S., 2008. Bitcoin: A Peer-to-Peer Electronic Cash System. www.bitcoin.org.

Rakhiemah, A.N., Xu, Y., 2022. Economic viability of full-chain CCUS-EOR in Indonesia. Resour. Conserv. Recycl. 179, 106069. https://doi.org/10.1016/j.resconrec.2021.106069

Sadawi, A. Al, Madani, B., Saboor, S., Ndiaye, M., Abu-Lebdeh, G., 2021. A comprehensive hierarchical blockchain system for carbon emission trading utilizing blockchain of things and smart contract. Technol. Forecast. Soc. Change 173, 121124. https://doi.org/10.1016/j.techfore.2021.121124

Shu, Z., Liu, W., Fu, B., Li, Z., He, M., 2022. Blockchain-enhanced trading systems for construction industry to control carbon emissions. Clean Technol. Environ. Policy 24, 1851–1870. https://doi.org/10.1007/s10098-022-02292-3

Thakur, K., Pathan, A.-S.K., Ismat, S., 2023. Blockchain Technology BT - Emerging ICT Technologies and Cybersecurity: From AI and ML to Other Futuristic Technologies, in: Thakur, K., Pathan, A.-S.K., Ismat, S. (Eds.), . Springer Nature Switzerland, Cham, pp. 125–145. https://doi.org/10.1007/978-3-031-27765-8_4

Uddin, M., Selvarajan, S., Obaidat, M., Arfeen, S.U., Khadidos, Alaa O., Khadidos, Adil O., Abdelhaq, M., 2023. From Hype to Reality: Unveiling the Promises, Challenges and Opportunities of Blockchain in Supply Chain Systems. Sustain. 15. https://doi.org/10.3390/su151612193

Zhang, S., Zhuang, Y., Liu, L., Zhang, L., Du, J., 2020. Optimization-based approach for CO2 utilization in carbon capture, utilization and storage supply chain. Comput. Chem. Eng. 139. https://doi.org/10.1016/j.compchemeng.2020.106885

Flavio Manenti, Gintaras V. Reklaitis (Eds.), Proceedings of the 34th European Symposium on Computer Aided Process Engineering / 15th International Symposium on Process Systems Engineering (ESCAPE34/PSE24), June 2-6, 2024, Florence, Italy

Hydrothermal liquefaction data for use in machine learning models

Geert Haarlemmer [a], Lucie Matricon [a], Anne Roubaud [a]

a Univ. Grenoble Alpes, CEA, LITEN, DTCH, LRP, F-38000 Grenoble, France
geert.haarlemmer@cea.fr

Abstract

Hydrothermal liquefaction is a sustainable pathway to generate biogenic liquids from organic resources. The technology is compatible with a wide variety of resources such as ligno-cellulosic resources, organic waste, algae, and sewage sludge. The chemistry is complex and predictions of product yields are notoriously difficult. Understanding and modelling of hydrothermal liquefaction is currently mostly based on a simplified biochemical analysis, product yield data and for a small application field. This paper presents a large dataset of 2587 experiments in batch reactors that were extracted from 173 publications in the scientific literature. This paper presents how machine learning can contribute to the field of hydrothermal processes. The presented techniques allow a better understanding of the data and its accuracy.

Keywords: Hydrothermal liquefaction, Yield data, Data analysis, Machine learning.

1. Introduction

The hydrothermal liquefaction (HTL) of biomass is now an established technology, making it possible to produce high quality biofuels from low value biogenic waste. Hydrothermal processes operate with hot compressed water, typically above 200 °C and at high pressures converting bio-resources in a crude oil. The field of hydrothermal processes remains very empiric, mostly based on experiments. This is mainly due to the complexity of the resources as well as its chemistry.

Hydrothermal reactions are performed in reactors that are capable to resist to high pressures. There are two major categories of laboratory reactors. The vast majority of scientific papers present work using batch reactors, where the resource is placed in the reactor and the closed system is heated. A large number of experiments can be conducted under controlled conditions. The validity of batch experiments to represent a future industrial transformation is however limited as the heating and cooling phases play an important role on the experiments. Continuous reactors in the academic laboratories are less numerous and experiments are longer to conduct. Batch reactors do have an important role to play in contributing to the understanding of the chemistry.

Modelling of the hydrothermal conversion is an important subject in the literature (Shahbaz et al. 2023). Modelling is done by (non)linear correlations (Déniel et al. 2016) and kinetic models (Hietala and Savage 2021). Most of these approaches have been limited in the past to specific resources. Exploitation at a larger scale can be done with machine learning algorithms as shown by (Li et al. 2021) among others. The advantage of this approach is that the data can be less structured and more voluminous than is common practice in a design of experiment approach. The validity of this approach is however often limited due to the limited amount of data used, typically a few hundred or even less experiments.

There are many incomplete data sets in the literature, insufficient data to understand the resource, but also missing crucial details concerning the reactor and the experiments, making interpretation of the results difficult and reproduction impossible. Resource and product analysis also form an important obstacle in the interpretation of reported hydrothermal experiments.

This study presents results on the HTL of a wide variety of resources, compiled from 173 literature references. This paper aims to show how modern data analysis techniques can make sense of the experimental data in the literature. The data was used to create a model that allows an accurate prediction of the hydrothermal process. The objective is to evaluate the accuracy of the data, not for each experiment but the ability to predict an arbitrary experiment from the literature data.

2. Biomass analysis

The description of biomass solely by ultimate analysis (CHONS, Ash, Heating Value) is useful for high temperature gasification but not so useful for low temperature processes such as HTL as mentioned in the introduction. Conversion in hot compressed water starts with the hydrolysis of the biopolymers, followed by the conversion of the produced molecules. For this reason, it is essential to be able to distinguish different common biopolymers (lignin, cellulose, proteins, and lipids) from simpler molecules (sugars, fatty acids, amino acids and pigments). It has been well established that proteins tend to be depolymerised to amino acids and dissolved under hydrothermal conditions with the formation of bio-oil through Maillard reactions. Lipids (not limited to triglycerides) are hydrolysed into glycerol and fatty acids. The latter contributes mainly to bio-oil formation. Compositional data is however not always reported. Most papers present an ultimate analysis and around half of the papers present details compositional analysis. Literature on hydrothermal carbonisation rarely include compositional analysis data. A majority of publications present compositional data that does not add up to 100 %. While this in itself can be understood, it is a problem in the usage of the results.

The compositional analysis in the form of lignin, carbohydrates, proteins and lipids remains a gross simplification compared to the vast complexity of actual biomass. In addition, measurements are often uncertain and can easily produce inaccurate results. In practice however, the full analysis, including profiling amino acids, fatty acids, sugar, and pigments analysis, and others are complex and are not performed on a routine basis.

3. Hydrothermal experiments

HTL experiments in batch reactors follow a common pattern. The resource is placed in the autoclave reactor with the desired water content and heated. The products are recovered and quantified after opening the reactor. This makes it possible to compare the data and to exploit it. Reactors and experimental procedures are quite constant across the literature. Product recovery techniques do show some variations but can easily be classified in families.

A typical experiment consists of a biomass slurry with a determined dry matter to water ratio being placed in a batch reactor. The reactor is then heated to the reaction temperature with a certain heating rate of that often varies from 4 to 100 °C/min, depending on the size and the heating technology. Once the reactor reaches the desired reaction temperature, it is held during a specified holding time. The pressure inside the reactor is the result of the reaction temperature, due to the water vapour pressure, and to a minor extend the initial nitrogen pressure and the quantity of gas produced. After this holding time, the reactor is cooled to room temperature. This procedure is constant across most studies.

The oily or solid product is referred to as biocrude in this study; this is anything not in the aqueous or gaseous phases. Biocrude is extremely variable in aspect, ranging from a free flowing viscous liquid to a dry powder. Extraction with a solvent separates the biocrude in bio-oil and biochar. Reliable bio-oil and bio-char yields can be obtained relatively easily from the HTL experiments. The yield of the aqueous and the gaseous phases largely depend on the applied techniques. There different product recovery techniques and yield definitions. The solid yield definition is relatively standard as the product not dissolving in water and the organic solvent. The oil yield is the oil retrieved by extraction from the oily residue after liquefaction.

For each reported experiment in this study, the biochemical composition of the biomass is used as presented in the publication. Each experiment is further described by the dry matter content in the biomass slurry, additional chemicals, heating rate, reaction temperature, holding time, extraction order and solvent used. The reported results are bio-oil, char, gas and aqueous phase yields whenever they are available.

4. Data collection

All the data in this paper has been previously described in publications. The data was collected from the websites from scientific publishers (only peer reviewed articles were considered). In this study, we only consider fully presented and documented data sets, including an adequate analysed biomass, the experiments fully described and results are presented in an accessible way.

Table 1. Range of the data in the included dataset.

Independent variables	Range
Temperature	20 - 600 °C
Heating rate	1 - 850 °C/min
Holding time	0 - 1320 min
Dry matter concentration	1 - 50 %
Composition	Ash, lignin, carbohydrates, proteins, lipids, guaiacol, amino acids, carboxylic acids, fatty acids, glycerol
Solvents	Ethyl acetate, ether, dichloromethane, chloroform, acetone, n-hexane, toluene, dimethyl sulfoxide, ethanol, isopropanol
Method	Order solvent extraction after or before water separation (values 1 and 2 respectively)

5. Numerical methods used

The algorithms used in this study are well known algorithms from the SciKit-Learn library and are implemented in Python 3.9. The regressor used in this study is the random forest regressor. The random forest regressor is a robust ensemble method based on multiple decision trees. A decision tree is a graph that, based on tests, proposes an outcome starting from a set of input parameters. As a measurement of the quality of the fit, the coefficient of determination is used as calculated by the function `r2_score` in the SciPy library. This formulation of R^2 ensures that the upper limit is 1 for a perfect fit.

Data from studies in any field are subject to uncertainties. In the machine learning and artificial intelligence field, process variables (independently modifiable parameters) are referred to as features. Uncertainties come from experimental errors variations in biomass analysis techniques and experimental practices. The accuracy that can be obtained from modelling with the data in this study is evaluated using MAPIE (Model Agnostic Prediction Interval Estimator). This Python library allows the identification of confidence intervals on data modelling with an arbitrary regressor. The theoretical basis of this library is described by (Kim et al. 2020). Analysis of the data is also performed using the SHAP library that supplies algorithms for interpretable AI. The library uses a game theory approach initially proposed by Lloyd Shapely and developed by (Lundberg et al. 2019) as a python library. The algorithms in this library allow the evaluation of individual variables and their interactions on the global results as well as individual experiments.

6. Data Analysis

The content of the dataset is difficult to visualise to check for coherency, as there are nine dimensions. Figure 1 shows how the composition of the resources in the database covers the full spectrum. Most real biomasses contain a well balances mixture of compounds required for life. In practice, the extremes and high lipid experiments are mainly covers by experiments on model mixtures and pure compounds.

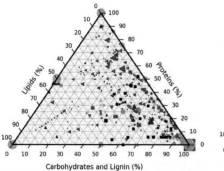
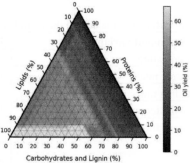

Figure 1 Ternary diagram with compositions, the size is proportional to the number of occurrences. The resource categories are colour coded, FW ▲, FPW ▼, Algae ◄, Sewage x, Mixture ■, Model ●, Herbs, and Wood +.

Figure 2 Ternary diagram with random forest predictions of bio-oil yields

To improve the understanding of the data a random forest model was generated and asked to predict the oil yield as a function of the composition as shown in Figure 2. The model was build using 16 parameters, or features. This modelling only takes into account the compositional effect and ignores all other process parameters.

It is obvious that the composition is not the only process parameter that is important. Figure 3 shows the feature importance on the oil yield prediction as predicted by the SHAP algorithm. The value on the horizontal axis give the influence of the parameter on the deviation from the global average.

The composition plays an important role. The most important process parameter is the temperature. The model compounds such as glycerol, lignin, carboxylic acids and amino acids do not play a significant role, mostly because they contribute little to the oil yield. Products from guaiacol experiments are classed as bio-oil. To check whether it is possible to reduce the dimensions of the modelling problem; a principal component analysis was conducted and presented in Figure 4.

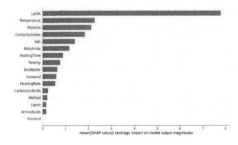

Figure 3 Feature importance   Figure 4 Principle component analysis

The model accuracy (R^2) of the bio-oil prediction is 97.7 % on the training data (70 % of the data) and 87.8 % on the test data (30 % of the data). This is a good score for this type of modelling (Zhang et al. 2021). Typical values oscillate around 90 % for training data and can be as low as 75 % for test data.

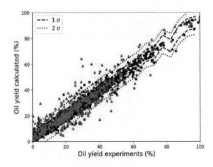

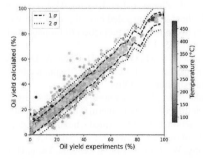

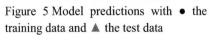

Figure 5 Model predictions with ● the training data and ▲ the test data

Figure 6 Model predictions coloured by temperature

It is also possible to evaluate the quality of the random forest model by the evaluation of the confidence interval. This will put an accuracy on the model, rather than a goodness of fit. Figure 5 shows the predictions on the training set in black circles (●) and the test set in red triangles (▲). The confidence interval as calculated by the MAPIE algorithm is traced in the same graph. The 2σ confidence interval is around ± 10 % absolute of the calculated yield.

Figure 6 shows the same data with the colour now indicating the temperature for which each experiment was performed. It shows that there is a light tendency for low temperatures below 250 °C to produce low oil yields. The 300 to 400 °C range favours medium oil yields in the 40 to 60 % yield range. High yields above 80 % are obtained by low and high temperatures alike; most likely, these are experiments with lipids or very high fat resources that produce oil no matter what other process parameters.

7. Conclusions

The large volume of data in the literature shows that there is a significant interest in hydrothermal experiments. This paper presents 2578 experiments from 173 scientific papers. Each individual experiments may be well done; their use for the scientific community is limited when the results cannot be exploited in larger meta studies. Meta studies are essential for the better understanding of the hydrothermal field as a whole. Globally, taking all the data into account the expected absolute uncertainty of the data can be estimated at 10 % absolute. This value should be interpreted as the 2σ uncertainty of the prediction for a new resource, based on existing data.

References

Déniel, M., G. Haarlemmer, A. Roubaud, E. Weiss-Hortala and J. Fages (2016). "Modelling and Predictive Study of Hydrothermal Liquefaction: Application to Food Processing Residues." Waste and Biomass Valorization 8(6): 2087-2107.

Hietala, D. C. and P. E. Savage (2021). "A molecular, elemental, and multiphase kinetic model for the hydrothermal liquefaction of microalgae." Chemical Engineering Journal 407: 127007.

Kim, B., C. Xu and R. F. Barber (2020). Predictive Inference Is Free with the Jackknife+-after-Bootstrap. 34th Conference on Neural Information Processing Systems.

Li, J., W. Zhang, T. Liu, L. Yang, H. Li, H. Peng, S. Jiang, X. Wang and L. Leng (2021). "Machine learning aided bio-oil production with high energy recovery and low nitrogen content from hydrothermal liquefaction of biomass with experiment verification." Chemical Engineering Journal 425: 130649.

Lundberg, S. M., G. Erion, H. Chen, A. DeGrave, J. M. Prutkin, B. Nair, R. Katz, J. Himmelfarb, N. Bansal and S.-I. Lee (2019). "Explainable AI for Trees: From Local Explanations to Global Understanding." ArXiv.

Shahbaz, M., M. Alherbawi, P. Parthasarathy, G. McKay and T. Al-Ansari (2023). Process modelling of the hydrothermal liquefaction of oil-palm waste for biocrude and hydrochar production. Computer Aided Chemical Engineering. A. C. Kokossis, M. C. Georgiadis and E. Pistikopoulos, Elsevier. 52: 1475-1481.

Zhang, W., J. Li, T. Liu, S. Leng, L. Yang, H. Peng, S. Jiang, W. Zhou, L. Leng and H. Li (2021). "Machine learning prediction and optimization of bio-oil production from hydrothermal liquefaction of algae." Bioresource Technology 342: 126011.

Flavio Manenti, Gintaras V. Reklaitis (Eds.), Proceedings of the 34th European Symposium on
Computer Aided Process Engineering / 15th International Symposium on Process Systems
Engineering (ESCAPE34/PSE24), June 2-6, 2024, Florence, Italy

Application of a Predictive Maintenance Strategy Based on Machine Learning in a Used Oil Refinery

Francesco Negri[a,b], Andrea Galeazzi[b], Francesco Gallo[a], Flavio Manenti[b,*]

[a]Itelyum Regeneration S.p.A., Via Tavernelle 19, Pieve Fissiraga 26854, Lodi, Italy
[b]Politecnico di Milano, CMIC Dept. "Giulio Natta", Piazza Leonardo da Vinci 32, Milan 20133, Italy
*flavio.manenti@polimi.it

Abstract

The Itelyum Regeneration used oil re-refining plant in Pieve Fissiraga currently employs a condition-based maintenance strategy for its thermodeasphalting (TDA) section, particularly focusing on the TDA T-401 column. This strategy involves monitoring the real-time pressure differential (ΔP) between the column's top and bottom, which increases in time due to fouling phenomena. Maintenance is scheduled when ΔP exceeds a predetermined empirical threshold, ensuring that the T-401 column operates within normal operations limits. However, this approach has limitations with non-conventional used oils. To address this, a data-driven machine learning algorithm, previously successful in predicting key performance indicators of the PH-401B furnace in the TDA section, was applied to the T-401 column datasets. This algorithm, based on Gaussian Process Regressions, effectively predicts the evolution of ΔP and reduces the time during which T-401 operates in suboptimal conditions. The implementation of this machine learning approach marks a significant improvement in the maintenance strategy, shifting from a static, condition-based approach to a dynamic, predictive one, thus ensuring more efficient and reliable operations, even with non-conventional used oil.

Keywords: Data-driven, Machine learning, Predictive maintenance, Thermodeasphalting, Used oil.

1. Introduction

Maintenance is a crucial aspect of every industrial plant to ensure continuity of operations and safety of the workers. Typical approaches in the European industrial context are corrective, preventive, opportunistic, condition-based, and predictive maintenance (Bevilacqua and Braglia, 2000). The combination of a vacuum distillation column and its feedstock fired heater are critical pieces of equipment in crude oil refineries and used oil re-refineries that suffer from fouling due to the characteristics of the heavy hydrocarbon feed, thus requiring careful maintenance planning (Fuentes et al., 2007; Morales-Fuentes et al., 2014). One of the most robust and efficient processes for the regeneration of used oil is based on the patented Revivoil® technology, and is currently operated in the Itelyum Regeneration re-refining facility in Pieve Fissiraga, Lodi, Italy (Gallo, 2016). The maintenance approach in the case of the TDA section of the process is typically condition-based, using the pressure differential across pieces of equipment as a sentinel key performance indicator to be monitored. Maintenance is planned once the parameter overcomes a warning threshold value. This static approach is typical for the refining industry, where fouling is an ever-present problem. Data-driven approaches have shown good results in modeling fouling in refinery equipment such as heat exchangers, with better fitting compared with equation-based, mechanistic modeling approaches, which instead often show poor results due to the extremely complex and partially random nature of fouling phenomena (Mei et al., 2023). This work uses said data-driven algorithms to develop a dynamic predictive maintenance strategy that is more effective in avoiding runtime within suboptimal operating regions and it is more adaptable to changes in feedstock composition, a typical situation for used oil waste.

2. Materials and Methods

2.1. Current Maintenance Strategy

The thermodeasphalting (TDA) section of the Revivoil® process works by fractionating dehydrated used oil in a vacuum column. The main products from the TDA T-401 column are three semi-finished base lube oil cuts. The TDA column starts every run with a project-specified pressure differential between top and bottom which is characterized by a dynamic evolution in time, as shown in Figure 1. The graph reports normalized values to preserve industrial secret, which have been cleared of gross errors by applying a robust methodology (Manenti and Buzzi-Ferraris, 2009). The vertical axis shows the pressure differential (ΔP) normalized with respect to the project value, which is the one observed at every start-of-run. The horizontal axis shows the length of run normalized so that the longest run is divided into ten equally and arbitrarily long time periods (τ). Figure 1 shows two curves, each representing a run in which T-401 was processing a certain type of used oil. Used oil type "A" is representative of a typical used oil that is treated in Pieve Fissiraga facility. Used oil type "B" is a non-conventional type of used oil, more volatile than type "A", for which an industrial test was carried out to understand the possible impact on the existing re-refining technology. Both curves show an evolution in time in which the ΔP gradually increases, firstly at a relatively slow pace, followed by a sudden and rapid degeneration, which is a typical fouling behavior for distillation systems working with heavy and unstable hydrocarbon feedstock (Seegulam et al., 2017).

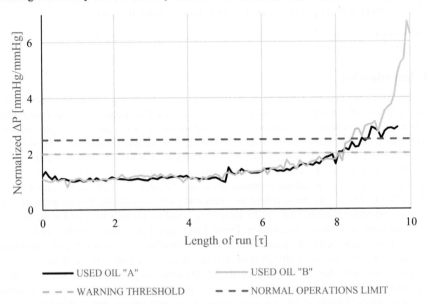

Figure 1. Normalized pressure differential in the TDA column vs time for two types of used oil

The evolution of the ΔP in time may be explained by an initial, gradual reduction of the effective cross sectional area in the column packed beds, which corresponds to a gradual increment in the overall pressure differential. When the ΔP approaches the flooding value in one (or more) of the beds, gas and liquid fail to flow correctly through the column, eventually leading to a unit shutdown (Rocha et al., 1993). The graph in Figure 1 also shows two important thresholds. The first is the warning threshold of 2 mmHg/mmHg, which is the value of normalized ΔP at which, according to the historical condition-based strategy, maintenance must be scheduled. This threshold has been determined by a statistical analysis on the ΔP evolution in time with typical used oil (type "A"). The second is the normal operations threshold of 2.5 mmHg/mmHg, which is the value at which T-401 starts to perform poorly due to suboptimal hydraulic working conditions, thus it is independent from the type of used oil that is being processed. The strategy works well for the case with conventional used oil of type "A", in which T-401 works in an inefficient operating region only for a short amount of time, roughly equal to 0.8τ. However, the strategy proved to be quite poor for the case with the non-conventional used oil of type "B". The different composition of the oil lead to an unexpected fast worsening of the column conditions, with a significant amount of T-401 run time inside the inefficient operating region, roughly equal to 1.6τ.

2.2. Data-driven Algorithm for Predictive Maintenance

Machine-learning-based frameworks have already been successfully implemented in the domain of Pieve Fissiraga re-refinery. Some examples of this are the performance prediction of the PH-401B furnace of the TDA section (Galeazzi et al., 2023a) and the development of a surrogate model for the amine scrubbing section of the plant (Galeazzi et al., 2023b, 2022). The data-driven algorithm shown in the work by Galeazzi et al. (2023a) was already successfully applied to forecast the pressure differential across the PH-401B furnace, which has a dynamic evolution in time due to fouling phenomena. Given the data-driven nature of the algorithm that requires no physical description of the fundamental phenomena governing a given process unit, it is possible to apply it on the T-401 datasets previously shown in Figure 1, to understand the forecast capabilities of the method and the possible implications of its usage inside a predictive maintenance strategy. The algorithm performs a regression of real plant time-dependent datasets by using two different methodologies, a polynomial regression and a Gaussian Process Regression (GPR), then performs future forecasting of the possible evolution of the dataset. The general polynomial relationship between ΔP and time is shown in Eq. (1), where θ are the features of the model, n_P is the selected degree of the polynomial, t is the time, and ε is the residual normally distributed error (Galeazzi et al., 2023a).

$$\Delta P(t) = \sum_{i=0}^{n_P} \theta_i t^i + \varepsilon \qquad (1)$$

The GPR method uses Gaussian Processes to model the dataset. According to this methodology, the time-dependent dataset is modeled as a function of some unknown functions of time f(t), and to specify a prior distribution over each function f(t) that is Gaussian (Galeazzi et al., 2023a). The advantage of this type of approach is that it is possible to model complex relationships in the data without specifying model parameters (Rasmussen and Williams, 2008), a feature that is ideal for modeling a complex phenomenon such as fouling in the vacuum TDA T-401 column. The functional form of a Gaussian Process expressing ΔP as a function of time is shown in Eq. (2), where m(t) and k(t,t') are respectively the mean and covariance functions (Galeazzi et al., 2023a).

$$\Delta P(t,t') = GP\{m(t),k(t,t')\} \tag{2}$$

The covariance functions included in the method (also referred to as kernels) are the Linear (LIN), the Radial Basis Function (RBF), and the Rational Quadratic (RQ) kernels. The optimal solution for the regression is found through a greedy search in which the kernels are combined through specific operators by following the local optimum at each combination step rather than finding the global optimum, due to computational constraints (Galeazzi et al., 2023a).

3. Results and Discussion

3.1. Application of a Novel Predictive Maintenance Strategy

The aforementioned data-driven algorithm is applied to the dataset shown in Figure 1. Considering a horizontal time axis divided into 10τ periods as shown previously in Figure 1, it was found that an acceptable compromise between prediction accuracy and length of run to be fed to the algorithm is a dataset with a length of 7τ. Forecast accuracy is shown in Figure 2. It is possible to notice that the most probable evolution in time predicted by the algorithm (the orange dashed line in the middle of the green-shaded prediction area) almost never precisely follows the real data from the plant. This is to be expected due to the complexity of the situation that is being analysed, which consists of a gradual increment in ΔP due to fouling that gradually modifies the hydraulic behaviour of the T-401 column, until an unfeasible operating region characterized by flooding is approached. The abrupt change from a feasible to an unfeasible hydraulic operating region translates effectively in an abrupt change in the behaviour of the ΔP as a function of time. The data-driven nature of the algorithm does not allow it to model the future change in the behaviour of the ΔP if no signs of this change are present in past data. Despite this, it is interesting to notice that the natural variability of the dataset generates a 95% confidence interval for the prediction which almost in all cases, shown in Figure 2, fits the real data up to the normal operations limit of 2.5 mmHg/mmHg. This can be explained by observing that the time period of 7τ includes both a "clean" operating condition which oscillates around the start-of-run value of ΔP, and a later different operating condition in which the ΔP starts increasing at a certain rate due to fouling phenomena. This effective change in the underlying physics generates a variability in the data that is noticed by the method, which then proposes a more conservative confidence interval for the forecast. The reason why the algorithm overall predictive capabilities are remarkably different between type "A" and type "B" oil is due to the unexpected early occurrence of the unfeasible hydraulic working condition for type "B" oil, with no past data showing the sign of this change. A similar behaviour would be shown for oil "A" as well, if enough time was given to the system. Defining a robust and adaptable strategy for maintenance in this domain is crucial. One may define a predictive-maintenance approach based on ΔP forecasting combined with a proper reference threshold, namely the normal operations limit. In this case, a dataset having a length of 7τ is used as input, and the algorithm is rolled daily. Daily rolling stops when the 2.5 mmHg/mmHg normal operations limit falls within the 95% forecast confidence interval. This threshold is used since it is representative of T-401 hydraulics and thus it is independent from the oil type. Maintenance can be scheduled for the day in which it is forecasted with a 95% confidence interval that the 2.5 mmHg/mmHg threshold will be overcome. Table 1 reports T-401 run time in the suboptimal operating region above the normal operations limit under different strategies. It is possible to see that in three cases out of four, the algorithm allows the length of the suboptimal operating region to be reduced down to zero. In those three cases, the algorithm contains within the 95% confidence interval the moment in which T-401 overcomes the normal operations limit, meaning that the prediction can be reliably used to schedule the maintenance much in advance compared to what usually happens with the condition-based approach. The only case in which the prediction does not provide benefits is the polynomial regression for used oil of type "A". It is interesting to notice that Gaussian Process Regressions proved to be effective both with type "A" and type "B" oil.

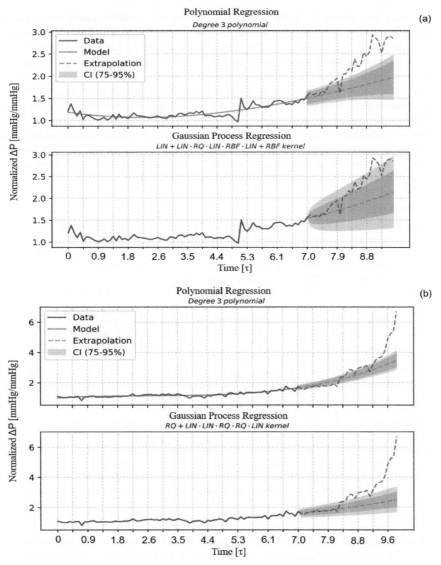

Figure 2. Forecasts on the ΔP time profile for used oil of type "A" (a) and type "B" (b)

Table 1. T-401 run time in suboptimal operating region under different strategies

Used oil type	Condition-based approach	Polynomial predictive approach	GPR predictive approach
Type "A"	0.8 τ	0.8 τ	0.0 τ
Type "B"	1.6 τ	0.0 τ	0.0 τ

4. Conclusions

The work has shown the limitations of a conventional condition-based maintenance strategy applied to a thermodeasphalting section in a used oil re-refinery. This approach is acceptable for typical used oil due to the consistency of its composition, but it fails when non-conventional, more volatile feedstock is processed, leading to long periods of run time inside a suboptimal operating region. It is possible to solve this problem by applying a data-driven algorithm to T-401 datasets. The algorithm predicts correctly the evolution in time of the pressure differential between top and bottom of the column up to the normal operations limit of 2.5 mmHg/mmHg, inside a 95% confidence interval. This allows to schedule the maintenance in advance and avoid altogether suboptimal run time periods. Gaussian Process Regressions have proven to be systematically better for this purpose, even with non-conventional used oil feedstock. Prediction capabilities of the algorithm may be upgraded in the future with hybrid modelling.

References

M. Bevilacqua, M. Braglia, 2000. Analytic hierarchy process applied to maintenance strategy selection. Reliability Engineering and System Safety 70, 71–83.

M.J. Fuentes, R. Font, M.F. Gómez-Rico, I. Martín-Gullón, 2007. Pyrolysis and combustion of waste lubricant oil from diesel cars: Decomposition and pollutants. Journal of Analytical and Applied Pyrolysis 79, 215–226.

A. Galeazzi, F. de Fusco, K. Prifti, F. Gallo, L. Biegler, F. Manenti, 2023a. Predicting the performance of an industrial furnace using gaussian process and linear regression: A comparison. Computers & Chemical Engineering 108513.

A. Galeazzi, K. Prifti, C. Cortellini, A. Di Pretoro, F. Gallo, F. Manenti, 2023b. Development of a surrogate model of an amine scrubbing digital twin using machine learning methods. Computers and Chemical Engineering 174.

A. Galeazzi, K. Prifti, F. Gallo, F. Manenti, 2022. A Methodology for The Optimal Surrogate Modelling of Digital Twins Using Machine Learning. Computer Aided Chemical Engineering 51, 1543–1548.

F. Gallo, 2016. Procedimento di rigenerazione di olii usati. ITUB20151298A1.

F. Manenti, G. Buzzi-Ferraris, 2009. Criteria for Outliers Detection in Nonlinear Regression Problems. Computer Aided Chemical Engineering 26, 913–917.

X. Mei, H. Kiyomoto, S. Kato, Y. Kansha, 2023. Data-Driven Soft Sensor for Crude Oil Fouling Monitoring in Heat Exchanger Networks. IEEE Sensors Journal 23, 26336–26346.

A. Morales-Fuentes, M. Picón-Núñez, G.T. Polley, S. Méndez-Díaz, 2014. Analysis of the influence of operating conditions on fouling rates in fired heaters. Applied Thermal Engineering 62, 777–784.

C.E. Rasmussen, C.K.I. Williams, 2008. Gaussian processes for machine learning, 3. print. ed, Adaptive computation and machine learning. MIT Press, Cambridge, Mass.

J.A. Rocha, J.L. Bravo, J.R. Fair, 1993. Distillation Columns Containing Structured Packings: A Comprehensive Model for Their Performance. 1. Hydraulic Models. Industrial and Engineering Chemistry Research 32, 641–651.

N. Seegulam, F. Coletti, S. Macchietto, 2017. Effect of Fouling on Control and Energy Recovery in an Industrial CDU Column. Computer Aided Chemical Engineering 40, 1555–1560.

Flavio Manenti, Gintaras V. Reklaitis (Eds.), Proceedings of the 34th European Symposium on Computer Aided Process Engineering / 15th International Symposium on Process Systems Engineering (ESCAPE34/PSE24), June 2-6, 2024, Florence, Italy

A novel hybrid framework integrating artificial intelligence and mathematical programming approaches for chemical batch scheduling

Dan Li, [a] Taicheng Zheng, [a] Jie Li [a,*]

aCentre for Process Integration, the Department of Chemical Engineering, The University of Manchester, Manchester, M13 9PL, United Kingdom
jie.li-2@manchester.ac.uk

Abstract

In this work, a novel hybrid algorithm that combines a gene expression programming and a sequence-based mixed-integer linear programming model is introduced for the short-term scheduling of multipurpose batch plants. It operates in three stages: the gene expression programming is implemented to generate its best possible solutions; an extracting algorithm is then executed to extract batching, sequencing and allocation information from solutions generated in the first stage; finally, a sequence-based model, with most binary variables being pre-fixed, is solved to optimize task timings and batch sizes. Computational results demonstrate that the proposed hybrid algorithm is capable of handling variable processing times and limited storage capacities. It effectively improves the solution quality by reducing the makespan, with a maximum reduction of up to 21.2%, in comparison to existing hybrid algorithms.

Keywords: Multipurpose batch facilities, scheduling, hybrid framework, gene expression programming, mathematical programming

1. Introduction

The multipurpose batch process is a collective definition of plants where products have specific processing steps sharing limited resources, such as machines, material, and utilities. To realize reasonable utilization of resources and achieve economic benefits, effective decision tools on scheduling are desirable but challenging to develop due to its NP-hardness. Mathematical formulations have been considerably developed to address the scheduling problems of multipurpose batch plants. These approaches demonstrated that mathematical programming approaches dominate on high solution qualities even the guarantee of global optima. However, excessive computational resources are essential to solve these formulations especially for complex systems with large time horizons or enormous customer demands. Artificial intelligence algorithms, including genetic algorithms, abbreviated as GA (He and Hui, 2010), and evolution algorithms (Han and Gu, 2021), have been developed to tackle the large-scale scheduling challenges, demonstrating commendable computational efficiency. However, these algorithms have been observed to yield solutions of inferior quality compared to those generated by the exact approaches. In our previous study (Li et al., 2022), we endeavored to address this limitation by introducing a hybrid algorithm that combines the strengths of a GA approach in rapid search capability with a mixed-integer linear programming (MILP) model for the superior solution quality. This approach exhibited good performance on reduced computational burdens and the generations of high-quality solutions. However, the genetic algorithm lacks transparency in problem knowledge. Specifically, we are hard to discern why certain scheduling decisions result in a high quality of their corresponding scheduling solution, and we lack insight into which parameters or variables exert the most significant influence on the solution quality. The problem knowledge, partially manifested in dispatching rules (DRs), is crucial to understand the essence of the scheduling problems and make determinations to rapidly respond to the occurrence of uncertainties.

Gene expression programming (GEP) is capable of acquiring problem-specific knowledge through the extraction of DRs. These rules play a crucial role in calculating priorities of tasks or units and serve as the basis for decision-making. They are constructed using attributes related to problem features and objective functions, offering advantages in terms of easy implementation and remarkably rapid computation. In this work, a novel hybrid algorithm (denoted as HA), integrating an enhanced GEP algorithm and a MILP formulation, is proposed to address the multipurpose batch scheduling problems. The objective is to minimize makespan (i.e. time horizon required to complete the production) under a given production requirement. In GEP, DRs are generated to determine the machine assignments and operation sequences individually. The efficacy of these DRs is enhanced through genetic operators. Subsequently, the acquired solution from GEP is further refined using a simplified MILP formulation to orientate the most-reasonable operation timings. Computational studies show that HA is capable to locate the optima in a short time frame for most considered examples and exhibits a significant advantage in computational efficiency relative to the reference mathematical programming approach.

2. Problem statement

In the scheduling problem of a multipurpose batch facility, several tasks i from the set $\mathbf{I}$ can be executed in their available processing units $j \in \mathbf{J}$. Units j able to perform a task i constitute a set $\mathbf{J}_i$. Processing times of tasks on the assigned units are variable with their batch sizes. And the variable and fixed processing time of a task i on unit j are denoted by a_{ij} and β_{ij}, respectively. Batch size of a task i performed on one unit j is bounded by its maximum B_{ij}^{max} and minimum B_{ij}^{min} unit capacity. There are $\mathbf{S}$ states involved in the process, including raw material $\mathbf{S}^R$, intermediate material $\mathbf{S}^{IN}$ and products $\mathbf{S}^P$. One state s is consumed or produced by a task i with the proportion ρ_{is}. The production process route to produce a product $s \in \mathbf{S}^P$ is expressed using $p \in \mathbf{P}$, which includes all involved tasks $i \in \mathbf{I}_p$ and states $s \in \mathbf{S}_p$. Four types of storage policies, including zero-wait (ZW), unlimited intermediate storage (UIS), finite intermediate storage (FIS), and no intermediate storage (NIS) are discussed. The objective considered in this work is to minimize the makespan.

3. Methodology

3.1. Hybrid framework

In the proposed hybrid algorithm, there are three stages as illustrated in Figure 1. The improved GEP in the first stage generates good-quality solutions where processing times of tasks are fixed as the maximum and independent on the batch size. Then in the second stage, scheduling information concerning batch numbers of tasks, unit allocations and performing sequence for batches of tasks are extracted and expressed using algorithmic parameters. Finally, the great majority of binary variables within a sequence-based MILP model are prefixed using the above extracted parameters, and an improved solution would be yield by solving the MILP formulation to refine the batching and timing determinations.

A pre-processing step is required in the first-stage algorithm of HA to fix the processing times τ_{ij} of tasks i on its available unit j as the maximum value that can be calculated using the maximum batch size (i.e. $\tau_{ij} = a_{ij} + \beta_{ij} \cdot B_{ij}^{max}$), as shown in Figure 1. This step is necessary because heuristics on batch size in GEP solutions indicate that solutions featuring tasks with maximum batch sizes and minimum batch numbers are likely to exhibit a higher level of quality in minimizing makespan. The third stage in HA employs a sequence-based MILP formulation from Li et al. (2022).

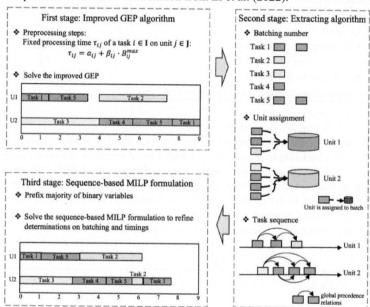

Figure 1. Framework of the proposed hybrid algorithm

3.2. Gene expression programming

3.2.1. Transformation of GEP individuals

In a GEP algorithm, each individual in a population can be transformed into a unique set of algebraic expressions, specifically DRs. These rules play a crucial role in determining the priority values of candidates, including products to be produced, units for a required task, and tasks producing a necessary state. The production sequence, unit allocation, and task selection are thus established. Subsequently, all batches are assumed to be processed with maximum batch sizes and processing times. To minimize makespan, batches of tasks start at the earliest possible time, allowing for the insertion of a batch before a previously performed one if all storage constraints and material balance are satisfied (Li et al., 2022). Consequently, a feasible scheduling solution can be generated as all variables for required tasks to meet production demands are determined. The makespan for this solution is then to evaluate the fitness of the individual.

In a GEP chromosome, the terminal sets employed to derive DRs for determining production sequence, unit allocation, and task selection encompass various attributes. For instance, when selecting a final product for the next production step, eleven attributes, denoted as $a_1^P \sim a_{11}^P$, are considered to calculate the priority values of candidate products, as outlined in Table 1. The product with the minimum priority result is then chosen for execution.

Table 1. Terminal sets for constructing DRs to decide the production sequence

Attribute description	Notation
Remaining production amount	a_1^P
Storage inventory ratio of states $s \in \mathbf{S}_p$ in p	a_2^P
Remaining reaction amount for tasks $i \in \mathbf{I}_p$ in p	a_3^P
Minimum production amount for one batch of p	a_4^P
Maximum production amount for one batch of p	a_5^P
Number of states involved in p	a_6^P
Number of tasks involved in p	a_7^P
Number of recycle stream included in p	a_8^P
Accumulate processing times of tasks in p	a_9^P
States $s \in \mathbf{S}_p$ are subject to ZW or NIS	$a_{10}^P \in \{0,1\}$
p is included in production process route for other final products	$a_{11}^P \in \{0,1\}$

3.2.2. Chromosome representations

A multigene structure is employed to construct the chromosome, as exemplified by Figure 2, which depicts the segment of a chromosome constructing the DR for the production sequence. Each gene, consisting of a head and tail with a fixed length of symbols, can be encoded as an expression tree using the breadth-first searching method. Different genes are connected using linking functions, represented by a linking gene (see the last gene in Figure 2). The terminal set in the linking gene differs from those in other genes, where terminals denote the ordinal numbers of genes (i.e. G1, G2 denoting the Gene 1 and 2, respectively) in the chromosome. The function sets in all genes comprise of five operators $(+, -, \times, \div, \sqrt{})$.

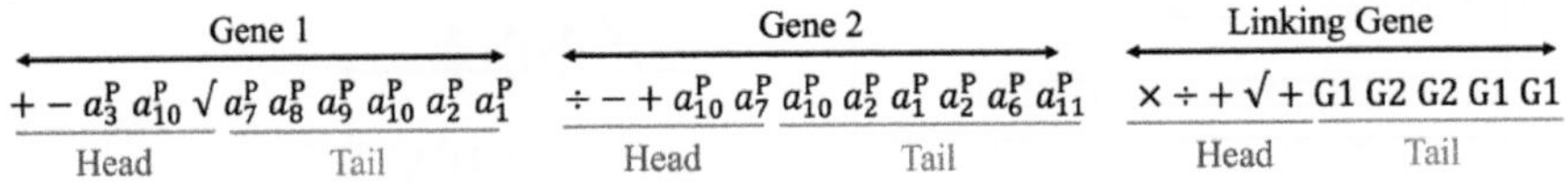

Gene 1		Gene 2		Linking Gene	
$+ - a_3^P\, a_{10}^P\, \sqrt{}\, a_7^P\, a_8^P\, a_9^P\, a_{10}^P\, a_2^P\, a_1^P$		$\div - + a_{10}^P\, a_7^P\, a_{10}^P\, a_2^P\, a_1^P\, a_2^P\, a_6^P\, a_{11}^P$		$\times \div + \sqrt{} + $ G1 G2 G2 G1 G1	
Head	Tail	Head	Tail	Head	Tail

Figure 2. The part of chromosome constructing DRs for the production sequence

3.2.3. Evolution of population in GEP

The evolutionary process of the population in GEP involves fitness evaluation, selection, crossover, and mutation. These operators are crucial for identifying individuals with exceptional adaptability, inheriting valuable metrics, and preserving genetic diversity. The tournament selection strategy is employed, where two candidate individuals are compared, and the more fit individual survives. To address the possibility of premature convergence, particularly in the mid to late stages of evolution, adaptive crossover and mutation approaches are implemented. The adaptive crossover (C_g^r) and mutation (M_g^r) rates at current generation g can be calculated using equations (1-2), respectively. In these equations, the variables MS_g^{avg}, MS_g^{max} and MS_g^{min} represent the average, maximum and minimum values of makespan across all individuals in generation g. One-point crossover is performed in each gene of the parent chromosome. And the head and tail segments in each gene individually execute the one-point mutation to generate a child from a parent.

$$C_g^r = C_0^r \cdot \left(1 + 0.2 \cdot \frac{g}{g^{max}} \cdot \frac{MS_g^{avg2}}{\left(MS_g^{max} - MS_g^{min}\right)^2 + MS_g^{avg2}}\right) \tag{1}$$

$$M_g^r = M_0^r \cdot 1.2^{\left(\frac{(g-1)\cdot MS_g^{avg}}{(MS_g^{max}-MS_g^{min})+MS_g^{avg}}\right)^{0.3}} \tag{2}$$

4. Computational studies

To assess the performance of the proposed hybrid algorithm (denoted as HA), we conducted tests on ten examples, including seven benchmark examples (Exs 1-7) with states subject to UIS, and three examples (Exs 8-10) considering the storage policy of FIS. Specifically, the examples 1-6 correspond to the examples 1, 2, 3, 7, 8 and 9 sourced from Li et al. 2022, while examples 8-10 originate from the work of Maravelias and Grossmann (2003), involving seven instances (Ins) with varying demand requirements. We evaluate the computational performance of HA by comparing it with a unit-specific event-based MILP model from Li et al. (2022) (referred to as L&R), as it is demonstrated superior to other continuous-time MILP formulations. We also compare with the model L&M (Lee and Maravelias, 2018), recognized as an effective hybrid algorithm that combines the advantages of the discrete- and continuous-time MILP formulations.

Table 2 presents a comparison between the HA and existing approaches L&M and L&R for addressing facilities involving unlimited storage capacities. Here, the model L&R guarantees the generation of globally optimal solutions with sufficient computational resources. Remarkably, the proposed HA yield identical objective results to the L&R except the Ex 3, underscoring that our proposed HA attains the global optimum across six out of seven examples. In terms of computational performance, the HA reduces the computational time by over an order of magnitude relative to L&R for Ex 2 (i.e. 4.8 s vs. 3600 s). While comparing with L&M, solutions from the HA outperform those from L&M in Exs 1, 3, 4, 5, and 6 with the maximum improvement in makespan reduction of 21.2% (e.g. 16.5 h vs. 20.0 h in Ex 6). This highlights the superiority of HA in producing more favourable outcomes.

Table 2. Computational results for examples 1-7 from model HA, L&M and L&R

Ex	HA		L&M		L&R	
	MS (h)	CPU (s)	*MS* (h)	CPU (s)	*MS*(h)	CPU(s)
1	4.4	0.8	5.3	0.1	4.4	0.1
2	46.1	4.7	46.1	0.6	46.1[a]	3600
3	14.8	108	14.6	0.3	13.4	0.3
4	193.3	4.7	197.2	0.6	193.3	0.2
5	16.5	2.8	17.0	0.4	16.5	0.8
6	16.5	3.9	20.0	0.2	16.5	7.3
7	14.3	1.0	14.3	0.5	14.3	0.1

Relative gap, [a]: 1.17%

As the model L&M is proposed for processes characterized by unlimited storage capacities, its implementations are tailored to solve examples 1-7. Computational results for Exs 8-10 from HA and L&R are presented in Table 3. For complicated systems (e.g. Ins 3 with enormous production demands and finite storage constraints), the advantage of the proposed hybrid algorithm primarily manifests in the reduced computational burdens. Specifically, computational times are decreased by 99% (i.e. 2.9 s vs. 3600 s), 96.5% (i.e. 125 s vs. 3600 s), 95.6% (160 s vs. 3600 s) and 99.8% (i.e. 7.4 s vs. 3600 s) in HA relative to L&R for Ins 1, 2, 3, and 5 (see Table 3), respectively.

Table 3. Computational results for examples 8-10 with FIS from the proposed HA and the MILP model L&R

Ex	Ins	HA			L&R	
		MS-GEP(h)	*MS*-HA(h)	CPU(s)	*MS*(h)	CPU(s)
1	1	37	37	2.9	37[a]	3600
	2	108	108	125	109[b]	3600
	3	217	217	160	NA	3600
2	4	37	37	1.7	37	0.3
	5	100	100	7.4	100[c]	3600
3	6	44	44	15.1	44	2.6
	7	158	158	119.4	158	30.6

Relative gap, [a]: 1.1%, [b]: 1.4%, [c]: 9.1%

5. Conclusion

In this study, we introduce a hybrid algorithm designed for optimizing the short-term scheduling of multipurpose batch plants. The hybrid algorithm is proposed to harness the strengths of both gene expression programming and mathematical programming approaches on computational efficiency and solution accuracy, respectively. And it is capable to address various operational characteristics, such as various or fixed processing time and constrained storage capacity. The computational results for ten benchmark examples demonstrate that the proposed algorithm outperforms the literature hybrid approach in terms of objective results with a maximum reduction of 21.2% in makespan. Furthermore, the computational time is significantly reduced by the proposed algorithm over one order of magnitude, compared to a representative unit-specific event-based continuous-time formulation.

Acknowledgement

Dan Li and Taicheng Zheng appreciate financial support from China Scholarship Council - the University of Manchester Joint Scholarship (201908130170, 202106440020). Jie Li appreciates financial support from Engineering and Physical Sciences Research Council (EP/T03145X/1, EP/V051008/1).

References

Y. Han, and X. Gu, 2021, Improved multipopulation discrete differential evolution algorithm for the scheduling of multipurpose batch plants, Industrial & Engineering Chemistry Research, 60(15), 5530 - 5547.
Y. He, and C.W. Hui, 2010, A binary coding genetic algorithm for multi-purpose process scheduling: A case study, Chemical Engineering Science, 65(16), 4816 - 4828.
H. Lee, and C.T. Maravelias, 2018, Combining the advantages of discrete-and continuous-time scheduling models: Part 1. Framework and mathematical formulations, Computers & Chemical Engineering, 116, 176 - 190.
D. Li, D. Zhang, N. Zhang, L. Zhang, and J. Li, 2022, A novel hybrid algorithm for scheduling multipurpose batch plants, Computer Aided Chemical Engineering, 51, 961 - 966.
D. Li, N. Rakovitis, T. Zheng, Y. Pan, J. Li, and G. Kopanos, 2022, Novel Multiple Time-grid Continuous-time Mathematical Formulation for Short-term Scheduling of Multipurpose Batch Plants, Industrial & Engineering Chemistry Research, 61(43), 16093 - 16111.
C.T. Maravelias, and I.E. Grossmann, 2003, Minimization of the Makespan with a Discrete-Time State-Task Network Formulation, Industrial & engineering chemistry research, 42(24), 6252 - 6257.

Flavio Manenti, Gintaras V. Reklaitis (Eds.), Proceedings of the 34th European Symposium on Computer Aided Process Engineering / 15th International Symposium on Process Systems Engineering (ESCAPE34/PSE24), June 2-6, 2024, Florence, Italy

Benders Decomposition to Integrate MILP and Discrete-Event Simulation for Flow Shop Scheduling

Roderich Wallrath* [a,b], Edwin Zondervan [b], Meik Franke [b]

[a] *University of Twente, Faculty of Science and Technology, Sustainable Process Technology, Drienerlolaan 5, 7522 NB Enschede, The Netherlands*
[b] *Bayer AG, Kaiser-Wilhelm Allee 1, 51368 Leverkusen, Germany*

r.wallrath@utwente.nl

Abstract

Optimization-based decision-making in the chemical industry is highly beneficial but also very difficult, because many decision variables must be considered, and their interrelation is complicated. Different modeling techniques exist each with individual strengths. We propose Benders decomposition to integrate mixed-integer linear programming (MILP) and discrete-event simulation (DES) to solve flow shop scheduling problems. The basic idea is to generate valid Benders cuts based on sensitivity information of DES models which can be found in the critical path of a DES solution. We apply our Benders-DES approach to a scaled literature flow shop with secondary resource constraints and find that near optimal solutions can be found quickly. From the optimality gap information during the solution process we can conclude that Benders-DES is a promising approach to combine rigorous optimization capabilities with high-fidelity modeling capabilities.

Keywords: Benders decomposition, Mixed-integer programming, Discrete-event simulation, Simulation-optimization, Flow shop scheduling

1. Introduction

For companies in the process and chemical industry optimization-based decision-making is a critical advantage in today's fast-paced and interconnected world. However, the complexity when optimizing chemical processes is very high: A chemical process which is operated by personnel on process units, consumes raw materials and utilities, and produces goods into a manufacturing supply chain, which is naturally subjected to many constraints and objectives. While simulation models can describe complex real-world processes to a great level of detail for which solutions can be obtained in reasonable computation time, their results might still be far from optimal. Mathematical optimization models, on the other hand, quickly grow to intractable size, when trying to include all relevant constraints. Simulation optimization (SO) has emerged as a powerful tool to solve complex problems without compromising solution quality and computation time (Amaran et. al., 2016, Chen et. al. 2012). For example, Paulo et. al. (2023) successfully use rigorous optimization and discrete-event simulation for the optimal design of biomass supply chains including the uncertainty of conversion factors in the fermentation for bioethanol and transesterification for biodiesel. However, there are two drawbacks of SO methods. First, due to the evaluation-intensive search process massive computational resources may be required when solving complex problems. Second, these methods do not provide optimality gap information and the user must decide when to terminate the search process. The potential upside of finding a better solution remains unknown. Wan et. al. (2005) suggest a simulation-based optimization framework in which a surrogate model is derived from the simulations to decrease the computational burden. Combining simulation with rigorous optimization techniques is still relatively unexplored field. Forbes et. al (2023) propose a logic-based Benders approach that evaluates a discrete-event simulation sub-problem to derive cuts for the master problem. Zhang et. al. (2017) derive Benders cuts from a discrete-event simulation model to find the optimal design parameters of a joint workstation, workload and buffer allocation system. The objective of this work is to integrate MILP and DES for flow shops by inferring dual information from critical paths to build valid Benders cuts.

2. Model Integration

We argue that the Benders decomposition framework as shown in Eq. (1) can be used to integrate mathematical optimization and discrete-event simulation directly. The basic idea is to generate valid optimality cuts $\mu \geq u^T(g - Bx)$ and feasibility cuts $0 \geq u^T(g - Bx)$ based on sensitivity information of DES models.

$$\min c^T x + \mu$$

$$\text{s.t.} \quad \begin{aligned} Ax &\geq b \\ \mu &\geq u^T(g - Bx) \quad \forall u \in O' \\ 0 &\geq u^T(g - Bx) \quad \forall u \in F' \\ x &\geq 0 \end{aligned} \tag{1}$$

We consider the original flow shop problem shown in Eq. (2) where c_{max} is the makespan, c_{im} the completion time of the job taking position i on machine m, $y_{ji} \in \{0,1\}$ the indicator variable of job j being in position i, and t_{jm} the processing time of job j on machine m. Any solution of this flow shop problem contains dual variables u_{im} corresponding to the constraints (2e) and (2f) which are equal to 1 if a job in position i on machine m lies on the critical path. By solving a DES model of this flow shop problem, we also obtain a critical path that consists of a jobs in positions i on machines m. Therefore, we can map the critical path of a DES solution to the dual variables u_{im} and build valid Benders cuts of the form $u^T(g - Bx)$. In Figure 1 a flow shop featuring 3 machines and 4 jobs is shown with the critical path and the active constraints.

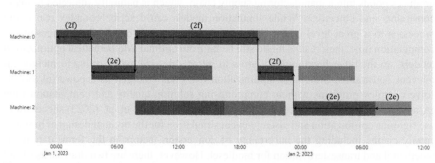

Figure 1: Example Gantt chart and critical path of flow shop with 3 machines and 4 jobs.

$$\min c_{max} \tag{2a}$$

$$\text{s.t.} \quad c_{max} \geq c_{im} \quad \forall \ i \in N, m \in M \tag{2b}$$

$$\sum_{i \in N} y_{ji} = 1 \quad \forall j \in N \tag{2c}$$

$$\sum_{j \in N} y_{ji} = 1 \quad \forall i \in N \tag{2d}$$

$$c_{im} + \sum_{j \in N} y_{ji} t_{jm} = c_{i+1m} \quad \forall i \in N_0, m \in M] \tag{2e}$$

$$c_{im} + \sum_{j \in N} y_{ji} t_{jm+1} = c_{im+1} \quad \forall i \in N, m \in M_0 \tag{2f}$$

$$y_{ji} \in \{0,1\} \tag{2g}$$

Our Benders master problem shown in (3) obtains an optimality cut $\mu \geq \sum u_{im} y_{ji} t_{im}$ from the DES solution in each iteration k, where u_{im} contains the dual information of the critical path and y_{ji} encodes the job order. If the DES solution is does not improve the upper bound a feasibility cut $N > \sum y_{ji}$ is added as well. In iteration $k+1$ the master problem is solved and its solution y_{ji} represents a new job order which is then simulated by the DES sub-problem to give new dual information and the next Benders cuts.

$$\min \mu \tag{3a}$$

$$\text{s.t.} \quad \mu \geq \sum_{\substack{(i,j,m) \\ \in (N,N,M)}} u_{im} y_{ji} t_{im} \ \forall \ u \in O' \tag{3b}$$

$$N > \sum_{(i,j)} y_{ji} \ \forall \ i,j \in F' \tag{3c}$$

$$\sum_{i \in N} y_{ji} = 1 \quad \forall j \in N \tag{3d}$$

$$\sum_{j \in N} y_{ji} = 1 \qquad \forall\, i \in N \qquad\qquad (3e)$$

$$y_{ji} \in \{0,1\} \qquad\qquad (3f)$$

3. Computational Studies

To test the performance of our Benders approach we apply it to the literature flow shop problem from Edgar et. al. (2001). Thereafter, we scale this problem, solve random instances, and introduce additional resource constraints.

3.1. Literature flow shop

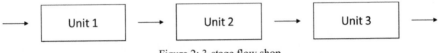

Figure 2: 3-stage flow shop

We consider the flow shop problem from Edgar et. al. (2001) as shown in Figure 2, in which 4 jobs visit 3 units with machine-specific processing times. The objective is to minimize the makespan of all jobs. As shown in Figure 3, the Benders cuts give good lower bounds on the optimum, while the DES solutions approach the optimum quickly. As a result, we find the optimal job order with a makespan of 34.8 hours after 5 iterations. Since there are only 24 different job orders in this example, our investigations in the following focus on larger instances.

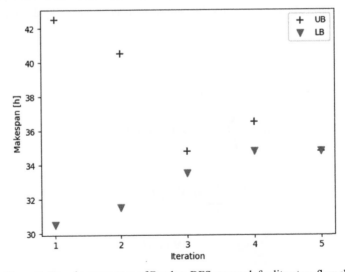

Figure 3: Bound convergence of Benders-DES approach for literature flow shop

3.2. Scaled Literature flow shop

We scale the literature flow shop of Chapter 3.1 with respect to the number of units and jobs and introduce the consumption of steam by each job as an example of secondary resource constraints. Note that we do not include the secondary resource constraints into the Benders cuts or the master problem but only into the DES model. In Figure 4 the remaining gaps and number of iterations of random instances of different problem sizes are shown after 2, 10, 60, 600, 1800 and 3600 seconds of solution time. For example, the problem size "10x5, 50Steam" corresponds to a setup with 10 jobs, 5 units, and 50 consumable units of steam. For each problem size we solve 30 instances with randomized processing times and steam consumption per job. From Figure 4 we observe that near optimal solutions with less than 10% remaining gap can be found for most of the problem sizes after less than 10 minutes. While we see that all problems with 10 jobs and 5 units converged to 0% gap after 200 iterations, we also recognize that for most of the larger problems achieving 0% gap is very difficult. Although, this might be due to the exponentially growing search space we also know that the Benders cuts omit the secondary resource constraints. Therefore, if secondary resource constraints are active in the optimum, the master problem is not able to proof optimality. This means dual variables of the secondary resource constraints could extend the cuts.

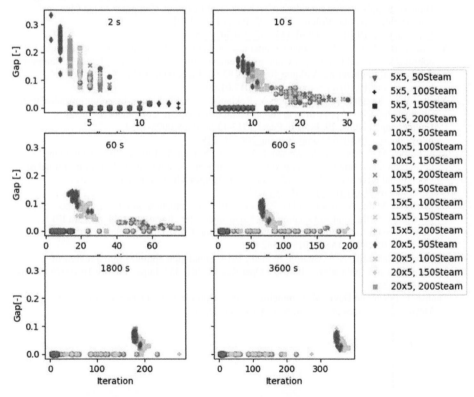

Figure 4: Remaining gap and number of iterations of different-sized, randomized problems with secondary resource constraints after 2, 10, 60, 600, 1800 and 3600 seconds of solution time.

4. Conclusions

We showed that it is possible to integrate MILP and DES for flow shops by inferring dual information from critical paths to build valid Benders cuts. With this integration, rigorous optimization capabilities can be combined with high-fidelity modeling and simulation capabilities. Our computational studies showed that the Benders-DES approach solves small to realistic-size flow shop scheduling problems in less than 30 minutes with an optimality gap of 10%. We were able to generate guaranteed near-optimal solutions of DES models after 200 iterations. Furthermore, when adding secondary resource constraints to the DES model, the master problem still guides the search process to near-optimal solutions in short time while reporting optimality gap information. Since DES models can include these constraints more efficiently than a MILP model, we argue that the Benders-DES approach extends the scope optimization models in general. Future research should focus on the applicability to a realistic case study, other types of optimization problems as well as speeding up the solution times.

References

Helena Paulo, Miguel Vieira, Bruno S. Gonçalves, Susana Relvas, Tânia Pinto-Varela, Ana P. Barbosa-Povoa, 2023, A Discrete-Event Simulation Approach to the Design and Planning of Biomass Supply Chains considering Technological Learning, Computer Aided Chemical Engineering, Elsevier, Volume 52, 2023, Pages 1285-1291, ISSN 1570-7946, https://doi.org/10.1016/B978-0-443-15274-0.50205-5

Ye Chen, Linas Mockus, Seza Orcun, Gintaras V. Reklaitis, 2012, Simulation-optimization approach to clinical trial supply chain management with demand scenario forecast, Computers & Chemical Engineering, Volume 40, Pages 82-96, ISSN 0098-1354, https://doi.org/10.1016/j.compchemeng.2012.01.007

Xiaotao Wan, Joseph F. Pekny, Gintaras V. Reklaitis, 2005, Simulation-based optimization with surrogate models—Application to supply chain management, Computers & Chemical Engineering, Volume 29, Issue 6, Pages 1317-1328, ISSN 0098-1354, https://doi.org/10.1016/j.compchemeng.2005.02.018

M.A. Forbes, M.G. Harris, H.M. Jansen, F.A. van der Schoot, T. Taimre, 2023, Combining optimisation and simulation using logic-based Benders decomposition, European Journal of Operational Research,Volume 312, Issue 3,2024,Pages 840-854, ISSN 0377-2217, https://doi.org/10.1016/j.ejor.2023.07.032.

M. Zhang, A. Matta, A. Alfieri and G. Pedrielli, 2017, A simulation-based benders' cuts generation for the joint workstation, workload and buffer allocation problem, 13th IEEE Conference on Automation Science and Engineering (CASE) , Xi'an, China, 2017, pp. 1067-1072, doi: 0.1109/COASE.2017.8256247

Amaran, S., Sahinidis, N.V., Sharda, B. et al., 2014, Simulation optimization: a review of algorithms and applications. 4OR-Q J Oper Res 12, 301–333. https://doi.org/10.1007/s10288-014-0275-2

Thomas F. Edgar and David M. Himmelblau, 2001, Optimization of Chemical Processes, McGraw-Hill, Pages 560 – 564, New York, NY, USA

Flavio Manenti, Gintaras V. Reklaitis (Eds.), Proceedings of the 34th European Symposium on Computer Aided Process Engineering / 15th International Symposium on Process Systems Engineering (ESCAPE34/PSE24), June 2-6, 2024, Florence, Italy

High-dimensional derivative-free optimization via trust region surrogates in linear subspaces

Damien van de Berg[a], Nilay Shah[a], Antonio del Rio-Chanona[a,*]

[a]*Sargent Centre for Process Systems Engineering, Roderic Hill Building South Kensington Campus. London, SW7 2AZ, United Kingdom*

a.del-rio-chanona@imperial.ac.uk

Abstract

Maintaining the benefits of derivative-free optimization in higher-dimensional decision spaces presents challenges for existing optimization methods. We introduce CUATRO_PLS - an extension of the CUATRO quadratic trust region optimizer that leverages intrinsic structures across high-dimensional black-box variables. CUATRO_PLS shows competitive convergence with leading derivative-free optimization algorithms in three high-dimensional chemical engineering case studies even in the absence or underestimation of known intrinsic dimensionality and is significantly faster than other model-based derivative-free optimization algorithms.

Keywords: black-box optimization, reduced-order optimization, dimensionality reduction

1. Introduction

Derivative-free optimization (DFO) is an effective tool for optimizing chemical engineering systems without explicit gradient expressions. However, state-of-the-art (SOTA) DFO solvers usually scale poorly in the number of decision variables and often even in their evaluation budget (van de Berg et al., 2022). Many existing methods for high-dimensional black-box optimization, from linear-quadratic trust region (Cartis and Roberts, 2023) to Bayesian optimization (BO) (Wang et al., 2016; Letham et al., 2020) methods, rely on random (Gaussian) subspace projections to find embeddings over which to construct and optimize surrogates. While end-to-end learning of linear (Garnett et al., 2014) or nonlinear embeddings (Moriconi et al., 2019) with Gaussian processes or variational autoencoders is possible, limited evaluations can compromise performance.

In this work, we introduce CUATRO_PLS, which integrates end-to-end learning concepts into the scalable Convex qUAdratic Trust Region Optimizer (CUATRO). At each iteration, Partial Least Squares regression (PLS) identifies the linear embedding that best predicts the output of all evaluations within a trust region. Surrogate fitting and minimization are then performed within this subspace and the minimization candidate is evaluated after reconstruction in the original space. This approach maintains the tractability of working with convex quadratic surrogates in low dimensions while enhancing the quality of the subspaces as compared to Gaussian projections by incorporating response information.

We benchmark CUATRO_PLS against a random baseline (Latin Hypercube Sampling) and seven SOTA DFO solvers: Py-BOBYQA, DIRECT-L, HEBO, ALEBO, TuRBO, and CMA-ES. We first use a synthetic toy problem with up to 1000 dimensions and a true linear latent space to show that CUATRO_PLS shows consistent convergence to a high-accuracy solution and is multiple orders of magnitude faster than other model-based methods. We then assess all algorithms on three high-dimensional chemical engineering problems exhibiting intrinsic structure: reactor control policy optimization (61 dimensions), value chain coordination under privacy considerations (72 dimensions), and bi-level planning-scheduling optimization (172 dimensions).

In Section 2, we discuss latent embeddings in DFO and introduce our algorithm CUATRO_PLS, before describing our benchmarking problems in Section 3. In Section 4, we then show that CUATRO_PLS ranks among the top three algorithms on all problems and outperforms competitors in high-dimensional scenarios favoring exploitation over exploration.

2. Methodology

2.1. Derivative-free optimization and latent structure

First, we consider derivative-free optimization (DFO) problems of the following form:

$$\min_{\mathbf{x} \in \mathcal{X}} f(\mathbf{x}) \tag{1}$$

where $\mathbf{x} \in \mathcal{X} \subset \mathbb{R}^{n_x \times 1}$ denotes the variables within box bounds $\mathcal{X}$ used to optimize the expensive black-box objective $f(\cdot)$. Underlying our work is the assumption that there is an embedding $\mathbf{z}$ in the latent space $\mathcal{Z}$ with effective dimensionality n_z capable of explaining or approximating the response of $f(\cdot)$.

$$\min_{\mathbf{x} \in \mathcal{X}} f(\mathbf{x}) \approx \min_{\mathbf{z} \in \mathcal{Z}} f\big(T(\mathbf{z})\big) \quad s.t. \quad T(\mathbf{z}) \in \mathcal{X} \tag{2}$$

where $n_z \ll n_x$, and $T(\cdot): \mathbb{R}^{n_z \times 1} \to \mathbb{R}^{n_x \times 1}$ is the reconstruction of the latent embedding into the original space such that $\mathbf{x} \approx T(\mathbf{z})$. The existence of a latent embedding allows us to construct and optimize surrogates in the lower-dimensional space $\mathbf{z} \in \mathbb{R}^{n_z \times 1}$ of the black-box objective, "breaking" the curse of dimensionality.

2.2. High-dimensional derivative-free optimizations

Before introducing our approach CUATRO_PLS, we present the DFO algorithms we benchmark against.

Py-BOBQYQA is a trust-region optimizer constructing linear-quadratic surrogates using interpolation and regression techniques. The algorithm exhibits strong exploitative properties by making quick progress, sometimes at the expense of exploration.

DIRECT-L is a search space partitioning direct DFO solver that elegantly trades off exploitation and exploration. The method is more robust to ill-conditioning in the objective as it does not rely on surrogates.

Latin hypercube sampling (LHS) is a space-filling design method. Any proposed high-dimensional DFO should outperform random search in the form of LHS.

CMA-ES, as an evolutionary search method, shines in highly nonlinear, stochastic applications with a high evaluation budget.

HEBO, short for Heteroscedastic and Evolutionary Bayesian Optimization solver, is the winning submission to the *NeurIPS 2020 Black-Box Optimisation challenge*.

TuRBO is a high-dimensional Bayesian optimization solver that leverages Thompson sampling within trust regions for scalability.

ALEBO revisits some design considerations of previous high-dimensional BO solvers relying on random embeddings.

A considerable part of the high-dimensional Bayesian optimization and DFO literature is predicated on the idea of finding projections to and reconstructions from latent spaces over which to optimize. These methods differ considerably however in the projection and reconstruction techniques used, the choice of surrogates in the latent space and how these are updated. Cartis and Roberts (2023) for example employ random Gaussian projection matrices within trust-region DFO solvers, which improves their scalability on nonlinear least squares problems. While random embeddings preserve theoretical guarantees useful for convergence proofs, we believe that we can integrate response information to improve the sample efficiency of high-dimensional trust region methods.

2.3. CUATRO_PLS

We propose CUATRO_PLS based on CUATRO (van de Berg et al., 2022). CUATRO_PLS iterates over the following steps until running out of evaluation budget:

1) We sample input-output evaluations within the current quadratic trust region $T(\mathbf{x}; \mathbf{x}_c, r) = \{\mathbf{x} \in \mathcal{X} \mid (\mathbf{x} - \mathbf{x}_c)^T(\mathbf{x} - \mathbf{x}_c) \leq r^2\}$ of radius r around the trust region center $\mathbf{x}_c$ in the original space $\mathcal{X}$, until we have n_{PLS} evaluations $y = f(\mathbf{x})$.

2) We then train PLS on all samples within $T(\cdot)$ to find the projection $M \in \mathbb{R}^{n_z \times n_x}$ and (imperfect) reconstruction $R = (M^T M)M^T \in \mathbb{R}^{n_x \times n_z}$ matrices that identify the linear embedding from which to best linearly predict $f(\cdot)$ such that $\mathbf{z} = M\mathbf{x}$ and $\mathbf{x} \approx R\mathbf{z}$.

3) We then train convex quadratic surrogates in the lower-dimensional embedding:

$$\min_{P \succcurlyeq 0, \mathbf{q}, r} f(\mathbf{x}) = \sum_{k=1,\dots,n_s} \left(y_k - \left(\mathbf{z}_k^T P \mathbf{z}_k + \mathbf{q}^T \mathbf{z}_k + k \right) \right)^2 \tag{3}$$

where $P \in \mathbb{R}^{n_z \times n_z}$ is the positive semi-definite matrix defining the quadratic, $\mathbf{q} \in \mathbb{R}^{n_z \times 1}$ the linear, and k the scalar coefficients.

4) Minimization is then performed within this subspace such that the reconstruction remains in the original trust region $T(\cdot)$:

$$\min_{\mathbf{z}} \mathbf{z}^T P \mathbf{z} + \mathbf{q}^T \mathbf{z} + k \quad \text{s.t.} \quad (R\mathbf{z} - \mathbf{x}_c)^T(R\mathbf{z} - \mathbf{x}_c) \leq r^2 \tag{4}$$

Since we implement our algorithm within a convex programming framework, we relax (4), and define a heuristic trust region in the latent space as follows:

$$\min_{\mathbf{z}} \mathbf{z}^T P \mathbf{z} + \mathbf{q}^T \mathbf{z} + k \quad \text{s.t.} \quad (\mathbf{z} - \mathbf{z}_c)^T(\mathbf{z} - \mathbf{z}_c) \leq \hat{r}^2 \tag{5}$$

where $\hat{r} = \max\limits_{\mathbf{z} \in \{\mathbf{z}_1, \dots, \mathbf{z}_{n_s}\}} (\mathbf{z} - \mathbf{z}_c)^T(\mathbf{z} - \mathbf{z}_c)$ is the furthest distance in the embedding space between the TR center and all samples within.

5) We then evaluate the suggested minimization candidate of (5) after reconstruction to the original space, and go to step 1) if the termination criteria are not met.

For a given latent dimensionality, if we were to use linear, instead of quadratic surrogates in the latent space, PLS would give the optimal embedding. In practice, we find that PLS works well even in combination with quadratic surrogates. The intuition behind this is that the black-box function should display increasingly linear behaviour as the trust region decreases. Next, we describe the case studies used for benchmarking.

3. Case studies

3.1. High-dimensional Rosenbrock with low effective dimensionality

We first define a synthetic high-dimensional Rosenbrock function with a known linear embedding dimensionality similar to (Wang et al., 2016) with the difference that we mix up the informative and uninformative inputs using an orthogonal Gaussian matrix $G \in \mathbb{R}^{n_h \times n_h}$ to make all dimensions informative. This allows us to control the original n_h and effective n_e dimensionality in studying the effect of over- or underestimating the embedding dimensionality n_{PLS} used as input to our solver.

3.2. Chemical engineering applications with low effective dimensionality

We benchmark all algorithms on three high-dimensional chemical engineering problems. While we believe these to exhibit intrinsic structure, the dimensionality of the *true* latent embedding is unknown, and does not have to be linear. The *reactor control policy* problem consists in finding the $n_h = 61$ neural network weights and biases that optimize a control policy of a standard CSTR control problem. The parameters of neural networks are known to exhibit low effective dimensionality.

In the *value chain coordination* (van de Berg et al., 2023a), we want to find the material flows ($n_h = 72$) that maximize the constituent agents' planning profits which can only be obtained as a result of privacy-preserving proprietary simulations. We believe that these embeddings are caused by temporal and spatial correlations between material flows.

In the *hierarchical planning-scheduling*, we solve for $n_h = 172$ planning targets that optimize a bi-level planning-scheduling objective as described in (van de Berg et al., 2023b). Intrinsic subspaces are again believed to arise from similar temporal correlations.

4. Results and discussion

4.1. Synthetic low-dimensional case study

On the 100-dimensional Rosenbrock instance on the top of Figure 1, CMA-ES, ALEBO, and TURBO display the best convergence. CUATRO_PLS seems to be competitive with other SOTA solvers, with a median and worst-case final convergence comparable to that of CMA-ES. As expected, CUATRO_PLS has a runtime at least an order of magnitude lower than that of other model-based DFO solvers while displaying comparable performance. HEBO and ALEBO are not investigated further given their exploding runtime on high-dimensional, high-budget problems.

When the dimensionality and budget are then increased to 1,000 on the bottom of Figure 1, we see that CUATRO_PLS, despite displaying a slightly worse median run than TURBO, displays the best final run of all samples and seems to be the most consistent. Additionally, while TuRBO's runtime increased by an order of magnitude when doubling the budget, CUATRO_PLS's runtime only doubled.

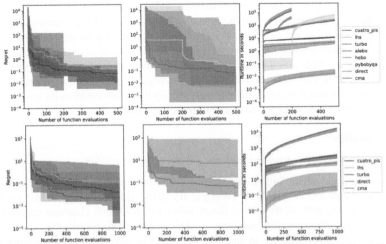

Figure 1. Regret versus evaluation budget convergence plot for the synthetic high-dimensional Rosenbrock case study with respective evaluation budget, original dimensionality and effective dimensionality of 500, 100, and 2 on the top and 1000, 1000 and 2 on the bottom.

Figure 2 investigates the effect that the input effective dimensionality has on CUATRO_PLS performance with other hyperparameters fixed to default heuristics. We keep the RB original dimensionality at 1,000, and the *true* effective dimensionality at 10. We see no major difference in performance when perfectly or overestimating the true latent dimensionality at 6 or higher. To the contrary, the best performance is found when *underestimating* the effective dimensionality at 2 and 6. This suggests that CUATRO_PLS stands as a powerful high-dimensional DFO solver, even if no knowledge about the intrinsic dimensionality is suspected. It might even be encouraged to use CUATRO_PLS in fewer effective dimensions. In other words, there is merit to the idea of performing surrogate optimization in the *most* informative linear combination of dimensions for surrogate optimization, rather than capturing *all* information.

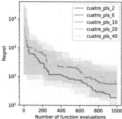

Figure 2. Regret versus evaluation budget convergence plot on the 1000-dimensional Rosenbrock with an effective dimensionality of 10 when CUATRO_PLS is used with different input dimensionalities and all other hyperparameters fixed to default heuristics.

4.2. Chemical engineering applications

Throughout all case studies in Figure 3, the CUATRO_PLS runs (on the left) generally display consistency across different hyperparameters and input embedding dimensionalities. This supports our hypothesis that CUATRO_PLS performs well even in the absence of problem-specific knowledge about embedding structure or effective dimensionality. In the policy training on the top, CUATRO_PLS outperforms most methods and is only outperformed in consistency and in the median run by CMA-ES and TURBO respectively. In the value chain coordination in the middle, all CUATRO_PLS median runs outperform the best runs of all other DFO methods, and even the original distributed optimization benchmark ADMM. In the hierarchical integration case study on the bottom, CUATRO_PLS and Py-BOBYQA are the only methods that make any progress. While CUATRO_PLS makes significant initial progress, Py-BOBYQA manages to better fine-tune the solution. Overall, the above findings are not surprising: CUATRO_PLS, as a high-dimensional quadratic trust region optimizer, excels in finding *good* nearby optima *quickly*. However, CUATRO_PLS remains a competitive optimizer even in the policy tuning, where more explorative methods like CMA-ES are encouraged.

5. Conclusion

We introduce CUATRO_PLS as a scalable high-dimensional DFO solver that capitalizes on learned linear structures in the decision variables to display competitive performance with SOTA alternatives at significantly lower runtime compared to other model-based methods. Our solver converges on three high-dimensional chemical engineering DFO problems where intrinsic dimensionality is suspected, and excels in fine-tuning solutions, and finding good optima quickly. CUATRO_PLS, by performing surrogate optimization in the most informative linear embedding dimensions, can even be used if no intrinsic dimensionality is known or suspected. In future work, we will combine our method with exploration routines to trade-off exploitation and exploration in the solution space.

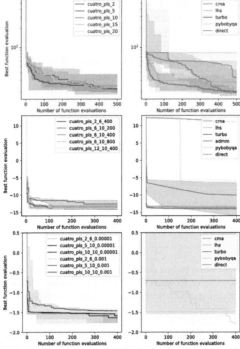

Figure 3. Best function evaluation versus evaluation budget convergence plots on the policy training (top), value chain coordination (center), and hierarchical planning-scheduling (bottom) case studies. Left: CUATRO with different hyperparameters (embedding dimensionality, number of TR samples, and TR initial radius). Right: competitive solvers.

References

C. Cartis, L. Roberts, 2023, "Scalable subspace methods for derivative-free nonlinear least-squares optimization," Mathematical Programming, 199, 461–524.

R. Garnett, M. A. Osborne, P. Hennig, 2014, "Active learning of linear embeddings for Gaussian processes," In Proceedings of the 30th Conference on Uncertainty in Artificial Intelligence (UAI), 230–239.

B. Letham, R. Calandra, A. Rai, E. Bakshy, 2020, "Re-Examining Linear Embeddings for High-Dimensional Bayesian Optimization," ArXiv, abs/2001.11659.

R. Moriconi, K. S. S. Kumar, M. P. Deisenroth, 2019, "High-dimensional Bayesian optimization with manifold Gaussian processes," arXiv preprint arXiv:1902.10675.

D. van de Berg, T. Savage, P. Petsagkourakis, D. Zhang, N. Shah, E. A. del Rio-Chanona, 2022,"Data-driven optimization for process systems engineering applications," Chemical Engineering Science, 248, 117135.

D. van de Berg, P. Petsagkourakis, N. Shah, E. A. del Rio-Chanona, 2023a, "Data-driven coordination of subproblems in enterprise-wide optimization under organizational considerations," AIChE Journal, 69(4), e17977.

D. van de Berg, N. Shah, E. A. del Rio-Chanona, 2023b, "Hierarchical planning-scheduling-control – Optimality surrogates and derivative-free optimization," arXiv:2310.07870

Z. Wang, F. Hutter, M. Zoghi, D. Matheson, N. De Feitas, 2016, "Bayesian optimization in a billion dimensions via random embeddings," Journal of Artificial Intelligence Research, 55, 361–387.

Flavio Manenti, Gintaras V. Reklaitis (Eds.), Proceedings of the 34th European Symposium on Computer Aided Process Engineering / 15th International Symposium on Process Systems Engineering (ESCAPE34/PSE24), June 2-6, 2024, Florence, Italy

Sequential Design of Experiments for Parameter Estimation with Markov Chain Monte Carlo

Xinyu Cao[a], Xi Chen[a,*], Lorenz T. Biegler[b]

[a]*State Key Laboratory of Industrial Control Technology, College of Control Science and Engineering, Zhejiang University 310027, Hangzhou China.*
[b] *Chemical Engineering Dept., Carnegie Mellon University, Pittsburgh, PA 15213, United States*
xi_chen@zju.edu.cn

Abstract

Parameter estimation involves deducing unknown parameters from empirical data or observational measurements. By iteratively selecting informative experiments based on current knowledge about the parameters, sequential design of experiments (DoE) is a useful tool to estimate parameters efficiently and precisely. Aiming at more efficient use of resources with reliable and accurate results, sequential DoE with updated parameter uncertainties obtained by Markov Chain Monte Carlo (MCMC) is proposed in this study. Bayesian model updating accomplished by MCMC offers a comprehensive approach to enhance model accuracy by integrating observational data into the modeling and simulation processes. Consequently, both the variance of estimated parameters and measurement noise can be updated iteratively to optimize the operation conditions and parameters for the next batch. The proposed method is applied to kinetic parameter estimation for a batch reactor system described by differential-algebraic equations. Comparative analysis demonstrates the superior accuracy of this approach over traditional sequential DoE methods without the MCMC technique.

Keywords: MCMC, Sequential design of experiments.

1. Introduction

Parameter estimation from empirical data or observational measurements has long captivated researchers and engineers, prompting the development of various strategies over time (Biegler et al., 1986). Bayesian parameter estimation (BPE) stands prominently among these methods. By combining the "prior" and "data distributions" through Bayes' theorem, Bayesian statistics allows us to update our beliefs about the parameters in light of the observed data and obtain the "posterior" distribution, which represents our updated knowledge about the parameters after taking the data into account.

While the choice of estimation strategies holds significance, the role of experimental data in augmenting parameter accuracy cannot be overstated. Conducting experiments within an industrial context proves resource-intensive, demanding both time and cost investments. Moreover, the quality of experimental data significantly influences parameter estimation outcomes. Hence, design of experiments (DoE) emerges as an invaluable mathematical framework encompassing the planning, execution, analysis, and interpretation of experiments (Durakovic, 2017). In numerous instances, a single experiment is inadequate to accurately estimate the model parameters. Therefore, the process of experimental design, execution, and parameter estimation needs to be conducted iteratively until a satisfactory fit to the experimental data is achieved (Barz et al., 2010). Despite the systematic approach, uncertainties like measurement noise skew the parameter estimates. To address these challenges, this study proposes an efficient approach by integrating Markov Chain Monte Carlo (MCMC) into DoE for parameter estimation, accounting for measurement noise and parameter uncertainties. An isothermal batch reaction process is presented to validate the efficacy of this method.

2. Methodology

2.1. Sequential DoE for parameter estimation basis

Parameter estimation adjusts the parameters to make the simulated model output as close as possible to the real measurement. Consider a set of experimental data that includes various measurement values $\hat{y}_{i,t} \in R$ $(i = 1,2,3, \dots, N_y)$ measured at time t. For each measurement value, we make assumptions that the measurement errors $\epsilon_i (i = 1,2,3, \dots, N_y)$ are additive, independent and normally distributed. To make it easier to analyze and apply in various process applications, the state variables are divided into differential variables $z(t)$ and algebraic variables $x(t)$. The ith calculated output at time t under parameters set as θ is defined as $y_i(t_k, \theta)$. The sum of squares of the residuals is minimized for the estimation of the model parameters, weighted by the inverse of the variances.

In a parameter optimization problem, operating conditions $u(t)$ can affect the estimate result as a part of that. Enhancing parameter precision in the context of statistical modeling entails reducing the uncertainty of model parameters. Mathematically, this reduction corresponds to diminishing the elements of the parameter variance-covariance matrix. To uphold dimensional coherence, Thompson et al.(Thompson et al., 2009) created a matrix representing the scaled local sensitivity, $\overline{Q}_i$, as defined in Eq. (1):

$$
\overline{Q}_i = \begin{bmatrix} \dfrac{\partial y_i(t_1)}{\partial \theta_1} \cdot \dfrac{\sigma_{\theta_1}}{\sigma_i} & \cdots & \dfrac{\partial y_i(t_1)}{\partial \theta_{N_\theta}} \cdot \dfrac{\sigma_{\theta_{N_\theta}}}{\sigma_i} \\ \dfrac{\partial y_i(t_2)}{\partial \theta_1} \cdot \dfrac{\sigma_{\theta_1}}{\sigma_i} & \cdots & \dfrac{\partial y_i(t_2)}{\partial \theta_{N_\theta}} \cdot \dfrac{\sigma_{\theta_{N_\theta}}}{\sigma_i} \\ \cdots & \cdots & \cdots \\ \dfrac{\partial y_i(t_{N_t})}{\partial \theta_1} \cdot \dfrac{\sigma_{\theta_1}}{\sigma_i} & \cdots & \dfrac{\partial y_i(t_{N_t})}{\partial \theta_{N_\theta}} \cdot \dfrac{\sigma_{\theta_{N_\theta}}}{\sigma_i} \end{bmatrix}, i = 1,2,3, \dots, N_y \tag{1}
$$

where σ_{θ_k} signifies a scaled factor linked to the uncertainty of the kth model parameter (which is standard deviation in this paper) and σ_i represents a user-provided estimation of the standard deviation to the ith measurement noise. The Fisher information matrix (FIM) can be calculated using the scaled local sensitivity matrix(Shahmohammadi et al., 2019): FIM $= \overline{Q}^T.\overline{Q}$, where $\overline{Q}$ is composed of $\overline{Q}_i (i = 1,2,3, \dots, N_y)$. The inverse of FIM provides an estimate of the variance-covariance matrix that will be obtained after that experiment with the operating condition $u(t)$. When performing sequential DoE calculations, $\overline{Q}$ contains two parts, i.e., $\overline{Q} = [\overline{Q}_{old}, \overline{Q}_{new}]^T$ and the resulting nonlinear program is solved with respect to $u(t)$, and with θ fixed. Popular choices of the objective function Φ(FIM) in DoE include A-(minimize trace of variance-covariance matrix), D-(minimize determinant of variance-covariance matrix), and E-(minimize the largest eigenvalue of variance-covariance matrix) design criteria. Among these, D-optimal designs are widely regarded as highly effective when compared to other optimality criteria (Kessels et al., 2006). Thus, in this study, designing the operating conditions for the next batch uses the following objective function that minimizes the determinant of the variance-covariance matrix: min Φ(FIM) $= det(\text{FIM}^{-1})$. Typically, model-based DoE and parameter estimation are carried out together in a sequential manner, including three phases: 1) experimental design phase, 2) complete execution of the experiment, and 3) parameter estimation phase.

2.2. The MCMC-based Strategy

Both sequential DoE and parameter estimation processes are central to obtaining accurate and reliable models (Bock et al., 2013). However, the standard deviations of the kth model parameter $\sigma_{\theta_k}(k = 1,2,...,N_\theta)$ and i^{th} measurement noise $\sigma_i(i = 1,2,...,N_y)$ in DoE and parameter estimation are not directly available from the model. The values of these hyperparameters are often unknown. Thus, they need to be either estimated using statistical methods or directly determined by experimenters. Bayes' rule relates the prior, posterior, likelihood, and the scaling factor. Usually, directly computing the posterior distribution is difficult due to its complex and high-dimensional nature. Specifically, when the conditioning variable (θ in this study) is continuous, the summation or integration becomes an integral, which can be challenging to solve analytically. Instead, MCMC (Brooks, 1998) can indirectly obtain inference on the posterior distribution using computer simulations. Thus, MCMC is integrated into the iterative cycle to give an approximation for them. As shown in the left segment of Fig.1, the MCMC-based method begins with design of experiments, which is pivotal for establishing the conditions for the next batch. The execution of the experiment follows, and then progresses to the MCMC phase. Subsequently, the process of parameter estimation is carried out, where parameters are inferred from the collected data. The completion of the method is then marked by reaching the predetermined iteration threshold.

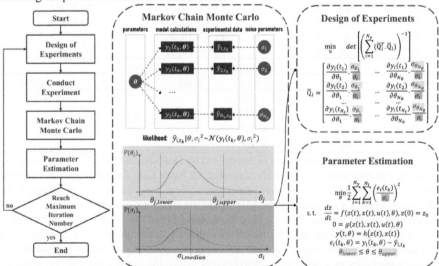

Figure 1: The MCMC-based strategy for DoE and parameter estimation.

The upper-middle segment of Fig.1 elucidates the process of calculating the likelihood within a two-layer Bayesian modeling approach employed in the MCMC-based method. The original estimated parameters $\theta \in R^{N_\theta}$ are extended to generalized parameters $[\theta, \sigma_1, \sigma_2, ..., \sigma_{N_y}] \in R^{N_\theta+N_y}$ under Bayesian model structure through the likelihood function. The experimental data $\hat{y}_{i,t_k}$ follows the Gaussian distribution, given all the extended parameters. Its mean is $y_i(t_k, \theta)$ and its variance is the same as that of independent white noise σ_i^2. Thus, given the prior of the generalized parameters, the posterior can be obtained with the help of MCMC. It needs to be clarified that not only the probability density distribution of θ but also that of σ_i can be updated once the new experimental data is obtained, as both constitute the likelihood function and have prior forms. As a result, the variance of parameters $\sigma_{\theta_i}^2 (i = 1,2, ..., N_\theta)$ and the variance of measurement noise $\sigma_j^2 (j = 1,2, ... N_y)$ can be updated. Once they are estimated, the scaled factors in the numerator and denominator can be obtained for DoE, as shown in top-right section in Fig. 1. On the other hand, the weights in the objective function can be updated for parameter estimation, as shown in the bottom-right segment. Additionally, to bolster the reliability of parameter estimation results in noisy environments, the 95% confidence intervals of the marginal distribution of θ serve as the upper and lower bounds in the parameter estimation problems. This step further enhances the credibility of the parameter estimation outcomes.

3. Results and discussion

To verify the effectiveness of the above-proposed method, this section presents an application for dynamic scenarios. The model of the Dow Chemical batch reactor describes a kinetic model of an isothermal batch reactor system (Biegler et al., 1986). Assume that four measured concentrations can be obtained with independent white noise and the true parameters exist. Detailed information is listed in Tables 1 & 2.

Table 1. Measured concentrations and corresponding white noise

index	$y(t,\theta) = h(z(t), x(t))$	distribution of ϵ	the true value of σ
1	$y_1 = x_1 + \epsilon_1$	$\epsilon_1 \sim \mathcal{N}(0, \sigma_1^2)$	$\sigma_1 = 0.1$
2	$y_2 = x_2 + \epsilon_2$	$\epsilon_2 \sim \mathcal{N}(0, \sigma_2^2)$	$\sigma_2 = 0.2$
3	$y_3 = x_3 + \epsilon_3$	$\epsilon_3 \sim \mathcal{N}(0, \sigma_3^2)$	$\sigma_3 = 0.1$
4	$y_4 = x_4 + \epsilon_4$	$\epsilon_4 \sim \mathcal{N}(0, \sigma_4^2)$	$\sigma_4 = 0.01$

Table 2. Parameters and their values

index	parameter	true value	index	parameter	true value
1	k_{10}	2.45×10^0	5	E_2	1.90×10^4
2	k_{20}	2.67×10^0	6	E_{-1}	2.69×10^4
3	k_{-10}	4.47×10^3	7	K_1	1×10^{-16}
4	E_1	1.91×10^4			

In this case, the batch temperature is determined by DoE sequentially. To ensure fairness, 5 batches of data were used for each method. Each batch lasts for 200 h and the sampling time is fixed for every 20 h, where the measurement data for $y_1 - y_4$ is obtained. To design experiments sequentially and to unify the experimental objective function, the first batch temperature is fixed at 70 °C. Then the temperature of the 2nd, 3rd, 4th, and 5th batches are sequentially optimized. The probability density function (pdf) of the estimated parameters after these batches are shown in Fig. 2. We observe that as the number of batches increases in a sequential experimental setup, the confidence interval tends to shrink. Herein the MCMC-based method is compared with the traditional method where MCMC is neither used in DoE nor parameter estimation. Specifically, the parameter variance $\sigma_{\theta_i}^2$ becomes three times larger than the parameter itself, the noise variance σ_j^2 is uniformly set to 1, and the boundary constraint of parameter estimation vanishes. To ensure that the outcomes of our study remain relatively independent of any specific set of initial assumptions, each method is conducted 15 times with different random initial parameters. A global accuracy index I_α, which considers the contribution of relative errors, is introduced as defined in Eq.(2) to assess the quality of the estimated parameters (Galvanin et al., 2009).

$$I_\alpha = \sqrt{\sum_{k=1}^{N_\theta} \left(\frac{\hat{\theta}_k - \theta_k}{\theta_k}\right)^2} \tag{2}$$

In Fig. 3, a box plot serves as a visual representation summarizing the distribution of the global accuracy index I_α. A smaller I_α value denotes superior estimation results. Within the traditional sequential DoE approach, I_α spans a range from 0.24 to 7.02. Instead, employing the MCMC-based method condenses the I_α range considerably, narrowing it down to a more favorable 0.05 to 0.44. Simultaneously, this integration reduces the median value from 0.96 to 0.23. A noticeable disparity emerges between the methods with and without MCMC. As seen in Figure 3, the traditional DoE exhibits a greater number of outliers in the final global accuracy index. In essence, the introduction of MCMC into the DoE for parameter estimation yields substantial enhancements in both the accuracy and reliability of the parameter estimation outcomes, mainly due to the robustness conferred upon estimated results by the confidence intervals obtained through MCMC in Bayesian models.

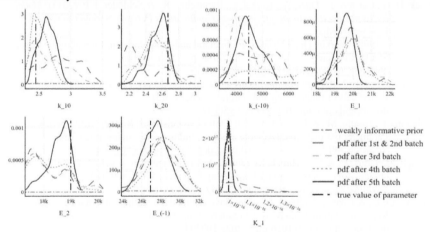

Figure 2. MCMC results for 7 parameters.

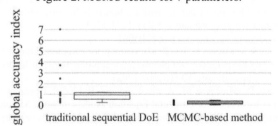

Figure 3. Box plot of global accuracy index of two methods.

4. Conclusions

This study proposes a parameter estimation method with DoE and Bayesian techniques. By iteratively selecting informative experiments based on the current knowledge about the parameters, this method allows for more efficient use of resources while obtaining accurate and reliable estimates of the parameters. It turns out that the proposed MCMC-based method obtains better parameter estimation results compared with traditional sequential DoE methods. However, there are still challenges to be considered in the future of the MCMC-based method. For example, the implementation of MCMC requires a significant amount of time, though this can be reduced by considering the time and resource costs of experiments. According to Bayesian parameter estimation, future work can focus on faster acquisition of the posterior distribution. Also, how to deal with over-parameterized systems is still challenging. Design of experiments, as a useful tool to detect parameter estimability and to save resources, can guide these advances.

Reference

Barz, T., Arellano-Garcia, H., & Wozny, G. (2010). Handling Uncertainty in Model-Based Optimal Experimental Design. Industrial & Engineering Chemistry Research, 49(12), 5702-5713. doi:https://doi.org/10.1021/ie901611b

Biegler, L. T., Damiano, J. J., & Blau, G. E. (1986). Nonlinear parameter estimation: A case study comparison. AIChE Journal, 32(1), 29-45. doi:https://doi.org/10.1002/aic.690320105

Bock, H. G., Carraro, T., Jäger, W., Körkel, S., Rannacher, R., & Schlöder, J. P. (2013). *Model based parameter estimation: theory and applications* (Vol. 4): Springer Science & Business Media.

Brooks, S. (1998). Markov chain Monte Carlo method and its application. Journal of the Royal Statistical Society: Series D (The Statistician), 47(1), 69-100. doi:https://doi.org/10.1111/1467-9884.00117

Durakovic, B. (2017). Design of experiments application, concepts, examples: State of the art. Periodicals of Engineering and Natural Sciences, 5(3). doi:http://dx.doi.org/10.21533/pen.v5i3.145

Galvanin, F., Barolo, M., & Bezzo, F. (2009). Online Model-Based Redesign of Experiments for Parameter Estimation in Dynamic Systems. Industrial & Engineering Chemistry Research, 48(9), 4415-4427. doi:https://doi.org/10.1021/ie8018356

Kessels, R., Goos, P., & Vandebroek, M. (2006). A comparison of criteria to design efficient choice experiments. Journal of Marketing Research, 43(3), 409-419. doi:https://doi.org/10.1509/jmkr.43.3.409

Liu, Y., Li, L., & Chang, Z. (2023). Efficient Bayesian model updating for dynamic systems. Reliability Engineering & System Safety, 236, 109294. doi:https://doi.org/10.1016/j.ress.2023.109294

Shahmohammadi, A., & McAuley, K. B. (2019). Sequential Model-Based A-Optimal Design of Experiments When the Fisher Information Matrix Is Noninvertible. Industrial & Engineering Chemistry Research, 58(3), 1244-1261. doi:https://doi.org/10.1021/acs.iecr.8b03047

Shahmohammadi, A., & McAuley, K. B. (2020). Using prior parameter knowledge in model-based design of experiments for pharmaceutical production. AIChE Journal, 66(11), e17021. doi:https://doi.org/10.1002/aic.17021

Smid, S. C., McNeish, D., Miočević, M., & van de Schoot, R. (2020). Bayesian Versus Frequentist Estimation for Structural Equation Models in Small Sample Contexts: A Systematic Review. Structural Equation Modeling: A Multidisciplinary Journal, 27(1), 131-161. doi:https://doi.org/10.1080/10705511.2019.1577140

Thompson, D. E., McAuley, K. B., & McLellan, P. J. (2009). Parameter estimation in a simplified MWD model for HDPE produced by a Ziegler‐Natta catalyst. Macromolecular Reaction Engineering, 3(4), 160-177. doi:https://doi.org/10.1109/9.395

Flavio Manenti, Gintaras V. Reklaitis (Eds.), Proceedings of the 34th European Symposium on Computer Aided Process Engineering / 15th International Symposium on Process Systems Engineering (ESCAPE34/PSE24), June 2-6, 2024, Florence, Italy

From legacy systems to data pipelines modernization in fermentation process

Anaëlle Dessaigne[a], Amelie Briane[a], Fayza Daboussi[a], Julien Cescut[a], David Camilo Corrales[a]

[a]*INRAE, UMS (1337) TWB, 135 Avenue de Rangueil, 31077 Toulouse, France*
David-Camilo.Corrales-Munoz@inrae.fr

Abstract

Developments in biotechnology using high throughput systems are increasingly and consequently the creation and consumption of data continue to grow rapidly. Data migration is an essential part of legacy system modernization in bioprocess. Migration process involves transferring data from outdated platforms or unknown data schemas to more advanced and secure systems. Data migration can be represented through data pipelines including data extraction, transformation and loading (ETL). The data pipelines are implemented in order to increase the overall efficiency of data-flow from the source (raw data) to the knowledge generation (Mohanty et al., 2013). Legacy systems in fermentation generally occur in bioreactor components as sensors, protocols, software or databases. These issues can limit the integration with modern tools and systems as Process Analytical Technology (PAT) instruments (Gerzon et al., 2022), avoiding real-time data on process parameters and thereby fail to assist operators in maintain optimal conditions for cell growth and production. The aim of this research is to present a guided process for designing data pipelines in bioreactors legacy systems. We present as use case a set of 24 mini-bioreactors of 50 mL. We conducted unit testing for components of the ETL process in order to ensure the integration and migration process of the legacy DB.

Keywords: Extract, Transform, Load (ETL); Database (DB); Dashboard; Directed Acyclic Graph (DAG); Mini-bioreactor

1. Introduction

The propagation of Internet-enabled technologies; the capability to collect, manage, and use "big data"; as well as the evolution of refined analysis and predictive techniques are now facilitating and pushing towards the implementation of Industry 4.0 – also known as smart manufacturing (Oliveira, 2019). Industry 4.0 represents a new paradigm in our society since the industrial revolution. This new paradigm demands the integration of digital systems and devices to enable online processing of vast quantities of data (Gargalo et al. 2021). This is therefore leading progressively to the introduction and adoption of digital solutions to predict and optimize the behavior of the production process at each product life cycle stage in real time.

Currently, legacy systems and legacy databases are confronted by the demands of Industry 4.0, which emphasizes interconnectedness, real-time data analytics, and adaptability. The historical legacy systems has impeded the integration into dynamic data pipelines essential for Industry 4.0 advancements. Moreover, the integration challenges within the field of fermentation, marked by historical data capture methods and limited real-time monitoring capabilities; emphasize the need for a paradigm shift in data management strategies for the legacy data acquisition software that controls bioreactors.

In this paper, we propose a data pipeline solution for enhanced data management in a robotic bioprocessing platform that integrates a set of 24 mini-bioreactors. By introducing a comprehensive and adaptable data pipeline, our goal is overcome the obstacles concerned to legacy databases retrieval and improve the data accessibility and data integration. The rest of the paper is organized as follows. Section 2 describes the bioprocess platform. Section 3 presents the proposed data pipeline. Section 4 provides the results, Section 5 presents the conclusions, and future works.

2. Bioprocessing platform

The robotic bioprocessing platform built in 2013 integrates a set of 24-instrumented mini-bioreactors (Hamilton, 2015). These mini-bioreactors consist in a miniaturization of 50 mL reactor with measurement and control by mini-probes of the temperature, pH, agitation speed, airflow, and oxygen concentration. The set of 24-minibioreactors is distributed equally among three polyBLOCKs (PB). The polyBLOCK is responsible for heating, cooling and stirring. Each reactor has its own heating zone which is heated electrically.

The microorganism growing in the mini-bioreactors is monitored by 'in-line' turbidity probes. The platform is designed to perform automated sampling (up to one sampling every 20 min on the 24 mini-reactors). The pipetting robot collects a sample in a reactor and immediately places it in a microplate maintained at -20°C. The data acquisition software (DAS) allows to export the fermentation parameters (T°, pH, pO2, etc.).

3. Data pipeline architecture

Data pipelines transport raw data from database sources for use by analytics tools. This paper details the composition of the data pipeline for 24 mini-bioreactors mentioned before. The data pipeline is composed by a set of steps used to move the raw fermentation data from the legacy database to a more appropriate and modernized time series database. It involves the flow of data through a series of stages where data is extracted, transformed, and loaded efficiently. **Figure 1** depicts the data pipeline architecture for 24 mini-bioreactors.

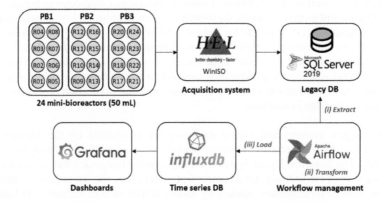

Figure 1. Data pipeline architecture for 24 mini-bioreactors

The key components of the data pipeline architecture include five steps:

3.1. Data acquisition software (DAS)

It serves as the bridge between the physical mini-bioreactors and the digital side representing by the legacy DB. DAS communicates with sensors as pH, temperature, oxygen, agitation in order to collect information. The data acquisition software called WinISO provides an interface to configure, control, and receive data from mini-bioreactors. WinISO 2.3.3 is Windows based program provided by H.E.L Group (Martin, 2013). Currently, H.E.L Group launched a new DAS called labCONSOL, which replaces the older WinISO software.

3.2. Legacy DB

The data generated by sensors of the mini-bioreactors are stored in a legacy database SQL Server 2019. This database is part of the WinISO software. The proprietary software imposes a limitation by not allowing direct access to the data persistence. Although the restriction to the access to the database is intended to protect the data and obviously create a long-term dependency on the proprietary software provider, this limitation restricts the integration with other tools. The main challenge to accessing the database was to understand its data schema, particularly in deciphering the complex relationships and dependencies between tables.

3.3. Workflow management

Once the data schema of the legacy DB was deciphered, different workflows were coded in order to apply the ETL process. We used Apache Airflow as workflow management platform. Airflow allows creating, scheduling and monitoring workflows coded in Python.
The workflows are expressed as Directed Acyclic Graphs (DAGs), where each node represents a specific task. Each task in the DAG is a unit of work that can encompass running a Python script to executing a database query. DAGs are executed in parallel, enabling the concurrent execution of multiple DAG runs. Upon completion of a DAG run, Apache Airflow notifies its final status using either a "success" or "failed" tag.

We built three workflows, represented by three DAGs to manage ETL process from legacy DB to a time series DB (**Figure 1**). Each DAG is responsible for performing the ETL process for each PolyBLOCK. These DAGs contains four tasks:
- *Waiting_data* checks whether new DoEs have been created. WinISO creates a Design of Experiment (DoE) and this is stored in the legacy database.
- *Creating_time_interval* has been implemented as function to trigger the execution of DAGs at regular intervals, specifically every five minutes.
- *Searching_data* looks new data from DoE identified in *Waiting_data* function
- *ETL* applies on detected data the ETL process:
    o *Extract:* during data extraction, data of the mini-bioreactors is copied by batch from legacy DB to a staging area. The extraction process involved mixing SQL queries and code written in python due to the complexity of the data schema of the legacy DB.
    o *Transform*: in the staging area, the raw fermentation data is preprocessed. Missing values were handled through imputation methods. Additionally, the names of the variables of the mini-

bioreactors were harmonized due to inconsistencies or variations in nomenclature of the sensor names.

○ *Load:* in this last step, the transformed data is moved from the staging area into a time series DB. The data that were already in the legacy DB were loaded. Data from running experiments are continuously loaded in periods of 5 minutes.

3.4. Time series DB

We used InfluxDB as time series database. InfluxDB was designed for handling and managing time-stamped or time-series data. Time series data consists of sequences of data points (e.g., the temperature of one mini-bioreactor by minute), each associated with a specific timestamp, ordered chronologically. This type of database uses a tag-value data model which is well-suited for scenarios where data points are indexed based on time, and each data point is associated with additional metadata in the form of tag-value pairs.

3.5. Dashboards

A dashboard provides a visual data representation in a consolidated and easy-to-digest-form. Dashboards in fermentation are useful for monitoring the key parameters (temperature, pH level), the bioreactor performance (agitation and aeration), the nutrient levels (e.g., glucose, nitrogen, glycerol, ethanol, etc.), and the biomass and product concentration. We built the dashboards for visualizing the processed data of the mini-bioreactors in Grafana open-source platform. Subsequently, we connected Grafana to InfluxDB for the visualization and analysis of mini-bioreactors data of previous experiments or running experiments. The dashboards were designed with an expert panel from fermentation service.

4. Results

In order to ensure the integration and migration process of the legacy DB to the time series database, we conducted unit testing for components of the ETL process, such as source extraction, data transformation, and target loading (Zhu et al., 1997). We used data from four experiments that were already in the legacy DB. Table 1 presents the dimensionality of those experiments characterized by average experiment length, the number of mini-bioreactors for each experiment, the number of variables of the mini-bioreactors and the data points for each variable.

Table 1. Dimensionality of experiments run in the mini-bioreactors.

Experiments	Average experiment length (hours)	Mini-bioreactors	Variables	Data points
RUN 1	48h25	8	557	581
RUN 2	72h55	15	557	875
RUN 3	75h	16	557	300
RUN 4	72h	16	557	864

We employed the four experiments presented in Table 1 to conduct unit testing for the ETL components. These experiments correspond to the production of monoclonal antibodies. The application of the ETL process was conducted considering that the data of the four experiments are already stored in the database. **Figure 2** presents the execution time for the components Extract, Test and Load.

In Run 1, the duration of the experiment was 48 hours and 25 minutes with 8 mini-bioreactors, 557 variables, and 581 data points, the Extract, Transform, and Load stages consumed times of approximately 37.63, 138.88, and 150.67 seconds, respectively. Run 2 encompasses an experiment duration of 72 hours and 55 minutes with 15 mini-bioreactors, 557 variables, and 875 data points, demonstrated increased processing times in all stages: 78.96, 459.76, and 334.02 seconds for Extract, Transform, and Load, respectively. Notably, Run 3, with 75 hours of experiment duration, 16 mini-bioreactors, 557 variables, and 300 data points, presented a reduction in the Extract and Load stages, with 49.26 and 225.37 seconds, while the Transform stage maintained a relatively high time of 315.88 seconds. The Run 4 with a 72 hours of experiment and featuring 16 mini-bioreactors, 557 variables, and 864 data points, the Extract, Transform, and Load stages displayed times of 114.19, 598.26, and 293.26 seconds, respectively.

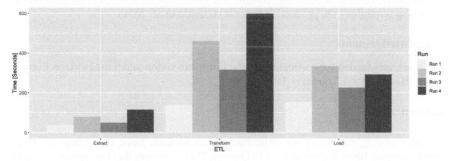

Figure 2. Unit testing for ETL components based on four experiments stored in the legacy DB. Execution time expressed in seconds.

On average, the Transform stage exhibits the highest processing time, with an average of approximately 378.94 seconds, followed by the Load stage with an average time of around 250.83 seconds. On the other hand, the Extract stage shows the shortest average time at approximately 69.76 seconds. These findings indicate the Transform stage consumes a significant portion of the overall processing time due this stage involves the mix of SQL queries and code written in python due to the complexity of the data schema of the legacy DB.

5. Conclusions and future works

Accessibility to legacy databases presents a multitude of problems, primarily the outdated and often proprietary nature of these systems. The simplest solution is to pay for the new version of the data acquisition system; however, this incurs additional costs and in the future, will become a legacy system. In order to address these issues in the field of fermentation, we proposed a data pipeline for 24 mini-bioreactors with the objective to deal the data management of legacy software systems. The data pipeline proposes a set of steps to move the raw data from the legacy database to a more appropriate and modernized time series database through ETL process.

In summary, the Transform was the stage that demanded most processing time, primarily attributed to the legacy data schema. The complexity of the legacy database structure necessitates intricate transformations to align the data of bioreactors, variables

(Temperature, pH, Oxygen, etc.) and values with the target schema, introducing additional processing steps with SQL queries and python scripts.

In conclusion, the implementation of the data pipeline for 24 mini-bioreactors improved the data management of the legacy databases by providing a structured and efficient mechanism for data integration, transformation, and migration. In general, the data pipelines can be an opportunity to facilitates the smooth transition from outdated bioreactor DAS, ensuring data consistency, improved accessibility, and enhanced interoperability with open source applications as Apache Airflow, InfluxDB and Grafana.

In addition, data pipelines play an important role in the construction of digital twins in bioprocess. These pipelines serve to collect, process, and integrate data in real-time, ensuring that the digital twin stays synchronized with its physical counterpart or the system it represents. As future work, we propose the construction of digital thread, an essential component to connect the physical objects with the digital objects, by facilitating measurement, sensing, monitoring, control, and communication about everything that is happening throughout the production process (Gargalo et al. 2021).

Acknowledgements

This work was funded (or co-funded) by the European Union under the Horizon Europe project Bioindustry 4.0, grant n. 101094287.

References

Gargalo, Carina L., Simoneta Caño de las Heras, Mark Nicholas Jones, Isuru Udugama, Seyed Soheil Mansouri, Ulrich Krühne, et Krist V. Gernaey. 2021. "Towards the Development of Digital Twins for the Bio-Manufacturing Industry". P. 1-34 in Digital Twins: Tools and Concepts for Smart Biomanufacturing, Advances in Biochemical Engineering/Biotechnology.

Gerzon, G., Sheng, Y., & Kirkitadze, M. (2022). Process Analytical Technologies – Advances in bioprocess integration and future perspectives. Journal of Pharmaceutical and Biomedical Analysis, 207, 114379. https://doi.org/10.1016/j.jpba.2021.114379

Hamilton Company. TWB and Hamilton Develop a Unique and Custom Made Microbial Culture Robot, Utilizing Cutting-Edge Technology for the Field of Industrial Biotechnology High Throughput Culture Platform. (2015). https://www.hamiltoncompany.com/press-releases/twb-and-hamilton-develop-a-unique-and-custom-made-microbial-culture-robot-utilizing-cutting-edge-technology-for-the-field-of-industrial-biotechnology#top.

Martin, David. 2013. WinISO Data Acquisition and Control Software (User Manual 2.0.1.). H.E.L Group.

Mohanty, S., Jagadeesh, M., & Srivatsa, H. (2013). "Big Data" in the Enterprise. In S. Mohanty, M. Jagadeesh, & H. Srivatsa (Éds.), Big Data Imperatives : Enterprise Big Data Warehouse, BI Implementations and Analytics (p. 1-24). Apress. https://doi.org/10.1007/978-1-4302-4873-6_1

Oliveira, A. L. (2019). Biotechnology, Big Data and Artificial Intelligence. Biotechnology Journal, 14(8), 1800613. https://doi.org/10.1002/biot.201800613

Zhu, H., Hall, P. A., & May, J. H. (1997). Software unit test coverage and adequacy. Acm computing surveys (csur), 29(4), 366-427.

Flavio Manenti, Gintaras V. Reklaitis (Eds.), Proceedings of the 34th European Symposium on Computer Aided Process Engineering / 15th International Symposium on Process Systems Engineering (ESCAPE34/PSE24), June 2-6, 2024, Florence, Italy

A Convexication-based Outer-approximation Method for Convex and Nonconvex MINLP

Zedong Peng[a], Kaiyu Cao[a], Kevin C. Furman[b], Can Li[a], Ignacio E. Grossmann[c], David E. Bernal Neira[a,d,e]

[a]*Davidson School of Chemical Engineering, Purdue University, 480 Stadium Mall Drive, West Lafayette, IN, 47907, USA*
[b]*ExxonMobil Upstream Research Co, 22777 Springwoods Village Parkway, Spring, TX, 77389, USA*
[c]*Department of Chemical Engineering, Carnegie Mellon University, Pittsburgh, PA 15213, USA*
[d]*Research Institute for Advanced Computer Science, Universities Space Research Association, Mountain View, CA, USA*
[e]*Quantum Artificial Intelligence Laboratory (QuAIL), NASA Ames Research Center, Mountain View, CA, USA*
dbernaln@purdue.edu

Abstract

The advancement of domain reduction techniques has significantly enhanced the performance of solvers in mathematical programming. This paper delves into the impact of integrating convexification and domain reduction techniques within the Outer-Approximation method. We propose a refined convexification-based Outer-Approximation method alongside a Branch-and-Bound method for both convex and nonconvex Mixed-Integer Nonlinear Programming problems. These methods have been developed and incorporated into the open-source Mixed-Integer Nonlinear Decomposition Toolbox for Pyomo-MindtPy. Comprehensive benchmark tests were conducted, validating the effectiveness and reliability of our proposed algorithms. These tests highlight the improvements achieved by incorporating convexification and domain reduction techniques into the Outer-Approximation and Branch-and-Bound methods.

Keywords: Mixed-Integer Nonlinear Programming, Outer-Approximation, LP/NLP Branch and Bound, Domain Reduction.

1. Introduction

Mixed-integer nonlinear programming (MINLP) has broad applications in process systems engineering (PSE), including planning, scheduling, and control. It offers a powerful modeling framework that optimizes discrete and continuous variables involved in linear and nonlinear constraints. However, the combinatorial complexity, nonlinearity, and even nonconvexity lead to substantial challenges in optimizing such problems.

Generally, MINLP can be classified as convex and nonconvex, depending on the convexity of its continuous relaxation. The algorithms for MINLP are primarily categorized into Branch-and-Bound (B&B) methods and decomposition methods (Kronqvist et al., 2019). The main idea of MINLP decomposition algorithms is to generate linear inequalities to approximate nonlinear constraints and iteratively solve the relaxed Mixed-Integer Linear Programming (MILP) main problem and Nonlinear Programming (NLP) subproblems. Decomposition methods for convex MINLP problems include the Outer-Approximation (OA) method (Duran and Grossmann, 1986). This method involves solving an MILP defined by linear inequalities that relax the nonlinear constraints, known as OA cuts, and an NLP with the main problem's integer solution fixed. The first-order Taylor approximation of the nonlinear constraints defines these OA cuts. To reduce the MILP problem solution time, the Linear Programming and Nonlinear Programming-based B&B (LP/NLP-B&B) method (Quesada and Grossmann, 1992) maintains the same B&B for the MILP, solves NLPs at the tree's integer nodes, and uses OA cuts to improve the searching bounds. Consequently, these decomposition methods are often called multi-tree and single-tree, based on their management of the MILP problem. A significant limitation of these methods is their initialization, usually given by relaxing the nonlinearity of the problem and relying on the cuts generated at each iteration to provide a better linear approximation as iterations progress.

While the OA method is effective for convex MINLPs, its limitations become apparent for nonconvex MINLP, where OA cuts do not guarantee validity in relaxations of nonlinear functions, precluding global optimality guarantees. Other relaxation techniques have been developed for nonconvex MINLPs addressing this challenge. Among these, the Auxiliary Variable Method (AVM) and McCormick relaxations are successful strategies for generating relaxations of nonconvex factorable functions (Tawarmalani and Sahinidis, 2013). AVM achieves this by introducing an auxiliary variable and a corresponding equality constraint for each intermediate nonlinear factor in a function, leading to computational efficiency by decomposing the function into simpler, lower-dimensional components. However, this method entails incorporating many auxiliary variables and constraints. In contrast, McCormick relaxations maintain the dimension of the original function and use a recursive approach to produce the required convex and concave relaxations effectively (Chachuat, 2013).

In addition to advancements in reformulations and optimization algorithms, the performance of optimization solvers has significantly improved through domain reduction techniques. These techniques encompass bound tightening, eliminating redundant variables and constraints, and convexification (Zhang et al., 2020). The bound tightening techniques include Feasibility-based Bound Tightening (FBBT), Optimality-based Bound Tightening (OBBT), and Marginals-based Bound Tightening (Zhang et al., 2020). Domain reduction methods, including convexification cuts and bound tightening techniques, have been successful for spatial B&B methods. These tighter relaxations provide stronger dual bounds, accelerating the B&B process by facilitating node pruning and efficiently identifying optimal solutions. However, decomposition-based MINLP solvers have not yet fully harnessed the potential of domain reduction techniques.

This work investigates the efficacy of domain reduction techniques within OA methods, applicable to both convex and nonconvex MINLP problems. It is understood that domain reduction techniques can be used during the presolve stage and at each node within the B&B tree, a strategy known as the branch-and-reduce method. Similarly, in the OA method, these techniques can be employed both in the presolve phase and during solving integer-fixed NLP subproblems. However, this work focuses on the impact of domain reduction methods at the method's initialization stage.

2. Solution algorithm

The general form of a MINLP problem is as follows.

$$\min_{x,y} \quad f(x,y)$$

$$s.t. \quad g_j(x,y) \le 0 \ , \forall j = 1, ..., l \qquad\qquad (MINLP)$$

$$x \in [\underline{x}, \overline{x}] \subseteq \mathbb{R}^n, y \in \{\underline{y}, ..., \overline{y}\} \subseteq \mathbb{Z}^m,$$

Where x and y represent continuous variables and discrete variables, respectively. Upper and lower variable bounds are determined by over- and underbars, respectively. Both the objective $f(x,y)$ and constraints $g_j(x,y)$ are potentially nonlinear functions.

The OA solution method for MINLP involves an iterative two-step procedure. The first step in iteration k determines the integer variables' values y^{k+1} by solving problem (OA-MILP), defined by the OA cuts. Its optimal objective function value, encoded in variable μ, provides a dual lower bound (LB) to the original MINLP problem's optimal objective.

$$\min_{x,y,\mu} \quad \mu$$

$$s.t. \quad f(x^i, y^i) + \nabla f(x^i, y^i)^T \begin{bmatrix} x - x^i \\ y - y^i \end{bmatrix} \le \mu \quad \forall i = 1, ..., k$$

$$g_j(x^i, y^i) + \nabla g_j(x^i, y^i)^T \begin{bmatrix} x - x^i \\ y - y^i \end{bmatrix} \le 0 \ \ \forall i = 1, ..., k, \forall j \in I \qquad (OA - MILP)$$

$$x \in [\underline{x}, \overline{x}] \subseteq \mathbb{R}^n, y \in \{\underline{y}, ..., \overline{y}\} \subseteq \mathbb{Z}^m, \mu \in \mathbb{R}^1.$$

The second step is determining the continuous variables' values x^{k+1} by solving problem (NLP-I) whose optimal solution yields a primal upper bound (UB) to problem (MINLP).

$$\min_{x,y} \quad f(x, y^{k+1})$$

$$s.t. \quad g_j(x, y^{k+1}) \le 0 \ , \forall j = 1, ..., l \qquad\qquad (NLP - I)$$

$$x \in [\underline{x}, \overline{x}] \subseteq \mathbb{R}^n.$$

If problem (NLP-I) is infeasible, the following feasibility subproblem is solved to minimize a norm p of the constraint violations s, as a result updating x^{k+1}.

$$\min_{x,y,s} \quad \|s\|_p$$

$$s.t. \quad g_j(x, y^{k+1}) \le s_j \ \ \forall j = 1, ..., l \qquad\qquad (NLP - f)$$

$$x \in [\underline{x}, \overline{x}] \subseteq \mathbb{R}^n, s \in [0, \infty) \subseteq \mathbb{R}_+^l.$$

As shown in Figure 1.a, the OA method begins by solving the relaxed NLP problem and then iteratively solves the (OA-MILP), (NLP-I), and (NLP-f) problems. The key to this process is the progressive accumulation of OA cuts, which incrementally narrows the gap between the LB and the UB. The iterations continue until LB and UB converge, culminating in the OA method reaching the optimal solution. This method is guaranteed to find the global optimal solution of convex MINLPs (Duran and Grossmann, 1986).

Maintaining a single MILP tree for the LP/NLP-B&B method can be implemented using the *LazyConstraint* callback function through callback functions in current MILP solvers, as shown in Figure 1.b. This method initializes by solving the relaxed NLP problem as well. Then, a B&B method is used to solve problem (OA-MILP). Whenever an incumbent solution is found in the search tree, (NLP-I) is solved, and OA cuts are added as lazy constraints to the MILP tree. This B&B process is guaranteed to terminate at the global optimal solution of convex MINLP problems (Quesada and Grossmann, 1992).

The OA and LP/NLP-B&B methods generate tight cuts at the boundary of the nonlinear feasible region defined by the original problem constraints by incurring the cost of solving NLP subproblems. If the (NLP-I) subproblem is infeasible, (NLP-f) is solved to find the point closest to the feasible region to generate the tightest possible cuts. Since the linear inequality constraints are accumulated iteratively, the main problem in the early iterations is that a poor approximation of the original MINLP model is obtained. Consequently, the integer combination provided by the main problem tends to yield an infeasible (NLP-I) subproblem, and no primal bound can be obtained.

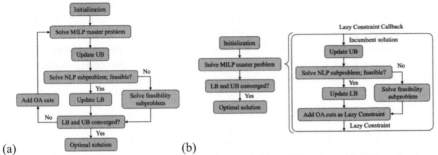

(a)   (b)

Figure 1. (a) Outer-Approximation method and (b) LP/NLP-based B&B method

In this work, we apply the domain reduction methods to the initialization stage of the OA method to resolve this issue. Eq. (1) shows the tightened bounds of the discrete and continuous variables, $[\underline{x}', \overline{x}']$ and $\{\underline{y}', ..., \overline{y}'\}$, respectively. Eq. (2) corresponds to the convexification linear cuts generated by the auxiliary variable method or reformulations, where z are auxiliary variables. Since both Eq. (1) and (2) are applied at the initialization stage, they are valid for (OA-MILP), (NLP-I), and (NLP-f).

$$x \in [\underline{x}', \overline{x}'] \in [\underline{x}, \overline{x}] \subseteq \mathbb{R}^n; \ y \in \{\underline{y}', ..., \overline{y}'\} \in \{\underline{y}, ..., \overline{y}\} \subseteq \mathbb{Z}^m \qquad (1)$$

$$Ax + By + Cz \leq b \qquad (2)$$

Considering that the convexification cuts are the relaxation of nonlinear constraints, they are redundant in the NLP subproblems where the original nonlinear constraints are included. Therefore, we denote the (NLP-I) and (NLP-f) problems with convexification cuts and tightened bounds as complete-scale NLP problems. The (NLP-I) and (NLP-f) problems with only tightened bounds are denoted reduced-scale NLP problems.

This work also considers modified alternatives of the OA and LP/NLP-B&B methods to guarantee global optimality for nonconvex MINLP problems. Several modifications have been introduced to provide such global optimality guarantees, denoted as global OA (GOA) and global LP/NLP-B&B (GLP/NLP-B&B). First, instead of adding OA cuts, the affine underestimators and overstimators are generated based on the convex and concave McCormick relaxations using subgradient propagation (Chachuat, 2013). Second, to guarantee the algorithm's convergence, no-good cuts are generated to cut off the explored integer combinations and prevent the algorithm from repeatedly cycling through the same combinations. These enhancements enable the global algorithms to converge to the global optimum of nonconvex MINLP problems if the NLP subproblems are solved to global optimality (Kesavan et al., 2004). Furthermore, we integrate the domain reduction techniques in GOA and GLP/NLP-B&B and investigate their effect on its performance.

3. Benchmarking and Results

To evaluate the impact of domain reduction techniques, we use test instances from the problem library MINLPLib (Vigerske, 2014). 434 convex instances and 181 nonconvex instances are selected, adhering to the criteria that each instance must have at least one discrete variable and at least one continuous variable. For clarity in our analysis, we use (r) and (c) to distinguish between the reduced-scale and complete-scale NLP subproblems used in the convexification-based OA and LP/NLP-B&B methods. Moreover, we indicate the results with convexification with the prefix (C-) in the following results.

The benchmark implementation is based on the **M**ixed-**i**nteger **n**onlinear **d**ecomposition **t**oolbox for **Py**omo-MindtPy (Bernal et al., 2018). We use both the multi-tree and single-tree implementation of OA and GOA strategy, maintaining their default configurations as a baseline. Moreover, a special version of BARON 19.4.4 is used to tighten the bounds and generate convexification cuts. Option *dolocal* is set to 0, and *numloc* is set to 0 to turn off local search during upper bounding and preprocessing in BARON. All range reduction and relaxation options are retained at their default settings. Nonlinear FBBT, OBBT, marginals-based, and linear-feasibility-based bound tightening are applied. Outer approximations of convex univariate functions and cutting planes are also applied. For the termination criteria of the algorithm, we set the absolute tolerances $\epsilon = 10^{-5}$ and $\epsilon_{rel} = 10^{-3}$, along with a time limit of 900s. We use GUROBI 10.0.0 as the MILP solver, IPOPTH 3.14 as the NLP solver for convex instances, and BARON 23.6.22 as the NLP solver for nonconvex instances. All tests ran on a Linux cluster with 48 AMD EPYC 7643 2.3GHz CPUs and 1 TB RAM, with each test restricted to using only a single thread.

The time and iteration performance profiles of the convex instances are presented in Figure 2. For the LP/NLP-B&B method, the number of iterations refers to the number of (NLP-I) subproblems solved. Overall, the convexification-based OA and LP/NLP-B&B methods utilizing reduced-scale NLP subproblems outperform the other solver alternatives regarding solution time. Regarding the number of iterations, both the OA and LP/NLP-B&B methods benefit from the convexification cuts and the bound tightening techniques. Interestingly, the choice between complete-scale and reduced-scale NLP subproblems does not significantly impact iteration performance.

However, it is noteworthy that the convexification-based LP/NLP-B&B method with complete-scale NLP subproblems underperforms in time performance compared to the standard LP/NLP-B&B method. This coincides with our previous statement that the convexification cuts are redundant and increase the computational complexity of (NLP-I) and (NLP-f) subproblems. For instances that can be solved within one second, both the standard OA method and the LP/NLP B&B method are more efficient than their convexified counterparts, as both bound tightening and convexification cuts entail additional processing time. Nonetheless, the bound tightening and convexification cuts generally enhance the performance of both the OA and LP/NLP B&B methods.

The benchmark results of nonconvex instances are presented in Figure 3. Similar to the convex cases, the convexification-based OA and LP/NLP B&B methods outperform the others in solution time and number of iterations. This consistent performance across convex and nonconvex MINLP problems demonstrates the effectiveness of the proposed convexification-based OA and LP/NLP B&B methods.

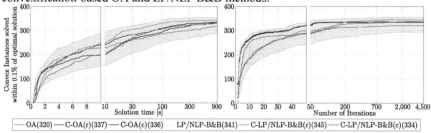

Figure 2. Time and iteration performance profile of 434 convex MINLP instances

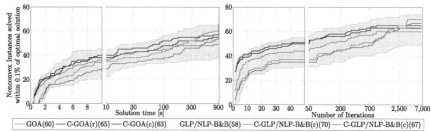

Figure 3. Time and iteration performance profile of 181 nonconvex MINLP instances

4. Conclusions

This work explores the impact of domain reduction techniques implemented in B&B-based solvers on the OA and the LP/NLP-B&B methods. These effects were investigated for variations of these methods to solve both convex and nonconvex MINLPs to global optimality. The proposed convexification-based OA and LP/NLP-B&B methods are implemented within the open-source solver MindtPy. Our benchmarking results highlight the significant improvements by domain reduction techniques in enhancing the efficiency of the OA and LP/NLP-B&B methods, observed by reducing the computational times and the number of iterations required for solving convex and nonconvex MINLP problems to global optimality. These results highlight the value of implementing domain reduction techniques, which are successful for B&B methods, in MINLP decomposition algorithms.

References

1. Kronqvist, J., Bernal, D. E., Lundell, A., Grossmann, I. E., 2019. A review and comparison of solvers for convex MINLP. Optimization and Engineering, 20, 397-455.
2. Duran, M. A., Grossmann, I. E., 1986. An outer-approximation algorithm for a class of mixed-integer nonlinear programs. Mathematical programming, 36, 307-339.
3. Quesada, I., Grossmann, I. E., 1992. An LP/NLP based branch and bound algorithm for convex MINLP optimization problems. Computers & chemical engineering, 16(10-11), 937-947.
4. Tawarmalani, M., Sahinidis, N. V., 2013. Convexification and global optimization in continuous and mixed-integer nonlinear programming: theory, algorithms, software, and applications, 65.
5. Zhang, Y., Sahinidis, N. V., Nohra, C., Rong, G, 2020. Optimality-based domain reduction for inequality-constrained NLP and MINLP problems. Journal of Global Optimization, 77, 425-454.
6. Chachuat, B.: MC++, 2013: a versatile library for bounding and relaxation of factorable functions. http://www3.imperial.ac.uk/environmentenergyoptimisation/ software.
7. Kesavan, P., Allgor, R. J., Gatzke, E. P., Barton, P. I. 2004. Outer approximation algorithms for separable nonconvex mixed-integer nonlinear programs. Mathematical Programming, 100, 517-535.
8. Vigerske, S., 2014. Towards MINLPLib 2.0 Model instance collections.
9. Bernal, D. E., Chen, Q., Gong, F., Grossmann, I. E., 2018. Mixed-integer nonlinear decomposition toolbox for Pyomo (MindtPy). In Computer Aided Chemical Engineering, 44, 895-900.

Flavio Manenti, Gintaras V. Reklaitis (Eds.), Proceedings of the 34th European Symposium on Computer Aided Process Engineering / 15th International Symposium on Process Systems Engineering (ESCAPE34/PSE24), June 2-6, 2024, Florence, Italy

Hybrid Symbolic-Numeric Computation based on Resultant Theory for Process Simulation

Shuhui Zhang,[a] Fei Zhao,[a*] Xi Chen[a*]

[a] *State Key Laboratory of Industrial Control Technology, College of Control Science and Engineering, Zhejiang University, Hangzhou, Zhejiang, China*
xi_chen@zju.edu.cn, zhaofeizju@zju.edu.cn

Abstract

Solving nonlinear equation systems stands as a fundamental challenge within the realm of process systems engineering (PSE). At present, numerical computation stands as the primary technical avenue for tackling these complexities. This approach boasts computational efficiency and has found extensive utility across numerous real-world scenarios, whereas limited by numerical instability. This article aims to leverage the characteristics of symbolic computation to address the inherent deficiencies of numerical computation. Drawing on the classical theories within the realm of symbolic computation, particularly the resultant theory, this study proposes a symbolic-numeric hybrid computational method tailored for nonlinear equation systems in the field of PSE. The proposed method primarily addresses the challenge of limitation to polynomial systems. The existing resultant theory is only applicable to polynomial equations. This proposed method summarizes a general model of the transcendental terms with respect to variables. Then symbolic representations are introduced for these terms, followed by triangularization of the original nonlinear system to obtain a new equivalent system. This enables solving the new system dimension-wise to enhance solution convergence and reduce initial-value dependency.

Keywords: symbolic-numeric computation, resultant theory, transcendental terms.

1. Introduction

The intricate nature of industrial processes demands robust solutions to nonlinear equation systems, as they are the mathematical backbone of process modeling. Numerical computation, with its efficiency and versatility, has long been the method of choice in PSE (Grossman and Westerberg, 2000). However, its limitations, including susceptibility to local solution traps and dependence on initial conditions, have spurred the exploration of alternative methodologies. Symbolic computation, rooted in mathematical logic and algebraic manipulation, emerges as a compelling alternative that holds the promise of overcoming the drawbacks associated with purely numerical approaches.

Motivated by the challenges of conventional numerical methods, this research seeks to introduce a paradigm shift in nonlinear equation system solving for PSE. By integrating symbolic computation, particularly leveraging resultant theory, the proposed hybrid approach aims to provide solutions that guarantee completeness and accuracy—qualities often elusive in purely numerical methods.

The resultant theory holds paramount significance in engineering, particularly in the analysis of equation systems. This mathematical framework plays a pivotal role in determining the combined effect of multiple forces or variables acting on a system. Engineers rely on resultant theory to simplify complex equations and streamline the solution process, enabling efficient problem-solving in various fields such as structural engineering, fluid dynamics, and control systems (Chiasson et al., 2003). The application of resultant theory enhances the understanding of system behavior and facilitates the design of robust and optimized engineering solutions.

However, the traditional utilization of resultant is confined to polynomial equations, posing a limitation in its utility for the diverse transcendental terms encountered in PSE. To overcome this limitation, the proposed method introduces a comprehensive model for transcendental terms, enabling their symbolic representation. This innovation facilitates the triangularization of the original nonlinear system, transforming it into an equivalent system that can be solved dimension-wise. The symbolic-numeric hybrid approach thus combines the accuracy of symbolic computation with the computational efficiency of numeric methods, providing a robust solution to the challenges posed by nonlinear equation systems in PSE.

The structure of this paper is designed to comprehensively present the proposed hybrid symbolic-numeric computational method. Section 2 provides a detailed exploration of the theoretical foundations of symbolic computation, focusing on resultant theory and its limitations. Section 3 outlines the methodology, describing the extension of resultant theory to transcendental terms by reformulating models appropriately and the subsequent solution of triangularized systems dimension by dimension. Section 4 presents the application of the proposed method to the Pressure-Enthalpy flash problem, illustrating the effectiveness of the method in real-world scenarios and discussing the obtained results through the hybrid method. Finally, Section 5 concludes the paper by summarizing key findings and discussing potential directions for future research.

2. Resultant theory for equation system

Resultant is a classic operation in symbolic computation, used to solve systems of polynomial equations. The resultant of two polynomials can be defined as follows while the property of resultant with two polynomials is presented subsequently in Property 1.

Definition 1. Resultant.

Given two multi-variate polynomials $f, g \subseteq \mathbb{R}[x_1, \cdots, x_n]$, f and g can be formulated into the univariate polynomial with main variable x_n as follows:

$$
\begin{aligned}
f(x_1, \ldots, x_n) &= a_m x_n^m + a_{m-1} x_n^{m-1} + \cdots + a_0 \\
g(x_1, \ldots, x_n) &= b_l x_n^l + b_{l-1} x_n^{l-1} + \cdots + b_0
\end{aligned}
\tag{1}
$$

where $a_i, b_j \subseteq \mathbb{R}[x_1, \cdots, x_{n-1}]$, $i = 0, \cdots, m$, $j = 1, \cdots, l$. The resultant of f and g with respect to x_n is thus the determinant of the Sylvester matrix (Chtcherba and Kapur, 2004).

Property 1 (Gelfand et al., 2008): Given two multi-variate polynomials $f, g \subseteq \mathbb{R}[x_1, \cdots, x_n]$, their resultant with respect to x_n is denoted by $r \subseteq \mathbb{R}[x_1, \cdots, x_n]$. If and only if f and g have a common root in the real domain $\mathbb{R}[x_n]$, the resultant r is equal to zero.

According to the property of resultants, we can deduce a chain of dimension reduction for a polynomial equation system, as shown in Figure 1. Given a polynomial system with n equations and n variables, the dimension of the equation system can be reduced by choosing a polynomial and a main variable to compute resultants with other polynomials with respect to the main variable. When the equations are homogeneous, the numbers of the variables and equations are consistent. The solutions in n-dimensional space will be projected into the 1-dimensional space. Geometrically, the set of solutions forms a series of scatters distributed in projective space. However, it might occur that the excess components are deduced in the set of solutions. For example, only one equation is generated in $\mathbb{R}[x_1, x_2]$ describing a curve with infinite solutions. This scenario appears due to certain dependencies between the high–dimensional equations, which bothers the generalization of the resultant theory to solve equation systems. But for a process in reality, the physical attributes impel the solutions shrinking into exact points without aforementioned dependencies. This characteristic intensively motivates us to introduce the resultant to solve the process simulation problems by reducing the dimension of systems.

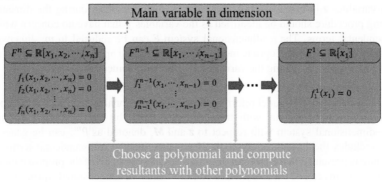

Figure 1. The chain of dimension reduction for a polynomial equation system.

3. Hybrid symbolic-numeric method

Based on the dimension-reducing chain presented in Figure 1, it is natural to apply the resultant theory to projecting high-dimensional equational systems into 1-dimensional systems and to solve the triangularized equations subsequently. In our previous work, the similar procedure has been proposed and applied to several cases through the CAD algorithm (Zhang et al., 2021). However, the primary obstacle in this procedure is that resultant operation is confined to polynomial systems. On the contrary, transcendental function terms are often involved in practical process systems. Therefore, resultant theory cannot be directly applied to such systems to reduce system dimensionality and enhance solution stability.

Nevertheless, we can leverage the capability of symbolic computation to manipulate symbolic entities. By introducing symbolic representations for transcendental function terms, we can reformulate the equation system into an algebraic form. Subsequently, employing knot theory allows us to execute dimensionality reduction operations on the reconstructed algebraic system, resulting in an equivalent system in trigonometric form, which is helpful to solve the system effectively and obtain solutions in a more manageable and interpretable format.

3.1. Model reformulation

A process simulation problem can always be formulated into an equation system, denoted as $F(x) = 0$. Given the presence of transcendental terms, it becomes imperative to treat the variables within these terms distinctly from other variables first. Building upon this distinction, symbolic representation is introduced to facilitate the model formulation, as shown as Eq. (2).

$$F(x) = 0 \Leftrightarrow \hat{F}(y, z, T(z)) = 0 \xrightarrow{\text{Model reformulation}} P(y, z, M) = 0 \qquad (2)$$

where $\boldsymbol{z} \subseteq \boldsymbol{x}$ represents the variable involved in transcendental terms and $\boldsymbol{y} = \boldsymbol{x} \backslash \boldsymbol{z}$. Then by representing the transcendental terms $T(\boldsymbol{z})$ in $\hat{F}$ with new symbols denoted as $\boldsymbol{M}$, a new algebraic system is generated with respect to variables $\boldsymbol{y}$, $\boldsymbol{z}$ and $\boldsymbol{M}$.

In the sequel, the similar dimension-reducing procedure is executed as shown in Figure 1. Although the number of variables excesses the number of equations caused by introducing the new variables $\boldsymbol{M}$, the resultant of two polynomials in P can also be computed to reduce the dimension of system. However, the choice of main variables in every dimension cannot be casually determined since the new variables are related to the origin variables $\boldsymbol{z}$ in essence. Thus, the order of main variables during the dimension-reducing procedure should be identified as the variables $\boldsymbol{y}$ that have no concern with the transcendental terms. The $n-$dimensional system F can be reduced to $m-$dimensional system by utilizing the appropriate model reformulation and applying the resultant theory into the new model assuming the variables $\boldsymbol{z}$ include m elements.

3.2. Dimension-wise solution

In the above section, the model reformulation and dimensionality reduction are proposed to handle equation systems with transcendental terms by resultant theory. Then a lower−dimensional system with respect to $\boldsymbol{z}$ and $\boldsymbol{M}$, denoted as P^m, can be generated, which includes the introduced symbols $\boldsymbol{M}$ representing the transcendental terms. The procedure is presented in the left part of Figure 2, as the first part of the proposed method. Thus, these terms can be substituted into $\boldsymbol{M}$ in P^m and a $m−$dimensional equation system with respect to $\boldsymbol{z}$, denoted as $\hat{P}$, can be solved to locate the solution of $\boldsymbol{z}$.

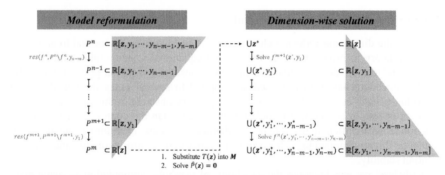

Figure 2. Procedure of the proposed hybrid symbolic-numeric method.

Subsequently, the solution $\boldsymbol{z}^*$ can be substituted into the chosen polynomials in every dimension of y. For example, the chosen polynomial for $y_1−$dimension is denoted as f^{m+1}. By solving $f^{m+1}(\boldsymbol{z}^*, y_1)$, which is a univariate polynomial with respect to y_1, the solution of y_1 can be rooted. The same steps of substitution and polynomial rooting are repeated dimension by dimension from y_1 to y_{n-m}. The all solutions exactly constitute the solution $\boldsymbol{x}^*$ of the origin system $F(\boldsymbol{x}) = 0$ without the dependency on the whole initial value of $\boldsymbol{x}$. The complete procedure of the proposed hybrid symbolic-numeric method is presented in Figure 2. In addition, it can be more stable to solve a lower-dimensional non-linear system while the univariate polynomials dimension by dimension can be solve without much effort.

4. Case study

A case of pressure-enthalpy flash in Figure 3, where n-Hexane (component 1) is separated from n-Octane is adopted to illustrate the hybrid symbolic-numeric method.

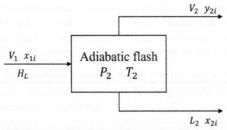

Figure 3. Diagram of pressure-enthalpy flash with involved variables.

The vapor-liquid equilibrium ratios can be determined utilizing the Antoine equation, while the molar enthalpies of individual compounds can be computed through empirical polynomials. Eq. (3) delineates the model for the pressure-enthalpy flash, in which $V_1 = 69$ kmol/h, $x_{11} = 0.331121$, $H_L = 572658$ cal/h and $P_2 = 760$ mm Hg. Noted that the model contains two exponential terms on account of the Antoine equation. By introducing new variables M_1 and M_2 to represent the two exponential terms, Eq. (3) is reformulated into a polynomial equation system.

$$
\begin{cases}
H_{L2} = L_2(51.72x_{21}T_2 + 66.07x_{22}T_2) \\
V_1 - V_2 - L_2 = 0 \\
x_{11}V_1 - L_2x_{21} - V_2x_{21} = 0 \\
x_{21} + x_{22} = 1 \\
y_{21} + y_{22} = 1 \\
y_{21} - \dfrac{10^{\left(6.87776 - \frac{1171.530}{(224.366+T_2)}\right)}}{P_2} \times x_{21} = 0 \\
y_{22} - \dfrac{10^{\left(6.92374 - \frac{1355.126}{(209.517+T_2)}\right)}}{P_2} \times x_{22} = 0 \\
H_{V2} = V_2\left(y_{21}(7678 + 31.83T_2 + 0.0903T_2^2) + y_{22}(10444.7 + 41.836T_2 + 0.1218T_2^2)\right) \\
H_{V2} + H_{L2} = H_L \\
50,0,0,0,0 \leq T_2, x_{21}, y_{21}, x_{22}, y_{22} \leq 150,1,1,1,1 \\
V_2, L_2 \geq 0,0
\end{cases}
\tag{3}
$$

Through computing the resultants based on the reformulated model, an equation with M_1 and M_2 can be generated in T_2-dimension. By substituting the exponential terms represented with M_1 and M_2, the deduced system is essentially an equation with respect to T_2. Due to the exponential terms, the initial value of T_2 have to be specified to solve the equation, which is initially given as 85 °C. Then, once the solution of T_2 is obtained, the other variables can be solved dimension by dimension. Finally, the result is $T_2 = 88.0400$ °C, $x_{21} = 0.474662$, $y_{21} = 0.838120$, $x_{22} = 0.525338$, $y_{22} = 0.161880$, $V_2 = 32.2351$ kmol/h, $L_2 = 36.7931$ kmol/h, $H_{V2} = 380704$ cal/h, $H_{L2} = 191954$ cal/h. In addition, we compare the proposed hybrid symbolic-numeric method with other two methods as presented in Table 1, in which one is applied in SyPSE of our previous work via projection operation of CAD as another hybrid method and the other is a numeric method by iterations.

In contrast to the hybrid method in SyPSE, the proposed approach represents a significant advancement, particularly in the part of symbolic computation, contributed by the computational efficiency of resultant theory. Furthermore, the part of numeric computation by dimension-wise solution is consistent in time consumption. In comparison to purely numeric methods, the enhanced computational efficiency of solving triangularized systems dimension by dimension is noteworthy. Overall, the proposed method not only encompasses additional advantages when compared to existing approaches but also exhibits superior performance in computational efficiency.

Table 1. Time cost comparison of the proposed method with other methods.

Methods	SyPSE (Zhang et al., 2021)		Proposed method		Numeric method[a]
	Projection of CAD	Dimension-wise solution	Resultant theory	Dimension-wise solution	
Time cost	0.186 s	5.92e-4 s	1.37e-3 s	5.92e-4 s	5.23e-3 s
Total cost	0.187 s		1.96e-3 s		5.23e-3 s

a. The numeric method is to invoke "fsolve" function in Python.

5. Conclusions

The primary contribution of this research lies in the development of a hybrid symbolic-numeric method that addresses the inherent deficiencies of traditional numerical approaches. By leveraging resultant theory, the proposed approach offers enhanced solution convergence and reduces reliance on initial value choices. The significance of this lies not only in the realm of theoretical advancements but also in practical applications within PSE.

The methodology is not only theoretically sound but also practical, as demonstrated through its application to the Pressure-Enthalpy flash problem. The results underscore the effectiveness of the proposed approach in providing solutions more robustly. Additionally, the method's utility extends to scenarios involving inequality constraints, showcasing its ability to expedite the elimination of infeasible solutions and thereby enhancing overall computational efficiency.

References

The authors gratefully acknowledge the Fundamental Research Funds for the Central Universities under Grant 226-2023-00109 and the financial support from the National Key Research and Development Program of China (2022YFB3305901).

References

J. Chiasson, L. Tolbert, K. McKenzie, 2003, Control of a Multilevel Converter Using Resultant Theory, IEEE Transactions on Control Systems Technology, 11(3), 345–354.

A. Chtcherba, D. Kapur, 2004, Constructing Sylvester-type resultant matrices using the Dixon formulation, Journal of Symbolic Computation, 38(1), 777-814.

I. Grossmann, A. Westerberg, 2000, Research Challenges in Process Systems Engineering, AIChE Journal, 46(9), 1700–1703.

I. Gelfand, M. Kapranov, A. Zelevinsky, 2008, Discriminants, Resultants, and Multidimensional Determinants, Springer Science & Business Media.

S. Zhang, F. Zhao, C. Zheng, L. Zhu, X. Chen, 2021, SyPSE: A Symbolic Computation Toolbox for Process Systems Engineering Part II—Design for PSE Applications, Ind. Eng. Chem. Res. 60(45), 16317–16329.

Flavio Manenti, Gintaras V. Reklaitis (Eds.), Proceedings of the 34th European Symposium on Computer Aided Process Engineering / 15th International Symposium on Process Systems Engineering (ESCAPE34/PSE24), June 2-6, 2024, Florence, Italy

Scenario Reduction Methods for Risk-Averse Demand Response Scheduling under Price Uncertainty

Sonja H. M. Germscheid,[a,b] Alexander Mitsos,[c,a,d] Manuel Dahmen[a,*]

[a]*Forschungszentrum Jülich GmbH, Institute of Energy and Climate Research, Energy Systems Engineering (IEK-10), Jülich 52425, Germany*
[b]*RWTH Aachen University, Aachen 52062, Germany*
[c]*JARA-CSD, Jülich 52425, Germany*
[d]*RWTH Aachen University, Process Systems Engineering (AVT.SVT), Aachen 52074, Germany*
*m.dahmen@fz-juelich.de

Abstract

Risk-averse demand response scheduling of power-intensive production processes can reduce financial risk resulting from electricity price uncertainty but is computationally expensive. Only few works discuss scenario reduction methods tailored to risk-averse optimization. In this work, we compare four scenario reduction methods from the literature and a heuristic sequential scheduling approach from our prior work. For the comparison, we schedule a continuous process by means of a generalized model for optimal simultaneous participation on both day-ahead and intraday electricity markets where uncertain intraday prices are modeled by a set of scenarios. We evaluate the performance of the scenario reduction methods by comparing cost and risk of the reduced and original problem. We find that k-means clustering outperforms the other three scenario reduction methods. Furthermore, the heuristic sequential scheduling appears best suited for participation on both markets while avoiding a computationally expensive stochastic scheduling.

Keywords: Risk-averse scheduling, scenario reduction, conditional value-at-risk, price uncertainty

1. Introduction

Risk-averse demand response scheduling under price uncertainty has shown great potential to significantly reduce financial risk with a small increase of expected cost in comparison to both risk-neutral stochastic scheduling and deterministic scheduling, see, e.g., Zhang et al. (2016) and Germscheid et al. (2022). In general, the necessary stochastic scheduling is connected to a high computational burden due to the large number of optimization variables arising from the consideration of many scenarios, calling for the use of scenario reduction methods to keep the optimization tractable.

Most scenario reduction approaches focus on *risk-neutral* stochastic programming (SP), i.e., optimization of the expected cost, see, e.g., Heitsch and Römisch (2003). In contrast, only few works (Alkhaleel et al., 2022; Arpón et al., 2018; Fairbrother et al., 2018, 2022; García-Bertrand and Mínguez, 2014; Pineda and Conejo, 2010) discuss scenario reduction methods for *risk-averse* approaches such as minimization of the conditional value-at-risk (CVaR), i.e., the expected cost of a certain percentage of worst-case scenarios. Importantly, while scenario reduction decreases computational times, it can lead to suboptimal solutions and thus a higher risk in risk-averse scheduling compared to the original risk-averse problem. This trade-off calls for a comparison of the existing approaches in the context of a particular application.

We compare four scenario reduction methods from the literature for which implementations are available, i.e., the methods proposed by Heitsch and Römisch (2003), Pineda and Conejo (2010), and Alkhaleel et al. (2022), and k-means clustering (Lloyd, 1982). Additionally, we consider the heuristic sequential scheduling approach proposed in our prior work (Germscheid et al., 2023). We consider the risk-averse demand response scheduling of a generalized, continuous process for simultaneous participation on both day-ahead and intraday electricity markets introduced in Germscheid et al. (2022). Here, day-ahead decisions must be made while intraday electricity prices are subject to uncertainty. We evaluate the performance of the reduction methods by solving the stochastic problem with a reduced set of scenarios and comparing expected cost and risk to the respective solution values of the original risk-averse problem. Note that in Germscheid et al. (2023) we already demonstrated that scenario reduction leads to strong computational benefits and that our proposed sequential scheduling is faster than the stochastic scheduling.

The remainder of this paper is structured as follows: In Section 2, we review existing risk-averse scenario reduction approaches. In Section 3, we specify our evaluation approach. In Section 4, we compare the reduction methods and Section 5 concludes the findings.

2. Risk-averse scenario reduction methods

Risk-neutral scenario reduction can be based on probability distances, i.e., metrics that describe the closeness between probability distributions. Dupačová et al. (2003) suggest choosing scenarios such that the probability distance of the original and the reduced set of scenarios is minimal:

$$\hat{\mu}_c(P, \tilde{P}) = \min_{\eta_{i,j}} \sum_{i=1}^{N} \sum_{j=1}^{M} c(p_i, \tilde{p}_j) \eta_{i,j}$$

$$s.t. \left\{ \eta_{i,j} \geq 0, \sum_{i=1}^{N} \eta_{i,j} = \pi_j, \sum_{j=1}^{M} \eta_{i,j} = \tilde{\pi}_j \right\} \quad \forall \, i,j \tag{1}$$

In Eq. (1), $\hat{\mu}_c(P, \tilde{P})$ is the optimal distance for the probability distributions $P = \sum_{i=1}^{N} \pi_i \delta_{p_i}$ and $\tilde{P} = \sum_{i=1}^{M} \tilde{\pi}_i \delta_{\tilde{p}_i}$, with scenarios $\{p_1, \ldots, p_N\}$ and $\{\tilde{p}_1, \ldots, \tilde{p}_M\}$ and probabilities π_i and $\tilde{\pi}_i$, respectively. δ_p denotes the Dirac measure. The function $c(p_i, \tilde{p}_j)$ is continuous, symmetric, and gives $c(p, \tilde{p}) = 0$ iff $p = \tilde{p}$. The optimization variables $\eta_{i,j}$ add up to the probabilities π_i and $\tilde{\pi}_i$, respectively. Based on the probability distance, Heitsch and Römisch (2003) suggest algorithms for scenario reduction with implementations available in the tools SCENRED and SCENRED2 of GAMS (GAMS Development Corporation, 2022). In the following, we refer to the approach of Heitsch and Römisch (2003) as *risk-neutral approach*.

Risk-averse SP can be tackled with minimization of CVaR, i.e., the expected cost of the $(1 - \alpha)$ worst-case scenarios (Rockafellar and Uryasev, 2000, 2002):

$$\min_{x_i, \Psi, \phi_i} \text{CVaR} \quad s.t. \quad \text{CVaR} = \psi + \sum_{i=1}^{N} \frac{\pi_i \phi_i}{(1 - \alpha)}, \{f(x_i, p_i) - \psi \leq \phi_i, \phi_i \geq 0\} \, \forall i \tag{2}$$

In Eq. (2), CVaR is determined for the confidence level α and the objective function f with the decision variables x_i, the continuous auxiliary variables ϕ_i and ψ, and N scenarios p_i. Note that only the $(1 - \alpha)$ worst-case scenarios have non-zero values for ϕ_i, i.e., they affect the objective value.

Pineda and Conejo (2010) and Alkhaleel et al. (2022) tailored scenario reduction to *risk-averse* SP by adjusting the probability distance-based reduction approach. Specifically, Pineda and Conejo (2010) suggested to replace the scenarios $\{p_1, \dots, p_N\}$ in the probability distance with information from the expectation of expected value (EEV) solution that is obtained by optimizing with a mean-valued scenario followed by solving the original problem with fixed first-stage decisions. To this end, they used values of the auxiliary variables $\{\phi_1, \dots, \phi_N\}$ of the EEV solution. Apart from that, Pineda and Conejo (2010) used the scenario reduction of Heitsch and Römisch (2003) to solve the risk-averse problem. In contrast, Alkhaleel et al. (2022) suggested to apply the scenario reduction of Heitsch and Römisch (2003) to a pre-selected set of scenarios, i.e., the $(1 - \alpha)$-worst case scenarios of the wait-and-see (WS) solution that is obtained by optimizing the scenarios separately assuming perfect foresight. Consequently, they assumed that the reduced set would represent only worst-case scenarios and applied risk-neutral SP in the final step as suggested by García-Bertrand and Mínguez (2014). In the following, we refer to the approaches of Pineda and Conejo (2010) and Alkhaleel et al. (2022) as *EEV-based* and *WS-based approach*, respectively.

It should be noted that further risk-averse reduction methods have been proposed, i.e., by García-Bertrand and Mínguez (2014), Arpón et al. (2018), and Fairbrother et al. (2018, 2022). These approaches build on repeatably solving the stochastic program with a small subset of scenarios. However, the respective algorithm implementations are not publicly available and thus considered beyond the scope of this paper.

3. Model specification and evaluation approaches

For comparison, we consider the generalized continuous process introduced by Schäfer et al. (2020) that considers generalized process characteristics, i.e., oversizing, minimal part load, ramping, storage capacity, efficiency losses, and temporary shutdowns. As introduced in Germscheid et al. (2022), we optimize the demand response scheduling considering simultaneous market participation on both the day-ahead and the intraday electricity market, i.e., considering known day-ahead and uncertain intraday electricity prices. For the analysis, we consider the same reference process and the same 201 intraday price scenarios as in Germscheid et al. (2022). We solve the stochastic program by means of the deterministic equivalent and Gurobi 9.1.1 with default settings on an Intel Core i7-9700 processor and 32GB RAM. For CVaR, we consider the confidence level $\alpha = 0.9$. For probability distance-based scenario reduction, we use the fast forward scenario reduction by Heitsch and Römisch (2003) implemented in SCENRED2 by GAMS (GAMS Development Corporation, 2022).

We compare the approaches listed in Table 1. As a further reduction approach, we consider k-means clustering using the scikit-learn module in Python (Pedregosa et al., 2011). Additionally, we compare the stochastic scheduling to a heuristic approach that we have previously introduced (Germscheid et al., 2023) and that is tailored to the simultaneous market participation. In particular, our heuristic sequential day-ahead and intraday scheduling optimizes the day-ahead schedule neglecting the intraday market and then solves the original problem with fixed day-ahead decisions. Thus, the sequential scheduling results in improved or equal expected cost and financial risk compared to day-ahead-only scheduling and simultaneously avoids the computational cost of the stochastic scheduling. In contrast, scenario reduction methods cannot guarantee such a specific upper bound of expected cost or risk but they can be applied to any stochastic problem.

Similar to our prior work (Germscheid et al., 2023), we evaluate the reduction methods by, first, solving the stochastic problem with the reduced set of scenarios, followed by an optimization of the stochastic program with the full set of scenarios but fixed first-stage decisions. We compare the results of the reduced problem to the results of the full problem, i.e., the original problem optimizing the CVaR with the full set of scenarios, by evaluating the relative differences in the CVaR. Additionally, we evaluate the relative difference in expected cost of the reduced compared to the full problem. Note that the expected cost is not the objective of the risk-averse problem but a key measure to evaluate the profitability of scheduling under uncertainty.

Table 1: Overview of the considered methods.

Reduction methods with use of stochastic scheduling	
Risk-neutral approach	Probability distance-based reduction by Heitsch and Römisch (2003) using the distance of intraday electricity price scenarios
Risk-averse EEV-based approach	Probability distance-based reduction by Pineda and Conejo (2010) using the distance of auxiliary variable ϕ_s of EEV solution
Risk-averse WS-based approach	Probability distance-based reduction by Alkhaleel et al. (2022) using distance of scenario cost of $(1 - \alpha)$ worst-case WS solutions
K-means clustering	Use centroids from clustering as scenarios
Sequential scheduling	See Germscheid et al. (2023)

4. Results

Figure 1 shows the relative difference in CVaR and relative difference in expected cost of all methods compared to the full problem. A positive value of either measure indicates an impairment of CVaR or expected cost, respectively, due to the scenario reduction. Note that an improvement of expected cost, i.e., a negative value, is possible at the cost of an impaired risk. Furthermore, note that for risk-neutral and EEV-based reduction, SCENRED2 of GAMS reduces the 201 original scenario to at most 126 scenarios due to an automatic reduction of SCRENRED2. In case of WS-based reduction, there are at most 20 scenarios due to the pre-selection of the worst-case scenarios.

Figure 1 reveals that for risk-neutral reduction, the difference in risk shows a monotonic trend, i.e., with an increasing number of scenarios the difference asymptotically approaches zero. In contrast, the EEV-based approach shows a pronounced kink for a reduced set with 25 scenarios leading to a significant impairment of both risk and expected cost. The WS-based approach shows an overall large difference in risk and is outperformed by both the k-means clustering and the risk-neutral reduction. Interestingly, k-means clustering has the lowest difference in expected cost and risk compared to the other reduction methods. It, however, shows an erratic behavior with respect to the difference in expected cost.

Figure 1a) -1d) show the relative difference in CVaR and expected cost of the sequential scheduling by means of a dashed line. Sequential scheduling and risk-averse stochastic scheduling are very similar with respect to both measures, i.e., the relative difference of both CVaR and expected cost is rather low in comparison to the other reduction methods. This behavior can be explained by similar day-ahead purchases, i.e., first-stage decisions, for both risk-averse scheduling and sequential scheduling, which were already noted in Germscheid et al. (2022).

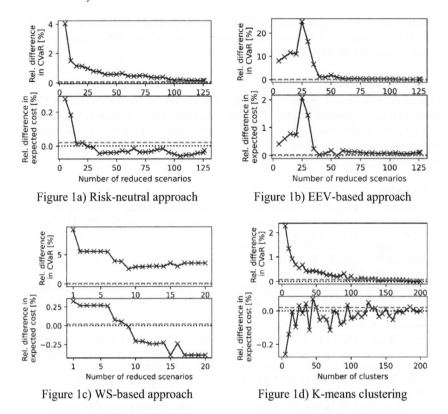

Figure 1a) Risk-neutral approach

Figure 1b) EEV-based approach

Figure 1c) WS-based approach

Figure 1d) K-means clustering

Figure 1: Comparison of the reduction methods: Figures a) to d) each consider a scenario reduction method. Each subfigure shows both the difference in CVaR (upper part) and in expected cost (lower part) of the reduction methods relative to the solutions of the original risk-averse problem. In all figures, the dashed lines correspond to the relative difference in CVaR and in expected cost, respectively, of the sequential scheduling approach introduced in Germscheid et al. (2023). Additionally, each figure contains a dotted, horizontal line at value zero for visual guidance.

Overall, k-means clustering leads to the lowest difference in both expected cost and risk compared to the other reduction methods. Compared to all reduction methods, the sequential scheduling shows particularly low differences in both expected cost and risk and appears to be a promising heuristic to bound financial risk and expected cost for this particular application.

5. Discussion and conclusion

In this work, four scenario reduction methods are compared for risk-averse stochastic demand response scheduling of a power-intensive process for combined day-ahead and intraday electricity market participation. Additionally, the previously introduced sequential day-ahead and intraday scheduling approach is considered. In the case study, the heuristic risk-averse reduction methods are outperformed by risk-neutral scenario reduction and k-means clustering. Furthermore, the sequential scheduling approach yields expected cost and CVaR that are very similar to those of the original problem due to highly similar day-ahead decisions.

6. Acknowledgment

This work was funded by the Helmholtz Association of German Research Centers through program-oriented funding (PoF) and under the grant *Uncertainty Quantification – From Data to Reliable Knowledge (UQ)* (grant number: ZT-I-0029). This work was performed as part of the *Helmholtz School for Data Science in Life, Earth and Energy* (HDS-LEE).

References

B.A. Alkhaleel, H. Liao, K.M. Sullivan, 2022, Risk and resilience-based optimal post-disruption restoration for critical infrastructures under uncertainty, Eur. J. Oper. Res. 296, 174–202.

S. Arpón, T. Homem-de-Mello, B. Pagnoncelli, 2018, Scenario reduction for stochastic programs with Conditional Value-at-Risk, Math. Program. 170, 327–356.

J. Dupačová, N. Gröwe-Kuska, W. Römisch, 2003, Scenario reduction in stochastic programming. Math. Program. 95(3), 493–511.

J. Fairbrother, A. Turner, S.W. Wallace, 2018, Scenario generation for single-period portfolio selection problems with tail risk measures: Coping with high dimensions and integer variables, INFORMS J. Comput. 30, 472–491.

J. Fairbrother, A. Turner, S.W. Wallace, 2022, Problem-driven scenario generation: An analytical approach for stochastic programs with tail risk measure. Math. Program. 191(1):141–182.

GAMS Development Corporation, 2022. General algebraic modeling system (GAMS) release 40.4.0, accessed 25th Oct 2022. https://www.gams.com/download/.

R. García-Bertrand, R. Mínguez, 2014, Iterative scenario based reduction technique for stochastic optimization using conditional value-at-risk, Optim. Eng. 15, 355–380.

S.H.M. Germscheid, A. Mitsos, M. Dahmen, 2022, Demand response potential of industrial processes considering uncertain short-term electricity prices, AIChE J. 68, e17828.

S.H.M. Germscheid, F.T.C. Röben, H. Sun, A. Bardow, A. Mitsos, M. Dahmen, 2023, Demand response scheduling of copper production under short-term electricity price uncertainty, Comput. Chem. Eng., 108394.

H. Heitsch, W. Römisch, 2003, Scenario reduction algorithms in stochastic programming. Comput. Optim. Appl. 24(2):187–206.

S. Lloyd, 1982, Least squares quantization in PCM, IEEE Trans. Inf. Theory. 28, 129–137.

F. Pedregosa, G. Varoquaux, A. Gramfort, V. Michel, B. Thirion, O. Grisel, M. Blondel, P. Prettenhofer, R. Weiss, V. Dubourg, J. Vanderplas, A. Passos, D. Cournapeau, M. Brucher, M. Perrot, E. Duchesnay, 2011. Scikit-learn: Machine learning in Python. J Mach Learn Res 12, 2825–283

S. Pineda, A.J. Conejo, 2010, Scenario reduction for risk-averse electricity trading, IET Gener. Transm. Distrib. 4, 694.

R. T. Rockafellar, S. Uryasev, 2000, Optimization of conditional value-at-risk, J. Risk 2(3), 21–41.

R. T. Rockafellar, S. Uryasev, 2002, Conditional value-at-risk for general loss distributions, J. Bank. Financ. 26(7), 1443–1471.

P. Schäfer, T.M. Daun, A. Mitsos, 2020, Do investments in flexibility enhance sustainability? A simulative study considering the German electricity sector, AIChE J. 66, 1–14.

Q. Zhang, J.L. Cremer, I.E. Grossmann, A. Sundaramoorthy, J.M. Pinto, 2016, Risk-based integrated production scheduling and electricity procurement for continuous power-intensive processes, Comput. Chem. Eng. 86, 90–105.

Flavio Manenti, Gintaras V. Reklaitis (Eds.), Proceedings of the 34th European Symposium on Computer Aided Process Engineering / 15th International Symposium on Process Systems Engineering (ESCAPE34/PSE24), June 2-6, 2024, Florence, Italy

Hybrid Optimization Strategy Applied to an Industrial Natural Gas Processing Plant

Roymel R. Carpio[a,*], Carlos R. Paiva[a], Thamires A. L. Guedes[a], Bruno V. Pinho[a], Tayná E. G. Souza[b], Letícia C. Santos[b], Leonardo D. Ribeiro[b], Argimiro R. Secchi[a]

*a*Chemical Engineering Program, COPPE, Universidade Federal do Rio de Janeiro (UFRJ), Rio de Janeiro - RJ, Brazil
*b*Petróleo Brasileiro S.A. (PETROBRAS), Rio de Janeiro - RJ, Brazil
*roymel@peq.coppe.ufrj.br

Abstract

This study introduces an integrated simulation and hybrid optimization framework to identify the optimal operating condition for an industrial natural gas processing plant. To achieve this goal, a comprehensive simulation of the plant was developed in Aspen Hysys. A bidirectional communication connection between Aspen Hysys and Python was established to automate and oversee the optimization framework. The adopted optimization strategy comprises two sequential stages: (1) Global optimization employing the Particle Swarm Optimization method to identify a promising region near to the global optimum and (2) Local optimization with the Powell method to fine-tune the results obtained from the preceding global optimization stage. Surrogate Gradient Boosting models for both the objective function and constraints were developed, training them using data derived from process simulations. During the global optimization phase, these surrogate models were employed instead of running Aspen Hysys simulations. In contrast, the local optimization stage employed Aspen Hysys simulations to ensure that the final optimal solution adheres to all the constraints. The optimization problem involves five decision variables, an economic objective function and five inequality constraints. Meanwhile, the Aspen Hysys simulation ensures the fulfillment of equality constraints by accounting for the physical and chemical equations governing the process. The hybrid optimization proved to be more efficient compared to isolated approaches for several reasons: (1) when applying only the local optimization method, the outcome resulted in a local optimum with a less favorable objective function value; (2) employing just the global optimization method led to a near-global optimum, but with a lower objective function value than that achieved by the combined strategy; and (3) the utilization of surrogate models during the global optimization stage reduced computing time by over 78 %.

Keywords: global optimization, gradient boosting, surrogate optimization.

1. Introduction

Natural gas processing facilities receive raw natural gas from oil extraction platforms and produce mainly three products: (1) Sales Gas (SG), (2) Liquefied Petroleum Gas (LPG), and (3) a stream with components heavier than C4 (C5+). The market conditions, especially sale prices, for each of these products are highly dynamic, often resulting in a shift of the most valued from one product to another. This frequently changing behaviour on sale prices in addition to the operational possibility of prioritizing the production of some products could often lead to suboptimal operating conditions. Hence, it is crucial to adeptly adjust the operational parameters of the plant in response to the prevailing market conditions (Souza et al., 2023).

Some previous studies have dealing with optimization on natural gas processing plants (Bullin and Hall, 2000; Bullin and Chipps, 2005; Zheng et al., 2010; Campos et al., 2012; Sobhi and Elkamel, 2015; Zhang et al., 2016; Souza at al., 2023), however none of them assessed the using of surrogate models during the global optimization stage. In this work, a hybrid global - local optimization framework, which considers surrogate models for the global optimization stage is proposed.

2. Methodology

2.1. Process modelling and simulation

The natural gas processing plant was modelled and simulated using Aspen Hysys considering first principles and steady state approaches. The simulation encompasses two key units: a Dew Point Plant (DPP), responsible for receiving the vapour phase from the slug catchers, and a Liquid Fractionating Unit (LFU), which handled the condensate from slug catchers, as well as the lighter condensate from the DPP. In addition to the primary condensate transfer line from DPP to LFU, another interconnection exists between these units in the form of recycle gas streams that flows from the LFU to the DPP. Therefore, both units are highly interdependent, as depicted in Figure 1.

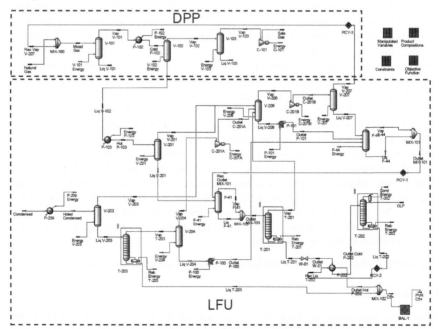

Figure 1. Aspen Hysys PFD of the natural gas processing plant.

Auxiliary units like the propane refrigeration cycle were deliberated excluded from the simulation, since the target of this study is the overall optimization of the plant. Consequently, the limitations of these auxiliary units were considered as operating constraints in the optimization problem. The unit operations considered on the process simulation are mainly: distillations columns, flash separators, heat exchangers, compressors and pumps. A total of 16 distinct components were included in the simulation: 14 alkanes (ranging from methane to n-dodecane, accounting for both normal and iso forms), nitrogen and carbon dioxide. While Peng-Robinson equation of state was employed as the thermodynamic model.

The operating conditions used for the base case simulation are based on the average values observed during a 60 minutes period on January 28, 2023, along with was detected an approximated steady-state condition of the plant.

2.2. Process optimization framework

After a pre-screening process, to identify controlled variables with certain flexibility on setpoint, and a local sensitivity analysis, to pinpoint the most influential variables, five operating variables were selected as decision variables for the optimization problem. In addition to the setting bounds for the decision variables, additional five quality constraints were considered. The codification and description of decision variables and inequality constraints are outlined in Table 1. It is worth mentioning that the equality constraints of the optimization problem, accounting for mass and energy balances and constitutive relations, are guaranteed by the Aspen Hysys simulation.

Table 1. Decision variables and inequality constraints of the optimization problem

Code	Decision variables	Code	Inequality constraints
x_1	Temp. on separation vessel of LRU	C_1	Methane in SG
x_2	Bottom temp. of deethanizer column	C_2	Ethane in LPG
x_3	Bottom temp. of debutanizer column	C_3	Ethane/Pentanes ratio in LPG
x_4	Bottom temp. of stabilizer column	C_4	Pentanes in LPG
x_5	Reflux ratio of debutanizer column	C_5	Reid vapour pressure in C5+

The objective function (OF) in this context aims to maximize economic profit. This profit is defined as the total income generated from the sale of various products, subtracting the associated expenses, which encompass operating costs such as electricity and fuel gas (see Equation 1).

$$Profit = \sum_{i=1}^{NP} [LHV_i \, F_i \, P_i] - [E_{cons} E_{cost} + F_{cons} F_{cost}] \tag{1}$$

where NP is the number of products (1 for SG, 2 for LPG, and 3 for C5+); LHV is the lower heating value [MMbtu/kmol] and F is the molar flowrate [kmol/h] of the product stream; P is the sale price [$/MMbtu] of the specific product; E_{cons} and E_{cost} are the consumption [kW] and cost [$/(kW.h)] of electricity; F_{cons} and F_{cost} are the consumption [MMbtu/h] and cost [$/MMbtu] of fuel gas.

The intrinsic non-linearity of the process model and the existence of several non-linear constraints generated non-convexities. Thus, the use of a global optimization algorithm is recommended to avoid get trapped on a local optimum near to the base case. On the other hand, applying global optimization on rigorous model simulations is typically computational-time expensive. For that reason, a hybrid optimization strategy was adopted. This strategy comprises two sequential stages: (1) global optimization using surrogate models, to fast identification of a promising region containing the global optimum and (2) local optimization utilizing the rigorous simulation to fine-tune the results obtained from the preceding global optimization stage while ensuring that the final optimal solution adheres to all the constraints.

Gradient Boosting models (Friedman, 2001) of the objective function and the constraints were trained using data derived from 100 process simulations. Then, these surrogate models were employed with Particle Swarm Optimization (PSO) algorithm (Kennedy and Eberhart, 1995) in the global optimization stage. On the other hand, Powell method (Powell, 1964) was applied direct into the simulation for the local optimization. A penalized objective function was defined for considering the quality and operational inequality constraints.

The optimization framework, which is totally automated by a Python script, including a bidirectional communication connection with Aspen Hysys, is depicted in Figure 2.

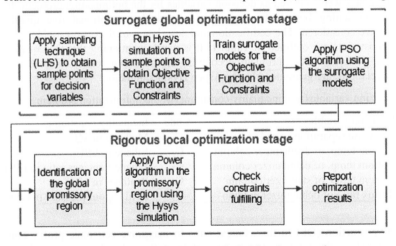

Figure 2. Schematic representation of the optimization framework.

3. Results and discussion

In order to asses the advantages of the proposed hybrid optimization framework, the result of isolated local/global approaches are shown on Table 2. Notice that the results achieved by the isolated local optimization correspond to a local optimum far from the optimum found by the isolate global optimization. It is worth to mention the relatively high computational time demanded by the global optimization since it is acting directly on the Aspen Hysys simulation. Summarizing the results of Table 2, the local optimization algorithm was trapped by a local optimum and the global optimization algorithm probably found a near global optimum but with a high computational cost.

Considering these findings, the proposed hybrid strategy was applied to solve the optimization problem, achieving the results detailed on Table 3. Notice that the time for the global optimization was reduced in more than 78 % by using surrogate models. It is worth mentioning that the reported time involves the whole process, i.e., running 100 simulations for obtaining the training data, train the surrogate models and executed the surrogated global optimization itself. Despite off the OF value in this case was lower than the obtained by the rigorous global optimization, it corresponds to a promising region near to the global optimum and was used as an initial guess for the local optimization stage.

Table 2. Optimization results when using isolated approaches

Code	Type	UoM	Base Case	Rigorous Local Optim.	Rigorous Global Optim.	LB	UB
x_1^a	Decision	-	0.56	0.04	0.02	0	1
x_2^a	Decision	-	0.61	0.66	0.36	0	1
x_3^a	Decision	-	0.52	0.03	0.45	0	1
x_4^a	Decision	-	0.53	0.65	0.61	0	1
x_5^a	Decision	-	0.46	0.38	0.33	0	1
OF^a	Objective	-	100	102.47	102.87	-	-
C_1	Constraint	% mol	82.08	83.02	83.33	80	-
C_2	Constraint	% vol	10.69	8.21	11.98	-	12
C_3	Constraint	-	6.565	12.36	10.23	-	16
C_4	Constraint	% vol	1.628	0.66	1.17	-	2
C_5	Constraint	kPa	60.13	74.88	61.63	-	76
Time	-	s	-	66.81	458.23	-	-

[a]In order to preserve proprietary information, the profit and decision variables are normalized.

Table 3. Optimization results when applying the hybrid strategy

Code	Type	UoM	Base Case	Surrogate Global Optim.	Rigorous Local Optim.	LB	UB
x_1^a	Decision	-	0.56	0.03	0.02	0	1
x_2^a	Decision	-	0.61	0.51	0.44	0	1
x_3^a	Decision	-	0.52	0.06	0.00	0	1
x_4^a	Decision	-	0.53	0.82	0.67	0	1
x_5^a	Decision	-	0.46	0.20	0.24	0	1
OF^a	Objective	-	100	102.72 [b]	102.88	-	-
C_1	Constraint	% mol	82.08	83.19 [b]	83.26	80	-
C_2	Constraint	% vol	10.69	10.31 [b]	11.15	-	12
C_3	Constraint	-	6.565	7.16 [b]	10.55	-	16
C_4	Constraint	% vol	1.628	1.44 [b]	1.06	-	2
C_5	Constraint	kPa	60.13	72.23 [b]	75.56	-	76
Time	-	s	-	97.46	76.57	-	-

[a]In order to preserve proprietary information, the profit and decision variables are normalized.
[b]Values obtained by Hysys simulation using the solution of the surrogate global optimization.

In this case, the result of the surrogate global optimization fulfilled all the constraints, but it is not guaranteed for all the cases. Therefore, the rigorous local optimization stage is necessary.

Notice that the final optimum obtained by the hybrid strategy was better, and represent 2.88 % improvement on profit. In addition, the total time consumption of the proposed framework was 174.03 s, a 62 % lower than the computational time demanded by the isolated rigorous global optimization.

4. Conclusions

The hybrid optimization framework demonstrated to be robust and efficient, successfully finding a feasible operating condition that improves the objective function on approximately 2.9 %. It has proven to be more efficient compared to isolated approaches for several compelling reasons: (1) when applying only the local optimization method, the outcome resulted in a local optimum with a less favourable objective function value; (2) employing just the global optimization method led to a near-global optimum, but with a lower objective function value than that achieved by the combined strategy; and (3) the utilization of surrogate models during the global optimization stage substantially reduced computing time by over 78 %.

Acknowledgements

Financial support from Petróleo Brasileiro S.A. (PETROBRAS) is gratefully acknowledged.

References

S. A. Al-Sobhi, A. Elkamel, 2015. Simulation and optimization of natural gas processing and production network consisting of LNG, GTL, and methanol facilities. J. Nat. Gas Sci. Eng. 23 (2015), 500–508.

K. A. Bullin, J. Chipps, 2005. Optimization of natural gas gathering systems and gas plants. In: Proceedings of the GPA Annual Convention Proceedings. ISSN: 00968870.

K. A. Bullin, K. R. Hall, 2000. Optimization of natural gas processing plants including business aspects. In: Proceedings of the GPA Annual Convention Proceedings, pp. 1–12. ISSN: 00968870.

M. Campos, M. Gomes, A. Souza, A. Barros, 2012. Optimisation of natural gas plant – Gains in profitability, stability and energy efficiency. In: Proceedings of the International Gas Union World Gas Conference Papers, 3, pp. 2089–2120.

J. Kennedy, R. Eberhart, 1995, Particle swarm optimization. IEEE International Conference on Neural Networks - Conference Proceedings, 4, pp. 1942-1948.

M. J. D. Powell, 1964. An efficient method for finding the minimum of a function of several variables without calculating derivatives. The Computer Journal 7: 155-162.

T. E. G. Souza, A. R. Secchi, L. C. Santos, 2023, Modeling and economic optimization of an industrial site for natural gas processing: A nonlinear optimization approach, Digital Chemical Engineering, 6, 100070.

B. J. Zhang, Q. L. Chen, J. Li, C. A. Floudas, 2016. Operational strategy and planning for raw natural gas refining complexes: process modeling and global optimization. AIChE J. 63 (2), 652–668.

Q. P. Zheng, S. Rebennack, N. A. Iliadis, P. M. Pardalos, 2010. Optimization models in the natural gas industry. Handbook of power systems I, energy systems. Springer, Berlin, pp. 121–148.

J. Friedman, 2001. Greedy Function Approximation: A Gradient Boosting Machine, The Annals of Statistics, Vol. 29, No. 5.

Flavio Manenti, Gintaras V. Reklaitis (Eds.), Proceedings of the 34th European Symposium on Computer Aided Process Engineering / 15th International Symposium on Process Systems Engineering (ESCAPE34/PSE24), June 2-6, 2024, Florence, Italy
© 2024 Elsevier B.V. All rights reserved. http://dx.doi.org/10.1016/B978-0-443-28824-1.50540-8

Multi-Parametric Programming for Design Space Identification

Simon Walsh[a†], Steven Sachio[a†], Cleo Kontoravdi[a], Diogo Narciso[b] , Maria M. Papathanasiou[a*]

[a]The Sargent Centre for Process Systems Engineering, Department of Chemical Engineering, Imperial College London, South Kensington Campus, London SW7 2AZ, UK

[b]Departamento de Engenharia Química, Instituto Superior Técnico, Universidade de Lisboa, Lisboa 1049-001, Portugal

*Corresponding author: maria.papathanasiou11@imperial.ac.uk
†These authors contributed equally to this work.

Abstract

Process design is often a challenging task that involves conflicting objectives. To ensure that processes operate within specifications and to accelerate their development, a design space (DSp) can be identified. The DSp is composed by combinations of operating and design decisions that yield a feasible operation. In this work, we present a model-based framework that employs multi-parametric programming for the identification of the DSp. The methodology is applied to the case study of a batch reactor design. The results are compared to the identification of the DSp via quasi-random sampling and the role of the fidelity of the process model in the identification of an accurate DSp is discussed.

Keywords: Design Space Identification, Multi-parametric Programming, Industry 4.0.

1. Introduction

Process and unit operation design is often challenged by the combination of conflicting objectives and underlying trade-offs with respect to target Key Performance Indicators (KPIs). Feasibility analysis (Grossmann et al., 2014) can be used as a tool to identify a region within which all performance and feasibility constraints are satisfied, also known as the design space (DSp). DSp identification has been an open challenge for the Process Systems Engineering (PSE) community, approached using various methods that include surrogate modelling (Geremia et al., 2023), (adaptive) sampling (Kusumo et al., 2019, Sachio et al., 2023) and probabilistic approaches (Kucherenko et al., 2020). All such approaches exhibit great potential in providing a systematic approach to explore and identify feasible design spaces, guiding process development. Most of such approaches are dependent to the generation of an informed dataset that will provide the basis for the classification of candidate operating points and, therefore, a feasible design space. This can often result into increased computational complexity, particularly in cases where nonlinear models are used.

Bansal et al. (2004) presented a methodology whereby process uncertainty can be integrated in the design and synthesis problem through flexibility analysis via parametric approaches. In this work, we harness the advantages of multi-parametric programming (mp-P) (Pistikopoulos, 2009) to develop a framework for design space identification. The capabilities of the methodology are assessed through a reactor design case study and results are compared to a previously published approach based on quasi-random sampling (Sachio et al., 2023).

2. The framework

The multi-parametric Design Space (mp-DSp) framework provides a rigorous methodology for model-based identification of multi-dimensional design spaces. A schematic representation of the multi-parametric Design Space (mp-DSp) framework is shown in Figure 1.

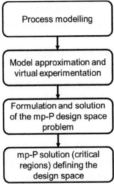

Figure 1 Multi-parametric Design Space (mp-DSp) framework

2.1. Step 1: Process modelling

The framework relies on the use of validated, high-fidelity process models that describe the unit operation(s) of interest. Such models most commonly comprise nonlinear ordinary or partial differential and algebraic equations ((P)DAEs) and can be simulated in any high-level environment, such as Python, gPROMS® ModelBuilder and MATLAB®.

2.2. Step 2: Model approximation and virtual experimentation

In this step, the high-fidelity model developed in Step 1 is linearised to harness the potential of linear mp-P and leverage its computational efficiency (Pistikopoulos 2009). For this, the expensive high-fidelity model is sampled within its validation region and a range of interest. In this case, quasi-random Sobol sampling is employed. The resulting dataset is used for the development of a discrete, linear state-space model. Equations 1 & 2 summarise the general formulation, where x, u, and y are the states, inputs, and outputs respectively, t equates to time, and T_s is the sample time. A, B, and C denote the matrices of the state-space model.

$$x(t + T_s) = Ax(t) + Bu(t) \tag{1}$$

$$y(t) = Cx(t) \tag{2}$$

2.3. Step 3: Formulation and solution of the mp-P design space problem

Step 3 is focused on the formulation and the solution of the mp-P problem that will determine the feasible design space. Here, we reformulate the traditional mp-P problem (Equations 3-9) and define θ as the set of design variables and/or uncertain system parameters. This will allow the mp-P solution (critical regions) to be expressed as a function of the manipulated (design) variables. This enables direct identification of the possible design space(s) as every critical region of the mp-P solution will be meeting the pre-specified constraints.

$$obj \qquad z(\theta) = \min_x f(x, \theta) \tag{3}$$

$$s.t \qquad x_{SS}(t + T_s) = Ax_{SS}(t) + B\theta(t) \tag{4}$$

$$\text{KPI}(t) = Cx_{SS}(t) \tag{5}$$

$$g(x, \theta) \leq 0 \tag{6}$$

$$h(x, \theta) = 0 \tag{7}$$

$$x \in \mathbb{R}^n \tag{8}$$

$$\theta \in \mathbb{R}^n \tag{9}$$

The linear state-space model from Step 2 is introduced in the mp-P problem as a set of equality constraints (Equations 4, 5). For this, the parameters of the state-space model are discretised over a chosen number of time steps. The density of the discretisation interval is user-specific and can be assessed based on the performance of the state-space model and system dynamics. However, it is noted that the computational complexity will increase when using a higher number of time steps. Slack variables are introduced in the system to calculate the constraint violations and are appended to the equality constraint matrices. For the state constraint matrices, the rows correspond to the variables, while the columns correspond to equations. To define the parameter space constraints, both the constraint matrix and the constant terms need to be specified. The optimisation variable is selected by assigning the linear cost term to the associated row in the cost vector. A linear objective function in terms of x and θ is defined. The purpose of this formulation is to get the DSp boundary projected onto the critical region. Therefore, the degrees of freedom in the mp-P formulation are equal to the size of theta (design variables). The resulting multi-parametric problem is solved via standard multi-parametric techniques, using the POP Toolbox in MATLAB® (Oberdieck et al., 2016).

3. The system case

The mp-DSp framework's capabilities are tested on the exemplar case study (Kucherenko et al., 2020) of a single batch reactor.

3.1. Step 1: Process modelling

The reactor is assumed to be of fixed volume and initially contains 1 m³ of component a, at a concentration of 2000 mol/m³. The objective is to produce product b from the following sequential reaction: $2a \xrightarrow{k_1} b \xrightarrow{k_2} c$. Equations 10-13 describe the dynamic model used in this case, whereby C_a, C_b, C_c are the concentrations of components a, b, and c respectively, τ and t_f are the process time and the final process time, k_j is the rate of reaction, E_j and Ai_j are the activation energy and the Arrhenius constant $\forall$ reaction $j = 1, 2$, R and T are the real gas constant and the process temperature, respectively.

$$\frac{dC_a}{d\tau} = t_f \cdot (-2 \cdot k_1 \cdot C_a^2) \tag{10}$$

$$\frac{dC_b}{d\tau} = t_f \cdot (k_1 \cdot C_a^2 - k_2 \cdot C_b) \tag{11}$$

$$\frac{dC_c}{d\tau} = t_f \cdot (k_2 \cdot C_b) \tag{12}$$

$$k_j = Ai_j \cdot e^{-\frac{E_j}{R \cdot T}}, j = 1,2 \tag{13}$$

The Ordinary Differential Equation (ODE) high-fidelity model (Equations 10-13) was simulated in MATLAB®, assuming: $E_1 = 20786.7$ J/mol, $E_2 = 41570.8$ J/mol, $Ai_1 = 0.0641$, $Ai_2 = 9938.1$. In this example, we identify two critical variables that impact the process performance; namely the temperature (T), and batch time (t_f) ranging 250-300 K and 250-350 min, respectively. We aim to identify a design space that will guarantee end-point component concentrations as follows: $C_a(t_f) \leq 185$ mol/m³, $C_b(t_f) \geq 790$ mol/m³, and $C_c(t_f) \leq 140$ mol/m³.

3.2. Step 2: Model approximation and virtual experimentation

The first step for the development of a linear, state space model is the generation of representative dataset. For this, the ODE model described in Step 1 was used as virtual experimentation platform for the generation of 1023 points via quasi-random Sobol sequence. Temperature and batch time were used as inputs and varied within a range of interest ($250 \leq T \leq 300$ and $250 \leq t_f \leq 350$) and the performance of the outputs (C_a, C_b, C_c) (KPIs) was monitored. The state space model followed the general format (Equations 1 and 2) and was created using the N4SID algorithm in MATLAB®. The final formulation comprises 6 states, with discretisation interval (T_s) of 3.5 min and the matrices (A, B, C) are displayed below.

$$A = \begin{bmatrix} 0.9598 & 0.004636 & -0.295 & -0.06569 & 0.1435 & -0.06415 \\ 0.09091 & 0.9325 & 1.745 & 0.4652 & -1.031 & 0.2766 \\ 0.00316 & 0.006644 & 0.8843 & -0.03831 & 0.03784 & -0.00751 \\ 0.005993 & -0.004314 & 0.08404 & 1.027 & -0.07491 & 0.007813 \\ -0.02049 & -0.0183 & 0.1308 & 0.0654 & 0.8188 & -0.03611 \\ -01463 & 6.334e-4 & -0.1921 & -0.02404 & 0.02537 & 0.9411 \end{bmatrix} \quad B = \begin{bmatrix} 0.0001318 & -0.0003536 \\ -0.0005707 & 0.002455 \\ -7.4e-7 & -0.0001534 \\ -2.539e-5 & 0.0001438 \\ 2.891e-5 & 0.0003407 \\ 0.001013 & -0.0001613 \end{bmatrix}$$

$$C = \begin{bmatrix} -3159 & -321.3 & -2909 & -2510 & 160.7 & -2056 \\ 1226 & 146.3 & 1016 & 216.2 & 69.62 & 1337 \\ 191.7 & 92.59 & 665.7 & -369.1 & -55.97 & -39 \end{bmatrix}$$

The model demonstrates good performance with mean absolute percentage errors 4-13 % for the three outputs.

3.3. Formulation and solution of the mp-P design space problem

The linear state-state space model from Step 2 is used for the formulation and solution of multi-parametric programming (mp-P) problem. In this case, the objective function is defined as the maximisation of the amount of target product b at the end of the batch. The mp-P formulation consists of 915 continuous variables, 2 parameters, 6 inequality constraints, and 915 equality constraints and is solved via the POP® Toolbox (Oberdieck et al., 2016). The design space (DSp) defined by the mp-P problem is depicted by the dashed-line in Figure 2a. The space is two-dimensional and a function of the two variables considered as inputs: namely the temperature (T), and the batch time (t_f). It is observed that the mp-DSp framework can identify a DSp boundary for the system. The multi-parametric solution consisted of a single critical region defined in Equation 14.

$$\begin{bmatrix} -0.9932 & -0.1161 \\ 0 & -1 \\ 1 & 0 \\ 0 & 1 \end{bmatrix} \begin{bmatrix} t_f \\ T \end{bmatrix} \leq \begin{bmatrix} -308.8112 \\ -250 \\ 300 \\ 350 \end{bmatrix} \qquad (14)$$

For comparison, the mp-P solution is benchmarked against the DSp produced based on the high-fidelity process model (Figure 2a, continuous black line) and following the framework published by Sachio et al. (2023). The two design spaces consider the exact same feasible bounds for the process time (250-350 min), while the mp-DSp presents a lower acceptable bound for the temperature (262 K). As observed, the DSp identified by using the state-space formulation (mp-DSp) slightly overpredicts the acceptable design space by considering 7 % of false positive points.

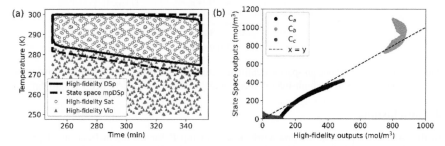

Figure 2 (a) *Comparison of the mp-DSp solution with the design space of the high-fidelity model and (b) Parity plot comparing the high-fidelity model outputs against the state-space model outputs.*

Although a 7 % error is not numerically high, there exist processes with low error tolerance. To further investigate the source of the observed discrepancy, the state-space/high-fidelity parity plot was constructed, as a function of the model outputs (C_a, C_b, C_c). For an accurate state-space model, the majority of the points would lie close or on the $x = y$ line. In this case, (Figure 2b) the state-space model presents inaccuracies particularly in the predictions of the concentrations for b and c. Specifically, the state-space model overestimates C_b, while underestimating C_c - particularly towards the end of the process. This can be translated into the concentration of b being predicted higher than its true value. The mismatch between the state space and the high-fidelity process model plays a key role in the formulation and solution of the mp-P and can be the main source for the mismatch observed between the DSps calculated with the two approaches (Figure 2a). Nonetheless, the mp-DSp presents great potential towards the identification of general representation of high-dimensional design spaces.

3.4. Design space uniqueness

In any model-based analysis it is critical to understand and confirm the trustworthiness of the solution, particularly in cases where parametric uncertainty is high. As discussed in Sachio et al. (2023), design spaces that are defined using computational geometry rely on the density of the point cloud generated up to a certain extent. Figure 3 compares six design spaces generated using quasi-random Sobol sampling on the validated high-fidelity model directly (Sachio et al., 2023). The DSps are defined based on different point cloud densities that range from 512 to 4096 points. It can be observed that as the data resolution decreases, the DSps decrease in size. This is expected, as fewer points are generated by the sampling method and, therefore, there is less information available to be utilised for the identification of the acceptable space boundaries. When comparing this methodology to the mp-DSp framework presented here, it is noted that, in the case of the latter, the DSp identified is unique. Critically, the mp-DSp is independent of any data generation as it is defined via the solution of an explicit optimisation problem that focuses solely on the identification of the bounds.

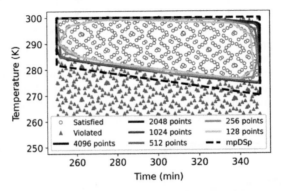

Figure 3 Assessment of design spaces identified using 128, 256, 512, 1024, 2048 and 4096 quasi-random samples of the high-fidelity model and the design space identified via mp-DSp.

4. Conclusions

In this work, we present a framework based on mp-P for the identification of process DSp. The methodology harnesses the computational efficiency of mp-P to identify the DSp bounds, without the need for expensive data generation. The capabilities of the presented approach are demonstrated through an established example of a reactor, whereby the DSp for product maximisation needs to be identified. The results indicate that the mp-DSp framework identifies the DSp satisfactorily, presenting a relatively low mismatch (7 %) to the DSp as identified using quasi-random sampling on the high-fidelity process model. The presented mismatch is attributed to the linear state space formulation required for the construction and solution of the mp-P problem. Current work is focusing on the assessment of different approximation methods to improve the solution of the mp-DSp and solving more complex design problems with larger number of design variables.

References

V. Bansal, J. D. Perkins, and E. N. Pistikopoulos, 2004, Flexibility analysis and design using a parametric programming framework, AIChE Journal, 48, 2851-2868

M. Geremia, F. Bezzo and M. G. Ierapetritou, 2023, A novel framework for the identification of complex feasible space, Comp. & Chem. Eng., 179

I.E. Grossmann, B.A. Calfa, and P. Garcia-Herreros, 2014, Evolution of concepts and models for quantifying resiliency and flexibility of chemical processes, Comp. & Chem. Eng., 70, 22-34

S. Kucherenko, D. Giamalakis, N. Shah and S. García-Muñoz, 2020, Computationally efficient identification of probabilistic design spaces through application of metamodeling and adaptive sampling, Comp. & Chem. Eng., 132

K. P. Kusumo, L. Gomoescu, R. Paulen, S. García Muñoz, C. C. Pantelides, N. Shah, et al., 2019, Bayesian Approach to Probabilistic Design Space Characterisation: A Nested Sampling Strategy, Ind. & Eng. Chem. Res., 59, 2396-2408

R. Oberdieck, N. A. Diangelakis, M. M. Papathanasiou, I. Nascu and E. N. Pistikopoulos, 2016, POP - Parametric Optimisation Toolbox, Ind. & Eng. Chem. Res., 55, 8979-8991

E. N. Pistikopoulos, 2009, Perspectives in multiparametric programming and explicit model predictive control, AIChE Journal, 55, 1918-1925

S. Sachio, C. Kontoravdi and M. M. Papathanasiou, 2023, A model-based approach towards accelerated process development: A case study on chromatography, Chem. Eng. Res. & Des., 197, 800-820

Flavio Manenti, Gintaras V. Reklaitis (Eds.), Proceedings of the 34th European Symposium on Computer Aided Process Engineering / 15th International Symposium on Process Systems Engineering (ESCAPE34/PSE24), June 2-6, 2024, Florence, Italy

Unveil the Subconscious Optimum: Near-Pareto-Optimal Design Alternatives for Industrial Energy System Transformation

Hendrik Schricker[a], Conrad Luka[a], Christiane Reinert[a], Dörthe Franzisca Hagedorn[a], Niklas von der Assen[a,*]

[a] Institute of Technical Thermodynamics, RWTH Aachen University, Schinkelstraße 8, 52062 Aachen, Germany
niklas.vonderassen@ltt.rwth-aachen.de

Abstract

Industrial decision-makers face challenges in identifying suitable transformations towards low-carbon energy systems due to multiple, often elusive, stakeholder decision criteria. Advanced optimization techniques can support the decision-making process: when facing multiple stakeholder criteria, multi-objective optimization identifies a set of Pareto-optimal alternatives. In addition, exploring near-optimal solutions provides insights into decision flexibilities.

In our work, we combine both approaches to identify near-Pareto-optimal energy system design alternatives. First, we determine Pareto-optimal alternatives using the augmented epsilon-constraint method. Second, we holistically explore the near-Pareto-optimal design space for a chosen Pareto-optimal alternative with the Modeling All Alternatives method, ensuring near-optimality in all objective values. Finally, we cluster representative design alternatives from the set of near-Pareto-optimal design alternatives to reduce decision complexity.

In a case study, we identify 5576 near-Pareto-optimal design alternatives for a multi-energy system to minimize annualized cost, investments, and energy import dependency. Moreover, we reduce the overall decision complexity to four representative designs. Our findings provide industrial decision-makers with a refined toolset for informed energy infrastructure investments amidst competing objectives.

Keywords: mixed-integer linear programming, decision support systems, modeling all alternatives, utility systems, decarbonization.

1. Introduction: Addressing current challenges in energy system modeling

Planning the transition towards low-carbon energy systems is a multifaceted decision-making challenge. Energy system optimization models can provide guidance for such decisions. Yet, most energy system optimization model formulations are limited to single-objective formulations and thus sideline the heterogeneity of preferences and subconscious preferences in the decision-making processes (DeCarolis et al., 2017). Consequently, relying solely on single-objective optimization often falls short, especially when key objectives and the inherent uncertainties of the model are neglected.

In response to the limitations, recent research trends in energy system modeling have pivoted toward more holistic modeling approaches, e.g., by integrating multiple objective functions, accommodating a range of parameter scenarios, and intensifying the exploration of near-optimal solutions to reveal subconscious preferences, which are not explicitly modeled (Chang et al., 2023). Combining these modeling approaches further increases insights for decision-makers: recent studies addressed parametric uncertainty in multi-objective optimization (Mores et al., 2023) and in near-optimal solution exploration (Grochowicz et al., 2023), and investigated near-optimal solutions in the face of multiple objectives (Dubois et al., 2023).

However, methods for exploring near-optimal solutions often focus on maximally distinct solutions in the near-optimal solution space (Jing et al., 2019) and thus potentially introduce bias towards solutions near the boundaries of the near-optimal solution space. The Modeling All Alternatives (MAA) method proposed by Pedersen et al. (2021) computes a geometric representation of the near-optimal solution space and thus enables complete and unbiased coverage. However, the applicability of MAA is hampered in industrial contexts, as MAA deals with continuous design variables, neglecting that many supply technologies come in specific, discrete capacity steps. Furthermore, MAA has so far only been applied to single-objective optimization problems.

Building upon the MAA method, our prior research introduced a method to sample all discrete alternatives from the continuous, near-optimal design space (Schricker et al., 2023). In this work, we extend our method for multi-objective optimization problems. To the extent of our knowledge, our work is the first MAA-based method, which identifies discrete design alternatives in the face of multiple objectives. Moreover, we apply clustering methods to the near-Pareto-optimal design alternatives to identify representative design alternatives analogously to Prina et al. (2023). Thus, we enable decision-makers to understand the inherent flexibilities in investment decisions.

2. Method: Identifying representative, near-Pareto-optimal design alternatives

In this section, we present the general problem statement for identifying representative, near-Pareto-optimal design alternatives in industrial energy systems and describe our methodological approach. The problem statement of our method is as follows: Given

- the existing infrastructure of an industrial energy system,
- a temporally resolved exogenous energy demand,
- a set of technology investment options, each with given discrete capacity expansion steps, and
- a set of n objective functions $\mathbf{z} = (z_j)$, where $j = 1 \ldots n$,

the task is to identify a set of representative energy system design alternatives, which are near-Pareto-optimal, i.e., representative alternatives, which are proximate to the Pareto-optimal design preferred by decision-makers. We consider the design of potential energy conversion and storage units by the discrete capacity expansion $\mathbf{d} \in \mathcal{D}$ and the operation of existing and newly installed units $\mathbf{o} \in \mathcal{O}$ as decision variables.

In the first step of our method, we identify Pareto-optimal design alternatives by solving the multi-objective optimization problem. We then select one Pareto-optimal alternative and explore all near-Pareto-optimal design alternatives close to the chosen alternative (cf. Section 2.1). In the second step, we identify representative design alternatives to reduce the decision complexity (cf. Section 2.2). Our method equips decision-makers with a representative selection of near-Pareto-optimal design alternatives and thus enables informed investment decisions.

2.1. Step 1: Exploration of discrete, near-Pareto-optimal design alternatives

To derive Pareto-optimal design alternatives, we employ a multi-objective mixed-integer linear program with the objective $\min_{\mathbf{d} \in \mathcal{D}, \mathbf{o} \in \mathcal{O}} \mathbf{z}(\mathbf{d}, \mathbf{o})$. We solve the multi-objective problem with the augmented epsilon-constraint method by Mavrotas (2009).

Next, to span the near-Pareto-optimal design space, we choose the best compromise solution according to the min-max-criterion (Li and Zio, 2018) by default. However, our method can be applied with any Pareto-optimal alternative i. We define the near-Pareto-optimal design space $\mathcal{W}_\varepsilon^{\mathcal{P}}(i)$ with respect to the Pareto-optimal alternative i with its objective function values $\mathbf{z}^{(i)}$:

$$\mathcal{W}_\varepsilon^{\mathcal{P}}(i) = \{\mathbf{d} \in \mathcal{D} | \min_{\mathbf{o} \in \mathcal{O}} \mathbf{z}(\mathbf{d}, \mathbf{o}) \leq \mathbf{z}^{(i)} \cdot (1 + \varepsilon)\}. \tag{1}$$

Here, the parameter $\varepsilon = (\varepsilon_j), j = 1 \ldots n$, represents the allowed relative slack for the objective function j. Thus, near-optimality is guaranteed for all objective functions $j = 1 \ldots n$.

Our method then follows the Modeling All Alternatives method considering discrete capacity steps by Schricker et al. (2023). First, we relax the discrete character of the design variables and iteratively span the continuous, near-Pareto-optimal design space. We systematically explore new search directions $\mathbf{n}$ to obtain vertices $\mathbf{v}$ of the near-Pareto-optimal design space by solving $\mathbf{v} = \max_{\mathbf{d} \in \mathcal{W}_\varepsilon^{\mathcal{P}}} \mathbf{n}^{\mathsf{T}} \mathbf{d}$. Subsequently, we reintroduce the discrete capacity expansion steps. We employ the recursive polytope discretization algorithm introduced by Schricker et al. (2023) to identify all discrete, near-Pareto-optimal design alternatives $\mathbf{d}_k \in \mathcal{W}_\varepsilon^{\mathcal{P}}(i)$, where $k = 1 \ldots m$ within the convex hull defined by the vertices $\mathbf{v}$.

2.2. Step 2: Reduction to representative design alternatives

As a result of Step 1, the number of identified discrete, near-Pareto-optimal design alternatives can be large. To reduce decision complexity, we determine representative near-Pareto-optimal design alternatives from the set of near-Pareto-optimal design alternatives $\mathcal{W}_\varepsilon^{\mathcal{P}}$. For this purpose, we use the FasterPAM implementation of the k-medoids algorithm by Schubert and Lenssen (2022) and segment the design alternatives into k distinct clusters. For each cluster, we identify the medoid as the representative design alternative. Thus, we ensure that only feasible design alternatives are selected as cluster representatives. We measure the validity of clustering structures by the overall average silhouette width (Rousseeuw, 1987). We then choose the most suitable number of clusters k according to the elbow criterion (Syakur et al., 2018). Our method provides decision-makers with manageable sets of design alternatives, which are representative of the complete near-Pareto-optimal design space. Thus, we significantly reduce the decision-making complexity in energy system expansion problems.

3. Case study: Decision support for a multi-energy system expansion

We apply our methodology to examine near-Pareto-optimal energy system design alternatives for a case study from Reinert et al. (2023), based on a real-world system (cf. Figure 1). The installed capacities of the existing energy system are taken from Kämper et al. (2021) and marked in blue, whereas all other shown capacities can be built during capacity expansion. We consider annualized cost, investments, and energy import dependency as objective functions. The energy import dependency is defined as the total amount of purchased energy. The multi-energy system is designed to serve temporally resolved electricity (P_{el}), heating ($\dot{Q}_{heat}$), and cooling ($\dot{Q}_{cool}$) demands. Natural gas and electricity are available for purchase from the grid with temporally resolved prices. The price for CO_2 certificates for direct emissions remains constant. The existing energy system predominantly relies on fossil fuels. We evaluate photovoltaic systems, wind turbines, electrode boilers, high-temperature heat pumps, organic Rankine cycles, and storage technologies as technology investment options for the energy system expansion. Each of these technologies is modeled using techno-economic data, e.g., specific investment costs and technical efficiencies, as well as data on operational CO_2-emissions. We assume specific capacity expansion steps and a maximum installable capacity for each technology.

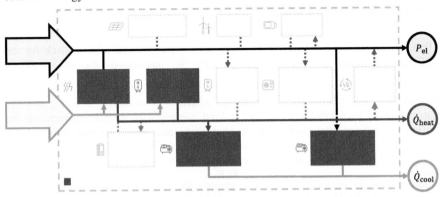

Figure 1. Superstructure of the multi-energy system case study taken from Reinert et al. (2023). The existing infrastructure is highlighted in blue.

We integrate our method into the energy system optimization framework SecMOD (Reinert et al., 2022). When exploring the Pareto- and near-Pareto-optimal design alternatives, we optimize one year of operation, aggregated into eight typical days with hourly resolution, resulting in 192 time steps. We assume a maximum storage period of 24 hours for the battery and the thermal storage unit. We set a relative objective slack of $\varepsilon_{j=1\dots3} = 5\,\%$ for all three objective functions compared to the best compromise solution. Furthermore, we scale the design decision variables with the specific investment costs before clustering to obtain representative design alternatives in terms of investment allocation.

In total, we identify 5576 near-Pareto-optimal design alternatives. The resulting capacity distributions (cf. Figure 2) reveal ranges of investment flexibility in terms of installable capacity for decision-makers. Specifically, we observe the largest flexibility in the design of the thermal storage unit, the electrode boiler, and the photovoltaic system.

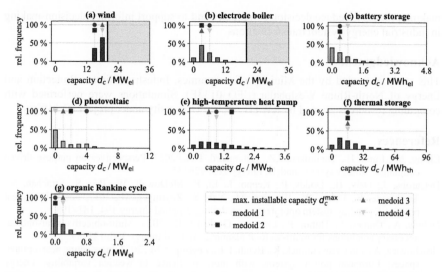

Figure 2. Capacity distributions for all technologies across the 5576 identified near-Pareto-optimal design alternatives. We highlight the capacities of the four representative design alternatives (the cluster medoids) and the maximum installable capacity if it lies in the range of the capacity axis.

The thermal storage unit enables electricity-driven operation of the existing combined heat and power plants. Electrifying the heat supply via electrode boilers or heat pumps is crucial for reducing natural gas imports. The installation of wind turbines with a capacity of at least 15 MW_{el} is a must-have decision for near-Pareto-optimality because wind turbines are crucial for reducing electricity imports. Collectively, the near-Pareto-optimal design alternatives facilitate the integration of renewable electricity sources and enable flexible system operation according to current energy carrier prices compared to the existing system.

We choose a clustering structure with four representative design alternatives according to the overall average silhouette width and the elbow criterion (cf. Section 2.2). The identified representative design alternatives show trade-offs in the renewable electricity source (wind turbine vs. photovoltaic system) and in the allocation of investments for the electrode boiler, high-temperature heat pump, and the organic Rankine cycle.

4. Conclusions

Acknowledging the intricacies and multifaceted challenges during the design optimization of energy systems, we introduce an extended version of the Modeling All Alternatives method incorporating multiple objective functions for industrial energy systems. First, we solve the underlying multi-objective design optimization problem to identify Pareto-optimal design alternatives using the augmented epsilon-constraint method. We then systematically explore the near-Pareto optimal design space around the Pareto-optimal alternative preferred by decision-makers and sample all contained design alternatives taking into account the discrete character of design decisions for industrial systems. Finally, we incorporate the k-medoids algorithm to reduce the decision complexity emerging from the potentially large amount of identified design alternatives. Our work combines multi-objective optimization with the exploration of near-optimal solutions to simultaneously increase insights from energy system models beyond single-objective considerations and beyond optimal solutions. We streamline the decision-making process to reduce decision complexity and to support informed decision-making in industrial energy system transformations.

Acknowledgments

This study is funded by the Ministry of Economics, Industry, Climate Protection and Energy of North-Rhine Westphalia (EFO 0133E). Simulations were performed with computing resources granted by RWTH Aachen University under project ID 1493.

References

Chang, M., Lund, H., Thellufsen, J.Z., Østergaard, P.A., 2023. Perspectives on purpose-driven coupling of energy system models. Energy 265, 126335.

DeCarolis, J., Daly, H., Dodds, P., Keppo, I., Li, F., McDowall, W., Pye, S., Strachan, N., Trutnevyte, E., Usher, W., Winning, M., Yeh, S., Zeyringer, M., 2017. Formalizing best practice for energy system optimization modelling. Applied Energy 194, 184–198.

Dubois, A., Dumas, J., Thiran, P., Limpens, G., Ernst, D., 2023. Multi-objective near-optimal necessary conditions for multi-sectoral planning. Applied Energy 350, 121789.

Grochowicz, A., van Greevenbroek, K., Benth, F.E., Zeyringer, M., 2023. Intersecting near-optimal spaces: European power systems with more resilience to weather variability. Energy Economics 118, 106496.

Jing, R., Kuriyan, K., Kong, Q., Zhang, Z., Shah, N., Li, N., Zhao, Y., 2019. Exploring the impact space of different technologies using a portfolio constraint based approach for multi-objective optimization of integrated urban energy systems. Renewable and Sustainable Energy Reviews 113, 109249.

Kämper, A., Leenders, L., Bahl, B., Bardow, A., 2021. AutoMoG: Automated data-driven Model Generation of multi-energy systems using piecewise-linear regression. Computers & Chemical Engineering 145, 107162.

Li, Y.-F., Zio, E., 2018. Rams Optimization Principles, in: Möller, N., Hansson, S.O., Holmberg, J.-E. (Eds.), Handbook of safety principles. Wiley, Hoboken, NJ, USA, pp. 514–539.

Mavrotas, G., 2009. Effe ε-constraint method in Multi-Objective Mathematical Programming problems. Applied Mathematics and Computation 213 (2), 455–465.

Mores, W., Nimmegeers, P., Hashem, I., Bhonsale, S.S., van Impe, J.F., 2023. Multi-objective optimization under parametric uncertainty: A Pareto ellipsoids-based algorithm. Computers & Chemical Engineering 169, 108099.

Pedersen, T.T., Victoria, M., Rasmussen, M.G., Andresen, G.B., 2021. Modeling all alternative solutions for highly renewable energy systems. Energy 234, 121294.

Prina, M.G., Johannsen, R.M., Sparber, W., Østergaard, P.A., 2023. Evaluating near-optimal scenarios with EnergyPLAN to support policy makers. Smart Energy 10, 100100.

Reinert, C., Nolzen, N., Frohmann, J., Tillmanns, D., Bardow, A., 2023. Design of low-carbon multi-energy systems in the SecMOD framework by combining MILP optimization and life-cycle assessment. Computers & Chemical Engineering 172, 108176.

Reinert, C., Schellhas, L., Mannhardt, J., Shu, D.Y., Kämper, A., Baumgärtner, N., Deutz, S., Bardow, A., 2022. SecMOD: An Open-Source Modular Framework Combining Multi-Sector System Optimization and Life-Cycle Assessment. Front. Energy Res. 10, 884525.

Rousseeuw, P.J., 1987. Silhouettes: A graphical aid to the interpretation and validation of cluster analysis. Journal of Computational and Applied Mathematics 20, 53–65.

Schricker, H., Schuler, B., Reinert, C., v.d.Aßen, N., 2023. Gotta catch 'em all: Modeling All Discrete Alternatives for Industrial Energy System Transitions. URL: <https://doi.org/10.48550/arXiv.2307.10687>.

Schubert, E., Lenssen, L., 2022. Fast k-medoids Clustering in Rust and Python. JOSS 7 (75), 4183.

Syakur, M.A., Khotimah, B.K., Rochman, E.M.S., Satoto, B.D., 2018. Integration K-Means Clustering Method and Elbow Method For Identification of The Best Customer Profile Cluster. IOP Conf. Ser.: Mater. Sci. Eng. 336 (1), 12017.

Flavio Manenti, Gintaras V. Reklaitis (Eds.), Proceedings of the 34th European Symposium on Computer Aided Process Engineering / 15th International Symposium on Process Systems Engineering (ESCAPE34/PSE24), June 2-6, 2024, Florence, Italy

A cell expansion framework for property-based automatic compartmentalization of Computational Fluid Dynamics (CFD) models

Lide Gonzalez-Sala,[a] Gorka Sánchez Larraona,[a] Paloma Grau,[a] Borja Hernández[a*]

[a] TECNUN Engineering School, University of Navarra, Manuel Lardizabal Ibibildea 13, San Sebastian, 20018, Spain.
bhernandezb@unav.es

Abstract

This work presents a framework for compartment model generation through the cell aggregation method. The framework aggregates the cells with a similar value of a target property directly from the mesh of the CFD model. This aggregation is performed directly from the results in the mesh of the CFD model, which has two main advantages against other compartmentalization frameworks. First, it identifies irregular 3D zones with similar properties. Second, it does not require the user to generate a new mesh on top of the results, which significantly improves automatizing the procedure and saves time for the user. Two case studies have been conducted to validate the framework: a Venturi that determines the cuts according to the axial velocity and an elbow that mixes two pipes with different temperatures and determines the cut according to temperature and velocity.

Keywords: Compartment models, CFD, scale-up, data management.

1. Introduction

Computational Fluid Dynamic (CFD) models have been widely used for modeling unit operations in chemical pharmaceutical or environmental industries. Despite their high computational cost, CFD provides internal fluxes and a detailed distribution of properties within the unit. One alternative to reduce its computational cost is the use of compartment models (CM) (Jourdan et al., 2018). CM can be classified in two approaches: Systemic compartment models based on the equivalent reactor network theory, and Zonal Models (ZM), which introduce a topological description within the unit. The first approach has been mainly employed for tracing and determining residence time distribution (RTD) into a unit (Danckwerts, P.V. 1953). The second approach, introduced by Bermingham et al. (1998), is based on the extraction of information on the fluxes within the unit to obtain a model based on a network of reactors that are equivalent to the finite volumes of the CFD model (Jourdan et al., 2018). These fluxes generated from the CFD model can be implemented in the reactor network following a data-driven approach or by means of surrogates. The flexibility of surrogate models has made this second approach the most interesting. Multiple surrogate modeling techniques (e.g., neural networks (Queipo et al. 2005), kriging (Boukouvala et al. 2013), dimensionless groups correlations (Hernández et al. 2022)) have been applied to modeling the fluxes in ZMs.

Apart from focusing on generating the surrogate models for the fluxes, research in ZM generation has also focused on automatizing the extraction of fluxes. The first work developed by Bezzo et al. (2004) introduced the automatic construction of compartments by aggregating the cells with similar properties. The aggregated cells were generated by the user on top of the results obtained from the CFD model, and its accuracy was limited by the number of cuts re-defined by the user. The first alternative and less automatized approach for identifying the right cuts was proposed by Alvarado et al. (2012). They measured the property through a set of lines and generated cuts at sections exhibiting changes. Due to the extensive size of the resulting zones in the ZM, they integrated the ZM approach with a systemic one. Within each zone, they incorporated an internal set of equivalent reactors. In another alternative to cell aggregation, Delafosse et al. (2014) proposed the layer-by-layer method for generating the network of reactors. Among the three approaches (cell aggregation, combined cell aggregation and systemic, and layer-by-layer), the most extended one is the one proposed by Bezzo et al.. It has been applied to different properties and is commercialized through the Multizonal tool developed by Process Systems Enterprise (Siemens, 2020). Following this approach, most recent works have also provided a higher automatization of compartment models by following a cell aggregation method with more than one property for CFD models (Tajsoleiman et al. 2019) and with particle concentration for Discrete Element Models (DEM) (Bhalode et al. 2021). However, the construction in both cases was still based on generating a mesh on top of the results. The generation of this mesh requires user intervention to define the number of cuts to be performed on top of the results. Furthermore, the results of this new mesh may not be accurate enough if the cell size is too large or when irregular zones exist. To overcome these drawbacks, this work proposes a new automatic framework that identifies the location of the compartments, directly analyzing the results obtained in each of the cells of the CFD simulation.

2. Methodology

2.1. Description of the Framework
The novel framework does not require generating a mesh on top of the results since all the information is extracted directly from the cells. The framework combines User Defined Functions (UDFs) from Ansys Fluent® and data analysis in Python for extracting the data and determining the optimal aggregation of cells based on a set of target properties and a desired increment. A general description of the framework is given in Figure 1, and more details with two case studies are given in the following paragraphs. The framework consists of four steps: First, all the information contained in the CFD model is extracted through UDFs. Second, the properties are set, and their difference between adjacent cells is computed. Third, the zones according to a defined maximum allowed difference are defined. Fourth, the fluxes are extracted between the zones.

2.1.1. Extraction from CFD.
The first step after running the CFD simulation consists of extracting information from all the cells. The extraction of information is divided into two steps. The first one extracts all the target properties of every cell with its identification number (ID) and location, generating an ASCII file named *"Properties-File"*. The extraction of all these properties is performed from *Export → Solution Data* in Ansys Fluent ® and selecting the values in the Cell Center for all the properties. The second extraction, *"Fluxes-File"*, employs a UDF that tracks all the cells extracting the ID and the mass flow rate through each face. The mass flow rate is calculated using the function *F_FLUX*, which provides the value calculated internally in Fluent®. Therefore, mass conservation is ensured with the same degree of accuracy as in the CFD simulation.

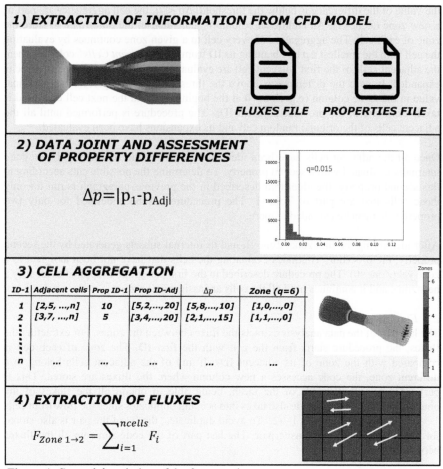

Figure 1. General description of the framework.

2.2. Data joint and analysis of property differences

The two data files are first merged into a unique *dataframe* in Python. The data extracted in *"Fluxes-File"* contains a column with the ID of the tracked cell (ID-1) and a second column with the IDs of its adjacent cells (ID-Adj). For each ID and its adjacent cell, a search is performed in *"Properties-File"* extracting the values of the target property in the two cells and computing the difference, Δp. The difference is stored in a column of the *dataframe,* see Step 3 of Figure 1. After storing the values, the distribution of differences is determined which allows us to set up the value for cutting the zones as a quantile of the distribution or as a specified set given by the user, see the example in step 2 of Figure 1.

2.3. Cell aggregation algorithm

The user defines a quantile or a threshold difference, q, that is employed in determining the regions by cell aggregation. Then, the cell aggregation algorithm begins from a random cell of the column ID-1. The cell is compared with its adjacent ones, and in case the value of the difference is below the threshold, $\Delta p < q$, the cell aggregates are part of a new zone (Zone=1). An additional column is generated in the *dataframe* to store the zone of each cell. The aggregation of every cell to a given zone continues by evaluating the cell with the smallest Δp by obtaining its ID from the *"Adjacent Cells"* column. Then, the adjacent cells of the first adjacent cell are evaluated, and the definition of the zone is expanded. In case the difference is above the threshold, the cell preserves its original value in the Zone column (e.g. Zone=0 at the beginning), and the next cell evaluated is taken from one of the previous adjacent IDs. The procedure is performed until all the adjacent cells of the original random cell and its expansions have been evaluated.

Once all the adjacent cells have been identified as part of the first (Zone=1), they are internally evaluated with a second property. To determine the possible cuts according to this second property, the algorithm described in the previous paragraph is run for only those cells that are part of Zone=1. The procedure has been defined for only two properties but can be extended to more.

After identifying the first zone, Zone=1, and its internal subsets generated by the second property, the procedure continues evaluating the cells that have not been assigned to a zone yet (Zone=0). The procedure described in the first paragraph is applied to identify a new zone, and it continues until all the cells are assigned to a zone.

2.4. Flux extraction
The last part of the data analysis extracts the fluxes between the zones. For extracting the fluxes, the procedure starts from the cell with the first ID. The zone of each cell is compared with the zone of its adjacent IDs. If any of the adjacent cells belong to a different zone, the code accesses a new column where the fluxes are stored. This is performed for all the cells of the mesh, being able to obtain all the fluxes of the boundaries. The resultant code also takes into account duplicates since the flow from cells $1 \rightarrow 2$ is the opposite of cells $1 \rightarrow 2$. To avoid duplicates, the ID of the pair is also stored for not considering the opposite pair. The last part of the code sums up all the fluxes between the zones.

2.5. Case Studies
The framework has been evaluated in two case studies with different properties for the generation of the zones: a Venturi tube and an elbow with two inlets (one with hot air and another with cold air). The physical property considered for the division of the zones is the axial velocity in the Venturi, and the temperature and velocity for the elbow.

3. Results
The framework has been tested with the case studies provided, and shows consistency with the cell results reported in Ansys Fluent® as shown in Figure 2 a). Here, the case of a Venturi is presented where the threshold for cutting the regions has been defined as the quantile 85% of the distribution in differences in the axial velocity; see Figures 2,b) and 2,c). If the difference between velocities accepted for aggregation is smaller, quantile 80%, we can see that the number of zones increases, see Figure 2, c). For validating the fluxes, we have evaluated if continuity is ensured. This has been done by comparing the inflow between zones 1 and 3, which has reported no difference in the mass flow.

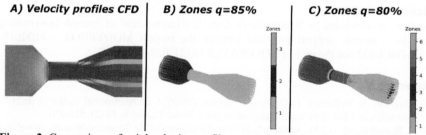

Figure 2. Comparison of axial velocity profile reported in a plane by a) Ansys Fluent®, b) zones with similar properties identified by the algorithm with a threshold defined as the quantile 85% of all the differences, and c) zones identified with a threshold defined as the quantile 80%.

The second case study evaluating the elbow considers two properties for cutting the regions, the temperature and the velocity magnitude of the flow. In this case, the zones with similar properties are more irregular than in the Venturi, highlighting the importance of the proposed tool. Generating the cuts with a single property is easier to visualize, but under more than one property, it is not that straightforward. A summary of the zones with these two properties is given in Figure 3.

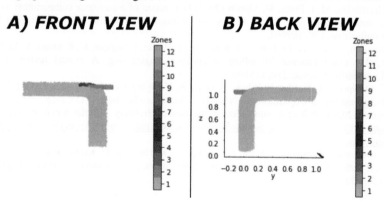

Figure 3. Compartment model generated for the elbow with two properties. A) Front and B) back views of the elbow.

4. Conclusions

This work has presented a framework for compartment model generation through the cell aggregation method. For the first time, a framework aggregates the cells directly from the results in the mesh of the CFD model. This allows us to identify better the cutting regions, especially if those zones are in 3D with irregular shapes. Furthermore, this significantly advances the automatization procedure and can reduce the time in generating CMs since the novel approach minimizes user interaction. The work has only been validated for CFD schemes and it only focuses on momentum and heat transfer. Future work can extend the framework to other applications (e.g., multiphase flow simulations), coupling chemical reactions with CFD, or be part of new computational methodologies that aim to speed up CFD simulations.

Acknowledgments

Authors acknowledge to "Ministerio de Ciencia e Innovación" of Spanish Government for the economic support provided through the project MODYPHOS - PID2019-108378RB-I00 and the project HOLIWATER -RED2022-134350-T.

References

A. Alvarado, S. Vedantam, P. Gethals, I. Nopens (2012) A compartmental model to describe hydraulics in a full-scale waste stabilization pond. Water Research, 46 (2), 521-530.

S. K. Bermingham, H.J.M. Kramer, G.M. van Rosmalen (1998) Towards on-scale crystalliser design using comparmental models. Computers & Chemical Engineering, 22, 1, S355-S362.

F. Bezzo, S. Macchietto (2004) A general methodology for hybrid multizonal/CFD models: part II. Automatic zoning. Computers & Chemical Engineering, 28 (4), 513-525.

P. Bhalode, M. Ierapetritou (2021) Hybrid multi-zonal compartment modeling for continuous powder blending processes. International Journal of Pharmaceutics, 602, 120643.

F. Boukouvala, Y. Gao, F. Muzzio, MG. Ierapetritou (2013) Redued-order discrete element method modeling. Chemical Engineering Science, 95, 12-26.

P.V. Danckwerts (1953) Continuous flow systems: distribution of residence times. Chemical Engineering Science, 2 (1), 1-13.

A. Delafosse, M.L. Collignon, S. Calvo, F. Delvigne, M. Crine, P. Thonart, D. Toye (2014) CFD-based compartment model for description of mixing in bioreactors. Chemical Engineering Science, 106, 76-85.

B. Hernández, M.A. Pinto, M. Martin (2022) Generation of a surrogate compartment model for counter-current spray dryer. Fluxes and momentum modeling. Computers & Chemical Engineering, 159, 107664.

N. Jourdan, T. Neveux, O. Potier, M. Kanniche, J. Wicks, I. Nopens, U. Rehman, Y. Le Moullec (2019) Compartmental Modelling in chemical engineering: A critical review. Chemical Engineering Science, 210, 115196.

N.V. Queipo, R.T. Haftka, W. Shyy, T. Goel, R. Vaidyanathan, P.K. Tucker (2005) Surrogate-based analysis and optimization. Progress in Aerospace Science, 41 (1), 1-28.

Siemens (2020) Multiscale simulation in the process industry – better together. Available in: https://blogs.sw.siemens.com/simcenter/multiscale-simulation-in-the-process-industry-better-together/

T. Tajsoleiman, R. Spann, C. Bach, KV. Genaey, J.K. Huusom, U. Krühne (2019) A CFD based automatics method for compartment model development. Computers & Chemical Engineering, 123, 236-245.

Flavio Manenti, Gintaras V. Reklaitis (Eds.), Proceedings of the 34th European Symposium on Computer Aided Process Engineering / 15th International Symposium on Process Systems Engineering (ESCAPE34/PSE24), June 2-6, 2024, Florence, Italy

Application of Co-Simulation Techniques in Process Systems Engineering and Algorithmic Challenges

Alexander Zinser*, Martin Arnold

Martin Luther University Halle-Wittenberg, Institute of Mathematics, Halle, Germany
alexander.zinser@mathematik.uni-halle.de

Abstract

With regard to process optimisation and process control, the efficient simulation of high dimensional spatially distributed systems is vital in process engineering. Co-simulation enables the parallel simulation of multiple subsystems. In this contribution, a basic co-simulation algorithm is introduced and exemplified on a model of an adiabatic plug flow tubular reactor (PFTR). Algorithmic parameters of the co-simulation such as the signal extrapolation method and the macro step size are investigated in detail. It is shown that the co-simulation approach for the stated test problem consisting of three coupled partial differential equations (PDE) already has the ability to compete with a monolithic reference simulation.

Keywords: Co-Simulation, Process Simulation, Process Systems Engineering

1. Introduction

Mathematical modelling and simulation are fundamental tools in process systems engineering. Modern reactor models are typically described by coupled spatially distributed partial differential equations (PDE). The discretisation of these systems often leads to a system of several thousand ordinary differential equations (ODE) that have to be solved numerically (Bremer et al., 2017). While such problems are typically simulated in a monolithic manner, co-simulation enables the parallel simulation of several subsystems. Co-simulation is a well-established tool in mechanical and electrical engineering (Eguillon et al., 2022), but there are just a few works on co-simulation in the field of process engineering (Gomes et al., 2017). Existing standards for co-simulation are investigated by Oppelt et al. (2015) and they conclude that the availability of co-simulation approaches is limited to specific industries.

In this contribution, we investigate the potential of co-simulation techniques in the parallel solution of systems of coupled PDE models. In sec. 2 a basic co-simulation algorithm is introduced, sec. 3 states our proposed test model of a PFTR, and in sec. 4 the proposed co-simulation approaches are analysed in detail w.r.t. their performance in terms of error and CPU time.

2. Co-Simulation

Co-simulation refers to simultaneous simulation of coupled subsystems. Consider dynamical systems, described by an ODE for the states, $\dot{x}_i = f_i(x_i, u_i)$, and an output $y_i = g_i(x_i, u_i)$ for a given input u_i. A basic example of two subsystems with outputs $y_i = g_i(x_i, u_i) := x_i$ and the corresponding monolithic system is shown in Fig. 1 (a)-(b).

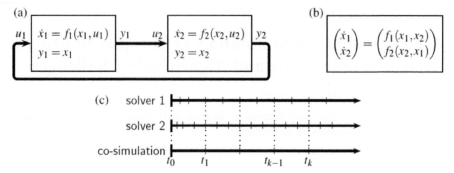

Figure 1: (a) Co-simulation of two subsystems and (b) the corresponding monolithic system. (c) Micro time steps of the ODE solvers, and macro time steps of the co-simulation for the communication between the subsystems.

2.1. Basic concept of a co-simulation algorithm

For known inputs u_i, each subsystem can be simulated independently of the other subsystems in parallel. While each ODE solver can proceed using its own step size controller, the information of the outputs y_i has to be propagated back to the corresponding inputs u_i at certain communication points. At each macro time step, a signal extrapolation for each input u_i is performed (Eguillon et al., 2022). Fig. 1 (c) visualises the solver-specific micro time steps and the macro time steps of the co-simulation in which the communication between the subsystems takes place.

2.2. Signal extrapolation

In this work, the input signals of the subsystems are extrapolated linearly at each communication point t_k. Let $p_i^{(k)}(t)$ the linear extrapolation based on the input signal at communication points t_{k-1} and t_k as shown in Fig. 2 (a). This extrapolation method is not continuous at the communication points, i.e. $p_i^{(k-1)}(t_k) \neq p_i^{(k)}(t_k)$. Therefore, a continuous and a continuously differentiable extrapolation method are additionally used. The continuous linear (C^0) extrapolation $p_{C,i}^{(k)}(t)$ is a linear extrapolation that satisfies $p_{C,i}^{(k)}(t_k) = p_i^{(k-1)}(t_k)$ and $p_{C,i}^{(k)}(t_{k+1}) = p_i^{(k)}(t_{k+1})$, Fig. 2 (b). Additionally, the linear C^1 extrapolation is a cubic polynomial based on the linear extrapolation, that satisfies also $\partial_t p_{C1,i}^{(k)}(t_k) = \partial_t p_i^{(k-1)}(t_k)$ and $\partial_t p_{C1,i}^{(k)}(t_{k+1}) = \partial_t p_i^{(k)}(t_{k+1})$, as shown in Fig. 2 (c).

A quadratic or cubic signal extrapolation would also be possible. However, in order to achieve a better asymptotic behaviour of the error than in the linear case, Arnold (2021) showed that a sophisticated start-up procedure of the co-simulation is required.

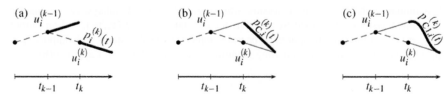

Figure 2: (a) Linear signal extrapolation, (b) continuous C^0, and (c) continuously differentiable C^1.

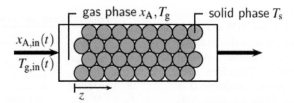

Figure 3: Schematic overview of the adiabatic PFT reactor model.

3. Modelling

In this work, we consider an adiabatic plug flow tubular reactor (PFTR), such as an exhaust gas treatment of a species A. Similar exothermic gas phase processes of high impact for the transition from fossil sources towards a sustainable recycling industry are, for example, the methanation of carbon dioxide, or the methanol synthesis from CO_2.

3.1. PFTR model

In our model, we consider two phases in one spatial dimension as depicted in Fig. 3. The gas phase is described by the molar fraction $x_A(t,z)$ and the temperature $T_g(t,z)$. The solid phase consists of a fixed bed catalyst layer and is described by the temperature field $T_s(t,z)$. While in the gas phase only convective mass and energy transport is considered, in the solid phase only diffusive energy transport, i.e. heat conduction, occurs. The governing equations of the model are stated as follows:

$$\frac{\partial x_A}{\partial t} = -v\frac{\partial x_A}{\partial z} - \frac{a}{c_{tot}}r(x_A, T_g), \tag{1a}$$

$$(\rho c_p)_g \frac{\partial T_g}{\partial t} = -(\rho c_p)_g v\frac{\partial T_g}{\partial z} - \Delta_r h\, r(x_A, T_g) - a\, q(T_g, T_s), \tag{1b}$$

$$(\rho c_p)_s \frac{\partial T_s}{\partial t} = \lambda\frac{\partial^2 T_s}{\partial z^2} + a\, q(T_g, T_s). \tag{1c}$$

The reaction rate $r(x_A, T_g)$ is described by a basic power law with Arrhenius equation,

$$r(x_A, T_g) = k_0 \exp\left(\frac{-E_A}{R\,T_g}\right)x_A, \tag{2a}$$

and the heat exchange between gaseous and solid phase is described by

$$q(T_g, T_s) = \alpha(T_g - T_s). \tag{2b}$$

The gas phase velocity v is calculated from the inlet volumetric flow F_{in} and the free cross-section area $A_{free} = 0.4\pi(d/2)^2$ by $v = F_{in}/A_{free}$. A summary of the system parameters that are used in the simulations is given in Tab. 1.

3.2. Boundary conditions

The boundary conditions of the gas phase equations are given by the inlet mole fraction $x_A(t,0) = x_{A,in}(t)$ and temperature $T_g(t,0) = T_{g,in}(t)$, respectively. In the boundary conditions of the solid phase equation, it is assumed that no heat conduction across the system boundary occurs, i.e. $\partial_z T_s(t,0) = \partial_z T_s(t,L) = 0$. In our simulations, two different sets of boundary conditions are used. First, a constant feed with a molar fraction of $x_{A,in}(t) = 0.0025$ and a temperature of $T_{g,in}(t) = 500K$. Second, a fluctuating feed in the molar fraction is applied. This is simulated by a Wiener process with a sampling rate of 1s, i.e. $x_{A,in}(t) \sim |W(t)|$, and normalised to $\frac{1}{t_f}\int_0^{t_f} x_{A,in}(t)dt = 0.0025$. Here, only the feed temperature is kept constant, $T_{g,in}(t) = 520K$.

3.3. Discretisation

In order to solve the PDE (1), it is discretised along the spatial coordinate using a finite volume method (LeVeque, 2002). Therefore, the domain of the spatial coordinate $\Omega = [0, L)$ is discretised into n_{FV} finite cells $\Omega_i = [z_{i-1/2}, z_{i+1/2})$ such that $\bigcup_{i=1}^{n_{FV}} \Omega_i = \Omega$ and $\Omega_i \cap \Omega_j = \emptyset$ for $i \neq j$, and an equidistant grid is assumed. Within a cell, the values of the spatially distributed variables are approximated by their integral mean. In the discretisation of the

accumulation terms, the Leibniz integral rule is applied. In the case of the convective and diffusive transport terms, the divergence theorem is utilised. The values on the boundaries of the cells are reconstructed by a first order upwind, and the gradients are interpolated linearly from the neighbouring values. This leads to a stiff set of $3 \cdot n_{FV}$ coupled ODE.

Table 1: System parameters.

Symbol	Description
$a = 10^4 \, \mathrm{m^2/m^3}$	specific surface area
$\alpha = 50 \, \mathrm{W/m^2 K}$	heat transfer coefficient
$d = 0.09 \, \mathrm{m}$	reactor diameter
$E_A = 80 \, \mathrm{kJ/mol}$	activation energy
$F_{in} = 7 \, \mathrm{m^3/h}$	inlet volume flow
$\Delta_r h = -1200 \, \mathrm{kJ/mol}$	enthalpy of reaction
$k_0 = 10^6 \, \mathrm{mol/m^2 s}$	kinetic constant
$L = 0.3 \, \mathrm{m}$	reactor length
$\lambda = 5 \, \mathrm{W/m \, K}$	heat conductivity
$R = 8.3145 \, \mathrm{J/mol \, K}$	gas constant
$(\rho c_p)_g = 1.2 \, \mathrm{kJ/m^3 K}$	density/heat capacity..
$(\rho c_p)_s = 950 \, \mathrm{kJ/m^3 K}$	..of gas/solid phase

4. Simulations

The simulation of the proposed model was implemented in PYTHON using NUMPY and SCIPY packages. The integration of the ODE was done using a backward differentiation formula (BDF) according to Shampine and Reichelt (1997) which is part of the SCIPY package. The integration interval was always chosen to be $[0, t_f]$ with the upper bound of $t_f = 750$s. All simulations were performed on a system with the following configuration: *Hardware* — Intel® Core™ i5-10500T CPU (6 Cores, 2.3 GHz), 8.0 GiB RAM, *Software* — Windows 10 Pro, PYTHON 3.8.10, NUMPY 1.24.1, SCIPY 1.10.1, SPYDER 5.4.5. Besides the Monolithic simulation of the overall set of $3 \cdot n_{FV}$ ODE, the system was simulated by means of a co-simulation as described below. The number of communication points in a co-simulation is denoted by n_{CP}.

4.1. Structure of the co-simulations

Since the system consists of three coupled PDE, it is natural to regard each discretised PDE as one subsystem. The outputs of the subsystems are the states itself, x_A, T_g, T_s. Fig. 4 shows different structures for a co-simulation. The first structure, Fig. 4 (a), performs direct feedback of the internal states and extrapolates them as described in sec. 2.2. This structure is denoted by Co-Simulation 1. In the structure shown in Fig. 4 (b), denoted by Co-Simulation 2, the reaction rate r is used as input to the subsystem for the gas

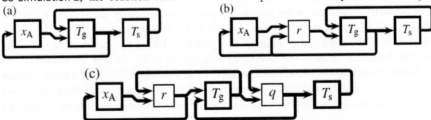

Figure 4: Different co-simulations. (a) Co-Simulation 1: Direct feedback of the internal states, (b) Co-Simulation 2: the reaction rate r, Eq. (1b), is extrapolated, and (c) intermediate calculation of reaction rate r and heat exchange q.

temperature T_g, Eq. (1b). This has the advantage, that the Jacobian of this subsystem becomes constant.

The third structure, Fig. 4 (c), performs a signal extrapolation on the reaction rate r and heat exchange q. It has to be noted that this structure does not lead to a feasible simulation. Consider the PDE for the mole fraction, Eq. (1a); this equation has a local stationary point at $x_A \to 0$. Replacing the reaction rate in this equation by a system input $u(t)$ leads to a disappearance of this stationary point and a co-simulation algorithm would require an infinitesimal small communication step size. The same holds for the two PDE for the temperatures which have their stationary points at $T_g \to T_s$ and vice versa.

4.2. Results

For all simulations, the CPU time, and the accuracy in terms of the L_2-error were measured. Let x_{jk} be the numerical solution of the j-th state of the overall simulation at the k-th communication time step t_k, and let $\tilde{x}_{jk}$ the corresponding value of a high-precision simulation. Then, the time-dependent L_2-error is defined by $\mathrm{err}(t_k) := \|\tilde{x}_{\cdot k} - x_{\cdot k}\|_2 / \|\tilde{x}_{\cdot k}\|_2$, and the global L_2-error is defined by $\mathrm{err} := \|\tilde{x}_{\cdot\cdot} - x_{\cdot\cdot}\|_2 / \|\tilde{x}_{\cdot\cdot}\|_2$.

A first simulation was conducted with $n_{FV} = 50$ finite volumes and $n_{CP} = 3001$ communication points in time with linear signal extrapolation for both types of boundary conditions, the constant feed system and the fluctuating feed system. Fig. 5 shows the L_2-error w.r.t. the simulated time t for both systems. The absolute and relative tolerances of the ODE solver were always fixed at 10^{-6}. Since the co-simulation employs a signal extrapolation of the states of the other subsystems, it is clear that a loss in accuracy can be observed. The CPU times of the simulations are shown in the legend of the figures. This indicates that the co-simulation approach has a higher potential at the fluctuating feed system.

Additionally, the signal extrapolation methods C^0 and C^1 lead to a slightly higher error, but also to a significantly better performance as shown in Fig. 6 (c). The reason is that the ODE solver does not have to handle the discontinuities at each communication point t_k. The influence of the number of communication points n_{CP} is shown in Fig. 6 (a)-(b) for the C^0 and the C^1 signal extrapolation, respectively. It was observed that one should not go below $n_{CP} \approx 2000$ communication points since this leads to problems because of a too large macro step size of the co-simulation. On the other hand, an increasing number of communication points leads to a higher CPU time. Hence, for the given system $n_{CP} = 2201$ communication points seem to be a reasonable choice.

Finally, Fig. 6 (d) shows the influence of the number of finite volumes n_{FV} of the spatial discretisation on the CPU time of the simulation. It can be seen clearly, that for every size

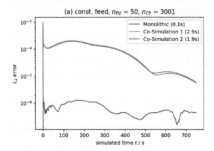
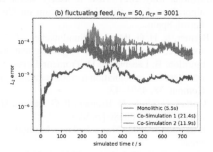

Figure 5: L_2-error w.r.t. simulated time t for (a) the constant feed system, and (b) the fluctuating feed system. Both simulations use the linear signal extrapolation.

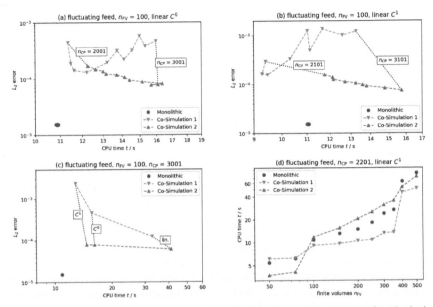

Figure 6: Influence of (a)-(b) the number of communication points n_{CP} for C^0 and C^1 signal extrapolation, (c) the type of signal extrapolation, and (d) the number of finite volumes n_{FV}.

of the problem, at least one of the two considered co-simulation structures shows a better performance than the Monolithic simulation. Especially for a fine discretisation with $n_{FV} \geq 400$, both co-simulation structures show a better performance than the monolithic simulation.

5. Conclusion

It was shown that the proposed co-simulation approaches enable the parallel simulation of spatially distributed PDE models in process engineering. Since the co-simulation of only three coupled PDE can already compete with a monolithic simulation, it is expected that a much higher performance can be achieved in simulations with much more coupled PDE.

References

M. Arnold, May 2021. How to verify worst case asymptotic error bounds for co-simulation algorithms. International Symposium on Co-Simulation and Solver Coupling in Dynamics, Ferrol, Spain.

J. Bremer, K. H. G. Rätze, K. Sundmacher, 2017. CO_2 methanation: Optimal start-up control of a fixed-bed reactor for power-to-gas applications. AiChE J. 63(1), 23–31.

Y. Eguillon, B. Lacabanne, D. Tromeur-Dervout, 2022. F₃ORNITS : a flexible variable step size non-iterative cosimulation method handling subsystems with hybrid advanced capabilities. Eng. Comput. 38, 4501–43.

C. Gomes, C. Thule, D. Broman, P. G. Larsen, H. Vangheluwe, 2017. Co-simulation: State of the art, arXiv:1702.00686 [cs.SY].

R. J. LeVeque, 2002. Finite Volume Methods for Hyperbolic Problems. Cambridge University Press.

M. Oppelt, G. Wolf, L. Urbas, 2015. Life Cycle Simulation for a Process Plant based on a Two-Dimensional Co-Simulation Approach. Comput. Aided Chem. Eng. 37, 935–40.

L. F. Shampine, M. W. Reichelt, 1997. The Matlab ODE Suite. SIAM J. Sci. Comput. 18(1), 1–22.

Flavio Manenti, Gintaras V. Reklaitis (Eds.), Proceedings of the 34th European Symposium on Computer Aided Process Engineering / 15th International Symposium on Process Systems Engineering (ESCAPE34/PSE24), June 2-6, 2024, Florence, Italy

Multi-Perspective Process Safety Analysis for Process Utility Systems under Industry 4.0

Qijia Peng,[a] Brent Young[a*]

[a] Chemical and Materials Engineering, University of Auckland
5 Grafton Road, Auckland Central, Auckland 1010, New Zealand
b.young@auckland.ac.nz

Abstract

Safety related factors can be measured, observed, or quantified in process safety management, but safety improvement is not easily validated. This paper initially presents a critical review of process safety analysis applied to process intensification, which is classified as an inherently safer design approach. The review revealed a lack of consensus on safety performance metrics for intensified processes, making it difficult to draw consistent conclusions on safety performance improvements.

Existing safety analysis approaches often focus on the design phase from a process lifecycle perspective. This work therefore also proposes a multi-perspective approach to safety analysis. The approach combines the hierarchy of controls perspective with the automation pyramid, and the digital twin concepts. This approach is applied and discussed in a case study of a retrofitted heat recovery system in an ammonia refrigeration plant.

Keywords: Process Safety, Safety Analysis, Digital Twins

1. Introduction

Over the past several decades, new process safety management concepts have been developed following investigations of major process safety incidents. Different process safety management (PSM) tasks are then performed throughout the life cycle of production facilities. In general, inherently safer designs are selected early in the process life cycle. Based on the hierarchy of controls, inherently-safer-design-decisions are the most effective in improving process safety. Process Intensification (PI) is the first of the four inherent safer design principles. A much-debated question is whether safety is improved in these PI processes compared to their conventional counterparts.

Current industry practice encourages the implementation of risk-based activities, i.e. risk-based safety management, risk-based inspection, and maintenance. A key activity in PSM is Hazard Identification & Risk Assessment (HIRA). A typical PSM activity is carried out by a multi-disciplinary team with different areas of expertise working together. As computer-aided tools become more available and used for PSM, it is important to have a smooth and safe transition from expert opinion-based approaches to more automated PSM and risk assessment processes.

In this work, we used the concept of hierarchy of controls to discuss the limitations of the computer-aided tools in the safety assessment of intensified processes. We also discussed the importance of considering multiple phases of the process lifecycle in the modelling for safety analysis the light of Industry 4.0 (I4.0). A multi-perspective safety analysis approach is proposed and discussed with a case study of a heat utility system.

2. Computer-Aided Process Safety Tools

In the past, quantitative risk assessment (QRA) has been the focus of computer-aided tools. In QRA, risk is composed of failure frequencies and consequences. Quantitative analysis uses empirical data for failure frequencies and different matrices are used for consequences. Risk-based analysis expresses risk in terms of consequence indices only. The Fire and Explosion Damage Index (FEDI) is commonly used, which deals with the consequences related to toxicity, flammability, and explosiveness. Another commonly used index is the Individual Risk (IR) indicator, which is a function of the distance between the epicentre of the accident and the location of the potential harm to personnel. FEDI and IR can be used in the selection of design alternatives in the inherently safer design approaches (Park *et al.*, 2019). The calculation of these safety indices can be automated in the safety analysis at the process design stage (Janošovský *et al.*, 2022). Traditional probabilistic risk assessment (PRA) at the design stage is static and only considers the risks at a snapshot in time. Unlike such PRA, the operational phase uses computer-aided tools to account for time-varying effects, i.e. disturbances, in risk estimation. Such a transition to dynamic risk analysis requires more sophisticated probabilistic models or data-driven approaches.

Digital visualisation is also used in PSM as a computer-aided tool. The tools range from graphical flowsheet interfaces to high-fidelity 3D plant models with virtual reality (VR) capabilities. There are also computational fluid dynamics (CFD) or finite element (FE) models for behavioural failure simulation. Such tools allow safety training to be conducted remotely in simulation environments and are ideal for improving operational procedures. With the advent of generative artificial intelligence (AI), intuitive human-machine interfaces (HMI) are expected to become increasingly available. Pioneering work has been done to make ChatGPT a participant in the HAZOP process, which was based on Large Language Modelling (LLM) (Xuan and Daniel, 2023). In the future, natural language processing (NLP) and generative AI may be used to translate the process-safety-relevant written work into more intuitive formats for human interaction, i.e., using AI to translate the written operational procedures, guidelines, best practices, and regulations into animated visual content with audio interfaces. Augmented Reality (AR) and Mixed Reality (MR) could also enable new interfaces for safety training and for promoting a good safety culture in engineering enterprises.

3. Safety Analysis Used in Process Intensification

Process Intensification (PI) is one of the inherently safer design principles. However, the results of process safety analysis of process intensified processes are conflicting. In this work, a literature review of process safety analysis applied to process intensification was conducted. This review involved entering the search terms "process intensification" AND "safety" into the Scopus (The University of Auckland) search engine on the 7th of November 2022. The search returned 234 peer-reviewed articles. After removing duplicates, 219 articles remained. These 219 articles come from 113 different sources. Chemical Engineering and Processing - Process Intensification is the most popular source, and 23 of the 219 articles came from this single source. After screening the 219 articles, some articles were identified as having a brief mention of "process safety" but no detailed work on safety. These articles were not considered further. 35 of the 219 articles had more specific discussions of process safety and process intensification. 14 of the 35 articles had further investigated process safety in process intensification using some quantitative methods.

36% of the papers used Individual Risk (IR) as a quantitative indicator to measure the safety improvement achieved through intensification. 28% of the papers used the Fire and Explosion Damage Index (FEDI). The remaining papers used the Process Stream Index (PSI), Process Route Index (PRI), Inherent Safety Index (ISI), and the Inherent Safety Key Performance Indicator (IS-KPI). 80% of the papers using the IR indicator considered the cost and environmental impact simultaneously. IR is the most used indicator in multi-criteria comparison methodologies developed to compare the performance of PI processes. A common goal of process intensification is to achieve cheaper, more sustainable, and safer processes in chemical manufacturing. These comparative studies suggest very small safety improvements in PI processes, when compared to their conventional counterparts.

A limitation of this research is the small number of papers found on the "process safety performance of the PI processes". In the literature reviewed, computer-aided tools are used to build mathematical models for the safety analysis of PI processes. All the papers reviewed only discuss the safety performance of PI processes in their design phase. There is a lack of discussion of PI plants during the operational phase, i.e. PSM, dynamic risk assessment. No firm conclusion could be drawn as to whether safety improvements can be guaranteed by PI over the whole life cycle.

4. Multi-Perspective Process Safety Analysis under Industry 4.0

As part of industry convergence, the chemical process industry is becoming increasingly digitalised and moving towards I4.0. Cloud-based computing, real-time optimisation, and interoperable devices are bringing disruptions to the traditional PSM activities. This work proposes a multi-perspective framework to apply existing safety theories and PSM concepts to computer-aid tools under I4.0, as shown in Figure 1.

The Basic Process Control System (BPCS) is at the bottom of the 5-level pyramid, which was adapted from ANSI/ISA-95, shown in Figure 1 (a). In the chemical process industry, I4.0 technologies enabled streaming of process data, cloud-based process analytics, advanced real-time control optimisation, and the use of interoperable equipment & instruments. Figure 1 (b) shows the Hierarchy of Controls adapted from the Centre for Chemical Process Safety (CCPS). Procedural improvement is at the lowest level of effectiveness in the hierarchy of controls. An example of procedural activity is using computer vision to detect whether personal protective equipment (PPE) is being worn. Automated control on process equipment, i.e. valves, may be considered an active safety barrier, which is the second lowest in the hierarchy, as shown in Figure 1 (b).

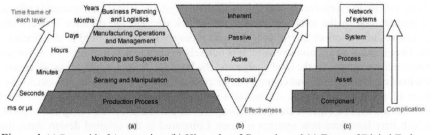

Figure 1 (a) Pyramid of Automation, (b) Hierarchy of Controls, and (c) Types of Digital Twin

Figure 1 (c) shows a pyramid of five different types of Digital Twin (DT) with increasing complexity. The lowest level DT requires a model of a physical component in the cyberspace, which can be analytical, empirical, data-driven/machine learning (AI) or regression-based. Flowsheet simulation is a common type of model found in chemical processes, which is (semi-) empirical. In the process safety practice, FE models of process piping, CFD dispersion models of chemical release, or VR tools used for safety training also have the potential to form the basis of DTs. The above mentioned are physics-based models and some have high fidelity. Due to the different levels of model abstraction, these models are heterogeneous. It is difficult to achieve data exchange between these models.

5. Case Study: Multi-Perspective Safety Analysis of an Ammonia System

In this section, safety analysis is discussed from 1) a life cycle perspective and 2) a hierarchy of controls perspective using a case study of an ammonia refrigeration system. The aim is to form a future-proof theoretical framework for the safety analysis of heating and cooling utility systems in the food processing industry under I4.0.

Food products and by-products make up 45% of New Zealand's total exports and 60% of these products are in refrigerated state (Carson & East, 2018). Meat products require refrigeration after slaughter, while dairy products require refrigeration of raw milk prior to factory processing. Ammonia systems are widely used in NZ for food processing and storage. Anhydrous ammonia (R717) has a zero Ozone Depletion Potential (ODP) and zero Global Warming Potential (GWP). It is also relatively inexpensive, volatile, and has a high latent heat of evaporation.

A waste heat recovery system was retrofitted in an aquatic product processing facility with several ammonia-based chillers (Xie, 2018). The chillers have a cooling capacity of 800kW. The heat recovery system replaced an on-site hot water boiler. The recovered energy is used to heat hot water on site to 40-70 °C and is also sufficient for space heating in winter. Latent heat recovery accounts for 85% of the total energy recovered, which was achieved by a water sourced heat pump. Sensible heat recovered accounts for the remaining 15% by a plate heat exchanger type device. The heat recovery system was installed after the original ammonia refrigeration had been in operation. For life cycle risk analysis, this change in risk profile before and after the retrofit should be captured. A different ranking of hierarchy of controls may be introduced between the existing ammonia refrigeration system, the new water sourced heat pump, and other additional heat recovery equipment.

5.1. Risk Assessment from the Life Cycle Perspective

Toxic release is a well-recognised risk of ammonia systems. The risk of ammonia release is proportional to the total charge, the rate of release, and the distance between the epicentre and personnel. Retrofitting the heat recovery system has little or no effects on the likelihood of an ammonia release. It is unlikely to change the IR as the location of the ammonia storage space, the total charge and the layout of the ammonia pipework remain unchanged. Using the IR indicator, it can be concluded that 'no safety improvement' has been achieved by the retrofit. Ammonia is mildly flammable, and explosive under strict circumstances. The water sourced heat pump was installed close to the refrigeration plant, which may introduce new ignition sources. Compared to the original design state, the FEDI of the ammonia system may be worse due to these new electrical components.

5.2. Safety Evaluation from the Hierarchy of Controls Perspective

'Moderation' is one of the four inherently safer principles. Moderation is usually achieved by reducing the process temperature or pressure. In this case study, the aquatic product processing plant has similar temperature requirements to meat processing plants. For refrigeration (chillers), the temperature requirements are typically at 20-30°C for process cooling, 10°C for boning, 0°C for chilling, and -20°C for freezing. Hot water temperature requirements are 60°C for washdown and 45°C for hand washing. Due to the nature of the relatively mild temperature requirements, the heat recovery system does not significantly affect the process conditions, i.e. temperature or pressure. The heating requirements were met by a boiler prior to the retrofit. At the passive safety barrier level, the overall system safety performance is improved due to the elimination of the boiler. There are minor impacts on the active safety barriers due to changes in the temperature control strategy. The waste heat recovery system may require cooling and heating loads to be matched during operation. The heat recovery equipment also led to changes at the operational procedures level and additional PSM tasks. There is insufficient information to determine whether these will have a negative or positive safety impact.

5.3. Multi-Perspective Framework for Process Safety Enhancement

To improve the energy efficiency of food processing plants, large utility systems are also gradually introducing I4.0 solutions, i.e. DT, Industrial Internet of Things (IIoT). At the same time, smart equipment may also be retrofitted into the facility with live document tracking the design changes. Existing industry best practice guidelines will soon become obsolete as the new operational strategies emerge.

As part of projects to improve the energy efficiency of industrial process plants, on-site personnel trained to operate boilers will be retrained to operate high-temperature heat pumps, absorption chillers or even hydrogen-powered equipment. These retraining programmes will also provide a good opportunity to improve the safety culture of the company. Meanwhile, asset owners will need to rely on refrigeration service providers during this technology transition. Refrigeration as a service (RaaS) could become the new norm in the specialist refrigeration sector. In the future, the introduction of industrial symbiosis and shared utility systems in large industrial complexes may require more systematic process safety assessment. Figure 2 shows a potential approach to multi-perspective process safety analysis for industrial refrigeration systems. In this framework, multi-physics and multi-timescale modelling is to be achieved with DTs at component, asset, system, and network levels for the safety of an ammonia refrigeration system.

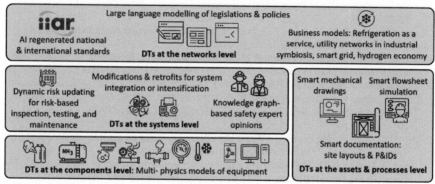

Figure 2 Heterogeneous abstractions in modelling for process safety enhanced DTs

6. Conclusions

The literature review conducted in this work showed that computer-aided safety assessment is found in the design phase of PI. There is a lack of published work on the performance of these 'inherently safer designs' after their construction. Therefore, there is a lack of validation on whether the inherently safer designs have better safety performance throughout the process lifecycle. There is weak evidence on whether process safety is guaranteed by PI processes.

Computer-aided tools are used in safety analysis and other PSM activities. These tools are based on heterogeneous abstractions for computer modelling. Hence, it is difficult to achieve data exchange between different process-safety-related computer-aided tools.

In the process industry, the current implementation of I4.0 technology is mostly found at the lower levels of the automation pyramid. High-fidelity and multi-physics co-simulation may be required to achieve a 'Process Safety Enhanced DT'. With the expanding applications of generative AI, a further step change in PSM is expected soon. To provide a new lens on the safety performance of industrial utility systems under I4.0, this work proposes a multi-perspective approach from the perspective 1) the process lifecycle and 2) the hierarchy of controls.

Considering the Sustainable Development Goals (SDGs), natural refrigerants such as ammonia (NH_3), carbon dioxide (CO_2), and hydrocarbons (propane, isobutane, or zeotropic mixtures) are becoming popular. The refrigeration as a service (RaaS) business model is also gaining momentum in the large industrial utility systems. Future research on safety analysis should be carried out to investigate heat utility system under the new business models and towards the hydrogen economy.

References

J. K. Carson, & A. R. East, 2018, The cold chain in New Zealand – A review. *International Journal of Refrigeration, 87,* 185-192.

J. Janošovský, I. Rosa, G. Vincent, B. Šulgan, M. Variny, Z. Labovská, J. Labovský, & Ľ Jelemenský, 2022, Methodology for selection of inherently safer process design alternatives based on safety indices. *Process Safety and Environmental Protection, 160,* 513–526.

J. Jiménez-Romero, A. Azapagic, & R. Smith, 2023, Systematic Development of Strategies for the Decarbonization of Process Utility Systems. *Computer Aided Chemical Engineering, 52,* 2995–3000.

J. Lee, I. Cameron, & M. Hassall, 2022, Information needs and challenges in future process safety. *Digital Chemical Engineering, 3,* 100017.

S. Park, S. Xu, W. Rogers, H. Pasman, & M. M. El-Halwagi, 2020, Incorporating inherent safety during the conceptual process design stage: A literature review. Journal of Loss Prevention in the Process Industries, 63 (October 2019), 104040.

T. R. Wanasinghe, M. Galagedarage Don, R. Arunthavanathan, & R. G. Gosine, 2022, Industry 4.0 based process data analytics platform. In *Methods in Chemical Process Safety, 6(6),* 101–137.

T. Xie, 2018, Study on Application of Waste Heat Recovery in Ammonia Refrigerator. In *American Journal of Physics and Applications,* 6,162-168.

J. Xuan & T. Daniel, 2023, The Future of Chemical Engineering in the Era of Generative AI. *The Chemical Engineers.* https://www.thechemicalengineer.com/features/the-future-of-chemical-engineering-in-the-era-of-generative-ai/

Flavio Manenti, Gintaras V. Reklaitis (Eds.), Proceedings of the 34th European Symposium on Computer Aided Process Engineering / 15th International Symposium on Process Systems Engineering (ESCAPE34/PSE24), June 2-6, 2024, Florence, Italy

Decomposition methods applied to the design of large-scale CO₂ supply chains

José A. Álvarez-Menchero*, Rubén Ruiz-Femenia, Raquel Salcedo-Díaz, José A. Caballero

Department of Chemical Engineering, University of Alicante. Ap. Correos 99, E-03080, Alicante. Spain.
joseantonio.alvarez@ua.es

Abstract

Global warming poses a significant contemporary challenge, and one proposed solution in literature is Carbon Capture and Storage (CCS). This study focuses on optimizing a CCS Supply Chain, specifically a multi-period design for Europe encompassing carbon capture, transport, and sequestration with diverse data sources and technologies. The inherent complexity of the resulting Mixed Integer Linear Programming problem for high CO_2 reduction targets necessitates exploration of alternative solution methods. To address this, the study proposes an algorithm that combines Generalized Disjunctive Programming and Augmented Lagrangian Relaxation decomposition. The results demonstrate enhanced efficiency and reduced computational time compared to traditional methods, rendering it suitable for large-scale supply chain challenges.

Keywords: Carbon Capture and Storage, Augmented Lagrangian Relaxation, Generalized Disjunctive Programming, decomposition, large-scale, supply chain

1. Introduction

Global warming has emerged as one of the most significant challenges that society faces today. The battle against climate change and the search for innovative solutions to mitigate its effect has turned into the centre of the researcher's attention. One potential approach to reduce the global warming effects could be the design of a Carbon Capture and Storage Supply Chain (CCS SC), as proposed by D'Amore and Bezzo (2017). This supply chain design was obtained from the optimisation of a Mixed Integer Linear Program (MILP), minimising the total cost of the CCS SC while simultaneously trying to reach a CO_2 reduction target over twenty-year horizon. These considerations lead to a large and complex model (No. Variables > 13 Millions & No. Equations > 8 Millions) which becomes intractable for model instances with CO_2 reduction targets exceeding 70%. Furthermore, when introducing new features such as multi-period or parameter uncertainties, it becomes compulsory to explore alternative resolution methods.

In this work, a CCS multi-period supply chain for Europe, based on that presented by D'Amore and Bezzo (2017), is designed. Post-combustion, oxy-fuel combustion and pre-combustion are considered as possible capture technology options. Data on CO_2 emissions and storage sites have been sourced from EDGAR database and CO2Stop Project, respectively. Regarding the CO_2 transport between the capture points and the storage locations, two types of pipelines are available—onshore and offshore pipelines. To incorporate the information from these databases into our model, the following data preprocessing steps are required: i) split into regions the Europe territory, ii) classify the regions based on their location (coastal, inland or maritime), and iii) identify the regions associated with both CO_2 emissions and the storage sites.

Furthermore, if uncertainty of CO_2 emissions with time is considered, it results in an even more complex model to be solve. To overcome the intractability of this model, the CCS supply chain is modelled using both Generalized Disjunctive Programming (GDP) and Augmented Lagrangian Relaxation decomposition. The combination of both techniques is not only useful to reduce the solution time, but also to optimise the supply chain even when the model becomes extremely large and cannot be solve using the classical approaches.

2. Model Description

In this contribution a Carbon Capture and Storage (CCS) system is optimized. To achieve this, the territory under consideration must be divided into regions. Once this division is complete, the model's constraints can be established, which can be classified into four groups: capture constraints, transport constraints, sequestration constraints, and logic constraints, which are described below. Each group has, in turn, a principal variable.

Table 1 shows the main parameters and variables of the CCS multi-period supply chain model.

Table 1. Nomenclature used in the equations.

Indexes
g: regions
t: time
c: capture technologies
l: transport form
q: transport range
$SR_{g,g}$: Regions g' surrounding region g
Parameters
η_c: Capture technology efficiency.
$UC_c^{Capture}$: Capture technology c unitary cost.
$E_{g,t}^{CO_2}$: CO_2 emissions in each region g.
α: Reduction target.
Q_q^{Max}: Range q minimum CO_2 transported.
Q_q^{Max}: Range q maximum CO_2 transported.
C^{IR}: Inshore intra-connection cost.
$Size_g$: Region g size.
$CF_{g,g',l,q}$: Gas pipeline l between regions g and g' fixed cost
$OPEX_{q,l}$: Unitary transport cost.
$Cap^{Injection}$: Well injection capacity.
S_g: Region g storage capacity

Continuous Variables
$Processed_{c,g,t}^{CO_2}$: Processed CO_2 through technology c in region g at time t.
$Q_{g,g',l,q,t}^{CO_2}$: Transported CO_2 from region g to region g' by transport form l in a quantity of q at time t.
$Sequestred_{g,t}^{CO_2}$: Sequestered CO_2 in region g at time t.

Binary Variables

$y_{g,g',t}$ $w_{g,g',l,t}$ $y_{g,g',l,q,t}$

2.1. Capture constraints

- **Constraints 1.** The available CO_2 in each region sets the upper limit for the total processed CO_2.
- **Constraints 2.** Imposes the maximum CO_2 that can be processed for each technology in each region.
- **Constraints 3.** Specifies the minimum CO_2 that must be processed.

2.2. Transport constraints

- **Constraints 4.** Mass balance for each region and time period (eq. **Errore. L'origine riferimento non è stata trovata.**).

$$\sum_c Captured_{c,g,t} + \sum_{g',l,q \in SR_{g,g}} Q_{g',g,l,q,t} = Sequestred_{g,t} + \sum_{g',l,q \in SR_{g,g}} Q_{g,g',l,q,t} \qquad \forall g,t \qquad (1)$$

- **Constraints 5.** Defines the upper and lower bounds of the transport ranges. While transported CO_2 is a continuous variable, it has been discretized due to the variation of transportation cost with the amount of CO2 being carried.

2.3. Sequestration constraints

- **Constraints 6.** Limits the maximum amount of CO_2 that can be sequestered in each region based on its storage capacity.

2.4. Logic constraints

- **Constraints 7.** Prevents cross-transport between regions (eq. (1)).

$$y_{g,g',t} + y_{g',g,t} \leq 1 \qquad \forall g,g,t \in SR_{g,g} \wedge g < g \qquad (2)$$

- **Constraints 8.** The primary binary variable z depends on five indexes. To simplify optimization, two constraints link the binary variable z with two binary variables having a lower number of indexes ($y_{g,g,t}$ and $w_{g,g,l,t}$)
- **Constraints 9.** Impedes transport from a region to itself and prohibits direct transport between non-adjacent regions.
- **Constraints 10.** Constraints to prevent transport in specific cases:
  Onshore pipelines are disallowed if one of the regions is maritime.
  Offshore pipelines are prohibited if one or both of the regions are coastal, and if one of the regions is inland.

3. Decomposition methods: Augmented Lagrangian Relaxation

To face the high complexity of the problem, a strategy based on both GDP and Augmented Lagrangian Decomposition has been tested. To apply Augmented Lagrangian Relaxation, it is necessary to identify what are commonly referred to as "complicating constraints. These constraints are the ones that, when relaxed, enable the decomposition of the model into smaller and less complex problems.

In this problem, the complicating constraints are identified within the transport constraints, specifically the mass balances (eq. (1)). These equations work a bond between capture, sequestration, and transport variables, and consequently, between these groups. Without the presence of mass balances, the model could be divided into three separate problems (capture, transport, and sequestration). These problems could further be

subdivided based on their indexes (g, l, q, t) if the problem's structure allows it. This constitutes the first complicating constraint. Additionally, eq. (2) which links each region g with their surrounding regions g', prevents the decomposition of the transport subproblem into regions. Therefore, it constitutes the second complicating constraint.
Once the complicating constraints have been identified, the subsequent subproblems result from dividing the model through the application of Augmented Lagrangian Relaxation.

3.1. First subproblem (Capture subproblem)

$$\underset{Processed_{c,g,t}^{(k)}}{Minimize} \; z^p = \sum_{c,g,t} \left(UC_c^{Capture} \eta_c Processed_{c,g,t}^{(k)} \right) + C^{IR} \sum_{c,g,t} \left(Size_g \eta_c Processed_{c,g,t}^{(k)} \right)$$

$$+ \sum_{c,g,t} \left(\rho_{g,t}^{(k-1)} \eta_c Processed_{c,g,t}^{(k)} \right)$$

$$+ \gamma \left[\sum_{g,t} \left(\sum_c \left(\eta_c Processed_{c,g,t}^{(k)} \right) + \sum_{g',l,q \in SR_{g,g'}} Q_{g',g,l,q,t}^{(k-1)} - Sequestred_{g,t}^{(k-1)} - \sum_{g',l,q \in SR_{g,g'}} Q_{g,g',l,q,t}^{(k-1)} \right)^2 \right]$$

Subject to

$$\sum_c Processed_{c,g,t}^{(k)} \le E_{g,t}^{CO_2} \quad \forall g,t \tag{3}$$

$$Processed_{c,g,t}^{(k)} \le \gamma_{g,c} E_{g,t}^{CO_2} \quad \forall c,g,t \tag{4}$$

$$\alpha \sum_{g,t} E_{g,t}^{CO_2} - \sum_{c,g,t} Processed_{c,g,t}^{(k)} \le 0 \tag{5}$$

3.2. Second group of subproblems (Transport subproblems)

$$\underset{z_{g,g',l,q,t}^{(k)}, Q_{g,g',l,q,t}^{(k)}, y_{g,g',t}^{(k)}}{Minimize} \quad z_{g,g',t}^Q = \sum_{l,q} \left(CF_{g,g',l,q} z_{g,g',l,q,t} + D_{g,g'} Q_{g,g',l,q,t}^{CO_2} OPEX_{q,l} \right)$$

$$- \rho_{g,t}^{(k-1)} \left(\sum_{l,q} Q_{g,g',l,q,t}^{(k)} \right) + \lambda_{g,g,t}^{(k-1)} y_{g,g',t}^{(k)}$$

$$+ \gamma \left[\left(\sum_c \left(\eta_c Processed_{c,g,t}^{(Calc)} \right) + \sum_{g'',l,q \in SR_{g,g'}} Q_{g'',g,l,q,t}^{(k-1)} + \sum_{g'',l,q \in SR_{g,g'}} Q_{g'',g,l,q,t}^{(Calc)} \right. \right.$$
$$\left. \left. - Sequestred_{g,t}^{(k-1)} - \sum_{g'',l,q \in SR_{g,g'}} Q_{g,g'',l,q,t}^{(k-1)} - \sum_{g',l,q \in SR_{g,g'}} Q_{g,g'',l,q,t}^{(Calc)} - \sum_{l,q \in SR_{g,g'}} Q_{g,g',l,q,t}^{(k)} \right)^2 \right]$$

$$+ \gamma \left[\left(y_{g,g',t}^{(k)} + y_{g',g,t \in (g' \ge g)}^{(k-1)} + y_{g',g,t \in (g' \le g)}^{(Calc)} - 1 + h_{g,g',t}^{(k)} \right)^2 \right]$$

Subject to

$$Q_{g,g',l,q,t}^{(k)} \le Q_q^{Max} \cdot z_{g,g',l,q,t}^{(k)} \quad \forall l,q \tag{6}$$

$$Q_{g,g',l,q,t}^{(k)} \geq Q_q^{Min} \cdot z_{g,g',l,q,t}^{(k)} \qquad \forall l,q \tag{7}$$

$$\sum_l w_{g,g',l,t}^{(k)} - y_{g,g',t}^{(k)} = 0 \tag{8}$$

$$\sum_q z_{g,g',l,q,t}^{(k)} - w_{g,g',l,t}^{(k)} = 0 \qquad \forall l \tag{9}$$

$$y, w, z \in \{0,1\}$$

3.3. Third group of subproblems (Sequestration subproblem)

$$\underset{Sequestred_{g,t}^{(k)}}{Minimize} \; z_g^S = \sum_t \left(\frac{CS}{Cap^{Injection}} Sequestred_{g,t}^{(k)} \right) - \sum_t \left(\rho_{g,t}^{(k-1)} Sequestred_{g,t}^{(k)} \right)$$

$$+ \gamma \left[\sum_t \left(\sum_c \left(\eta_c Processed_{c,g,t}^{(Calc)} \right) + \sum_{g',l,q \in SR_{g,g'}} Q_{g',g,l,q,t}^{(calc)} - Sequestred_{g,t}^{(k)} - \sum_{g',l,q \in SR_{g,g'}} Q_{g,g',l,q,t}^{(Calc)} \right)^2 \right]$$

Subject to

$$\sum_t Sequestred_{g,t}^{(k)} - S_g \leq 0 \tag{10}$$

$$Sequestred_{g,t}^{(k)} \geq 0 \quad \forall t \tag{11}$$

3.4. Algorithm
The augmented Lagrangian decomposition method has been applied to our case study following this algorithm:

Step 1. Fix an initial value for the multipliers $\rho_{g,t}^{k-1}$, $\lambda_{g,g',t}^{k-1} = 1$, and variables $Q_{g,g',l,q,t}^{k-1}$, $Sequestred_{c,g,t}^{k-1}, y_{g,g,t}^{k-1} = 0$.

Step 2. Compute the first subproblem and obtain $Processed_{c,g,t}^k$.

Step 3. $Processed_{c,g,t}^{calc} = Processed_{c,g,t}^k$. Compute the second group of subproblems. Whenever subproblems were being solved, the values of $Q_{g,g',l,q,t}^k$ and $y_{g,g',t}^k$ are obtained. These values are used in the subproblems that are not computed yet, being
$Q_{g,g',l,q,t}^{calc} = Q_{g,g',l,q,t}^k$ and $y_{g,g',t}^{calc} = y_{g,g',t}^k$.

Step 4. Compute the third group of subproblems and obtain $Sequestred_{c,g,t}^1$.

Step 5. Evaluate the value of the complicating constraints $(CM_{g,t}^k, CL_{g,g',t}^k)$ at the current iteration.

Step 6. Update the penalty parameter γ:

if $\left| CM_{g,t}^k \right| + \left| CL_{g,g',t}^k \right| \geq 0.8 \left| CM_{g,t}^{k-1} \right| + \left| CL_{g,g',t}^{k-1} \right|$, set $\gamma^{k+1} = 1.2\gamma^k$, otherwise, set $\gamma^{k+1} = \gamma^k$

Step 7. Update multipliers:

$$\rho_{g,t}^k = \rho_{g,,t}^{k-1} + \gamma^{k+1} CM_{g,t}^k$$

$$\lambda_{g,g',t}^k = \lambda_{g,g',t}^{k-1} + \gamma^{k+1} CL_{g,g',t}^k$$

4. Results

The computational results obtained using the original and the decomposed formulation are shown below in Table 2 and Table 3, respectively. As can be seen, the computational time has been significantly reduced, even the originally intractable problem has been solved. Furthermore, the gap has been considerably diminished.

Table 2. Computational results of without decomposition.

α	Time, s	Gap, %
0.6	623	1.11
0.7	1530	2.06
0.8	3600	7.02
0.9	Intractable	-

Table 3. Computational results applying Augmented Lagrangian relaxation.

α	Time, s	Gap, %
0.6	91	0.63
0.7	140	0.85
0.8	511	1.11
0.9	854	3.68

5. Conclusions

To tackle the challenge of solving large-scale supply chains, we propose an algorithm that integrates both Generalized Disjunctive Programming (GDP) and Augmented Lagrangian Relaxation decomposition. This formulation enables the attainment of a feasible supply chain design for instances that were previously intractable without decomposition techniques, particularly for CO2 reduction targets exceeding 70%. Furthermore, the decomposition algorithm markedly diminishes computation time for instances that are tractable in both approaches.

Acknowledgments

The authors gratefully acknowledge financial support to the Generalitat Valenciana, Spain, PROMETEO/2020/064 and to the Spanish "Ministerio de Ciencia e Innovación" under project PID2021-124139NB-C21.

References

D'Amore, F., Bezzo, F., 2017. Economic optimisation of European supply chains for CO2 capture, transport and sequestration.
JRC, 2021. Emission Database for Global Atmospheric Research (EDGAR).
JRC, 2014. CO2StoP project.
Li, Z., Ierapetritou, M.G., 2009. Production planning and scheduling integration through augmented Lagrangian optimization.

Flavio Manenti, Gintaras V. Reklaitis (Eds.), Proceedings of the 34th European Symposium on Computer Aided Process Engineering / 15th International Symposium on Process Systems Engineering (ESCAPE34/PSE24), June 2-6, 2024, Florence, Italy

Enhancing Chemical Process Simulation through a GPU-Optimized Framework: Implementation and Validation of Equation-Oriented Methods using CUDA

Shaoyi Yang, Xufei Tian, Shifeng Qu, Zhaoyang Duan, Minglei Yang, Feng Qian, Wenli Du*

Key Laboratory of Smart Manufacturing in Energy Chemical Process, Ministry of Education, East China University of Science and Technology, Shanghai, 200237, China
E-mail: wldu@ecust.edu.cn

Abstract

In the realm of chemical engineering, the simulation of complex process systems frequently entails solving interconnected equations on a large scale. Traditional methods are difficult to handle higher-dimensional computing, particularly hose necessitating increased real-time processing capabilities. This study aims to significantly enhance the computational efficiency of equation-oriented (EO) methods by leveraging Graphics Processing Units (GPUs), primarily utilizing the CUDA programming paradigm exploit the parallel processing capabilities of GPUs. We present a novel GPU-based framework tailored for chemical process simulations. This framework segments the thermodynamic computations and other complex tasks within the EO method, using GPU's massive parallel capabilities to simultaneously update each thermodynamic parameter in batches, significantly enhancing the overall efficiency of parameter computation.

This work first demonstrates the tasks split method within the EO structure, followed by the utilization of CUDA graph on GPUs for parallel computation of thermodynamic parameters after the breakdown of tasks. Extensive result analyses are provided, validating that using a consumer-grade GPU achieve nearly a 100-fold enhancement in performance, while preserving identical accuracy.

Keywords: Equation-Oriented, GPU, nonlinear solver, CUDA.

1. Introduction

In industrial process simulation, the Sequential Modular (SM) method simulates each module separately and resolves them iteratively, whereas the Equation-Oriented (EO) approach achieves synchronous optimization of the process by establishing and solving a set of nonlinear equations. The EO method excels in simultaneously handling all equations and variables, employing efficient large-scale solvers and precise derivative computations, making it particularly suited for complex processes with nested loops and intricate design specifications. Compared to the SM approach, the EO method offers greater accuracy and flexibility in process design and performance optimization.

Although the EO approach has distinct advantages in simultaneous optimization and convergence efficiency, solving large-scale models still requires substantial computational effort. Dowling & Biegler (2015) designed a framework for large scale EO modelling, putting forward a large-scale parallel outlook. The IDAES project (Miller, 2018) demonstrates the power of the EO method when integrated with modern modeling tools.

The duration required to solve equations serves as a crucial performance metric for the solver's efficiency. Despite the possibility of accelerating convergence and reducing iteration numbers through mathematical techniques, each iteration necessitates updating the thermodynamic state for all equations, with the computational speed of the thermodynamic parameters involved in each equation directly impacting the actual execution time of the program. On the other hand, despite the mature applications of GPUs in scientific computing tasks such as deep learning and fluid dynamics, there is almost no generic parallel solution based on GPUs in the field of process simulation. Ma (2016) attempted to accelerate the large sets of equations using multicore processors and GPU but faced limitations due to inadequate computational distribution. This led to excessive computational loads on individual GPU threads and insufficient degrees of parallelism, failing to significantly improve GPU performance. Nikolić (2018) developed CUDA based parallel program for DAE equations, yet it was limited to relatively simple computational tasks and fell short in handing complex chemical simulation. To addressing these gaps, we propose a novel, large-scale parallel framework designed specifically for chemical process simulation based on the GPU architecture. This framework systematically organizes the thermodynamic computations and other complex tasks within the EO method, leveraging the GPU's massive parallel capabilities to simultaneously update each thermodynamic parameter in batches, thereby significantly enhancing the overall computation efficiency.

2. Thermodynamic calculations based on CUDA graph

A typical workflow of the EO approach in process simulation and optimization consists of several steps, including initialization, parameter calculation, function evaluation and/or gradient evaluation, iterate updating, and termination judgment. Within this workflow, the computation of thermodynamics parameters is notably time intensive. Conventional platforms such as gPROMS and AspenPlus update parameters serially by calling external thermodynamic interfaces. As depicted in Figure 1, for the large sparse matrices establish by actual processes, computing each thermodynamic equation involves numerous parameter calculations. Given that the independence of these parameter updates, they can be grouped into batches. These batches of thermodynamic parameters awaiting computation are dispatched in parallel to the GPU. Here, the updates occur simultaneously. Upon completion, the updated results are fed back into the sparse matrix, setting the stage for the subsequent iterative resolution of the nonlinear equations system.

Enhancing Chemical Process Simulation through a GPU-Optimized Framework: Implementation and Validation of Equation-Oriented Methods using CUDA

3273

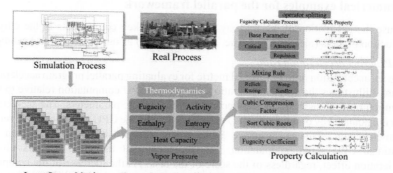

Figure 1. The calculation process and calculation elements of EO method

Figure 2 illustrates the workflow and execution strategy of large-scale parallel computation of thermodynamic parameters on GPUs. This process entails breaking down the thermodynamics calculations into specific functional operators, which are then scheduled for parallel execution via a computational graph. In practical applications, state parameters such as component fractions, temperature, and pressure are extracted from each equation and fed into the parallel program, allowing for the simultaneous resolution of all thermodynamic parameters required by each equation.

Taking the cubic state equation of state SRK as an example, the basic workflow for the computation of thermodynamic parameters, such as the fugacity coefficient, can be decomposed into the following steps: calculating base state parameters, computing mixing rules, solving the cubic equation for the compression factor, sorting the compression factors, and calculating the fugacity coefficients. These operators are individually written as CUDA kernel functions, tailored with specific computational tasks. During execution, CUDA Graphs are utilized to schedule each kernel, enabling the distribution of computational tasks across the GPU threads. Thermodynamic calculations require access to certain fundamental physical properties, which remain read-only during computation and therefore are loaded into shared memory for more efficient access by all threads within the same block, as depicted by the memory structure in Figure 2. This approach maximizes the efficient utilization of the GPU, and the execution of each kernel is carried out by the GPU's Streaming Multiprocessors. Leveraging the GPU's architectural design, our program significantly outperforms multicore CPU parallelism in terms of acceleration ratios.

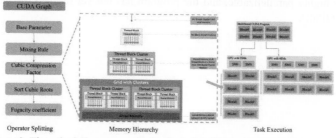

Figure 2. The calculation process and calculation elements of EO method

In this paper, the SRK Thermodynamic model is coded in C++, the GPU version program is developed using CUDA. The implementation has been conducted on both an Intel multi-core-processor platform and an NVIDIA GPU GTX4060 platform.

S. Yang et al.

3. Numerical examples for the parallel framework

We use the calculation of the fugacity coefficient for key components in the ethylene production process (methane, ethylene, ethane, propane) as our numerical test example.

3.1. Program acceleration ratio

Program acceleration ratio is a crucial metric for evaluating parallel program acceleration. Figure 3 illustrates the acceleration ratio achieved by GPU computation relative to CPU execution time, across various numbers of thermodynamic parameters. The acceleration ratio is calculated by dividing the CPU execution time by the GPU execution time, serving as an indicator of the performance enhancement afforded by GPU parallelism over traditional CPU serial computation. It is evident that the GPU delivers obvious acceleration effect, regardless of the scale of the task. As the increase of the computing scale, the overall acceleration ratio significantly improves, and different kernel functions have different acceleration performance. Observing the trends, we can categorize the calculations into two distinct groups based on their acceleration profiles: consistent acceleration group and variable acceleration group.

3.1.1. Consistent Acceleration Group

Consistent acceleration group includes the Base Parameter, Cubic Compression Factor, and Sort Cubic Roots computations. These three metrics demonstrate a relatively uniform trend in the acceleration ratio as the number of parameters increases. The slight upward trajectory suggests that while the GPU provides a consistent computational advantage over the CPU for these tasks, the extent of the advantage does not dramatically increase with the task complexity. This indicates that the program reaches the memory and computing limits of the GPU prematurely and fails to fully harness its performance potential.

3.1.2. Variable Acceleration Group

The Mixing Rule and Fugacity Coefficient calculations, on the other hand, exhibit distinct profiles:

Mixing Rule: The acceleration ratio for the Mixing Rule calculation maintains a stable profile as the number of thermodynamic parameters increases. With the expansion of scale, the acceleration ratio further improves. Although it exhibits a greater acceleration ratio than other kernel functions, it can still be clearly found that the calculation has reached its performance bottleneck.

Fugacity Coefficient: In stark contrast, the Fugacity Coefficient computation shows a significant upward trend, indicating a notable performance improvement when transitioning from CPU to GPU as the number of parameters grows. This suggests that the task is highly parallelizable, and the program has not yet reached the memory and computing limits.

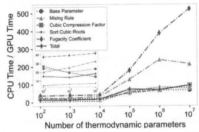

Figure 3. The calculation process and calculation elements of EO method

Enhancing Chemical Process Simulation through a GPU-Optimized
Framework: Implementation and Validation of Equation-Oriented Methods
using CUDA   3275

Overall, Figure 3 suggests that while GPUs can provide computational benefits for all types of tasks, the extent of these benefits varies depending on the nature of the computations involved. Tasks with greater inherent parallelizability exhibit more substantial acceleration, which highlights the importance of aligning computational tasks with the most suitable hardware architecture to maximize performance efficiency.

3.2. Time-consuming analysis of different kernel functions

Due to the sequential execution of the calculation graph, the most time-consuming function will limit the execution of the whole system as a shortcoming for the whole process, so it is important to analyze the time-consuming of specific programs.

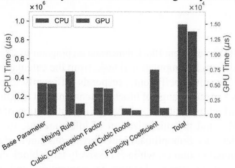

Figure 4. Specific time-consuming analysis of the program

Figure 4 illustrates the computational times, measured in microseconds, for various functions executed on CPUs and GPUs. The left y-axis corresponds to CPU time ($\times 10^6 \mu s$), while the right side corresponds to GPU time($\times 10^4 \mu s$), because of the GPU times are significantly lower, hence the need for a separate scale to accommodate the smaller values. Fugacity Coefficient and Mixing Rule calculation spend the most time in CPU mode, however these two functions have the largest acceleration ratio on the GPU, this indicates that the significant improvement offered by the GPU is also significant for the overall operation. In addition, it is important to highlight that the total time of each function is not equal to the time consuming of the whole calculation graph Total because the compiler will fuse the assembly code to reduce unnecessary data replication.

4. Optimize GPU execution efficiency.

The block dimension (blockdim) is a pivotal configuration parameter in GPU programming that directly influences the granularity of parallelism and the efficiency of resource allocation within the GPU's architecture. The selection of an appropriate blockdim is essential to achieve an optimal balance between parallel workload distribution and hardware utilization. To illustrate this, experiments have been conducted to observe the effect of different blockdim on program acceleration under different model sizes.

The Figure 5 illustrates the acceleration ratio across varying computational scales, with the horizontal axis representing different block dimensions (blockdim), and the vertical axis depicting the corresponding acceleration ratio. The data is segmented into multiple graphs representing different values of model size (n), denoting the number of thermodynamic parameters being computed. These graphs collectively demonstrate the performance impact of block dimension on GPU execution time relative to CPU time for several thermodynamic calculation tasks.

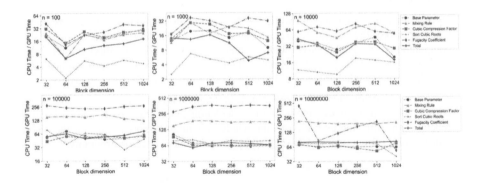

Figure 5. Effect of different Block dimension on program acceleration

As showed in Figure 5, each computational task, from the calculation of base parameters to the evaluation of fugacity coefficients, responds differently to changes in blockdim. Notably, there exists a specific range of block dimensions that maximizes the acceleration ratio for each task, which is indicative of the optimal utilization of the GPU's streaming multiprocessors (SMs) and the minimization of idle time due to thread divergence or memory access bottlenecks. Suboptimal block dimensions can lead to underutilization of the GPU's computational resources, while excessively large block dimensions may cause an oversubscription of resources, leading to contention and reduced throughput. Therefore, the careful tuning of blockdim is instrumental in harnessing the full computational prowess of GPU.

Consequently, the insights underscore the critical role of blockdim in the optimization of GPU programs. The findings serve as a testament to the necessity of deliberate parameter tuning to align with the architecture-specific characteristics of GPUs, thereby ensuring that the parallel computational capabilities are fully leveraged for enhanced scientific computing performance.

5. Conclusions

This paper advances the calculation of the EO model by introducing a parallel architecture based on the GPU platform. It proposes a method for large-scale parallel calculation of thermodynamic parameters and conducts a comparative analysis of GPU acceleration performance in different problem dimensions and shows the acceleration effect of the program at the performance bottleneck. Moreover, the execution of the program on the GPU is optimized by blockdim. This work will provide a far-reaching impact on the GPU parallel programming of process simulation.

References

Ma, Y., Shao, Z., Chen, X., & Biegler, L. T. (2016). A parallel function evaluation approach for solution to large-scale equation-oriented models. Computers & Chemical Engineering, 93, 309-322.

Nikolić, D. D. (2018). Parallelisation of equation-based simulation programs on heterogeneous computing systems. PeerJ Computer Science, 4, e160.

Dowling, A. W., & Biegler, L. T. (2015). A framework for efficient large scale equation-oriented flowsheet optimization. Computers & Chemical Engineering, 72, 3-20.

Miller, D. C., Siirola, J. D., Agarwal, D., Burgard, A. P., Lee, A., Eslick, J. C., ... & Gunter, D. (2018). Next generation multi-scale process systems engineering framework. In Computer Aided Chemical Engineering (Vol. 44, pp. 2209-2214). Elsevier.

Flavio Manenti, Gintaras V. Reklaitis (Eds.), Proceedings of the 34th European Symposium on Computer Aided Process Engineering / 15th International Symposium on Process Systems Engineering (ESCAPE34/PSE24), June 2-6, 2024, Florence, Italy

A hybrid evolutionary algorithm for multi-energy system planning under uncertainty

Hagen Seele[a], Florian Seibel[a], Dörthe Franzisca Hagedorn[a], Christiane Reinert[a], Niklas von der Assen[a,*]

[a]*Institute of Technical Thermodynamics, RWTH Aachen University, Schinkelstr. 8, 52062 Aachen, Germany*
[*]niklas.vonderassen@ltt.rwth-aachen.de

Abstract

The transition from fossil-based to renewable energy systems is accompanied by many uncertainties. Thus, reliable decision-making tools for energy system planners are vital. This paper introduces a hybrid evolutionary algorithm (HEA) for energy system planning while considering multiple sources of uncertainty. The HEA minimizes the expected total annualized cost of a sector-coupled energy system by solving a two-stage stochastic program. The algorithm combines an evolutionary algorithm for the first-stage investment decisions with global optimization for second-stage operational decisions. Our HEA contains three key developments: (i) a graph-based representation of energy systems rendering the definition of a superstructure obsolete, (ii) a subsystem recombination operator for refining design candidates, and (iii) an extendable mutation operation based on a so-called energy conversion hierarchy. We evaluate the HEA in terms of computational performance and solution quality within a case study. The case study focuses on designing an industrial energy system. As a benchmark approach, we use a superstructure-based design optimization. We compare the approaches for design tasks of increasing complexity, i.e., we increase the number of scenarios for the two-stage stochastic programs. We find that the HEA can identify designs of slightly lower total annualized cost compared to the superstructure-based optimization. Furthermore, we find that the computational time of the HEA increases less strongly when considering a higher number of scenarios. Thus, the HEA can be a promising alternative to superstructure-based approaches for identifying energy system designs under uncertainty.

Keywords: Synthesis, Distributed multi-energy systems, Multiple uncertainties, Graph-based representation.

1. Introduction

Transitioning from fossil-based to renewable energy systems necessitates prompt investments in complex infrastructure, despite facing uncertainties (Roald et al., 2023). Here, process system engineering techniques as reviewed by Pistikopoulous et al. (2021), can aid solving design tasks regarding synthesis and design decisions. For example, superstructure-based optimization has been successfully applied to energy system planning problems. To consider uncertainty in energy system planning, various methods exist, e.g., stochastic programming (Fodstad et al., 2022). However, developing feasible solution strategies can be challenging as superstructure-based optimization models often yield large-scale non-convex optimization problems which can be hard to solve (Mencarelli et al., 2020). To deal with the potentially prohibitive computational burden of solving the design task, evolutionary algorithms (EAs) can be a valuable search heuristic. Zhou et al. (2013) develop a superstructure-based hybrid EA adopting an EA for chemical batch scheduling and apply it to an energy system planning problem. However, the loss in computational performance did not outweigh the benefits of considering uncertainty in their case study. Furthermore, defining superstructures can already be a cumbersome task. Voll et al. (2012) develop a sophisticated superstructure-free approach featuring a problem-specific EA for solving the design task; however, without the consideration of uncertainty. In this paper, we build upon their superstructure-free approach by considering uncertainty with a two-stage stochastic program and using a two-stage decomposition like Zhou et al. (2013). As the EA of Voll et al. (2012) does not address component sizing, adopting their approach is non-trivial: We extend the mutation operator of Voll et al. (2012) to also adjust component capacities, introduce a recombination operator, and propose a graph-based representation. Besides, we note that our approach adopts an evolution strategy and parameter control, both being outlined by Eiben and Smith (2015). In the following, we present our superstructure-free hybrid evolutionary algorithm for energy system planning under uncertainty.

2. Method: Hybrid evolutionary algorithm for energy system planning

2.1. Overview

Our hybrid evolutionary algorithm (HEA) aims to solve a two-stage stochastic program with recourse for energy system planning under uncertainty. Here, uncertainty is represented by a set of probability-weighted scenarios. The HEA aims to identify the individual, i.e., energy system design, with the highest fitness. We measure the fitness of an individual by the expected total annualized cost to be able to rank designs candidates. The key idea of our HEA for solving the stochastic program is to address the investment decision variables with an EA and the operational decision variables with global optimization: an EA addresses the first stage of the here-and-now decisions while the second stage of the wait-and-see decisions is addressed by solving mixed-integer linear programs (MILPs). As a consequence, we can define independent MILPs for determining operational expenditure for each scenario removing the ties between the scenario subproblems. This decoupling reduces subproblem complexity and allows for parallel computation.

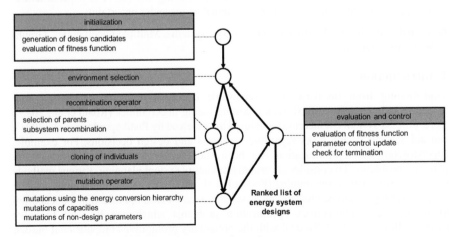

Figure 1: Steps of the hybrid evolutionary algorithm.

Figure 1 shows the steps of our HEA explained in the following. To approach the design task, the HEA starts off with an initialization step. The initialization randomly generates a large set of individuals, evaluates their fitness, and conducts a tournament selection to obtain the initial population of a predefined size. The fitness evaluation involves determining capital expenditure using cost correlations and solving MILPs for determining operational expenditure for the considered scenarios. The population, i.e., a set of individuals representing energy system designs, is updated in each iteration of the HEA. To update a population, the HEA performs environment selections constraining the population size, recombinations, mutations, and fitness evaluations until reaching a predetermined number of iterations or a time limit. Ultimately, the HEA yields the design with the lowest expected total annualized cost identified during its runtime.

2.2. Novel key components

The three key components introduced in this work are the graph-based representation, the recombination operator, and the extended mutation operator. We define a **graph-based representation** using a weighted graph $G = (V, E, l_V)$ and graph weight l_G to specify an individual. The graph G encodes an energy system design as well as additional parameters influencing the HEA's behavior during runtime. Each vertex in the set of vertices V of the graph corresponds to one component of the energy system. The vertex weight l_V defines the type and capacity of each component as well as a parameter influencing the strength of capacity mutations. The graph weight l_G defines parameters influencing the frequency of mutations resulting in the removal, exchange, or addition of components. For encoding designs, we assume lossless connections for each energy carrier and thus an implicit definition of component connections. Consequently, the set of edges E remains empty. By using this graph-based representation, the HEA does not require the cumbersome definition of a superstructure. For superstructure-based approaches, problem complexity can increase exponentially with the number of equipment considered in the superstructure. As our graph-based representation puts no restrictions on the types and number of components, we classify our approach as superstructure-free.

Building upon the work of Voll et al. (2012), we develop an EA for investments decisions by extending their mutation operator and introducing a recombination operator. Alike the graph-based representation, the two variation operators (i.e., recombination and mutation operator) are adapted to the energy system planning problem. Adapting the variation operators to the design task aims to enhance the performance of the HEA by incorporating problem-specific knowledge. Our **recombination operator** seeks to combine beneficial properties from two distinct individuals using a subsystem recombination approach and is inspired by Emmerich et al. (2001). Furthermore, the recombination operator addresses the issue that common recombination operators cannot be applied to graphs. For recombining, the components of an individual are assigned to a subsystem according to their main function (e.g., a heat pump is assigned to the heating subsystem). The recombination operator randomly chooses for each subsystem which individual ought to provide the respective components, i.e., component type and capacity. Certain other parameters of the HEA, i.e., the parameters influencing the HEA's behavior, are recombined either similarly or by determining the arithmetic mean. As recombining individuals can reduce diversity of a population, the recombination operator is bypassed at times and individuals are cloned instead. The **extended mutation operator** aims to allow exploring the solution space and escaping local optima by addressing the four principles for the design of mutation operators also considered by Voll et al. (2012): scalability, reachability, locality, and symmetry. The mutation operator of Voll et al.

(2012) utilizes an energy conversion hierarchy (ECH) offering an easily definable yet rational component replacement strategy but does not adjust the capacity of components. Our extended mutation operator uses an ECH and additionally alters component types as well as component capacities.

3. Results

We evaluate the developed HEA in terms of computational performance and solution quality using a case study adapted from the literature. The case study is based on the work of Sass et al. (2020) and aims for designing an industrial energy system to fulfill heating, cooling, and electricity demands. We construct probability-weighted scenarios similarly to Mavromatidis et al. (2018). The scenarios $s \in S$ occurring with the probability π_s exhibit different energy demands, electricity prices, and gas prices. As a benchmark approach, we use a superstructure-based design optimization. The benchmark solves the same two-stage stochastic programs directly while also minimizing the expected total annualized cost as given in Eq. (1). Both approaches use identical component models and identical model parameters to determine the capital expenditure $CAPEX$, the operational expenditure $OPEX$, and the expected total annualized cost TAC.

$$\min \mathbb{E}(TAC) = \underbrace{\underbrace{CAPEX}_{\substack{\text{capital} \\ \text{expenditure}}} + \underbrace{\sum_{s \in S} \pi_s \cdot OPEX_s}_{\substack{\text{expected operational} \\ \text{expenditure}}}}_{\text{expected total annualized cost}} \tag{1}$$

We compare the HEA with the benchmark approach for design tasks of increasing complexity: we set up four two-stage stochastic programs with 1, 4, 16, and 64 scenarios, respectively. Figure 2 shows the observed solution quality over time for multiple algorithm runs. All runs are terminated after 40 hours, and we repeat runs to examine the stochastic nature of the HEA. For the cases of 1, 4, and 16 scenarios, both approaches yield similar high-quality solutions. For the case of 16 scenarios, the HEA yields a design with slightly lower expected total annualized cost (i.e., -0.1 % compared to benchmark solution; remaining optimality gap of benchmark: 1.1 %). As expected, increasing the number of scenarios considered severely lowers the computational performance of both approaches. However, even though the HEA matches the benchmark in terms of solution quality, the HEA's convergence rate is worse in three of the four cases and the superstructure-based approach excels particularly for the easier design tasks (e.g., the benchmark approach finds the final design approx. 100 times faster than the HEA when only one scenario is considered). Nevertheless, notably, both approaches show a comparable increase in solution quality over time for the hardest design task. This trend indicates that the HEA is less penalized by an increased problem difficulty suggesting that the HEA can be a promising solution strategy for design tasks of elevated complexity. Furthermore, we observe a consistent convergence behavior for the cases in which we run the HEA multiple times, in spite of the stochastic nature of EAs. However, no general statements regarding the HEA's reliability to find high-quality solutions can be made, as we consider only a limited set of problem instances. Besides, it is worth noting that our preliminary results indicate that adding promising design candidates to the initialization, e.g., designs obtained by a superstructure-based optimization considering only one scenario, can significantly improve the overall performance.

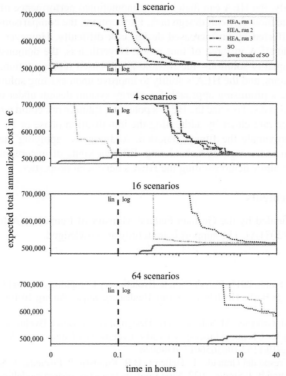

Figure 2: Progress of the developed hybrid evolutionary algorithm (HEA) in comparison to the upper and lower bound of the superstructure-based optimization (SO) as reference.

4. Conclusions

Prompt investments in energy infrastructure are required despite multiple sources of uncertainty (e.g., due to uncertain energy prices, demands, availability of renewables, extreme events, potential component or grid outages, future technology parameters, investment costs, or policies). Uncertainties increase the complexity of design tasks underscoring the need for reliable energy system planning methods. In this work, we present a superstructure-free hybrid evolutionary algorithm (HEA) for designing energy systems under uncertainty. The HEA utilizes stage decomposition enabling parallel computing and reducing subproblem complexity. The three key components of the developed approach are (i) the graph-based representations making the algorithm superstructure-free; (ii) the subsystem recombination enabling the usage of a recombination operator for refining the solution quality; and (iii) the extended mutation operator featuring an energy conversion hierarchy (ECH). The developed components aim to avoid the generation of invalid design candidates and thus to increase computational performance. In a case study adapted from the literature, we compare the HEA with a superstructure-based design optimization using four design tasks of increasing difficulty. We show that the HEA can reach similar or, in certain cases, a slightly better solution quality than the benchmark. As expected, the complexity added by considering uncertainty impedes the computational performance of both approaches.

In the case study, the HEA can match the computational performance of the benchmark approach for the most difficult design task. Furthermore, the comparisons shows that the HEA is less affected by an increased design task difficulty. However, the benchmark outperforms the HEA in three of four cases. Nevertheless, the demonstrated ability to generate high-quality solutions, the flexible graph-based representation, the extendable variation operators, and the HEA's ability to improve upon existing solutions renders the algorithm to be a promising approach for energy system design under uncertainty, i.e., complex design tasks. To seize the HEA's potential, future work could aim for improving the convergence rate either by addressing the initialization phase or by using surrogate models to approximate the fitness function. Additionally, applying the HEA to more difficult design tasks, e.g., by considering different kinds of uncertainties or seasonal storages, might allow demonstrating the HEA's beneficial properties.

Acknowledgements

This study is funded by the German Federal Ministry of Economic Affairs and Energy (ref. no.: 03EN2031A). The support is gratefully acknowledged.

References

A.E. Eiben, J.E. Smith, 2015. Introduction to Evolutionary Computing, Natural Computing Series. Springer Berlin Heidelberg, Berlin, Heidelberg. https://doi.org/10.1007/978-3-662-44874-8

M. Emmerich, M. Grötzner, M. Schütz, 2001. Design of Graph-Based Evolutionary Algorithms: A Case Study for Chemical Process Networks. Evolutionary Computation 9, 329–354. https://doi.org/10.1162/106365601750406028

M. Fodstad, P. Crespo del Granado, L. Hellemo, B.R. Knudsen, P. Pisciella, A. Silvast, C. Bordin, S. Schmidt, J. Straus, 2022. Next frontiers in energy system modelling: A review on challenges and the state of the art. Renewable and Sustainable Energy Reviews 160, 112246. https://doi.org/10.1016/j.rser.2022.112246

G. Mavromatidis, K. Orehounig, J. Carmeliet, 2018. Design of distributed energy systems under uncertainty: A two-stage stochastic programming approach. Applied Energy 222, 932–950. https://doi.org/10.1016/j.apenergy.2018.04.019

L. Mencarelli, Q. Chen, A. Pagot, I.E. Grossmann, 2020. A review on superstructure optimization approaches in process system engineering. Computers & Chemical Engineering 136, 106808. https://doi.org/10.1016/j.compchemeng.2020.106808

E.N. Pistikopoulos, A. Barbosa-Povoa, J.H. Lee, R. Misener, A. Mitsos, G.V. Reklaitis, V. Venkatasubramanian, F. You, R. Gani, 2021. Process systems engineering – The generation next? Computers & Chemical Engineering 147, 107252. https://doi.org/10.1016/j.compchemeng.2021.107252

L.A. Roald, D. Pozo, A. Papavasiliou, D.K. Molzahn, J. Kazempour, A. Conejo, 2023. Power systems optimization under uncertainty: A review of methods and applications. Electric Power Systems Research 214, 108725. https://doi.org/10.1016/j.epsr.2022.108725

S. Sass, T. Faulwasser, D.E. Hollermann, C.D. Kappatou, D. Sauer, T. Schütz, D.Y. Shu, A. Bardow, L. Gröll, V. Hagenmeyer, D. Müller, A. Mitsos, 2020. Model compendium, data, and optimization benchmarks for sector-coupled energy systems. Computers & Chemical Engineering 135, 106760. https://doi.org/10.1016/j.compchemeng.2020.106760

P. Voll, M. Lampe, G. Wrobel, A. Bardow, 2012. Superstructure-free synthesis and optimization of distributed industrial energy supply systems. Energy 45, 424–435. https://doi.org/10.1016/j.energy.2012.01.041

Z. Zhou, J. Zhang, P. Liu, Z. Li, M.C. Georgiadis, E.N. Pistikopoulos, 2013. A two-stage stochastic programming model for the optimal design of distributed energy systems. Applied Energy 103, 135–144. https://doi.org/10.1016/j.apenergy.2012.09.019

Flavio Manenti, Gintaras V. Reklaitis (Eds.), Proceedings of the 34th European Symposium on Computer Aided Process Engineering / 15th International Symposium on Process Systems Engineering (ESCAPE34/PSE24), June 2-6, 2024, Florence, Italy

Cost Optimal Desalinated Water Production

Shashank Prabhakar,[a*] Santanu Bandyopadhyay,[b]

Department of Energy Science and Engineering, Indian Institute of Technology Bombay, 400076, India
shashank.prabhakar@iitb.ac.in

Abstract

Industrial parks require a significantly large amount of water for industrial activities. The water requirement for these industries is fulfilled by using locally available freshwater sources like surface water, groundwater, external water diversion, reclaimed water, etc. Using these water sources for industrial demand stresses them for the demand satisfaction of other sectors. Due to different water sources having different costs of water generation, desalinated water can be one of the options for industrial water supply because of their abundance. Since desalination is a more cost-intensive water production process, it becomes mandatory to have cost optimal water production. This work proposes a Pinch-based, non-iterative graphical method to determine the cost-optimal water mix production to satisfy demand. The method determines the minimum subsidy required to meet overall water demand. A case study to demonstrate the applicability of the method is done.

Keywords: Optimization, Desalination, Pinch Analysis.

1. Introduction

Water, an indispensable resource for life, plays a vital role in sustaining ecosystems, supporting agriculture, and meeting the basic needs of human societies. As global population growth, urbanization, and climate change place increasing pressure on water resources, effective water management becomes paramount. Water management involves planning, developing, distributing, and conserving water resources to ensure equitable access, environmental sustainability, and resilience in the face of evolving challenges (World Bank, 2016). Water scarcity is expected to worsen with the current policy and climate change in developing countries (Tan and Foo, 2018). Pinch Analysis is used for systematic planning of resources, which was developed by Linnhoff et al. (1978) for heat exchanger applications. Later, its applications expanded to include the conservation of mass-separating agents (El-Halwagi and Manousiouthakis, 1989) and various material resources (Foo, 2012). Bandyopadhyay et al. (2009) later extended the concepts of Pinch analysis to address segregated targeting problems, proposed a decomposition method. Prabhakar and Bandyopadhyay (2023) extended the concept of Pinch analysis for decarbonization and proposed a graphical optimization method. Pinch Analysis has proven its versatility by tackling diverse engineering challenges across mechanical, chemical, process, energy, and environmental domains (Klemeš et al., 2018).

Industrial water demand is rising rapidly, posing a significant threat to water resources and exacerbating water scarcity in many regions due to the substantial amount of water required for manufacturing, cooling, and other operational needs. Climate change is further compounding the challenge by altering precipitation patterns and reducing the reliability of existing water supplies.

Desalination technologies offer a promising solution to mitigate the strain on conventional freshwater sources by converting seawater or brackish water into freshwater. However, implementing desalination comes with challenges, including high energy consumption, environmental impacts, and cost-intensive. Balancing the increasing industrial water demand with sustainable desalination practices is crucial for ensuring water security and minimizing adverse effects on ecosystems and local communities. Addressing the challenge of water desalination is crucial for enhancing water resource planning. Various quantitative methodologies, including game theory as demonstrated by Yamamoto et al. (2012) and input-output analysis as illustrated by Yang et al. (2015), have been employed to optimize policies in the realm of integrated water management.

In this work a new graphical methodology for determining the minimum desalinated water production needed for the satisfaction of demand is presented. The method also determines the minimum subsidy requirement to support the desalinated water production. The proposed method can be used as a planning too and can determine the maximum water demand that can be satisfied for a given subsidy. A mathematical optimization formulation to solve the above problem is also presented in the subsequent section which is used to verify the graphically obtained results. In subsequent section the mathematical optimization formulation is presented which is followed by graphical methodology and case study. At last conclusion is presented.

2. Mathematical Optimization Formulation

Let W_i is the capacity of water produced, and the capacity factor be x_i for the i th water source. Therefore, the total water produced by source i annually is $x_i W_i$. The cost of water produced by i th source is C_i and the total cost of water produced is $x_i W_i C_i$. Similarly, W_j be the water demand of j th sector. The capacity factor for the sector j be y_j and hence, it consumes annual water of $y_j W_j$ while producing a fund of $y_j W_j C_j$ from the system. C_j is the maximum acceptable price of the j th sector. W_{des} is the amount of desalinated water produced and C_s is subsidy provided to support the production of desalinated water. The primary objective is to determine the minimum subsidy required to support desalinated water production for the demand satisfaction of specified geographic regions. The mathematical equations for the optimization problem can be written as:

Minimize:

$$Z_1 = C_s \tag{1}$$

Constraints:

$$\sum_{i=1}^{n} x_i W_i + \sum W_{des} = \sum_{i=1}^{m} y_j W_j \tag{2}$$

$$C_s \leq \sum_{i=1}^{n} x_i W_i C_i - \sum_{j=1}^{m} y_j W_j C_j \tag{3}$$

Equation (2) implies that the summation of the total freshwater produced and the water produced after desalination should satisfy the total water demands of various sectors. Similarly, equation (3) represents that the total subsidy provided for desalinated water produced should be either less than or equal to the difference of the total cost of water product and the total fund generated by water consumption by various sectors. In addition to these constraints, the capacity factors are non-negative, and their values should lie between 0 and 1.

3. Graphical Methodology

A new graphical method is proposed to determine the minimum subsidy required for desalinated water production to meet industrial demand. This method involves constructing a piecewise linear water production composite curve, which plots water production against its corresponding production cost (Figure 1a). The cost intensity, or the cost per unit of water production, is calculated for each water source, and these sources are then arranged in ascending order of their cost intensity. The water production composite curve is constructed to ensure the utilization of the least cost-intensive water sources first. The resulting cumulative water produced versus cumulative cost incurred curve represents the optimal sequence for utilizing water sources to meet the specified water demand while minimizing production costs.

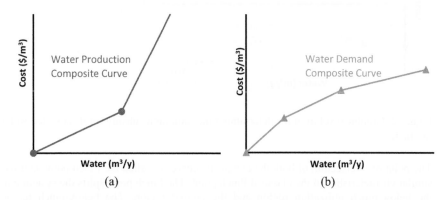

Figure 1(a): Water demand composite curve (b) water production composite curve.

Similarly, a piecewise linear water demand composite curve is drawn to represent the relationship between water consumption and the cost of water consumption (as shown in Figure 1b). This curve is created by calculating the cost intensity (i.e., fund generated per unit of water consumed) for each water source and arranging the sources in descending order of their cost intensity. The resulting curve ensures that the highest cost-intensive water sources are used first for water consumption in the region. For every point on the composite curve of water, the fund generated by the water source is represented by the y-axis, and the x-axis represents the amount of water consumed.

To meet the water demand of a specific region, the water production composite curve (Figure 1a) is adjusted by shifting it vertically downwards. This shift is equivalent to the subsidy provided by the government. After this adjustment, the shifted water production composite curve and the water demand composite curve are plotted together on the cumulative water versus cumulative cost graph to determine the minimum subsidy provided to meet the industrial water demand. This process ensures the region's water needs are fulfilled while minimizing the subsidy required for desalinated water production.

The first point of intersection of both the shifted composite curves of water production and water demand composite curve gives the optimum solution to the problem (see Figure 2). This intersection point is called the Pinch point. The Pinch point ensures that the optimum mix of water is produced. The horizontal projection of the production composite curve represents the amount of water produced by the different water sources, which must satisfy the given water demand (as indicated by the horizontal projection of the water demand composite curve). Thus, the horizontal projections of the composite curve ensure that the water balance constraint is met. Likewise, the vertical projection of the composite curve corresponds to the cost for the system, ensuring that the fund balance constraints are satisfied.

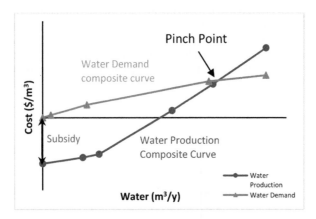

Figure 2: Graphical solution for determining the minimum subsidy for desalinated water production.

The point of intersection of both the composite curves is called the Pinch point as it has similar characteristics to the classical Pinch point. The Pinch point splits the system into the below-pinch utilization region and the unused region. The below-pinch region contains all water-producing sources and demands that must operate at full capacity to meet the system's demands. The water sources and water demand that are not needed are included in the above-pinch region and can be shut down. The water production and water demand operate at partial capacity at Pinch Point. Following the golden rule of Pinch Analysis, transferring water across the Pinch point is not allowed.

4. Case Study

The case study is based on Qingdao, a city in Shandong Province on the east coast of China. It is one of the cities which suffers from water shortage issues. The case study is taken from Jia et al. (2019). The tabulated data in Table 1 represents the various sectoral demands for water and the acceptable cost of water paid by these sectors. Table 2 represents the water production capacities of various existing water sources. The total water demand from multiple sectors is 275 kt/d, and the total water produced by the existing sources is 210 kt/d. The remaining water demand is satisfied using desalinated water, and the cost of freshwater generated from desalination is 1.15 $/t. The objective of this case study is to find the cost-optimal water mix production for the satisfaction of the overall demand for water.

Table 1: Sectoral water demand and the cost of water (Jia et al., 2019).

Sector	Water demand (kt/d)	Cost ($/t)
Residential sector	70	0.36
Industrial sector	150	0.65

Commercial Sector	45	0.94
Others	10	1.05

Table 2: Water production capacity and the corresponding cost of water production (Jia et al., 2019).

Water sources	Capacity pf production (kt/d)	Cost ($/t)
Ground water	20	0.55
Reclaimed water	50	0.78
Surface water	50	0.43
External diversion water	90	0.72

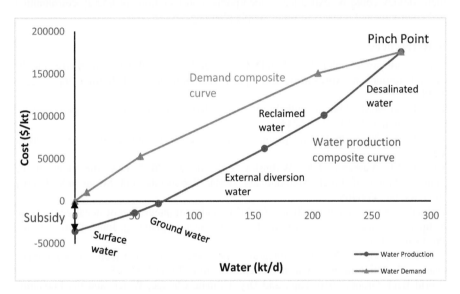

Figure 3: Graphical solution for determining the cost-optimal water mix production to satisfy the overall water demand.

The production composite curve and the demand composite cure in Figure 3, drawn using the proposed method. The production composite curve is drawn according to the increasing cost per unit of water production. Similarly, the demand composite curve is drawn according to decreasing per unit of acceptable price. The production composite curve is shifted vertically downwards until it covers the total water demand. The amount of vertical downward movement gives the amount of subsidy to be provided for desalinated water generated. The point of intersection of both curves gives the optimum solution and is also called the Pinch point. The solution implies that after using the locally available resources completely, the seawater desalination fulfills the remaining water demand. Total water produced by desalination to satisfy the water demand of 65 kt/d at a generation cost of 74750 $/kt. The subsidy provided by the government is equal to 35550 $/kt. These results are identical to those reported by Jia et al. (2019), where the limiting composite curve is used to determine the minimum subsidy.

5. Conclusion

This paper introduces a novel non-iterative graphical targeting approach to optimize subsidies for desalinated water production. The method determines the minimum subsidy and desalinated water production necessary to meet demand requirements. The graphical outcomes obtained through the proposed technique can be verified using a mathematical formulation presented in the paper to ascertain the optimal subsidy. The applicability of this method is demonstrated through a case study presented focusing water scarcity of Qingdao city in China. The obtained results suggest that, at a generation cost of 74,750 $/kt, the desalination process produces a total of 65 kt/d of water to meet demand, with a corresponding government subsidy of $35,550/kt.

This graphical method, outlined in this paper, is adaptable to changes in water demand and subsidy levels, providing an optimal solution. It serves as a valuable planning tool for achieving cost-effective desalinated water production. In subsequent studies, the methodology could be expanded to incorporate considerations of energy consumption and environmental impacts in water supply planning.

6. References

Bandyopadhyay S., Sahu G. C., Foo D. C. Y., Tan R. R., 2009, Segregated targeting for multiple resource networks using decomposition algorithm, AIChE Journal, 56(5), 1235-1248.

El-Halwagi M.M., Manousiouthakis V., 1989, Synthesis of mass exchange networks, AIChE Journal, 35(8), 1233-1244.

Foo D.C.Y., 2012, Process integration for resource conservation, CRC Press, Florida, USA.

Klemeš J.J., Varbanov P.S., Walmsley T.G., Jia X., 2018, New directions in the implementation of Pinch Methodology (PM), Renewable and Sustainable Energy Reviews, 98, 439-468.

Prabhakar, S. and Bandyopadhyay, S., 2023. Optimum integration of negative emission technologies for carbon-constrained energy sector planning. Journal of Cleaner Production, 411, p.137302.

Tan, R.R., Foo, D.C.Y., 2018. Integrated multi-scale water management as a climate change adaptation strategy. Clean. Technol. Environ. 20, 1123e1125.

World Bank Group, 2016. High and Dry: Climate Change, Water, and the Economy. World Bank, Washington, DC.

Yamamoto, T., Jalaldin, A., Nagasawa, T., 2012. Factors responsible for the effective introduction of water-saving irrigation facilities in the tarim river basin. WIT Trans. Ecol. Environ. 168, 245e253.

Yang, W., Song, J., Higano, Y., Tang, J., 2015. An integrated simulation model for dynamically exploring the optimal solution to mitigating water scarcity and pollution. Sustainability 7, 1774e1797.

Flavio Manenti, Gintaras V. Reklaitis (Eds.), Proceedings of the 34th European Symposium on Computer Aided Process Engineering / 15th International Symposium on Process Systems Engineering (ESCAPE34/PSE24), June 2-6, 2024, Florence, Italy
© 2024 Elsevier B.V. All rights reserved. http://dx.doi.org/10.1016/B978-0-443-28824-1.50549-4

Development of a computational tool for the solution of optimal control problems with metaheuristic techniques

Eduardo Herrera-Álvarez [a], Oscar Daniel Lara-Montaño [b], Mayra Margarita May-Vázquez [c], Fernando Israel Gómez-Castro [a,*], Claudia Gutiérrez-Antonio [b], Manuel Toledano-Ayala [b]

[a] *Departamento de Ingeniería Química, División de Ciencias Naturales y Exactas, Campus Guanajuato, Universidad de Guanajuato, Noria Alta S/N, Guanajuato, Guanajuato, 36050, México. fgomez@ugto.mx*
[b] *Facultad de Ingeniería, Universidad Autónoma de Querétaro, Cerro de las Campanas S/N, Querétaro, Querétaro, 76010, México.*
[c] *Unidad Académica de Educación Virtual, Dirección General de Desarrollo Académico, Universidad Autónoma de Yucatán, Benito Juárez 421 Cd. Industrial, Mérida, Yucatán, 97288, México.*

Abstract

This study explores the solution of a dynamic optimization problem with a focus on a Continuous Stirred-Tank Reactor (CSTR) known for its output multiplicities. The dynamic optimization problem is discretized into a non-linear programming (NLP) problem. The effectiveness of three metaheuristic algorithms—Differential Evolution (DE), Grey Wolf Optimizer (GWO), and Cuckoo Search (CS)— in solving this NLP problem is evaluated, considering both solution quality and computational efficiency. The findings provide insights into applying metaheuristic methods in dynamic optimization, highlighting the importance of discretization in transforming dynamic problems into manageable NLP tasks.

Keywords: dynamic optimization, optimal control, metaheuristic algorithms, continuous stirred-tank reactor

1. Introduction

Dynamic optimization is a key procedure widely used in various engineering and scientific fields to optimize the behavior of systems that predominantly depend on time or space. Typically, the goal is to optimize these systems based on a performance index, which is either maximized or minimized to achieve optimal outcomes. In the realm of chemical engineering, dynamic systems play a crucial role. Examples of such systems in this field include the determination of kinetic constants from time-series data, the control of batch and semi-batch chemical reactors, the start-up and shut-down processes of continuous systems, and the switching between different steady-state operating points. Differential-algebraic mathematical models are employed to represent and analyze these complex systems accurately. These models provide a robust framework for understanding and optimizing the dynamic behavior of various chemical engineering processes, mostly focusing on the analysis of the state variables, implying optimal control problems.

Traditional approaches to solve dynamic optimization problems, such as the calculus of variations, the Pontryagin's Maximum Principle, and the dynamic programming, each have their own drawbacks (Diwekar, 2008). The calculus of variations becomes complex when dealing with intricate constraints. Pontryagin's Maximum Principle often struggles with non-linear systems. On the other hand, although versatile and robust, dynamic programming becomes less effective and more computationally demanding when the dynamic optimization problem increases in dimensions; furthermore, these classic techniques necessitate a comprehensive system model, which may not be practical for extensive or complex problems, particularly those with uncertain variables. These challenges underscore the importance of choosing the most suitable method for each unique dynamic optimization scenario. Another alternative to address dynamic optimization problems is discretizing and solving the problem numerically as a non-linear programming (NLP) problem. An example of this approach has been reported for a fermentation system by Sridhar and Lopez Saucedo (2015). However, to solve relatively complex models by deterministic approaches, it is mandatory to determine adequate values for the variables at the initial time (May-Vázquez et al., 2022). Also, determining proper initial guesses for the trajectory of the variables could be difficult.

This research examines the use of various metaheuristic optimization algorithms in a case study of a Continuous Stirred-Tank Reactor (CSTR) exhibiting output multiplicities. The case study, initially reported by Hicks & Ray (1971) and later modified by Flores-Tlacuahuac et al. (2008), serves as the basis for this exploration. The study begins by discretizing the dynamic optimization problem, converting it into a Nonlinear Programming (NLP) problem. Then, the NLP problem is solved using metaheuristic algorithms. The use of metaheuristic optimization algorithms can be a suitable strategy to solve optimal control problems, mainly due to the non-linear behavior that the model can present, and the capacity of the metaheuristics to perform a global search and identify the feasible sub-space that contains the best solution. Three distinct optimization algorithms—differential evolution (DE), grey wolf optimizer (GWO), and cuckoo search (CS)—are then applied to solve the resulting NLP. The effectiveness of these algorithms is compared based on the number of iterations and the variety of candidate solutions generated. A dynamic optimization solution tool is also provided, enabling users to apply these methodologies to different case studies.

The document's structure is organized in the following manner: Section 2 outlines the methodology used in developing the tool. Section 3 presents and discusses the results of this specific case study, including an analysis of the tool's scope and limitations. The document concludes with Section 4, which summarizes the findings and conclusions of the work.

2. Methodology

2.1. Case study

The case study under consideration involves a CSTR exhibiting output multiplicities, as detailed in the work of Flores-Tlacuahuac et al. (2008). This model operates within a highly non-linear region. For enhanced analysis and to facilitate the emergence of multiple steady states, the model is formulated in a dimensionless form, as shown in equations 1 and 2.

$$\frac{dy_1}{dt} = \frac{1-y_1}{\theta} - k_{10}\,exp(-N/y_2)y_1 \tag{1}$$

$$\frac{dy_2}{dt} = \frac{y_f - y_2}{\theta} + k_{10}\,exp(-N/y_2)\,y_1 - \alpha u(y_2 - y_1) \tag{2}$$

In this model, y_1 denotes the dimensionless concentration, expressed as c/c_f, while y_2 is the dimensionless temperature, represented as T/Jc_f. The term y_f corresponds to the dimensionless feed temperature, defined as T_f/Jc_f, and u represents the cooling flow rate. Table 1 shows the values employed in the parameters used by the model. The measured variable is y_1, and the manipulated variable is u.

Table 1. Parameters required by the model.

Parameter	θ	J	c_f	α	T_f	k_{10}	T_c	N
Value	20 min	100 K-L/mol	7.6 mol/L	1.95×10^{-4} 1/L	300 K	300 l/min	290 K	5

Table 2 presents four distinct nominal steady states applicable to our case study. These states represent different operational conditions, and the system can transition between these steady states as required.

Table 2. Nominal steady states for the case study.

	A	B	C	D
y_1	0.0944	0.1367	0.1926	0.2632
y_2	0.7766	0.7293	0.6881	0.6529
u	340	390	430	455

2.2. Optimal control problem

The optimal control problem is shown in equations 3 to 6.

$$\begin{array}{c} \text{min:} \\ z, u \end{array} \int_{t_0}^{t_f} \left\| z(t) - \hat{z} \right\|^2 dt \tag{3}$$

$$\dot{x}(t) = F(z(t), u(t), t)\,z(0) = z^0 \tag{4}$$

$$z^l \le z \le z^u \tag{5}$$

$$u^l \le u \le u^u \tag{6}$$

In this optimal control problem, the objective is to minimize $\int_{t_0}^{t_f}\left\| z(t) - \hat{z} \right\|^2 dt$, representing the squared deviation of the state vector $z(t)$ from the target $\hat{z}$ over time t_0 to t_f. The system's evolution is governed by $\dot{x}(t) = F(z(t), u(t), t)$, with $z(t)$ as the state variables, $u(t)$ as the control variables, and $z(0) = z^0$ defining the initial state. In this case study, such relationships are given by equations (1) and (2). Constraints $z^l \le z \le z^u$ and $u^l \le u \le u^u$ limit the state and control variables within feasible ranges.

This dynamic optimization problem is solved using a Python-based tool. The process involves discretizing the time variable, which is independent, into equal intervals. To minimize the integral, its value is computed numerically using the 1/3 Simpson's method. The optimization of the integral is carried out using metaheuristic algorithms from the Mealpy library. The code for solving this dynamic optimization problem, after converting it into a Nonlinear Programming (NLP) problem, can be accessed at https://github.com/DanlaraIQ/DynamicOpt.

The explicit discretized objective function is shown in equations 7-9. Δt is the discretized time, 20 intervals are used for its calculation. β_1, β_2, and β_3 are weights for each squared term.

$$f_{obj} = \frac{\Delta t}{3} \sum_{i=0}^{N-2} [\beta_1 \cdot (y1_i - y1_{\text{final}})^2 + \beta_2 \cdot (y2_i - y2_{\text{final}})^2 + \beta_3 \cdot (u_i - u_{\text{final}})^2] \tag{7}$$

$$y_{1_{i+1}} = y_{1_i} + \Delta t \cdot \left(\frac{1 - y_{1_i}}{\theta} - k_{10} \cdot \exp\left(-\frac{N}{y_{2_i}} \right) \cdot y_{1_i} \right) \tag{8}$$

$$y_{2_{i+1}} = y_{2_i} + \Delta t \cdot \left(\frac{y_f - y_{2_i}}{\theta} + k_{10} \cdot \exp\left(-\frac{N}{y_{2_i}} \right) \cdot y_{1_i} - \alpha \cdot u_i \cdot (y_{2_i} - y_c) \right) \tag{9}$$

The parameters of the metaheuristic optimization algorithms are given in Table 3. 50 candidate solutions and 500 iterations are employed. The lower and upper limits used for the control variable are 200 and 550, respectively.

Table 3. Parameters used in the metaheuristic algorithms.

CS	DE	GWO
$n = 50$	$n = 50$	$n = 50$
$p_\alpha = 0.25$	$w_f = 0.7$	
	$cr = 0.9$	
	$DE/best/1/bin$	

3. Results

Table 4 displays the results for the objective function's value and the CPU time taken for each optimization algorithm across various steady-state transitions. This table highlights the best performances regarding the objective function's quality and CPU time efficiency in bold. These results show that the CS algorithm is not the best choice for solving this optimization problem. This is not only due to its longer computational time for completing 500 iterations, which might be attributed to the inherent structure of the code but also because of its inability to effectively minimize the value of the objective function through the optimal selection of the vector of u values.

Table 4. Comparative results for the objective function value/time (seconds) in each transition between steady states.

transition	CS	DE	GWO
A→B	2,141.8058/13.58	2,051.2866/**12.05**	**2,040.9517**/12.54
B→A	2,151.7355/14.01	1,957.2324/12.43	**1,951.9298/12.56**
A→C	18,017.8751/14.43	15,337.9467/13.11	**15,315.1204/12.83**
C→A	13,331.4591/14.06	12,814.7678/**13.10**	**12,718.0579**/14.79
A→D	67,931.6923/15.07	**58,127.4895/13.39**	58,140.7994/14.52
D→A	44,602.0470/14.09	**42,802.0694/12.66**	42,811.31/13.43
B→C	4,707.0856/14.03	4,268.6486/13.38	**4,257.5752/13.57**
C→B	3,775.9691/13.70	**3,506.7442**/13.30	3,507.2127/**12.84**
B→D	36,388.9497/13.75	30,688.6344/13.16	**30,484.4022/13.35**
D→B	24,548.2092/13.39	**22,476.6771/12.01**	22,498.8302/13.08
C→D	9,542.4709/13.81	8,156.1741/**13.07**	**8,127.4643**/13.38
D→C	7,309.2156/13.80	**6,144.5463/13.17**	6,151.5801/18.59

The efficiency in execution time is generally comparable across the three optimization algorithms. However, GWO shows some variability in certain instances, notably in the transition from D to C. Regarding the best solution's quality, the DE and GWO algorithms demonstrate very similar performances. With comparison purposes, the problem has been discretized using the orthogonal collocation on finite elements approach and codified in the GAMS Studio environment. By solving for the first transition using the deterministic IPOPT solver, a value of 2,677.63 is obtained for the objective function. This value is comparable to those obtained with the metaheuristic methods, although slightly higher. This may reflect the existence of various local optima. On the other hand, the deterministic solution is obtained in 0.227 seconds with the deterministic approach, which is a considerably lower computing time.

Figure 1 presents the plotted trajectories of y_1 and y_2 during the transitions from state B to A and from D to C. It is observable that the GWO and DE algorithms produce comparable trajectories for the B to A transition, with minor differences observed in the transition from C to D. The plots visually demonstrate the CS algorithm's inability to identify satisfactory solutions within the given number of iterations for this optimization problem.

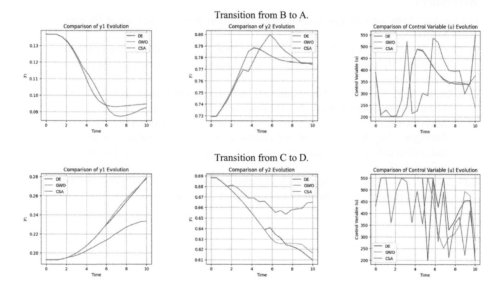

Figure 1. The behavior of the transitions between steady-state B→A and C→D.

A notable challenge associated with the strategy involving metaheuristic optimization algorithms is the exponential increase in running time as the number of dimensions grows. Specifically, in this optimization problem, the dimensionality is directly tied to the discretization of the independent variable, which, in this context, is time. This aspect becomes particularly critical in scenarios with broader time frames. In such cases, a larger number of discrete time points is required to represent the system's trajectory accurately.

Consequently, as the time frame expands, the increased need for finer discretization leads to a higher dimensional space, thereby significantly impacting the computational time.

4. Conclusion

The research indicates that DE and GWO outperform CS in addressing the discretized dynamic optimization problem, demonstrating superior solution quality and time efficiency performance. The strategy of discretizing the dynamic optimization into an NLP problem is critical for effectively applying these metaheuristic algorithms. The limitations of the CS algorithm are noted within the iteration constraints of the NLP context. The developed computational tool, capable of adapting these algorithms, proves versatile for various dynamic optimization scenarios. The study underscores the significance of a well-chosen strategy in discretized dynamic optimization and opens new avenues for future research in this field. It is also noted that an increase in problem complexity leads to an exponential growth in the computational time required for these metaheuristic algorithms.

References

U. Diwekar, 2008, Introduction to applied optimization, Springer Science & Business Media.

A. Flores-Tlacuahuac, S.T. Moreno, L. Biegler, 2008. Global Optimization of Highly Nonlinear Dynamic Systems, Industrial & Engineering Chemistry Research, 47, 2643–2655.

G.A. Hicks, W.H. Ray, 1971, Approximation methods for optimal control synthesis, The Canadian Journal of Chemical Engineering, 49, 522–528.

M.M. May-Vázquez, F.I. Gómez-Castro, E.S. Rawlings, V. Rico-Ramírez, M.A. Rodríguez-Ángeles, 2022, Optimal control of a rate-based modelled batch distillation column: Initialization strategy, Computers & Chemical Engineering, 162, 107811.

L.N. Sridhar, E.S. López Saucedo, 2015, Optimal control of Saccharomyces cerevisiae. Fermentation process, Chemical Engineering Communications, 203, 318-325

Flavio Manenti, Gintaras V. Reklaitis (Eds.), Proceedings of the 34th European Symposium on Computer Aided Process Engineering / 15th International Symposium on Process Systems Engineering (ESCAPE34/PSE24), June 2-6, 2024, Florence, Italy

Progressive Hedging for Optimization of Tree Ensembles as Objective Functions

Bashar L. Ammari,[a] Sergio Bugosen,[a] Jean-Paul Watson,[b] Emma S. Johnson,[c] Carl D. Laird,[a]

[a] *Carnegie Mellon University*
[b] *Lawrence Livermore National Laboratory*
[c] *Sandia National Laboratories*
bammari@andrew.cmu.edu

Abstract

Ensembles such as random forests and gradient boosted decision trees have become popular as surrogates in optimization problems. Large ensembles, however, may result in computationally impractical optimization problems. In this work, we adapt the parallelizable progressive hedging algorithm to accommodate ensembles of trees, leveraging mathematical equivalence in block-angular structures of stochastic programming and machine learning ensemble models. We study this algorithm on a large-scale example and show that there are computational benefits to utilizing progressive hedging to find high-quality heuristic solutions.

Keywords: Machine Learning, Optimization, Decomposition

1. Introduction

The operations research and engineering communities have increasingly adopted integrated machine learning (ML) and optimization in recent years. These communities have developed an extensive body of literature for ML models as surrogates within optimization problems ranging from security constrained alternating current optimal power flow (AC-OPF) for reliable electricity operation (Kilwein et al., 2021) to designing combination chemotherapy regimens to treat cancer (Bertsimas et al., 2016). Much of this adoption is not only driven by recent advancements in open-source ML modeling tools such as Pytorch, Tensorflow, and Scikit-learn, but by additional development of Python libraries such as the Optimization & Machine Learning Toolkit (OMLT) (Ceccon et al., 2022) that enable embedding trained ML models within optimization problems.

Tools such as OMLT that perform this embedding rely on the ability to formulate trained ML models as constraints in mathematical programs. That is, these tools take trained ML models, generate the algebraic expressions required to represent such models, and embed them within broader optimization problems coded within an algebraic modeling language such as Pyomo (Bynum et al., 2021). For example, several authors have proposed formulations for decision trees and ensembles of decision trees. Biggs et al. (2018), Mišić (2020), and Mistry et al. (2021) present mixed-integer linear programming formulations of ensembles of standard decision trees such as random forests (RFs) and gradient-boosted decision trees (GBDTs). Recently, Ammari et al. (2023) explored extensions of standard trees called linear model decision trees and showed how to formulate them as mixed-integer linear programs and mixed-integer quadratic programs.

Although the ML community has shown ensembles such as RFs and GBDTs to be effective models (Caruana and Niculescu-Mizil, 2006), embedding large ensembles in broader decision-making problems may lead to computationally intractable optimization problems. We note that, like stochastic programming problems, these problems often contain a block-angular structure. Therefore, decomposing these large problems into their individual trees may be computationally advantageous. In this work, we use progressive hedging (Rockafellar and Wets, 1991) as a decomposition strategy for optimization over large GBDTs and RFs embedded as objective functions to provide good heuristic solutions with faster computational performance compared with the direct solution of the full-space model. This algorithm is implemented in mpi-sppy, a Python package for parallel decomposition of stochastic programs (Knueven et al., 2023). Although this work does not consider stochastic programming problems, we are interested in solving problems of the form Eq. (1) – Eq. (3).

$$\min \quad d \tag{1}$$

$$\text{s.t.} \quad g(x) \le 0 \tag{2}$$

$$d = \Phi(x) \tag{3}$$

To state the problem explicitly, we are optimizing the output, d, of a tree ensemble, Φ, subject to constraints on the inputs to the tree ensemble, x. Specifically, we are interested in the case where Φ is a large tree ensemble. Biggs et al. (2017) previously studied this problem for RFs as objective functions and proposed Bender's decomposition to improve solution time over the direct approach. We extend this work by applying progressive hedging (PH) to get good heuristic solutions to Eq. (1) – Eq. (3). While this methodology is heuristic and does not come with optimality guarantees, several algorithmic advances have resulted in successful application of progressive hedging to solve mixed-integer programming problems (Watson and Woodruff, 2011).

The remainder of this paper is structured as follows. In Section 2, we review the relevant generalized disjunctive programming (GDP) formulation for individual trees used in this work. Furthermore, we draw analogies to the extensive form (EF) of a stochastic program and present an EF of the problem described by Eq. (1) – Eq. (3). In addition, we introduce the PH algorithm to accommodate GBDTs and RFs and present the computational environment and example problem used to compare performance. In Section 3, we compare the computational time and solutions using both PH and direct solution of the EF. We discuss concluding remarks and future avenues of research in Section 4.

2. Overview of Methods

2.1 Formulation for Embedding Individual Trees
When decomposing an ensemble into its individual trees, we can apply the GDP formulation presented in Ammari et al. (2023) for a single linear model decision tree, by using constant values at the leaf nodes. This formulation is as follows:

$$\bigvee_{l \in L} \begin{bmatrix} Z_l \\ \underline{x_l} \le x \le \overline{x}_l \\ d = F_l \end{bmatrix} \tag{4}$$

$$\text{exactly\_one}\{Z_l : l \in L\} \tag{5}$$

$$x^L \leq x \leq x^U \tag{6}$$

$$x \in R^n \tag{7}$$

$$Z_l \in \{\text{True, False}\} \qquad\qquad \forall\, l \in L \tag{8}$$

The Boolean variable Z_l indicates which leaf is selected, implying the bound constraints and the constant value F_l that are enforced. The bound vectors $\underline{x}_l$ and $\overline{x}_l$ are calculated by traversing the tree and finding the tightest lower and upper bounds taken from the tree's splitting thresholds. Constraint Eq. (5) and the use of the "or" operator, $\vee$, enforces selection of only one disjunct per disjunction (i.e., exactly one leaf is returned by the tree). To acquire a mixed-integer programming representation of this disjunctive formulation, we apply a Big-M transformation on the disjuncts as is common in GDP literature.

2.2 Progressive Hedging

Progressive Hedging (PH) is an effective algorithm for solving stochastic optimization problems. In this work, we apply PH to find good heuristic solutions for large tree ensembles that are otherwise prohibitively computationally expensive or intractable. In this section, we review the PH algorithm, and show how this algorithm can accommodate ensembles of trees.

Many stochastic optimization problems are formulated as two-stage problems. There are "here-and-now" decisions in the first stage (variables x) and "wait-and-see" decisions in the second stage (variables y_s). That is, a modeler may identify a finite set of realizations of the second stage (called scenarios), S, and their probability of occurrence, π_s. The objective, Eq. (9), is to minimize the cost associated with making those first stage decisions and the expected value of the cost over all scenario realizations, while ensuring that any first and second stage decision will satisfy constraints in Eq. (10).

$$\min \quad c^T x + \sum_{s \in S} \pi_s f(y_s) \tag{9}$$

$$\text{s.t.} \quad g(x, y_s) \leq 0 \qquad\qquad \forall\, s \in S \tag{10}$$

To extend this idea to ensembles of trees, we treat each tree, t. as a scenario. The input variables to the tree, x will be analogous to our "first stage variables," and the output of each tree d_t as well as the binary variables z_l associated with correct selection of the leaves (this variable is introduced when Eq. (4) – Eq. (8) is transformed), will be our analog to the "second stage variables." If we reconsider Eq. (1) – Eq. (3), we can rewrite that optimization problem equivalently as follows.

$$\min \quad \frac{1}{|T|} \sum_{t \in T} d_t \tag{11}$$

$$\text{s.t.} \quad g(x) \leq 0 \tag{12}$$

$$d_t = \Phi_t(x) \qquad\qquad \forall\, t \in T \tag{13}$$

The output of an RF is the average of the outputs of the individual trees and therefore our objective is given in Eq. (11). The constraints on the input given by Eq. (12) remain the same, however we embed each tree, Φ_t using the GDP formulation in Eq. (13). We refer to this problem as the extensive form (EF) representation due to its analog to the extensive form of a stochastic programming problem. Note that the output of a GBDT is the sum of the individual trees, and the objective function is easily modified to accommodate this.

Given the equivalent formulation of Eq. (1) – Eq. (3) described by Eq. (11) – Eq. (13), the PH algorithm for tree ensembles as objective functions can be written as follows.

Algorithm 1: Progressive Hedging for Tree Ensembles as Objective Functions

1. $k := 0$
2. For all $t \in T$
$$x_t^{(k)} := \mathrm{argmin}_{x,d_t} \{d_t : g(x) \le 0, d_t = \Phi_t(x)\}$$
3. $\bar{x}^{(k)} := \frac{1}{|T|} \sum_{t \in T} x_t^{(k)}$
4. For all $t \in T$
$$w_t^{(k)} := \rho(x_t^{(k)} - \bar{x}^{(k)})$$
5. $k := k + 1$
6. For all $t \in T$
$$x_t^{(k)} := \mathrm{argmin}_{x,d_t}\{w_t^{(k)}x + \frac{\rho}{2}\left|\left|x - \bar{x}^{(k-1)}\right|\right|^2 + d_t : g(x) \le 0, d_t = \Phi_t(x)\}$$
7. $\bar{x}^{(k)} := \frac{1}{|T|} \sum_{t \in T} x_t^{(k)}$
8. For all $t \in T$
$$w_t^{(k)} := w_t^{(k-1)} + \rho(x_t^{(k)} - \bar{x}^{(k)})$$
9. Terminate if criterion is met, otherwise go to step 5.

As explained in Knueven et al. (2023), there are many possible termination criteria in Step 9 of Algorithm 1 including iteration limits, primal convergence, primal-dual convergence, or convergence of ρ. Selection of this criterion is often left for the user and can be problem dependent. Note that steps 2, 4, 6, and 8 are straightforwardly parallelizable which is a key advantage of utilizing PH. In this work, we show that with a fixed number of PH iterations, and the addition of an *incumbent finder* (Knueven et al., 2023), we can acquire good heuristic solutions with faster solution times when compared to the direct solution of the EF. Solution quality and computational benefit also depend on proper selection of ρ values, and automated ρ update schemes are available in mpi-sppy. See Watson and Woodruff (2011) for additional information on ρ calculations.

2.3 Case Study and Computational Setup

We use the *ex2_1_5* instance from MINLPLib.org. The objective is a nonlinear function, all the constraints are linear, and all the variables are continuous and bounded between 0 and 1. We replace the objective function by sampling the input variables randomly between their bounds, evaluating the objective function, and training a random forest on the resulting data (i.e. the features are the sampled input variables and the label is the value of the nonlinear objective expression evaluated at each sampled point). We fix the maximum depth of the individual trees in the RF to 10 layers and increase the size of the ensemble by adding more trees. This enables comparison of the different solution approaches at increasing scales. To train the RFs, we use Scikit-learn 1.2.2 and Python

3.11.3. We embed each trained RF using Big-M transformations of the individual tree formulation from Eq. (4) – Eq. (8). We use Pyomo 6.6.2 and its extension, Pyomo.GDP.

To utilize the PH algorithm, we use mpi-sppy. In addition, mpi-sppy can generate the EF given by Eq. (11) – Eq. (13) automatically using the same workflow required for utilizing the PH algorithm. For each trained RF, we fix the number of PH iterations to 20. In addition, we utilize the *xhatshuffle* incumbent finder, as well the dynamic ρ update capabilities of the *norm-rho-updater,* both of which are available in the mpi-sppy library. We utilize 30 processors, openmpi 4.0.5, and mpi4py 3.1.4 to take advantage of the parallelizability of the PH algorithm. The computational studies were performed on a Linux server running Ubuntu with 1TB of RAM and 4 Intel(R) Xeon(R) Gold 6234 CPUs (3.30GHz) with 8 cores each. The EF solution and the PH algorithm both use Gurobi 10.0.4 as the optimization solver with 8 solver threads.

3. Results

Results for the computational performance are shown in Table 1. With 20 iterations of PH, the best incumbents found are variable, although all are within 2% of the true solution. In certain cases, these PH solutions are almost exactly the true optima. It is again important to note that convergence to the true optimum is not guaranteed due to limitations of PH on second stage binary variables. However, we can see that the PH algorithm scales better than the EF method and can provide high-quality solutions. This improved performance is more evident with larger ensembles. Although not shown here, there is an additional computational benefit to using PH since model generation is also parallelized and the Gurobi-Persistent interface in Pyomo eliminates the need to generate new Pyomo models at each iteration of the PH algorithm.

Table 1. Computational performance results on MINLPLib.org example ex2_1_5. *Num Trees* indicates the number of trees in the RF. *EF Time* is the solution time using the extensive form in mpi-sppy, and *PH Time* using progressive hedging. *True Obj* is the objective value from the optimal solution of EF. *PH Obj* is the best incumbent after 20 iterations of PH. *% Difference* compares these two objective values.

Num Trees	EF Time [sec]	PH Time [sec]	True Obj	PH Obj	% Difference
30	26.82	21.87	-8.917	-8.756	1.81
50	69.93	40.87	-5.323	-5.276	0.88
70	81.62	48.95	-3.814	-3.764	1.31
90	128.5	59.38	-2.942	-2.928	0.48
110	203.4	74.92	-2.408	-2.379	1.20
130	210.6	89.18	-2.044	-2.042	0.01
150	294.0	98.55	-1.772	-1.758	0.79

4. Conclusions

Tree ensembles such as random forests (RFs) have become popular machine learning models. In the framework of mathematical optimization, these RFs are mixed-integer programming representable, which has driven increased adoption of these models as surrogates in the engineering community. However, large ensembles may result in computationally intractable optimization problems. Our contributions include using progressive hedging (PH) as an approach to acquire good heuristic solutions with improved solution times. We introduced how to apply the PH algorithm to accommodate ensembles, and results showed that PH scales better than the extensive form solution as problem size increases. Future work remains to determine whether we can acquire better solutions or optimal solutions in comparable computational time. Additionally, other decomposition strategies such as Lagrangian relaxation may be future research directions.

Disclaimer

This work was performed under the auspices of the U.S. Department of Energy by Lawrence Livermore National Laboratory under Contract DE-AC52-07NA27344 and was supported by the Department of Energy's Office of Electricity's Advanced Grid Modelling (AGM) program. This work was also funded by Sandia National Laboratories Laboratory Directed Research and Development (LDRD) program. Sandia National Laboratories is a multi-mission laboratory managed and operated by National Technology & Engineering Solutions of Sandia, LLC, a wholly owned subsidiary of Honeywell International Inc., for the U.S. Department of Energy's National Nuclear Security Administration under contract DE-NA0003525.

References

Ammari, B. L., Johnson, E. S., Stinchfield, G., Kim, T., Bynum, M., Hart, W. E., Pulsipher, J., and Laird, C. D. (2023). "Linear model decision trees as surrogates in optimization of engineering applications." Computers & Chemical Engineering, 178:108347.

Bertsimas, D., O'Hair, A., Relyea, S., and Silberholz, J. (2016). "An analytics approach to designing combination chemotherapy regimens for cancer." Management Science, 62:1511–1531.

Biggs, M., Hariss, R., and Perakis, G. (2017). "Optimizing objective functions determined from random forests." SSRN Electronic Journal.

Birge, J. R. and Louveaux, F. (2011). "Introduction to Stochastic Programming." Springer New York.

Bynum, M. L., Hackebeil, G. A., Hart, W. E., Laird, C. D., Nicholson, B. L., Siirola, J. D., Watson, J.-P., and Woodruff, D. L. (2021). "Pyomo — Optimization Modeling in Python", volume 67. Springer International Publishing, 3 edition

Caruana, R. and Niculescu-Mizil, A. (2006). "An empirical comparison of supervised learning algorithms." pages 161–168. ACM Press.

Ceccon, F., Jalving, J., Haddad, J., Thebelt, A., Tsay, C., Laird, C. D., and Misener, R. (2022). "OMLT: Optimization & machine learning toolkit." Journal of Machine Learning Research, 23:1–8.

Kilwein, Z., Boukouvala, F., Laird, C., Castillo, A., Blakely, L., Eydenberg, M., Jalving, J., and Batsch-Smith, L. (2021). "Ac-optimal power flow solutions with security constraints from deep neural network models." Computer Aided Chemical Engineering, 50:919–925

Knueven, B., Mildebrath, D., Muir, C., Siirola, J.D., Watson, J.-P., and Woodruff, D. L. (2023), "A parallel hub-and-spoke system for large-scale scenario-based optimization under uncertainty," Mathematical Programming Computation, pp. 1–29.

Mistry, M., Letsios, D., Krennrich, G., Lee, R. M., and Misener, R. (2021). "Mixed-integer convex nonlinear optimization with gradient-boosted trees embedded." INFORMS Journal on Computing, 33:1103–1119.

Mišić, V. V. (2020). Optimization of tree ensembles. Operations Research, 68:1605–1624.

Rockafellar, R. and Wets, R. J.-B. (1991). "Scenarios and policy aggregation in optimization under uncertainty." Mathematics of Operations Research, 16:119–147.

Watson, J.-P. and Woodruff, D. L. (2011). "Progressive hedging innovations for a class of stochastic mixed-integer resource allocation problems." Computational Management Science, 8:355–370.

Flavio Manenti, Gintaras V. Reklaitis (Eds.), Proceedings of the 34th European Symposium on Computer Aided Process Engineering / 15th International Symposium on Process Systems Engineering (ESCAPE34/PSE24), June 2-6, 2024, Florence, Italy

An Improved Oracle Adaption for Bilevel Programs

Daniel Jungen,[a] Alexander Mitsos[b,a,c],*

[a]*Process Systems Engineering (AVT.SVT) RWTH Aachen University, 52074 Aachen, Germany*
[b]*JARA-CSD, 52056 Aachen, Germany*
[c]*Institute of Energy and Climate Research: Energy Systems Engineering (IEK-10), Forschungszentrum Jülich GmbH, 52425 Jülich, Germany.*
amitsos@alum.mit.edu

Abstract

Bilevel programs with nonconvex lower levels occur in many applications in engineering but are notoriously challenging: A global optimization problem must be solved even to check the feasibility of a given candidate solution point. We present an adaption of the approach of Tsoukalas et al. [J. Glob. Optim. 44, 235–250 (2009)]. Our algorithm adaption changes the oracle to minimize directly the lower-level objective, with the target objective value inscribed into its constraints. With this formulation, we aim to obtain lower-level-optimal solution points to the oracle, and thus faster generation of good upper bounds. We implement and compare our approach to the original approach and the state-of-the-art solvers of Mitsos et al. [J. Glob. Optim. 42, 475–513 (2008)] and Djelassi et al. [J. Glob. Optim. 75, 341–392 (2019)] using a comprehensive benchmark test set comprising more than 160 problem instances. Our approach outperforms the original oracle algorithm and the solver of Mitsos et al. but not the one of Djelassie et al.

Keywords: bilevel programming, benchmark, oracle.

1. Introduction

Bilevel programs (BLPs) are optimization problems where a so-called lower-level problem is embedded into an upper-level problem. We consider optimistic BLPs of the form

$$
\begin{aligned}
f^* = \min_{x \in \mathcal{X}, y \in \mathcal{Y}} \quad & f(x, y) \\
\text{s.t.} \quad & g^u(x, y) \le 0 \\
& y \in \arg\min_{z \in \mathcal{Y}} h(x, z) \\
& \quad\text{s.t.} \; g^l(x, z) \le 0 \\
& \quad\quad v^{il}(z) \le 0,
\end{aligned}
\tag{BLP}
$$

with the upper-level objective function $f^u \colon \mathbb{R}^{nx} \times \mathbb{R}^{ny} \to \mathbb{R}$, the lower-level objective function $h \colon \mathbb{R}^{nx} \times \mathbb{R}^{ny} \to \mathbb{R}$, the coupling upper- and lower-level inequality function $g^u \colon \mathbb{R}^{nx} \times \mathbb{R}^{ny} \to \mathbb{R}^{ngu}$ and $g^l \colon \mathbb{R}^{nx} \times \mathbb{R}^{ny} \to \mathbb{R}^{ngl}$, respectively, and the non-coupling lower-level inequality function $v^{il} \colon \mathbb{R}^{nx} \times \mathbb{R}^{ny} \to \mathbb{R}^{nvil}$. A reliable and fast solution to such optimization problems is paramount due to their many applications, e.g., chemical engineering (Clark and Westerberg, 1990; Mitsos et al., 2009) or even gemstone cutting (Küfer et al., 2008). However, the solution of (BLP) is very challenging: the lower-level optimization problem must be solved globally even to check the feasibility of a given candidate pair $(\overline{x}, \overline{y})$. (BLP) can be reformulated as a single-level problem if the lower-level problem is convex and satisfies some regularity conditions. However, convexity of the lower level can, in many applications, not be assumed.

A prominent approach for solving (BLP) absent any convexity assumptions is the adaptive discretization approach. Over the last decades, discretization-based algorithms have been published for the global solution of (BLP), e.g., (Mitsos et al., 2008; Tsoukalas et al., 2009; Djelassi et al., 2019). We are especially interested in the approach Tsoukalas et al. (2009) proposed, which we implemented as the *BLP-Oracle* solver in libDIPS (Jungen et al., 2023). This approach performs a bisection search in the objective space by iteratively solving an oracle problem to determine whether a target objective value f^t is attainable or not. We believe the *BLP-Oracle* is promising as it might inherit strong convergence guarantees through the bisection approach. The oracle problem is an unconstrained minmax problem, where the objective function combines the upper- and lower-level objectives and constraints. Tsoukalas et al. (2009) solve the minmax problem through a smoothing technique based on the Laplace method.

Our algorithm (*BLP-AdaptOracle*) adapts the concept of Tsoukalas et al. (2009) by letting the oracle directly minimize the lower-level objective, with the target objective value inscribed into its constraints. With this formulation, we aim to enhance the chance that the computed candidate point is lower-level optimal, which may lead to a faster generation of good upper bounds (UBD). Although unconstrained subproblems, as proposed by Tsoukalas et al. (2009), might be easier to solve, we do not expect any performance losses since we require a global solution of the subproblems.

2. The *BLP-AdaptOracle* Approach

2.1. Algorithm Description and Subproblem Formulations

For the bisection search in the objective space, we need an initial lower bound (LBD) and UBD on the objective. We compute an initial LBD for (BLP) by

$$LBD^{init} = \min_{x \in X, y \in Y} f(x, y)$$
$$\text{s.t. } g^u(x, y) \leq 0 \tag{LBP}$$
$$g^l(x, y) \leq 0$$
$$v^{il}(y) \leq 0$$

and an initial UBD by

$$UBD^{init} = \max_{x \in X, y \in Y} f(x, y)$$
$$\text{s.t. } g^u(x, y) \leq 0 \tag{UBP}$$
$$g^l(x, y) \leq 0$$
$$v^{il}(y) \leq 0.$$

Once an initial LBD and UBD are computed, the target objective value is set to $f^t \leftarrow \frac{UBD+LBD}{2}$. We formulate our adapted oracle problem as

$$\bar{h} = \min_{x \in \mathcal{X}, y \in \mathcal{Y}} h(\boldsymbol{x}, \boldsymbol{y})$$
$$\text{s.t. } \boldsymbol{g}^u(\boldsymbol{x}, \boldsymbol{y}) \leq \boldsymbol{0}$$
$$\boldsymbol{g}^l(\boldsymbol{x}, \boldsymbol{y}) \leq \boldsymbol{0}$$
$$\boldsymbol{v}^{il}(\boldsymbol{y}) \leq \boldsymbol{0} \qquad \text{(ORA)}$$
$$\min \left\{ h(\boldsymbol{x}, \boldsymbol{y}) - h(\boldsymbol{x}, \boldsymbol{y}^k), \min_{i \in \{1 \ldots np\}} -g_i^l(\boldsymbol{x}, \boldsymbol{y}^k) \right\}, \forall \boldsymbol{y}^k \in \mathcal{Y}^{ORA}$$
$$f(\boldsymbol{x}, \boldsymbol{y}) \leq f^t.$$

If the optimal objective value of (ORA) is ≥ 0 or infeasible, then f^t is not attainable. Then, the current *LBD* is set to f^t and (ORA) is solved again. Whenever (ORA) is feasible, first, feasibility of the computed candidate point $\bar{\boldsymbol{x}}$ is checked by solving the lower-level problem for fixed $\bar{\boldsymbol{x}}$, which reads

$$h^*(\bar{\boldsymbol{x}}) = \min_{y \in \mathcal{Y}} h(\bar{\boldsymbol{x}}, \boldsymbol{y})$$
$$\text{s.t. } \boldsymbol{g}^l(\bar{\boldsymbol{x}}, \boldsymbol{y}) \leq \boldsymbol{0} \qquad \text{(LLP)}$$
$$\boldsymbol{v}^{il}(\boldsymbol{y}) \leq \boldsymbol{0}.$$

If the candidate point $\bar{\boldsymbol{x}}$ is ϵ_h-feasible, i.e., $\bar{h} \leq h^*(\bar{\boldsymbol{x}}) + \epsilon_h$, or the corresponding upper-level objective value is better than the incumbent *UBD*, f^t is updated, and (ORA) is solved again. If the candidate point is infeasible, the discretization $\mathcal{Y}^{ORA}$ is populated with a suitable discretization point, and (ORA) is solved again. An auxiliary problem needs to be solved to compute a valid discretization point, similar to the algorithm of Mitsos and Tsoukalas (2015) for generalized semi-infinite programs. The auxiliary problem is given by

$$a(\bar{x}) = \min_{x \in \mathcal{X}, y \in \mathcal{Y}} \max_{i \in \{1 \ldots np\}} g_i^l(\bar{\boldsymbol{x}}, \boldsymbol{y})$$
$$\text{s.t. } h(\bar{\boldsymbol{x}}, \boldsymbol{y}) \leq \boldsymbol{1} \cdot \alpha \cdot h^*(\bar{\boldsymbol{x}}) \qquad \text{(AUX)}$$
$$\boldsymbol{v}^{il}(\boldsymbol{z}) \leq \boldsymbol{0},$$

with $\alpha < 0$. If no valid discretization point is computed, α is decreased and (AUX) is resolved. The complete algorithm description of *BLP-AdaptOracle* is given in Algorithm 1.

2.2. Assumptions and Proof of Convergences

The following assumptions are primarily standard in global optimization and very similar to the assumptions used in Mitsos et al. (2008) of the solver *BLP-Box*.

Assumption 1 (Compactness of Sets): The sets $\mathcal{X} \subsetneq \mathbb{R}^{nx}$ and $\mathcal{Y} \subsetneq \mathbb{R}^{ny}$ are compact.

Assumption 2 (Continuous Functions): All occurring functions are continuous on their respective host sets.

Assumption 3 (Global solution of subproblems): All subproblems are solved to global optimality.

Algorithm 1: Algorithm description of *BLP-AdaptOracle*. User inputs are the initial finite discretization set $\mathcal{Y}^{init} \subsetneq \mathcal{Y}$, an initial value for $\alpha < 0$, a decreasing rule for α, and the termination tolerances ϵ^a and ϵ_h.

1   solve (LBD) to obtain LBD^{init}
2   **if** (LBD) is infeasible **then**
3   set $LBD \leftarrow +\infty, UBD \leftarrow +\infty$ and terminate;
4   **end**
5   Set $LBD \leftarrow LBD^{init}$;
6   solve (UBD) to obtain UBD^{init};
7   set $UBD \leftarrow UBD^{init}$;
8   set $f^t \leftarrow \frac{UBD+LBD}{2}$ and $\mathcal{Y}^{ORA} \leftarrow \mathcal{Y}^{init}$;
10   **if** $UBD - LBD \leq \epsilon^a$ **then**
11   terminate;
12   **end**
13   solve (ORA) to obtain $\boldsymbol{x}^{ORA}, \boldsymbol{y}^{ORA}$ and $\bar{h}$;
14   **if** (ORA) is infeasible **then**
15   set $LBD \leftarrow f^t$ and $f^t \leftarrow \frac{UBD+LBD}{2}$;
16   got to line 13;
17   **end**
18   solve (LLP) for fixed $\boldsymbol{x}^{ORA}$ to obtain $h^*(\boldsymbol{x}^{ORA})$ and $\boldsymbol{y}^{LLP}$;
19   **if** $\bar{h} \leq h^* + \epsilon_h$ and $\boldsymbol{g}^u(\boldsymbol{x}^{ORA}, \boldsymbol{y}^{LLP}) \leq 0$ **then**
20   set $UBD \leftarrow f^t, \boldsymbol{x}^* \leftarrow x^{ORA}, \boldsymbol{y}^* \leftarrow \boldsymbol{y}^{ORA}$, and $f^t \leftarrow \frac{UBD+LBD}{2}$;
21   go to line 10;
22   **end**
23   **If** $f(\boldsymbol{x}^{ORA}, \boldsymbol{y}^{LLP}) < UBD$ and $\boldsymbol{g}(\boldsymbol{x}^{ORA}, \boldsymbol{y}^{LLP}) \leq 0$ **then**
24   set $UBD \leftarrow f(\boldsymbol{x}^{ORA}, \boldsymbol{y}^{LLP}), \boldsymbol{x}^* \leftarrow \boldsymbol{y}^{ORA}$, and $f^t \leftarrow \frac{UBD+LBD}{2}$;
25   go to line 10;
26   **end**
27   solve (AUX) for fixed $\boldsymbol{x}^{ORA}$ to obtain $a(\boldsymbol{x}^{ORA})$ and $\boldsymbol{y}^{AUX}$;
28   **if** $a(\boldsymbol{x}^{ORA}) \geq 0$ **then**
29   decrease α;
30   go to line 27;
31   **end**
32   set $\mathcal{Y}^{ORA} \leftarrow \mathcal{Y}^{ORA} \cup \boldsymbol{y}^{AUX}$;
33   go to line 10;

Assumption 4 (Inner Problem): For each point $\bar{x} \in X^{outer} \cap \mathcal{Y}^{inner}$ with $X^{outer} = \{x \in X : \exists \bar{y} \in Y : g^u(x, \bar{y}) \leq 0\}$ and $\mathcal{Y}^{inner} = \{x \in X : \exists \bar{y} \in \mathcal{Y} : g^l(x, \bar{y}) \leq 0, v^{il}(\bar{y}) \leq 0\}$ it holds: For any $\epsilon_{h1} > 0$ there exists a point $\bar{z} \in \mathcal{Y}$ such that

$$
\begin{aligned}
&\boldsymbol{g}^l(\boldsymbol{x}, \boldsymbol{z}) < \boldsymbol{0}, \\
&\boldsymbol{g}^u(\boldsymbol{x}, \boldsymbol{z}) \leq \boldsymbol{0}, \\
&\boldsymbol{v}^{il}(\boldsymbol{z}) \leq \boldsymbol{0}, \\
&h(\boldsymbol{x}, \boldsymbol{z}) < \bar{h}(\boldsymbol{x}) + \epsilon_{h1}.
\end{aligned}
\tag{A3}
$$

Note that Assumption 4 is stronger than Assumption 4 in Mitsos et al. (2008).

2.3. Outline of Proof of Convergence

First, we show that if $f^t < f^*$, i.e., the target objective value is not attainable, (ORA) will become infeasible after finitely many iterations. The only interesting iterates are the pairs $(\hat{x}, \hat{y})$ satisfying all lower- and upper-level constraints but $\hat{y}$ not satisfying optimality in (LLP). Suppose a pair $(\hat{x}, \hat{y})$ is found, which exhibits this. The discretization point y^k computed by (AUX), which is added, forbids in all following iterations to revisit $(\hat{x}, \hat{y})$, and a neighborhood around it. Therefore, after finitely many iterations, (ORA) becomes infeasible, and it is proven that f^t is not attainable. Second, we show that if $f^t \geq f^*$, i.e., the target objective value is attainable, (ORA) will furnish a feasible point after finitely many iterations. Like in the first case above, we exclude all pairs $(\hat{x}, \hat{y})$ that do not satisfy lower-level optimality after a finite number of iterations. Because at least one pair $(\hat{x}, \hat{y})$ fulfills all lower- and upper-level constraints and is optimal in the lower level, we must obtain such a point after finitely many iterations. Whenever the target value f^t is proven to be not attainable or a feasible pair $(\hat{x}, \hat{y})$ is found satisfying $f(\hat{x}, \hat{y}) \leq f^t$, the target objective value f^t is updated via bisection. Through bisection, we terminate finitely with proof of ϵ^a-optimality.

3. Numerical Experiments

We use our library libDIPS (Jungen et al., 2023) to compare *BLP-AdaptOracle* to our implementation of the approach of Tsoukalas et al. (2009), i.e., *BLP-Oracle,* and the solvers *BLP-Box* (Mitsos et al., 2008) and *BLP-noBox* (Djelassie et al. 2019). To enable a fair comparison to the underlying algorithm idea of Tsoukalas et al. (2009), we do not apply the smoothing method proposed in the original application but rather directly solve the discrete minmax problem, and all other occurring subproblems, using the subsolver MAiNGO v0.7.1. (Bongartz et al., 2018) with its default settings. We use the bilevel benchmark test set provided by libDIPS (Jungen et al. 2023) for the numerical experiments, which consists of 167 problem instances. All calculations were conducted on the RWTH High-Performance Computing cluster running Rocky Linux 8 on a single core with an Intel Xeon Platinum 8160 Processor 'SkyLake' running at 2.1 GHz. We use the 'best-working' hyperparameters of *BLP-Box*, as reported in Jungen et al. (2023). For BLP-AdaptOracle we use an initial $\alpha = 0.5$ and decrease it by 1.5 whenever (AUX) fails to produce a discretization point.

Figure 1 shows the time factor performance plot for the different solvers. It can be seen that *BLP-AdaptOracle* exceeds *BLP-Oracle* as well as slightly outperforms *BLP-Box*. However, *BLP-noBox* is still by far the best solver.

4. Conclusion

We presented an adaptation of the BLP algorithm proposed by Tsoukalas et al. (2009). While our adaptation outperforms our implementation of the original approach and the state-of-the-art solver of Mitsos et al. (2008), it is superseded by the approach of Djelassi et al. (2019). However, our results (likely) depend on the composition of the benchmark test set, the subproblem formulation, and the used subsolver. The bilevel community might benefits from our algorithm adaption and its integration into libDIPS because the seamless transition between the bilevel solvers within libDIPS enhances accessibility, and our algorithm adaptation might be advantageous in specific applications. Furthermore, our contribution shows that there is likely some undetected potential in the existing approaches, as a simple adaptation resulted in significant performance improvements.

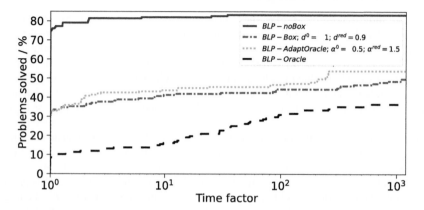

Figure 1: Time factor performance plot showing the numerical performance of the solvers *BLP-noBox* (Djelassi et al., 2019); *BLP-Box* (Mitsos et al. 2008); our algorithm adaptation *BLP-AdaptOracle*; and *BLP-Oracle,* our implementation of Tsoukalas et al. (2009).

Acknowledgements

Funded by the Deutsche Forschungsgemeinschaft (DFG, German Research Foundation) under Germany's Excellence Strategy – Cluster of Excellence 2186 'The Fuel Science Center' – ID: 390919832. Computations were performed with computing resources granted by RWTH Aachen University.

References

Bongartz, D., Najman, J., Sass, S., & Mitsos, A. (2018). MAiNGO - McCormick-based Algorithm for mixed-integer Nonlinear Global Optimization. *Technical Report, Process Systems Engineering (AVT.SVT), RWTH Aachen University, Germany. http://permalink.avt.rwth-aachen.de/?id=729717*

Clark, P. A. & Westerberg, A. W. (1990). Bilevel programming for steady-state chemical process design—I. Fundamentals and algorithms. *Computers & Chemical. Engineering, 14,* 87–97.

Djelassi, H., Glass, M. & Mitsos, A. (2019). Discretization-based algorithms for generalized semi-infinite and bilevel programs with coupling equality constraints. *Journal of Global Optimization, 92,* 341–392.

Küfer, K.-H., Stein, O. & Winterfeld, A. 2008. Semi-infinite optimization meets industry: A deterministic approach to gemstone cutting. *SIAM News, 41* (8).

Jungen, D., Zingler, A., Djelassi, H., Mitsos, A. (2023; in preperation) libDIPS – Discretization-Based Semi-Infinite Programming Solvers. https://git.rwth-aachen.de/avt-svt/public/libdips.

Mitsos, A., Lemonidis, P. & Barton, P. I. (2008). Global solution of bilevel programs with a nonconvex inner program. *Journal of Global Optimization, 42,* 475–513.

Mitsos, A., Bollas, G. M. & Barton, P. I. (2009). Bilevel optimization formulation for parameter estimation in liquid–liquid phase equilibrium problems. *Chemical Engineering Science, 64,* 548–559.

Mitsos, A. & Tsoukalas, A. (2015). Global optimization of generalized semi-infinite programs via restriction of the right hand side. *Journal of Global Optimization, 61,* 1–17.

Tsoukalas, A., Rustem, B. & Pistikopoulos, E. N. (2009). A global optimization algorithm for generalized semi-infinite, continuous minimax with coupled constraints and bi-level problems. *Journal of Global Optimization, 44,* 235–250.

Flavio Manenti, Gintaras V. Reklaitis (Eds.), Proceedings of the 34th European Symposium on Computer Aided Process Engineering / 15th International Symposium on Process Systems Engineering (ESCAPE34/PSE24), June 2-6, 2024, Florence, Italy

Modeling and Economic Optimization of an Industrial Site for Natural Gas Processing: an MINLP Approach

Tayná E. G. Souza[a,b*], Argimiro R. Secchi[a], Letícia C. Santos[b]

aChemical Engineering Program, COPPE, Universidade Federal do Rio de Janeiro (UFRJ), Rio de Janeiro – RJ, Brazil
bPetróleo Brasileiro S.A. (PETROBRAS), Rio de Janeiro - RJ, Brazil
taynaegs@gmail.com

Abstract

In this work, a multi-step MINLP (mixed-integer nonlinear programming) strategy was proposed for high-level enterprise-wide economic optimization of a multi-unit and - feedstock natural gas processing site. The framework was studied in a Petrobras facility using Aspen HYSYS for process simulation, Python for optimization and Microsoft Excel as data transfer interface. MINLP was broken down into a hybrid nonlinear programming (NLP - particle swarm plus flexible polyhedron) added to a mixed-integer programming (MIP - branch-and-bound plus linear programming as initial estimate generator for NLP subproblems). A potential profit increase of 9.1 % (118.78 R$ / 1000 m^3) was found by optimizing raw gas distribution to process units and selecting their operating status, thus showing how successful the proposed strategy is.

Keywords: Multi-unit NGPUs, Process Simulation, Enterprise-wide Optimization

1. Introduction

Natural gas is a mixture of mostly paraffin hydrocarbons from underground reservoirs (MONDAL et al., 2013). Its primary use is as fuel (MONDAL et al., 2013), specially as a transition source from oil to renewable energy. Although field conditioning usually takes place near the wellhead, further onshore processing is needed to guarantee market specification – this is carried out by natural gas processing plants. Those facilities are subject to variations in the inlet streams from upstream.

Although several papers have been published on modeling and optimization of gas plants, there is a lack of focus on high-level integrated business perspective, embracing the enterprise-wide optimization concept. Souza et al. (2022) tried to fulfill this gap by introducing an NLP approach via global optimization and rigorous simulation. However promising, this approach is still limited, since multi-unit natural gas processing facilities also have the flexibility of putting one or more plants on standby when inlet feed flowrate is low – reduction of operating costs (OpEx). Besides, gas processing units (NGPUs) have lower feed boundaries – below which continuous operation is not feasible and plant is shut down – those conditions generate binary decision variables. Thus, a robust mixed integer nonlinear programming (MINLP) approach is required for daily basis application. This work intends to fill this gap by proposing an MINLP optimization strategy for economic optimization of an industrial multi-unit natural gas processing site and comparing results with the NLP approach from Souza et al. (2022).

2. Background

2.1. Process description

The system in study is the same Petrobras facility presented by Souza et al. (2022) – the largest natural gas processing facility in Brazil. This site receives non-processed raw gas from three different offshore sources and processes it into four products: sales gas, NGL (C_2^+), LPG, and C_5^+, plus two intermediate streams: NGL (C_3^+) and residual gas. The site is composed of five NGPUs that may differ by refrigeration technology, performance and capacity. There are also three liquid fractionating units (LFUs) that receive: 1) unstabilized condensate from slug catchers (SG), 2) intermediate NGL (C_3^+) from NGPU-A, 3) lighter liquid formed in knockout drums. A general schematic of the industrial site is presented in Fig. 1(a) (further details in Souza et al., 2022).

There are several possible configurations to send the multi-feedstock raw gas to the five process units. Those possible routes are the continuous decision variables (u) of the optimization problem proposed by Souza et al. (2022). In this work, binary decision variables (y) are also added, representing the NGPUs operating status, plus two degrees of freedom: u_{11}, fraction of the residual gas from NGPU-E that is reprocessed, and u_{12}, fraction of the residual gas from NGPU-A that is reprocessed (Fig. 1(a)). Product profile and overall OpEx will vary according to feed route configuration and NGPU operating status. It is important to mention that currently this is a manual decision of the Operations team, which may lead to suboptimal operating conditions.

2.2. Process modeling and simulation

HYSYS commercial simulator was the tool chosen to build a static first-principles model of the facility. The model has already been presented, discussed and validated in the previous work of Souza et al. (2022), where further details can be found. Validation showed good agreement with plant data, thus presenting itself as a good starting point to the simulation-optimization framework proposed here and detailed in the next section.

3. Methodology

The high-level methodology of this work is similar to the one from Souza et al. (2022). Difference here lies in the MINLP approach: at each iteration, process simulation receives continuous and integer decision variables, carries out mass/energy balances and passes back model variables to the MINLP optimizer, which computes the objective function. Upon convergence, an optimum operating point is found, associated with maximum business profit and optimum values of the decision variables (Fig. 1(b)).

3.1. Optimization framework

Each individual gas plant is represented by several non-linear processes (ZHANG et al., 2016). and has the flexibility of changing operating status, which leads to integer binary decision variables. Thus, this work proposed an MINLP optimization strategy. This agrees with the literature, which states that MINLP techniques are well-suited to such problems: nonlinear process plus desired selection of process alternatives, possibly with discrete variables (MENCARELLI et al., 2020).

Figure 1(b) summarizes the proposed methodology: particle swarm (PSO) global method is used as pre-screening with relaxed integers to generate initial estimates for MINLP; branch-and-bound and flexible polyhedrons (FPO) are used in a loop to find an

MINLP solution via tree-search – this step defines the integer values that are translated into plant operating status in HYSYS simulation; PSO and FPO are used in series with tighter tolerances to refine the MINLP result and reach a final optimal solution. Based on the experience provided by Souza et al. (2022), it was studied the possibility of using *PSO + FPO* in each NLP subproblem from tree-search. Unfortunately, time consumption would make it unfeasible for industrial application, so an LP was used instead to generate feasible estimates to each NLP subproblem.

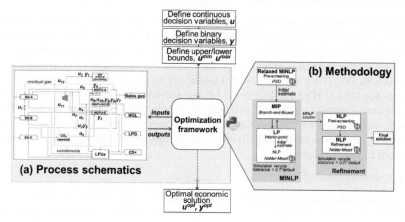

Figure 1: Simulation-optimization framework proposed in this work (created by the authors): (a) model schematic including the decision variables. (b) MINLP optimization methodology proposed. PSO, branch-and-bound and FPO methods are employed in three main steps: pre-screening, MINLP solution and post-refinement.

3.2. Optimization problem formulation

The proposed optimization problem has the goal of achieving the optimal feed allocation (u) and NGPUs operating status (y) to maximize business profit. For the sake of result comparison, the objective function (S in Eq. (1)) is the profit, calculated as revenue minus OpEx. The costs used in this work are from Souza et al. (2022).

$$S[x(u,y),u,y] = \sum_{i=1}^{n_p} m_i Q_{pi} - [c_{EE} Power_{EE} + c_{FG} Q_{FG}] + \text{Pen}[x(u,y),u,y,r] \quad (1)$$

where x are model variables, $n_p = 5$ is the number of products, m_i is market product price, Q_p are product flowrates, c are average costs of electricity and fuel gas. $Power_{EE}$ is electricity demand and Q_{FG} is fuel gas consumption, which uses lower heating value to match units. r is the scale factor for magnitude equalization. Inequality constraints were accounted for by adding a penalty term (Pen) to the objective function, with adjusted magnitude, thus avoiding numerical issues in the optimization search. Equality constrains are guaranteed from feasible path approach. Constraint values and penalty function mathematics can be found in Souza et al. (2022).

3.3. Computational Aspects

Figure 1 summarizes the complete strategy. The optimization problem was implemented in Python. For PSO algorithm, *pyswarm* package was customized to create continuous intervals based on the choice of binary variables. For local NLP, spicy package (*spicy.optimize.minimize*) was adapted to include an LP (interior point) for initial estimate generation. Size of the initial simplex was modified to ensure proper exploration. A Matlab implementation of branch-and-bound (SOARES, 2001) was adapted to Python and tailored for this work. Excel was used as user interface with VBA procedures and a bidirectional communication with Aspen HYSYS and Python.

4. Results and Discussion

4.1. Optimization results

Optimization framework was implemented in three main steps: 1) PSO relaxed pre-screening with 190 particles and 20 iterations generated a feasible initial estimate to the 2) MINLP step, which was solved by branch-and-bound (MIP tree-search with tolerance of 0.1 for integer variables, 0.00001 for the continuous ones and 0.01 for constraints) coupled with FPO (NLP with 0.1 overall tolerance). In this step, convergence of recycle streams was 10% of HYSYS default; an LP was solved with interior-point to generate a feasible initial estimate for NLP problem. 3) Lastly, NLP variables of the MINLP solution were refined by PSO post-screening (120 particles and 20 iterations) followed by NLP – FPO local refinement (0.001 overall tolerance) with recycle convergence tightened to 1% of default.

4.1.1. Computational effort

Process modeling and optimization were executed in an Intel Core™ i5 10210U processor, 1.60GHz. Model execution time was dependent on how close input conditions were from previous execution, varying from 40s to nearly 3min. This dependence is a consequence of HYSYS convergence strategy, which utilizes the current converged solution as initial guess for the next run (SOUZA et al., 2022).

For each optimization step, total execution time was: 1) PSO pre-screening: 8h 2min; 2) MINLP: 15h 20min; 3) post-refinement: 10h 39min. Thus, total execution time was 34h, which is consistent with the dimension and complexity of the system: i) rigorous phenomenological simulation approach, ii) global non-deterministic optimization method (PSO), iii) utilization of several solution steps and optimization algorithms.

4.2. Analysis of the Variables Search Space

PSO was used to explore and better understand the MINLP space of variables. A total of 6592 feasible points were gathered from individual PSO executions and the results for u_8 (NGPU-A feed gas flowrate) are shown in Fig. 2. This is a very representative plot to understand the space of variables, since it shows a wall-shaped region at u_8=0.5 where some of the best objective function values are and which corresponds to the lowest value of u_8 when NGPU-A is under operation (y_4=1). This is the region where an NLP approach would find its optimum. However, the region with u_8=0 is not only feasible in this MINLP approach (y_4=0), but concentrates a region of economically interesting points, where the MINLP optimum might lie.

4.2.1. MINLP results

The MINLP problem was successfully solved and the tree-search step-by-step results are presented in Table 1. Results show that the MINLP optimizer found an optimum at y_4=0. This means that NGPU-A was put in standby, in agreement with the search space analysis in Section 4.2 and shows the advantage of formulating an MINLP approach in comparison to NLP – the optimizer used the plant flexibility of putting NGPUs in standby to find an optimum economic operating point better than the one found in Souza et al. (2022) from NLP approach (objective function of 0.985 versus 0.979).

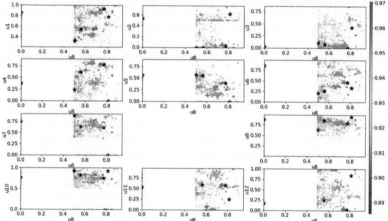

Figure 2: Plots of u_8 (NGPU-A feed flowrate) u_1 to u_{12}. Colors refer to objective function (S) value (color-bar in the right). Star symbols: five highest S values.

Table 1: Tree-search results from MINLP solution. Table shows number of executions, tree node, binary variables (y_1 to y_7), iterations, function evaluation of each NLP run.

#	Node	y_1	y_2	y_3	y_4	y_5	y_6	y_7	S	Iterations	Feval.
1	1	1	0.509	0.970	0.628	0.955	0.902	0.965	0.955	202	342
2	1	0	0.395	0.997	0.997	0.891	0.996	0.969	0.969	209	337
3	2	0	1	0.929	0.589	0.968	0.930	0.973	0.973	217	361
4	2	0	0	0.900	0.526	0.909	0.969	0.972	0.972	100	198
5	3	0	1	0.821	0	0.998	0.986	0.967	0.967	158	257
6	3	0	1	0.968	1	0.934	0.974	0.973	0.972	130	251
7	4	0	1	0.972	1	0.993	0.993	0.934	0.934	187	301
8	4	0	1	0.692	1	0.886	0.945	0.973	0.973	119	212
9	4	0	1	0	0	0.980	0.980	0	0	4	67
10	4	0	1	1	0	0.829	0.995	0.985	0.985	108	186
11	5	0	1	1	0	0	0.850	0	0	4	63
12	5	0	1	1	0	1	0.973	0.983	0.983	175	308
13	Final	0	1	1	0	1	1	0.985	0.985	19	62

4.3. Profit Gain

Economic results from optimization solution are shown in Table 2.

Table 2: Potential profit gain resulting from the solution of NLP and MINLP problem formulations in comparison to a base case, defined as initial estimate.

Problem formulation	Objective function	Potential profit gain (%)	Potential profit gain (R$/1000m³)
NLP – FPO (Souza et al., 2022)	0.9704	6.4 %	83.73
NLP – PSO + FPO (Souza et al., 2022)	0.9790	7.3 %	96.11
MINLP	0.9852	8.0 %	104.94
MINLP + post refinement	0.9948	9.1 %	118.78
Base case (Souza et al., 2022)	0.9120		

By adding the operating status of the NGPUs as integer decision variables, better economic results were found. Additionally, coupling the MINLP solution with a post-refinement step showed the best overall results, bringing a potential gain of over 9 % in plant variable profit. Results show that it is overall advantageous to work with an MINLP strategy in comparison to NLP, even considering the higher computation demand for MINLP, and this is a consequence of the gas plant dynamic scenarios that might lead to the possibility of putting one or more NGPUs in standby, reducing OpEx.

5. Conclusions

This work had the objective to formulate a high-level economic optimization framework for a multi-unit industrial natural gas processing facility, considering the flexibility of having NGPUs in standby. This resulted in an MINLP optimization problem, aiming at the optimum operating point for maximum business profit. MINLP model was broken down into an NLP combined with MIP, both solved as a simulation-optimization integrated framework, using HYSYS for simulation, Python for optimization and Excel as data transfer interface. An augmented objective function was used to incorporate inequality constraints. The problem was successfully solved using branch-and-bound coupled with flexible polyhedron, preceded by a PSO pre-screening, in 23h 22min (Intel ® Core™ i5 10210U processor with 1.60 GHz). An LP problem was formulated with interior-point to generate feasible initial estimates for Nelder-Mead. Results were then refined in a with PSO in series with Nelder-Mead, considering tighter tolerances for both the NLP problem and process simulation. Results were in agreement with the graphical analysis from PSO. Both resulted in disfavouring the three process units that have the lowest liquid recovery fractions, a consequence of the products sales prices, defining higher values for liquid streams. An objective function of 0.9948 was obtained, in comparison to 0.9120 of base-case, indicating a potential increase of 9.1 % or 118.78 R$/1000 m^3 in industrial plant variable profit. This work thus provided a contribution to the literature by successfully proposing an MINLP optimization framework and methodology for the business economic optimization of a natural gas processing site. Although the methodology was implemented and tested in a specific industrial case, it is applicable to other midstream sites. It also makes way for new works and developments regarding digital transformation in the natural gas processing research field.

References

L. Mencarelli, Q. Chen, A. Pagot, 2020, A review on superstructure optimization approaches in process system engineering, Computers and Chemical Engineering, v. 136.

S. Mokhtab, W. A. Poe, J. Y. Mak, 2012, Handbook of natural gas transmission and processing, Elsevier Inc.

S. Mondal, M. R. Uddin, A. K. Azan, 2013, Simulation and Optimization of natural gas processing plant, International conference on mechanical, industrial and materials engineering.

R. Soares, 2001, Modificação e implementação de algoritmos para problemas MINLP.

T. Souza, A. R. Secchi, L. C. Santos. Modeling and economic optimization of an industrial site for natural gas processing: A nonlinear optimization approach, 2023, Digital Chemical Engineering, 6, 100070.

B. Zhang, Q. L. Chen, J. Li, C. A. Floudas, 2016. Operational strategy and planning for raw natural gas refining complexes: process modeling and global optimization. AIChE J., 652–668.

Q. Zheng, S. Rebennack, N. A. Iliadis, P. M. Pardalos, 2010. Optimization models in the natural gas industry. Handbook of power systems I, energy systems. Springer, Berlin, pp. 121–148.

Flavio Manenti, Gintaras V. Reklaitis (Eds.), Proceedings of the 34th European Symposium on Computer Aided Process Engineering / 15th International Symposium on Process Systems Engineering (ESCAPE34/PSE24), June 2-6, 2024, Florence, Italy

Solving Inverse Optimization Problems via Bayesian Optimization

Yen-An Lu,[a] Vikram Kumar,[a] Wei-Shou Hu,[a] Joel Paulson,[*b] Qi Zhang[*a]

[a] *Department of Chemical Engineering and Materials Science, University of Minnesota, Minneapolis, MN 55455, USA*
[b] *Department of Chemical and Biomolecular Engineering, The Ohio State University, Columbus, OH 43210, USA*
* paulson.82@osu.edu, qizh@umn.edu

Abstract

Data-driven inverse optimization refers to the learning of unknown optimization models from optimal or near-optimal solutions of that optimization problem. As such, it can be used to uncover hidden decision-making processes, assuming that they can be described as optimization problems. However, the inverse optimization problem is commonly formulated as a large-scale bilevel program, which is often very difficult to solve, especially when the lower-level problems are nonconvex. In this work, we propose a black-box optimization approach based on Bayesian optimization to tackle general inverse optimization problems. Here, the objective function is approximated using a probabilistic surrogate model and can, for fixed parameter values, be evaluated by directly solving the given lower-level optimization problems. In a computational case study, we apply the proposed method to estimate the missing parameters in a standard pooling problem that is nonlinear and nonconvex. The results demonstrate the ability of the proposed framework to accurately estimate the model parameters with small numbers of data points and Bayesian optimization iterations.

Keywords: Inverse optimization, Bayesian optimization, decision making.

1. Introduction

Data-driven inverse optimization (IO) is an emerging approach to learning the explicit rules behind complex decision-making processes (Chan et al., 2021). It leverages mathematical optimization as a model for decision making, where observed decisions are assumed to be the optimal or near-optimal solutions to an underlying optimization problem. The primary objective of IO is to decipher the optimization model that best mirrors an agent's decision-making patterns based on their past decisions. A key strength of IO is its ability to directly account for constraints, thereby harnessing the full modeling versatility of mathematical programming and providing a natural mechanism to incorporate domain knowledge, ultimately yielding interpretable decision models.

Inverse optimization problems (IOPs) are typically formulated as bilevel programs, which involve as many lower-level problems as there are training data points. Each lower-level problem represents an instance of the forward optimization problem (FOP) with the corresponding model inputs and observed decisions, whereas the objective of the upper-level problem is to estimate model parameters that yield FOP solutions that best align with the observed decisions. Common approaches to solving IOPs apply single-level reformulations and cutting-plane methods (Chan et al., 2019; Keshavarz et al., 2011). Recent works have also proposed decomposition methods to handle IOPs with high-dimensional FOPs and large datasets (Gupta and Zhang, 2022, 2023). However, these existing exact solution methods often become intractable when the FOP is nonconvex.

In this work, we propose to solve general IOPs using Bayesian optimization (BO) where we treat the loss function of the IOP as a black box. Here, the key advantage of BO is that, at each iteration, it only requires the evaluation of the loss function with the current parameter estimates; this can be achieved by directly solving the FOP for every data point, which circumvents the need of a single-level reformulation or a cutting-plane algorithm. Consequently, BO remains applicable even when the FOP is nonlinear and nonconvex. In a computational study, we demonstrate that the proposed BO framework can efficiently identify robust estimates of model parameters in a nonlinear and nonconvex pooling problem with relatively small numbers of iterations and observations, particularly when the number of unknown model parameters is limited.

2. Mathematical formulation

We assume that the decision-making process of interest can be formulated as an optimization problem of the following general form, which we refer to as the FOP:

$$\underset{x \in \mathbb{R}^n}{\text{minimize}} \quad f(x, u; \theta)$$
$$\text{subject to} \quad g(x, u; \theta) \leq 0, \tag{1}$$

where objective function f and constraint functions g are parameterized by θ, x denotes the n-dimensional vector of decision variables, and $u \in \mathbb{R}^m$ denote the contextual inputs that describe the system conditions. Here, we assume that the model parameters $\theta \in \mathbb{R}^d$ are unknown; however, we can measure decisions $\{x_i\}_{i \in I}$ under varying input conditions $\{u_i\}_{i \in I}$ for a given set of observations I. We further assume that the observations are noisy due to, for example, measurement errors, suboptimal decisions, or model mismatches. The goal of IO is to estimate the unknown θ such that the model predictions best fit the observed decisions, which gives rise to a data-driven IOP that can be formulated as the following bilevel optimization problem (Gupta and Zhang, 2023):

$$\underset{\hat{\theta} \in \Theta, \hat{x}}{\text{minimize}} \quad l(\hat{\theta}) = \sum_{i \in I} (x_i - \hat{x}_i)^{\mathsf{T}} W (x_i - \hat{x}_i)$$
$$\text{subject to} \quad \hat{x}_i \in \arg \min_{\tilde{x} \in \mathbb{R}^n} \{ f(\tilde{x}, u_i; \hat{\theta}) : g(\tilde{x}, u_i; \hat{\theta}) \leq 0 \} \quad \forall i \in I \tag{2}$$

where the objective of the upper-level problem is to obtain estimates of the model parameters, denoted by $\hat{\theta}$, that minimize the decision loss $l(\hat{\theta})$ defined as the weighted sum of squared residuals of predicted and observed decisions. Here, W denotes the diagonal matrix of weighting factors. The bilevel optimization problem (2) is commonly solved using a single-level reformulation where the lower-level problems are replaced by their optimality conditions; however, this is only applicable when the FOP is convex. To address nonconvex FOPs, we propose a BO-based approach as described in the following.

3. Solution approach

In this work, we treat the upper-level objective of problem (2) as a black-box function and directly optimize it through BO (Frazier, 2018). Problem (2) is thus converted to the following black-box optimization problem:

$$\underset{\hat{\theta} \in \Theta}{\text{minimize}} \quad l(\hat{\theta}). \tag{3}$$

3.1. Gaussian process regression

We approximate the loss function l with a Gaussian process (GP) surrogate $\hat{l}(\hat{\theta}) \sim \mathcal{GP}\left(m(\hat{\theta}), \kappa(\hat{\theta}, \hat{\theta}')\right)$, where the prior GP distribution is specified by the choice of the mean function $m(\hat{\theta})$ and covariance (kernel) function $\kappa(\hat{\theta}, \hat{\theta}')$ (Rasmussen and Williams, 2005). By maximizing the log marginal likelihood, the hyperparameters of the kernel κ are calibrated to a set of t past evaluations $\mathcal{D}_t = \left\{\left(\hat{\theta}_n, l(\hat{\theta}_n)\right)\right\}_{n=1}^{t}$, where $l(\hat{\theta}_n)$ denotes the evaluation of the decision loss obtained by solving $|I|$ FOPs at $\hat{\theta}_n$.

We consider a zero mean, which can be achieved by normalizing the output data, and focus on the stationary covariance functions from the Matérn class. Conditioned on the evaluations $\mathcal{D}_t$, the predicted posterior distribution of the function l at a future input $\hat{\theta}_{t+1}$ remains Gaussian with the following posterior mean and covariance:

$$
\begin{aligned}
\mu_t(\hat{\theta}_{t+1}) &= \kappa_t^{\mathsf{T}}(\hat{\theta}_{t+1})\mathbf{K}_t^{-1}\boldsymbol{l}_t, \\
\sigma_t^2(\hat{\theta}_{t+1}) &= \kappa(\hat{\theta}_{t+1}, \hat{\theta}_{t+1}) - \kappa_t^{\mathsf{T}}(\hat{\theta}_{t+1})\mathbf{K}_t^{-1}\kappa_t(\hat{\theta}_{t+1}),
\end{aligned}
\tag{4}
$$

where $\boldsymbol{l}_t = \left[l(\hat{\theta}_1), \dots, l(\hat{\theta}_t)\right]^{\mathsf{T}}$, $\kappa_t = \left[\kappa(\hat{\theta}_{t+1}, \hat{\theta}_1), \dots, \kappa(\hat{\theta}_{t+1}, \hat{\theta}_t)\right]$, and $\mathbf{K}_t$ is a $t \times t$ matrix whose ij^{th} entry is $\kappa(\hat{\theta}_i, \hat{\theta}_j)$.

3.2. Bayesian optimization

The BO framework aims to minimize the function l over the input domain $\hat{\theta} \in \Theta$ by sequentially querying particular $\hat{\theta}$ values based on the posterior of the GP surrogate that provides uncertainty quantification of function l over the input domain. In each BO iteration the next sample point $\hat{\theta}_{t+1}$ is queried by optimizing an acquisition function that is defined in terms of the posterior information and the t past evaluations $\mathcal{D}_t$:

$$
\hat{\theta}_{t+1} \in \arg\min_{\theta \in \Theta} \mathbb{E}[\max(\hat{l}_t(\theta) - l^*, 0)].
\tag{5}
$$

We use the expected improvement (EI) acquisition function (Jones et al., 1998), where the GP surrogate conditioned on the past evaluations $\mathcal{D}_t$ is denoted by $\hat{l}_t$, and l^* denotes the minimum decision loss across the previous evaluations (also known as the incumbent). Based on the new query point $\hat{\theta}_{t+1}$, the true loss function value $l(\hat{\theta}_{t+1})$ is evaluated by solving the solving $|I|$ FOPs. The dataset $\mathcal{D}_t$ is then appended with the new evaluation $\left(\hat{\theta}_{t+1}, l(\hat{\theta}_{t+1})\right)$ to create a concatenated dataset $\mathcal{D}_{t+1}$. The new dataset $\mathcal{D}_{t+1}$ is later used to update the GP model, and the same process is repeated until the termination criterion is met. A pseudocode for the BO algorithm is shown in Algorithm 1.

Algorithm 1 Bayesian optimization for inverse optimization

Input: GP prior m and κ, input domain Θ, initial data $\mathcal{D}_0$, total number of iterations T, and $|I|$ experiments with pairs of $\{(x_i, u_i)\}_{i=1}^{|I|}$ and corresponding FOPs

1: **for** $t = 0,1,2 \dots T$ **do**
2:      Update GP model using $\mathcal{D}_t$
3:      $\hat{\theta}_{t+1} \leftarrow \arg\min_{\theta \in \Theta} \mathbb{E}[\max(\hat{l}_t(\theta) - l^*, 0)]$
4:      Evaluate $l(\hat{\theta}_{t+1})$ by solving $|I|$ FOPs at current $\hat{\theta}_{t+1}$
5:      $\mathcal{D}_{t+1} \leftarrow \mathcal{D}_t \cup \{(\hat{\theta}_{t+1}, l_{t+1})\}$
6: **end for**

Output: Optimal solution $\hat{\theta}_T$

---

4. Computational case study

We consider a standard pooling problem where an operator blends a set of feedstocks in a pooling network to create various final products that meet desired qualities and demands while minimizing the total cost. Provided below is the formulation of a standard pooling problem (Misener and Floudas, 2009):

$$\underset{f,y,z,q}{\text{minimize}} \sum_{(s,l)\in T_f} c_s f_{sl} - \sum_{(l,j)\in T_y} d_{lj}^y y_{lj} - \sum_{(s,j)\in T_z} d_{sj}^z z_{sj} \tag{6a}$$

$$\text{subject to } \sum_{l:(s,l)\in T_f} f_{sl} + \sum_{j:(s,j)\in T_z} z_{sj} \le A_s^U \quad \forall s \in \mathcal{S} \tag{6b}$$

$$\sum_{s:(s,l)\in T_f} f_{sl} - \sum_{j:(l,j)\in T_y} y_{lj} = 0 \quad \forall l \in \mathcal{L} \tag{6c}$$

$$\sum_{s:(s,l)\in T_f} C_s f_{sl} = p_l \sum_{j:(l,j)\in T_y} y_{lj} \quad \forall l \in \mathcal{L} \tag{6d}$$

$$\sum_{l:(l,j)\in T_y} p_l y_{lj} + \sum_{s:(s,j)\in T_z} C_s z_{sj} \le P_j^U \left(\sum_{l:(l,j)\in T_y} y_{lj} + \sum_{s:(s,j)\in T_z} z_{sj} \right) \quad \forall j \in \mathcal{J} \tag{6e}$$

$$\theta_j D_j \le \sum_{l:(l,j)\in T_y} y_{lj} + \sum_{s:(s,j)\in T_z} z_{sj} \quad \forall j \in \mathcal{J} \tag{6f}$$

$$f_{sl} \ge 0 \quad \forall s \in \mathcal{S}, l \in \mathcal{L} \tag{6g}$$

$$y_{lj} \ge 0 \quad \forall l \in \mathcal{L}, j \in \mathcal{J} \tag{6h}$$

$$z_{sj} \ge 0 \quad \forall s \in \mathcal{S}, j \in \mathcal{J} \tag{6i}$$

$$q_l \ge 0 \quad \forall l \in \mathcal{L}, \tag{6j}$$

where $\mathcal{S}$ is the set of input feedstocks, $\mathcal{L}$ is the set of mixing pools, and $\mathcal{J}$ is the set of output products. As incoming feedstocks can connect to a pool or directly to an output, sets T_f, T_y, and T_z denote the existing streams from input s to pool l, pool l to output j, and input i to output j, respectively. The cost per unit of feedstock s is denoted by c_s. The revenue per unit flow from pool l to output j and input s to output j are denoted by d_{lj}^y and d_{sj}^z, respectively. We use variables f_{sl}, y_{lj}, and z_{sj} to denote the flow from input s to pool l, pool l to product j, and input s to output j, respectively, whereas the quality level in pool l is denoted by p_l.

In problem (6), we assume that each feedstock s has a limited availability A_s^U as indicated in constraints (6b); the material and quality balance at pool l are maintained through constraints (6c) and (6d), respectively; the upper acceptable product quality P_j^U of each product j is set in (6e). We consider a scenario in which the demand for each product j (D_j in constraints (6f)) is known; however, due to the limited input availability, the operator has varying unknown preferences on the minimum demand they would like to satisfy for each product j, where θ_j denotes the minimum fraction of demand j that needs to be satisfied. Notably, constraints (6e) contain bilinear terms that render the overall optimization problem nonconvex. The goal is to apply IO to estimate the θ_j values by observing a part of the decisions, namely f_i and y_i, based on varying input conditions $u_i = (D, A^U, P^U, d^y, d^z)_i$ in a set of experiments I.

We test the proposed BO framework on two benchmark pooling networks, Haverly1 and Foulds2 (Adhya et al., 1999), where their network specifications ($|\mathcal{S}|, |\mathcal{L}|, |\mathcal{J}|$) are (3,1,2) and (6,2,4), respectively. For each random instance of the IOP, we first generate a set of ground truth $\theta_j \ \forall \ j \in \mathcal{J}$ and create a training dataset of $|I|$ experiments with randomized demand $D \sim \mathcal{U}(100,200)$, feedstock availability $A^U \sim \mathcal{U}(133,167)$, upper acceptable quality $P^U \sim \mathcal{U}(1.5,3)$, and revenue d^y and $d^z \sim \mathcal{U}(6,15)$. Lastly, we solve these $|I|$ experiments of problem (6) to collect the true optimal solutions $x_i^* = (f_i^*, y_i^*)$, and a Gaussian noise is added to generate noisy observations of decisions $x_i = x_i^* + \gamma$, where $\gamma \sim \mathcal{N}(0, \sigma^2 \mathbb{I})$. A separate set of testing data is generated based on the same randomization procedure with 25 experiments. The computational statistics are obtained from the results of 10 random instances of each IOP.

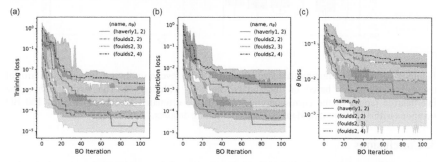

Figure 1: Effect of network size and dimensionality of θ (n_θ) on the accuracy of the estimated FOPs. Convergence analysis of (a) training loss, (b) prediction loss, and (c) θ loss on haverly1 and foulds2 networks with varying n_θ. Training and prediction loss describe the normalized decision loss on the training and testing datasets, respectively, whereas θ loss denotes the difference between the ground truth and estimate θ values. Here the solid lines and shaded areas respectively denote the medians and confidence intervals of the corresponding loss across the 10 random instances.

We first implement the proposed method to solve the IOPs for the two networks with $|I| = 50$ under varying dimensionality of θ (n_θ), i.e., n_θ number of θ_j is selected to be unknown. *Figure* 1 shows the convergence of three different types of losses over the BO iterations, including decision loss on the training and testing data as well as θ loss compared to the ground truth values. A similar trend in loss convergence is observed in all problems, where a rapid and consistent decrease is observed in the first 20-30 iterations followed by small and discrete improvements. The estimated models in all cases show good generalizability in predicting the decisions under unseen conditions, as a similar convergence between training and prediction losses is observed. A comparable rate of convergence is obtained in the two benchmark networks with $n_\theta = 2$, indicating that the algorithm is robust with respect to the network size, which directly affects the number of decision variables in the FOP. While the algorithm shows a slower convergence for increasing n_θ in the foulds2 problem, it converges to good estimates of θ that show accurate predictions on decisions within 100 iterations.

Next, we examine the impact of the size of training datasets $|I|$ on the prediction accuracy of the estimated FOPs at 100 BO iterations, as shown in *Figure* 2a. A monotonic decrease in prediction loss is observed with increasing $|I|$ up to 150 data points; however, 50-100 data points seem to be enough to estimate models that provide accurate predictions under the given 10 random instances. Lastly, we test the algorithm performance under varying noise levels in terms of the observed decisions (*Figure* 2b), where the algorithm provides robust θ estimates even under relatively high measurement noises ($\sigma = 0.1$). These results demonstrate that the IO approach is data-efficient and robust in learning unknown optimization model parameters, which can be especially advantageous when experiments for collecting decision data are expensive and subject to high levels of noise.

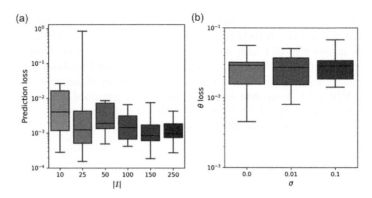

Figure 2: Effect of (a) training data size $|I|$ and (b) noise level σ on the prediction and θ error of the estimated models based on the foulds2 network with $n_\theta = 4$. The boxplots show the interquartile ranges of the corresponding losses of the estimated models obtained at 100 BO iterations with 10 different random instances of training datasets.

5. Conclusions

In this work, we proposed a solution algorithm for solving general inverse optimization problems, where the goal is to learn unknown parameters of optimization models. This was achieved by treating the objective of an IOP as a black box and iteratively optimizing it using Bayesian optimization. To assess the performance of the algorithm, we apply it to a nonlinear and nonconvex pooling problem with unknown model parameters. The results demonstrate the effectiveness and robustness of the proposed method for estimating model parameters based on a small set of noisy data within a limited number of BO iterations.

References

Adhya, N., Tawarmalani, M., and Sahinidis, N.V., 1999. A Lagrangian approach to the pooling problem. *Industrial and Engineering Chemistry Research*, *38*(5), 1956–1972.

Chan, T. C. Y., Lee, T., and Terekhov, D., 2019. Inverse optimization: Closed-form solutions, geometry, and goodness of fit. *Management Science*, *65*(3), 1115–1135.

Chan, T. C. Y., Mahmood, R., and Zhu, I. Y., 2021. Inverse optimization: Theory and applications. *ArXiv Preprint,* ArXiv:2109.03920.

Frazier, P. I., 2018. *A Tutorial on Bayesian Optimization. ArXiv Preprint,* ArXiv:1807.02811.

Gupta, R. and Zhang, Q., 2022. Decomposition and Adaptive Sampling for Data-Driven Inverse Linear Optimization. *INFORMS Journal on Computing.*

Gupta, R. and Zhang, Q., 2023. Efficient learning of decision-making models: A penalty block coordinate descent algorithm for data-driven inverse optimization. *Computers and Chemical Engineering*, *170*, 108123.

Jones, D. R., Schonlau, M., and Welch, W. J., 1998. Efficient Global Optimization of Expensive Black-Box Functions. *Journal of Global Optimization*, *13*(4), 455–492.

Keshavarz, A., Wang, Y., and Boyd, S., 2011. Imputing a convex objective function. *IEEE International Symposium on Intelligent Control - Proceedings*, 613–619.

Misener, R., and Floudas, C. A., 2009. Advances for the pooling problem: Modeling, global optimization, and computational studies Survey. *Applied and Computational Mathematics*, *8*(1), 3–22.

Rasmussen, C. E., and Williams, C. K. I., 2005. Gaussian Processes for Machine Learning. *The MIT Press.*

Flavio Manenti, Gintaras V. Reklaitis (Eds.), Proceedings of the 34th European Symposium on Computer Aided Process Engineering / 15th International Symposium on Process Systems Engineering (ESCAPE34/PSE24), June 2-6, 2024, Florence, Italy

Learning reduced-order models for dynamic CO_2 methanation using operator inference

Luisa Peterson[a], Pawan Goyal[a], Ion Victor Gosea[a], Jens Bremer[b], Peter Benner[a,c], Kai Sundmacher[a,c,*]

[a]*Max Planck Institute for Dynamics of Complex Technical Systems, Sandtorstraße 1, Magdeburg, 39106, Germany*
[b]*Clausthal University of Technology, Leipnizstraße 17, Clausthal-Zellerfeld, 38678, Germany*
[c]*Otto von Guericke University, Universitätsplatz 2, Magdeburg, 39106, Germany*
sundmacher@mpi-magdeburg.mpg.de

Abstract

The efficient modeling of dynamic systems in process engineering is becoming increasingly important in the modern industrial landscape. Our study addresses this challenge by employing reduced-order modeling and model order reduction techniques, with a focus on the non-intrusive operator inference method. This method excels at handling the complexity of nonlinear dynamics, a key factor in ensuring both computational efficiency and accuracy of approximations. We demonstrate the potential of operator inference by applying it to a CO_2 methanation reactor model within the power-to-x framework. The results show the ability of the reduced-order model to provide an accurate yet streamlined solution, which is essential for the analysis of dynamic systems in the Industry 4.0 era.

Keywords: Dynamic systems, Model order reduction, Operator inference, Reactor modeling, Power-to-X, Methanation, Model identification.

1. Introduction

The emergence of Industry 4.0, along with increasing sustainability demands, is driving industrial plants toward dynamic operations. The rapid technological advances of Industry 4.0 require flexible, real-time process control, which aligns well with sustainability demands for resource-efficient, environmentally friendly operations. Despite a historical preference for steady-state operation due to its economic and safety benefits (Fischer and Freund, 2020), industry is increasingly adopting dynamic control systems to meet these evolving demands. A prime example of this shift is Power-to-X (PtX), a family of processes that convert renewable energy into a spectrum of green chemicals. These chemical products have a wide range of applications, serving as green fuels and platform chemicals, or even being converted back to electricity. However, there are significant challenges in effectively managing the dynamics of renewable energy sources (Güttel et al., 2013). Given these challenges, the development of robust models for real-time optimization and control becomes critical to ensure operational efficiency and reliability. Traditional models based on differential equations have been instrumental in understanding dynamic processes. These models face the challenge of dealing with uncertain parameters and large state spaces that include dimensions such as temperature, pressure, and chemical concentrations. In addition, dealing with nonlinearities and the dynamic behavior of industrial processes requires the control of time-varying process variables. Integral to these models is the incorporation of real-time data, a critical factor in adapting to changing operating conditions. Spatial resolution in these models is achieved through discretization into finely spaced elements, either in two or three dimensions, a process that is computationally intensive but essential to accurately represent the multidimensional nature of these systems. The need for dynamic system models that are not only computationally efficient but also maintain high accuracy, especially in scenarios with frequent model evaluations, becomes apparent (Benner et al., 2021).

Reduced-Order Models (ROMs) and Model Order Reduction (MOR) serve as an effective strategy to meet computational demands. They simplify dynamical models by reducing the number of variables and equations while preserving the core dynamics. Order reduction typically involves the projection of system state variables into a lower dimensional subspace. Such a projection uses a different coordinate system, allowing for a more efficient computational representation that preserves the essential dynamics of the original system (Benner et al., 2021). ROMs fall into two main categories: "intrusive" (Bremer et al., 2017), which refine high-fidelity models, and "non-intrusive" (Bremer et al., 2021), which generate simplified models from data when detailed equations are not available. Among the non-intrusive methods, sparse identification of nonlinear dynamical systems (SINDy), dynamic mode decomposition (DMD), and operator inference (OpInf) are notable for their utility in systems with complex or unknown equations. In particular, OpInf (Peherstorfer and Willcox, 2016) is distinguished by its ability to develop models that are consistent with the structural principles of the original partial differential equations. It encapsulates nonlinear dynamics within the ROM framework, often including terms up to second order. In the following, we will explore the use of OpInf to develop efficient ROM for CO_2 methanation reactor models. Our goal is to demonstrate how these models capture the dynamics of the system and thereby effectively address the computational challenges of process engineering.

2. Methodology

The proposed methodology consists of two steps: First, we collect detailed data from a full-order model (FOM) of a methanation reactor. This provides a solid basis for our study. Second, we build a reduced-order model (ROM) that simplifies these data.

2.1. Full order reactor model

We use a one-dimensional full-order reactor model as described by Zimmermann et al., 2022. This model consists of a system of coupled PDEs that encapsulate an energy balance (expressed in terms of temperature, T) and a mass balance (focused solely on the conversion of CO_2, X), while intentionally ignoring axial mass dispersion. We have adapted this model to our research objectives by assuming a catalyst efficiency factor of 1, as a simplification of the original work. The operating and design parameters are consistent with an industrial packed-bed reactor, which enhances the practical relevance of our research. The equations governing the evolution of X and T with respect to the axial coordinate (z) over time (t) are as follows:

$$\varepsilon_R \frac{\partial X}{\partial t} = -u \frac{\partial X}{\partial z} + \frac{M_{CO_2}}{\rho y_{CO_2,in}} (1 - \varepsilon_R) \zeta \sigma_{eff}, \tag{1}$$

$$\left(\rho c_p\right)_{eff} \frac{\partial T}{\partial t} = -u_{in} \rho_{in} c_p \frac{\partial T}{\partial z} + \frac{\partial}{\partial z}\left[\Lambda_{ax} \frac{\partial T}{\partial z}\right] + \frac{4U}{D}(T - T_{cool}) - \Delta H_r (1 - \varepsilon_R) \zeta \sigma_{eff}. \tag{2}$$

The model incorporates constants such as heat capacity (c_p), packed-bed reactor void fraction (ε_R), coolant temperature (T_{cool}), CO_2 molar mass (M_{CO_2}), inlet CO_2 mass fraction ($y_{CO_2,in}$), catalyst particle fraction (ζ), and tube diameter (D). For details on the non-constant quantities, we refer to the work of Zimmermann et al., 2022. These parameters include reaction rate (σ_{eff}), axial heat conductivity (Λ_{ax}), heat transfer coefficient (U), enthalpy of reaction (ΔH_r), gas mixture density (ρ), and surface gas velocity (u). The initial and boundary conditions can be summarized as follows, taking into account the reactor length (L):

$$X|_{z=0} = 0, \quad \Lambda_{\text{ax}} \frac{\partial T}{\partial z}|_{z=0} = u_{\text{in}}\rho_{\text{in}}c_{\text{p}}(T - T_{\text{in}}), \quad \frac{\partial^2 T}{dz^2}|_{z=L} = 0, \tag{3}$$

$$X|_{t=0} = X_0, \quad T|_{t=0} = T_0. \tag{4}$$

The reactor in our study is modeled by discretizing its governing equations into 200 equally-sized control volumes using the finite volume method. This approach, chosen to deal with the significant nonlinearity of the equations and to ensure an accurate representation of the reactor's behavior, results in a large system of ODEs. While this granularity captures the dynamics with high fidelity, it also significantly increases the computational requirements. To solve this intricate system, we use the Kvaerno5 integrator from the diffrax library in Python (Kidger 2021).

2.2. Operator inference (OpInf)

The used methodology employs ROMs to approximate the high-dimensional FOM (dimension n) with a significantly lower dimension (r), thereby reducing computational complexity. The ROM formulation with the inferred reduced operators $\hat{\mathbf{A}} \in \mathbb{R}^{r \times r}$ (linear), $\hat{\mathbf{H}} \in \mathbb{R}^{r \times r^2}$ (quadratic), and $\hat{\mathbf{B}} \in \mathbb{R}^{r \times 1}$ (constant) is as follows:

$$\dot{\hat{x}}(t) = \hat{\mathbf{A}}\hat{x}(t) + \hat{\mathbf{H}}(\hat{x}(t) \otimes \hat{x}(t)) + \hat{\mathbf{B}}, \quad \hat{x}(0) = \hat{x}_0 \tag{5}$$

The reduced states and their derivatives are denoted by $\hat{x} \in \mathbb{R}^r$ and $\dot{\hat{x}} \in \mathbb{R}^r$, respectively. The symbol $\otimes$ represents the Kronecker product, which represents the quadratic approach of our model. This quadratic formulation balances computational simplicity with the ability to capture essential nonlinear behavior.

ALGORITHM 1: OPERATOR INFERENCE (OPINF) APPROACH

Input: State snapshots matrix $X = [x_1, x_2 \ldots x_m] \in \mathbb{R}^{n \times m}$, derivative data $\dot{X} = [\dot{x}_1, \dot{x}_2 \ldots \dot{x}_m] \in \mathbb{R}^{n \times m}$, user-specific-tolerance **tol**

1 **Construct a reduced basis, $V_r \in \mathbb{R}^{m \times r}$:** The basis V is derived from the principal right singular vectors of X, obtained by PCA via SVD. Based on **tol** the first r columns are selected to form the reduced basis V_r.

2 **Project the snapshots and derivatives:** The snapshots and derivatives are projected onto the r-dimensional subspace spanned by V_r. This results in the reduced state snapshot matrix $\hat{X}$ and its derivatives $\dot{\hat{X}}$.

3 **Define the structure of the ROM:** The structure of the ROM is defined based on the characteristics of the system being modelled.

4 **Solve the optimization problem:** Address the optimization problem of obtaining the stable reduced operators $\hat{\mathbf{A}}, \hat{\mathbf{H}}, \hat{\mathbf{B}}$ using the parameterization method recommended by Goyal et al. (2023), which ensures global asymptotic stability.
Output: Operators of the ROM for the defined model structure. The model leads to trajectories of the reduced state variables $\hat{x}$ over time.

Our dimensionality reduction procedure employs Singular Value Decomposition (SVD) for Principal Component Analysis (PCA) on the state snapshot matrix X. In SVD, X is decomposed into its singular vectors and values, represented as $X = U\Sigma V^T$, where U and V are matrices of left and right singular vectors, respectively, and Σ is the diagonal matrix of singular values. The first r columns of V are selected to form V_r, effectively capturing the key dynamics for PCA, while maintaining computational efficiency and the integrity of the original model's dynamics. Using V_r, the reduced states $\hat{x}$ and their derivatives $\dot{\hat{x}}$ are then constructed as approximated by the equation $\hat{x}(t) \approx V_r^T x(t)$. This projection of x onto a lower-dimensional space through V_r results in the derived reduced trajectories, $\hat{x}$. In the next phase of the proposed methodology, these reduced operators are inferred using a gradient-based optimization method, specifically the Adam optimizer. This approach facilitates the effective tuning of the model parameters. Furthermore, to ensure a global asymptotic stability of our inferred quadratic models, we adhere to the parameterization guidelines proposed by (Goyal et al. 2023). The presented algorithm outlines the steps involved in determining a ROM using the OpInf approach.

3. Results and Discussion

To account for rapid variations in the control parameters, especially the cooling temperature T_{cool}, we first solve equations (1) and (2) in the start-up phase. This involves setting the initial conditions $X|_{t=0} = 0$ and $T|_{t=0} = T_{cool}$. At the end of this phase, steady-state profiles are obtained for the reactor. These profiles are then used as the basis for the next phase, where T_{cool} is abruptly increased from 270 to 280 °C. This sudden increase induces a hotspot in the reactor, resulting in an abrupt and intense perturbation in the behavior of the system. It is important to recognize that this rapid increase in T_{cool} is an atypical, extreme case, demonstrating its computationally challenging nature. More commonly, cooling temperature changes occur gradually. Nevertheless, this extreme scenario is critical for investigating the effectiveness of OpInf under severe scenarios. The full-order state trajectory is captured in snapshots, which are then compiled into a state snapshot matrix $X(t) \in \mathbb{R}^n$ encompassing conversion and temperature data across all volumes. These data are normalized by subtracting the final value of each trajectory to set the equilibrium point to 0, aligning with the data centering requirement for PCA via SVD. We also obtain the derivatives by using the right-hand side of the equilibrium equations. If direct access to these equations is not available, numerical approximations can be used, however this may introduce numerical errors.

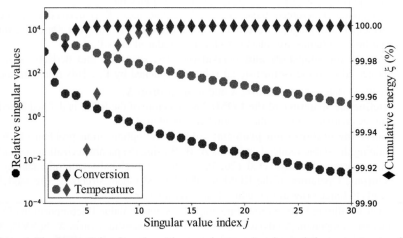

Figure 1: The decay of singular values (shown as hexagons) and cumulative energy captured by the initial dominant modes (shown as rhombi). Data are shown for the conversion (in red) and temperature (in green).

Next, for analyzing dynamic reactor changes, we apply PCA using SVD to the state snap-shot matrix $X(t)$, initiating the OpInf procedure. Figure 1 illustrates the singular value decay resulting from this transformation. The decay's pattern, which is rather gradual than steep, indicates a complex distribution among the singular values. This suggests the complex and highly nonlinear nature of our application. To capture the dynamics of the system, we derive reduced models over dimensions r with the goal of capturing 99.9% to 99.99% of the total energy present in the data. This is measured by the cumulative sum of squared singular values, which reflects the information content of the system state. The number of singular values required to meet this threshold is determined by their cumulative proportion to the total.

We construct the low-dimensional data and its derivatives by projecting high-dimensional data onto dominant modes using a reduced-order basis. By treating temperature and conversion separately, the projection matrix V_r, is formed by combining left leading singular vectors from separate PCAs of these data subsets. Using the Adam optimizer, in accordance with the stability parameterization of Goyal et al., 2023, we infer the reduced operators $\widehat{A}$, $\widehat{H}$ and $\widehat{B}$. Figure 2 presents a 3D plot comparing the actual data with a ROM that captures 99.9% of the energy for both conversion and temperature. This model, selected with a rank of $r = 7$ ($r_X = 2$ and $r_T = 5$), is chosen because increasing the energy threshold beyond this point does not significantly improve the ROM's performance. The ROM shows a high degree of agreement with the actual data, effectively capturing the dynamics of the system with accepted accuracy for the application. However, we observe minor variations in temperature and conversion at the hotspot location. These significant discrepancies provide valuable insight for future improvements in the accuracy of the model. A quantitative evaluation using the Frobenius norm shows a remarkably small deviation of only 0.43% from the original model. In addition, the reduced model achieves a significant speedup, solving the initial value problem in only 0.44% of the time required by the mechanistic model. Specifically, the ROM completes 100 iterations in a cumulative time of only 2.47s, compared to 553.74s for the mechanistic model, underscoring a significant improvement in the computational

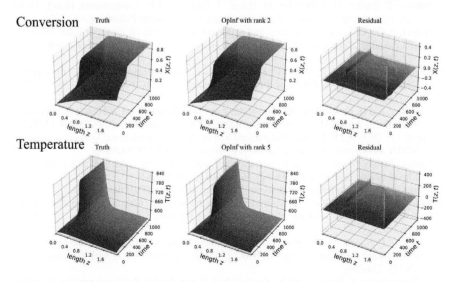

Figure 2: 3D representation comparing true reactor response with the inferred model, highlighting deviations in both conversion and temperature.

efficiency. This efficiency not only demonstrates the effectiveness of the ROM, but also expands its potential applications in complex chemical engineering scenarios. With its quadratic nonlinearity and an optimized rank of $r = 7$, the ROM manages to reproduce the true system's dynamics excels both efficiently and accurately, promising significant advances in dynamic system analysis.

4. Conclusion

Our study successfully demonstrates the ability of the ROM to capture complex system dynamics with significant computational efficiency. In future work, we aim to apply the "lift-and-learn" approach, which uses auxiliary variables to simplify nonlinear system interactions and make them more computationally tractable. This method will allow us to efficiently model the dynamics as quadratic systems. In the future, our goal is to further extend the versatility of the model by integrating variable parameters. This extension, exemplified by our case study of CO_2 methanation, includes adaptation to variable input loads that affect species volume flow. In addition, the incorporation of specific control terms, such as T_{cool}, into our model will enhance its adaptability. These advancements will not only refine the ROM's adaptability and precision across different parameters and control settings, but also solidify its role as a versatile and accurate tool for complex challenges in dynamic system analysis and a variety of computational scenarios.

Acknowledgment

This contribution is funded by the Bundesministerium für Bildung und Forschung (BMBF) and Project Management Jülich (PtJ) under grant 03HY302R. This work is part of the research initiative "SmartProSys: Intelligent Process Systems for the Sustainable Production of Chemicals" funded by the Ministry for Science, Energy, Climate Protection and the Environment of the State of Saxony-Anhalt.

References

P. Benner, T. Breiten, H. Faßbender, M. Hinze, T. Stykel, and R. Zimmermann, (Eds.), *Model reduction of complex dynamical systems*. Springer International Publishing AG, 2021.

J. Bremer, P. Goyal, L. Feng, P. Benner, and K. Sundmacher, "POD-DEIM for efficient reduction of a dynamic 2D catalytic reactor model." *Computers & Chemical Engineering* 106 (2017): 777-784.

J. Bremer, J. Heiland, P. Benner, and K. Sundmacher, "Non-intrusive Time-POD for Optimal Control of a Fixed-Bed Reactor for CO2 Methanation." *IFAC-PapersOnLine* 54.3 (2021): 122-127.

K.L. Fischer, and H. Freund, "On the optimal design of load flexible fixed bed reactors: Integration of dynamics into the design problem." *Chemical Engineering Journal* 393 (2020): 124722.

P. Goyal, I.P. Duff, and P. Benner. "Guaranteed Stable Quadratic Models and their applications in SINDy and Operator Inference." *arXiv preprint arXiv:2308.13819* (2023).

R. Güttel, "Study of unsteady-state operation of methanation by modeling and simulation." *Chemical Engineering & Technology* 36.10 (2013): 1675-1682.

P. Kidger, *On Neural Differential Equations*. University of Oxford, PhD thesis, 2021.

B. Peherstorfer, and K. Willcox, "Data-driven operator inference for nonintrusive projection-based model reduction." *Computer Methods in Applied Mechanics and Engineering 306* (2016): 196-215.

W.I.T Uy, D. Hartmann, and B. Peherstorfer, "Operator inference with roll outs for learning reduced models from scarce and low-quality data." *Computers & Mathematics with Applications* 145 (2023): 224-239.

R.T. Zimmermann, J. Bremer, and K. Sundmacher, "Load-flexible fixed-bed reactors by multi-period design optimization." *Chemical Engineering Journal 428* (2022): 130771.

Flavio Manenti, Gintaras V. Reklaitis (Eds.), Proceedings of the 34th European Symposium on Computer Aided Process Engineering / 15th International Symposium on Process Systems Engineering (ESCAPE34/PSE24), June 2-6, 2024, Florence, Italy

Discontinuous Galerkin spectral element method for continuous chromatography: Application to the Lumped Rate Model without pores

Jesper Frandsen[a], Jan Michael Breuer[b], Eric von Lieres[b], Johannes Schmölder[b], Jakob K. Huusom[a], Krist V. Gernaey[a], Jens Abildskov[a]

aDept. of Chemical and Biochemical Engineering, Technical University of Denmark, Søltofts Plads, Building 228A, 2800 Kgs. Lyngby, Denmark
bForschungszentrum Jülich, IBG-1: Biotechnology, Jülich 52428, Germany
Corresponding author: jespfra@kt.dtu.dk

Abstract

This study presents CADET-Julia, an implementation of the Discontinuous Galerkin spectral element method (DGSEM) in Julia, applied to the Lumped Rate Model (LRM) and multi-component Langmuir isotherm for binary separation in both batch and simulated moving bed (SMB) operation. A comparative analysis was made of CADET-FV and CADET-DG, C++ implementations of finite volume and DGSEM found in CADET, respectively. For stiff systems operated in batch mode, CADET-FV, CADET-Julia and CADET-DG showed similar performance, however, for less stiff systems, CADET-Julia and CADET-DG were superior. For stiff systems in SMB operation, CADET-Julia was significantly faster than CADET-FV. CADET-DG could not be benchmarked at the current time.

Keywords: Chromatography, Continuous chromatography, SMB, numerical solver

1. Introduction

Chromatography is an essential unit operation for the purification of biopharmaceutical products and proteins. Continuous chromatography has the potential to increase productivity and reduce solvent consumption compared to batch chromatography. However, operating continuous chromatography is significantly more complex as it requires the use of multiple columns in series and/or parallel in either open or closed loops (Schmidt-Traub et al., 2020). Although shortcut design methods are fast tools to design some continuous operations such as the simulated moving bed (SMB) (Frandsen et al., 2023), the reliability of the design method when taking non-ideal phenomena into account such as film diffusion and pore diffusion is doubtful. Instead, design of operation can be carried out by solving comprehensive models numerically. While modelling can aid the design and operation of continuous chromatography, the simulation time required to solve the partial differential equation (PDE) models can become significant. One continuous chromatography operation, where the simulation time is significant, is the SMB operation (He et al., 2020).

Long simulation times strengthen the need for fast PDE solvers. To reduce the simulation time, Meyer implemented an arbitrary order Discontinuous Galerkin spectral element method (DGSEM) for solving the general rate model for batch chromatography (Meyer et al., 2020). More recently, Breuer developed a slightly different DGSEM and implemented it in C++. The code is open-source and publicly available in the software CADET (Breuer et al., 2023; Leweke & von Lieres, 2018). Whereas C++ is a high-performing computational language, it is a low-level compiled language and thus demands more programming expertise compared to languages like Python. Conversely, Python is a high-level programming language that is very dynamic and easy to use but also slower. The programming language Julia is a dynamic, high-level programming language, yet it produces fast, low-level machine code (Bezanson et al., 2017).

In this study, an implementation of the DGSEM in Julia is made and applied to the Lumped Rate Model (LRM) without pores and the multi-component Langmuir isotherm for a binary separation. The Julia implementation is compared to the C++ implementation in CADET in terms of convergence of overall maximum absolute error (MAE) of the outlet and simulation time for both batch and SMB operation. The Julia implementation allows for rapid prototyping and customized isotherms. The package is called CADET-Julia and can be found on Github (github.com/jespfra/CADET-Julia).

2. Methodology

2.1 Model

In this study, the LRM model with the multi-component Langmuir isotherm was studied. The model and isotherm are given for each component $i \in [1, \ldots, N_C]$ in eq. (1)-(2).

$$\frac{\partial c_i}{\partial t} = D_{ax} \frac{\partial^2 c_i}{\partial z^2} - u \frac{\partial c_i}{\partial z} - \frac{1 - \varepsilon}{\varepsilon} \frac{\partial q_i}{\partial t} \tag{1}$$

$$\frac{\partial q_i}{\partial t} = k_{kin,i} \left(k_{eq,i} c_i q_{max,i} \left(1 - \sum_{j=1}^{N_c} \frac{q_j}{q_{max,j}} \right) - q_i \right) \tag{2}$$

Here, t is time, c_i is the mobile phase concentration, N_c is the total number of solutes, q is the corresponding stationary phase concentration, z is the spatial coordinate, D_{ax} is the axial dispersion coefficient, ε is the total porosity, k_{eq} is the equilibrium adsorption constant, q_{max} is the maximum adsorption capacity and k_{kin} is a kinetic constant. The boundary and initial conditions are given in eq. (3)-(4), respectively.

$$u c_{in,i} = u c_i(t, 0) - D_{ax} \frac{\partial c_i(t, 0)}{\partial z} \tag{3a}$$

$$\frac{\partial c_i(t, L)}{\partial z} = 0 \tag{3b}$$

$$c_i(0, z) = 0, \qquad q_i(0, z) = 0 \tag{4}$$

Where L is the column length. If assuming isotherm equilibrium, the PDE system in eq. (1)-(2) must be discretized and solved as a differential algebraic equations (DAE) system, setting eq. (2) equal to 0. Alternatively, one can set a large k_{kin} value to approximate the equilibrium and still discretize and solve the system as an ODE system. In CADET-Julia, the latter approach was used. For the SMB operation, four columns were used. To connect the four columns, simple mass balances were set up (Frandsen et al., 2023).

2.2 Numerical methods

To discretize the spatial coordinate, the same mathematical formulation as (Breuer et al., 2023) was implemented in Julia (Breuer et al., 2023). A brief description is given here.

The idea of the DGSEM is to break down the spatial domain into cells to approximate the solution by a piece-wise polynomial approximation. The polynomials are Lagrange polynomials on Legendre-Gauss-Lobatto nodes. The transport equation (1) can be translated into an ODE system with element-wise discrete operators, given in eq. (5),

$$\dot{\underline{c}}_i = \frac{2}{\Delta z}\left(-D\left(u\underline{c}_i - \underline{g}\right) + M^{-1}\beta\left(\left(u\underline{c}_i - \underline{g}\right) - \underline{h}^*\right)\right) - \frac{1-\epsilon}{\epsilon}\frac{\partial \underline{q}_i}{\partial t} \tag{5a}$$

$$\underline{g} = \frac{2}{\Delta z}D_{ax}\left(D\underline{c}_i - M^{-1}\beta\left(\underline{c}_i - \underline{c}_i^*\right)\right) \tag{5b}$$

Here $\dot{\underline{c}}$ is the vector of polynomial coefficients of the temporal derivative of the polynomial approximation, M is the mass matrix, D is the is the polynomial differentiation matrix, $\underline{g}$ is an auxiliary variable, β is the lifting matrix, Δz is equidistant cell-spacing, $\underline{h}^*$ and $\underline{c}^*$ are the feasible numerical fluxes. The mass matrix can either be determined exactly or approximated using collocation of interpolation and quadrature nodes. Here the collocation method can be computationally less demanding but at a cost of accuracy. More details can be found elsewhere (Breuer et al., 2023).

For the comparison of numerical solvers, the performance of CADET-Julia was compared with the Finite Volume and Discontinuous Galerkin solvers in CADET, called CADET-FV and CADET-DG, respectively. The solutions of the solvers were compared with a very finely discretized solution using CADET-FV. Here, 60000 axial cells were used for the batch operation whereas 15000 axial cells were used for the SMB operation for each column. For all tests, the ODE systems were solved using absolute and relative time integration tolerances of 10^{-12} and 10^{-10}, respectively, to make

Table 1: Parameters for the Batch (Breuer et al., 2023) and the SMB case studies.

Parameter	Value	Unit
D_{ax}	$1.0 \cdot 10^{-4}$	m^2/s
Column Length	1	m
u	0.1	m/s
k_{eq}	$[0.1, 0.05]$	m^2
q_{max}	$[10, 10]$	-
ε	0.4	-
Feed concentration 1	$[10, 10]$	mol/L
Feed concentration 2	$[0, 0]$	mol/L
Time sections (Batch)	$[0, 12, 40]$	s
Switching time (SMB)	20	s
Number of cycles (SMB)	2	-
$[u_1, u_2, u_3, u_4]$	$[5.6, 3.8, 4.7, 3.2]$ $\cdot 10^{-2}$	m/s
$[u_D, u_F]$	$[2.4, 0.9] \cdot 10^{-2}$	

the discretization error dominate. For all the CADET solvers, the initial time-step was set to 10^{-10}. The solutions of the PDEs were evaluated at each 0.1 second. To investigate convergence, the polynomial orders and number of cells were varied. In CADET-FV and CADET-DG, the system was solved as a DAE system using IDAS BDF solver (Hindmarsh et al., 2005). In CADET-Julia, the DifferentialEquations.jl package was used to solve the ODE systems, and specifically, the QNDF solver was chosen for the multi-component Langmuir isotherm as it was the fastest solver in initial tests (Rackauckas & Nie, 2017). All tests were run on an Asus Vivobook equipped with Intel® Core ™ i5-1035G1 CPU 1.00 GHz processor, 8Gb Ram and 64-Bit Windows 11 operating system.

3. Results and Discussion

As case studies, the separation of two components described by the Lumped Rate Model with the Langmuir isotherm using batch and SMB operation was studied. The parameters for the case study are given in table 1 (Breuer et al., 2023), where u_1, u_2, u_3 & u_4 are the SMB inlet velocities in column 1,2,3 and 4, u_D and u_F are the SMB desorbent inlet and SMB feed inlet velocities, respectively.

With the multi-component Langmuir isotherm, the concentration profiles and the convergence in terms of simulation time and MAE are shown in Figure 1. To approximate the Langmuir equilibrium in CADET-Julia, the kinetic constant was set to 10^8 $1/s$. The concentration profiles and convergence are shown in Figure 1.

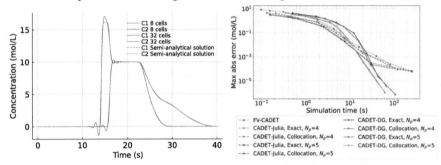

Figure 1: *(a) Concentration profiles for Batch operation, simulated solutions using CADET-Julia with fourth order polynomials and 8 and 32 cells. (b) Convergence in terms of simulation time and overall maximum absolute error of the outlet.*

Figure 1a shows the concentration profiles during batch operation as well as the solution simulated using CADET-Julia using up to fourth order polynomial and 8 and 32 spatial cells. The concentrations increase rapidly, and large gradients contribute to stiffness. Furthermore, when the problem is under-resolved (i.e., fewer cells), the DGSEM oscillates near these gradients which results in larger approximation errors and even negative concentration values. These oscillations disappear when increasing the number of cells as previously observed (Breuer et al., 2023). These oscillations could be corrected using for example weighted essentially non-oscillatory methods which have been implemented for CADET-FV (Leweke & von Lieres, 2018).

Figure 1b compares the simulation time and the MAEs. The figure shows similar convergence using CADET-FV, CADET-DG and CADET-Julia initially, however, at MAEs less than 10^{-4} mol/m^3, CADET-DG is significantly faster.

For SMB operation, the concentration profiles and the convergence are shown in Figure 2. At the current time of writing, CADET-DG did not support cyclic systems for the LRM. Figure 2a shows the concentration profiles for raffinate and extract during SMB operation along with simulations using CADET-Julia using up to fourth order polynomial and 8 and 32 cells. As for the batch operation, the simulations oscillate when using 8 cells for the raffinate concentration profiles which disappear when increasing the number of cells. In terms of convergence in Figure 2b, CADET-Julia is significantly faster despite using the same parameters as for the batch operation. This suggests that the DGSEM method for SMB systems can significantly reduce simulation time. To investigate the convergence for less stiff systems, the same simulations for batch operation have been performed using an increased axial dispersion coefficient of $1 \cdot 10^{-3}$ m^2/s.

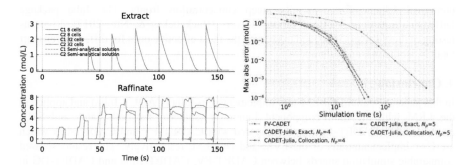

Figure 2: *(a) Concentration profiles for SMB operation, simulated solutions using CADET-Julia with fourth order polynomials and 8 and 32 cells. (b) Convergence in terms of simulation time and overall maximum absolute error of the outlet.*

The concentration profiles and the convergence are shown in Figure 3. The concentration profiles in Figure 3a show that few cells are adequate to simulate the profiles accurately and no oscillations were observed. The convergence in Figure 3b shows that both CADET-Julia and CADET-DG converge significantly faster than CADET-FV as expected. Comparing CADET-Julia and CADET-DG, the convergence is very similar in terms of simulation time. As in Figure 1, CADET-Julia seems to be slightly faster for a small number of cells whereas CADET-DG seems to be faster when using a larger number of cells. For Figure 3, CADET-Julia is faster at MAEs between 10^{-1} to 10^{-4} mol/m^3 whereas CADET-DG is faster at MAEs larger than $10^{-5} mol/m^3$. This is because CADET-Julia scales worse than CADET-DG when increasing the number of cells for discretization.

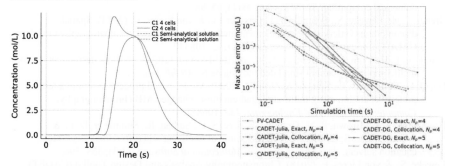

Figure 3: *(a) Concentration profiles for batch operation with $D_{ax} = 10^{-3}$ m^2/s, simulated solutions using CADET-Julia with fourth order polynomials and 4 cells. (b) Convergence in terms of simulation time and overall maximum absolute error of the outlet.*

The next step would be to compare CADET-Julia, CADET-FV and CADET-DG using more complex transport models such as the lumped rate model with pores or the general rate model and incorporating various isotherms. Conducting more extensive analysis would enhance the understanding of the performance differences between the C++ implementation in CADET and the Julia implementation in CADET-Julia. Another reasonable step for CADET-Julia would be to implement actual equilibrium isotherms which requires solving the PDEs as system of DAEs instead of approximating the equilibrium using a high kinetic constant and solving the system as system of ODEs. Additionally, correcting oscillatory solutions and negative concentrations should be implemented using an oscillation suppression mechanism for DG. This ensures a robust numerical scheme for especially steep concentration fronts. The Julia package DifferentialEquations.jl offers various solvers (Rackauckas & Nie, 2017). Rigorous testing of these solvers is needed to identify the most effective ones for different transport models, isotherms, and tolerances.

4. Conclusion

In this paper, a spatial DGSEM was implemented in Julia (CADET-Julia) and applied to the LRM with the multi-component Langmuir isotherm for both batch and SMB operation. The CADET-Julia was compared with CADET-FV and CADET-DG which are C++ implementations of the FVM and DGSEM, respectively. The results showed comparable simulation speeds between CADET-FV, CADET-Julia and CADET-DG in batch operation for a stiff system. For SMB operation, CADET-Julia was significantly faster compared to CADET-FV. In general, using too few cells with the DGSEM for stiff systems can lead to oscillating solutions with negative concentrations. Hence, when using DGSEM for stiff problems, care should be taken on the number of cells for discretization. For less stiff batch operation, CADET-Julia and CADET-DG were significantly faster than CADET-FV.

Acknowledgements

This study was financially supported by the Technical University of Denmark. Johannes Schmölder and Krist V. Gernaey have received support from the IMI2/ EU/EFPIA joint undertaking Inno4Vac under grant n° 101007799.

References

Bezanson, J., Edelman, A., Karpinski, S., & Shah, V. B. (2017). Julia: A fresh approach to numerical computing. *SIAM Review, 59*(1), 65–98.

Breuer, J. M., Leweke, S., Schmölder, J., Gassner, G., & von Lieres, E. (2023). Spatial discontinuous Galerkin spectral element method for a family of chromatography models in CADET. *Computers & Chemical Engineering*, 108340.

Frandsen, J., Huusom, J. K., Gernaey, K. V., & Abildskov, J. (2023). Shortcut design method for multicomponent gradient simulated moving beds. *AIChE Journal*.

He, Q. Le, von Lieres, E., Sun, Z., & Zhao, L. (2020). Model-based process design of a ternary protein separation using multi-step gradient ion-exchange SMB chromatography. *Computers and Chemical Engineering, 138*, 106851.

Hindmarsh, A. C., Brown, P. N., Grant, K. E., Lee, S. L., Serban, R., Shumaker, D. E., & Woodward, C. S. (2005). SUNDIALS: Suite of nonlinear and differential/algebraic equation solvers. *Acm Transactions on Mathematical Software, 31*(3), 363–396.

Leweke, S., & von Lieres, E. (2018). Chromatography Analysis and Design Toolkit (CADET). *Computers and Chemical Engineering, 113*, 274–294.

Meyer, K., Leweke, S., von Lieres, E., Huusom, J. K., & Abildskov, J. (2020). ChromaTech: A discontinuous Galerkin spectral element simulator for preparative liquid chromatography. *Computers and Chemical Engineering, 141*, 107012.

Rackauckas, C., & Nie, Q. (2017). DifferentialEquations.jl – A Performant and Feature-Rich Ecosystem for Solving Differential Equations in Julia. *Journal of Open Research Software, 5*(1), 15.

Schmidt-Traub, H., Schulte, M., & Seidel-Morgenstern, A. (2020). Preparative Chromatography for Separation of Proteins. In *John Wiley & Sons* (3rd edition). John Wiley & Sons.

Flavio Manenti, Gintaras V. Reklaitis (Eds.), Proceedings of the 34th European Symposium on Computer Aided Process Engineering / 15th International Symposium on Process Systems Engineering (ESCAPE34/PSE24), June 2-6, 2024, Florence, Italy

A multi-agent system for hybrid optimization

Eric S. Fraga[a*], Veerawat Udomvorakulchai[a], Lazaros G. Papageorgiou[a]

[a]*Sargent Centre for Process Systems Engineering, University College London (UCL), Gower Street, London WC1E 7JE, United Kingdom*
e.fraga@ucl.ac.uk

Abstract

Optimization problems in process engineering, including design and operation, can often pose challenges to many solvers: multi-modal, non-smooth, and discontinuous models often with large computational requirements. In such cases, the optimization problem is often treated as a *black box* in which only the value of the objective function is required, sometimes with some indication of the measure of the violation of the constraints. Such problems have traditionally been tackled through the use of *direct search* and *meta-heuristic* methods. The challenge, then, is to determine which of these methods or combination of methods should be considered to make most effective use of finite computational resources.

This paper presents a multi-agent system for optimization which enables a set of solvers to be applied simultaneously to an optimization problem, including different instantiations of any solver. The evaluation of the optimization problem model is controlled by a scheduler agent which facilitates cooperation and competition between optimization methods. The architecture and implementation of the agent system is described in detail, including the solver, model evaluation, and scheduler agents. A suite of direct search and meta-heuristic methods has been developed for use with this system. Case studies from process systems engineering applications are presented and the results show the potential benefits of automated cooperation between different optimization solvers and motivates the implementation of competition between solvers.

Keywords: multi-agent system, hybrid optimization, direct search, meta-heuristic.

1. Introduction

Optimization problems in process engineering, including design and operation, can often pose challenges to many solvers. In particular, these problems may be multi-modal, non-smooth, and even discontinuous. In such cases, the optimization problem is often treated as a *black box* in which only the value of the objective function is required, sometimes with some indication of the measure of the violation of the constraints. Such problems have traditionally been tackled through the use of *direct search* and *meta-heuristic* methods. The challenge, then, is to determine which of these methods or combination of methods may be most appropriate. Further, these methods often have a number of parameters which affect their behaviour and choosing values for these parameters may be difficult to do without significant experimentation.

2. A multi-agent system

A multi-agent system is software that enables autonomous pieces of software, known as *agents*, to interact through the sending and receiving of *messages* (Nwana, 1996; Bradshaw, 1997). Multi-agent systems have been developed for engineering design problems, e.g. (Hanna and Cagan, 2008; Zhang et al., 2020) and references cited there-in. These previous implementations support cooperation by sharing information between solvers but do not provide the necessary control of model evaluation to enable an implementation for competition. The latter motivates a new multi-agent system implementation which decouples the optimization methods from the evaluation of the models. The system consists of the following agents:

- **solver**: a particular optimization method with specific parameter values which affect the method's behaviour;
- **model evaluation**: an agent which evaluates the model, consisting of the objective function and all constraints, given a point in the search domain;
- **scheduler**: an agent which accepts requests from solver agents for the evaluation of points in the search domain and allocates these requests to model evaluation agents; and,
- **analysis**: an agent which analyses all points evaluated and provides the scheduler with information about the search domain.

There will always be more than one solver agent as the aim is to explore the effect of cooperation and competition between different solvers. There may also be more than one model evaluation agent which is particularly useful to make use of modern multi-core computers for concurrent evaluation of different points.

The diagram in Figure 1 shows the multi-agent system along with the communications links between them, including both persistent links that exist throughout the execution of the agent system and ephemeral links (shown in a dashed line and labelled as a *wormhole*) which come into existence when required and disappear once used. The double circles around the model and solver agents indicate that there may be more than one instance of each of these agents. The *user*, i.e. the process systems engineer wishing to solve a particular optimization problem, is included in this diagram although obviously is not necessary a software agent.

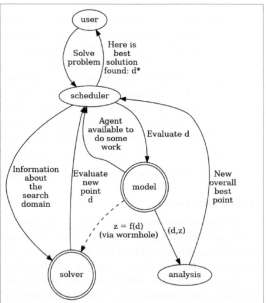

Figure 1: The agents in the agent based system including the scheduler, the model evaluation agents, the solver agents, and the analysis agent, showing the communications links between the agents. Solid lines are persistent communication links; the dashed line represents ephemeral links to receive the result of the evaluation of the model, $f(d)$, at a given point, d, in the search domain. The best solution found is indicated by d^*.

At the centre of the multi-agent system is the *scheduler*. The main purpose of this agent is to process requests from the solvers for the evaluation of points in the search domain. When such a request is received, it is added to an evaluation queue. This queue is used to allocate the evaluation of these points when model evaluation agents become available. The availability of model evaluation agents is handled by a different queue. The current scheduling algorithm, for deciding which evaluation request to allocate to a model evaluation agent, when the latter is available, is based on the least recently used (LRU) algorithm used by operating systems to implement multi-tasking on single processor systems (Madnick and Donovan, 1974). This algorithm prioritises solvers which have not been given access to a model evaluation agent more recently than other solver agents.

The scheduler also enables sharing of information between solvers; in the first instance, it sends any new *best* solution found by any solver to all other solvers. It is up to the solvers individually to decide what to do with this information. The individual behaviour of the solvers and how they use this information is described in the next section.

The multi-agent system has been implemented in the Julia language (Bezanson et al., 2017), a fast and modern programming language ideal for numerical analysis and computational science. Julia provides easy and transparent access to the multiple processors now typically available in modern multi-core desktop and laptop computers. Agents are easily created using the `Threads.@spawn` directive; communications links are instances of the `Channel` type. Messages between agents are encoded using our own format. Each message consists of the type of message, the agent that sent the message, and the content (which depends on the type of message). The results presented below are based on Julia 1.9.2. The resulting code is open source, portable, easy to use, and makes effective use of the computational processing capabilities available.

3. The solvers

Two types of solvers are considered: meta-heuristic methods inspired by nature (Fraga, 2022) and direct search methods (Kelley, 1999). A suite of methods has been implemented in the Julia language and the methods have been instrumented to enable the agent based system to share information when appropriate with each solver. The full list of solvers used in this paper follows:

- **genetic algorithm** (GA) inspired by Darwinian evolution (Holland, 1975) using crossover and mutation with fitness based selection to explore the solution space and exploit the better solutions. In what follows, the size of the population modelled is the key parameter that is explored by having multiple instances of this solver. This method incorporates new best solutions found by other solvers by simply adding the new solution to the population before the start of a generation. This is similar to the metaphor of multi-island genetic algorithms (Alba and Tomassini, 2002).
- **plant propagation algorithm** (PPA) based on the original paper (Salhi and Fraga, 2011) which is inspired by the propagation of strawberry plants using runners where the number of runners propagated by a solution is proportional to the fitness of that solution and the length of the runners inversely proportional to the fitness. This combination leads to a balance between exploitation and exploration of the solution space. The number of solutions to consider for propagation at each iteration is the key parameter explored. As with the genetic algorithm, new solutions sent by the scheduler are added to the population at the start of an iteration. In terms of nature inspiration, this could be considered as incorporating a further means of propagation used by plants: seeds carried over from other areas by animals or the wind.

- **steepest descent** is a gradient based hill-climbing method which has been implemented using finite differences for the numerical approximation of the gradient (Burden and Faires, 1989). The initial population is treated as a multi-start optimization problem where a search is started with each member of this population in turn. New solutions from the scheduler are added to the list of starting points yet to be attempted and inserted at the beginning of this list.
- **coordinate search** which searches along each dimension in turn, using a simple line search method (also used by the steepest descent method) (Kelley, 1999). The initial population and any points from the scheduler are treated as for the steepest descent method.

4. Illustrative case study

Two case studies in the design of heat exchanger network synthesis are presented to explore the impact of the sharing of information to allow solvers to cooperate. One is a small example, with 2 hot streams and 2 cold streams, and the other is a larger problem with 5 cold and 5 hot streams based on case study 5 in (Fraga, 2009). The first is solved as an MINLP and the second as a pure NLP using a fully continuous representation of the superstructure (Fraga, 2006). Heat exchanger network design problems are combinatorial in nature and solutions often have a subset of design variables at the constraints. Previous work (Fraga, 2006) has shown that manually applying a sequence of methods can lead to better final outcomes. By using the multi-agent system, it will be interesting to see if and how the methods can cooperate to obtain good solutions.

The solvers considered are those described above with multiple instances of the meta-heuristic methods with different parameter settings. The base population size, np, is the number of design variables for both problems. This is adjusted for different instances of the solvers: for the GA are np (small) and $5 \times$ np (large); for the PPA, the sizes are np/2 (small) and $2 \times$ np (large). There is only one instance of each of the direct search methods. All methods are started with the same randomly generated population of size np with values of 10 for the smaller problem and 25 for the larger case.

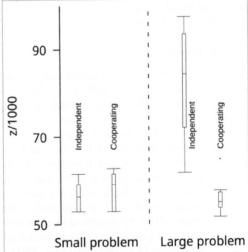

Figure 2: Box plot of the outcomes of 10 runs for both problems, comparing the outcomes for both when solvers are fully independent and when they are cooperating by sharing improved solutions when found.

The stopping criterion for the search is 60 thousand messages received by the scheduler agent, which can otherwise be thought of as 60 thousand iterations over the main loop of the scheduler. The schedule iteration loop considers not just function evaluations but also updates on the solution space by the analysis agent. The end result is that this stopping criterion equates to on the order of 5 thousand function evaluations by each of the 6 solvers.

Figure 2 presents the box plots of the variation of the objective function value for the best solution found over 10 runs, both when each solver works independently or when the solvers share any new better solution found. For the smaller problem, not sharing information actually leads to better outcomes, although only marginally. It would seem that sharing may lead to premature convergence in some cases. However, for the larger problem, sharing information leads to better solutions more quickly.

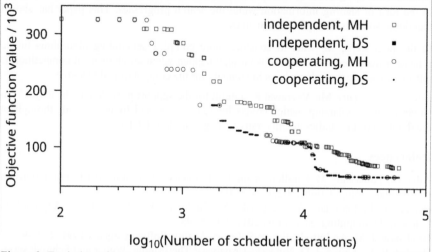

Figure 3: Evolution of best solution found, for the larger case study, as a function of the number of scheduler iterations indicating the solver responsible for the identification of the best solution to that point. The top trail of points is for when the solvers operate independently; the bottom trail is the outcome when the best solutions found are shared. MH is meta-heuristic and DS is direct search.

Figure 3 shows the evolution of the best solution found as a function of the number of scheduler iterations for both independent and cooperating cases. For the independent case, only the meta-heuristic methods are able to find good solutions. When the methods cooperate, both meta-heuristic and direct search methods are able to find improved solutions. It appears that when one of the meta-heuristic methods identifies a better solution, this solution is immediately improved by one of the direct search solvers. Although the methods are stochastic and repeated attempts will lead to different outcomes, the outcomes presented here are representative.

For the larger case study, the behaviour when solutions are shared is what we expected. The meta-heuristic methods are good at exploration but less effective at exploitation for constrained problems. The direct search methods have better exploitation properties. It should be noted, however, that the results obtained in this case study are not as good as the known optimum for this problem. This motivates the future work described below.

5. Conclusions

Optimization problems that arise in the process industries may often exhibit properties that preclude the use of mathematical programming, properties such as nonconvexity, nonlinearity, discontinuities, and differential equations. For those problems, a variety of meta-heuristic and direct search methods, that may treat the objective function as a black box, can be considered. However, there is a large choice of these methods, each of which may also have a large number of tunable parameters. As a result, choosing the appropriate method may be difficult a priori. Furthermore, each of these methods may have beneficial behaviour in different parts of the search space. These two factors motivate the development of a multi-agent system to enable a variety of methods, with different instances of many, to be applied to a problem simultaneously. The simultaneous application of multiple methods and instances of methods leads naturally to the idea of sharing information while the search progresses. This paper has shown that doing so leads to improved outcomes.

In the next steps, we wish to consider more complex scheduling algorithms in the scheduler agent and also explore what may happen when an element of competition is introduced where the solvers have to compete for the computational resource.

Acknowledgements. Mr. Veerawat is grateful for the support provided by the Royal Thai Government Scholarship, which covers his tuition fees and living stipends throughout the duration of his studies at University College London (UCL).

References

Alba, E.; Tomassini, M. Parallelism and Evolutionary Algorithms. IEEE transactions on evolutionary computation 2002, 6, 443–462.

Bezanson, J.; Edelman, A.; Karpinski, S.; Shah, V. B. Julia: A Fresh Approach to Numerical Computing. SIAM rev. 2017, 59, 65–98.

Bradshaw, J. M. An Introduction to Software Agents. Software agents 1997, 4, 3–46.

Burden, R. L.; Faires, J. D. Numerical Analysis; The Prindle, Weber and Schmidt series in Mathematics; Fourth.; PWS-Kent Publishing Company: Boston, 1989.

Fraga, E. S. Hybrid Methods for Optimisation. In Computer aided methods for optimal design and operations; Zilinskas, J.; Bogle, I. D. L., Eds.; World Scientific Publishing Co., 2006; pp. 1–14.

Fraga, E. S. A Rewriting Grammar for Heat Exchanger Network Structure Evolution with Stream Splitting. Engineering optimization 2009, 41, 813–831.

Fraga, E. S. Nature Inspired Methods for Optimization: A Julia Primer for Process Engineering; doi:10.5281/zenodo.7016482, 2022.

Hanna, L.; Cagan, J. Evolutionary Multi-Agent Systems: An Adaptive and Dynamic Approach to Optimization. Journal of mechanical design 2008, 131, 011010.

Holland, J. H. Adaptation in Natural and Artificial Systems; University of Michigan Press: Ann Arbor, MI, 1975.

Kelley, C. T. Iterative Methods for Optimization; SIAM, 1999.

Madnick, S. E.; Donovan, J. J. Operating Systems; McGraw-Hill Book Company, 1974.

Nwana, H. S. Software Agents: An Overview. The knowledge engineering review 1996, 11, 205–244.

Salhi, A.; Fraga, E. S. Nature-Inspired Optimisation Approaches and the New Plant Propagation Algorithm. In Proceedings of ICeMATH 2011, the international conference on numerical analysis and optimization; Yogyakarta, 2011; pp. K2:1–8.

Zhang, Z.; Han, Q.; Li, Y.; Wang, Y.; Shi, Y. An Evolutionary Multiagent Framework for Multiobjective Optimization. Mathematical problems in engineering 2020, 9147649.

Flavio Manenti, Gintaras V. Reklaitis (Eds.), Proceedings of the 34th European Symposium on Computer Aided Process Engineering / 15th International Symposium on Process Systems Engineering (ESCAPE34/PSE24), June 2-6, 2024, Florence, Italy

Graphical Deterministic Equivalent Algorithm for Robust Process Optimization

Albertus Fuad,[a,*] Edwin Zondervan,[a] Meik Franke,[a]

[a]*Sustainable Process Technology, Department of Chemical Engineering, Faculty of Science and Technology, University of Twente, Drienerlolaan 5, Enschede 7522NB, The Netherlands*
albertus.fuad@utwente.nl

Abstract

The uncertainty of process parameters is always a challenge during the design of chemical processes. There are several ways to consider uncertainty during process optimization, for example: stochastic programming, chance-constrained programming, and robust optimization (Li and Grossman, 2021). Robust optimization, in particular, yields the highest risk avoidance, i.e. to plan for the worst-case scenario (Li and Grossman, 2021).

In this contribution, a graphical method is proposed to estimate the robust optimum of an optimization problem, given a bounded uncertainty set. This method is based on the Monte Carlo method to find a combination of uncertain parameters that would give the robust optimum. With the robust uncertain parameter as the input, the optimization problem can be solved deterministically to obtain the robust optimum.

To demonstrate the method, a reactor-separator system with recycle, where the uncertain parameters follow Gaussian distribution is used. The proposed method was benchmarked and compared against PyROS solver that is based on the Generalized Robust Cutting Set algorithm (Isenberg et al., 2021).

The results show that compared to the more robust PyROS solver, the graphical method with 5000 samples gives a 3% difference in the objective value function with 33% computation time requirement. The speed can be increased further by utilizing parallelization during the feasibility checks of each sample.

Keywords: Graphical algorithm, Robust Optimization, Uncertainty.

1. Introduction

Optimal design of chemical processes is important in the chemical industry for safe and economic operation. One of the main challenges in process design is the uncertainty of the process parameters. Uncertainty in process parameters can lead to overdesign requirements that can be costly or even lead to infeasible designs. One of the possible solutions is robust optimization. Robust optimization is an optimization method that considers the worst-case, i.e., risk-averse, scenario given a bounded set of possible scenarios (Li and Grossman, 2021). Due to the risk-averse nature of robust optimization, the solution can have conservativism issue (Ning and You, 2018), but this conservative result gives a baseline for the possible outcome, which can also be beneficial to plan for the worst outcome. Wiebe and Misener (2021) stated that the large number of methods for robust optimization and the relatively steep background knowledge requirements inhibits the application of robust optimization. This paper proposes a graphical robust optimization method based on Monte Carlo simulations. The method can be used to graphically obtain a combination of uncertain parameters that would give the robust optimum.

2. Methodology

The proposed method can be used find the robust optimum of an optimization program under uncertainty, with two uncertain parameters. The optimization problem is constructed as a minimization program:

$$\min f(x, y, q)$$

$$\text{s. t. } g_i(x, y, q) \leq 0, \forall i \tag{1}$$

$$h_j(x, y, q) = 0, \forall j$$

Where f is the objective function, g are inequality constraints including variable boundaries, and h are equality constraints. The uncertain parameters are denoted as q, decision variables as x, and state variables as y. The state variables y are outside the degree of freedom and solved such that the equality constraints holds.

This method solves the uncertainty by finding a realization of the uncertain parameters, denoted $\hat{q}$, that will give the robust optimum when the problem is solved deterministically with $\hat{q}$ as the input. In the first step, the optimization problem is solved deterministically at the nominal value of the uncertain parameters. The feasibility optimal argument of the deterministic solution is checked against random scenarios of uncertain parameters.

A feasibility boundary, which separates feasible and infeasible samples, is then drawn for each inequality constraint based on a linear classifier:

$$-\frac{1}{2}(\mu_1 + \mu_0)^T \Sigma^{-1}(\mu_1 - \mu_0) + q^T \Sigma^{-1}(\mu_1 - \mu_0) + \ln\left(\frac{N_1}{N - N_1}\right) = 0 \tag{2}$$

Where μ_1 and μ_0 are the mean of feasible and infeasible samples, respectively, and N_1 is the number of feasible samples. This equation approximates the feasibility boundary, and it approaches the true feasibility boundary as the number of samples increases. This feasibility boundary is then translated to be a tangent to the boundary of the uncertainty set, and the intersection between the infeasibility boundaries is the robust parameter. The optimization problem is finally solved with this robust parameter to obtain the robust optimum.

3. Case Study

To test the method an ideal reactor-separator system (Figure 1) from Isenberg et al. (2021) is used as a case study. The system consists of an ideal isothermal mixed-flow reactor with elementary reactions in liquid phase as follows:

$$A \rightarrow B \rightarrow C$$

$$A \rightarrow D \tag{3}$$

$$B \rightarrow E$$

There is also a separator where pure C is completely recovered as top product. The remaining A, B, D, and E go to the bottom of the splitter. One recycle stream with a recycle ratio of δ contains A and B only, and another recycle stream contains only D and E with a recycle ratio of β. The objective is to minimize the annualized operating cost of the system where the decision variables are reactor volume and recycle ratios β and δ. The uncertainty set is defined to cover 99.7% (3σ) of the normal distribution.

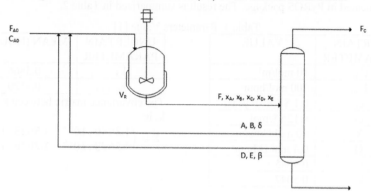

Figure 1. Process Flow Diagram of the Reactor-Separator System

The full optimization problem is as follows:

$$\min c_1 V^2 + c_2 F[\delta(x_A + x_B) + \beta(x_D + x_E)] \tag{4}$$

subject to:

- equality constraints (mass balances):

$$F_{A_0} - x_A F(1 - \delta) - C_{A_0} x_A V(k_1 + k_3) = 0 \tag{5}$$

$$-x_B F(1 - \delta) + C_{A_0} V x_A k_1 - C_{A_0} V x_B(k_2 + k_4) = 0 \tag{6}$$

$$-x_C F + C_{A_0} V x_B k_2 = 0 \tag{7}$$

$$-x_D F(1 - \beta) + C_{A_0} V x_A k_3 = 0 \tag{8}$$

$$-x_E F(1 - \beta) + C_{A_0} V x_B k_4 = 0 \tag{9}$$

$$x_A + x_B + x_C + x_D + x_E - 1 = 0 \tag{10}$$

- inequality constraints (performance requirements):

$$\chi - F x_C \leq 0 \tag{11}$$

$$\omega - F x_D \beta \leq 0 \tag{12}$$

- and boundaries:

$$0 \leq \delta \leq 1 \tag{13}$$

$$0 \leq \beta \leq 1 \tag{14}$$

The parameter data (Isenberg et al., 2021) is presented in Table 1.

4. Result and Discussion

4.1. Robust Optimization

The robust solution can be calculated from the optimization problem with the robust parameter as the input. Figure 2 shows how the graphical method progresses. The result of the robust optimization by this algorithm is then compared with the result from Isenberg et al. which uses the Generalized Robust Cutting Set (GRCS) method implemented in PyROS package. The result is summarized in Table 2.

Table 1. Parameters Value [1]

CERTAIN PARAMETER	VALUE
C_{A0}	10 mol/m³
F_{A0}	100 mol/hour
c_1	0.1 $/((m³)² year)
c_2	0.125 $/mol
X	40 mol C/hour
Ω	0.4 mol D/hour
k_1	0.9945
k_2	0.5047

UNCERTAIN PARAMETER	MEAN (HOUR^{-1})
k_3	0.3866
k_4	0.3120

The covariance matrix between k_3 and k_4 is:

$$\Sigma = \begin{pmatrix} 1.3830 \cdot 10^{-4} & 4.5623 \cdot 10^{-5} \\ 4.5623 \cdot 10^{-5} & 1.2078 \cdot 10^{-4} \end{pmatrix}$$

Table 2. Robust Optimization Result

Algorithm	GRCS (PyROs)	Graphical		
No. of runs	1	1	1	200 (averaged)
Solvers	IPOPT	fmincon	fmincon	fmincon
Parallelization	No	No	Yes 8 workers	Yes 4 workers
No. scenarios	n/a	5000	5000	5100
V (m³)	109.5	107.1	107.1	Not recorded
β	0.77	0.78	0.78	
δ	0.016	0.016	0.016	
Total cost	25823	25071	25071	24645
Time	12.1 s	4.5 s	1.5 s	1.99 s

The proposed algorithm is used both with parallel computing and serial computing during the handling of the 5000 scenarios. For both parallelized and serial computation, there is no difference on result of the optimization problem. However, the implementation of parallel computing with 8 workers reduces the computation time to one third as compared to the one without parallelization. This shows that the required time is not linearly proportional on the number of workers, because the handling of the parallelization also requires additional computational power.

4.2. Effect of Sampling

The use of randomly generated samples can affect the outcome of the optimization over different runs. The method was tested with number of random scenarios ranging from 100 to 5100 scenarios, with a step size of 250 scenarios. In each number of scenarios, 200 different set of random scenarios are used. However, given enough samples, the optimization results converge reliably with a rather small variation between runs. The number of samples also increases the required computation time, therefore a balance between them needs to be determined. At larger sample size, the variation in computation time increases, this is possibly due to longer convergence for certain samples.

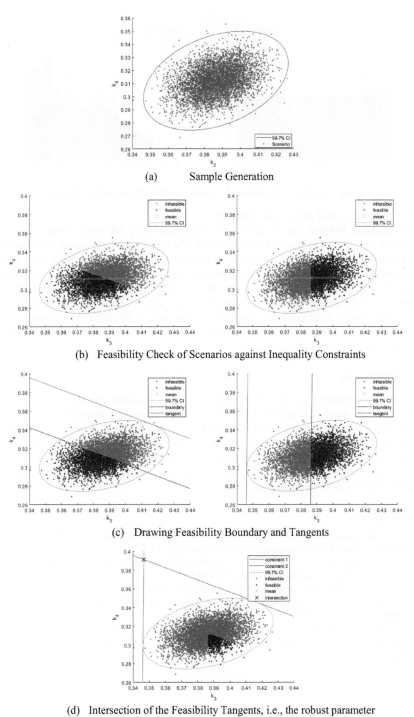

(a)   Sample Generation

(b)   Feasibility Check of Scenarios against Inequality Constraints

(c)   Drawing Feasibility Boundary and Tangents

(d)   Intersection of the Feasibility Tangents, i.e., the robust parameter

Figure 2. The Progression of the Graphical Method

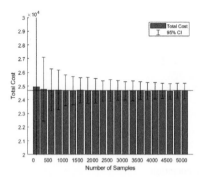 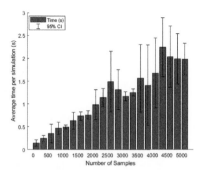

Figure 3. Effect of Number of Samples to the Optimization Results

4.3. Advantages and Further Improvements

This graphical method can estimate robust optimum in a relatively short time. The graphical nature of the method also gives an illustration on how robust optimization works, which helps learning process for optimization under uncertainty. However, it still has some limitations for further improvements. First, it can only handle two uncertain parameters and two inequality constraints that are affected by the uncertain parameters. Further research is still required for upscaling to higher dimension, but the graphical illustration would be difficult for dimension higher than 3. The second limitation is that the uncertain parameters must be linear to the objective function and constraints within the domain of the uncertainty set.

5. Conclusions

The proposed graphical method is a promising way to estimate a robust optimum in a short time. It also gives consistent results as long as enough samples are provided. Compared to the more robust GRCS method, the graphical method with 5000 samples gives a 3% difference in the objective value function with 33% computation time requirement, which can still be accelerated by parallelization. The algorithm also works consistently as long as enough random scenario are provided. Further research is required for upscaling to higher dimensions.

References

C. Li, I.E. Grossman, 2020, A Review of Stochastic Programming Methods for Optimization of Process Systems Under Uncertainty, Front. Chem. Eng, 2:622241.

J. Wiebe, R. Misener, 2021, ROmodel: A Python Robust Optimization Modeling Toolbox, Computer Aided Chemical Engineering, 50, 683-688.

C. Ning, F. You, 2018, Leveraging the Power of Big Data Analytics for Process Scheduling under Uncertainty using a Stochastic Robust Optimization Approach, Computer Aided Chemical Engineering, 43, 319-324.

N.M. Isenberg, P. Akula, J.C. Eslick, D. Bhattacharyya, D.C. Miller, C.E. Gounaris, 2021, A generalized cutting-set approach for nonlinear robust optimization in process systems engineering, AIChE J., 67.

Flavio Manenti, Gintaras V. Reklaitis (Eds.), Proceedings of the 34th European Symposium on Computer Aided Process Engineering / 15th International Symposium on Process Systems Engineering (ESCAPE34/PSE24), June 2-6, 2024, Florence, Italy

Portfolio-based Strategy for Bayesian Optimization for Autonomous Selection of Multiple Acquisition Functions and Hyperparameters

Runzhe Liang,[a] Haoyang Hu,[a] Zhihong Yuan[a],*

aDepartment of Chemical Engineering, Tsinghua University, Beijing 100084, China
*Corresponding author's E-mail: zhihongyuan@mail.tsinghua.edu.cn

Abstract

Bayesian optimization has become an effective tool in chemical research in recent years. Acquisition functions act as a vital part of the Bayesian optimization framework to determine the most promising experimental point, however, it is difficult for most chemists to select appropriate acquisition functions for different chemical reactions. In this investigation, a novel portfolio-based strategy for Bayesian optimization (PCR-BO) is proposed, which consists of multiple acquisition functions and selects the most suitable one autonomously. Based on a multi-armed bandit strategy, the proposed method considers historical observations and recent progress together. Benchmark tests and case studies indicate that the proposed portfolio-based strategy can significantly outperform other portfolio strategies and approach the upper bound of its individual components, demonstrating its excellent adaptability and selectivity.

Keywords: Bayesian optimization, acquisition function, portfolio strategy, multi-armed bandit

1. Introduction

Experimental conditions play a critical role in the performance of chemical reactions. However, when faced with complex chemical systems or unclear reaction mechanisms, it can be a challenging task for chemists to select an appropriate combination of parameters. A traditional approach is to fit the response surface model by DoE. However, it strongly depends on the prior knowledge of chemists and the optimum cannot be guaranteed. Bayesian optimization, as a global search framework that can deal with expensive black-box functions (Shahriari et al., 2016), has attracted increasing attention in experimental condition screening. By incorporating and translating the uncertainty of regression models, Bayesian optimization combines existing observations with unknown information properly to drive towards the optimum step by step. Generally, for an unfamiliar reaction system, suitable combinations of experimental parameters (e.g., temperature, pressure, and concentration) can be found after several experiments by the guide of Bayesian optimization, leading to high yield, selectivity or reaction rate. At present, Bayesian optimization has proven its efficiency in several areas, such as organic synthesis, material design, photoreactions, and electrochemistry (Shields et al., 2021).

The key components of Bayesian optimization can be divided into two parts: building a probabilistic surrogate model and optimizing acquisition functions, wherein the Gaussian process (GP) is a common approach to build the surrogate model, and the acquisition function is utilized to determine the next experimental point by making a trade-off between expectations and variances. There exist multiple acquisition functions as reported in the literature, such as PI, EI, and UCB. Nevertheless, different acquisition functions may have distinctly different behavior when confronted with different chemical systems, and it is a non-trivial decision on which one should be selected. Furthermore, the suitable acquisition function may change as the optimization campaign progresses. Therefore, how to design and update the selection of acquisition functions is an essential issue to be addressed.

Inspired by the aforementioned problems, a novel portfolio-based strategy for Bayesian optimization, named PCR-BO (Portfolio-based strategy with Customized Reward function for Bayesian Optimization), is proposed in this work, which is developed based on a multi-armed bandit (MAB) strategy. Instead of using a single acquisition function, the portfolio-based strategy contains a set of acquisition functions and optional hyperparameters. At each iteration, the acquisition functions are selected randomly with different probabilities determined by cumulative rewards, and the appropriate one gradually emerges and iterates as the rewards accumulate. The following sections elaborate on the method of the proposed portfolio strategy and practical performance.

2. Method

The proposed strategy is inspired by GP-Hedge (Hoffman et al., 2011) and No-PASt-BO (Vasconcelos et al., 2019), and manages to tackle their undesirable properties while maintaining the simplicity of the algorithm. Compared to the previous investigations, two main contributions are included in the proposed method: 1) the variance of GP is considered when calculating the reward of each arm, and 2) the reward is set as the improvement upon the incumbent target. The overall framework is clarified as follows.

2.1. Hierarchical hedging strategy

To realize the selection of different acquisition functions from the portfolio, a MAB strategy is employed in this investigation, in which each acquisition function is treated as a single "arm". Given K available individual acquisition functions, K possible arms are formulated, with unknown and maybe dynamically variable reward probability distribution for each one. The task is to find the approach to select the arm combination that corresponds to the maximal cumulative rewards. Specifically, we are confronted with a trade-off between exploration and exploitation: Due to the unknown reward probability distribution, different arms need to be tested repeatedly to obtain the ground-truth distribution, which implies they should be chosen equally. However, to obtain the maximal cumulative rewards, existing information should be fully utilized, which means the best arm up to now should be chosen as much as possible.

Hedge is a suitable algorithm to deal with this problem, which was also adopted by GP-Hedge and No-PASt-BO. Its main idea is to allocate different probabilities $p_t(i)$ for each arm i for selection based on cumulative rewards. In the Bayesian optimization framework, each acquisition function i proposes an experimental point $x_t(i)$ at each iteration t. The probability of each arm i can be determined by $p_t(i) = \exp(\eta G_t(i)) / \sum_j \exp(\eta G_t(j))$,

where η is a hyperparameter and $G_t(i)$ is the cumulative rewards of the arm i up to the time t. In this way, the hedging algorithm enables possible exploration of every arm while focusing on the arms with high cumulative rewards.

2.2. Reward customization

Based on the hedging strategy, how to measure and calculate the reward $r_t(i)$ of each step t is a crucial part of determining the probability of each arm. Previous investigations suggested that if the arm i proposed an experimental point $x_t(i)$, the expected value of the GP model at $x_t(i)$ could be a reasonable evaluation for the reward (i.e., $r_t(i) = \mu_t(x_t(i))$), which acts as a reasonable and natural approach.

However, it is flawed due to its simplistic formulation and inaccurate consideration. On the one hand, the reward function only focuses on the expectation, and the variance of the GP model is neglected. In Bayesian optimization settings, observations are usually rather limited, and exploration of the variances contributes to searching for possible global optimum. To take the variance into account, we propose to sample the reward function f_t from the posterior of GP, by which the expectation and variance can be handled together. The arm with the highest reward is selected at step t.

On the other hand, the formulation $r_t(i) = \mu_t(x_t(i))$ is myopic and deviated from the ultimate target. Since we aim to reach the optimum within the limited number of iterations, it is desirable to make steady progress towards the optimum; that is, step-by-step improvements should be treasured during iterations. Therefore, in this investigation we propose to use the potential improvement $I(f_t(x_t(i)) - \tau_t)$, instead of pure expectation $\mu_t(x_t(i))$, as the reward function to make the selection concentrate on potential better value, where τ_t represents the best observation up to the time t and $I(\Box)$ is the improvement function (i.e., $I(\Box) = \max(\Box, 0)$).

2.3. Memory factor and reward normalization

Different from the vanilla MAB problem, one prominent feature of the portfolio strategy is that the optimal acquisition function may change and evolve as the optimization campaign progresses. Too distant reward evaluation hardly provides efficient information for the current decision. Therefore, a memory factor is introduced to reduce the influence of previous iterations and enables the optimizer to focus more on the recent reward. In detail, the cumulative reward can be calculated by the equation $G_t(i) = mG_{t-1}(i) + r_t(i)$, where m is a memory hyperparameter and its range is [0, 1]. The recommended range for m in No-PASt-BO is [0.7, 1]; however, since the proposed portfolio strategy involves sampling from the posterior, more randomness may be introduced so that a smaller value of m is encouraged to recover from numerical fluctuation quickly. A recommended value for m in this investigation is 0.7.

The hedging framework also suffers from the scale of the reward function. Suppose the difference of $G_t(i)$ is huge for each arm i, the probability of one arm may occupy a dominant position over the others. On the contrary, if all remains unchanged except for scaling down $G_t(i)$ by a large number, the rewards may be close enough to make the portfolio degenerate into a completely random one. To avoid this undesirable behavior, the reward function is normalized as shown in Eq. (1):

$$R_t(i) = \frac{G_t(i) - \max_j(G_t(j))}{\max_j(G_t(j)) - \min_j(G_t(j))} \tag{1}$$

In this way the reward $R_t(i)$ is constrained between -1 and 0. Then $G_t(i)$ is replaced by $R_t(i)$ to calculate the probability to realize the normalization of the reward function:

$$p_t(i) = \frac{\exp(\eta R_{t-1}(i))}{\sum_j \exp(\eta R_{t-1}(j))} \tag{2}$$

2.4. The PCR-BO algorithm

The above is the basic idea of the PCR-BO algorithm. Its detailed realization is summarized in Algorithm 1.

Algorithm 1 PCR-BO

Input: hyperparameter $\eta \in \mathbb{R}^+$, $m \in [0,1]$

1. Let $G_0(i) = 0, i = 1,2,...,I$
2. **for** $t = 1,2,...$ **do**
3.   for each acquisition function α_i in the portfolio:
4. $x_t(i) = \arg\max_x \alpha_i(x)$
5.   Normalize rewards $R_{t-1}(i) = \frac{G_{t-1}(i) - \max_j(G_{t-1}(j))}{\max_j(G_{t-1}(j)) - \min_j(G_{t-1}(j))}$
6.   Nominate a point c_t from $x_t(i)$ with probability $p_t(i) = \frac{\exp(\eta R_{t-1}(i))}{\sum_j \exp(\eta R_{t-1}(j))}$
7.   Evaluate objective function on point c_t and update the GP model
8.   Sample f_t from the GP posterior
9.   Update the rewards $G_t(i) = mG_{t-1}(i) + I(f_t(x_t(i)) - \tau_t)$
10. **end for**

---

3. Case study

To test the performance of the proposed PCR-BO algorithm, a few case studies including several benchmark experiments and a simulated real-world application were carried out, and the performance of PCR-BO, GP-Hedge, No-PASt-BO, and the upper bound and average effect of individual acquisition functions was recorded for comprehensive comparison. The portfolio involved three common acquisition functions: PI, EI, and UCB, and various hyperparameters of these acquisition functions were included in the portfolio for optional selection: $\xi = 0$ and 0.001 for PI and EI, $\kappa = 1.5$ and 3.0 for UCB. To ensure the reliability and stability of the test, 50 runs were executed for each method and case to obtain average results. For hyperparameters, η was set as 2.5 and m was set as 0.7 in the proposed method, while the hyperparameters in the other methods were consistent with the recommended values in their original references.

3.1. Benchmark test

Before large-scale application in practical scenarios, the statistical performance of the proposed method was determined via benchmark mathematical functions. Here four common benchmark functions were selected for testing, with different and multiple local optima: Branin, Hartman3, Ackley, and Hartman6, with 2, 3, 5, and 6 dimensions respectively. Figure 1 illustrates the comparison results of the logarithm of regret versus iteration for different methods, where regret denotes the difference between the actual optimum and the observed one.

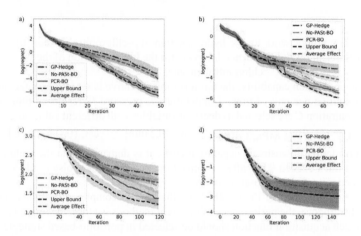

Figure 1. Average results and 95% confidence intervals of PCR-BO, GP-Hedge, No-PASt-BO, and the upper bound and the average performance of individual acquisition functions in the portfolio for various benchmark functions. a) Branin, b) Hartman3, c) Ackley, d) Hartman6.

According to Figure 1, the proposed PCR-BO algorithm can outperform the other portfolio-based methods and approaches the best performance of individual acquisition functions in most cases. For the Ackley function, due to its significant multimodal characteristics (there exist thousands of local optima for the 5-dimensional Ackley function), it is difficult to determine the appropriate acquisition function, and wrong decisions may occur repeatedly during iteration. However, after wandering in the beginning, PCR-BO manages to find the suitable acquisition function to drive the regret decrease rapidly, especially after 60 iterations. In contrast, the regret of GP-Hedge and No-PASt-BO remains at high levels all along.

3.2. Hydrogenation of p-chloronitrobenzene

It is an essential transformation from halogenated nitroaromatics to their corresponding aromatic anilines in the fine chemical industry. However, low selection and yield may occur due to incomplete conversion and dehalogenation when applied in the traditional batch mode. For better controllability and economic benefits, a simulated optimization campaign of the hydrogenation of *p*-chloronitrobenzene is conducted using continuous flow synthesis techniques, which provide uniform temperature distribution, intensified mass transfer, and easy implementation.

Previous investigations have determined the mechanism and kinetic parameters of the reaction (Duan et al., 2022). Figure 2a explains its competitive pathways, where apart from the target product, nitrobenzene and aniline as byproducts are generated via slow reaction steps. It implies that by precise control, it is feasible to enhance the yield of *p*-chloroaniline while keeping side reactions at low levels.

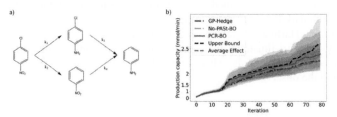

Figure 2. a) Reaction network for the hydrogenation of *p*-chloronitrobenzene. b) Average results and 95% confidence intervals for the hydrogenation of the *p*-chloronitrobenzene.

To maximize the production capability, the optimization objective is set to maximize the yield of *p*-chloroaniline per unit of time. Temperature T, pressure P, residence time R, and reagent concentration C are selected as decision variables with different value ranges:

$$T \in [40\ ^\circ C, 70\ ^\circ C] \quad , \quad P \in [1\ \text{MPa}, 3\ \text{MPa}] \quad , \quad R \in [0, 5\ \text{min}] \quad , \quad C \in (0, 0.5\ \text{mol/L}) \quad .$$

Furthermore, considering downstream separation costs, it is demanded that the yield of the target product must exceed 90 % after optimization, and moderate noise is added to the objective function to make it closer to reality.

Comparison results are shown in Figure 2b. Note that due to complex constraints and potential noise disturbance, the performance of different methods is close, making it hard to distinguish which acquisition function should be selected in portfolio-based strategies. However, PCR-BO is still the one that is the closest to the upper bound of individual acquisition functions, demonstrating its superior performance when faced with complex real-world applications.

4. Conclusions

A novel portfolio-based strategy for Bayesian optimization (PCR-BO), which assists chemists in selecting the appropriate acquisition function autonomously, is proposed in this investigation. Compared with existing methods, PCR-BO manages to tailor suitable reward functions and take into account the variances of GP models, forming a more complete hedging framework. Case studies demonstrate that PCR-BO can be close enough to the upper bound of its individual acquisition functions in most cases, and shows competitive performance when applied in practical applications.

References

B. Shahriari, K. Swersky, Z. Wang, R. P. Adams and N. de Freitas, 2016, Taking the Human Out of the Loop: A Review of Bayesian Optimization, Proc. IEEE, 104, 148-175.

B. J. Shields, J. Stevens, J. Li, M. Parasram, F. Damani, J. I. M. Alvarado, J. M. Janey, R. P. Adams and A. G. Doyle, 2021, Bayesian reaction optimization as a tool for chemical synthesis, Nature, 590, 89-96.

M. Hoffman, E. Brochu and N. De Freitas, 2011, Portfolio Allocation for Bayesian Optimization. In UAI, pp. 327-336.

T. D. P. Vasconcelos, D. A. de Souza, C. L. Mattos and J. P. Gomes, 2019, No-PASt-BO: Normalized portfolio allocation strategy for Bayesian optimization. In 2019 IEEE 31st International Conference on Tools with Artificial Intelligence (ICTAI), pp. 561-568.

X. Duan, J. Yin, M. Huang, P. Wang and J. Zhang, 2022, Hydrogenation kinetics of halogenated nitroaromatics over Pt/C in a continuous Micro-packed bed reactor, Chem Eng Sci, 251.

Flavio Manenti, Gintaras V. Reklaitis (Eds.), Proceedings of the 34th European Symposium on Computer Aided Process Engineering / 15th International Symposium on Process Systems Engineering (ESCAPE34/PSE24), June 2-6, 2024, Florence, Italy

Evaluation Method for Power-to-Liquids Concepts for e-Kerosene Production

Fredrik Nyholm,[a,b] * Henrik Saxén[a]

[a]*Åbo Akademi University, Henriksgatan 8, Åbo 20500, Finland*
[b]*Neste Oyj, Kägelstranden 21, Esbo 02150, Finland*
fredrik.nyholm@abo.fi

Abstract

The escalating climate crisis has prompted stringent regulations to curb emissions. However, many solutions are insufficient and face challenges in certain sectors. Biofuels offer partial relief, yet sustainable biomass availability is limited. Power-to-liquids (PtL) technologies provide a means to produce renewable drop-in fuels independently of biomass constraints. Increased R&D and commercial activity necessitate a standardized method for evaluating PtL technologies. This study introduces a 3E performance criteria framework for PtL technologies, employing the Analytical Hierarchy Process to establish a weighed evaluation system. Initial findings revealed a notable bias towards specific indicators, highlighting the need for further indicator inclusion under economic and environmental criteria for a balanced assessment. The framework's future validation involves PtL technology assessment through spreadsheet modelling. Enhancements may include additional indicators and sensitivity analysis to bolster route ranking robustness.

Keywords: Power-to-Liquids, Sustainable Aviation Fuel, Analytical Hierarchy Process

1. Introduction

The escalating climate crisis has spurred a growing interest in new sustainable technologies. As sustainable biomass is increasingly utilized, the need for renewable solutions decoupled from biomass becomes imperative. Moreover, technologies capable of demand-side response are essential to support the large-scale deployment of intermittent renewable electricity generators. Power-to-X (PtX) technologies, particularly Power-to-Liquids (PtL), offer intriguing drop-in solutions. To navigate the diverse landscape of PtL, a tailored approach is necessary for a levelized, comprehensive assessment. This research focuses on developing an evaluation framework designed for concept-level assessment of PtL fuel production routes, specifically targeting e-kerosene production. The framework comprises 17 indicators grouped under the 3E (Engineering, Economic, and Environmental) performance criteria. The goal is to facilitate an initial screening of PtL technologies, aiding in the selection of promising alternatives for further in-depth evaluation. The more detailed motivation and description of the approach, along with a case-study of evaluating a Fischer-Tropsch (FT) route using the framework, will be given in a full-length journal paper (Nyholm et al., 2024).

This paper introduces the evaluation method and key performance indicators for a nuanced assessment of PtL technologies in conceptual e-kerosene production. The framework integrates indicators under the 3E criteria, providing a holistic evaluation of engineering performance, economic viability, and environmental sustainability. Scores for PtL routes are determined based on their performance against the indicators. The Analytical Hierarchy Process (AHP), developed by Thomas L. Saaty in the 1970s, is employed to weight indicator and criteria scores objectively, considering their perceived importance (Saaty, 1977). Previous studies utilizing similar evaluation frameworks have focused on hydrogen production or general carbon capture, utilization, and storage (Janosovský et al., 2022) (Chauvy et al., 2019). Other studies, such as those by Dieterich et al. (2020) and Schemme (2020), have reviewed several PtL technologies, but without focus on a single product and the use of a multi-criteria evaluation framework. This study narrows its focus to PtL technologies for kerosene production, customizing indicators to reflect the challenges of synthesizing sustainable liquid hydrocarbons. By developing a robust, early concept stage evaluation framework specific to kerosene production via PtL processes, this research aims to contribute to the advancement and adoption of sustainable and efficient methods for meeting the aviation industry's fuel requirements.

2. Evaluation framework

2.1. Selection of key performance indicators

This section introduces the chosen indicators essential for the comprehensive evaluation of PtL production routes under the 3E criteria. Each indicator is described, accompanied by the reasoning behind its selection. Details including definitions and scoring considerations are presented in Table 1, Table 2 and Table 3. The main references used for setting the scoring limits are provided under the tables. The engineering performance indicators are intended to capture technical feasibility, energy utilization, carbon efficiency, selectivity to kerosene and liquid hydrocarbon products in general, along with safety and logistical aspects of PtL routes. The economic indicators reflect the economic viability, financial attractiveness and investment recovery potential. The environmental indicators assess the environmental impact, sustainability and resource efficiency.

Table 1. Engineering evaluation indicators and requirements for scoring.

Indicator	Notes on requirement selection	Requirements	Score	Source
TRL		R&D (1 - 3)	0	a
		Development Scale (4 - 6)	1	
		Demonstration Scale (7 - 9)	2	
Energy Efficiency (%)	Around 50 % in literature, requirements set slightly lower due to lack of heat integration in the concept level study.	< 40	0	b
		40 - 80	1	
		> 80	2	
Carbon-to-Jet Efficiency (mol-%)	Researchers and vendors typically report kerosene or diesel selectivity around 70 - 80 %, target limit set accordingly and outstanding limit a bit higher.	< 70	0	c
		70 - 90	1	
		> 90	2	
CO_2 Intensity ($t_{CO2}/t_{HC,liquid}$)	Stoichiometric minimum, if every carbon atom from the CO_2 ends up in the -CH_2- units of the fuel, is 3.1 t/t. Gaseous byproducts increase the intensity.	> 5	0	d
		3.5 - 5	1	
		< 3.5	2	
H_2 Intensity ($t_{H2}/t_{HC,liquid}$)	Similar minimum as above is 0.14 t/t. If removal of O from CO_2 by H_2 is considered, the minimum is 0.43 t/t. Gaseous byproducts increase the intensity.	> 0.6	0	d
		0.45 - 0.6	1	
		< 0.45	2	
Recycle Ratio ($t_{recycle}/t_{kerosene}$)	A FT modeling study found a recycle ratio of 2.4 per liquid hydrocarbon product for the model with highest distillate selectivity.	> 3	0	e
		2 - 3	1	
		< 2	2	
CISI	No suitable references found in literature for the limits. The FT score calculated in this work ±50 % was used instead.	> 835	0	f
		278 - 835	1	
		< 278	2	
Flexibility and Dynamic Operation	Ability to follow the electricity profile gets max. points. Some credit is given for handling capacity adjustments.	No/No information	0	g
		Considerable turndown	1	
		Fully flexible	2	
Storage and Shipping of Intermediates	Processes with intermediate products that can be stored/shipped without significant extra measures receive max points.	Practically impossible	0	
		To some extent	1	
		Readily storable	2	

[a] (Chauvy et al., 2019). [b] (Becker et al., 2012), (Peters et al., 2022), (Schmidt et al., 2018). [c] (Conkle et al., 2011), (Dieterich et al., 2020), (Haldor Topsoe, 2022). [d] (Schemme 2020), (Hank et al., 2023). [e] (Kauppi, 2021). [f] (Gangadharan et al., 2013), (Nyholm et al., 2024). [g] (Karjunen, 2022).

Technology Readiness Level (TRL) serves as a measure of the system's technical maturity, offering insights into technical feasibility and development stage. It provides valuable information about the readiness of PtL production routes (Chauvy et al., 2019).

Energy Efficiency reflects the effectiveness of energy utilization in the conversion process, quantifying the ratio of energy content in produced hydrocarbons to the energy input required for the PtL process. (Hannula et al., 2020. **Carbon-to-Jet Efficiency** measures the carbon conversion efficiency from CO_2 by considering the amount of input carbon atoms bound to the final jet fuel product (Hannula et al., 2020). **Recycle Ratio** quantifies the mass of material recycled in the PtL process per ton produced kerosene in order to raise the yield of jet fuel. The magnitude of recirculation required in the process gives an indication of the efficiency, complexity and selectivity of the process.

CO_2 and H_2 **intensities** measure the material efficiency and environmental load of a technology by indicating the CO_2 and hydrogen consumption per unit of liquid hydrocarbon output (Calemma et al., 2013).

Comprehensive Inherent Safety Index (CISI) is a method of quantifying the inherent safety of chemical processes during the early design stage. It is based on chemical, process and connectivity scores and its application ensures prioritization of safety (Gangadharan et al., 2013). **Flexibility and dynamic operation** evaluates a PtL route's capacity to address electricity grid imbalances caused by intermittent renewable energy generation (Karjunen, 2022). **Storage and shipping of intermediates** examines the practical aspects of storing and transporting intermediate products within PtL production routes, with a key role in enabling geographically decentralized production concepts and flexible operation using storage of intermediates.

Table 2. Economic evaluation indicators and requirements for scoring.

Indicator	Notes on requirement selection	Requirements	Score	Source
CAPEX Intensity ($€/t_{kerosene}$)	Previous studies indicate a range of 1,000-10,000 €/t, but most estimates seem to fall around 3,000-5,000 €/t.	> 5,000 3,000 – 5,000 < 3,000	0 1 2	a
OPEX Intensity ($€/t_{kerosene}$)	These estimates also vary widely, roughly around 1,000-5,000 €/t. A suitable range could be 1,000-2,000 €/t, due to most estimates falling within it..	> 2,000 1,000 – 2,000 < 1,000	0 1 2	a
NPV (M€)	Rough estimates scaled from previous work range from negative to over 600 M€, the average being ca 200 M€. Limits set around the average, with some margin.	< 150 150 - 250 > 250	0 1 2	a
IRR (%)	To add value to the company, the IRR should exceed the company's Weighted Average Cost of Capital, which is the average rate that a company expects to pay to finance its business. Various oil & gas and chemical industries have a WACC of around 10 %. An IRR clearly exceeding this level is given the highest score.	< 6.1 6.1 - 20 > 20	0 1 2	b
Payback Time (years)	Previous studies roughly indicate payback times of 5-10 years. Periods above this are not given any points, while periods below this receive maximum points.	> 10 5 - 10 < 5	0 1 2	c

[a] (Schemme, 2020), (Peters et al., 2022), (Kauppi, 2021). [b] (McCamish, 2021), (Neste Oyj, 2023). [c] (Oztemel et al., 2022).

CAPEX intensity measures the capital investment required per ton installed capacity of kerosene production. This describes the economic efficiency and cost-effectiveness of investments. **OPEX intensity** represents the operational and maintenance costs associated with PtL production per ton of e-kerosene output (Janosovský et al., 2022).

Net Present Value (NPV) is a common economic indicator for assessing investments. It assesses the economic attractiveness of PtL routes by quantifying the net monetary value of the project over its lifetime. **Internal Rate of Return** (IRR) is the discounting rate at which the NPV becomes zero. It is used to describe the annualized return rate of an investment and can be regarded as an indicator of the project's profitability and efficiency over time. **Payback time** is the duration required for the initial investment in the PtL routes to be recovered through generated revenues (Scipioni et al., 2023). It describes the time it takes for an investment to reach break-even.

GHG reduction quantifies the potential percentage of greenhouse gas emissions reduced by the e-kerosene versus a fossil comparator specified by the European Parliament (2022) Renewable Energy Directive RED II. **Water footprint** measures the net amount of water consumed per unit of e-kerosene output, with the assumption that all generated wastewater can be recycled as feed for the water electrolysis (Peters et al., 2022). This indicates the water consumption of the process and its load on surrounding water bodies.

Wastewater generation quantifies the volume of wastewater produced per unit of e-kerosene output. It evaluates the environmental impact associated with wastewater treatment and disposal (Peters et al., 2022).

Table 3. Environmental evaluation indicators and requirements for scoring.

Indicator	Notes on requirement selection	Requirements	Score	Source
GHG Reduction (%)	The technology is given full points if it can fulfill the RED II reduction target. If no reductions are achieved, the route does not receive any points.	< 0 $0 - 70$ > 70	0 1 2	a
Water Footprint ($t_{H2O}/t_{kerosene}$)	Other studies indicate a bit above 1 $t_{H2O}/t_{kerosene}$, assuming the wastewater is recirculated. A process causing double the load receives no score, while a ratio of under 1 gets max. score.	> 2 $1 - 2$ < 1	0 1 2	b
Wastewater Generation ($t_{WW}/t_{kerosene}$)	Stoichiometry gives a 2.57 ratio. E-factors and results from previous studies land at around 2-3 $t_{WW}/t_{kerosene}$. Limits set accordingly.	> 3 $2 - 3$ < 2	0 1 2	c

[a] (European Parliament, 2022). [b] (Peters et al., 2022). [c] (Schemme, 2020), (Peters et al., 2022), (Janosovský et al., 2022).

2.2. Weighing framework

This section outlines the application of the Analytical Hierarchy Process (AHP) in assessing PtL technologies for e-kerosene production. Developed by Saaty, AHP is widely used across various disciplines (Janosovský et al., 2022). It facilitates systematic comparison and prioritization of options based on multiple criteria, making it particularly useful for complex problems with conflicting objectives.

Table 4. Indicator weights and comparison matrix consistency ratios (CR) calculated with the Excel file of Goepel (2013) using the traditional linear 1-9 AHP scale. A CR < 0.10 is generally considered acceptable.

Indicator	Weight	Indicator	Weight	Indicator	Weight
Engineering	CR = 0.01	Economic	CR = 0.01	Environmental	CR = 0.00
TRL	*0.313*	*CAPEX Intensity*	*0.097*	*GHG Reduction*	*0.571*
Energy Efficiency	*0.203*	*OPEX Intensity*	*0.128*	*Water Footprint*	*0.286*
Carbon Efficiency	*0.137*	*NPV*	*0.238*	*Wastewater gen.*	*0.143*
CO₂ Intensity	*0.040*	*IRR*	*0.436*		
H₂ Intensity	*0.062*	*Payback Time*	*0.101*		
Recycle Ratio	*0.035*				
CISI	*0.035*				
Flexibility	*0.088*				
Storage and Shipping	*0.088*				

AHP breaks down decision problems hierarchically, starting with the overall objective, followed by criteria and sub-criteria. A pairwise comparison method is employed, where decision-makers assign scores based on perceived importance (Chauvy et al., 2019). These scores populate comparison matrices used to derive weights reflecting the relative importance of each criterion or indicator. The weights assigned to these criteria are 0.20, 0.31, and 0.49, respectively, as proposed by Chauvy et al. (2019). Indicator weights are derived using classical AHP and the resulting weights are presented in Table 4.

Inconsistencies are addressed by keeping the consistency ratio below 0.1, following Saaty's rule of thumb. The final score for each PtL route is determined by the weighed sum of its performance against the 3E criteria.

3. Results and conclusions

The 3E performance criteria framework for PtL technologies studied exhibits significant weighting towards a single indicator. The concentration is exacerbated by the limited number of indicators in the environmental and economic criteria. Introducing additional indicators would distribute the weight more evenly, allowing for a well-rounded performance. More indicators would give a good criterion score if the route's performance is good all-around in that aspect, like the engineering criterion now does. A good performance in a single engineering indicator will not significantly increase the route's performance, but decent all-around performance in the engineering aspect will still give a noticeable boost to the total score of the route.

Despite the apparent concentration issue, a strong engineering performance is crucial for achieving good environmental and economic outcomes. In the context of deploying PtL technologies for environmental benefits, poor performance in the environmental aspect diminishes the significance of engineering and economic considerations. The indicator weights in this study are not extreme compared to the largest indicator weights per criterion in the work by Chauvy et al. (2019), which were in the range of $0.69 - 0.74$.

Another paper by the authors of this work details the application of the here presented framework for the evaluation of a FT pathway as a case study (Nyholm et al., 2024). The route scored a 1 on most of the indicators, which was somewhat expected as it was intended to act as a baseline for further evaluations and with most of the literature reviewed for setting the scoring requirements also focused on the FT. The route did well regarding utilizing the CO_2 feedstock and in the GHG reduction, and consequently it scored a 2 in both indicators. On the other hand, it is notable that the route scored a 0 on both CAPEX and OPEX intensity, indicating that the cost of producing the fuel was higher than anticipated based on the literature review. The generation of other hydrocarbon byproducts pushed up the kerosene-specific wastewater generation enough to cause the route to score a 0 for this indicator too. The route achieved a total score of 1.15, with the Environmental Performance score making up 60.9 % of the final score, the other criteria contributing roughly equally to the result.

The next step involves deploying the framework to evaluate PtL routes, enabling a meaningful comparison of the fundamental characteristics of various technologies. A large and diverse sample of routes will validate the framework's robustness and functionality. Further development could include adding more indicators under the economic and environmental criteria to distribute the criterion's influence more evenly over its indicators. Additionally, incorporating sensitivity analysis, either on model inputs or framework weights, as proposed by Janosovský et al. (2022), or a combination of both, would enhance the reliability of rankings and reduce the subjectivity in the framework.

References

Becker W., Braun R., Penev M., Melaina M., 2012, Production of Fischer-Tropsch liquid fuels from high temperature solid oxide co-electrolysis units, Energy, 47, 1, 99-115.

Calemma V., de Klerk A., 2013, Fischer-Tropsch Syncrude: To Refine or to Upgrade?, Greener Fischer-Tropsch Processes for Fuels and Feedstocks, First Edition, 281-309, Weinheim, Germany.

Chauvy R., Meunier N., Thomas D., De Weireld G., 2019, Selecting emerging CO2 utilization products for short- to mid-term deployment, Applied Energy, 236, 662-680.

Conkle H., Marcum G., Griesenbrock E., Jones W., Morris Jr. R., Robota H., Thomas D., 2011, Production of Synthetic Paraffinic Kerosene by Hydrocracking Fischer-Tropsch Wax, AlChE Annual Meeting.

Dieterich V., Buttler A., Hanel A., Spliethoff H., Fendt S., 2020, Power-to-liquid via synthesis of methanol, DME or Fischer-Tropsch-fuels: a review, Energy & Environmental Science, 13, 3207-3252.

European Parliament, Council of the European Union, 2022, Directive (EU) 2018/2001 of the European Parliament and of the Council of 11 December 2018 on the promotion of the use of energy from renewable sources (recast).

Gangadharan P., Singh R., Cheng F., Lou H., 2013, Novel Methodology for Inherent Safety Assessment in the Process Design Stage, Industrial & Engineering Chemistry Research, 52, 17, 5921-5933.

Goepel K., 2013, Implementing the Analytical Hierarchy Process as a Standard Method for Multi-Criteria Decision Making In Corporate Enterprises - A New AHP Excel Template with Multiple Inputs, Proceedings of the International Symposium on the Analytical Hierarchy Process.

Haldor Topsoe, 2022, Renewable synthetic fuels technology.

Hank C., Holst M., Thelen C., Kost C., Längle S., Schaadt A., Smolinka T., 2023, Power-to-X country analyses: Site-specific, comparative analysis for suitable Power-to-X pathways and products in developing and emerging countries, Fraunhofer Institute for Solar Energy Systems.

Hannula I., Kaisalo N., Simell P., 2020, Preparation of Synthesis Gas from CO2 for Fischer-Tropsch Synthesis - Comparison of Alternative Process Configurations, Journal of Carbon Research, 6, 3, 55.

Janosovský J., Bohácíková V., Kraviarová D., Variny M., 2022, Multi-criteria decision analysis of steam reforming for hydrogen production, Energy Conversion and Management, 263, 115722.

Karjunen H., 2022, Analysis and Design of Carbon Dioxide Utilization Systems and Infrastructures, Lappenranta, Finland.

Kauppi M., 2021, Comparison of Synthetic Fuel Production Routes for Kerosene Range Hydrocarbons, Lappeenranta, Finland.

McCamish B., 2021, Internal Rate of Return | IRR (InvestingAnswers).

Neste Oyj, 2023, Neste Capital Markets Day 2023, London, United Kingdom.

Nyholm F., Toppinen S., Saxén H., 2024, Holistic Evaluation Method for Concept-Level Study of Power-to-Liquids Technologies. Submitted manuscript.

Oztemel H., Salt I., Salt Y., 2022, Carbon Dioxide Utilization: Process Simulation of Synthetic Fuel Production From Flue Gases, Chemical Industry & Chemical Engineering Quarterly, 28, 4, 305-317.

Peters R., Wegener N., Samsun R., Schorn F., Riese J., Grünewald M., Stolten D., 2022, A Techno-Economic Assessment of Fischer-Tropsch Fuels Based on Syngas from Co-Electrolysis, Processes, 10, 4, 699.

Saaty T.L., 1977, A scaling method for priorities in hierarchical structures, J. Math. Psych. 15, 234.

Schemme S., 2020, Techno-ökonomische Bewertung von Verfahren zur Herstellung von Kraftstoffen aus H_2 und CO_2, Energy & Environment, 511, Jülich, Germany.

Schmidt P., Batteiger V., Roth A., Weindorf W., Raksha T., 2018, Power-to-Liquids as Renewable Fuel Option for Aviation: A Review, Chemie Ingenieur Technik, 90, 1-2, 127-140.

Scipioni A., Manzardo A., Ren J., 2023, Hydrogen Economy - Processes, Supply Chain, Life Cycle Analysis and Energy Transition for Sustainability (2nd ed.), London, United Kingdom.

Smith R., Tan E., Ruiz-Mercado G., 2019, Applying Environmental Release Inventories and Indicators to the Evaluation of Chemical Manufacturing Processes in Early Stage Development, ACS Sustainable Chemistry & Engineering, 7, 12, 10937-10950.

Flavio Manenti, Gintaras V. Reklaitis (Eds.), Proceedings of the 34th European Symposium on Computer Aided Process Engineering / 15th International Symposium on Process Systems Engineering (ESCAPE34/PSE24), June 2-6, 2024, Florence, Italy

TSeC: an efficient transition state search tool driven by machine learning potential

Kun Tang,[a] Lei Zhang,[a] Qingwei Meng,[a] Jian Du,[a] Qilei Liu[a,*]

[a]State Key Laboratory of Fine Chemicals, Frontiers Science Center for Smart Materials Oriented Chemical Engineering, Institute of Chemical Process Systems Engineering, School of Chemical Engineering, Dalian University of Technology, Dalian 116024, China

Qilei Liu (liuqilei@dlut.edu.cn)

Abstract

The density functional theory (DFT) has achieved success in the study of reactive systems by combining diverse transition state search algorithms in various electronic structure calculation packages. However, due to the complexity and high cost of the DFT-based computation of the complex reactive systems, there has been continuous development in machine learning potential (MLP) in recent years. It has been demonstrated that MLP is feasible to approximate the potential derived from electronic structure methods on the basis of certain data, and it has a computational cost comparable to that of semi-empirical methods. In this work, an efficient transition state search (TSeC) tool driven by MLP is developed for reactive system research. Multiple transition state search algorithms are combined with the MLP model to achieve efficient evaluations of the reaction properties of organic reaction systems within the scope of traditional DFT research.

Keywords: machine learning potential, transition state, reaction barrier, deep learning.

1. Introduction

With the continuous progress of machine learning modelling techniques, the machine learning potential (MLP) is now recognized for its capability to approximate the computational accuracy of density functional theory (DFT), a widely employed method in molecular simulations. Additionally, MLP exhibits a computational speed several orders of magnitude faster than DFT (Schreiner et al., 2022a). This provides a cheap and accessible way to study chemical reactions, as the search process for chemical reaction paths and transition states require iterative calculations of molecular energies and atomic forces. But the prerequisite for doing so is that the MLP needs to well describe the potential energy surface (PES) of the transition state regions, depending on whether the database used for training the model is sampled from these regions. Recently, Schreiner et al. (2022b) have constructed such a database (Transition 1x) and developed the corresponding MLP model (a model trained on Transition 1x database), making it feasible that the MLP can be applied to study the properties of reactive systems (Schreiner et al., 2022a). However, the known transition state search algorithms have more or less individual shortcomings and more effective transition state search algorithms need to be combined with MLP.

Searching for transition states in chemical reactions is an inherently challenging task, primarily due to two key factors. First, the molecule system involves multiple atoms and numerous degrees of freedom, rendering the PES a high-dimensional surface. Navigating this space to pinpoint transition state positions is exceedingly difficult due to the vast array of potential configurations that must be considered. Second, in the realm of large molecule systems or intricate reactions, the computational cost associated with determining the energy and structure of transition states can be prohibitively high. This necessitates the use of advanced and computationally cheap computational methods to complete this task more quickly and accurately.

Researchers have proposed numerous transition state search algorithms. For example, the Berny algorithm used in Gaussian software (Frisch et al., 2016), which is based on the initial guess structure. It needs to calculate the Hessian matrix and check the eigenvalue at each step. In addition, there is an efficient Dimer algorithm (Henkelman and Jónsson, 1999) that does not require time-consuming calculation of the Hessian matrix at each step, but only calculates the first derivative of energy (i.e., force) to determine the direction of the searching steps. Recently, Liu et al. (2023) has proposed a transition state search algorithm, GENiniTS-RS, based on the reactive sites, which significantly accelerates the identification of transition states for specific reaction types and demonstrates a high success rate. Besides, the nudged elastic band (NEB) algorithm (Henkelman and Jónsson, 2000) is also an efficient and widely used dual ended transition state search method. It constructs an energy elastic band on the reaction coordinates by interpolating between the reactants and products structures. However, the original NEB algorithm could not provide accurate transition state structures. To this end, an improved version of the climbing image-nudged elastic band (CI-NEB) algorithm (Henkelman et al., 2000) has been proposed. The above methods do not use Hessian matrices to determine the direction of the reaction coordinates, so it is necessary to further identify and refine the transition state structures rigorously. But completing this task requires time-consuming calculations of the complete Hessian and iterative diagonalization for molecular systems. Therefore, Hermes et al. (2022) have proposed the Sella algorithm, a novel efficient algorithm for the optimization of molecular structures to saddle points using a redundant internal coordinate system. This algorithm converges to saddle point structures in fewer effective steps than that of popular quantum chemistry codes.

In this work, an efficient MLP-based transition state search (TSeC) framework is developed to predict reaction barriers of organic reactions in an automatic, fast manner. In Section 2, the TSeC framework that combines the MLP model and advanced transition state search algorithms is discussed in detail. In Section 3, a benchmark test comprising 55 initial guesses of transition states generated by the GENiniTS-RS algorithm is introduced to highlighting the applications of TSeC tool in reactive system research.

2. TSeC framework

The execution of transition state search algorithms of the TSeC framework is shown in **Figure 1**. Here, a hybrid transition state search strategy is developed by combining CI-NEB (Henkelman et al., 2000), GENiniTS-RS (Liu et al., 2023), and Sella (Hermes et al., 2022) algorithms and integrated with the Transition 1x MLP model (Schreiner et al., 2022a; Schreiner et al., 2022b), which is used as a calculator for energies and forces in the atomic simulation environment (ASE) package (Larsen et al., 2017). If the user only inputs the SMILES of products or reactants, it will be transferred to GENiniTS-RS to obtain the transition state initial guess of this reaction as long as the reaction exists in the template library. If the SMILES is not in the reaction template library, it is necessary to prepare the structures of reactants and products for the CI-NEB algorithm. Then the Sella algorithm is used for further refinement of the saddle point obtained from the two technical routes of CI-NEB and GENiniTS-RS. Finally, the Sella algorithm is used to perform the intrinsic reaction coordinate (IRC) calculation of the saddle point obtained by Sella refinement, and determine the final IRC path and corresponding reaction barrier. This also confirms the correctness of the searched reaction transition states.

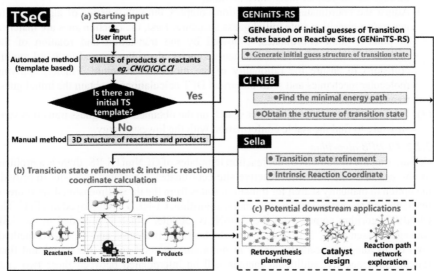

Figure 1. The overview of the TSeC framework. **a** There are two input methods for searching reaction transition states: CI-NEB requires manual preparation of appropriate three-dimensional structures of reactants and products, and GENiniTS-RS only requires the inputs of the SMILES representations of reactants or products to automate the search. **b** Transition state refinement and intrinsic reaction coordinate calculation. **c** Research scenarios of reactive systems applied by the TSeC framework.

2.1. Transition 1x MLP model

Transition 1x is a dataset providing a collection of molecular configurations on and along reaction paths for approximately 10k reactions. Schreiner et al. (2022b) published the dataset and trained the Transition 1x MLP model, which is built upon the PaiNN (Schütt et al., 2021) architecture that employs equivariant message passing graph neural networks. The reactions in the database involve four types of elements (C, H, O, N), and the molecular structures are sampled from reactive and high energy regions (non-equilibrium molecular structure) by the NEB algorithm to ensure that the MLP trained in this dataset can accurately understand the reaction process.

2.2. Reaction path and transition state search algorithms

As shown in **Figure 1**, for reactions within the reaction templates of the GENiniTS-RS algorithm, it can be started from the SMILES representations of products or reactants. For other types of reactions, the CI-NEB algorithm started from the three-dimensional structures of reactants and products has been integrated into the TSeC framework. In addition, the Sella algorithm is also integrated for further refinements of transition state and acquisitions of IRC paths.

2.2.1. GENiniTS-RS algorithm

GENiniTS-RS has a reactive site coordinate database containing a few common organic chemical reactions, which are sufficient for ordinary organic retrosynthesis research. Searching for reaction transition states through GENiniTS-RS mainly involves the following three steps.

(1) The roughly initial three-dimensional geometries of reactive complex are automatically and fast generated from the SMILES strings of reactants or products through the molecular mechanics method.

(2) Adjust the coordinates of the reaction complex through a series of algorithms to generate a transition state initial guess structure. First, the reaction sites are matched in point-to-point coordinates, followed by the translation and rotation of the molecular branches, and the distance geometry algorithm is used to avoid atomic collisions to ensure the rationality of the molecular structure. Finally, applying molecular mechanics and semi-empirical DFT calculations to obtain the initial guess transition state.

(3) Perform a conformational isomer search on the obtained initial guess transition state structure to find the stable conformation with the lowest energy.

2.2.2. CI-NEB algorithm

Considering the limitations of the reaction templates of GENiniTS-RS, there is a problem of absence of initial structural reactive site coordinates, it remains necessity to provide the option to manually search for transition states from the three-dimensional structure of reactants and products. Thus, a dual-ended algorithm, CI-NEB, is employed in TSeC. The CI-NEB algorithm comes from the AutoNEB module, which is provided in the ASE package (Larsen et al., 2017) employing the basic NEB method and a CI-NEB method. First of all, the user needs to supply at minimum two end-points (the initial and final states). Subsequently, additional images will be interpolated between these two end-points dynamically, and in each step, a small force is applied through "nudged" atom pushing, adjusting the band structure along the energy gradient direction, and then minimizing the energy to ensure that the lowest energy point on the path is found. After this process is completed, the climbing image is performed to locate the saddle point on the minimal energy path (MEP). In this work, the spring constant between images on the path is set to $0.1 \ eV \cdot Å^{-2}$, the maximum force along the NEB path is set to $0.025 \ eV \cdot Å^{-1}$, and the max images along the NEB path when done is set to 20.

2.2.3. Sella algorithm

Sella is a novel algorithm for the automated optimization of molecules to saddle points in a basis of redundant internal coordinates. Iterative diagonalization of the Hessian is necessary for the refinement of the rough transition state structures found by the above algorithms. Sella provides a method to incorporate the information obtained from iterative differentiation algorithm into the construction of approximate Hessian matrices, which accelerates the refinement task. In this study, the preliminary transition state structure, obtained through the above two algorithms, is served as the initial input for the Sella algorithm calculation. Following refinement, the first-order saddle point structure undergoes additional IRC calculations to delineate the reaction pathway. And ultimately save the reaction kinetics information and optimization trajectory file of the reaction.

3. Results and discussions

To showcase the efficiency of the transition state search algorithm and the Transition 1x MLP utilized in TSeC, 55 transition state initial guess of the reactions derived from the GENiniTS-RS reaction templates are employed for benchmark test. **Table 1** compares the success rate, average time consumption, and average number of steps calculated using the DFT method (the calculation level is b3lyp/6-31g(d,p) em=gd3bj) in the Gaussian software (Frisch et al., 2016) combined with its transition state search algorithm, the MLP model combined with Sella algorithm, and the DFT method (b3lyp/6-31g(d,p) em=gd3bj) combined with Sella algorithm for these 55 reactions.

From **Table 1**, it is evident that, under the same transition state search algorithm, MLP significantly expedites this task and exhibits a high success rate. This further substantiates the efficacy of the Transition 1x MLP. In the case of using DFT calculation, Sella algorithm is also more efficient than the search algorithm in Gaussian (Higher success rate and lower average single step computation time), and its Python implementation also facilitates the combination with MLP.

Table 1. The success rate, average time consumption, and average number of steps calculated using the DFT method in the Gaussian software, the MLP model combined with Sella algorithm, and the DFT method combined with Sella algorithm.

	DFT in Gaussian	Sella+MLP	Sella+DFT
Success rate	87%	98%	100%
Average time consuming (s)	1699	216.4	4,861.6
Average steps	29.83	154.2	146.53

To demonstrate the effectiveness of the Sella algorithm in refining the initial guess structure of the transition states, 54 reactions that successfully searched for transition states are selected. Using the DFT calculation results as the benchmark. The root mean squared error (RMSE) of the transition state structures generated by MLP model combined with CI-NEB is 0.887 Å, and the RMSE of the transition state structure refined by the MLP model combined with GENiniTS-RS + Sella algorithm is 0.879 Å. This indicates that Sella has improved the geometric structure accuracy of the transition state to a certain extent.

The Sella algorithm is employed to conduct IRC searches using MLP and DFT as potential, respectively. The differences in the reaction barriers derived from these two potentials are then compared in **Figure 2**. Based on the results obtained using the DFT potential, the mean average error (MAE) of the potential barriers calculated by Sella + MLP on this dataset is 0.423 eV. This indicates that there is still some room for improvement in Transition 1x MLP on the dataset derived from the template reactions of GENiniTS-RS. For reactions containing a large number of heavy atoms, new MLPs need to be trained.

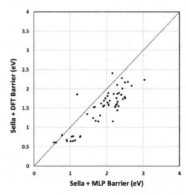

Figure 2. Comparison of reaction barriers found with Sella using MLP as potential on the x-axis vs. DFT on the y-axis.

4. Conclusions

In this paper, a computational tool (TSeC) is developed for transition state and MEP searches. It combines the MLP and advanced transition state search algorithms. On the test dataset, the combination of MLP + Sella algorithm in TSeC achieves a 98% success rate in transition state searches and MAE of 0.423 eV on reaction barrier. Additionally, TSeC integrates the CI-NEB algorithm, which can switch between algorithm modes based on various scenario requirements, such as the absence of reaction templates, providing broad applicability. TSeC can also be employed for the swift generation of extensive reaction kinetics databases, providing data for better performing MLPs. For instance, the Transition 1x database exclusively encompasses heavy atoms C, N, O, rendering it incapable of predicting reactions involving halogens in GENiniTS-RS. Consequently, the need arises to train dedicated MLPs on new datasets in the future.

Finally, although there are various search algorithms for reaction transition states, it is still difficult to achieve chemical reactions *in silico* without relying on human intervention. GENiniTS-RS currently relies on templates. In the future, it is imperative to develop new generative artificial intelligence models to enable the generation of transition state initial guesses without the need for prior experience.

References

Q. Liu, K. Tang, L. Zhang, J. Du, and Q. Meng, 2023. Computer ‐ assisted synthetic planning considering reaction kinetics based on transition state automated generation method. AIChE Journal, 69(7), e18092.

M. Schreiner, A. Bhowmik, T. Vegge, P. B. Jørgensen, and O. Winther, 2022a. NeuralNEB—neural networks can find reaction paths fast. Machine Learning: Science and Technology, 3(4), 045022.

M. Schreiner, A. Bhowmik, T. Vegge, J. Busk, and O. Winther, 2022b. Transition1x ‐ a dataset for building generalizable reactive machine learning potentials. Scientific Data, 9(1), 779.

M. J. Frisch, G. W. Trucks, H. B. Schlegel, et al., 2016. Gaussian 16 Rev. C.01. Wallingford, CT.

K. T. Schütt, O. T. Unke, and M. Gastegger, 2021. Equivariant message passing for the prediction of tensorial properties and molecular spectra. Paper presented at the International Conference on Machine Learning.

G. Henkelman, B. P. Uberuaga, and H. Jónsson, 2000. A climbing image nudged elastic band method for finding saddle points and minimum energy paths. The Journal of Chemical Physics, 113(22), 9901-9904.

G. Henkelman, and H. Jónsson, 2000. Improved tangent estimate in the nudged elastic band method for finding minimum energy paths and saddle points. The Journal of Chemical Physics, 113(22), 9978-9985.

G. Henkelman, and H. Jónsson, 1999. A dimer method for finding saddle points on high dimensional potential surfaces using only first derivatives. The Journal of Chemical Physics, 111(15), 7010-7022.

E. D. Hermes, K. Sargsyan, H. N. Najm, and J. Zádor, 2022. Sella, an Open-Source Automation-Friendly Molecular Saddle Point Optimizer. Journal of Chemical Theory and Computation, 18(11), 6974-6988.

A. H. Larsen, J. J. Mortensen, J. Blomqvist, et al., 2017. The atomic simulation environment—a Python library for working with atoms. Journal of Physics: Condensed Matter, 29(27), 273002.

Flavio Manenti, Gintaras V. Reklaitis (Eds.), Proceedings of the 34th European Symposium on Computer Aided Process Engineering / 15th International Symposium on Process Systems Engineering (ESCAPE34/PSE24), June 2-6, 2024, Florence, Italy

Supply chain optimization for biopropane production in Brazil

Larissa Thais Bruschi,[a*] Luiz Alexandre Kulay,[a] Moisés Teles dos Santos[a]

[a]*Department of Chemical Engineering, Polytechnic School, University of São Paulo, Av. Prof. Luciano Gualberto, Trav. 3, 380, São Paulo, 05508-900, Brazil*
larissabruschi@usp.br

Abstract

The present work proposes an optimization model for the supply chain design for biopropane production in Brazil, aiming to identify trade-offs and aid the decision-making process. The proposed model is a mixed integer linear programming formulation, considering a maximum net present value as the objective function. The model considers the feedstock availability, location and purchasing costs; the multiple technological routes with their average yield, raw materials, and utilities, potential production and storage facilities location, with their capacities, capital and operational costs; and the market location and demands; as well as taxes and the logistic between the layers. Using a case study covering São Paulo and Paraná regions, the analysis showed the influence of biopropane prices and feedstock costs on net present value. The optimized network determined glycerin dehydration as the preferred conversion route due to its higher biopropane yield and lower costs compared to other methods. The study also reveals two production and storage centers strategically located near feedstock sources, emphasizing the complex relations between location decisions, taxes, and efficient supply chain management.

Keywords: biopropane, optimization, supply chain

1. Introduction

Renewable fuels can be an alternative to fossil fuels, aiding the supply of the growing world demand for energy and mitigating the emissions of greenhouse gases. Biopropane (propane from renewable feedstocks) is a potential candidate to compete in the decarbonized fuel market due to its variety of raw materials and technological routes (Menezes et al., 2022). Brazil has a great potential for producing biopropane, because of its agricultural capacity and diversity of feedstocks. Among the known feasible production routes for biopropane, are the hydrotreatment of vegetable oils (in which biopropane is a byproduct), the gasification of lignocellulosic materials followed by Fischer Tropsch synthesis and the dehydration of glycerin (Johnson, 2019). The diverse technological processes and feedstocks appeal to multi-scale systems engineering approaches, which can model the distribution of feedstocks, biofuel production technologies and analyze supply chains, to meet regional and national biofuels economies. The real-world deployment of renewable fuels projects requires careful evaluation of decisions along the entire project value chain. In this sense, optimization techniques have been extensively applied. Kostin et al. (2018) explored the supply chain of ethanol production from sugarcane in Brazil using a mixed integer linear programming (MILP) formulation to maximize the net present value (NPV). The authors identified optimal strategies to allocate new biorefineries, compared with the current supply chain, considering the cultivation areas of sugarcane in different regions, production plants, storage facilities, transportation modes, and final markets. In some studies, more than one criterion is required to support better decisions. In the study of Tesfamichael et al. (2023), a multi-objective modeling was developed, covering an environmental monetary indicator, based on life cycle analysis, together with economic objective functions of maximizing profits and minimizing investment costs, in the supply chain for biodiesel and bioethanol production from biomass. As results, the refineries are mainly situated near biomass sources, rather than areas with high biofuel demand. The optimized planning indicates the use of a raw material in the first production years and later incorporate another biomass. Theozzo and Teles dos Santos (2021) evaluated the design of forest biomass biorefinery in Brazil, using a MILP framework interconnecting forest, production, storage, and market decisions. A case study on eucalyptus biorefinery in Brazil has shown that taxes policies and transportation costs were the largest NPV detrimental factors and highlighted that non-technical parameters, such as prices and taxes, significantly impacted decisions along the entire supply chain. In the present work, an optimization model is proposed for the supply chain design for biopropane production in Brazil, aiming to identify trade-offs and aid the decision-making process. The proposed model is a MILP formulation, considering a maximum net present value as the objective function. A case study for biopropane production in the São Paulo and Paraná region was analyzed. The conversion technologies considered in the model were hydrogenation of vegetable oils, dehydration and gasification. The feedstocks included were soybean and sunflower, glycerin, sugarcane bagasse, rice husk and soybean straw.

2. Methodology

A previous work (Theozzo and Teles dos Santos, 2021) is expanded and adapted to represent the Brazilian supply chain for biopropane production. The MILP formulation model is divided into four decision layers: feedstock, production, storage and market. In the feedstock layer, the constraints represent the purchase of raw material, considering its type (set B), availability, location (set O) and prices. A set for each period (set T) is included in the model, to capture uncertainties in prices and in feedstocks availabilities along time in future works, as well as changes in products demand, as covered in this study. The purchased flowrate of feedstock b, from location o, $FB_{o,b,t}^{buy}$, is equivalent to the amount of material processed in the conversion facilities (set P) ($FP_{p,b,t}$), presented in Eq. (1), and accounted in the overall costs, affecting the NPV.

$$\sum_{o \in O} FB_{o,b,t}^{buy} = \sum_{p \in P} FP_{p,b,t} \qquad \forall (b \in B, t \in T) \tag{1}$$

In the production layer, the conversion technology (set Z) is defined as a binary variable, coupled with the location of the facility p ($y_{p,z}$). To produce biopropane, some inputs are used by the technology besides the feedstock, as chemicals (set I), electricity, hot and cold utilities (set U). Each input cost is summed as the operational cost, for each period. The investments costs are related to the decision variable of the facility and are included in the NPV function. The maximum installed capacity of the production facility is fixed, but the model is flexible to operate with a capacity less or equal to the maximum. The biopropane (set G) produced in facility p, by the technology z ($FG_{p,z,g=prop,t}$) can be transferred directly to the market m, $FG^{p-m}_{p,m,g=prop,t}$, or can be sent to a warehouse s, $FG^{p-s}_{p,s,g=prop,t}$, presented in Eq. (2), while coproducts , also defined by the set G, are sold, free on board, from the production location, summed in the revenue value.

$$\sum_{z \in Z} FG_{p,z,g=prop,t} = \sum_{m \in M} FG_{p,m,g=prop,t}^{p\_m} + \sum_{s \in S} FG_{p,s,g=prop,t}^{p\_s} \quad \forall (p \in P,\ t \in T) \qquad (2)$$

The transportation costs of the biopropane from the production facility to the market or the storage facility are accounted in the overall costs for each period. For the biopropane sold to the market, taxes related to origin and destiny of the product, are accounted, and reflect on the selling price. In the storage layer, the facilities are defined with a binary variable (y_s), and a mass balance constraint, represents the biopropane storage in each period considering the amount of product received from the production center, the transference between storage centers, and the amount sold to the markets. For the market layer, the product g sold to each market m ($FM_{m,g,t}^{market}$) must be less or equal to its demand ($F_{m,g,t}^{dem}$), for each period, presented in Eq. (3).

$$FM_{m,g,t}^{market} \le F_{m,g,t}^{dem} \qquad \forall (\, m \in M, g \in G,\ t \in T) \qquad (3)$$

The profit (L_t) accounts for the revenue less the cost for each period, and taxes are considered. For the NPV equation, Eq. (4), the profit is discounted by an interest rate (*int_rate*), and the investment cost of production (C^{invest_P}) and storage (C^{invest_S}) are incident only in the first period of operation.

$$NPV = \sum_{t \in T} \frac{L_t}{(1 - int\_rate)^t} - \left(C^{invest\_P} + C^{invest\_S} \right) \qquad (4)$$

The optimization model was developed using Python language and the Pyomo software package. For solving the problem, the Gurobi (Gurobi Optimization, 2023) solver was used, with the Branch and Bound method.

3. Case study

As a preliminary case study, the model was applied to the region of São Paulo because of its economic relevance (gas demand, population size, and industrial relevance in Brazil). The conversion route used in the model was the hydrotreatment of vegetable oils and the feedstock was soybean, the most available oilseed in the region. For the feedstock used in the model, 26 localities were covered, representing 64 % of the soybean produced by the region. For the market layer, a scenario of substitution of a fraction of the liquefied petroleum gas (LPG) demand of a typical year in São Paulo was used, considering 7 locations. The optimization outcomes indicated that, only a small portion of the regional demand could be substituted by biopropane, even when using all the soybeans available. To accurately represent the potential and viability of biopropane production in Brazil, the model was expanded to incorporate a broader range of feedstocks, regions and conversion technologies.

Therefore, the proposed model was applied to a case study to substitute 10 % of the LPG demand from the capital of São Paulo and Paraná (set M) by biopropane. The demand has an increase of 1.4 % by year, following a Brazilian government energy forecast (EPE, 2022). The set O included the biggest producers of each feedstock in the regions, soybean and sunflower, glycerin, sugarcane bagasse, rice husk and soybean straw, covering 25 localities. 4 localities in each region were included in the set P, as possible production centers, geographically distributed in the state, as well as 3 localities as possible storage centers. The model solved had 222,814 equations, 77,083 continuous variables and 30 binary variables. The binary variables are the representation of the 3 technologies coupled with 8 possible locations to install the production facilities, accounting 24 variables, and 6 variables representing the possible locations to install the storage facility. The superstructure is illustrated in Figure 1, showing examples of the objects in each set.

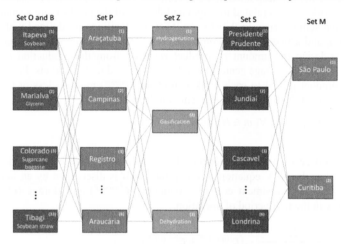

Figure 1: Superstructure of the optimization model

The results of a sensitivity analysis, presenting the influence of variation in biopropane selling price, and the variation in the feedstock costs in the NPV, are showed in the Figure 2.

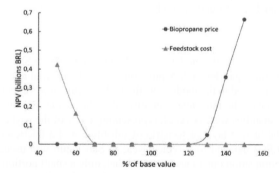

Figure 2: NPV dependence in variation of biopropane price and feedstock costs

For the current prices of all the feedstocks, products, capital and operational costs, the supply chain evaluated was not feasible. However, when the biopropane selling prices increase, from 130 % in relation to the base value, the NPV of the networks exceed 50 million reais. Observing the results for the variation in feedstock costs only, the project became feasible when the feedstock costs are lower than 60 % of the base value, presenting the significant influence of the raw materials on biofuel prices. For transportation costs, a sensitivity analysis was realized, but even for costs lower than 50 % of the base value, the projects were not viable and the results were not included in the figure. Although variations in biopropane prices and feedstock costs had a major impact on NPV, the technology route selected, as result of the optimization, was the same for all scenarios: glycerin dehydration. Considering the scenario of the current prices and the biopropane selling price representing 130 % of the base value, the NPV breakdown of the optimized network is presented in Figure 3.

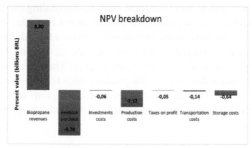

Figure 3: NPV breakdown for the scenario of biopropane selling price of 130 % of the base value, and glycerin dehydration conversion route as a result of the optimization

The feedstock purchase, for the glycerin dehydration technology chosen by the optimization, is the major negative factor of the NPV for the scenario; this is due to the relatively low yield of the process. The optimized network presented the installation of 2 production facilities, both using the dehydration of glycerin as conversion technology. Although this conversion route has the highest biopropane yield when compared to hydrogenation and gasification: 30 % in mass of biopropane (Johnson, 2019), large quantities of feedstock are still needed to supply the demand. Besides the dehydration product yield, the glycerin costs are lower than the oilseed costs (feedstock for the hydrogenation route), making the dehydration route more attractive than the hydrogenation, even considering the profits from the sale of green diesel, the main product of the conversion by the hydrogenation route. When comparing the dehydration to the gasification, although the raw materials are cheaper than the glycerin, the biopropane yield is lower, close to 1 %, making the process unfeasible. The production costs are the second negative portion of the NPV, and represent the electricity, hot and cold utilities and hydrogen purchases. The optimized network is shown in Figure 4, with the installation of 2 production centers (P), and 2 storage centers (S). The NPV of the network, considering a time horizon of 20 years, is 50.6 million reais.

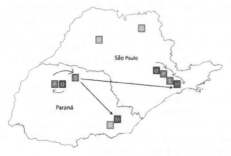

Figure 4: Optimized network for the biopropane production in São Paulo and Paraná (O: source location of feedstock purchased, P: production facility location, S: storage facility location, M: market location)

The feedstock origins (O) presented in Figure 4 are the locations where glycerin is available. The optimized network presented the production center (P) close to the location of feedstock (O) and the storage center (S), for both regions, minimizing transportation costs. The supply chain to meet the São Paulo demand receive biopropane from the Paraná storage center, instead of transporting the feedstock from distant locations or installing another production center inside the region. This occurs because the biopropane produced in São Paulo is insufficient to meet the local market, demanding the transportation from another region. Installing a new production facility is not feasible, since in the model a fixed maximum capacity and fixed investments were adopted, indicating that even installing a production facility that does not operate at the maximum capacity, the investment costs will represent an unnecessary charge. The taxes on product sales also influence the supply chain decision, as the product sales taxes between Paraná and São Paulo are lower than the internal sales taxes of each region, making the biopropane transportation from Paraná more advantageous than internal transportation in São Paulo.

4. Conclusions

A MILP optimization model was developed to evaluate the design of the biopropane supply chain in Brazil, considering factors such as feedstock availability, conversion technologies, storage, market demand, and associated costs. By applying the model to a case study in São Paulo and Paraná regions, the analysis demonstrates the impact of biopropane prices and feedstock costs on the NPV. The results showed the glycerin dehydration as the optimal conversion route, due to its higher biopropane yield compared to other technologies, and due to glycerin prices lower than the other materials. The optimized supply chain illustrates two production and storage centers, emphasizing proximity to feedstock sources and markets, demonstrating the intricate relationship between location decisions, taxes, and efficient supply chain management. As future works some points can be highlighted: expanding the feedstock availability and market demand to the whole country, evaluate the uncertainties associated with the model parameters and add the installed production capacity associated with a variable investment cost. The supply chain optimization model revealed that biofuel projects, such as biopropane production, can face financial challenges due to high production and logistics costs, despite its environmental advantages, highlighting the complexity of balancing economic strategic decisions when implementing biorefinery projects.

References

A. Kostin, D. H. Macowski, J. M. T. A. Pietrobelli, G. Guillén-Gosálbezc, L. Jiménez, M. A. S. S. Ravagnani, 2018, Optimization-based approach for maximizing profitability of bioethanol supply chain in Brazil, Computers and Chemical Engineering, 115, 121-132.

B. Tesfamichael, L. Montastruc, S. Negny, 2023, Developing a Comprehensive Decision Support Optimization Model for Biofuel Supply Chain. Computer Aided Chemical Engineering, 52, 3307-3312.

B. Theozzo, M. T. dos Santos, 2021, A MILP framework for optimal biorefinery design that accounts for forest biomass dynamics, Computers and Chemical Engineering, 146, 107201.

E. Johnson, 2019, Process Technologies and Projects for BioLPG, Energies, 12, 250.

EPE (Empresa de Pesquisa Energética), 2022, Estudos prospectivos sobre oferta, demanda, investimentos e o abastecimento de GLP no Brasil, Ministry of Mines and Energy. Available at: https://www.epe.gov.br/. Acessed in: 12 Jan. 2023.

Gurobi Optimization, LLC. Gurobi Optimizer Manual. 2023. Available at: https://www.gurobi.com. Accessed in: 28 Nov. 2023.

N. A. Menezes, I. L. C. Cunha, M. T. dos Santos, L. Kulay, 2022, Obtaining bioLPG via the HVO Route in Brazil: A Prospect Study Based on Life Cycle Assessment Approach, Sustainability, 14, 15734.

Flavio Manenti, Gintaras V. Reklaitis (Eds.), Proceedings of the 34th European Symposium on Computer Aided Process Engineering / 15th International Symposium on Process Systems Engineering (ESCAPE34/PSE24), June 2-6, 2024, Florence, Italy

Coupling Rule-based reasoning, Exergy analysis and Pinch analysis to optimize and improve the Energy efficiency of Processes

Noha-Lys Senoussaoui,[a] Raphaële Théry Hétreux,[a] Gilles Hétreux,[a]

[a]*Laboratoire de Génie Chimique, Département PSI, 4 allée Emile Monso, 31432 Toulouse CEDEX 4, France*
nohalys.senoussaoui@toulouse-inp.fr

Abstract

Global efforts target carbon neutrality by 2050, with a focus on Carbon Capture Utilization and Storage in industries like, for example, methanol production. While sustainability analysis like exergy analysis lacks practical solution proposals, integrating artificial intelligence allows to bridges this gap. The COOPERE approach combines pinch analysis, exergy analysis and optimization for the design and retrofit of processes. This study applies COOPERE to a methanol production process with CO_2 recovery, and highlighting the strength of the rule-based reasoning tool in suggesting improvements. COOPERE significantly reduces energy and electric consumption, offering economic benefits with initial investments.

Keywords: Rule-based reasoning, Exergy analysis, Energy integration, Superstructure optimisation, decarbonation.

1. Introduction

Efforts worldwide to combat climate change, like Europe's Fit for 55 plan, aim for carbon neutrality by 2050 (European Commission, 2019). In the industrial sector, Carbon Capture Utilization and Storage (CCUS) technologies are being explored, such as for methanol production processes (Nami et al., 2019). In addition, the implementation of innovative and conceptual approaches stands as a key to the emergence of more sustainable and sober production paths. Innovative approaches like pinch analysis, life cycle assessment, and exergy analysis already enhance sustainability (Bachmann et al., 2023; Blumberg et al., 2017; Kemp, 2011). However, these approaches while insightful, often lacks practical improvement solutions and usually relies on engineer's expertise. The integration of artificial intelligence (AI), discussed by (Venkatasubramanian, 2019), addresses this gap for chemical engineering. The COOPERE approach was developed at the Toulouse Chemical Engineering Laboratory by (Gourmelon et al., 2017) to associate pinch analysis, exergy analysis and optimization to propose retrofitted process structures. To fill the gap between diagnosis and practical solutions, a case-based reasoning was first introduced, but has proven its limits because of its inability to express general knowledge. Moreover, case based reasoning requires an extensive cases database which is difficult to build when there is only a scarce number of relevant cases (Prentzas and Hatzilygeroudis, 2007). A Rule based expert systems (RBES) seems to be a more suitable approach as it could lead to the intuitive application of the appropriate set of heuristics to a given defect. This paper demonstrates the COOPERE approach's application to a methanol production process presented by (Yang et al., 2018), emphasizing the role of the developed rule-based reasoning tool in suggesting improvements.

2. Principle of the COOPERE method

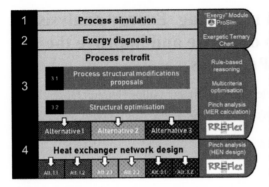

Figure 1: The COOPERE approach to improve the energy efficiency of processes

The COOPERE method supports the engineer in the retrofit or the design of energetically efficient chemical processes. This approach is divided in four steps as in Figure 1. (1) First, data is collected and a process simulation is built on ProSimPlus, a flowsheeting software that proposes automatic energy and exergy balance on any simulated process (Gourmelon et al., 2014). (2) Then, the exergy analysis of the process is carried out and the *exergy ternary diagram* is displayed to pinpoint the most critical exergy losses in the process. (3) Based on this exergy diagnosis, the process retrofit is performed. Solutions for improvement are proposed for each operation or set of operations using a RBES knowledge base that was recently introduced. These improvement suggestions consisting of a set of structural modifications and ranges for operating parameters are combined to build a process superstructure. This superstructure enables the user to get an overall view of the suggested solutions for each part of the process. To determine the set of alternative scenarios combining solutions that fit best together, a multicriteria multivariable optimization is performed using a MIDACO optimization algorithm embedded on the ProSimPlus simulator. This solver is able to solve multiobjective MINLP relying on an extended evolutionary Ant Colony Optimization and the Oracle Penalty Method, enabling to find a global optimum. (4). Lastly, a heat exchanger network is designed for each alternative process proposed, then ensuring a compromise between economic viability and heat recovery.

3. Presentation of the process

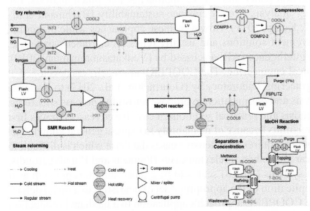

Figure 2: Schematic diagram of the methanol production process (Yang et al., 2018)

The investigated process, depicted in Figure 2, involves the production of methanol (MeOH) and was detailed by (Yang et al., 2018). To reduce CO_2 footprint of the process, they introduced an original *parallel-series* methane reforming reactors configuration. This configuration enables to optimize syngas production by incorporating a proper amount of carbon monoxide (CO). This, enhances the conversion of CO_2 in the methanol reaction loop. The process comprises two reactors: the first operates independently for steam methane reforming (*parallel* part), and its products are then introduced as reactants into the second reactor (*series* part) for dry methane reforming. (Yang et al., 2018) reported a significant improvement in carbon efficiency, increasing from 93.34% to 97.35%, and a decrease in the total annual cost compared to their reference scenario. However, the overall energetic performance of the process remained unexplored. To address this gap, the present article aims to investigate the system's energy efficiency using the COOPERE method. The goal is to identify and rectify potential irreversibilities, ensuring that any improvements do not compromise the process's energy consumption.

4. Analysis of the methanol process using the COOPERE approach

4.1. Step 1: Process simulation

The process proposed by (Yang et al., 2018) is replicated and enriched in ProSimPlus. For the sake of this study, a generic "input-output" integration is implemented for all reactors of the process in order to give more industrial relevance to the system, since the original process does not show any form of heat integration. Furthermore, hot and cold utility stream have been introduced in the model. Specifically, utilities consist in fumes from a natural gas-fuelled furnace at 1850 °C, and cold river water at 18 °C. Intermediate heat carrier fluids are also introduced in closed loops such as high-pressure steam (280 °C, 60 bar) and R134a refrigerant (-21.4 °C, 1 bar).

4.2. Step 2: Exergy diagnosis

The exergy analysis performed in the COOPERE approach (Gourmelon et al., 2017) relies on a form of exergy balance that focuses on the effective transformation of exergy on the considered system (see Eq. (1)).

$$\Delta B^{consumed} = \Delta B^{produced} + B_{out}^{M,waste} + I \tag{1}$$

Dividing each side of Eq. (1) by $\Delta B^{consumed}$, we obtain the final formulation in Eq. (2) that enable to locate a representative point of each process section on an *Exergy ternary diagram*.

$$1 = IE + IW + II \tag{2}$$

The diagram of Figure 3 acts as a radiography of the process. The closer a dot is to the *intrinsic efficiency* vertex IE, the more efficient the related sector is. Operations close to the *intrinsic irreversibility* vertex II suffer from non-optimal operational parameters, while sections close to the *intrinsic waste* vertex IW illustrate the presence of waste streams that could be recovered or be mechanically, chemically or thermally recovered. The size of each dot represents the amount of global exergy loss (i.e., irreversibility and waste) relatively to the whole process. Of course, every process section has been studied. This contribution will however only focus on the retrofit of the Separation & Concentration (Sep. & Conc.) section as it is the least efficient one.

4.3. Step 3: Process retrofit

The COOPERE RBES tool aims to mimic the expert reasoning and to suggest structural improvement relying on the ternary exergy diagram analysis. Figure 4 displays the

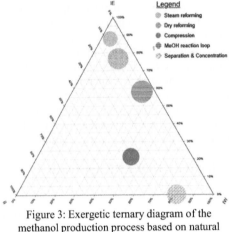

Figure 3: Exergetic ternary diagram of the methanol production process based on natural gas and recovered CO_2

forward chaining reasoning based on the expert's knowledge and analysis of the ternary chart; the RBR thus applied on the Sep. & Conc. section leads to the following improvement proposals. The high value of IW in this section is caused by: (a) utility that is release to the environment, (b) the purge of the first distillation's column gas distillate and (c) the second distillation column's wastewater. To reduce the IW (a), Pinch Analysis will be performed during Step 4 and then reduce the use of hot utility. The IW (b), mainly composed of chemical exergy, suggests to burn purged gas to produce combustion fumes, thus saving on hot utility. The IW (c) is a rich in methanol (48 % mol.) and could be recovered by installing another distillation column. The high value of II is caused by (d) heat exchangers, displaying a large difference between hot and cold streams that could be reduced by improving the Heat Exchanger Network, and (e) a pressure valve, which shifts the inlet stream pressure from 78 bar to 5 bar. A turbine would significantly improve the exergy efficiency. The proposed alternatives are thus compiled and added in the nominal process to end up with the process superstructure displayed in Figure 5.

The MIDACO optimization, using both operational (real) and structural (integer) variables, lead to several optimal alternate scenarios that include suggested modifications. In our approach, we chose to maximize the process integrability and to minimize the

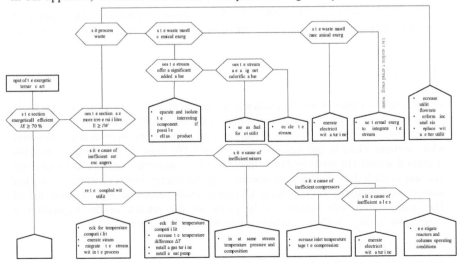

Figure 4: Heuristics turned into a chain of questions

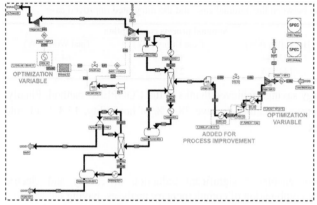

Figure 5: ProSimPlus superstructure simulation of the
Separation & Concentration section

required mechanical work. The optimization leads to a Minimal Hot Utility requirement, Minimal Cold Utility requirement and Minimal Work respectively equal to 19,975 kW, 149,525 kW and 44,973 kW. Table 1 summarizes the technical changes that were implemented in Figure 2 to reach the previously stated results.

Table 1: Improved process new parameters and design details

Section	Layout	Description
Compression	COOL3 / COMP2-1 / COMP2-2 / COOL4 / COMP3	Optimisation results in modifying $P_{COMP2-1}$ from 6 bar to 10.5 bar and T_{COOL3} from 57.3 °C to 69.1 °C. Non-variable optimisation changes T_{COOL4} from 115.8 °C to 30.0 °C to perform isothermal mixing
MeOH reaction loop	HX-A1 / TURB-A1 / Purge	Exchanger-turbine sequence added to both reco er t e purge's mec anical exerg and preheat the turbine inlet stream to introduce a new cold stream to the process. Optimisation results in setting $T_{HX-A1} = 467.8\,°C$ and $P_{TURB-A1} = 67.4\ bar$
Separation & Concentration	HX-A2 / TURB-A2 / COOL-A7	Exchanger-turbine-exchanger sequence added on stream input of the Topping column to replace a pressure valve. Optimisation results in setting $T_{HX-A2} = 467.0\,°C$. Process specifications gives $P_{TURB-A2} = 5\ bar$ and $T_{COOL-A7} = 28.1\,°C$

4.4. Step 4: Heat exchanger network design

In this last step, the improved scenario goes under a pinch analysis to determine an optimized heat exchanger network that includes all newly generated streams. The design of this network aims to get as close as possible to the Minimum Energy Requirement (MER). This step is performed using RREFlex, a software developed in Toulouse Chemical Engineering Laboratory (ADEME, 2020).

Table 2: Process comparison between the nominal case and the integrated improved case

Process	Nominal process consumption		
	Hot Utility (kW)	Cold Utility (kW)	Total Work (kW)
Reference	232,744	323,629	64,340
Improved	144,174	273,723	44,973

Table 2 displays the energy savings achieved thanks to the COOPERE method. Finally, the use of COOPERE approach enabled to save 38.1 % of hot utility, 15.4 % of cold utility and 30.1 % of work.

5. Conclusions

The COOPERE approach enables a significant reduction of energy and electric consumption thanks to the combination of complementary analyses, paving the way to a new economic profitability, provided that necessary investments are initially done. Greater results can be reached through a study extended to the whole process. Efforts should however be carried on the description of complex unit operations' exerg alance such as reactors, which were not regarded in this study but is talked in a research project entitled ANR NACREE. The question of a proper recovery of chemical exergy should be investigated further. Perspectives include the formulation of new rules based on other relevant process graphical representation such as the Grand Composite Curve.

References

2020.   nt èse de réseaux d'éc angeurs de c aleur flexi les - é eloppement d'un outil de reconfiguration totale ou remodelage partiel du réseau existant [WWW Document]. La librairie ADEME.

M. Bachmann, S. Völker, J. Kleinekorte and A. Bardow, 2023. Syngas from What? Comparative Life-Cycle Assessment for Syngas Production from Biomass, CO2, and Steel Mill Off-Gases. ACS Sustainable Chem. Eng. 11, 5356–5366.

T. Blumberg, T. Morosuk and G. Tsatsaronis, 2017. Exergy-based evaluation of methanol production from natural gas with CO2 utilization. Energy 141, 2528–2539.

European Commission, 2019. Going climate-neutral by 2050: a strategic long term vision for a prosperous, modern, competitive and climate neutral EU economy. Publications Office of the European Union, LU.

S. Gourmelon, R. Thery Hetreux and P. Floquet, 2017. A systematic approach: Combining process optimisation exergy analysis and energy recovery for a better efficiency of industrial processes. International Journal of Exergy 23, 298.

S. Gourmelon, R. Théry Hétreux, P. Floquet, P. Baudet and O. Baudouin, 2014. Premises for a combined Exergy and Pinch Optimization within ProSimPlus® simulator. Computer Aided Chemical Engineering 33, 1507–1512.

I. C. Kemp, 2011. Pinch Analysis and Process Integration: A User Guide on Process Integration for the Efficient Use of Energy, 2nd edition. ed. Butterworth-Heinemann.

H. Nami, F. Ranjbar and M. Yari, 2019. Methanol synthesis from renewable H2 and captured CO2 from S-Graz cycle – Energy, exergy, exergoeconomic and exergoenvironmental (4E) analysis. International Journal of Hydrogen Energy 44, 26128–26147.

J. Prentzas and I. Hatzilygeroudis, 2007. Categorizing approaches combining rule-based and case-based reasoning. Expert Systems 24, 97–122.

V. Venkatasubramanian, 2019. The promise of artificial intelligence in chemical engineering: Is it here, finally? AIChE Journal 65, 466–478.

Y. Yang, J. Liu, W. Shen, J. Li and I.-L. Chien, 2018. High-efficiency utilization of CO2 in the methanol production by a novel parallel-series system combining steam and dry methane reforming. Energy 158, 820–829.

Flavio Manenti, Gintaras V. Reklaitis (Eds.), Proceedings of the 34th European Symposium on Computer Aided Process Engineering / 15th International Symposium on Process Systems Engineering (ESCAPE34/PSE24), June 2-6, 2024, Florence, Italy

Scalable Modeling of Infinite-Dimensional Nonlinear Programs with InfiniteExaModels.jl

Joshua L. Pulsipher[a]* and Sungho Shin[b]

[a]*Department of Chemical Engineering, University of Waterloo, 200 University Ave. W., Waterloo, ON N2L 3G1, Canada*
[b]*Mathematics and Computer Science Division, Argonne National Laboratory, 9700 S. Cass Ave., Lemont, IL 60439, USA*
pulsipher@uwaterloo.ca

Abstract

In this work, we present InfiniteExaModels.jl as a modeling framework to efficiently solve nonlinear infinite-dimensional optimization problems. This framework seamlessly integrates InfiniteOpt.jl, a modeling platform tailored for infinite-dimensional optimization models, with ExaModels.jl, an algebraic modeling and automatic differentiation system for nonlinear optimization problems exhibiting repetitive patterns. Our primary focus lies in recognizing that the discretization of infinite-dimensional optimization problems often reveals repetitive patterns. Leveraging this structure allows us to significantly enhance the efficiency of derivative evaluations—a common computational bottleneck in nonlinear optimization procedures. By harnessing the efficient derivative evaluation capabilities of ExaModels.jl, we achieve substantial speed improvements in the evaluation of derivatives for objective and constraint equations. To illustrate the effectiveness of InfiniteExaModels.jl, we present numerical examples involving quadrotor optimal control and stochastic alternating current (AC) optimal power flow. Our findings demonstrate that by using InfiniteExaModels.jl, one can achieve a minimum fourfold acceleration in derivative evaluation performance compared to state-of-the-art algebraic modeling and automatic differentiation tools.

Keywords: infinite-dimensional optimization, nonlinear programming, algebraic modeling

1. Introduction

Nonlinear infinite-dimensional optimization (InfiniteOpt) problems appear in various application areas which include optimal control, stochastic optimization, and partial differential equation (PDE)-constrained optimization (Pulsipher et al., 2022). The infinite-dimensional nature of these problems typically mandates the use of discretization schemes (e.g., orthogonal collocation over finite elements) to solve these problems by numerical means (Biegler, 2010). Relying on a manual approach, given the intricate nature of the discretization procedures, is susceptible to errors and often falls short of employing the most effective discretization strategies (Nicholson et. al., 2018). Hence, modeling environments such as pyomo.dae (Nicholson et al., 2018), InfiniteOpt.jl (Pulsipher et al., 2022), and GEKKO (Beal et al., 2018) enable the use of sophisticated discretization schemes for a variety of InfiniteOpt problem types. Building on the popular algebraic modeling language JuMP.jl, InfiniteOpt.jl is uniquely able to model InfiniteOpt formulations with both stochastic modeling elements (e.g., risk measures) and differential & algebraic equations (DAEs).

The discretized formulations produced by these frameworks are often cast as large-scale nonlinear programs, potentially involving millions of variables which can surpass the capabilities of existing algorithms and software tools. Discretized InfiniteOpt problems typically exhibit a highly recurrent structure which is not exploited by most existing modeling environments. For example, a reaction kinetics equality constraint can be enforced over thousands of random scenarios (Chen et al., 2016). Leveraging this inherent structure has great potential to enable efficient (parallelizable) solution routines for discretized InfiniteOpt problems. For instance, exploiting the recurrent structure can significantly reduce the computational burden of expensive automatic-differentiation (AD) routines on complicated nonlinear expressions.

Shin et al. (2023) present a single-instruction, multiple-data (SIMD) abstraction for nonlinear programs (NLPs) which is implemented in the open-source Julia package ExaModels.jl. Contrary to general purpose algebraic modeling languages like JuMP.jl (Lubin et al., 2023), Pyomo (Hart et al., 2017), and Gravity (Hijazi et al., 2018) which do not save repeated structure, ExaModels.jl preserves the parallelizable structure in the model, and in turn, exploits that structure for more efficient computations on multi-threaded CPUs or GPU accelerators. Shin et al. (2023) demonstrate how ExaModels.jl leverages the repeated structure in large-scale AC optimal power flow (ACOPF) problems to speed up AD by 1 to 2 orders-of-magnitude relative to JuMP.jl. Moreover, Shin et al. (2023) obtain an order-of-magnitude speed on the overall solution time for ACOPF problems solved on GPUs using ExaModels.jl and MadNLP.jl in contrast to state-of-the-art CPU solvers. The utility of these modeling/solution approaches has not yet been investigated on discretized InfiniteOpt problems.

Thus, we present InfiniteExaModels.jl as a new backend for InfiniteOpt.jl to automatically discretize InfiniteOpt problems into the SIMD-NLP representation used by ExaModels.jl. This backend facilitates an intuitive modeling environment for InfiniteOpt problems that gives ExaModels.jl direct access to the repeated structures exhibited by discretized InfiniteOpt models which enable highly efficient AD routines that are parallelizable. This framework is general and can significantly accelerate derivative evaluations on nonlinear InfiniteOpt models across an array of applications.

This paper is structured as follows. Sections 2 discusses the modeling/solution abstractions behind InfiniteOpt.jl and ExaModels.jl. Section 3 describes the InfiniteExaModels.jl interface. Section 4 demonstrates the capabilities of the proposed framework on two real-world case studies. Finally, Section 5 summaries key findings and outlines plans for future work.

2. Modeling Abstractions

This section reviews key aspects of InfiniteOpt.jl and ExaModels.jl and their underlying modeling abstractions. We refer the reader to (Pulsipher et al., 2022) and (Shin et al., 2023) for more comprehensive discussions.

2.1. InfiniteOpt Modeling Abstraction

InfiniteOpt problems involve infinite parameters $d \in \mathcal{D} \subseteq \mathbb{R}^{n_d}$ that index infinite decision variables $y: \mathcal{D} \mapsto \mathcal{Y} \subseteq \mathbb{R}^{n_y}$ where $\mathcal{D}$ is often a continuous domain. Examples include time $t \in \mathcal{D}_t = [t_0, t_f]$ and uncertainty $\xi \in \mathcal{D}_\xi$ where ξ is randomly distributed. With these we define a general InfiniteOpt formulation with the core abstraction elements:

$$
\begin{aligned}
min \quad & M_d h(Dy(d), y(d), z, d) \\
s.t. \quad & g(Dy(d), y(d), z, d) \leq 0, \quad d \in \mathcal{D}
\end{aligned}
\tag{1}
$$

where $h(\cdot)$ is the objective function, $g(\cdot)$ are the constraint functions, $M_d: \mathcal{Y} \mapsto \mathbb{R}^{n_y}$ is a measure operator which summarize infinite variables $y(d) \in \mathcal{Y}$ over the function space $\mathcal{Y}$, $D: \mathcal{Y} \mapsto \mathcal{Y}$ are differential operators that capture the rate of change of infinite variables, and $z \in \mathcal{Z} \subseteq \mathbb{R}^{n_z}$ are finite variables. This captures many formulations in stochastic, dynamic, and PDE-constrained optimization.

Transformations are applied to Problem (1) to obtain a formulation that is compatible with standard optimization solvers (e.g., Ipopt). Direct transcription is a common transformation method where the InfiniteOpt problem is projected onto a set of discretization points $\widehat{\mathcal{D}} := \{\hat{d}: k \in \mathcal{K}\}$. Typically, this leads to the discretized formulation:

$$
\begin{aligned}
min \quad & \sum_{k \in \mathcal{K}} \alpha_k h(Dy_k, y_k, z, \hat{d}_k) \\
s.t. \quad & g(Dy_k, y_k, z, \hat{d}_k) \leq 0, \quad k \in \mathcal{K} \\
& q(Dy_k, y_k, \hat{d}_k) = 0, \quad k \in \mathcal{K}
\end{aligned}
\tag{2}
$$

where α_k are coefficients used to approximate the measure operator M_d and the equality constraints $q(\cdot) = 0$ employ a numerical scheme (e.g., orthogonal collocation over finite elements) to approximate the differentiated variables Dy which are treated as auxiliary variables. Note that different choices of discretization scheme and measures can lead to more complex formulations, but these are omitted for concision in presentation. The key observation for this work is that the objective and constraints inherently exhibit a repeated structure over the discretization index k.

InfiniteOpt.jl is an open-source Julia package that builds upon the modeling capabilities of JuMP.jl to intuitively model InfiniteOpt problems. This modeling environment centers around the InfiniteModel object which stores InfiniteOpt problems using the unifying abstraction discussed in the current section. To enable arbitrary solution approaches for InfiniteModels, InfiniteOpt.jl provides an extendible backend interface which automates the creation and mapping of underlying models that can be optimized (referred to as OptimizerModels) to provide a seamless experience for users. By default, InfiniteOpt.jl employs the TranscriptionOpt backend which uses a suite of direct transcription methods to transform an InfiniteModel into a JuMP.jl model which can be solved using the large collection of solvers supported by JuMP.jl (Lubin et al., 2023). Although this approach handles diverse model structures, one drawback is that JuMP.jl models are unable to leverage the repeated structure inherent in direct transcription formulations to boost computational performance. This motivates the development of InfiniteExaModels.jl as an alternative backend for solving InfiniteModels via direct transcription as discussed in

Section 3. To learn more about InfiniteOpt.jl, detailed documentation, tutorials, and examples are available at https://infiniteopt.github.io/InfiniteOpt.jl/stable/.

2.2. SIMD Modeling Abstraction for Nonlinear Programs

The SIMD-NLP modeling abstraction captures such repetitive patterns and facilitates the development of algorithms that exploit these patterns. The repetitive pattern in this abstraction allows for the evaluation of the model and derivative equations with SIMD parallelism. The general SIMD-NLP problem formulation is:

$$\min_{\underline{z} \leq z \leq \overline{z}} \sum_{l \in \mathcal{L}} \sum_{i \in \mathcal{I}_l} h_l(z; p_{i,l})$$

$$s.t. \quad g_m(z; q_k) + \sum_{n \in \mathcal{N}_m} \sum_{j \in \mathcal{I}_n} f_n(z; s_{j,n}) = 0, \quad m \in \mathcal{M}, k \in \mathcal{K}_m \tag{3}$$

where $z \in [\underline{z}, \overline{z}]$ are decision variables, $h_l(\cdot), g_m(\cdot), f_n(\cdot)$ represent the repetitive patterns constituting the objective and constraint functions, and p, q, s are data parameters. We note that only the data parameters change with each repetition indexed over i, k, j, meaning the algebraic structure in $h_l(\cdot), g_m(\cdot), f_n(\cdot)$ remains constant.

ExaModels.jl implements an algebraic modeling interface to construct SIMD-NLP models where the user specifies the optimization model equations via an iterator, which allows us to capture the repetitive patterns in the model equations and make them available to the AD backend. This enables us to construct derivative evaluation kernels for each computational pattern using a symbolic expression tree and reverse-mode AD. These kernels are compiled and executed over multiple data to numerically evaluate the derivative. This strategy facilitates parallelized sparse AD on GPUs (Shin et al., 2023), providing a remarkable speedup. However, even with serial execution on CPUs, the tailored derivative kernels provide more efficient derivative evaluations relative to conventional AD tools, as we demonstrate in Section 4.

3. InfiniteExaModels.jl

The repeated discretized structure of InfiniteOpt problems can be translated directly into the SIMD-NLP formulation behind ExaModels.jl shown in Problem (3). This is accomplished by appending all the discretized infinite variables Dy_k, y_k onto the finite variables z, transforming the inequality constraints into equalities via slack variables to obtain $g_m(\cdot)$, refactoring $\alpha_k h(\cdot)$ to obtain $h_l(\cdot)$, and setting $f_n(\cdot) = 0$. Inspired by this observation, InfiniteExaModels.jl is a new backend for InfiniteOpt.jl to convert nonlinear InfiniteModels into ExaModels using the same direct transcription methods supported by TranscriptionOpt. Principally it performs this conversion using the exa_model method which creates an ExaModel along with all the mappings between the model objects such that the optimal values can be queried once the ExaModel has been solved using a solver supported by NLPModels.jl. One current limitation of InfiniteExaModels.jl is the use of metaprogramming to generate generators for ExaModels.jl which induces additional compilation when first calling the AD kernels. However, this will soon be remedied by directly constructing the symbolic expression trees used by ExaModels. We refer the reader to https://github.com/infiniteopt/InfiniteExaModels.jl to learn more.

Table 1. Numerical results for quadrotor optimal control

ndisc	nvar	ncon	ExaModels		JuMP		AMPL	
			deriv. time	total time	deriv. time	total time	deriv. time	total time
2.0k	36.0k	36.0k	0.02	0.25	0.24	0.48	0.14	0.4
4.0k	72.0k	72.0k	0.04	0.55	0.48	1.01	0.33	0.88
8.0k	144.0k	144.0k	0.16	1.35	1.04	2.24	0.71	1.99
16.0k	288.0k	288.0k	0.2	2.94	1.97	4.7	1.48	4.39

Table 2. Numerical results for stochastic optimal power flow

nscen	nvar	ncon	ExaModels		JuMP		AMPL	
			deriv. time	total time	deriv. time	total time	deriv. time	total time
2.0k	68.0k	68.0k	0.2	1.8	1.91	3.53	0.87	2.38
4.0k	136.0k	136.0k	0.7	5.78	4.98	10.13	2.06	6.81
8.0k	272.0k	272.0k	1.08	17.84	10.45	27.08	4.51	19.93
16.0k	544.0k	544.0k	2.19	59.7	28.82	86.63	8.7	60.42

4. Cases Studies

In this section, we demonstrate the capabilities of InfiniteExaModels.jl with two examples: quadrotor optimal control and stochastic optimal power flow. We formulate each problem using InfiniteOpt.jl and solve the underlying discretized model with three different AD backends: JuMP.jl (i.e., MathOptInterface.Nonlinear.ReverseAD), AMPL (via AmplNLWriter.jl), and ExaModels.jl (via InfiniteExaModels.jl). Each is solved using Ipopt and we compare each AD backend based on the derivative evaluation times. The same solution is obtained for all different modeling tools. The source code and implementation details to reproduce the numerical results are available at https://github.com/infiniteopt/InfiniteExaModels.jl/tree/main/examples. All case studies were run on a server computer with two Intel(R) Xeon(R) Gold 6140 CPUs.

4.1. Quadrotor Optimal Control

We consider the quadrotor optimal control problem presented by Hehn and D'Andrea (2011) and use a sinusoidal setpoint trajectory. We formulate the optimal control problems with a 60 second time horizon and discretize it using a varied number of uniformly spaced discretization points (ndisc). The numerical results are shown in Table 1 and show that the InfiniteExaModels.jl backend consistently outperforms the other conventional backends. On average, AD on ExaModels.jl is 8.7 times faster than JuMP.jl, and 5.6 times faster than AMPL. This substantially improves the solution time since the AD comprises nearly half of solution time using JuMP.jl.

4.2. Stochastic AC Optimal Power Flow

We model a two-stage stochastic AC optimal power flow (ACOPF) problem based on the formulation presented in Coffrin et. al., (2018) augmented with multivariate Gaussian bus loads. We use the pglib_opf_case3_lmbd test case from the pglib-opf library

(Babaeinejadsarookolaee et. al., 2019) and vary the number of scenarios (nscen) used to discretize the model. The numerical results are shown in Table 2 and again the InfiniteExaModels.jl backend is the most performant. On average, the ExaModels.jl AD is 11.5 times faster than JuMP.jl, and 4.4 times faster than AMPL.

5. Conclusions and Future Outlook

We introduced InfiniteExaModels.jl as an effective tool to efficiently solve nonlinear InfiniteOpt problems. It bridges the intuitive modeling environment provided by InfiniteOpt.jl with the efficient SIMD-NLP modeling abstraction behind ExaModels.jl to accelerate AD performance by exploiting the repetitive structures inherent in discretized InfiniteOpt problems. With serial CPU computations, our numerical experiments in optimal control and stochastic ACOPF demonstrate approximately an order-of-magnitude reduction in NLP derivative evaluation times relative to state-of-the-art tools (i.e, JuMP.jl, AMPL). The SIMD-NLP abstraction also enables GPU acceleration within the solution routines which has potential to further accelerate solution times. In future work, we will investigate how InfiniteExaModels.jl performs using GPU-based AD evaluations in combination with the GPU interior-point solver available with MadNLP.jl.

References

S. Babaeinejadsarookolaee, A. Birchfield, R. D. Christie, C. Coffrin, C. DeMarco, R. Diao, M. Ferris et al., 2019, The power grid library for benchmarking ac optimal power flow algorithms, arXiv preprint arXiv:1908.02788

L. D. Beal, D. C. Hill, R. A. Martin, J. D. Hedengren, 2018, Gekko optimization suite, Processes 6 (8), 106

L. T. Biegler, 2010, Nonlinear programming: concepts, algorithms, and applications to chemical processes, SIAM, Philadelphia, USA

W. Chen, L. T. Biegler, S. G. Muñoz, 2016, An approach for simultaneous estimation of reaction kinetics and curve resolution from process and spectral data, Journal of Chemometrics 30 (9), 506–522

C. Coffrin, R. Bent, K. Sundar, Y. Ng, M. Lubin, 2018, Powermodels. jl: An open-source framework for exploring power flow formulations, In 2018 Power Systems Computation Conference (PSCC), pp. 1-8. IEEE, Dublin, Ireland

W. E. Hart, C. D. Laird, J.-P. Watson, D. L. Woodruff, G. A. Hackebeil, B. L. Nicholson, J. D. Siirola, et al., 2017, Pyomo-optimization modeling in python, Vol. 67, Springer

M. Hehn and R. D'Andrea, 2011, Quadrocopter trajectory generation and control, IFAC proceedings Volumes 44, no. 1: 1485-1491

H. Hijazi, G. Wang, C. Coffrin, 2018, Gravity: A mathematical modeling language for optimization and machine learning, NIPS 2018 Workshop MLOSS, Montreal, Canada

M. Lubin, O. Dowson, J. D. Garcia, J. Huchette, B. Legat, J. P. Vielma, 2023, Jump 1.0: recent improvements to a modeling language for mathematical optimization, Mathematical Programming Computation, 1–9

B. Nicholson, J. D. Siirola, J.-P. Watson, V. M. Zavala, L. T. Biegler, 2018, pyomo. dae: A modeling and automatic discretization framework for optimization with differential and algebraic equations, Mathematical Programming Computation 10, 187–223

J. L. Pulsipher, W. Zhang, T. J. Hongisto, V. M. Zavala, 2022, A unifying modeling abstraction for infinite-dimensional optimization, Computers & Chemical Engineering 156, 107567

S. Shin, F. Pacaud, M. Anitescu, 2023, Accelerating optimal power flow with gpus: Simd abstraction of nonlinear programs and condensed-space interior-point methods, arXiv preprint arXiv:2307.16830

Flavio Manenti, Gintaras V. Reklaitis (Eds.), Proceedings of the 34th European Symposium on Computer Aided Process Engineering / 15th International Symposium on Process Systems Engineering (ESCAPE34/PSE24), June 2-6, 2024, Florence, Italy

Bayesian Optimization Priors for Efficient Variational Quantum Algorithms

Farshud Sorourifar,[a,b,c] Diana Chamaki,[b,c] Norm M. Tubman,[b] Joel Paulson,[a] David E. Bernal Neira[b,c,d]

[a] *Department of Chemical and Biomolecular Engineering, The Ohio State University, Columbus, OH, USA*
[b] *Quantum Artificial Intelligence Laboratory (QuAIL), NASA Ames Research Center, Moffett Field, CA, USA*
[c] *USRA Research Institute for Advanced Computer Science, Mountain View, CA, USA*
[d] *Davidson School of Chemical Engineering, Purdue University, West Lafayette, IN, USA*
dbernaln@purdue.edu

Abstract

Quantum computing (QC) currently relies on hybrid quantum-classical methods known as Variational Quantum Algorithms (VQAs) to solve problems. Still, there are several challenges with VQAs on the classical computing side: they correspond to non-convex black-box optimization problems, the observations from quantum hardware are noisy, and quantum computing time is expensive. The first point is inherent to the problem structure, requiring the classical part of VQAs to be solved using global optimization strategies. However, there is a trade-off between cost and accuracy. QC returns a set of bitstrings, each referred to as a shot. The probabilistic nature of quantum computing demands many shots to measure its state accurately. Since QC time is charged per shot, reducing their number yields cheaper and less accurate observations. Recently, there has been an increasing interest in using Bayesian optimization (BO) methods to globally optimize quantum circuit parameters. This work proposes two modifications to the BO framework to provide a shot-efficient optimization strategy for VQAs. Specifically, we provide the means to place a prior on the periodicity of the rotation angles and a framework to set a topological prior using few-shot observations. We demonstrate the effectiveness of our proposed approach through an ablation study, showing that using both proposed features statistically outperforms a standard BO implementation within VQAs for computational chemistry simulations.

Keywords: Quantum computing, Bayesian optimization, Variational quantum algorithms

1. Introduction

Quantum computing (QC) has been the subject of growing interest in chemical engineering, owing to its potential to solve computationally challenging problems (Bernal et al., 2022). However, as a nascent technology, it has a limited number of processing units (qubits), and its quantum state rapidly decoheres. To circumvent current devices quick decoherence and a limited number of qubits, Variational Quantum Algorithms (VQAs) have been proposed, wherein a classical machine selects parameters for a quantum circuit representing a problem of interest, and a quantum machine evaluates it (Cerezo et al., 2020). This circuit encodes the evolution of prepared qubits through a series of parameterized operators or gates. The final qubit system state should follow a distribution representing the solution to a computational problem. Physically, the quantum gate parameters represent rotation angles, which modify the quantum state of the qubits system. The final states of the qubits are then measured by projecting them into a set of classical bits (bitstrings), with each bitstring measurement referred to as a shot. Thus, VQAs entail a feedback loop where a classical optimization algorithm selects the parameters for the quantum circuit based on a measure of the bitstrings.

Bayesian Optimization (BO) is a family of sample-efficient zeroth-order optimizers and has successfully solved various black-box problems, including VQAs. BO's sample efficiency results from using observations to construct a statistical surrogate model known as a Gaussian Process (GP), which generalizes a multivariate normal distribution to function space (i.e., a probability distribution over functions that fit the data). The GP's ability to quantify the model uncertainty allows us to systematically trade off exploring the parameter space and exploiting promising regions. BO has been gaining increased research interest for solving VQAs, spanning introductions to BO for VQAs (Tibaldi et al., 2023), benchmarking (Ciavarella and Chernyshev, 2022), and initialization strategies (Muller et al., 2022; Tamiya and Yamasaki, 2022). There is evidence that standard BO algorithms may benefit from lower-shot queries (Iannelli and Jansen, 2021).

This work provides background on BO algorithms and proposes two principled modifications to the vanilla BO algorithm (i.e., a standard GP built from a Matérn kernel with a zero-mean prior) to improve its efficiency in solving VQAs. Specifically, we propose encoding the parameter's 2π periodicity into the GP kernel function and a strategy for encoding a sample-based topological prior learned by fitting a second GP to low-shot measurements. Through an ablation study, we show that these modifications can significantly improve BO performance on VQAs.

2. Bayesian Optimization Preliminaries

First, let $J(\theta)$ be the true quantum circuit value evaluated at a given vector of rotation angles θ. When we query the circuit, we generate a noisy observation,

$$y(\theta, s) = J(\theta) + \epsilon(s), \tag{1}$$

where $\epsilon(s) \sim \mathcal{N}(0, \sigma^2(s))$, is an independent and identically distributed Gaussian noise whose variance is given by the number of observations (shots) s of the circuit. We let $\epsilon = \epsilon(\bar{s})$ be the noise evaluated at the largest number of shots $\bar{s}$ used to observe the circuit. BO starts with an initial data set $\mathcal{D}_0 = \{\theta_i, y_i\}_{i=1}^{J}$ consisting of J initial observations, which can be used to build a statistical surrogate model. The model choice in this framework is general, only requiring that the model is statistical, as it can quantify epistemic uncertainty in terms of a covariance function. This function, coupled with the model's mean, is used to guide the sample points selection that balances exploration with exploitation through constructing and optimizing an acquisition function. Typically, this is done in-between observations and can be cheaply optimized using gradient methods. While many statistical models exist, the GPs are the most common choice due to their rigorous statistical quantification and non-parametric nature.

We assume that the circuit has a GP prior to the form $f(\theta) \sim \mathcal{GP}(\mu_0, k)$ where $\mu_0 : \theta \rightarrow \mathbb{R}$ is the prior mean, and $k : \theta \times \theta \rightarrow \mathbb{R}$ is the prior covariance function. There are many possible choices for the covariance function. Here, we define the Matérn kernel function,

$$k_v(\theta_i, \theta_j) = (d(\theta_i, \theta_j) \sqrt{2v}/\ell)^v K_v(d(\theta_i, \theta_j) \sqrt{2v}/\ell) \sigma_f^2/(\Gamma(v)2^{v-1}), \tag{2}$$

where ℓ is a length-scale parameter, σ_f^2 is the measurement noise variance, $\Gamma(v), K_v$ are the modified Bessel and gamma functions, and $d(\cdot)$ is a Euclidean distance function. The choice of v is based on how smooth the function is believed to be, where larger values indicate a smoother function. Under the GP prior, the n function evaluations $\boldsymbol{y}_{1:n}$ are jointly Gaussian with mean $[m]_i = \mu_0(\theta_i)$, covariance $[K]_{i,j} = k(\theta_i, \theta_j)$, and $[k(\theta)]_i = k(\theta, \theta_i)$. This implies the corresponding function value $f(\theta)$ at any test point $\theta_{1:n}$ must be jointly Gaussian with $\boldsymbol{y}_{1:n}$. Due to the properties of jointly Gaussian random variables, we find that the posterior distribution of the objective given all available noisy observations $p(f(\theta)|y_{1:n}, \theta_{1:n}, \theta)$, is Gaussian with the following mean and covariance,

$$\mu_n(\theta) = \mu_0(\theta) + \boldsymbol{k}(\theta)^\top (K + \sigma^{2I_n})(\boldsymbol{y}_{1:n}^f - \boldsymbol{m}), \tag{3a}$$

$$\sigma_n^2(\theta) = k(\theta, \theta) - \boldsymbol{k}(\theta)^\top (K + \sigma^2 I_n)^{-1}\boldsymbol{k}(\theta). \tag{3b}$$

With the mean and variance functions defined, we introduce the acquisition function. We can select a point θ that provides the most information by optimizing the acquisition function. For example, the lower confidence bound acquisition function,

$$\alpha_{LCB}(\theta) = \mu(\theta) - \sqrt{\beta}\sigma(\theta), \tag{4}$$

balances exploration and exploitation by assigning an optimistic value to each candidate point. The exploitation term is represented by the mean, and the exploration term by the standard deviation scaled by a parameter $\sqrt{\beta}$. Small values of β result in an exploitative strategy, and large values in a more exploratory strategy.

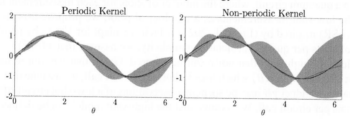

Figure 1: Periodic (left) vs. non-periodic (right) BO kernel on a periodic function. The periodic kernel has noticeably higher accuracy for $\theta > 5$ by recognizing the parameter space periodicity.

3. Specialized Quantum Computing Priors

3.1 Periodic Parameter Prior

While BO requires box constraints on the parameters, the periodic boundary conditions are not typically known or enforced. We can, however, use periodic kernels to codify the periodicity of the circuit measurements and uncertainty in the GP model using a periodic kernel (MacKay, 1998). The periodic kernel can be defined as

$$k_{Periodic}(\theta, \theta') = \sigma_f^2 \exp\left(-2\sum_i^{n_\theta} \sin^2\big((\theta_i - \theta_i')\,\pi/p\big)/\ell_i\right) \tag{5}$$

where p is the period, and ℓ_i is the length scale corresponding to the ith parameter. Typically, p is an unknown parameter fitted to data as most problems have no known periodicity. Given that $p = 2\pi$ for VQAs, this parameter is fixed during the model fitting. In Fig. 1, we provide an example of how knowledge of the periodic boundaries improves the surrogate model accuracy. The true function is represented as a black line, the data as red stars, and the mean and 95% CI as a blue line and clouds. Note the region $\theta \in [4.7, 2\pi]$, where uncertainty is substantially lower for the periodic kernel due to a measurement near $\theta = 0.2$. The non-periodic GP recommends the following sample near $\theta = 2\pi$, exploring the high uncertainty region, thus wasting samples.

3.2 Topological Prior

Although reducing the measured distribution of bitstrings to a single value, such as by taking the mean or conditional value at risk, allows traditional optimization strategies to be easily adapted to solve VQAs, they also result in a loss of information.

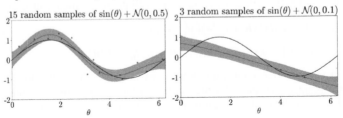

Figure 2: Effect of cheap and noisy (left) vs. expensive and precise data (right). Notice how samples with ×5 noise for ×1/5 cost may be more valuable than fewer, more accurate samples.

Consider Fig. 2, where a larger volume (five times more data points) of noisier data (with five times the standard deviation of additive noise) may still result in a better surrogate model than fitting to a smaller, although more precise, dataset. This example can be likened to a quantum circuit, where the number of shots for each measurement is tunable. To use the low-shot measurements as a topological prior, we propose using a low-shot residual (LSR) inspired by (Lu et al., 2021), which we adapt for VQAs by regulating the number of shots per query. For notation simplicity, we assume that $y(\theta, \bar{s}) = J(\theta)$, i.e., $\bar{s}$ is sufficiently high such that noise can be ignored. Given that we aim to minimize a high-shot circuit output $J(\theta)$ which uses $\bar{s}$ shots per circuit call, we assume that a fraction of the total shot budget γB may be spent on observations of a low-shot circuit $g(\theta)$, which uses $\underline{s}$ shots per circuit call. We assume that the high-shot model can be defined as

$$J(\theta) = g(\theta) + \epsilon(\theta), \tag{6}$$

where function $\epsilon(\theta)$ is a residual between the high and low-shot observations for a given θ. However, this assumption must be satisfied by construction. Let $\mathcal{D}_0 = \{\theta_i, g_i\}^m$ be the set of m low-shot observations obtained from spending γB uniformly over θ, and $\mu_g(\theta), \sigma_g(\theta)$ be the mean and variance functions obtained from fitting a GP to $\mathcal{D}_0$. With the low-shot budget exhausted, $\mu_g(\theta)$ becomes a deterministic function that approximates $g(\theta)$, the topological prior used to improve learning $J(\theta)$. With each measurement k, we construct a data set $\mathcal{D}_k = \{\theta_i, J_i - \mu_g(\theta_i)\}_{m+1}^k$ to build a mean and variance function of the residual $\mu_\epsilon(\theta), \sigma_\epsilon(\theta)$, while satisfying Eq. (6). Eq. (3a) becomes

$$\mu_J(\theta) = \mu_g(\theta) + \mu_\epsilon(\theta), \tag{7}$$

and can optimize the circuit by minimizing $\mu_J(\theta)$. Since the low-shot model can no longer reduce its variance, it serves no value in informing the exploration of the parameter space. Instead, we can formulate the Eq. (4) acquisition function as

$$\alpha_{LCB,LSR}(\theta) = (\mu_g(\theta) + \mu_\epsilon(\theta)) - \sqrt{\beta}\sigma_\epsilon(\theta), \tag{8}$$

where we use the mean function in Eq. (7) but only use the residual standard deviation σ_ϵ for exploration. Note that the low-shot residual acquisition needs a larger exploration constant β, given that the residual magnitudes are significantly smaller than the means.

4. Experimental Results

In Fig. 3.a, we compare the periodic kernel (yellow lines) versus a Matérn kernel (blue lines) using statistical convergence on a VQA simulation to find molecular hydrogen's ground state using as number of shots per evaluation $\bar{s} = 10000$, and $B = 100\bar{s}$ as total budget. Additionally, we vary the fraction of the total shot budget for initialization $\gamma = \{0.1, 0.4, 0.8, 1.0\}$, spent on random samples over the parameter space. Note that $\gamma = 1.0$ is a random sampling strategy (red line) with the worst performance, whereas smaller values of γ improve convergence for the periodic kernel. For the Matérn kernel, the trend isn't as apparent; convergence is faster with $\gamma = 0.4$ (blue-dashed line) than $\gamma = 0.1$ (blue-dotted line). Note that with a larger random sampling budget, the performance difference between the kernels diminishes since the highly explorative random sampling reduces the need for further exploration and, thus, the benefits derived from the periodic kernel. Finally, large γ allows the BO algorithms to focus on exploitation, evident by the faster convergence when switching from random to Bayesian sampling strategies.

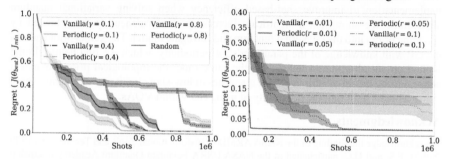

Figure 3: (left) Comparison of Matérn versus periodic kernel-based GPs in BO for multiple γ, (right) comparison of LSR-BO using a Matérn and periodic kernels for different ratios of r

We present the results of the LSR-BO strategy in Fig. 3.b, where for the ratio of shots between the high and low shot circuits, we use $r = \underline{s}/\bar{s} \in \{0.01, 0.05, 0.1\}$, with $\bar{s} = 10000$. These results show a clear trend favoring residual models constructed from very few shots. In contrast, with small r values, the algorithm finds near-optimal parameters on the high-shot circuit within the first few queries. However, larger r values may diminish performance, as seen in the $r = 0.1$ case with a vanilla kernel. While the results suggest that smaller r could further improve performance, it would result in numerical issues. As shown in Eq. (3b), the GP fitting requires a matrix inversion, which results in cubic scaling and increased risk of singularity as the number of data points grows.

The ablation study in Fig. 4 compares the base strategy to one with a periodic kernel and two LSR strategies using Matérn and periodic kernels. The vanilla strategies can be considered a case of the LSR where $r = 1$. The vanilla periodic kernel (yellow) provides a clear advantage over the vanilla Matérn kernel (blue), and both LSR strategies provide an advantage over the vanilla strategies. Although the difference between the two kernels in the LSR is slight, the periodic kernel shows slightly lower regret and variance.

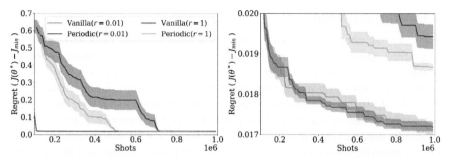

Figure 4: Full ablation study results. The periodic kernel and the LSR independently improve the BO performance relative to a Vanilla strategy. (right) Zoomed-in regret performance.

5. Conclusions

This work proposes two modifications to the standard Bayesian optimization implementation to improve shot-based efficiency when solving variational quantum algorithms. We show that a significant increase in performance can be achieved by encoding priors into the GP kernel function and surrogate model. The kernel prior endows the GP with knowledge of the parameter's 2π periodicity, which we find helpful in the limited circuit observation regime. At the same time, the topological prior provides a better starting model by utilizing large quantities of low-shot circuit measurements. These improvements highlight the possibility of using BO within VQAs.

Acknowledgments

We acknowledge the funding of the NASA ARMD Transformational Tools and Technology (TTT) Project. F.S. and D.C. participated in the NASA/USRA Feynman Quantum Academy internship program. D.B.N., F.S., and D.C. were supported by the NASA Academic Mission Services, Contract No. NNA16BD14C. The NSF Graduate Research Fellowship partially supported F.S.. J.P. acknowledges funding from the National Science Foundation, Award No. 2237616.

References

D. E. Bernal, A. Ajagekar, S. M. Harwood, S. T. Stober, D. Trenev, F. You, 2022. Perspectives of quantum computing for chemical engineering. AIChE Journal 68 (6), e17651.

M. Cerezo, A. Arrasmith, R. Babbush, S. C. Benjamin, S. Endo, K. Fujii, J. R. McClean, K. Mitarai, X. Yuan, L. Cincio, P. J. Coles, 2020. Variational quantum algorithms. Nature Reviews Physics 3, 625–644

A. N. Ciavarella, I. A. Chernyshev, Apr 2022. Preparation of the SU(3) lattice Yang-Mills vacuum with variational quantum methods. Phys. Rev. D 105, 074504.

G. Iannelli, K. Jansen, 2021. Noisy Bayesian optimization for variational quantum eigensolvers.

Q. Lu, L. D. Gonz´alez, R. Kumar, V. M. Zavala, 2021. Bayesian optimization with reference models: A case study in MPC for HVAC central plants. Computers & Chemical Engineering 154, 107491.

D. J. C. MacKay, 1998. Introduction to Gaussian processes.

J. Muller, W. Lavrijsen, C. Iancu, W. de Jong, sep 2022. Accelerating Noisy VQE Optimization with Gaussian Processes. In: 2022 IEEE International Conference on Quantum Computing and Engineering (QCE). IEEE Computer Society, Los Alamitos, CA, USA, pp. 215–225

S. Tamiya, H. Yamasaki, Jul 2022. Stochastic gradient line Bayesian optimization for efficient noise-robust optimization of parameterized quantum circuits. npj Quantum Information 8 (1), 90

S. Tibaldi, D. Vodola, E. Tignone, E. Ercolessi, 2023. Bayesian Optimization for QAOA

Flavio Manenti, Gintaras V. Reklaitis (Eds.), Proceedings of the 34th European Symposium on Computer Aided Process Engineering / 15th International Symposium on Process Systems Engineering (ESCAPE34/PSE24), June 2-6, 2024, Florence, Italy

Numerical simulation and experimental validation of a wind turbine using Generative Design

Martin Grardel [a], Cabrel Kengne Tokam [a], Maxime Denis [a], Olivier Bain [a], Arnaud Dujany [a*]

[a] U2R 7511, Basins-Reservoirs-Resources (B2R), GéoLab, UniLaSalle - University of Picardie Jules Verne, Beauvais, France

*Arnaud.dujany@unilasalle.fr

Abstract

With an energy demand in continuous growth over the last decade and new climate change stakes, ways to create more power has been studied. Offshore winds turbine which creates energy out of the wind was thus studied. Many studies have been led about the optimization stake that wind turbine are facing as actually, more than half of the wind power is lost when exploited by a classic horizontal wind turbine (HAWT). A particular new technology is now used in industry and can be applied to this problematic: Generative Design. It refers to all the numerical conception methods that automatically perform a design exploration with constraints defined by the user. To evaluate the relevance of this new conception methods on this subject, it was decided to create two prototypes of blades using two Generative Design applications of *CATIA*, a computer aided design (CAD) software. The first application (called *XGenerative Design*) has permitted to create a simple blade design only by using 3D parametric modelling, which make the process easier than creating it with actual means, those requiring precision and time. The second application (called *Parametric Design Study*) has permitted to ameliorate this previous blade design by implementing parametric ameliorations, a method of topology optimization. Two blades were tested: the blade created on *XGenerative Design* and a second similar blade model, but this time optimized with topology optimization. The blades were assembled on two separate classic wind turbine models and were evaluated in the fluid dynamic simulation software *XFlow* under an equivalent wind. The results proved that the optimized model with parametric ameliorations has a slightly better rotation speed than the non-optimized one. However, as these technologies are very recent, it wasn't possible to fully ameliorate the initial design. It was planned to ameliorate it by using mechanical evaluations methods of the blades. It seems that this conception method still needs some improvement in the future, even if in some other domains, it has already proved his efficiency.

Keywords: Wind turbine, Generative Design, topology optimization, Lattice-Boltzmann method, rotation speed

1. Introduction

For several decades, a real desire to develop renewable energies was born in the world to slow down climate change. Wind is one of these renewable energies, which is inexhaustible and clean. In 2022, wind energy created 7,6% of the world's total electricity. In comparison, it produced less 2,4% of it 10 years earlier, in 2012, according to Ember Climate. Wind can be exploited by wind turbines located on land (onshore) or at sea (offshore). Offshore wind turbines are more developed in the industry as it provides a better general yield (it can reach 40% for an offshore model while the best yield of an onshore wind turbine is 25%). In cause, the wind is faster and steadier at sea due to the lack of obstacle (Li et al., 2020).

Wind turbines are subject to studies to improve their yield, as a big part of the wind force is lost during energy transformation by the motor. Most of these studies talked about blades. The possibility of using other industrial blades (Lachenal et al., 2013) or other composite materials (Thomas et Ramachandra, 2018) were studied, however, these studies didn't permit to considerably ameliorate the best industrial designs already existing. Also, a large part of studies concerned vertical axis wind turbine (VAWT) models which are cheaper but less effective than a classic horizontal turbine (HAWT) (Marzec et al., 2023; Akbari et al., 2022). Generally, the blades are modelized using a CAD (computer aided design) software and then tested numerically using algorithms such as the BEM (blade element momentum) (Bavanish et Thyagarajan, 2013). Once a correct model is obtained, the blade is constructed and tested under real conditions in a wind tunnel. Now, with progress in the domain of (CAD), some studies were conducted about blades of HAWT turbines using topology optimization (Zhu et al., 2021). This method is part of the Generative Design which corresponds to all the numerical conceptions methods that explore design automatically under user-defined constraints (Tyflopoulos et al., 2018). These methods are difficult to handle as it requires advanced knowledge in the industrial domain. The purpose of this study is to create a blade model, without considering a typical industrial blade conception, and then optimize it as much as possible to evaluate the impact of Generative Design on the base design. For this purpose, a blade is modelized and optimized in *CATIA* using Generative Design conception methods. Two models, one optimized and one not, are then tested into the numerical simulation software *XFlow* to study their rotation speed. The goal is to demonstrate the advantages of Generative Design on an industrial-based subject.

2. Environment

To evaluate the performance of the wind turbine created, it was decided to simulate the wind conditions near the city of Quend, Somme department, France. This area was chosen because it was once subject to a project of an offshore wind farm construction in 2010. At the time it was decided to abort this project as offshore wind farms weren't as developed as of today and thus didn't convince locals. Also, with the strong oceanic currents, the Atlantic coastline of the north of France presents very strong winds. In fact, there are already big wind farms in Le Tréport and Fécamp (still in construction) a few hundred kilometers away from Quend (Pezy et al., 2020). Relooking at this subject can bring a new look about this abandoned project.

3. Model conception

The wind turbine model was created on *CATIA*, a CAD software developed by Dassault Systems. This software is widely used in industry nowadays.

3.1. Blade construction using XGenerative Design

The first step is to create a blade model using the *XGenerative Design* application, integrated in the 3DExperience platform, a cloud linked to *CATIA*. It uses parametric representation to permit an easy modification of forms created (**Figure 1 (a)**). Ultimately, it can allow the creation of complex 3D models. It was decided to create a blade from scratch only using this application. The blade construction followed 4 steps : The first step was to create the outlines of the blade (**Figure 1 (b)**). For this, a typical blade section was implemented and duplicated as well as circular sections to create the base of the blade. The second step was to implement a deformation and rotation of theses outlines to create a spiral movement which will permit a faster rotation during simulations (**Figure 1 (c)**). The third step was to close the blade by creating a hull which link these shapes together (**Figure 1 (d)**). The last creation step consisted of the extraction of construction parameters using specific functions.

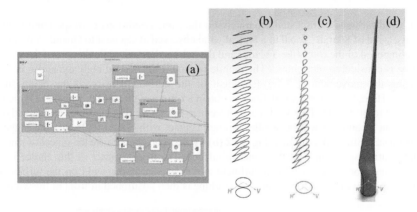

Figure 1 : Parametric representation of the first step (a), Visualization of the first step (b), second step (c) and third step (d) of creation of the blade

3.2. Blade optimization using Parametric Design Study

Parametric Design Study application was used to optimize the model previously created. This application uses two types of variables to ameliorate a 3D model: geometric variables and response variables. The first category corresponds to parameters that will be modified by the design exploration while response variables correspond to results parameters that will characterize the success of the study. These variables can correspond to lengths, areas, volumes, stresses, etc.

In this study, geometric variables are directly exported from *XGenerative Design* parameters. They correspond to the rotation angle and spacing between each blade section, the diameter and deformation ratio of the blade's tip and the total number of sections which defines the blade's height. With the response parameters, the objective of this study was to maximize the intrados area of the blade (the side that is facing the wind) while keeping a similar volume. At the end, two blades are obtained, one created with just *XGenerative Design* and the same one but optimized using the *Parametric Design Study* application.

3.3. Wind turbine assembly using Assembly Design

These two blades are assembled on the *Assembly Design* application. Blades are added to two prototypes of classic wind turbines composed of a hub, a nacelle and a tower. (**Figure 2 (a)**).

4. Numerical validation

To evaluate the efficiency of the two models created, the software *XFlow* was used. This computational fluid dynamics (CFD) software resolves the Lattice-Boltzmann method (LBM) to permit complex fluid simulations. The LBM method was preferred to the Navier Stokes method as it presents the best results for simple wind turbine models (Xu, 2016). For complex models, it may however not be the best solution (Schubiger et al., 2020).

Each wind turbines were tested separately on the same conditions corresponding to an average wind of 8 km.h^{-1} equal to a typical wind observed at sea next to Quend. A mobile part composed of the rotor (the 3 blades and the hub) is defined while the rest of the wind turbine is considered motionless. The mobile section follows rigid body dynamics laws, meaning the movement will be dependent of the defined density of the composite material. Here, the density was defined to obtain a rotor weight of 61 t, which is a typical industrial rotor weight. The wind mesh chosen for this study is categorized as adaptative refinement meaning it will be smaller through contact with blades (0.25 m^2) and bigger further away (8m^2 at maximum) (**Figure 2 (b)**). It was chosen because the object of study is the rotation speed and not the wind turbulence. The direct impact of this choice is a better simulation of the wind comportment as the impact of the wind on the turbine's rotation speed will be more realistic. The turbine is then positioned in front of the wind.

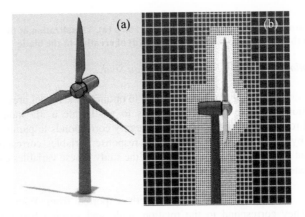

**Figure 2 : Assembly of the wind turbine with optimized
blades (a), mesh used in *XFlow* (b)**

5. Results

After simulations, the first model only created with *XGenerative Design* had a rotation speed of 12,71 deg.s^{-1} or 2,12 revolutions per minute while the second model had a rotation speed of 12,71 deg.s^{-1} or 2,16 revolutions per minute (**Figure 3**).

The two models presented similar final results. However, the optimized model with Parametric Design study has a slightly better rotation speed. Unfortunatly some elements of the *XGenerative Design* modelling couldn't be exported into *Parametric Design Study* which prevented a more realistic optimization. Moreover, *Mechanical Scenario Creation* application of *CATIA* was used to evaluate the resistance of the blades to different levels of stress, but excessive uncertainties prevented us from obtaining robust results.

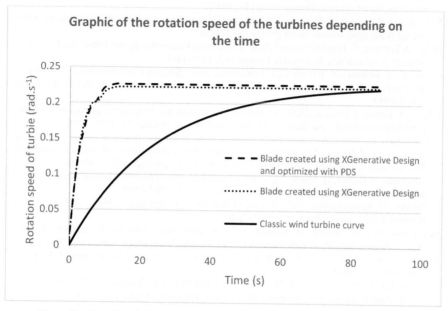

Figure 3 : Graphic of the rotation speed of the turbines depending on the time.

Conclusions

The Generative Design applications of *CATIA* allowed the creation of two simple blades. One of those was optimized using additional topology optimization methods. As it is recent technologies, it seems that the different applications have trouble communicating between each other meaning the results can still be ameliorated to obtained a more in-depth study. The *XGenerative Design* application has permitted a creation of a quick and easily modifiable wind turbine blade. It is a real advancement in industry as it accelerates and simplify the difficult conceptions steps of a piece. The conception method using Generative Design applications may be a revolution for future but still needs improvement. As already a big number of studies evocated that a significant amelioration of wind turbine may be compromised (Chehouri et al., 2015), this method enabled us to quickly and easily recover the optimization performed by industrial engineers on wind turbine blades. Moreover, Generative Design has already proven his efficiency in other industrial domains such as build information modelling (BIM) (Gan, 2022) or aerospace (Pilagatti et al., 2023).

References

V. Akbari, M. Naghashzadegan, R. Kouhikamali, F. Afsharpanah, W. Yaïci, 2022, Multi-Objective Optimization and Optimal Airfoil Blade Selection for a Small Horizontal-Axis Wind Turbine (HAWT) for Application in Regions with Various Wind Potential, Machines 10, 687

B. Bavanish, K. Thyagarajan , 2013, Optimization of power coefficient on a horizontal axis wind turbine using bem theory, Renewable and Sustainable Energy Reviews 26, 169-182

A. Chehouri, R. Younes, A. Ilinica, J. Perron, 2015, Review of performance optimization techniques applied to wind turbines, Applied Energy 142, 361-388

Ember Climate. (2023). Global Electricity Review 2023. https://ember-climate.org/insights/research/global-electricity-review-2023/

V.J.L. Gan, 2022, BIM-based graph data model for automatic generative design of modular buildings, Automation in Construction 134, 104062

X. Lachenal, S. Daynes, P. Weaver, 2013, Review of morphing concepts and materials for wind turbine blade applications, Wind energy 16, 283-307

H. Li , A.Teixeira, C. Guedes Soares, 2020, A two-stage Failure Mode and Effect Analysis of offshore wind turbines, Renewable Energy 162, 1438-1461

Ł. Marzec, Z. Buliński, T. Krysiński, J. Tumidajski, 2023, Structural optimisation of H-Rotor wind turbine blade based on one-way Fluid Structure Interaction approach, Renewable Energy 216, 118957

J. Pezy, A. Raoux, J. Dauvin, 2020, An ecosystem approach for studying the impact of offshore wind farms: a French case study, ICES Journal of Marine Science 77, 1238-1246

A.N. Pilagatti, E. Atzeni, A. Salmi, 2023, Exploiting the generative design potential to select the best conceptual design of an aerospace component to be produced by additive manufacturing, The International Journal of Advanced Manufacturing Technology 129, 5597-5612.

A. Schubiger, S. Barber, H. Nordborg, 2020, Evaluation of the lattice Boltzmann method for wind modelling in complex terrain, Wind Energy Science 5, 4, 1507-1519

L. Thomas, M. Ramachandra, 2018, Advanced materials for wind turbine blade- A Review, Materialstoday : proceedings 5, 1, 2635-2640

E. Tyflopoulos, F.D. Tollnes, M. Steinert, A. Olsen, 2018, State of the art of generative design and topology optimization and potential research needs, NordDesign, Linköping, Sweden

J. Xu, 2016, Wake Interaction of NREL Wind Turbines Using a Lattice Boltzmann Method, Sustainable Energy 4, 1-6

J. Zhu, X. Cai, D. Ma, J. Zhang, X. Ni, 2021, Improved structural design of wind turbine blade based on topology and size optimization, Low-Carbon Technologies 17, 69-79

Flavio Manenti, Gintaras V. Reklaitis (Eds.), Proceedings of the 34th European Symposium on Computer Aided Process Engineering / 15th International Symposium on Process Systems Engineering (ESCAPE34/PSE24), June 2-6, 2024, Florence, Italy

Development of an Energy Mix evaluation method of an infrastructure based on a multi-layered territorial approach.

Julien Jean Victor[a], Chloé Labauge[a], Philippe Trubert[b], Augustin Mpanda[a], Laurent Fontanelli[a], Sebastien Potel[a], Arnaud Dujany[a]

[a]U2R 7511, Basins-Reservoirs-Resources (B2R), Geosciences Department, UniLaSalle - University of Picardie Jules Verne, Beauvais, France
[b]Syndicat mixte de l'aéroport de Beauvais-Tillé (SMABT), 1 rue du Pont de Paris - 60000 Beauvais
arnaud.dujany@unilasalle.fr

Abstract

Modern global climate awareness has led governing institutions worldwide to encourage the reduction of CO_2 emissions and the development of sustainable production methods, including that of energy. Renewable energy sources are preferred to fossil fuels, and multiple studies have aimed to optimize energy mixes and include more renewable energy sources in them. This paper proposes and describes a methodology to evaluate the available energy mix potential of a territory, centred on an infrastructure. An application of this method to Oise (France) and the Paris Beauvais Airport is proposed.

Keywords: Energy Mix, Evaluation, Territorial Approach, Carbon Footprint

1. Introduction

The worldwide growing realization of climate change has induced new policies regarding CO_2 emissions and environmental impacts, especially concerning energy consumption and generation. Alongside with the increase of energy prices, fossil fuels are being disregarded and renewable energy sources grew massively in current energy mixes (Østergaard and Sperling, 2014). Multiple studies have aimed to model and evaluate renewable energy sources, technologies, and facility locations, trying to develop optimized energy mixes that include more renewable energies (Ilbahar et al., 2019). These studies have been conducted at international, national, and regional scales, each dealing with different challenges and levels of complexity. As the IPCC estimates 75% of ecological and energetic transitions are territorial, it appears suitable to assess the environmental impact of energy mixes at that level, for example by using a carbon footprint evaluation. In this domain, the most common methods are the input-output method and the Life-Cycle Assessment (LCA).

The input–output method works by analyzing each economic activity related to the sector of a product, to be able to economically track it. The LCA analyzes and agglomerates the different carbon footprints of each element and process used to create a final product (Wiedmann and Minx, 2008). The input-output method is used to evaluate the carbon footprint of processes in the LCA. (Von Der Assen et al., 2014). Such methods are effective to calculate the carbon footprint of processes or products.

This study proposes a method to evaluate the carbon footprint of a territory's energy mix potential centered on an infrastructure, to be used as a base for energy mix optimization.

This is conditioned by a multi-scale inventory of different energy sources in the considered territory, followed by the determination of evaluation criteria, complementary to an LCA evaluation. The sources are first evaluated individually, then results are aggregated in a global evaluation for the territory's energy mix, centered on a specific infrastructure.

2. Method

2.1. Method for the inventory of available energy sources

The first step to evaluate the energy mix potential for a territory is to build an inventory of its energy resources. This inventory is done with a multi-scale approach that enables to gather information on multiple energy sources and different energy categories.

2.1.1. Territorial scale

At a territorial scale, a first inventory is done on available gas and electricity resources. In addition to renewable energy sources, fossil fuels are also considered to cover all energy needs, since renewable sources can be insufficient to cover an energy mix. To be considered, the energy sources need to be available, which means they must be connected to the gas or electricity distribution network and produce energy. Electricity sources taken into account include thermal energy (fossil fuel combustion), nuclear energy, onshore and offshore wind turbines, solar photovoltaic panels, hydroelectric power, geothermal power (electricity generation), bioenergy and marine power plants. In the case of gas sources, natural gas extraction stations and biogas generation stations are considered. Other sectors that comply with the inventory requirements may also be included. Therefore, a state of play for electricity and gas resources can be created at a large scale, by using data from the government and/or from the network operators. The spatial perimeter proposed for the regional inventory is based on an administrative division, to facilitate compliance with governments and avoid multiplicity of environmental policies. However, some cases might find a distance-based perimeter definition better suited and could chose to proceed differently.

2.1.2. Infrastructure and city agglomeration scale

A second inventory can be done at smaller scale, namely the infrastructure on which the evaluation is centered, and the city agglomeration eventually surrounding it. The energy sources considered at this scale are heat networks that are already connected to the infrastructure. They can be based on multiple energy types: geothermal, solar, organic matter combustion or fossil fuels. The area of inventory is limited by the uncertainties in heat transfer efficiency (Kavvadias and Quoilin, 2018).

2.2. Individual Environmental Evaluation of energy sources by criteria development

Once the energy sources available in the studied area have been listed, they can be evaluated according to specific criteria. Their definition is highly dependent of the availability of data. Depending on the facilities, the necessary information is not always available. This study relies on information from public databases, such as the ADEME "Base Carbone" based on an LCA analysis to calculate three criteria that are then combined in a global indicator.

2.2.1. Gross Carbon Footprint by energy sector

The first criterion accounts for the energy sector impact, as addressed by the Lifecycle Assessment. The LCA focuses on the carbon footprint of production processes, from material extraction to marketing, transport of products, production, and packaging. This method also considers the potential of the product to be reused, recycled and how final waste may or may not be recycled. (Von Der Assen et al., 2014). Although this method is widely used to determine à product's carbon footprint, it does have limitations. In fact, it is easy to double-count hydroelectric dams and electricity supply, as they are not considered as dual function resources in this method (Evans et al., 2009). Some studies recommend adding other criteria to this calculation, such as environmental and social criteria, which are not always linked with carbon footprints (Turconi et al., 2013). In this study, the carbon footprint imputed to the energy sector CF_{ES} is expressed in gCO_2eq/y and calculated as shown in Eq. (1).

$$CF_{ES} = E_{ES} * P_y \tag{1}$$

Where E_{ES} are the source emissions by kWh produced as indicated in ADEME Base Carbone, in gCO_2eq/kWh, and P_y represents the yearly production of the installation (kWh/y), dependent on each source and collected in the inventory.

2.2.2. Urbanization and land use

As forests and green spaces absorb a part of carbon emissions, it is important to evaluate the impact of urbanization and global land use to correctly calculate a territory's carbon footprint (Harris and Gibbs, 2021). This is calculated from the ground area of the facility and an emission factor, dependent on the biome in which it is implanted (Lal et al., 2018). This emission factor is the opposite of the sequestration factor which comes from the database of the European Environment Agency (EEA). The carbon footprint due to urbanization is calculated as indicated in Eq. (2)

$$CF_U = EF_{LU} * A \tag{2}$$

With EF_{LU} the emission factor corresponding to the land use change ($gCO_2eq/ha/y$) and A the ground area of the installation (ha), which depends on the source and is collected in the inventory.

As the installation of solar panels on already urbanized areas (roofs, car parks) does not induce any additional urbanization on the ground, the ground area for these installations is counted as zero.

2.2.3. Distance

The distance between production facilities and consumption areas is considered in evaluation methods for facility-location purposes, in the evaluation of energy projects. Here, it is used to evaluate an energy mix, expressed through the energy losses in transportation and the emissivity of a compensation energy. In France, this compensation is considered equal to 598 gCO_2eq per kWh, which is the LCA carbon footprint of imported gas for electricity generation. The distance-related carbon footprint is expressed in Eq. (3)

$$CF_D = P_L * E_{CE} * D \tag{3}$$

Where P_L represents the accounted losses during transportation, in kWh/km/y which depends on the study zone, E_{CE} is the emissivity of the compensation energy in gCO_2eq/kWh, and D the distance between the energy source and the infrastructure studied in km, collected during the inventory.

2.2.4. Construction of global indicator

As all three criteria are expressed in gCO_2eq/kWh, they can be combined to obtain a final value as shown in Eq. (4). It represents the resulting evaluation of every precedent criterion and allows a comparison between different infrastructures.

$$CF_S = CF_{ES} + CF_U + CF_D \tag{4}$$

This value is expressed in gCO_2eq/y, to assess the yearly carbon emissions of installation.

2.3. Energy mix impact evaluation

Once the yearly carbon emissions of each source of energy of the infrastructure studied, they can all be agglomerated to calculate a global carbon footprint, as shown in Eq (5). This global carbon footprint is in fact an evaluation of the energy mix of the infrastructure. This evaluation is an innovation because it becomes a tool for monitoring and comparison over time and with other projects of infrastructures. It also is a decision-support tool as it can help deciding about the source of energy used in an infrastructure and evaluating the interest of a project. As the three main criteria, related to the energy sector, the urbanization, and the distance, are all expressed in the same unit, they can also be compared with values from other infrastructures.

$$CF_{EM} = \sum CF_S \tag{5}$$

It is also possible, and even interesting, to compare the carbon emission of each source, within the same infrastructure, with its total energy mix. This allows to study and assess the sustainability of an infrastructure's energy mix.

3. Application of the method to Paris Beauvais Airport and Oise, France

The spatial perimeter on which this method was applied is the French administrative division of Oise, the Hauts-de-France region, with an annual energy consumption of approximately 12 TWh (ODRE, 2023). The evaluation for its energy mix is centered on the Paris Beauvais Airport, for besides plane-related emissions and consumption, these infrastructures have important energy consumption.

3.1. Energy sources inventory

The inventory of energy sources available in Oise is done with the French public databases from ORE and ODRE agencies, as well as the website data.gouv.fr (ORE, 2023). These databases regroup an important amount of energy-related data, and therefore provide information on gas and electricity-producing installations. From the larger scale of inventory, Oise contains over 4000 solar photovoltaic installations regrouped in aggregations for individual setups, 71 wind turbine fields, 9 bioenergy installations, 9 thermal power plants and 24 biomethane injection points. No nuclear, hydroelectric, marine or geothermal power plants are present. There is also no production of natural gas in Oise. The smaller scale inventory showed that the airport is not connected to a heating network.

3.2. Criteria evaluation and indicator calculation

For the criteria evaluation, critical values provided for each source by the inventory are annual energy production in kWh, energy sector and position. The latter allowed surrounding biome registration and distance evaluation. For simplification purposes, surface was estimated globally for wind turbines (0.03 ha per wind turbine), bioenergy and biomethane injection points (0.05 ha) and thermal power plants (20 ha per installation). Power losses in transport were imputed for each energy (Gas or Electricity) from national loss ratio, total production and total network length. If it is assumed that these values are not the most precise on exact losses in Oise, they can however be representative of a "national responsibility".

This allows for the Energy sector, Urbanization and Distance carbon footprints to be calculated and compiled into the global indicator. Table 1 gathers some examples for results, expressed in tCO_2eq per year.

ID	Name	Energy	Sector	CF$_{ES}$	CF$_U$	CF$_D$	CF$_S$
5	BOISSY BIO	Gas	Biomethane	878.42	0.09	1.35	**879.86**
86	Confid	Elec	Thermal	5,080.01	36.60	165.82	**5,282.42**
179	BOUTAVEN	Elec	Wind	37.38	0.18	217.80	**255.36**
308	Bionerval	Elec	Bioenergy	167.76	0.09	391.12	**558.97**
285	AGOST	Elec	Solar	5.54	0.00	388.87	**394.41**

Table 1: Energy sources individual evaluation examples

The impact of distance for gas production facilities is noticeably smaller than for electricity production facilities. This is because losses on the French electricity network (>10,000 kWh/y) are significantly higher than on the gas network (ca. 35 kWh/y).

3.3. Global territorial energy mix carbon evaluation

Once all energy sources have been individually evaluated, all criteria and the indicator were summed to obtain the carbon evaluation for the territorial energy mix, as well as a compilation each energy sector (Table 2).

Sector	Count	CF$_{ES}$	CF$_U$	CF$_D$	CF$_S$
Solar	284	3050.11	32.94	69,912.86	**72,995.91**
Wind	71	13,767.24	12.99	13,028.07	**26,808.30**
Bioenergy	9	2,157.33	0.82	2,271.80	**4,429.96**
Thermal	9	48,822.34	329.40	1,982.83	**51,134.58**
Biomethane	24	12,728.82	2.20	21.85	**12,752.87**
Total	397	80,525.84	378.35	87,217.41	**168,121.61**

Table 2: Criteria compilation for all energy sectors

It can be noted that the global impact of urbanization is significantly lower than the other two criteria. This can be explained by the low surfaces accounted for in the calculation of the urbanization criteria, as well as for the values given in the EEA database.

The total carbon footprint for the territory is 168 ktCO$_2$eq per year, for a total annual production of 2 TWh of energy. Compared to the 2021 energy consumption of 12TWh for Oise, this shows that the territory is not energetically independent. It also enlightens the value of nuclear power in the French energy mix, as the nuclear power plant of Gravelines, in Nord, France, produces over 28 TWh a year.

4. Conclusion and prospects

The carbon evaluation method described in this paper is based on a territorial and spatial approach, and the innovative perspective of its centering on a given infrastructure allows to evaluate the situation of an energy mix at territorial scales. The flexibility it offers enables numerous possible variations of parameters, depending on the availability of data, thus allowing for eventual studies more precise than that made in the application. This method also has versatility in the use that can be made of its results. It can be used to monitor temporal evolution of the energy mix, as well as to assess the potential of an energy facility development project. Results of this study highlight the importance of proximity in the energy mix carbon footprint and correlates the IPCC statement that territorial levers are essential to the ecological and energetic transition worldwide.

References

Base Empreinte® [Online]. Date consulted: 27/10/2023. Available from: <https://base-empreinte.ademe.fr/documentation/base-carbone>.

Evans, A., Strezov, V., Evans, T.J., 2009. Assessment of sustainability indicators for renewable energy technologies. Renewable and Sustainable Energy Reviews, volume 13, n° 5. p. 1082-1088. DOI : 10.1016/j.rser.2008.03.008

European Environment Agency's home page [Online]. Date consulted : 13/11/2023. Available from: <https://www.eea.europa.eu/publications/carbon-stocks-and-sequestration-rates >.

Harris, N., Gibbs, D., 2021. Forests Absorb Twice As Much Carbon As They Emit Each Year. [Online]Date consulted: 23/11/2023. Available from: <https://www.wri.org/insights/forests-absorb-twice-much-carbon-they-emit-each-year>.

Ilbahar, E., Cebi, S., Kahraman, C., 2019. A state-of-the-art review on multi-attribute renewable energy decision making. Energy Strategy Reviews, volume 25, p. 18-33. DOI : 10.1016/j.esr.2019.04.014

Kavvadias, K.C., Quoilin, S., 2018. Exploiting waste heat potential by long distance heat transmission: Design considerations and techno-economic assessment. Applied Energy, volume 216, p. 452-465. DOI : 10.1016/j.apenergy.2018.02.080

Lal, R., Smith, P., Jungkunst, H.F., Mitsch, W.J., Lehmann, J., Nair, P.K.R., McBratney, A.B., Sá, J.C. de M., Schneider, J., Zinn, Y.L., Skorupa, A.L.A., Zhang, H.-L., Minasny, B., Srinivasrao, C., Ravindranath, N.H., 2018. The carbon sequestration potential of terrestrial ecosystems. Journal of Soil and Water Conservation, volume 73, n° 6. p. 145A-152A. DOI : 10.2489/jswc.73.6.145A

ORE [Online]. Date consulted: 20/09/2023. Available from: <https://www.agenceore.fr/opendata/registre-national-des-installations-de-production-et-de-stockage-delectricite-au-3108202 >

ODRE [Online]. Date consulted: 20/09/2023. Available from: <https://odre.opendatasoft.com/explore/dataset/points-dinjection-de-biomethane-en-france/information/>

Østergaard, P.A., Sperling, K., 2014. Towards Sustainable Energy Planning and Management. International Journal of Sustainable Energy Planning and Management, p. 1-5 Pages. DOI : 10.5278/IJSEPM.2014.1.1

Turconi, R., Boldrin, A., Astrup, T., 2013. Life cycle assessment (LCA) of electricity generation technologies: Overview, comparability and limitations. Renewable and Sustainable Energy Reviews, volume 28, p. 555-565. DOI : 10.1016/j.rser.2013.08.013

Von Der Assen, N., Voll, P., Peters, M., Bardow, A., 2014. Life cycle assessment of CO_2 capture and utilization: a tutorial review. Chem. Soc. Rev., volume 43, n° 23. p. 7982-7994. DOI : 10.1039/C3CS60373C

Wiedmann, T., Minx, J., 2008. A Definition of 'Carbon Footprint.' CC Pertsova, Ecological Economics Research Trends. 2. 55-65.

Flavio Manenti, Gintaras V. Reklaitis (Eds.), Proceedings of the 34th European Symposium on
Computer Aided Process Engineering / 15th International Symposium on Process Systems
Engineering (ESCAPE34/PSE24), June 2-6, 2024, Florence, Italy

Data-driven robust hydrogen infrastructure planning under demand uncertainty using a hierarchical-based decomposition method

Xu Zhou, Margarita E. Efthymiadou, Lazaros G. Papageorgiou and Vassilis M.
Charitopoulos[*]

*Department of Chemical Engineering, The Sargent Centre for Process Systems
Engineering, University College London (UCL), Torrington Place, WC1E 7JE, UK*
[*]*v.charitopoulos@ucl.ac.uk*

Abstract

Strategic planning of national hydrogen infrastructure constitutes a prominent topic
within the "Net-zero" agenda. Nevertheless, uncertainty surrounding future hydrogen
supply chains could lead to significant economic loss and even jeopardise the security of
energy systems. This work aims to provide an uncertainty-resilient scheme to alleviate
these disadvantages. We propose a data-driven adaptive robust mixed-integer linear
programming (MILP) optimisation framework with 5-year steps 2035-2050 and hourly
resolution by explicitly accounting for demand uncertainty typically introduced in energy
planning models through the introduction of representative days. To solve this complex
MILP problem, we propose an enhanced column-and-constraint generation algorithm
based on a hierarchical method that can significantly reduce the computational effort.

Keywords: Hydrogen infrastructure planning, Decomposition method, Polyhedral
uncertainty set, Adaptive robust optimisation, Column-and-constraint generation.

1. Introduction

In light of the increasing number of countries committing to "Net-zero" by 2050,
hydrogen as a low-carbon alternative to natural gas plays a significant role towards the
decarbonisation of the heat sector (Lowes and Woodman, 2020). Towards the
optimisation of hydrogen infrastructure planning, many uncertainties such as the
hydrogen demand and renewable energy generation are inherent to underlying problem.
Despite the plethora of research works examining this problem only a handful consider
risk-averse decision-making (Câmara et al., 2019). For the case of power sector only
decarbonisation, Lara et al. (2018) proposed a nested decomposition algorithm to solve
this class of multi-scale MILP problems, but it focused on the deterministic minimisation
problem. Hou et al. (2021) developed a modified decomposition algorithm based on
stochastic dual dynamic integer programming for large-scale renewable electricity
planning. Furthermore, energy-planning models typically involve representative days in
order to alleviate the computational complexity due to their multi-scale nature (Vaes and
Charitopoulos, 2023). The issue of systematically accounting for the uncertainty
introduced through the deployment of representative days within these models remains
largely unexplored. To this end, we employ a two-stage data-driven adaptive robust
optimisation (ARO) model.

ARO has been widely applied in network/transportation problems and power system
scheduling problems (Baringo et al., 2018) and has shown to mitigate the overly

conservative issue of a single-stage robust optimisation. However, two-stage ARO problems even in simple cases are NP-hard (Ben-Tal et al., 2004). The two most widely used methods in the literature to overcome the computational burden of ARO are the Benders-dual cutting plane algorithm and column-and-constraint generation (CCG) algorithm (Zeng and Zhao, 2013), both of which involve solving an MILP master problem and a bilinear sub-problem. In most cases, the inner max-min problem is reformulated as a single-level max problem through duality and the introduction of big-M constraints (Baringo et al., 2018; Ning and You, 2018). Nonetheless, finding the right values for big-M parameters in this case is a notoriously difficult problem. Motivated by the aforementioned problems, the contribution of this work is two-fold: (i) we propose a data-driven ARO-based way to explicitly account for the demand uncertainty introduced in energy planning models through the deployment of representative days; (ii) we develop an enhanced CCG-based hybrid solution scheme that reduces significantly the computational time of the resulting multi-scale and multi-level problem. In Section 2, we briefly discuss the hydrogen-planning problem we study, Section 3 details the proposed hybrid solution scheme while in Sections 4 & 5 results and conclusions are provided respectively.

2. Model Formulation

The hydrogen infrastructure planning problem considering demand uncertainties is formulated as an adaptive robust MILP optimisation problem. It involves choosing the optimal investment strategy for each region over the 5-year steps 2035-2050, and hourly operating strategy over a number of representative days (c) to meet the uncertain hydrogen demand. The total production rate of production technologies p in each region g, year t, cluster c and hour h is denoted by Pr_{pgcht}, and the flowrates of all transportation modes l from region g' to g is denoted by $Q_{lgg'tch}$. The number of investments of the new production technologies p and new transportation units of type l for hydrogen transportation in region g and time t by IP_{pgt} and $ITU_{lgg't}$, are denoted respectively. The uncertain hydrogen demand is TD_{gtch} which is modeled following the polyhedral uncertainty sets convention. The total cost TOC consists of the production capital & operational cost PCC & POC, the road transportation capital cost RCC and operating cost ROC, the carbon emissions cost CEC, fuels costs FC for the natural gas and biomass consumption (Efthymiadou et al., 2023). More specifically, we have

$$TOC = PCC(IP_{pgt}) + POC(Pr_{pgcht}) + RCC(ITU_{lgg't}) + ROC(Q_{lgg'tch}) \\ + CEC(Pr_{pgtch}) + FC(Pr_{pgtch}) . \tag{1}$$

The hydrogen energy demand-generation balance constraint is as below:

$$\sum_{p \in P} Pr_{pgtch} + \sum_{l \in L} \sum_{g' \in N_{gg'}} Q_{lg'gtch} \geq \sum_{l \in L} \sum_{g' \in N_{gg'}} Q_{lgg'tch} + TD_{gtch} \tag{2}$$

for all $g \in G$, $t \in T$, $c \in C$, $h \in H$. The hydrogen production constraints are:

$$Pr_{pgtch} \leq cap_p^{max} \cdot NP_{pgt}, \qquad \forall p \in P, g \in G, t \in T, c \in C, h \in H \tag{3}$$

$$NP_{pgt} = NP_{pg,t-1} + IP_{pgt} \qquad \forall p \in P, g \in G, t \in T . \tag{4}$$

Similarly, we have road transportation constraints:

$$Q_{lgg'tch} \leq cap_l^T \cdot NTU_{lgg't} \qquad \forall l \in L, \{g, g'\} \in N_{gg'}, t \in T, c \in C, h \in H \tag{5}$$

$$NTU_{lgg't} = NTU_{lgg',t-1} + ITU_{lgg't} \qquad \forall l \in L, \{g, g'\} \in N_{gg'}, t \in T \tag{6}$$

where NP_{pgt} and $NTU_{lgg't}$ denote the total number of available production technologies p and transportation units of type l in region g and time t, respectively. The total carbon emissions should satisfy an upper limit, which is formulated as the following constraint:

$$\sum_{p \in P} \sum_{g \in G} \sum_{c \in C} \sum_{h \in H} y_{ptc}^e \cdot Pr_{pgtch} \leq et_t \qquad \forall t \in T. \tag{7}$$

Concisely, the resulting data-driven adaptive robust optimisation (ARO) for the above hydrogen planning problem is formulated as the following compact form:

$$\min_{x} \; c^{\mathsf{T}} x + \max_{d \in \mathcal{D}} \min_{y \in \Omega(x,d)} b^{\mathsf{T}} y$$
$$\text{s.t.} \;\; Ax = B, \;\; \Omega(x,d) = \{y: \; Wy \geq h - Tx - Md\},$$
$$\mathcal{D} = \left\{ d \;\middle|\; \begin{array}{c} d = d_0 + P\xi, \; \xi = \underline{\xi} \circ z^- + \overline{\xi} \circ z^+ \\ 0 \leq z^-, z^+ \leq 1, \; z^- + z^+ \leq 1, \; 1^{\mathsf{T}}(z^- + z^+) \leq \Phi \end{array} \right\} \tag{8}$$

where the variable x is the first-stage integer variable including decision variables IP_{pgt}, $ITU_{lgg't}$, NP_{pgt} and $NTU_{lgg't}$, which is made prior to the uncertainty realisation. The variable y is the second-stage continuous variable including Pr_{pgcht} and $Q_{lgg'tch}$, which is made after the uncertainty is realised. $\mathcal{D}$ is the data-driven polyhedral uncertainty set derived from the historical demand data by using principal component analysis and kernel smoothing methods (Ning and You 2018) for modeling uncertain demand d, i.e., TD_{gtch} in (2), where vectors $\underline{\xi}$ and $\overline{\xi}$ define the confidence interval of latent uncertainties, and parameter Φ is an uncertainty budget describing the conservatism of uncertainty sets.

3. Enhanced CCG Algorithm for Adaptive Robust MILP Problems

The data-driven ARO problem is a complex tri-level optimisation that cannot be directly solved using off-the-shelf solvers. The CCG algorithm can decompose the adaptive robust MILP into a master problem and a sub-problem. The master problem passes the solved integer decision variables to the sub-problem, and then the sub-problem continuously generates scenarios for the master problem. The above process iterates until the gap between the upper and lower bounds satisfies a certain optimality tolerance. Its master problem is the relaxation of the original problem (8), and the sub-problem is a bilevel max-min problem determining the worst-case uncertainty realisations.

CCG-MP:

$$TC = \min_{x, \eta, y^k} c^{\mathsf{T}} x + \eta$$
$$\text{s.t.} \;\; Ax = B,$$
$$\eta \geq b^{\mathsf{T}} y^k, \;\; k = 1, \cdots, r$$
$$Tx + Wy^k \geq h - Md^k$$

CCG-SP:

$$\Xi(x) = \max_{d \in \mathcal{D}} \min_{y} b^{\mathsf{T}} y$$
$$\text{s.t.} \;\; Wy \geq h - Tx - Md$$

Note that the above CCG-MP is an MILP problem and its constraints and variables will grow as the iteration k proceeds. If the optimisation problem is large-scale and needs more iterations to obtain a feasible solution, like the planning problem proposed in this paper, the CCG-MP can become prohibitively large and needs more computing time to be solved. Therefore, we apply the Benders decomposition (Geoffrion, 1972) to decompose the large-scale CCG-MP into a small MILP problem and a large LP problem. The Benders decomposition process for CCG-MP is as follows:

Benders-MP:

$$\min_{x,\theta} c^\top x + \theta$$

s.t. $Ax = B,$

$$\theta \geq \sum_k \pi_{ik}(h - Md^k - Tx) \quad \forall i = 1, \cdots s$$

Benders-SP:

$$\min_{\eta, y^k} \eta$$

s.t. $\eta \geq b^\top y^k, \; k = 1, \cdots, r$

$$Tx + Wy^k \geq h - Md^k \; : \; \pi_{sk}$$

The Benders-SP is solved with the given x from the Benders-MP and then it passes the sensitivity parameter π_{sk} at iteration step s to the Benders-MP to generate an optimality cut. When the Benders algorithm converges, the obtained x is the optimal solution for the CCG-MP and then is given to the CCG-SP to calculate the worst scenario d^{k+1}. We can observe that the CCG-SP is an NP-hard problem and cannot be solved directly. We use a block coordinate descent (BCD) method (Minguez et al., 2018) to solve the CCG-SP, which overcomes the aforementioned challenges. The BCD method involves solving two linear programs alternatively until convergence:

BCD-Lower Level:

$$C(x) = \min_y b^\top y$$

s.t. $Wy \geq h - Tx - Md$

$$d = d^v \; : \; \mu^v$$

BCD-Middle Level:

$$\max_{d \in \mathcal{D}} C(x)^v + \mu^v(d - d^v)$$

The lower level problem is solved with a fixed scenario d^v at iteration v of the BCD method and iteration k of CCG algorithm. The operating cost is maximised in the middle level of BCD method with the sensitivities μ^v obtained from the lower level. It is built upon the first-order approximation of the operating cost $C(x)^v$ around the uncertainty realisations of the previous iteration.

To summarise, the above algorithms form the Enhanced CCG (ECCG) algorithm developed in this paper, which has one outer loop associated with CCG and two inner loops related to Benders decomposition & BCD method. It comprises the following steps:

1) Initialisation of the outer loop: Set the iteration counter k to 1 and tolerance ϵ.
2) Initialisation of the Benders inner loop: Set the iteration counter i to 1, and select initial values for d^1 and x^1.
3) Solve problems Benders-SP and Benders-MP, and increase the iteration counter $i \leftarrow i+1$. If converged, then set $x^k \leftarrow x^i$.
4) Initialisation of the BCD inner loop: Set the iteration counter v to 1.
5) Solve problems BCD-Lower Level $C(x^k)$ and BCD-Middle Level, and increase the iteration counter $v \leftarrow v + 1$. If the given tolerance is satisfied, set $d^{k+1} \leftarrow d^v$.
6) Outer loop convergence checking: If $|TC^k - C(x^k) - c^\top x^k| / TC^k \leq \epsilon$, the algorithm stops; otherwise, go to step 2).

Note that even though the ECCG algorithm has two inner loops and needs iterations for each of them, it is typically faster to solve the original MILP problem (8) than the CCG algorithm without inner loops, as illustrated in the next computational experiments.

4. Results & Discussion

The performance of the proposed ECCG method is evaluated on the hydrogen infrastructure planning for domestic heating in Great Britain (GB) from 2035 to 2050. GB is divided into 13 regions based on the local gas distribution zones of the incumbent natural gas network. In order to reduce the model size, we perform clustering on hydrogen demand data points by K-Medoids clustering method (Charitopoulos et al. 2022). We treat the highest demand day as one cluster and perform the polyhedral uncertainty set for other remaining clusters. The model is implemented in GAMS Studio 1.13.4 and solved by Gurobi 9.5.1. The relative tolerances for the Benders and BCD methods are 1×10^{-6} and 1×10^{-8}, respectively. The optimality tolerance of outer ECCG algorithm is 0.1%.

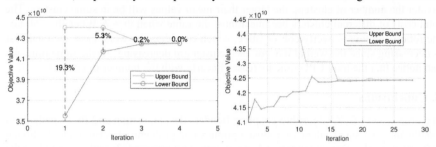

Figure 1: (Left) Upper and lower bounds of outer ECCG algorithm; (Right) Upper and lower bounds of inner Benders decomposition method when the iteration step of ECCG $k = 3$.

Fig. 1 shows the convergence of ECCG (outer loop) and Benders decomposition at iteration step $k = 3$ of ECCG for 4 clusters with uncertainty budget $\Phi = 15$ introduced in problem (8). In general, the ECCG can converge within typically 5 iterations, and its inner Benders loop converges within up to 40 iterations regardless of the number of clusters. BCD method can converge within 30 seconds because it only solves two simple LPs. In Table 1, we compare the final optimal objective values, i.e. the total system cost of the planning problem, and the total CPU execution time with and without Benders method in the ECCG under 6 Clusters and uncertainty budget $\Phi = 10$. As we can see, using Benders can sharply reduce the CPU time compared with using monolithic way to solve the CCG-MP directly. At the same time, it makes around 3% gap between the two converged values, which is acceptable in large-scale optimisation problems.

Table 1: Computational performance comparison of ECCG algorithm with and without Benders.

	Total Cost (£b)	CPU time (min)	Gurobi Optimality Tolerance
With Benders	41.978	22	0.01%
Without Benders	40.757	185	3%

Figure 2: (Left) Total cost for 4 clusters with different uncertainty budgets; (Right) Total cost and CPU time with different clusters and uncertainty budgets.

The conservatism of robust solutions depends on the uncertainty budgets which are chosen by decision makers. Fig. 2 (left) displays a robust solution profiles for 4 clusters with different uncertainty budgets. We can see that the overall trend of costs rises as the uncertainty budget increases. When the value of Φ is low, the increase in cost is significantly large, because the datasets in each cluster are relatively concentrated after performing clustering. In Fig. 2 (right), we compare the total cost difference with different number of clusters under a fixed uncertainty budget. When $\Phi = 0$, i.e., the demand of each cluster is the average value, the total cost increase at a slow rate. This shows that the greater the number of clusters, the larger their mean values will be in some clusters. The total costs of different clusters become almost the same when $\Phi = 2$. When $\Phi = 24$, i.e., the robust solution is overly conservative, which considers the worst case, the total cost is decreasing since the weight days of each cluster are decreasing. At the same time, we can notice that the total CPU time increases linearly with the number of clusters.

5. Conclusions

We propose an ECCG algorithm coupling Benders decomposition and BCD methods to handle the two-stage adaptive robust optimisation problem of large-scale hydrogen infrastructure planning under demand uncertainty. The proposed algorithm can reduce the computational time up to 80% as the experimental result shows. Furthermore, it can also be flexibly extended to deal with other uncertainties like the renewables uncertainty and other complex large-scale systems such as transportation systems. Ongoing research focuses on modifications to Benders decomposition to reduce the resulting optimality gap and apply it to the planning problems of coupled heat and power sectors.

Acknowledgements
Financial support from the Engineering & Physical Sciences Research Council (EPSRC) under the projects EP/T022930/1 and EP/V051008/1, is gratefully acknowledged.

References
A. Ben-Tal, A. Goryashko, E. Guslitzer, A. Nemirovski, 2004, Adjustable robust solutions of uncertain linear programs, Math. Program., 99, 2, 351-376.

L. Baringo and A. Baringo, 2018, A stochastic adaptive robust optimization approach for the generation and transmission expansion planning, IEEE Trans. Power Syst., 33, 1, 792-802.

D. Câmara, T. Pinto-Varela, A. P. Barbósa-Povoa, 2019, Multi-objective optimization approach to design and planning hydrogen supply chain under uncertainty: A Portugal study case, Comput. Aided Chem. Eng., 46, 1309-1314.

V.M. Charitopoulos, M. Fajardy, C.K. Chyong, D.M. Reiner, 2023, The impact of 100% electrification of domestic heat in Great Britain, Iscience, 26, 11, 1-12.

M. E. Efthymiadou, V. M. Charitopoulos, L. G. Papageorgiou, 2023, Hydrogen infrastructure planning for heat decarbonisation in Great Britain, Comput. Aided. Chem. Eng., 52, 3025-3030.

A. M. Geoffrion, 1972, Generalized benders decomposition. J Optim. Theory Appl., 10, 4, 237-260.

S. Hou, Y. Fan, B. Yi, 2021, Long-term renewable electricity planning using a multistage stochastic optimization with nested decomposition, Comput. Ind. Eng., 161, 1-13.

C. L. Lara, D. S. Mallapragada, D. J. Papageorgiou, A. Venkatesh, I. E. Grossmann, 2018, Deterministic electric power infrastructure planning: Mixed-integer programming model and nested decomposition algorithm, Eur. J. Oper. Res., 271, 1037-1054.

R. Lowes, B. Woodman, 2020, Disruptive and uncertain: policy makers' perceptions on UK heat decarbonization, Energy Pol., 142, 1-12.

R. Minguez, R. Garcia-Bertrand, J. M. Arroyo, N. Alguacil, 2018, On the Solution of Large-scale robust transmission network expansion planning under uncertain demand and generation capacity, IEEE Trans. Power Syst., 33, 2, 1242-1251.

C. Ning, F. You, 2018, Data-driven decision making under uncertainty integrating robust optimization with principal component analysis and kernel smoothing methods, Comput. Chem. Eng., 112, 190-210.

J. Vaes, V. M. Charitopoulos, 2023, A data-driven uncertainty modelling and reduction approach for energy optimisation problems, Comput. Aided Chem. Eng., 52, 1161-1167.

B. Zeng, L. Zhao, 2013, Solving two-stage robust optimization problems using a column-and-constraint generation method, Oper. Res. Lett., 41, 5, 457-461.

Flavio Manenti, Gintaras V. Reklaitis (Eds.), Proceedings of the 34th European Symposium on Computer Aided Process Engineering / 15th International Symposium on Process Systems Engineering (ESCAPE34/PSE24), June 2-6, 2024, Florence, Italy

Case study on quality assurance of third-party models for co-simulation using FMI

Isabell Viedt[a*], René Lorenz[b], Leon Urbas[a]

aTU Dresden, Chair of Process Control System and Process Systems Engineering Group, Helmholtzstr. 14, 01069 Dresden, Germany

bGerman Aerospace Center (DLR), Institute of Engineering Thermodynamics, Energy System Integration, Pfaffenwaldring 38-40, 70569 Stuttgart, Germany

*isabell.viedt@tu-dresden.de

Abstract

In this paper, the workflow for the quality assessment and assurance of modularized simulation models (Viedt et al., 2023) is utilized for the quality assessment of independent third-party simulation models in form of Functional Mock-up Units (FMUs). Besides the process of testing of third-party models, the paper discusses the required information exchange between the manufacturer and the end-user of the simulation models to allow quality assessment and execution in a co-simulation. The case study is based on the use case of a modular Solid Oxide Electrolysis (SOEL) plant. The co-simulation integrates third-party FMUs, such as a SOEL model, with in-house developed FMUs, including the water supply unit and the steam supply unit. A best practice for the quality assessment and exchange of simulation models is derived. This comprises the testing of the third-party models, their subsequent integration into the co-simulation as well as the definition of the information, that is required for the integration of an FMU into the co-simulation.

Keywords: Quality assurance, Quality assessment, Co-simulation, Model exchange, Solid Oxide Electrolysis, Modular plants.

1. Introduction

Co-simulation is a very powerful tool for the process of plant design, especially of modular plants, as it allows a detailed analysis of the system and the individual components' behavior in various steady-state and transient operating conditions. A co-simulation of modular process plants must combine, potentially confidential, partial models for each process unit from different manufacturers. As most manufacturers are assumed to be reluctant to share their internal model structure (Mädler et al., 2022), the co-simulation of the partial models can be realized via a standardized interface using Functional Mock-up Units (FMUs). This approach in return also requires a more flexible and modular approach to model quality assessment as, without knowledge of the internal structure, different quality factors like interoperability, usability and flexibility must also be considered.

In this paper, the workflow outlined in Viedt et al. (2023) to conduct quality assurance of modularized simulation models is applied specifically to the evaluation independent third-party simulation models represented as Functional Mock-up Units (FMUs). The paper not only delves into the testing process for third-party models but also explores the essential information exchange between the simulation model manufacturer and end-user. The presented case study focuses on FMUs related to modular solid oxide electrolysis

(SOEL) plants. The co-simulation integrates third-party FMUs, such as the SOEL reactor, with internally developed FMUs like the water supply unit and steam supply unit.

The case study results in the identification of a best practice for quality assessment and for the exchange of simulation models. This encompasses the comprehensive testing of third-party models, their seamless integration into the co-simulation framework, and the specification of essential information needed for the integration of a FMU into the co-simulation. This information must be transferred alongside the FMU to ensure a smooth and effective integration process.

2. Co-simulation and the Functional Mock-up Interface (FMI)

There are typically three approaches for integrating partial models into a full-system simulation (FMI, 2023):

- **Monolithic Approach:** Construct the entire full-system model within a single tool dedicated to simulation.
- **Model Exchange:** Transfer models between tools to conduct simulations in one of them, allowing for interoperability.
- **Co-simulation:** Loosely couple two or more simulators, enabling a modular, flexible full-system simulation composed of independent sub-simulators.

Co-simulation presents numerous advantages compared to the other two approaches (Hatledal et al., 2019. Its modular design and high flexibility allow the construction of a full-system simulation from distinct stand-alone sub-simulators. Co-simulation enables the utilization of specialized tool chains and domain-specific knowledge already employed by participants and partners, while safeguarding their intellectual property rights through the optional black box approach. Therefore, it is well-suited for addressing the complexity arising from the integration of diverse elements within the system, especially when dealing with numerous partial models originating from different fields and disciplines (Hatledal et al., 2019).

The Functional Mock-Up Interface (FMI) serves as a tool-independent standard, enabling binary compatibility among partial models. FMI is an open and freely usable standard, gaining support from a diverse array of tools such as Dymola, Python, SimulationX, and Simulink. A model adhering to FMI is referred to as a Functional Mock-Up Unit (FMU).

3. Quality assurance for simulation models for the exchange of models

The literature identifies various strategies for evaluating simulation model quality, with Balci and Sargent's verification and validation (V&V) methods being prominent (Murray-Smith, 2015; Sargent & Balci, 2017). Despite their comprehensive assessment techniques focusing on model accuracy, a meta-analysis reveals inconsistent use of V&V methods in simulation studies (Sargent & Balci, 2017).

An alternative perspective is presented by Mädler et al. (2021) and Viedt et al. (2023), who explore the applicability of quality assurance methods from software development to simulation models. In this approach, quality assessment strategies adopted from software development, such as test-driven development, and quality models defining features through FCM (factor–criteria–metrics) models, are employed to ensure test-driven modeling. This cross-disciplinary approach aims to enhance the reliability of simulation models by leveraging established practices from software development.

Since the partial models are compiled into a co-simulation framework, quality features outside of the models' behavior must also be considered to assure successful model interaction. In the realm of co-simulation, the distinction between the person overseeing quality assurance and the model builder introduces a significant challenge. Information exchange is essential for aligning expectations and ensuring that the co-simulation process is not only compliant with standards but also harmonized in terms of modeling methodologies and objectives. For more detail the reader is kindly referred to Mädler et al. (2022) and Viedt et al. (2023).

4. Case study

Scaling water electrolysis to the gigawatt level involves modularization following standards such as VDI 2776 and VDI/VDE/NAMUR 2658. This manufacturer-independent integration holds potential for efficient and flexible hydrogen production (Lange et al., 2023). However, implementing modular plants faces challenges from distributed knowledge and diverse simulation models by different manufacturers, hindering the simulation of connected cyber-physical systems (Hamzah et al., 2023).

Among the power-to-hydrogen converters the high-temperature Solid Oxide Electrolysis (SOEL) can operate at the highest efficiency. Its capabilities for heat integration and parallel reduction of CO_2 and H_2O unlocks further efficiency increase on the system level. Due to these unique features the SOEL is considered as a key technology for Power-to-X processes. In this case study the use case of modular SOEL is utilized to derive a best practice for the quality assessment and exchange of simulation models. The SOEL model (see 4.1) was developed and exported as a black-box FMU by DLR, and handed over to TU Dresden. Hence, the modelling details remained unveiled for TU Dresden and created a realistic test case for the quality-driven model assurance framework. This comprises of the testing of the third-party FMU and its subsequent integration into the co-simulation.

4.1. HTEL model

The SOEL model is developed using the modelling framework TEMPEST (Santhanam et al., 2018; Tomberg et al., 2022) and exported as an FMU from the commercial editor Dymola. The model represents a single reactor module, comprising the stacks and the power electronics. The stacks are modelled zero dimensionally (0D) with lumped mass, energy and species balances. This simplified model was compared to a more detailed and validated model (Tomberg et al., 2022). The simplified model gives a good estimate of the reactors operating conditions and transient behaviour, while solving very quickly.

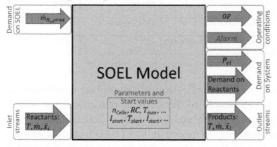

Figure 1: FMU of the SOEL model. The parameters being exchanged with other system components are indicated by arrows pointing into or out of the SOEL model.

For the integration into the co-simulation, certain information on conditions and demands have to be communicated between the component models. The exchanged parameters are represented by the arrows pointing into or out of the SOEL model in Fig.1. The time independent parameters and their start values can be set before starting the simulation run. These comprise parameters defining the reactors size, like number of cells, heat capacitance and area of insulation, operating parameters like nominal operating point, reactant conversion rate (RC) and forming gas flow in standby and operating limitations such as temperatures and voltage limits. The arrow in the top left sets the desired hydrogen production rate, which internally is converted into a current, based on Faraday's law and the RC. This leads to a demand on electrical power and reactant flow, which is transferred back to the system with the respective arrows on the right. The inlet streams pass the actual properties of the supply streams to the SOEL. Potential mismatches between supply and demand, which may lead to unbeneficial operation or malfunction and throwing of an alarm, can be identified.

Depending on the target of the analysis, the given level of modelling depth in the component models as well as the distribution of control intelligence between component and system level additional information might need to be exchanged. Exemplary, this can be details on supply and product stream qualities, state of health of the component or operation dependent degradation rate. However, the herein presented methodology itself, is generic and therefore independent of the components and exchanged parameters.

4.2. Model quality assessment

The quality assurance of the individual partial models defines if the FMU can be used in the context of the system simulation at all. If the model does not reach the desired quality as an individual model, the co-simulation will not be successful. In Table 1 an excerpt of the corresponding FCM model for the SOEL unit is shown. As the case study focuses on the applicability of the partial model in a system-wide co-simulation, the focus lays on the quality factors Functional Suitability and Compatibility. The quality assessment of the SOEL partial model shows that the models fulfill the necessary requirements and is therefore qualified to be utilized in the specified plant simulation. The interface specifications for the quality factor compatibility fulfills the required metrics. Furthermore, the FMU's behavior matches the defined criteria of functional correctness and therefore reaches the quality for the intended purpose.

Table 1: Excerpt of the tested FCM model for the SOEL partial model

Factor	Criteria	Metric	Target	Model value
Functional Suitability	Functional Correctness	Min. outlet mass flow SOEL	$0.18\ g{*}s^{-1}$	$0.184\ g{*}s^{-1}$
		Max. outlet stack temperature	850 °C	860°C
Compatibility	Interoperability	Interface standard adherence	FMI standard	FMI standard
		Unit outlet mass flow water/hydrogen	$kg{*}s^{-1}$	$kg{*}s^{-1}$

4.3. SOEL system co-simulation

To assess whether the partial model can be used effectively in a plant simulation, the SOEL-FMU is co-simulated below in a simplified plant configuration with the balance of plant components Water Supply, Steam Supply and Air Supply. These balance of plant components are realized as simple, dynamic 0D models in MATLAB/Simulink and also exported as FMUs. The co-simulation of the system is then implemented in Simulink. The system structure is shown in Fig. 2. The balance of plants components can in this context be considered quality assured. The defining factor for the success of the case study is the integration of the SOEL FMU into the plant co-simulation and its subsequent execution. Therefore, we define a simple test case which evaluates the SOEL behavior in the plant context. For that, a steady state scenario 1 at nominal operating point at 60 A is compared to scenario 2, which is a transition from hot-standby to an operating point above nominal. This is achieved by ramping-up the current from 0 to 70 A at a rate of 5 A/min.

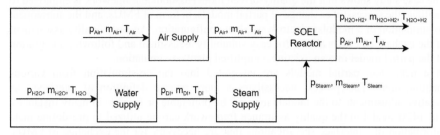

Figure 2: Simplified HTEL system configuration

Fig. 3 shows the product gas mass flow at the outlet of the Steam Supply Unit. The test scenario shows that the dynamic model behavior from the SOEL FMU is propagated in the balance of plant components and therefore correctly reflects the expected plant behavior. The higher mass flow at the beginning of both scenarios reflects the forming gas mass flow that is applied during hot standby.

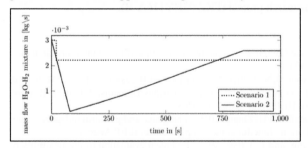

Figure 3: Selected results of the co-simulation, outlet mass flow H_2O-H_2 mixture

4.4. Best practice for quality assessment and exchange of simulation models

From the successful integration of the SOEL FMU into a co-simulation the critical information exchange for the simulation execution is derived. Without this meta information the behavior of the FMU cannot be assessed effectively. One valuable information about exchanged FMUs is the model's purpose. This must include a general understanding of the modeled process, which encompasses the implemented basic process functions and the employed modeling approach and goal. This allows an evaluation if a FMU is generally suitable for the covered process. Besides, detailed specifications about interfaces, including units, purpose and connections with other partial models are fundamental for connecting the partial models. Depending on the co-simulation platform, these interface specifications can either be defined as a formalized system configuration or lay the groundwork for manual model connection through a GUI. Lastly, the boundary conditions and model performance indicators, which allow the individual quality assessment, must also be exchanged along with the FMU. They function as a guideline as to how the FMU shall be utilized in the context of the system simulation by defining clear limits and operating ranges. The specification of key model performance indicators allows for quality assessment of the model's performance. One example for necessary exchanged information in the case study is the modeling approach of the SOEL model. Only because the dynamic modeling approach is known, the end-user expects this dynamic behavior to propagate into the plant simulation as well.

5. Conclusions and outlook

The case study shows that the quality-driven model assurance framework is employed to facilitate the successful exchange of partial models, in form of FMUs, and the subsequent co-simulation of a modular electrolysis plant configuration. An early quality assessment of the exchanged FMUs allows for easy suitability assessment and following integration of the partial model into an existing, simplified plant co-simulation.

In a next step, partial models are integrated into the co-simulation from various manufacturers. This process necessitates a more precise definition of interfaces, as iterative adjustments to the models may not be preferable or feasible in many instances. The FCM model in the quality assurance framework can be utilized to pre-define meta information like interface specifications that are necessary for the exchange of FMUs. With this information modeling and standardized interface descriptions come into focus for the exchange of models but also the quality assurance, bringing together standards such as FMI, ISO/IEC 25010, MTP, DEXPI and OntoCAPE.

Acknowledgements

We thank the German Federal Ministry of Education and Research for their financial support within the eModule research project (FKZ 03HY116A-B).

References

FMI. Functional Mock-up Interface Literature. Available online: https://fmi-standard.org/literature/ (accessed on 04 December 2023).

M. Hamzah, M.M. Islam, S. Hassan,M.N. Akhtar, M.J. Ferdous, M.B. Jasser, and A.W. Mohamed, 2023. Distributed Control of Cyber Physical System on Various Domains: A Critical Review. Systems, 11, 4. https://doi.org/10.3390/systems11040208

L.I. Hatledal, A. Styve, G. Hovland, and H. Zhang, 2019. A language and platform independent co-simulation framework based on the functional mock-up interface. IEEE Access, 7.

H. Lange, A. Klose, W. Lippmann, and L. Urbas, 2023. Technical evaluation of the flexibility of water electrolysis systems to increase energy flexibility: A review. International Journal of Hydrogen Energy, 48, 42, 15771–15783. https://doi.org/10.1016/j.ijhydene.2023.01.044

J. Mädler, I. Viedt, J. Lorenz, L. Urbas, 2022. Requirements to a digital twin-centered concept for smart manufacturing in modular plants considering distributed knowledge.In Computer Aided Chemical Engineering, 49, 1507-1512. https://doi.org/10.1016/B978-0-323-85159-6.50251-7

J. Mädler, I. Viedt, L. Urbas, 2021. Applying quality assurance concepts from software development to simulation model assessment in smart equipment, in: Türkay, M., Gani, R. (Eds.), Computer Aided Chemical Engineering. Elsevier, 50, 813–818. https://doi.org/10.1016/B978-0-323-88506-5.50127-3

D.J. Murray-Smith, 2015. Testing and Validation of Computer Simulation Models, Simulation Foundations, Methods and Applications. Springer International Publishing, Cham. https://doi.org/10.1007/978-3-319-15099-4

R.G. Sargent, O. Balci, 2017. History of verification and validation of simulation models. In 2017 winter simulation conference (WSC), 292-307. IEEE.

S. Srikanth, M. P. Heddrich, S. Gupta and K. A. Friedrich, 2018. Transient reversible solid oxide cell reactor operation – Experimentally validated modeling and analysis. Applied Energies. Elsevier, 232, 473–488. https://doi.org/10.1016/j.apenergy.2018.09.186

M. Tomberg, M. P. Heddrich, F. Sedeqi, D. Ullmer, S. A. Ansar and K. A. Friedrich, 2022. A New Approach to Modeling Solid Oxide Cell Reactors with Multiple Stacks for Process System Simulation. J. Electrochem. Soc. 169. https://iopscience.iop.org/article/10.1149/1945-7111/ac7009

I. Viedt, K. R. Gopa, J. Mädler, and L. Urbas, 2023. Quality assessment of partial models for co-simulation of modular electrolysis plants. In Computer Aided Chemical Engineering, 52, 217-1222. https://doi.org/10.1016/B978-0-443-15274-0.50194-3

Flavio Manenti, Gintaras V. Reklaitis (Eds.), Proceedings of the 34th European Symposium on
Computer Aided Process Engineering / 15th International Symposium on Process Systems
Engineering (ESCAPE34/PSE24), June 2-6, 2024, Florence, Italy

Fast Algorithm for the Continuous Solution of the Population Balance Equation

Menwer Attarakih[a], Mark W. Hlawitschka[b], Hans-Jörg Bart[c]

[a]*Department of Chemical Eng., The University of Jordan, Amman, 11942, Jordan*
[b]*Institute of Process Engineering, Johannes Kepler University, Linz, 4040, Austria*
[c]*RPTU Kaiserslautern., 67663, Germany*
m.attarakih@ju.edu.jo

Abstract

Population balance models are used because of different system heterogeneities due to complex prevailing phenomena governed by particle fusion, splitting and growth. We present a Minimum Relative Entropy Population Density Estimator (MREPDE) based on the fast Clenshaw algorithm for the evaluation of the Legendre series as the heart of our proposed scheme. The present MREPDE reduced the order of computational complexity from $O(M^2)$ to $O(M)$ with an accelerated implementation due to the low rank of the particle fusion matrix because of its tensorial decomposition. We implement the PBE and the MREPDE in a fully vectorized form, which results in a linear scaling of the CPU time with respect to M, instead of a cubic scaling using conventional methods. Therefore, our method is suitable for solving large-scale problems involving particle size distributions.

Keywords: Population Balances; Fast algorithm; Clenshaw; MREPDE.

1. Introduction

The population balance equation (PBE) is a deterministic integro-partial differential equation with applications that spans many fields in pure and applied sciences. The PBE is known to admit analytical solutions only for a few cases with restricted forms of particle interaction rates and kinetics. Therefore, numerical-based solutions are required in case of general fusion and splitting rates when artificial intelligence supervising (Neuendorf et al., 2023) and real-time monitoring are required (Mickler et al., 2014). As a fast computational model (Drumm et al., 2010), the reduced two-equation population balance model OPOSPM is used in modelling real chemical engineering problems. This ranges from modelling and CFD simulation of pilot extraction columns (Drumm et al., 2010) to annular centrifugal extractors used to recover spent nuclear fuels, bubble column reactors and online monitoring and analysis of the multiphase flow behaviour in industrial and chemical process engineering equipment (Mickler et al., 2014). Despite this, OPOSPM lacks the prediction of the full-size population distribution which is vital for online control purposes, estimation of individual particle physio-chemical properties and online inverse solution of the PBE (Mickler et al., 2014). To overcome this, we decoded the distribution behind OPOSPM by maximizing the Shannon entropy. The analytical form of this distribution is found to be the well-known Weibull distribution (Attarakih et al., 2020) which spreads as a function of time and space with mean particle size d30. The latter is a freely moving Lagrangian particle without bounds which is learned from the calculated moments of the corrected continuous solution of the PBE for which the Weibull distribution is used as prior information. The least biased posterior distribution, viewed as a correction to the prior information, is found by expanding the Kullback-Leibler divergence as a minimum solution to the relative entropy problem using a set of orthogonal Legendre polynomials. This allows us to derive the expansion coefficients in a closed form with integration quadrature based on careful sampling of the number concentration function.

The first challenge here is the complexity of the approximate continuous solution as it is represented by a series of orthogonal Legendre polynomials which has a summation complexity of $O(M^2)$ where M is the order of expansion which is repeated two times for each function evaluation. The second complexity comes from the quadratic source term for the formation of particles due to binary collisions with mechanisms embedded in the symmetric fusion rate. The complexity of this quadratic formation term depends on the used computational algorithm which in the order of $O(M^3)$. To overcome this challenge, we adapted the Clenshaw algorithm (Clenshaw, 1955) to evaluate the summation of Legendre polynomials series with a complexity of only $O(M)$, while the evaluation of the quadratic source term is decomposed into two levels. The first one is the tensorial decomposition of the binary fusion rate using the singular value decomposition (SVD) which results in a low-order approximation $O(2)$ for the Golovin fusion rate of turbulent diffusion and $O(5)$ for the realistic fusion rate of Coualaglou and Tavlarides based on the kinetic theory of gases. The second level is the complete vectorization of fusion and splitting source terms that are then implemented based on vectorized matrix computation techniques and popular vector-based software (e.g., MATLAB). This results in a compact algorithm which can be fast enough to meet the computational speed required when solving the PBE within real time monitoring and complex CFD environments.

2. Mathematical Model

2.1. The Discrete Population Balance Equation

Let the continuous number concentration function $f(x,t)$ that describes the population of particles in a homogeneous physical space at any given point in time be sampled M times with points $i = 0,1, \ldots M-1$ that are represented along the real line of the discrete particle space as ξ_i with a point population sample $N_i = f(x_i,t)$. Then, the discrete population balance model which accounts for binary particle fusion and splitting is written as:

$$\frac{\partial N_i(t)}{\partial t} + D(t)N_i(t) = \frac{1}{2}S_i - N_i\Omega^{|i)}N + B^{|i)}N \tag{1}$$

where $D(t)$ is the particle dilution rate, Ω is the discrete matrix of binary particle fusion rate per unit volume of the physical space. The upper triangular matrix B represents the discrete rate of binary particle splitting that depends on the given daughter particle distribution function and splitting rate. The discrete rate of birth of particles (S_i) due to binary fusion depends on the discretization schemes that is used to reduce the continuous source term into its discrete form which can be written in two distinctive forms:

$$S_i = \begin{cases} N^T\Psi^{(i)}N \\ \Pi^{|i)}(N \cdot N') \end{cases} \tag{2}$$

The difference is due to the discrete representation of the stretched particle phase space as presented by the product $f(x,t)f(x-u,t)$. In the above formulation N_i represents the particle sample at ξ_i and $N`_i$ is the respective sample at (ξ_i-u_j). Accordingly, Ψ and Π are the binary fusion rates (Ω) modified by the method of discretization. Note that the superscripts ($|i\rangle$ and $\langle i|$) represent the ith row and column vectors of the given matrix respectively. Also, both terms appearing in Eq.(2) are quadratic birth terms with complexity in the order of $O(M^2)$ at any given discrete point i. Hence the overall complexity for M grid points is in the order of $O(M^3)$ (Attarakih et al., 2004).

2.2. The Minimum Relative Entropy Population Density Estimator (MREPDE)

In our previous work (Attarakih et al., 2020) the general continuous solution of the PBE based on minimizing the relative entropy using the Kullback-Leibler divergence was presented. In this regard, the prior information (0 & 3rd moments) is decoded from the solution of the two-moment equation model (OPOSPM) using the maximum entropy principle. The posterior information is supplied from the local discrete samples (N_i) which were obtained from the solution of M-transport equations. The MREPDE has four striking advantages: Firstly, it is a continuous approximate solution satisfying the positivity physical conditions, secondly, it is consistent with total number and mass concentrations of the particles, thirdly, it supplies the local details of the number concentration function and fourthly, it is consistent with the low-order moments of the population density function. The main challenge in the original density estimator is the complexity arising from the Legendre series as the backbone of the functional estimator with order of complexity $2O(M^2)$ per sampling point. Two distinctive features were introduced to the present MREPDE: firstly, the Clenshaw algorithm (Clenshaw, 1955) is extended from evaluating the Chebyshev series to that of Legendre one and secondly, the MREPDE is completely vectorized to exploit the elegant representation of the complex discrete PBE in complete vectorized form (see Fig.(1)). This enables efficient and parallel execution of numerical algorithms on TPUs (Tensor Processing Units) by exploiting the inherent structure of vectors and matrices. The MREPDE initial learning phase starts by OPOSPM distribution followed by a learning phase that samples the discrete local information in a reinforcement loop. At the heart of the MREPDE is the Clenshaw algorithm which computes the series of Legendre polynomials using a backward recurrence formula based on the information stored in the expansion coefficients (λ) as shown in Fig.(1). The order of complexity is now only $O(M)$ thanks to the Clenshaw algorithm.

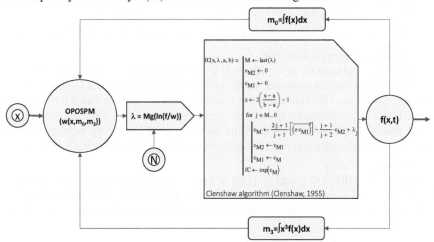

Figure (1): Minimum Relative Entropy Population Density Estimator (MREPDE).

2.3. Tensorial Decomposition of the binary fusion rate

To further enhance the computational speed of the discrete PBE model as given by Eq.(1), it is clear that the other cost of computation lies in the fusion rate matrix Ω (Matveev et al., 2015). In this work we used the tensorial decomposition of Ω to reduce its rank based on the singular value decomposition (SVD). This allows us to express Ω as a sum of rank-one tensors with set of coordinates arranged according to its decreasing magnitude.

3. Results and discussion

3.1. Low-order fusion rate approximation
A sample of results is presented to show the low order approximation of two popular fusion rates using the SVD. The first one is the tensorial decomposition of the Golovin fusion rate for turbulent diffusion which results in an exact low-order approximation of order two. The second case is the most realistic fusion rate of Coulaloglou and Tavlarides based on the kinetic theory of gases to model droplet and bubble coalescence. A five-rank approximation with an error in order of machine precision is found. Fig.(2) shows the contours of the exact (15×15 gris points) and approximate fusion rates ((5×5 grid points)) for a wide range of operating conditions prevailing in an industrial scale mixer used for liquid-liquid dispersions (Alopaeus et al., 1999). On the other hand, the information contents as represented by the singular values is shown in Fig.(3)-Left. This reduction in the rank of fusion rate matrix results in an accelerated computational time.

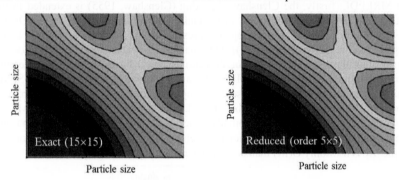

Figure (2): Exact and reduced contours of Coulaloglou and Tavlarides fusion rate using the SVD.

3.2. CPU time for the fast MREPDE
For comparison between the new MREPDE with enhanced vectorized features in terms of computational time (as measured by the CPU time), we performed a standard test on the implementation of the Golovin fusion rate for turbulent diffusion with 0.05/s dilution rate and 0.025/s pre-frequency factor. The particle size domain $x \in [a = 0.01, b = 4]$ with a grid that is distributed according to the distribution of Gauss-Legendre quadrature nodes. The initial condition is normal distribution with $\mu = 1.20$ mm and $\sigma = 0.30$ mm.

3.3. Reference solution
To validate the MREPDE model (Eq.(3)) in terms of the conserved moments; namely, the zero and third moments as well as higher order moments, the Chebyshev-QMOM is used with InvQMOM to reconstruct the particle size distribution (Attarakih et al., 2021).

$$f(x) = w(x,t) \, exp\left(\sum_{j=0}^{M-1} \lambda_j(t) \varphi_j(x) \right) \tag{3}$$

In Eq.(3) w is the Weibull pdf and φ is a Legendre polynomial. The system of Eqs.(1,2 and 3) were solved in the standard summation forms with the MREPDE in its classical form with no vectorization except for the calculation of the vector λ. On the other hand, the fully vectorized form of Eqs.(1 and 2) and the MREPDE with Clenshaw algorithm (see Fig.(1)) were also solved under the same conditions listed in section 3.2.

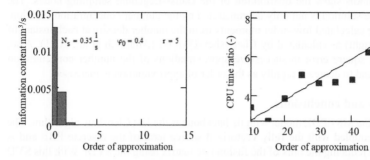

Figure (3): (Left) Information content (Singular values) of the Coulaloglou and Tavlarides fusion rate, (Right) CPU time ratio between the fast (vectorized) and slow (nonvectorized) algorithms.

Fig.(3)-Right shows the CPU time ratio between the vectorized MREPDE with Clenshaw algorithm and the classical nonvectorized PBE. It is obvious that as the order of approximation is increased, the CPU time ratio increases as well. This indicates the reduction in complexity from $O(M^2)$ to $O(M)$ per sampling point. Actually the CPU time for the fast vectorized MREPDE with Clenshaw algorithm shows linear dependency on the order of approximation (Fig.(4)-Left) while the classical nonvectorized one shows cubic dependency on the order of approximation as shown in Fig.(4)-Right.

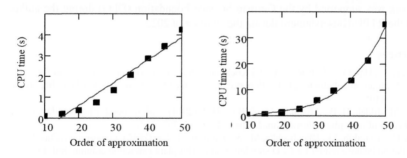

Figure (4): (Left) CPU time for the fast algorithm, (Right) CPU time for the classical algorithm.

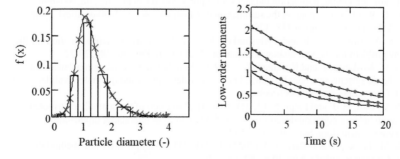

Figure (5): (Left) Estimated density with 30 nodes, (Right) Estimated low-order moments.

Fig.(5)-Left shows the estimated population number concentration at final simulation time of 20 seconds as calculated using the MREPDE (sloid line) and compared to the reconstructed solution (bars) using the InvQMOM (Attarakih et al., 2021) with 8 nodes. The cross symbols show the distribution of the Gauss-Legendre sampling nodes. The accuracy of the solution is not only demonstrated by the number concentration function, but also by the calculated low-order moments from the number density at each instant of time (Fig.(5)-right) as calculated by Chebyshev-QMOM (Attarakih et al., 2021). Also, the root mean square error in successive approximations of the number concentration function is found to decrease rapidly as the order of approximation is increased.

4. Summary and conclusions

We proposed the MREPDE model with its backbone is the fast Clenshaw algorithm. The MREPDE is coupled with the fully vectorized source term of the discrete PBE and is accelerated by reducing the rank of the fusion rate matrix using the SVD. With this SVD of the popular Coulaloglou and Tavlarides fusion rate, it is found a rank of order 5 is sufficient to produce accurate approximation of the exact matrix. On the other hand, the Clenshaw algorithm is extended and used to evaluate the Legendre series in the MREPDE which reduced the order of complexity from $O(M^2)$ to $O(M)$. Based on this, the CPU time average ratio between the fast and standard implementation of the MREPDE is found up to 7 times as the number of sampling points approaches 50 nodes. Our fast implementation is found extremely accurate in estimating the population density and its global moments when compared to the InvQMOM.

Acknowledgments

This work was supported by the German Science Foundation (DFG) during the author visit to the RTPU/Kaiserslautern during the summer of 2022.

References

Neuendorf, L., Hammal, Z., Fricke, A. and Kockmann, N. (2023). AI-based supervision for a stirred extraction column assisted with population balance-based simulation. Chem. Ing. Tech, 95,1134-1145.

Mickler, M., Jildeh, H. B., Attarakih, M., & Bart, H. J. (2014). Online monitoring, simulation and prediction of multiphase flows. Can. J. Chem. Eng., 92, 307–317.

Drumm, C., Attarakih, M., Hlawitschka, M. W. and Bart, H.-J. r. (2010). One-group reduced population balance model for CFD simulation of a pilot-plant extraction column. Ind. Eng. Chem. Res. 49:3442–3451.

Attarakih, M. and Bart, H.-J. (2020). Beyond OPOSPM: A Corrected maximum entropy Weibull distribution for solving population balances. Computer-Aided Chem. Eng., 48, 691-696.

Clenshaw, C. W. (1955). A note on the summation of Chebyshev series. Mathematical Tables and Other Aids to Computation 9:118–120.

Matveev, S. A., Smirnov, A. P. and Tyrtyshnikov, E. E. (2015). A fast numerical method for the Cauchy problem for the Smoluchowski equation. J. of Comp. Physics, 282, 23-32.

Alopaeus, V., Koskinen, J. and Keskinen, K. I. (1999). Simulation of population balances for liquid-liquid systems in a nonideal stirred tank. Part1 description and qualitative validation of model. Chem. Eng. Sci. 54:5887-5899.

Attarakih, M, Bart, H.-J. and Faqir, N. (2004). Numerical solution of the spatially distributed population balance equation describing the hydrodynamics of interacting liquid-liquid dispersions. Chem. Eng. Sci., 59:2567-2592.

Attarakih, M., Fricke, A. and Bart, H.-J. (2021). InvQMOM: A Simple inversion method that works. Computer-Aided Chem. Eng., 50, 535-540.

Flavio Manenti, Gintaras V. Reklaitis (Eds.), Proceedings of the 34th European Symposium on Computer Aided Process Engineering / 15th International Symposium on Process Systems Engineering (ESCAPE34/PSE24), June 2-6, 2024, Florence, Italy

A Logic-Based Implementation of the LP/NLP Branch and Bound Algorithm

Rubén Ruiz-Femenia[a*], Juan Javaloyes-Antón[a] and José A. Caballero[a].

[a]*Department of Chemical Engineering, University of Alicante, Ap. correos 99. E-03080, Alicante, Spain.*
ruben.ruiz@ua.es

Abstract

This study addresses discrete optimization problems in Process System Engineering (PSE) by introducing a Logic-Based LP/NLP Branch and Bound (LB LP/NLP BB) algorithm. We extend the LP/NLP BB algorithm to exploit disjunctive structures, enhancing its capabilities for discrete/continuous optimization. The proposed logic-based approach reduces combinatorial search efforts, showcasing superior performance compared to non-logic versions. Through a case study and computational results, we demonstrate a substantial reduction in both the number and size of LP problems solved in the logic version. The Logic-Based LP/NLP BB algorithm emerges as a promising tool for tackling large-scale disjunctive problems, offering potential applications superstructure optimization embedded with commercial process simulators.

Keywords: mathematical programming, generalized disjunctive programming, LP/NLP branch and bound, Mixed-Integer Non-Linear Programming (MINLP).

1. Introduction

The contributions of the Process System Engineering community to solving the complex problems emerging nowadays demands addressing large-scale discrete problems. Advancements in computer hardware and mathematical programming algorithms, as noted by Koch et al. (2022), show approximately a 20x speedup in hardware for LP/MILP (Linear Programming/Mixed-Integer Linear Programming) problems from 2001 to 2020, while MILP algorithms improved 50x, resulting in a total speed up of around 1,000 times. Continuing this growth, innovative algorithms may play an essential role in solving real-world problems.

In Mixed-Integer Non-Linear Programming (MINLP), two main approaches exist: i) single-tree and ii) multi-tree search. A well-known single-tree algorithm for solving MILPs is the Kelley's algorithm (Kelley, 1960), a branch-and-bound type algorithm that solves relaces MILP problems, where the feasible region is iteratively tightened by adding cutting planes derived from the fractional values of the solution in the previous iteration. Westerlund and Petterson extended this as the Extended Cutting Plane (ECP) algorithm (Westerlund and Pettersson, 1995). The main drawback of single-tree algorithms is that its convergence may be slow. An algorithm that exemplifies the multi-tree approach is the Outer Approximation (OA) algorithm (Duran and Grossmann, 1986), which solves the Non-Linear Programming (NLP) subproblem that arises from the original problem by fixing binary variables from the solution of the previous MILP. This significantly reduces the number of iterations compared to branch and bound algorithms (single-tree). However, it is less efficient because, at each iteration, an MILP must be solved, leading to the development of a new search tree. To leverage the strengths of both approaches, a hybrid algorithm, LP/NLP based branch and bound, was developed by Quesada and Grossmann (1992), that can be viewed as a single-tree implementation of the OA algorithm. The idea here is to relax the nonlinearities by linearizing the original problem and hence solve LP problems at the nodes of the tress while simultaneously relaxing the integrality by branching. This avoids solving an MILP master problem at each iteration. When an integer feasible solution is obtained at a node, an NLP subproblem is solved, providing an upper bound and outer approximation cuts that are updated to tighten all the open nodes of the single-tree search.

In this work, we extended the LP/NLP BB algorithm developed by Quesada and Grossmann into a logic equivalent customized algorithm that exploits the disjunctive structure of the model, thereby facilitating the modeling of discrete/continuous optimization problems by using symbolic expressions. The proposed LB LP/NLP BB algorithm solves the NLP subproblems within a reduced space (focusing exclusively on the Boolean variables that hold true in the current node). We assess the performance of the logic-based version by comparing it to the original LP/NLP algorithm through the use of a case study.

2. Example Logic-Based LP/NLP Brach and Bound Algorithm

2.1. Types of problems
In this section we formulate the problems involved in the LB LP/NLP BB algorithm. The problem P-GDP shows the Generalized Disjunctive Programming formulation (Raman and Grossmann, 1994) of an optimization problem involving discrete decisions (given a set of disjunctions K, at each disjunction D_k, only one term i must be selected).

$$\underset{x\in\mathbb{R}^n, z, c_k \in\mathbb{R}, Y_{ik}\in\{True, False\}}{minimize} \quad z = \sum_{k\in K} c_k + f(x) \ \big(\text{objective function}\big)$$

$$s.t. \quad h(x) = 0$$
$$g(x) \leq 0 \ \big(\text{common constraints}\big)$$

$$\underset{i\in D_k}{\vee} \begin{bmatrix} Y_{i,k} \\ r_{i,k}(x) \leq 0 \\ s_{i,k}(x) = 0 \\ c_k = \gamma_{i,k} \end{bmatrix} \quad k \in K \ \big(\text{disjunctions}\big) \qquad \text{(P-GDP)}$$

$$\Omega(Y) = True \ \big(\text{logic propositions}\big)$$
$$x^{lo} \leq x \leq x^{up}$$

From the above formulation, a GDP master problem, Eq (1), and GDP subproblem, Eq (2) can be derived. For convex problems, the GDP master problem is a relaxation of the original GDP problem generated by linear approximations at a set of given points, $x^j, j = 1,...,l$.

$$\underset{x \in \mathbb{R}^n, c_k, \alpha, z^M \in \mathbb{R}, Y_{i,k} \in \{True, False\}}{\text{minimize}} \quad z^M = \sum_{k \in K} c_k + \alpha$$

s.t.

$$\left. \begin{array}{l} \alpha \geq f(x^j) + \nabla f(x^j)^T(x - x^j) \\ T_h^j \left[h(x^j) + \nabla h(x^j)^T(x - x^j) \right] \leq 0 \\ g(x^j) + \nabla g(x^j)^T(x - x^j) \leq 0 \end{array} \right\}, \; j = 1,\ldots,l$$

$$\left. \underset{i \in D_k}{\vee} \left| \begin{array}{c} Y_{ik} \\ \left. \begin{array}{l} r_{i,k}(x^j) + \nabla r_{i,k}(x^j)^T(x - x^j) \leq 0 \\ T_s^j \left[\nabla s_{i,k}(x^j)^T(x - x^j) \right] \leq 0 \end{array} \right\}, \; j \in L_{i,k}^l = \left\{ j : Y_{i,k}^l = True, j = 1,\ldots,l \right\} \\ c_k = \gamma_{i,k} \end{array} \right| \; k \in K \right. \tag{1}$$

$$\Omega(Y) = True$$

$$x^{lo} \leq x \leq x^{up}$$

The GDP subproblem (Eq (2)), which is an NLP, is obtained from the GDP formulation by fixing the values of the Boolean variables.

$$\underset{x \in \mathbb{R}^n, c_k, z_l^{Sub} \in \mathbb{R}}{\text{minimize}} \quad z_l^{Sub} = \sum_{k \in K} c_k + f(x)$$

s.t. $\quad h(x) = 0$

$$\left. \begin{array}{l} g(x) \leq 0 \\ r_{i,k}(x) \leq 0 \\ s_{i,k}(x) = 0 \\ c_k = \gamma_{ik} \end{array} \right\} \text{for } Y_{i,k}^l = True, \; i \in D_k, k \in K \tag{2}$$

$$x^{lo} \leq x \leq x^{up}$$

The GDP master problem, Eq (1), is reformulated using the Hull Relaxation to obtain an MILP master problem, Eq (3):

$$\underset{x \in \mathbb{R}^n, v_{i,k}, \alpha, z_l^M \in \mathbb{R}^1, y_{i,k} \in \{0,1\}}{\text{minimize}} \quad z_l^M = \sum_{k \in K} \sum_{i \in D_k} \gamma_{i,k} y_{i,k} + \alpha$$

s.t.

$$\left. \begin{array}{l} \alpha \geq f(x^j) + \nabla f(x^j)^T(x - x^j) \\ T_h^j \left[h(x^j) + \nabla h(x^j)^T(x - x^j) \right] \leq 0 \\ g(x^j) + \nabla g(x^j)^T(x - x^j) \leq 0 \end{array} \right\}, \; j = 1,\ldots,l$$

$$\left. \left. \left. \begin{array}{l} \nabla r_{i,k}(x^j)^T v_{i,k} \leq \left(-r_{i,k}(x^j) + \nabla r_{i,k}(x^j)^T x^j \right) y_{i,k} \\ T_s^j \nabla s_{i,k}(x^j)^T v_{i,k} \leq T_s^j \nabla s_{i,k}(x^j)^T y_{i,k} \end{array} \right\}, \; j \in L_{i,k}^l \\ x^{lo} y_{i,k} \leq v_{i,k} \leq x^{up} y_{i,k} \end{array} \right|, i \in D_k \atop x = \sum_{i \in D_k} v_{i,k} \right\}, k \in K \tag{3}$$

$$Ay \geq a$$

2.2. Algorithm

The Logic-Based LP/NLP BB algorithm shown in Algorithm 1 keeps a list of the LP_i problems obtained from the GDP master HR reformulation, Eq. (3), by relaxing the integrality condition on the binary variables. Each LP_i problem represents a node within the branch-and-bound tree. The formulation of the LP_i at the initial node, N_1, requires an initialization step that provides, at least, a linearization point (x^j) for the nonlinear constraints for each term for all the disjunctions. These points, $x^j, j = 1,...,n^{Sub}$, comes from the solution of n^{Sub} initial GDP subproblems given by Eq. (2), where the fixed values of the Boolean variables, $Y_{i,k}^l = True, l = 1,...,n^{Sub}$, are determined by solving an iterative set covering problem. Let $\mathcal{L}$ denote the list of nodes that must still be solved (i.e., those not pruned or branched). Let z^{up} and z^{lo} denote the best upper and lower bound on the optimum value. Initially, the upper bound is derived from the lowest value of the objective function in the solved initial GDP subproblems. The proposed method is summarized as a pseudo code in Algorithm 1.

Algorithm 1. Logic-Based LP/NLP Branch and Bound algorithm.

---

0. Initialize

$\mathcal{L}= \{N_1\}$, $l' = \left\{ l : \min z_l^{Sub}, l = 1,...,n^{Sub} \right\}$, $z^{up} = z_{l'}^{Sub}$, $z^{lo} = -\infty$

$(x^\star, y^\star) = (x_{l'}^{Sub,\star}, \left\{ y_{i,k}^{Sub,\star}=1: Y_{i,k}^{l'} = True, y_{i,k}^{Sub,\star}=0: Y_{i,k}^{l'} = False \right\})$

1. Terminate?

If $\mathcal{L}= \varnothing$, the solution $(x^\star, y^\star)$ is optimal or the optimality gap $z^{up} - z^{lo}$ is below a specified tolerance.

2. Select node

Choose a node N_i in $\mathcal{L}$ and delete it from $\mathcal{L}$.

3. Bound

Solve LP_i. If it is infeasible, go to **Step 1**. Else, let $(x_i^\star, y_i^\star)$ be its solution and $z_i^\star$ its objective function value.

4. Prune

If $z_i^\star \geq z^{up}$, go to **Step 1**.

Else,

      if $(x_i^\star, y_i^\star)$ is infeasible to MILP (GDP master problem, Eq. (4)) go to **Step 6**.

      if $(x_i^\star, y_i^\star)$ is feasible to MILP, let $z^{lo} = z_i^\star$ if $z_i^\star \geq z^{lo}$, and go to **Step 5**.

5. Add cuts?

Solve the NLP (GDP subproblem, Eq. (3)) fixing the Boolean variables accordingly to $y_i^\star$ values. If $z_i^{Sub,\star} \leq z^{up}$, let $z^{up} = z_i^{Sub,\star}$, $(x^\star, y^\star) = (x_i^{Sub,\star}, y_i^\star)$ and delete from $\mathcal{L}$ all nodes N_i with $z_i^\star \geq z^{up}$. Strengthen LP_i and all nodes N_i in $\mathcal{L}$ by adding linearizations evaluated at the solution of the NLP, x_i^{Sub}. Go back to **Step 3**.

6. Branch

From LP_i, construct linear programs LP_i^1 and LP_i^2 with smaller feasible regions whose union contains all the solutions of LP_i with $y_i \in \{0,1\}^m$. Add the corresponding new nodes LP_i^1 and LP_i^2 to $\mathcal{L}$ and go to **Step 1**.

---

3. Case study

The proposed Logic-Based LP/NLP branch and bound algorithm has been tested in solving the illustrative eight-process problem taken from the work of Türkay and Grossmann (1996). This test problem comprises eigth Boolean variables, 33 continuous variables, and eight disjunctions with two terms each (five of them nonlinear), leading to 20 different feasible process topologies. The superstructure of the process syntesis problem is shown in Figure 1a.

4. Results

The case study is solved by the LB LP/NLP BB algorithm implemented in GAMS using the CONOPT solver for the NLP subproblems and the CPLEX 12.1.0 solver for LP problems. Figure 2 shows the search tree for the case study obtained with the proposed method. It follows a best-bound search strategy and a branching rule that selects the binary variable closest to 1. The optimal process configuration for the test problem is shown in Figure 1b. To assess the performance of the LP LP/NLP BB algorithm, the test problem has also been solved with the non-logic version of the LP/NLP BB algorithm and the Logic-Based Outer Approximation (LBOA) algorithm. Table 1 presents the main computational results. The number of LP problems solved decreased from 32 to 10 in the logic version of the LP/NLP BB algorithm. In comparison to the LBOA, the proposed method eliminates the need to solve 3 MILP problems.

Regarding the size of the LP problems, a typical LP problem in the logic version of the LP/NLP BB algorithm comprises 56 equations, whereas in the non-logic algorithm, it consists of 75 equations. In both cases, there are 33 continuous variables and 8 relaxed binary variables.

5. Conclusions

The application of logic version of the LP/NLP BB algorithm to our case study has resulted in two main advantages over the conventional LP/NLP BB. It achieves a significant descent in the number of LP problems solved and in the size of these problems. These results are promising when applied to larger-scale disjunctive problem. The logic feature of the LB LP/NLP BB algorithm is perfectly suited for superstructure optimization involving the use of commercial process simulators.

Further work involves adapting the LB LP/NLP BB algorithm to be used in conjunction with the state-of-the-art branch and bound commercial solvers through the user cuts facility available in these solvers.

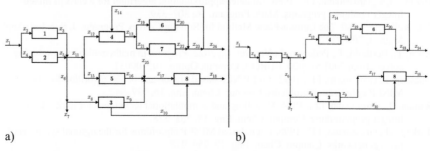

a)   b)

Figure 1. a) Eight-process problem superstructure and b) optimal flowsheet topology.

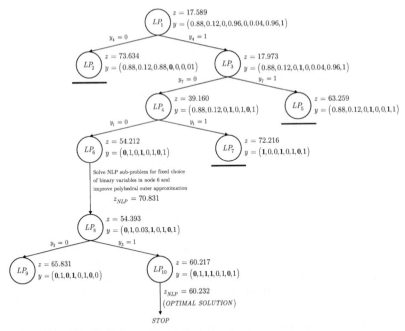

Figure 2. Search tree of the Logic-Based LP/NLP branch and bound algorithm.

Table 1. Computational results.

	LB LP/NLP BB	LBOA	LP/NLP BB
Initial NLP sub-problems	2	1	1
NLP sub-problems	2	2	3
LP problems	10	---	32
MILP problems	---	3	---

Acknowledgments

The authors gratefully acknowledge financial support to the Spanish "Ministerio de Ciencia e Innovación" under project PID2021-124139NB-C21.

References

Duran, M.A., Grossmann, I.E., 1986. An outer-approximation algorithm for a class of mixed-integer nonlinear programs. Math. Program. 36, 307–339.

J. E. Kelley, J., 1960. The Cutting-Plane Method for Solving Convex Programs. J. Soc. Ind. Appl. Math. 8, 703–712.

Koch, T., Berthold, T., Pedersen, J., Vanaret, C., 2022. Progress in mathematical programming solvers from 2001 to 2020. EURO J. Comput. Optim. 10, 100031.

Quesada, I., Grossmann, I.E., 1992. An LP/NLP based branch and bound algorithm for convex MINLP optimization problems. Comput. Chem. Eng. 16, 937–947.

Raman, R., Grossmann, I.E., 1994. Modelling and computational techniques for logic based integer programming. Comput. Chem. Eng. 18, 563–578.

Türkay, M., Grossmann, I.E., 1996. Logic-based MINLP algorithms for the optimal synthesis of process networks. Comput. Chem. Eng. 20, 959–978.

Westerlund, T., Pettersson, F., 1995. An extended cutting plane method for solving convex MINLP problems. Comput. Chem. Eng. 19, 131–136.

Flavio Manenti, Gintaras V. Reklaitis (Eds.), Proceedings of the 34th European Symposium on
Computer Aided Process Engineering / 15th International Symposium on Process Systems
Engineering (ESCAPE34/PSE24), June 2-6, 2024, Florence, Italy

FASTMAN-JMP: All-in-one Tool for Data Mining and Model Building

Kyle Territo, *Jose Romagnoli

Louisiana State University, Baton Rouge, United States
*kterri3@lsu.edu, *jose@lsu.edu*

Abstract

In the contemporary realm of big data, the adept exploration of vast multivariate datasets is indispensable. Addressing this imperative, FASTMAN-JMP emerges as an innovative add-in for SAS's JMP software, seamlessly amalgamating a diverse range of machine learning algorithms into a unified and user-friendly tool. This integration serves as a catalyst for extracting profound insights from intricate data sets, insights that could easily elude discovery otherwise. Boasting an intuitively designed graphical user interface, FASTMAN-JMP leads users through a methodically structured process of knowledge discovery, finely tailored to their specific use cases.

Keywords: data-mining, dimensionality reduction, software, data exploration

1. Introduction

Data is often regarded as the most important asset in the modern world because it holds the key to understanding complex patterns, behaviors, and trends, enabling informed decision-making in almost every aspect of business, science, technology, and even societal development. Due to the advancements brought about by Industry 4.0, such as the integration of the Internet of Things, artificial intelligence, and automation, data is now being generated at exponentially higher rates than ever before. The need for better ways to analyze this burgeoning big data is crucial for several reasons. Firstly, the sheer volume of data exceeds the capacity of conventional databases and analytical tools, necessitating more sophisticated and scalable solutions. Secondly, the complexity and diversity of this data require advanced analytics techniques, like machine learning and AI, to extract meaningful insights. These insights are vital for driving efficiencies, innovation, and competitive advantage in an increasingly data-driven world. Moreover, efficient analysis of big data enables predictive maintenance, enhanced customer experiences, and more informed decision-making, all of which are key components in realizing the full potential of Industry 4.0. This work introduces an environment designed to streamline the application of pattern recognition techniques to historical datasets. FASTMAN-JMP, an integrated tool for data exploration and fault detection, seamlessly merges the statistical data analysis software JMP [1] with the FASTMAN Python environment [2]. Packaged as an add-in utilizing JMP Scripting Language (JSL), FASTMAN-JMP eliminates the need for users to possess an in-depth understanding of the intricate implementation of each offered method. This includes tasks such as data cleaning, normalization, sampling, dimensionality reduction, and data clustering. Serving as the offline, model-building component in the process monitoring workflow, this tool conducts clustering on a historical database to train a model. This model can then be deployed for real-time process monitoring. All data used in this paper will be sourced from the Tennessee Eastman Process (TEP), a virtual plant that produces time series data often used for benchmark tests for process control and fault detection applications [3].

2. Data Mining & Knowledge Discovery

Data Mining

FASTMAN-JMP workflow is illustrated in *Figure 1*. It begins with the data pre-processing phase, a frequently underestimated yet vital stage in the process. Often times, data is not clean. There may be missing values, outliers, or non-numeric values. In the context of chemical plants, malfunctioning sensors, process downtime, or human errors could cause missing data or outliers in the data. The next pre-processing step is data scaling. Scaling is a crucial step in the machine learning pipeline due to different ranges of the features. The environment has implemented several dimensionality reduction methods, including Principal Component Analysis (PCA), Independent Component Analysis (ICA), Spectral Embedding, t-distributed Stochastic Neighbour Embedding (t-SNE), Uniform Manifold Approximation and Projection (UMAP), Triplet Manifold Approximation (TriMAP), and most recently, Pairwise Controlled Manifold Approximation (PaCMAP). Users do not need to have a deep understanding of each method before using them, as FASTMAN-JMP will employ default parameters if none are specified. This feature allows users to become more familiar with the methods and later fine-tune parameters as needed. Furthermore, FASTMAN-JMP offers a range of clustering methods, including K-Means, MeanShift, Balanced Iterative Reducing and Clustering using Hierarchies (BIRCH), Density-Based Spatial Clustering of Applications with Noise (DBSCAN), and Hierarchical Density-Based Spatial Clustering of Applications with Noise (HDBSCAN). Additionally, users have the option to upload custom cluster labels to overlay on the preprocessed and reduced data projection. Just like with the dimensionality reduction methods, FASTMAN-JMP does not demand that users fully comprehend each clustering method upfront, and default parameters are used in the absence of user specifications.

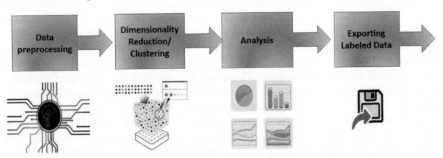

Figure 1: FASTMAN-JMP workflow for Data Mining

As an example, consider the data from the Tennessee Eastman Process (TEP). Specifically, data for TEP-1, where the A/C feed ratio is varied, and the B composition remains constant (step change). *Figure 2* displays 2D projections of the data using four combinations of DR (PCA, UMAP, t-SNE, and PaCMAP) and DBSCAN clustering techniques. It's worth noting that all the methods—namely t-SNE, UMAP, and PaCMAP-show excellent separability among classes (clusters). The only difference between them is that UMAP and PaCMAP subdivide the transient region between clusters (due to the action of the controller) into an additional region, showing a better characterization of the local process behavior. On the other hand, when using PCA for dimensionality reduction, the DBSCAN algorithm falls short in proper classification, illustrating the necessity of selecting an appropriate combination of techniques to fully and accurately classify the data.

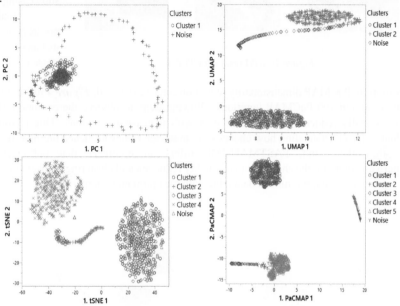

Figure 2: DR and Clustering results for TEP-1

Analysis Features

After gaining insight from the dimensionally reduced, clustered data, there are more features that can be used to extract more information and further reassure the users initial conclusions. First, contribution plots can be created. These serve a crucial role in identifying the features that most significantly influence the difference between two specific clusters. This is super effective—with just a few clicks of a button the user can go from knowing little about their data to quickly pinpointing the exact variables responsible for a fault in the process. Another notable feature is the use of Self-Organizing Maps (SOMs), which are unsupervised, neural network-based models that arrange data points onto a lower-dimensional grid. These maps serve as a valuable complement to traditional 2-D dimension reduction plots, offering comparable results and insights. *Figure 3* shows the raw SOM, an original cluster projected to the raw SOM, and a feature projected to the raw SOM.

After verifying the dimensionality reduction and clustering with SOM, the user can conduct sensitivity analysis with FASTMAN-JMP. This analysis, applicable to tasks like data cleaning and normalization, involves selecting parameters (e.g., outlier count for cleaning, cluster numbers for k-means) and setting their range and interval. As the parameter varies within this range, clustering metrics (silhouette, Davies-Bouldin scores)

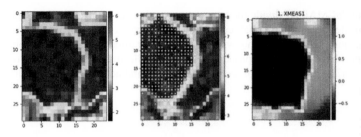

Figure 3: SOM results for TEP-1

and visual plots of the reduced and clustered data are generated, showcasing the analysis progression. For instance, the impact of varying iterations in PaCMAP dimensionality reduction can be examined. *Figure 4* illustrates the data at 50 and 100 PaCMAP iterations, allowing users to observe the evolution of the dimensionally reduced and clustered data with increasing iterations. This method is valuable for understanding how changes in parameter values influence the final results. On the other hand, FASTMAN-JMP offers an optimizer that optimizes all hyperparameters for the chosen dimensionality reduction and clustering algorithms. After the optimizer is run, it returns a data table with the optimum hyperparameters.

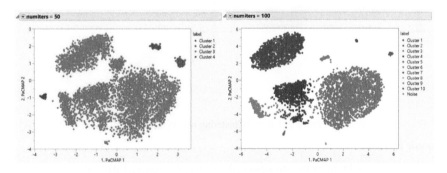

Figure 4: FASTMAN-JMP sensitivity analysis for PaCMAP number of iterations

3. Predictive Modelling

By this stage, the user is expected to have derived significant insights from their data via unsupervised techniques such as dimensionality reduction, clustering, and Self-Organizing Maps (SOMs). Understanding the impact of each feature on the clustering process is further enhanced by examining contribution plots. The next step involves developing predictive models. The analysed data will be employed to train a selected model. It's crucial to generate visualizations to validate the model's effectiveness, ensuring it is capable of making accurate predictions and that the model can be exported for external applications. This process is illustrated in *Figure 5*. FASTMAN-JMP provides the capability to produce both classification and regression models, tailored to the user's specific application. For instance, classification models can be developed for chemical plant data, labelling data points into predefined classes that represent various

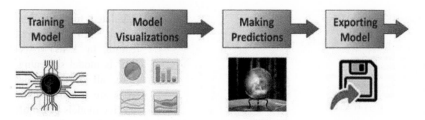

Figure 5: FASTMAN-JMP workflow for predictive modeling

plant operating conditions. Conversely, regression models can be constructed to function as 'soft sensors', predicting the value of one feature based on the values of other features. This is particularly useful for features that are challenging or costly to measure directly with physical sensors.

Classification Model Building

In FASTMAN-JMP, a classification predictive model is created using labelled data from prior clustering. This process involves choosing from available model types like Random Forest, Boosted Tree, Decision Tree, Neural Network, SVM, Linear Classifier, and Naïve Bayes classifier. The procedure includes dividing the data into training and test sets, adjusting hyperparameters, and training the model. After training, the model's accuracy is assessed using the test data, with the option to fine-tune hyperparameters through grid-search optimization if necessary. Depending on the chosen model, specific visualizations are generated, such as a confusion matrix and feature importance plot for a Random Forest model. As shown in *Figure 6*, the confusion matrix plots the true labels vs. the predicted labels and looks for mismatches that can be seen by a heatmap. A good confusion matrix results in a diagonal with darker colors—showing that the predicted labels match with the true labels. These visual aids are crucial for evaluating prediction accuracy and the impact of different features. Finally, the model can be either exported for further use or employed to predict new clustering labels on novel data.

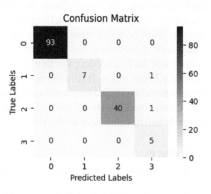

Figure 6: FASTMAN-JMP confusion

Regression Model Building

On the other hand, FASTMAN-JMP also offers regression model building. These models do not require labelled data as they are just predicting continuous values. The model types for use are Random Forest, Gradient Boosted Tree, Decision Tree, Linear, Ridge, SVR, ElasticNet, Lasso, and Ada Boost regressors. The process begins with splitting the data into training and testing sets and choosing a suitable model. Key steps involve defining the target variable and identifying predictors. Once the model is trained, its performance is evaluated by plotting actual values against predicted ones, with an ideal model showing data along a diagonal line. Metrics like R-squared value and mean-squared-error are

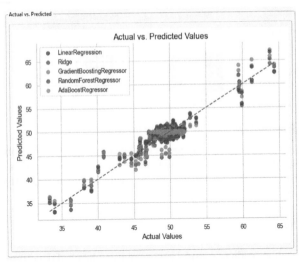

calculated to assess the model. An additional feature in FASTMAN-JMP is model screening. Here, all of the model types are tested and the top five models based off of MSE values are plotted. This model screening process is illustrated in *Figure 7*. Finally, one can optimize hyperparameters using grid-search, export the model, or use it to make predictions on new data.

Figure 7: FASTMAN-JMP plot for different regression models

4. Conclusions

By addressing the challenges posed by the volume, velocity, and variety of data generated in modern times, Fastman-JMP offers a comprehensive solution for data exploration and fault detection. Its capabilities in data pre-processing, dimensionality reduction, clustering, and predictive modelling make it an invaluable tool for extracting meaningful insights from complex datasets. The use of the Tennessee Eastman Process data in this study underscores the tool's applicability in real-world scenarios, particularly in process control and fault detection. As industries continue to evolve in a data-driven landscape, tools like FASTMAN-JMP will play a pivotal role in harnessing the power of big data to drive innovation, efficiency, and competitive advantage. This paper not only highlights the features and functionalities of FASTMAN-JMP but also sets the stage for future research and development in the realm of advanced data analytics.

References

[1] *Statistical Software*. JMP. (n.d.). https://www.jmp.com/en_us/home.html

[2] Romagnoli, J. (n.d.). Fault Detection and Knowledge Discovery. PSE LSU. https://pse.che.lsu.edu/DA.php

[3] Shen Yin, Steven X. Ding, Adel Haghani, Haiyang Hao, Ping Zhang, A comparison study of basic data-driven fault diagnosis and process monitoring methods on the benchmark Tennessee Eastman process, Journal of Process Control, Volume 22, Issue 9, 2012, Pages 1567-1581, ISSN 0959-1524, https://doi.org/10.1016/j.jprocont.2012.06.009. (https://www.sciencedirect.com/science/article/pii/S0959152412001503)

Flavio Manenti, Gintaras V. Reklaitis (Eds.), Proceedings of the 34th European Symposium on
Computer Aided Process Engineering / 15th International Symposium on Process Systems
Engineering (ESCAPE34/PSE24), June 2-6, 2024, Florence, Italy

A Fuzzy Interval Type 2 Logic Approach with Bow-tie Technique and Sensitivity Analysis

Vitor A. O. Silva[a], Raphael A. Santana[a], Raphael I. Tsukada[a], Savio S. V. Vianna[a], Flavio Vasconcelos da Silva[a]

[a]*University of Campinas, School of Chemical Engineering, Chemical Systems Engineering Department – Albert Einstein Ave., 500, Campinas – SP, 13083-852, Brazil*
v188321@dac.unicamp.br

Abstract

In the context of risk management in the process industries, a major concern arises due to the scarcity of data about frequencies of events, failure probabilities, and other critical parameters, largely dependent on operator and specialist experience. A fuzzy logic system designed for handling uncertain and vague information is proposed to address this issue. The study integrates fuzzy interval type-2 logic into the Bow-tie diagram, a visual tool depicting risk sources and control barriers. Moreover, the paper discusses applying sensitivity analysis techniques to support decision-making based on the Bow-tie model with fuzzy interval type-2 inference systems. Two sensitivity analysis methods — variance-based analysis (Sobol' method) and derivative-based analysis (method of Morris) — are considered to understand how uncertainty in input parameters affects output uncertainty. The proposed methodology is applied to a case study in the oil and gas industry, specifically focusing on the transportation of hydrocarbons through flexible pipelines (risers). This comprehensive approach is expected to enhance risk management practices in complex industrial processes, facilitating more informed decision-making and contributing to safer and more reliable operations.

Keywords: Process Safety, Risk Analysis, Bow-tie, Fuzzy Logic, Sensitivity Analysis.

1. Introduction

Accident prevention through risk assessment is crucial to risk management (Khan et al., 2020). There are various methods to quantify event frequencies and their risks. Bow-tie (Figure 1) is a well-known semi-quantitative method. This method employs a diagram in the shape of a bow-tie, where the right side represents initiating events that could develop into a major accident and the preventive barriers to avoid this, and the left side depicts consequences and their mitigation barriers. However, assessing these events involves inherent uncertainties due to imprecise information from insufficient data and specialist knowledge.

Figure 1. Simplified Bow-tie diagram.

The fuzzy logic emerges as a viable solution to deal with uncertainties in risk analysis. Almeida et al. (2023) used the Bow-tie to build a Mamdani fuzzy logic system, combining fault and event tree methods. Within this framework, they introduced "AND" and "OR" nodes, described by 49 rules outlining the relationships between events pairwise. This approach allows the estimation of frequency results considering the uncertainty. Once the uncertainty is addressed with a fuzzy logic system, a comprehensive approach is necessary to understand the importance of each barrier on risk control. This understanding aids in making assertive decisions and enhances the system safety performance. In this regard, Ferdous et al. (2013) also proposed the Bow-tie model as a combination of a fault tree and an event tree. However, Bayesian updating was used to assign the likelihood of undesirable events and a local sensitivity analysis was applied. The approach used Spearman's rank correlation coefficients to assess the contribution of each input event to the risk. While both referenced works utilized fuzzy type-1, this ongoing study advances by adopting fuzzy interval type-2 for a more robust treatment of uncertainty. Furthermore, this research incorporates and compares two distinct methods of global sensitivity analysis (Sobol indices method and method of Morris) to enhance the assessment of the importance of protective barriers. Given the significant impact these issues have on decision-making processes, this study aims to contribute to making the risk management system in process safety more informed and effective.

This work applies the developed framework in a case study on the loss of containment in risers, crucial components that link the seafloor to production and drilling facilities in the offshore oil and gas industry (Figueredo et al., 2023).

2.   Fundamentals and Proposed Framework

2.1.   Fuzzy Interval Type-2

A fuzzy set is an element grouping taken from a universe of discourse, represented through membership functions (μ_A). These functions assign a degree of belongingness to each observation. The fuzzy interval type-2 is derived from the fuzzy type-2 membership function, which can be mathematically described as $((x,u), \mu_A(x,u))|\forall x \in X, \forall u \in Jx \subseteq [0,1]$, where $0 \leq \mu_A(x,u) \leq 1$. To derive the fuzzy interval type-2, $\mu_A(x,u) = 1, \forall u \in Jx \subseteq [0,1]$. This membership function comprises an upper membership function (UMF) and a lower membership function (LMF). Together, these curves define a region known as the footprint of uncertainty. This mathematical construct serves as a tool for describing linguistic variables employed in classifying objects, particularly when uncertainties exist regarding their values. Figure 2 visually represents a simple triangular membership function (Castillo and Melin, 2008).

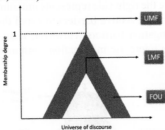

Figure 2. Simple representation of triangular interval fuzzy type membership function

After defining the fuzzy membership function, the subsequent stage involves applying a fuzzy logic system. This system is structured by:

1. **Fuzzifier:** Considering the membership functions previously defined by the specialists, the membership degree of each input is obtained.
2. **Rule base:** Specialists establish rules for the fuzzy logic system, structured as **"IF input 1 is A AND/OR input 2 is B THEN output is C"**, with A, B, and C representing membership functions.
3. **Fuzzy inference engine:** Each rule generates firing strength based on fuzzified inputs, the fuzzy operator ('OR' or 'AND'), and the implication operator ('MIN' or 'PRODUCT'). The engine aggregates these strengths.
4. **Output processor:** The aggregated result is reduced to a type-1 fuzzy system and the final crisp value is obtained through defuzzification.

2.2. Interval Type 2 Fuzzy Logic Bow-tie (IT2FLB)

The IT2FLB employs fuzzy inference nodes in each Bow-tie diagram connection based on the Layers of Protection (LOPA). Along each pathway linking a threat to the top event, inferences are performed representing nodes "AND" (with specific fuzzy set and rule base): the frequency of the threat is combined with the Probability of Failure on Demand (PFD) of the subsequent barrier, resulting in a new frequency. This new frequency is then combined with the PFD of the next barrier. After conducting inferences along the pathways, an "OR" inference is performed, aggregating pairwise the frequencies obtained to determine the frequency of the top event. The same reasoning used to obtain the frequencies of each pathway is applied to obtain the frequencies of consequences.

2.3. Sensitivity analysis

Sensitivity Analysis studies how the influence of uncertainty in a model's response is distributed among the various sources of input uncertainty. Sensitivity analysis assesses its robustness and clarifies complex relationships by offering a comprehensive understanding of a model. This work delves into two distinct sensitivity analysis methods.

2.3.1. Sobol indices method

The Sobol' indices is a variance-based global sensitivity analysis method that decomposes the variance of the model output into contributions from individual input factors and their interactions (Saltelli et al., 2010). The total sensitivity index equation for the Sobol' method is as follows (Equation 1).

$$S_{Ti} = \frac{E_{j \neq i}(V_{ij})}{V} \tag{1}$$

Where V_{ij} is the variance of the model output due to the interaction between the i-th and j-th input factors, and $E_{j \neq i}(V_{ij})$ is the expected value of V_{ij} over all possible combinations of the i-th and j-th input factors. Saltelli's sampling scheme is employed with 1024 samples in this work to explore the universe of input values.

2.3.2. Method of Morris

This derivative-based method involves conducting a sequence of randomized one-factor-at-a-time experiments given by optimized trajectories across p selected levels in the space of the input factors, where changes in the output are attributed to specific changes in the input parameters. The elementary effect d at point **X** of each factor X_i is calculated as shown in Equation 2 (Campolongo et al., 2007).

$$d_i(X) = \left(\frac{y(X_1, \dots, X_{i-1}, X_i + \Delta, X_{i+1}, \dots, X_k) - y(X)}{\Delta} \right) \tag{2}$$

Where Δ is a perturbation value. Then, from the distribution of the absolute values of the elementary effects we denote the estimated mean, μ^*, which provides a reliable ranking of factors in terms of their importance. In this work, using the SALib library (Ruano et al., 2012), the analysis has four levels and 1024 trajectories.

2.4.   Framework

The framework was developed using the Python programming language and leverages function libraries such as pyit2fls, SALib, Numpy, Pandas, and Matplotlib.

The case study Bow-tie is based on CCPS (2018) and Figueredo et al. (2023). For simplicity, this work aims to know the importance of each barrier in preventing the occurrence of the top event. So, the focus is on the left side of the diagram (Figure 3).

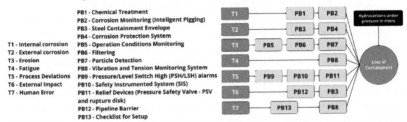

Figure 3. Bow-tie diagram (left side) for oil and gas flow under pressure in risers.

Applying the IT2FLB model in the constructed diagram, the framework involves:

1. Input sets of samples (varying in $[10^{-4}, 10^0]$) and obtain sensitivity indices for each sensitivity analysis method based on the outputs.
2. Generate a ranking of protective barriers with sensitivity indices, from highest to lowest, for each sensitivity analysis method.
3. Compare the two rankings using the Rank Biased Overlap (RBO) concordance measure (Equation 3), where X_d is the length of the overlapping list, n is the number of ranked observations, and p is set to 90% in this case, indicating that the top 4 ranks contribute 60.64% to the RBO.

$$RBO = \frac{X_n}{n} \cdot p^n + \frac{1-p}{p} \sum_{d=1}^{n} \frac{X_d}{d} \cdot p^d \qquad (3)$$

3.   Results

Drawing on the authors' expertise, a fuzzy set for input 1 and output (frequency), a fuzzy set for input 2 (PFD) (Figure 4), and the rule bases (for "AND" and "OR" nodes, with 36 rules each), have been established. Subsequently, the framework was implemented.

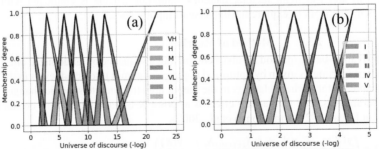

Figure 4. (a) Fuzzy set for input 1 and output. (b) Fuzzy set for input 2.

The normalized sensitivity indices obtained make it possible to view the importance of the protective barriers on the top event frequency reduction (Figure 5).

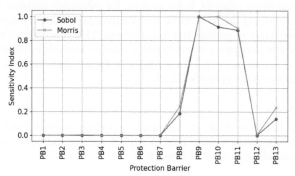

Figure 5. Normalized sensitivity indices for Sobol' and Morris.

With notable advantages, barriers PB9, PB10, and PB11 emerge as the most globally significant. It is inferred that this specific analysis prioritizes barriers associated with the threat of higher frequency, "Process Deviations" (0.003 year^{-1}), placing them at the forefront. Subsequently, PB8 and PB13 exhibit relevance. It's worth highlighting that PB8 functions as a barrier in multiple pathways, those associated with "Fatigue" and "Human Error" threats. Meanwhile, PB13 is within the "Human Error" pathway, with a threat frequency of 0.002 year^{-1} Moving down the list, barriers PB12 and PB3 stand out despite their tendency toward zero. In Sobol' method, they have sensitivity indices of $1.04 \cdot 10^{-6}$ and $2.96 \cdot 10^{-7}$, respectively, with others in the range of 10^{-13} and lower. Similarly, their sensitivity indices in the method of Morris are $2.14 \cdot 10^{-3}$ and $2.77 \cdot 10^{-3}$, respectively, compared to others with values in the order of 10^{-6} and lower., respectively, compared to others with values in the order of 10^{-6} and lower.

The respective rankings and the RBO measure are presented in Table 1.

Table 1. Rankings of protective barriers by the sensitivity analysis and the RBO.

Sobol' Method	Method of Morris	RBO [%]
PB9, PB10, PB11, PB8, PB13, PB12, PB3, PB7, PB5, PB2, PB6, PB1, PB4	PB10, PB9, PB11, PB8, PB13, PB3, PB12, PB1, PB2, PB5, PB7, PB6, PB4	86.89

With an RBO of 86.89%, it is reasonable to consider the rankings as highly concordant. Therefore, the decision regarding method selection for applications can be based on either profiling or the availability of application tools.

To operationalize these findings, let's consider a practical scenario in the oil and gas industry: designing a maintenance plan for risers, establishing a schedule, and managing a limited budget to ensure process safety. Using the IT2FLB built and the Sobol method, the prioritization order for protective barriers could be as follows: (1) PB9: Pressure and Level Switch High alarms (PSH and LSH), (2) PB10: Safety Instrumented Systems (SIS), and (3) PB11: Relief devices. Notably, the top three barriers are associated with process control systems and physical elements, underscoring the critical importance of maintaining these systems. This systematic approach should be applied across all systems within the plant to manage and control risks effectively.

4.   Conclusion

The proposed approach, integrating fuzzy interval type-2 logic with the Bow-tie technique and sensitivity analysis, holds promise for enhancing decision-making in risk management. Identifying the most influential barriers preventing the top event proved consistent and effective in guiding risk management. The robustness of the framework was demonstrated by comparing two different sensitivity analysis methods, as evidenced by the agreement in rankings of preventive barriers. Future applications to real plants are recommended to assess the system's effectiveness.

Acknowledgements

The authors would like to thank the National Council for Scientific and Technological Development (CNPq) grant number 130523/2020-8 and the National Petroleum Agency (ANP). Thanks are also due to Shell Brasil S.A.

References

Almeida, R. S., Vasconcelos da Silva, F., & Vianna, S. S. V. (2023). Combining the bow-tie method and fuzzy logic using Mamdani inference model. *Process Safety and Environmental Protection*, *169*, 159–168. https://doi.org/https://doi.org/10.1016/j.psep.2022.11.005

Campolongo, F., Cariboni, J., & Saltelli, A. (2007). An effective screening design for sensitivity analysis of large models. *Environmental Modelling & Software*, *22*(10), 1509–1518. https://doi.org/https://doi.org/10.1016/j.envsoft.2006.10.004

Castillo, O., & Melin, P. (2008). 3 Type-2 Fuzzy Logic. In *Type-2 Fuzzy Logic: Theory and Applications* (pp. 29–43). Springer Berlin Heidelberg. https://doi.org/10.1007/978-3-540-76284-3_3

CCPS. (2018). *Bow Ties in Risk Management: A Concept Book for Process Safety*. Wiley-AIChE.

Ferdous, R., Khan, F., Sadiq, R., Amyotte, P., & Veitch, B. (2013). Analyzing system safety and risks under uncertainty using a bow-tie diagram: An innovative approach. *Process Safety and Environmental Protection*, *91*(1), 1–18. https://doi.org/https://doi.org/10.1016/j.psep.2011.08.010

Figueredo, A. K. M., Coelho, D. G., Miranda, P. P., de Souza Junior, M. B., Frutuoso e Melo, P. F. F., & Vaz Junior, C. A. (2023). Subsea pipelines incidents prevention: A case study in Brazil. *Journal of Loss Prevention in the Process Industries*, *83*, 105007. https://doi.org/https://doi.org/10.1016/j.jlp.2023.105007

Khan, F. I., Amyotte, P. R., & Amin, Md. T. (2020). Chapter One - Advanced methods of risk assessment and management: An overview. In F. I. Khan & P. R. Amyotte (Eds.), *Advanced Methods of Risk Assessment and Management* (Vol. 4, pp. 1–34). Elsevier. https://doi.org/https://doi.org/10.1016/bs.mcps.2020.03.002

Ruano, M. V, Ribes, J., Seco, A., & Ferrer, J. (2012). An improved sampling strategy based on trajectory design for application of the Morris method to systems with many input factors. *Environmental Modelling & Software*, *37*, 103–109. https://doi.org/https://doi.org/10.1016/j.envsoft.2012.03.008

Saltelli, A., Annoni, P., Azzini, I., Campolongo, F., Ratto, M., & Tarantola, S. (2010). Variance based sensitivity analysis of model output. Design and estimator for the total sensitivity index. *Computer Physics Communications*, *181*(2), 259–270. https://doi.org/https://doi.org/10.1016/j.cpc.2009.09.018

Flavio Manenti, Gintaras V. Reklaitis (Eds.), Proceedings of the 34th European Symposium on Computer Aided Process Engineering / 15th International Symposium on Process Systems Engineering (ESCAPE34/PSE24), June 2-6, 2024, Florence, Italy

Disjunctive Programming meets QUBO

Pedro Maciel Xavier,[a,b,c] Pedro Ripper,[c,d] Joshua Pulsipher,[e] Joaquim Dias Garcia,[c] Nelson Maculan,[b] David E. Bernal Neira [a,f,g,]*

[a] *Davidson School of Chemical Engineering, Purdue University, West Lafayette, IN, USA*
[b] *Computer Science & Systems Engineering Program, COPPE, Federal University of Rio de Janeiro, RJ, Brazil*
[c] *PSR Energy Consulting & Analytics, Rio de Janeiro, RJ, Brazil*
[d] *PUC Department of Electrical Engineering, Pontifical Catholic University of Rio de Janeiro, Rio de Janeiro, RJ, Brazil*
[e] *Department of Chemical Engineering, University of Waterloo, 200 University Ave. W., Waterloo, ON N2L 3G1, Canada*
[f] *Quantum Artificial Intelligence Laboratory (QuAIL), NASA Ames Research Center, Moffett Field, CA, USA*
[g] *USRA Research Institute for Advanced Computer Science, Mountain View, CA, USA*
dbernaln@purdue.edu

Abstract

Optimization problems must often be reformulated from how they are modeled into a form solvers can tackle. This is the case for optimization problems over disjunctive sets that entail logic constraints, known as Generalized Disjunctive Programs (GDPs). GDPs are usually solved by reformulating them as Mixed-Integer Programs (MIPs), for which powerful solvers exist. Alternatively, physics-inspired methods have been proposed for Quadratic Unconstrained Binary Optimization (QUBO). MIPs can be approximated as QUBOs; for instance, GDPs can be solved by these physics-inspired solvers by using GDP-MIP-QUBO reformulations. We evaluate this approach empirically by solving resulting QUBOs from the well-known MIP reformulations of GDP, Big-M and Hull, and compare it to a proposed reformulation that directly encodes GDP as QUBO via indicator variables. Our results demonstrate an advantage in avoiding the intermediate MIP reformulations when obtaining QUBO problems from GDP.
Keywords: Disjunctive Programming, Quantum Computing, QUBO, Ising solver

1. Introduction

Optimization problems involving choosing among discrete alternatives are ubiquitous in decision-making processes, and many are relevant in process systems engineering (PSE). In many applications, these choices imply that certain constraints are active or not. A powerful framework for modeling these optimization problems is Generalized Disjunctive Programming (Grossmann and Trespalacios, 2013), where in addition to optimization objectives, $f(x)$, and constraints, $h(x)$, over continuous variables, x, that usually appear in mathematical programming; Boolean variables, Y, can activate sets of algebraic constraints or disjuncts, $g(x)$, and be involved in logical constraints, Ω, of which a common one is the disjunction or exclusive or over subsets of them, D_k.

$$\min_{x,Y} f(x) \quad \text{s.t.} \quad h(x) \leq 0, \; \underline{\vee}_{i \in D_k} \begin{bmatrix} Y_{i,k} \\ g_{i,k}(x) \in S_{i,k} \end{bmatrix}, k \in K, \Omega(Y) = \text{True}, \tag{1}$$

$$x \in X \subset \mathbb{R}^n; Y_{ik} \in \{\text{False}, \text{True}\}, i \in D_k, k \in K$$

To solve GDP problems, one usually relies on the beautiful theory of Disjunctive Programming (Balas, 2018), which allows these problems to be reformulated into Mixed-Integer Programs (MIPs) to access Branch-and-Bound-based solvers. Over the past decade, MIP solvers have provided increasing support for indicator constraints. This feature presents a way to preserve the semantics of GDP models, making it easier for modeling and enabling solvers to leverage structure that is sometimes lost during MIP reformulation.

Much of the difficulty in solving GDP problems comes from the combinatorial aspect of disjunct selection. Novel solution heuristics have been devised in the past decades to address combinatorial optimization problems that will classically require tremendous computational effort. Most notably, the development of quantum optimization algorithms and other physics-inspired methods for Quadratic Unconstrained Binary Optimization (QUBO) has been an active research area that has had several advancements since the first theoretical speedup projections were made two decades ago. QUBO problems can be written as follows

$$\min_{y \in \{0,1\}^n} y'Qy = \min_{y \in \{0,1\}^n} \sum_{i,j=1}^{n} Q_{i,j}\, y_i\, y_j \tag{2}$$

Even though interesting optimization problems are often described as constrained MIPs, many QUBO reformulation techniques have been derived and implemented to reframe general models and feed them to these novel optimization architectures (Maciel Xavier et al. 2023). Most QUBO platforms will be able to reinterpret MIP and MINLP problems. Still, there's no support for GDP native inputs or a reformulation path that considers the specificities of disjunctive programs.

Considering GDP's modeling flexibility and industrial relevance and the exciting possibility of solving them using advanced solvers, this work aims to develop reformulation techniques to transform GDP problems into QUBO and evaluate their performance using simulated and quantum annealing. We implement two alternative GDP-MIP-QUBO reformulations using Big-M and Hull reformulations. We compare them to a newly proposed reformulation based on indicator variables and problem-aware considerations to enhance the final formulation's conditioning. We test these reformulations with examples, including a PSE application involving a choice of reactors in a chemical process (Iftakher et al., 2023).

2. Reformulation Methods

Reformulation techniques of more general optimization problems into QUBO have been developed in the past decade to develop applications for physics-inspired methods, better known as Ising solvers, given the Ising model of spins in a transverse field, a model equivalent to the QUBO shown in Eq. (2).

The QUBO.jl ecosystem implements a wide range of tools and novel and existing developments from literature. A brief overview of the relevant aspects of QUBO reformulation is presented in the following sections. Nevertheless, a more detailed discussion about the subject can be found in Maciel Xavier et al. (2023).

To access QUBO solvers, it becomes necessary to represent real- and integer-valued variables using only binary variables. Let $x \in X \subset \mathbb{R}$ be a variable from an optimization model. We call an encoding a function $\xi[X]\colon \{0,1\}^n \to X$ one built to represent x using binary variables, even if approximately.

To enforce constraints while solving unconstrained problems, one can move them to the objective function through penalization. Each constraint of the form $g_i(\boldsymbol{x}) \in S_i$ will be represented by a penalty function $\|g_i(\boldsymbol{x})\|_{S_i}$ and a corresponding penalty factor ρ_i.

$$\min_{\boldsymbol{x} \in X} f(\boldsymbol{x}) \text{ s.t. } g_i(\boldsymbol{x}) \in S_i \ \forall i \xrightarrow{\text{yields}} \min_{\boldsymbol{x} \in X} f(\boldsymbol{x}) + \sum_i \rho_i \|g_i(\boldsymbol{x})\|_{S_i} \tag{3}$$

By composing the capabilities of the DisjunctiveProgramming.jl (GDP to MIP) and QUBO.jl (MIP to QUBO) packages, one can establish the complete bridge between GDP and QUBO in terms of mathematical formulation and software development. Using the indicator reformulation of GDPs opens a more general reformulation path. Given that it is possible to penalize a constraint of the form $g_i(\boldsymbol{x}) \in S_i$ as $\|g_i(\boldsymbol{x})\|_{S_i}$, one can encode $Y_i \implies \{g_i(\boldsymbol{x}) \in S_i\}$ as $y_i \|g_i(\boldsymbol{x})\|_{S_i}$ where y_i is the binary variable that corresponds to Y_i. When information regarding variable bounds is made available within disjunctions Y_i, as in $Y_i \implies \{\boldsymbol{x} \in X\}$, we propose the following encoding,

$$\xi \left[\bigcup_i X_i \right] = \sum_i y_i \, \xi_i[X_i] \text{ s.t. } \sum_i y_i = 1, y_i \in \{0,1\} \tag{4}$$

Note that no extra penalization terms are produced for enforcing each constraint $\boldsymbol{x} \in X_i$.

3. Results

Two GDP models and their reformulations were evaluated using both a classical (Neal Simulated Annealing) algorithm (D-Wave Systems Inc., 2022) and a quantum (D-Wave Quantum Annealing) solver (Finnila et al., 1994). For each problem reformulation, we consider: Δ, the largest magnitude among the QUBO coefficients; n_{vars}, the number of binary variables; n_{qubits}, the number of qubits after embedding the problem in the Quantum Processing Unit (QPU); TTT, the Time-to-target; and TTF, the Time-to-feasibility, both for Simulated and Quantum Annealing, SA and QA, respectively. We used the neal implementation for SA and executed it single-threaded in a Laptop with 2.80GHz processors and 16GB of RAM, where each problem variation was runned 1000 times, performing 4000 sweeps per run. For QA we used the D-Wave Advantage system to also obtain 1000 runs per problem, each requiring 200us of annealing time in the QPU.

We can interpret Δ as a rough measure of the problem's conditioning, where greater values are related to harder instances. n_{vars} and n_{qubits} indicate the amount of resources required to run SA and QA, respectively. Depending on the interaction between variables, multiple qubits might be necessary to represent a single variable when embedding a QUBO problem in quantum hardware. The Time-to-target (TTT) and Time-to-feasibility (TTF) values are calculated using the time spent running the algorithm t and the success probability p = #success/#samples as inputs for

$$\text{TTT}(t, p; s = 0.99) = t \frac{\log(1 - s)}{\log(1 - p)} \tag{5}$$

This quantity provides a performance metric for optimization heuristics that accounts for algorithmic effort and solution quality. The target is reached for TTT when getting a feasible solution within a 5% gap of the optimal value. All solutions feasible to the original problem are regarded as successful for TTF.

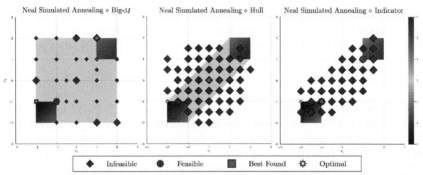

Figure 1: Solutions found via Simulated Annealing for (left) Big-M, (center) Hull, and (right) indicator reformulations of the Boxes Problem, Eq. (6).

3.1. Boxes

Our first example of a disjunctive model is the optimization of a linear function of two variables over a feasible region composed of two separate boxes, as in Eq. (8).

$$\min_{x,Y,\gamma} x_1 - x_2 + \gamma \quad \text{s.t.} \quad \begin{bmatrix} Y_1 \\ -2 \le x_1, x_2 \le -1 \\ \gamma = 1 \end{bmatrix} \vee \begin{bmatrix} Y_2 \\ 1 \le x_1, x_2 \le 2 \\ \gamma = 5 \end{bmatrix} \tag{6}$$

$$x \in [-2,2]^2; Y \in \{\text{False,True}\}^2; \gamma \in \mathbb{R}$$

Figure 1 shows how Simulated Annealing (SA) responds to the Big-M, Hull, and Indicator reformulations. As confirmed by Table 1, SA cannot find a feasible solution for the Big-M and Hull cases. In its last row is the interval-aware (IA) reformulation, highlighted in Figure 2, whose results from SA and Quantum Annealing (QA) indicate a clear advantage by yielding optimal solutions with SA and near-optimal with QA.

Table 1: Results for the Boxes Problem, Eq. (6)

Reformulation Method	$\log_{10}\Delta$	n_{vars}	TTT$_{SA}$	TTF$_{SA}$	n_{qubits}	TTT$_{QA}$	TTF$_{QA}$
Big-M	3.43	42	$\approx 10^3$	310.17	107	∞	∞
Hull	4.53	68	∞	∞	162	∞	∞
Indicator	3.15	286	∞	909.53	711	∞	∞
Indicator (IA)	1.34	34	3.8	≈ 0	37	∞	0.22

As expected, we can see from Table 1 and Figure 1 that the Hull will require more variables than the Big-M approach and also yield a worser conditioning, which can also be seen by its TTT/TTF values for SA. The indicator method, if applied naively, will narrow the coefficient range but will require auxiliary variables to reduce the final expression's high-degree terms to 2. An Interval-Aware (IA) technique that considers the disjunction of the variables' domains at the moment in which they are encoded will be able to produce much better results. As depicted in Figure 2., this will happen because there's no need to penalize such interval constraints, and their fulfilment arises from the values each variable's encoding is able to take.

Moreover, in Figure 2 it is possible to see that both samplers will output most solutions being distributed within each box, instead of having them to be more spread throughout the whole domain while subject to penalization as in Figure 1. Figure 2 also shows that the optimal within each box is consistently found using SA, something that did not happen as often with the Big-M, Hull and Indicator methods in Figure 1.

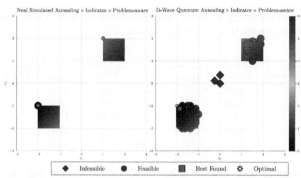

Figure 2: Solutions found via Simulated Annealing (left) and Quantum Annealing (right) for the problem-aware indicator reformulations of the Boxes Problem, Eq (6).

3.2. Reactors Problem

A reactor choice GDP presented by (Iftakher et al., 2023) is given by Eq. (7),

$$\min_{x,Y,\gamma} x' \text{diag}(c_x)\, x + \gamma \quad \text{s.t.} \quad \begin{bmatrix} Y_1 \\ x_2 \leq 0 \\ \gamma = 6.1 \end{bmatrix} \underline{\vee} \begin{bmatrix} Y_2 \\ x_1 \leq 0 \\ \gamma = 5.9 \end{bmatrix} ; \alpha' x \geq d \tag{7}$$

$$x \in [0,5]^2 ; Y \in \{\text{False, True}\}^2 ; \gamma \in \mathbb{R} ; c_x = (1.5,1)' ; \alpha = (0.75,8)' ; d = 3$$

The problem states the selection of one of two reactor designs under a global linear constraint. For this problem, leveraging knowledge from the problem and creating an interval-aware (IA), constraint-aware (CA) indicator reformulation was essential to produce a well-behaved reformulation, as shown in Table 2 and Figure 3. By using the global constraint to tighten each variable's bounds, it was possible to obtain good results for both SA and QA, as seen in Figure 3.

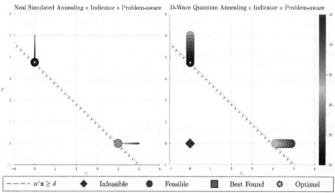

Figure 3: Solutions found via Simulated Annealing (left) and Quantum Annealing (right) for the constraint-aware indicator reformulation of the Reactors Problem, Eq. (7).

The Interval-Aware reformulation that provided the best setting in the previous example, will now interact catastrophically with the global constraint $\alpha' x \geq d$, producing high-order terms and, consequently, introducing many auxiliary variables. To address this issue, we use this same inequality combined with the knowledge from the disjuncts to derive bounds for x_1 and x_2 that will not only restrict their domain but enforce the global constraint as well. This method shows up in Table 2 as the Interval-Aware, Constraint-Aware (IA, CA) reformulation.

Table 2: Results for the Reactor Problem, Eq. (7)

Reformulation Method	$\log_{10} \Delta$	n_{vars}	TTT_{SA}	TTF_{SA}	n_{qubits}	TTT_{QA}	TTF_{QA}
Big-M	6.08	27	∞	∞	81	∞	∞
Hull	6.08	57	∞	∞	145	∞	∞
Indicator	6.08	77	$\approx 10^4$	$\approx 10^4$	176	∞	∞
Indicator (IA)	6.08	253	∞	∞	674	∞	∞
Indicator (IA, CA)	2.17	74	24.73	0	123	∞	20.11

Interesting to notice that despite using more variables than the Big-M and Hull variations, the (IA, CA) version presents a significant drop on the value of Δ, followed by better TTT/TTF records.

4. Conclusion & Future Work

This work shows different reformulations of GDP problems into QUBO and their effect when solving via physics-inspired methods, namely simulated and quantum annealing. Our results indicate that the reformulations that require an intermediate MIP reformulation, either Big-M or Hull, lead to QUBO problems that become challenging for Ising solvers. Notably, the Hull reformulation performs the worst given the introduction of extra variables and constraints and that annealing-based methods do not use the continuous relaxation for solving the problem. Reformulating considering the disjunctive structure of the original GDP problems results in more amenable QUBO problems for the simulated and quantum annealing algorithms, highlighted by our proposed indicator reformulation. These results highlight the importance of considering the solver features when reformulating a problem. Namely, metrics such as the conditioning and number of variables/qubits after embedding are determining factors for the QUBO-based solvers, contrary to the tightness of the continuous formulation, for example. We see this work as the first step towards deriving QUBO reformulations of GDP problems to solve practical problems efficiently and envision structure-specific reformulations as the enabling technique for allowing physics-inspired (including quantum) methods to address GDP problems. The code for reproducing the experiments can be found at "https://github.com/pedromxavier/DisjunctiveToQUBO.jl".

References

E. Balas, 2018. Disjunctive programming. Springer, New York, USA.

D-Wave Systems Inc., 2022. dwave-neal. https://https://github.com/dwavesystems/dwave-neal.

A. Finnila, M. Gomez, C. Sebenik, C. Stenson, J. Doll, 1994. Quantum annealing: A new method for minimizing multidimensional functions. Chemical Physics Letters 219 (5), 343–348.

I. E. Grossmann, F. Trespalacios, 2013. Systematic modeling of discrete-continuous optimization models through generalized disjunctive programming. AIChE Journal 59 (9), 3276–3295.

A. Iftakher, M.-K. Kazi, M. F. Hasana, 2023. Mixed-Integer Quadratic Optimization Using Quantum Computing For Process Applications. In: Foundations of Computer Aided Process Operations / Chemical Process Control (FOCAPO/CPC 2023).

S. Kirkpatrick, C. D. Gelatt Jr, M. P. Vecchi, 1983. Optimization by simulated annealing. Science 220 (4598), 671–680.

P. Maciel Xavier, P. Ripper, T. Andrade, J. Dias Garcia, N. Maculan, D. E. Bernal Neira, 2023. QUBO.jl: A Julia ecosystem for Quadratic Unconstrained Binary Optimization.

H. D. Perez, S. Joshi, I. E. Grossmann, 2023. Disjunctiveprogramming. jl: Generalized disjunctive programming models and algorithms for jump. arXiv preprint arXiv:2304.10492.

Flavio Manenti, Gintaras V. Reklaitis (Eds.), Proceedings of the 34th European Symposium on Computer Aided Process Engineering / 15th International Symposium on Process Systems Engineering (ESCAPE34/PSE24), June 2-6, 2024, Florence, Italy

Adopting Circular Economy Principals for Sustainable Manufacturing

Konstantina Stylianopoulou[a], Emilia Kondili[a], Christiana Papapostolou[a], John K. Kaldellis[b]

[a]Optimisation of Production Systems Lab., Mechanical Engineering Department, University of West Attica, Greece
[b]Soft Energy Applications and Environmental Protection Lab., University of West Attica, Greece
email for correpondence: kstilianopoulou@uniwa.gr

Abstract

The world is currently facing the concerning issue of an increasing consumption rate on a global scale. This is closely tied to the prevalent use of linear economy models in manufacturing processes. These models are fundamentally flawed in a way that they fail to consider a product's entire life cycle in terms of the environment, society, and economy. As a result, the notion of a better future in which no resources are depleted gains paramount importance. An out-of-the-box vision where all products, upon reaching the end of their primary utility, are not discarded but instead recuperated, entering into a cycle of reduce, reuse, recover, remanufacturing, recycling, and redesign, perpetuating their value across multiple lifecycles, known as "circular economy". As such, the notion of "circular economy" must shift from being a mere idea to an absolute necessity. However, as this notion gains attention rapidly, its practical implementation remains somewhat inadequate in its technological blueprint. In that regard, this paper represents an ongoing project focusing on developing a model that considers the 9R-based components of circularity which are essential not just for economic growth but also for environmental and social protection. Considering this complex problem, this study aims to develop a closed-loop supply chain model focusing on sustainable manufacturing. In a nutshell, this study aims to develop a model suitable for various products and purposes for a more sustainable future in manufacturing.

Keywords: Circular economy, Sustainable manufacturing, Life Cycle Assessment.

1. Introduction

The business transformation from the traditional model the linear economy, to the circular economy in the last few decades has become a global debate (T.B.J., Coenen et al., 2020). This debate has been fueled by a significant increase in attention from governments, non-government organizations, and academics towards environmentally friendly manufacturing policies. As consumers are becoming increasingly conscious of the sustainability aspects of their purchasing decisions, companies are advancing towards the implementation of circular economy principles (Giuffrida, G, M. and Mangiaracina, R., 2020). To achieve sustainability within manufacturing, companies need to focus on various perspectives such as reducing waste, reusing materials, recycling products, refurbishing goods, recovering resources, and redesigning processes (K.Stylianopoulou et al.,2023 & K.Stylianopoulou et al., 2022). Implementing the 9R strategies in sustainable manufacturing is crucial to achieving a circular economy. By adopting the 9R strategies, companies can not only reduce their environmental impact but also optimize resource utilization and create new business opportunities. This approach ensures that products and resources are used efficiently, waste is minimized, and the environmental impact is reduced. By embracing the 9R strategies for sustainable manufacturing and adopting circular economy principles, companies can transition from a linear economy model to a more sustainable and inclusive circular economy model that promotes economic growth, environmental protection, and societal well-being.

2. The 9R Framework

The 9R framework is a comprehensive approach designed to promote sustainability and circularity in the manufacturing industry. This framework consists of nine strategies, each beginning with the letter 'R', aimed at reducing waste and maximizing resource efficiency. In the realm of circular economy, the 9R framework plays a crucial role by emphasizing strategies like reduction, reuse, recycling, recovery, redesign, remanufacturing, refurbishing, repurposing, and rethinking. These strategies are crucial for optimizing the use of resources while minimizing waste generation. When implementing these strategies, it is essential to consider various elements, such as the availability and cost of resources, the environmental impacts, and the efficiency of the processes involved. While transitioning to a perfect circular economy free of waste is a challenge, the principles embodied in the 9R framework offer a guide away from disposable culture and adopting sustainable practices. Its core principle is to maintain the utility of resources for the longest possible duration, maximize their value during usage, and subsequently ensuring the recovery and rejuvenation of products and materials after their service life concludes. (K. Stylianopoulou et al., 2023, J. Mast et al.,2022 & European Commission, 2020).

R0	Refuse	Abandon product or offer the same product with a radically different product
R1	Rethink	Use of a product more intensive (e.g. Sharing products)
R2	Reduce	Increase efficiency in product manufacture or use by consuming fewer natural resources and materials
R3	Re-Use	Reuse by another consumer of discarded product which is still in good condition and fulfills its original function
R4	Repair	Repair and maintenance of defective product so it can be used with its original function
R5	Refurbish	Restore an old product and bring it up to date
R6	Remanufacture	Use parts of discarded product in a new product with the same function
R7	Repurpose	Use discarded product or its parts in a new product with a different function
R8	Recycle	Process materials to obtain the same (high grade) or lower (low grade) quality
R9	Recover	Incineration of material with energy recovery

Table 1: 9R Strategies for pursuing Sustainable Manufacturing in Circular Economy (adapted from J. Mast et al.,2022 & European Commission, 2020)

This strategy is particularly vital for sustainable development, especially in the manufacturing sector. It plays a significant role in resource conservation, reducing environmental impacts, and inspiring innovation and economic growth. Essentially, the 9R framework in sustainable manufacturing revolves around the concept of innovative utilization of resources to minimize consumption and waste, thereby maximizing efficiency (K. Stylianopoulou et al., 2023, J. Mast et al.,2022 & Eur. Commission, 2020).

3. Methodology

In the contemporary landscape of industrial manufacturing, sustainability has transitioned from a peripheral concern to a central operational imperative. This shift is driven by a growing recognition of environmental challenges, regulatory pressures, and evolving market expectations. Sustainable manufacturing, which aims to minimize environmental impact while maintaining economic viability, has emerged as a crucial practice. To this end, the development of an optimization model that holistically considers cost, environmental impact, and energy usage becomes paramount.

3.1. Model Development

The approach that is intended here is that the development process involves integrating sustainability principles into traditional manufacturing optimization, addressing complex interdependencies between various manufacturing aspects. The model was developed to address the complex interactions between various elements of manufacturing - resource utilization, waste management, energy consumption, and production efficiency - all under the umbrella of sustainability. The first step was to identify the critical elements affecting sustainable manufacturing, such as resource use, waste generation, energy consumption, and compliance with environmental standards. Then the principles of the 9R framework to ensure a comprehensive approach to sustainability were taken into account. Based on these factors, the model defines a set of variables (both decision and state variables) and constraints that represent the limitations or requirements of the manufacturing process.

3.2. The Objective function

The optimization model developed for sustainable manufacturing incorporates the principles of the 9R framework elements into a mathematical structure. The objective function is to achieve an optimal balance between cost, sustainability, and energy efficiency, with the understanding that advancements in one aspect may result in concessions elsewhere. At the core of the model is a multi-objective function, as presented in Eq. (1), placing emphasis on three primary objectives: minimizing cost (C), environmental impact (E), and energy use (U). The objective function is expressed as:

$$\text{Minimize } Z = \alpha C + \beta E + \gamma U \tag{1}$$

In this context, "Z" symbolizes the total weighted impact of the manufacturing process. Within Eq. (2) symbolized as C, includes the cost of materials, labor, production and miscellaneous costs that could influence the manufacturing process.

$$C = C_{materials} + C_{labor} + C_{process} + C_{other} \tag{2}$$

Regarding the environmental factor E, highlighted in Eq. (3), a scoring system is used to quantify the impact on the environment. Additionally U, as defined in Eq. (4), indicates the level of energy used throughout the production process. This adjustment was made to give a more comprehensive view that includes not merely the quantity of energy consumed but also accounts for the nature of the energy sources used and how long each process lasts, which collectively influence both energy efficiency and ecological consequences.

$$E = \sum (w_R * R_{iscore}) + (w_w * W_{kscore}) + \left(w_E * E_{jscore}\right) \tag{3}$$

$$U = \sum U_{jrate} * T_j * S_j \qquad (4)$$

The weighting factors (α, β and γ) included in Eq. (1) indicate the varying significance of distinct factors aligned with the strategic priorities and processes of a given industry. These factors underscore the importance of cost, environmental impact and energy use in the manufacturing process. They are determined based on objectives related to sustainability within the industry, regulatory requirements and market pressures. For instance, a higher weight on environmental impact (β) signifies a stronger emphasis on sustainability, possibly in response to strict environmental regulations or market demands for sustainable products.

3.3. Variables and Constraints

Fundamental to the model are the variables and constraints. Variables include decision variables such as resource usage, production output, and energy consumption rates, as well as state variables depicting current inventory levels and waste generation. Constraints were formulated to enclose the limitations and requirements underlying the manufacturing process, ensuring adherence to sustainability objectives. The variables and constraints are designed to balance cost-efficiency, environmental sustainability, and energy conservation.

3.3.1. Constraints

Firstly, the constraint of resource management is introduced. This constraint aims for optimal use of resources and a reduction of waste. Following that, the constraint on energy consumption and efficiency is presented, which controls energy use by encouraging energy efficient processes. They are presented as follows:

$$R_i \leq R_{iavailable} + R_{ipurchased} - R_{iwasted} \,, \forall i \qquad (5)$$

$$U \leq U_{jmax} \,, \forall j \qquad (6)$$

The next constraint is environmental scoring, which uses a scoring system in the manufacturing process where product are evaluated for their environmental impact and assigned corresponding scores. Each score reflects the relative environmental impact, with higher scores indicating a greater negative impact.

$$E \leq E_{limit} \qquad (7)$$

Additionally, the waste management constraint makes sure that waste management, including recycling, recovery and disposal, does not exceed waste generation.

$$W_{krecycled} + W_{krecoverd} + W_{kdisposed} \leq W_{kgenerated} \,, \forall k \qquad (8)$$

The next constraint is Quality and Compliance. This constraint ensures that the products meet established quality standards and compliance requirements, factoring in associated costs. The manufacturing process not only focuses on producing high quality products but also meticulously complies with necessary regulatory standards. It helps maintain customer satisfaction and legal compliance, critical in sustainable manufacturing.

$$Q_l + C_{lcomplince} \geq Q_{lstandard} \, , \forall l \tag{9}$$

Last but not least, Market Dynamics and Demand constrain is presented. This constraint aligns production with market demand, considering inventory levels to avoid overproduction or shortages. Matching production output to market demand, considering the inventory available. Thus, it ensures that the total production output minus the inventory available is sufficient to meet or exceed market demand. It avoids both the shortfall of not having enough product to meet demand and excessive overproduction, producing more than what is needed leading to wasted resources and increase storage costs. It is a crucial part of efficient inventory management and ensuring customer satisfaction.

$$\sum P_j - I \geq D \tag{10}$$

3.3.2. Variables

There are two main types of variables that were considered: decision variables and state variables. Decision variables are unknown in an optimization problem; they can change according to the needs of the manufacturing industry, while state variables are fixed parameters that the model uses to make decisions but does not directly control.

Category	Variable	Type
Resource Management	R_i	Decision
	$R_{iavailable}$	State
	$R_{ipurchased}$	Decision
	$R_{iwasted}$	Decision/State
Energy Consumption	U	Decision
	U_{jrate}	State
	T_j	Decision
	S_j	State
Environmental Scoring	E	Decision/State
	E_{limit}	State
Waste Management	$W_{krecycled}$	Decision
	$W_{krecoverd}$	Decision
	$W_{kdisposed}$	Decision
	$W_{kgenerated}$	State
Market Demand	P_j	Decision
	I	State
	D	State

Table 2: Key Variables in the Optimization Model for Sustainable Manufacturing

4. Conclusions

In conclusion, this optimization model offers a comprehensive approach for manufactures to address the complexities of sustainable production, balancing economic, environmental and energy considerations to achieve more sustainable and efficient outcomes. This optimization model presents a structured and comprehensive approach to sustainable manufacturing. The model integrates various aspects of sustainable manufacturing, including resource efficiency, energy management, environmental conservation, waste reduction, product quality and market alignment. It is adaptable to different industrial contexts and can be tailored to prioritize specific aspects, such as reducing environmental impact or minimizing costs, with the aim of guiding manufacturers toward more sustainable and efficient production methods. The model serves as a decision making tool guiding manufacturing in optimizing their processes for sustainability and efficiency. The constraints provide a structured approach to managing resources efficiently, controlling energy consumption, minimizing environmental impact, managing waste responsibly, ensuring product quality and compliance, and aligning production with market demand. The model's flexibility in weighting different objectives (cost, environmental impact, energy) makes it adaptable to various manufacturing contexts and sustainability goals. However, this optimization model represents a preliminary framework, and its empirical validation is pending. Future implementation is contingent upon extensive data collection, which is necessary to corroborate the model's efficiency and clarify its parameters. This ongoing process of data acquisition and analysis will enable a more robust and reliable application of the model in practical scenarios.

References

T.B.J. Coenen, W. Haanstra, A.J.J.J. Braaksama, J. Santos, 2020, CEIMA: A framework for identifying critical interfaces between the Circular Economy and stakeholders in the lifecycle of infrastructure assets, Resources, Consertation & Recycling, 155

European Commision, 2020, Categorisation System for the Circular Economy: A sector-agnostic approach for activities contributing to the circular economy

M. Giuffrida, R. Mangiaracina, 2020, Green Practices for Global Supply Chains in Diverse Industrial, Geographical, and Technological Settings: A Literature Review and Research Agenda, sustainability, 12

Q. Liu, A.H. Trevisan, M. Yang, J. Mascarenhas, 2022, A framework of digital technologies for the circular economy: Digital functions and mechanisms, Business Strategy and the Environment, 31, 2171-2192

J. Mast, F. von Unruh, W. Irrek, 2022, RETHINK: Enabling the Circular Economy, Available online at: www.prosperkolleg.ruhr/en/

T.A.C. de Melo, M.A. de Oliveira, S.R.G. de Sousa, R.K.Vieira, T.S.,2022, Amaral, Circular Economy Public Policies: A Systematic Literature Review, Procedia Computer Science, 204, 652-662

C. M. Papapostolou, E. M. Kondili, 2023, Modelling of reverse supply chains in the context of circular economy, Computer Aided Chemical Engineering, 52, 3325-3330

K.G. Stylianopoulou, E.M. Kondili, C.M. Papapostolou, J.K. Kaldellis, 2023, Optimisation modeling for decision support in the industrila cicruclar economy activities, Computer Aided Chemical Engineering, 52, 2131-2136

K.G. Stylianopoulou, E.M. Kondili, J.K. Kaldellis, 2022, Process Systems Engineering prospects in Circular Economy implementation in industry, Computer Aided Chemical Engineering, 51, 1309-1314

Flavio Manenti, Gintaras V. Reklaitis (Eds.), Proceedings of the 34th European Symposium on Computer Aided Process Engineering / 15th International Symposium on Process Systems Engineering (ESCAPE34/PSE24), June 2-6, 2024, Florence, Italy

Decarbonization strategies by industrial ecology

Marianne Boix[a]*, Henri de la Vaissière de Verduzan[a], Stéphane Négny[a]

[a]*Laboratoire de Génie Chimique, UMR5503, Toulouse INP/CNRS/UPS, 4 Allée Emile Monso, 31432 TOULOUSE Cedex 4, FRANCE*
marianne.boix@toulouse-inp.fr

Abstract

Eco-Industrial Parks (EIPs) are a way to enhance decarbonization of industrial activities by fostering collaboration among companies within an industrial park. Following this reorganization, a network can emerge in which companies exchange energy and raw materials. This work deals with the hypothetical implementation of a steam network among companies in an existing EIP. The objective is to demonstrate the benefits of multi-objective optimization in defining the most suitable network using a mixed-integer linear programming approach. Two criteria are considered to determine the optimal organization: cost and greenhouse gas emissions (GHG). This approach is implemented through a mathematical model that considers various utilities, production capacities, and industry demands seasonally. Subsequently, an epsilon constraint strategy is employed to select the best solution. The addition of a hybrid energy system and a CO_2 capture unit to the model allows for assessing potential benefits. The result of this work shows a waste-free organization and reduced GHG emissions by approximately 2000 metric tons of carbon dioxide equivalents per year. The addition of a hybrid energy system and CO_2 capture unit enables an additional reduction of 7000 tons of GHG emissions with a relatively modest increase in cost. This work could potentially be applied to another industrial park scenario in the future.

Keywords: Eco-Industrial Park, Multi-Objective Optimization, CO_2 capture unit, decarbonization.

1. Introduction

For several years, the impact of human activities on the planet has been observed and acknowledged, leading to the emergence of various concepts. The term "Anthropocene" first appeared in 1990, initially referring to an era from which the geological impact of these activities significantly influences the planetary system (IPCC Report, 2021). This concept later expanded to encompass all global environmental changes caused by humans. In 2009, nine planetary boundaries were identified (Rockström et al., 2009). Each of them corresponds to a process in the Earth's system that is essential for the stability of living conditions and is impacted by human activities. This will significantly alter living conditions on Earth. The awareness of the importance of acting by certain states can, however, be perceived. Commitments are made, and investment plans are created to fulfill them. This is notably the case with the France Relance 2030 plan, which aims to finance major technical projects and, among other goals, reduce the impact of industry. Industrial ecology is one of the practices that can be relied upon to achieve this objective.

One of the most common strategies in industrial ecology is the establishment of eco-industrial parks (EIP). By definition, an EIP is an industrial park where stakeholders share infrastructure, services, and implement common development strategies to apply the principles of industrial ecology. The term was first referenced in 1992 during the United Nations Conference on Environment and Development, and since then, numerous projects have been launched. Most of industrial symbioses have originated from commercial agreements between industries and have evolved over time. Therefore, this approach does not guarantee optimal functioning of the industrial park (Boix et al., 2015). An optimization process will enable the creation of an EIP with most positive environmental, economic, and social impacts according to specific objectives. This approach can be applied to various cases such as spatial arrangement and design, energy efficiency, resource efficiency, waste management, mobility, or collaboration and knowledge sharing. One key aspect of establishing EIP is the presence of an exchange network among the constituent industries. This exchange network can take various forms and, for example, be utilized to optimize the use of raw materials and energy or to valorize waste.

In the current study, the focus is on determining an optimal steam exchange network to meet the needs of each participant. The aim of this paper is to propose an optimization-based approach to design an industrial symbiosis by integrating into the superstructure numerous ways of producing electricity as well as new carbon capture facilities. The objective is also to develop a generic superstructure as complete as possible, integrating several technology bricks with different degrees of maturity.

2. Superstructure improvement

The superstructure includes the detailed description of the different companies involved in the industrial park; a hybrid renewable energy sources (HRES) and several equipment: turbines, boilers, CO_2 capture units. An illustration of the superstructure is represented in figure 1.

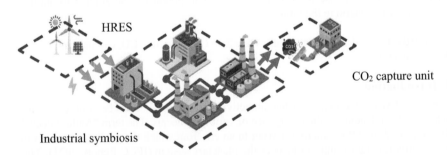

Figure 1. Schematic representation of superstructure

Three different cases of CO_2 capture are distinguished: oxy-combustion capture, pre-combustion capture, and post-combustion capture (Akeeb et al. 2022). The focus is done in this paper on the latter case that allows the capture of CO_2 emitted after combustion. Several technologies, more or less mature and suitable for industry, can be identified. For example, there is capture by cryogenic condensation, which is too energy-intensive, or capture by microalgae, which is too complex to implement. The three technologies mainly used in the industry are membranes, adsorption, and absorption. CO_2 capture through membrane filtration is based on the use of a semi-permeable barrier to filter the flue gas stream. This technology has several advantages, such as its low cost (operational and investment), simplicity, reliability with good adaptation to production, and a low maintenance frequency. It is also very compact, and up to 88% of CO_2 can be captured, but its performance is affected by the decrease in concentration. However, this technology is the least mature of the three and is the subject of numerous studies (Wu et al., 2023; Janakiram et al., 2023; Li et al., 2023).

Absorption involves bringing the gases to be treated into contact with a liquid solvent. The CO_2 is then absorbed by this liquid, which can be recycled for further use. This process is generally implemented in absorption columns that can reach several tens of meters in height. This technology is very effective for CO_2 capture. The solvents used are inexpensive while exhibiting high absorption capacities. However, most of them degrade over time and with temperature. In addition, these compounds generally have a high environmental impact. Nevertheless, this technology remains the most advanced.

Adsorption allows for CO_2 capture by circulating the flue gas through porous materials. The CO_2 is then physically or chemically fixed to these materials, which can be recycled afterward. Among the adsorbents used are activated carbon, zeolite, and polymers. In addition to its efficiency, this technology has a lower environmental impact and cost compared to absorption (Li et al., 2023). This process is thus the most promising for CO_2 capture.

3. Problem statement

Given is a set of companies composed of processes involving vapour, electricity and water demands. The goal is to find the optimal configuration (exchanges between companies) that leads to the minimum of the cost and the minimum of carbon release in the atmosphere. The decision variables of the mathematical model are all the flows exchanged between companies (their existence and their physical characteristics) as well as the sizing of equipment. A multi-objective optimization approach is carried out on an EIP with new add-on facilities to show impact on its GHG emissions (Figure 2):

- Optimal steam network
- Hybrid Power System (HPS)
- CO_2 capture unit

These facilities are integrated in the optimization model. The model is formulated as a multiperiod Mixed Integer Linear Programming (MILP) based on Mousqué et al. (2023) and solved using an epsilon-constraint approach to deal with two objective functions: minimum of total cost (investment, operational and raw materials cost) and minimum of Green House Gases (GHG) emissions. The constraints of the model consist in all the mass and energy balances and thermodynamic considerations. The presented results are issued by making a TOPSIS analysis among solutions on the Pareto fronts and a weight of 0.7 has been attributed to GHG emissions whereas 0.3 is affected to the total cost.

The model is formulated as an MILP (Mixed Integer Linear Programming) dealing with several thousands of variables (between 10234 and 12584 depending on the scenarios).

4. Case study

The work of Kim et al. (2010) on the Yeosu Industrial Park served as a case study. The aim of this work is also to demonstrate the applicability of an optimization approach for a steam exchange network within a real industrial complex. In this study, 15 industries were identified and classified into two types: producing and consuming companies. Their spatial distribution can be observed in the Figure 2.

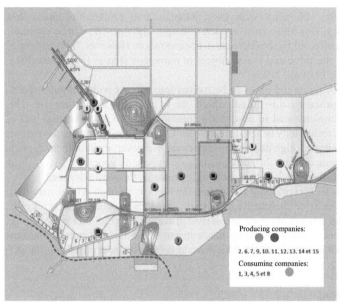

Figure 2. Map of industrial symbiosis of Yeosu

Producing industries have the ability to generate steam, unlike consuming industries, which are unable to produce it. Each of them has a different need, whether it be for the type or quantity of steam. Therefore, there is very high-pressure steam (THP), high-pressure steam (HP), medium-pressure steam (MP), and low-pressure steam (BP). As demand varies throughout the year, it has been divided into 4 periods based on seasons: t1 - Spring (April to June), t2 - Summer (July to September), t3 - Autumn (October to December), t4 - Winter (January to March).

In the first step, the flue gas to be treated must be defined. Assumptions will be made to simplify the system. Firstly, the flue gas stream to be treated will be assumed to be a binary mixture composed of 14% CO_2 and 86% N_2. In this case, the greenhouse gas (GHG) emissions from the boilers consist only of CO2. The reduction of its temperature to 25°C has also been assumed. We can then calculate the flue gas flow to be treated based on the GHG emissions from the boilers.

5. Results and discussion

This study was carried out considering climate and energy mix in South Korea and with weighting of criteria. A weight of 0.7 has been attributed to GHG emissions and 0.3 to the total cost for the multicriteria analysis. The choice of the energy source has a significant impact on GHG emissions. After optimizing this network, it can be discerned that the adsorption unit is much more environmentally advantageous than the membrane filtration unit. Additionally, the electricity demand of these CO_2 capture units can be quite significant. The hybrid energy production system found after the previous optimization is therefore not suitable. The optimal solution to this problem involves using an adsorption unit. A new energy supply system has also been defined with a production capacity of 1140 kW and 6850 kW for solar and wind, respectively. The exchange network, on the other hand, has not changed. The optimal solution has also been determined in the case of CO_2 capture through membrane filtration (Table 1).

Scenario explored	GHG emissions (tons CO_2eq / year)	Total cost (10^6 USD)
EIP with steam network	**10 416**	**1.898**
add of **HPS**	**7 131**	**1.909**
add of **HPS** and **adsorption** unit	**3 304**	**1.906**
add of **HPS** and **membrane** unit	**5 142**	**1.964**

Table 1. Comparison of results obtained

From table 2, it can be seen that this EIP organization emits approximately 2000 t eqCO_2 more with additional expenses of about $60 million, despite a lower investment cost for the membranes. Compared to the base case, with a little increase of the total cost (0.4%), the total GHG emissions can be decreased of more than 65% by using absoption for CO_2 capture. This is due to the fact that this technology is much more energy-intensive than adsorption. The hybrid power system must be more substantial than that needed for the other technology, increasing the total cost. However, emissions from electricity consumption still remain higher by a few hundred-ton eq. CO_2.

	Base case (w/o CO_2 capture)	CO_2 capture by absorption	CO_2 capture by membrane filtration
Total cost	1.899×10^9 \$/year	1.906×10^9 \$/year	1.964×10^9 \$/year
Investment cost for capture unit	-	1.35×10^6 \$/year	2.6×10^5 \$/year
Operating cost for capture unit	-	154530 \$/year	unknown
GHG total emissions	10416 T eq. CO_2/year	3304 T eq. CO_2/year	5142 T eq. CO_2/year
Amount of captured CO_2	-	5735 T CO_2/year	4205 T CO_2/year
GHG linked to electricity consumption	3947 T eq. CO_2/year	2667 T eq. CO_2/year	3012 T eq. CO_2/year

Table 2. Comparison of scenarios: base case compared to two different CO_2 capture technologies

Therefore, it can be seen that, despite a significantly higher investment cost, the implementation of an adsorption unit is markedly more advantageous than that of a membrane filtration unit, notably due to its capture capacity and lower energy demand. It is also worth noting that the capture of CO_2 entails a substantial energy demand. The use of carbon-neutral electricity thus serves to minimize the impact of this high consumption. However, in the absence of clean energy, one might question the relevance of establishing a CO_2 capture unit.

6. Conclusions and perspectives

Using the mathematical model and a multi-criteria optimization strategy, an optimal solution for a steam exchange network was determined. This led to a reduction in greenhouse gas emissions. Elements were then added to the model to assess their impact on the industrial eco-park. Initially, a hybrid electricity generation system and a post-combustion CO2 capture unit were tested. The use of a hybrid power system composed of carbon-neutral energy sources demonstrated a significant decrease in greenhouse gas emissions, approximately 30%. The additional integration of a CO2 capture unit resulted in a total reduction of 70% compared to the initial solution. The cost, on the other hand, was not greatly impacted by these additions. The result of this work shows an organization with zero waste and greenhouse gases emission reduced by around 2000 tons of carbon dioxide equivalent per year.

The main contribution of this work is the modelling and the implementation in the optimization model of several technologies including: the steam network (several level of pressure), the hybrid power system and a CO_2 capture unit Two capture unit technologies are tested and adsorption unit is revealed to be more efficient in both CO_2 capture and energy consumption. The implementation of both hybrid power system and CO_2 capture unit leads to an additional decrease of 7000 tons CO_2 eq. with a relatively modest increase in cost.

The perspective of the work is to extend the superstructure and the generic model to other kind of participants such as municipalities, neighbourhood and other kinds of material exchanges.

Acknowledgements

This work was supported by a government grant managed by the Agence Nationale de la Recherche under the France 2030 program, under the reference ANR-22-PESP-0004.

References

O., Akeeb, 2022, Post-combustion CO2 capture via a variety of temperature ranges and material adsorption process: A review. J. Environ. Manag. 313, 115026.

M. Boix, Montastruc, L., Azzaro-Pantel, C. & Domenech, S., 2015, Optimization methods applied to the design of eco-industrial parks: a literature review. J. Clean. Prod. 87, 303–317.

M. Boix, Négny, S., Montastruc, L., Mousqué, F., 2023, Flexible networks to promote the development of industrial symbioses: A new optimization procedure, Comp. Chem. Eng., 169, 108082.

IPCC report, 2021, Intergovernmental Panel on Climate Change. https://www.ipcc.ch/.

S. Janakiram, Lindbråthen, A., Ansaloni, L., Peters, T. & Deng, L., 2022, Two-stage membrane cascades for post-combustion CO2 capture using facilitated transport membranes: Importance on sequence of membrane types. Int. J. Greenhouse Gas Control 119, 103698.

S., Kim, Yoon, S.-G., Chae, S. H. & Park, S., 2010, Economic and environmental optimization of a multi-site utility network for an industrial complex. J. Env. Manag. 91, 690–705.

R. Li, Lian, S., Zhang, Z. & Song, C., 2023, Modeling of hollow fiber facilitated transport membrane modules for post combustion carbon capture process: Evaluation of non-ideal effect and module characteristic. Chem. Eng. Sc. 276, 11879.

J., Rockström et al. 2009, Planetary Boundaries: Exploring the Safe Operating Space for Humanity. Ecol. Societ.14.

H., Wu et al., 2023, Industrial-scale spiral-wound facilitated transport membrane modules for post-combustion CO2 capture: Development, investigation and optimization. J. Membr. Sc. 670, 121368.

Flavio Manenti, Gintaras V. Reklaitis (Eds.), Proceedings of the 34th European Symposium on Computer Aided Process Engineering / 15th International Symposium on Process Systems Engineering (ESCAPE34/PSE24), June 2-6, 2024, Florence, Italy

Comparison of Domino Effect Analysis Tools using Graph Theory

Niki Moradmand-Nia[a], Nelly Olivier-Maget[a], Franck Prats[b]

[a]Laboratoire de Génie Chimique INPT-ENSIACET, 4, allée Emile Monso - CS 44362, 31030 TOULOUSE Cedex 4, France
[b]INERIS; Parc Technologique Alata BP 2, 60550 Verneuil-en-Halatte
niki.moradmandnia@toulouse-inp.fr

Abstract

Domino effects refer to low-frequency accidents with critical consequences. During these accidents, one event triggers a more destructive event in a chain reaction. Modeling and assessing their safety are a considerable challenge due to their rarity, their complexity, and the limited data availability. This paper presents some graph-theory-based models used for domino effect assessment. The ultimate aim is to compare them, not in a mathematical way but from an industrial perspective. The framework of the comparison is defined: specifying the criteria of the analysis and the different case studies.
Instead of opposing the methods, it appears that a complementary use of the tools could be more beneficial.

Keywords: Domino effects, Risk analysis, Graph Theory, Bayesian Network, Petri Net.

1. Introduction

The definition of domino effects has evolved over the last decades, becoming increasingly precise over time. The current commonly accepted definition has the following key points: the propagation of a primary accident with an escalation or a worsening of the consequences (Alileche, 2015; Reniers and Cozzani, 2013). The escalation factor is what makes domino effects so devastating. The Feyzin disaster is a perfect illustration of a domino effect. On 4 January 1966, following an operating error, a propane leak generated a flammable cloud in an LPG storage area. The cloud is ignited on a nearby road, and quickly after, a torch fire is generated under one sphere. Emergency services tried to cool down the neighboring spheres for 1h30 and extinguish the giant flare, which expanded again after the safety valves at the top of the sphere opened. The sphere exploded (1st BLEVE) suddenly, killing 13 people. A neighboring propane sphere exploded 1 h later (2nd BLEVE) without causing any casualties. The human toll was high: 18 dead, including 11 firefighters, and 84 injured (BARPI, 2006).

Modeling the steps that make up domino effect accidents is therefore a challenge in order to avoid them or at least reduce their consequences. Dozens of methods have been developed to model domino effects with different approaches (Chen et al., 2020; Necci et al., 2015). Some of them aim to qualitatively find out the possible scenarios, others to precisely obtain the probability of a certain set of events occurring, and still others to help manage the accident during the crisis.

This diversity of methods is a proof of the interest into this topic and at the same time, the evidence that no consensus has yet emerged on how to correctly model domino effects (Alileche, 2015). Each method addresses a different aspect of the problem which makes their requirements and specificities unique: data input and output, precision, computation time. However, few, if any, articles test their method on identical case studies so comparing them is laborious.

Recently graph theory has been increasingly used as a way to represent domino effect. They are notably appealing as they are more visual and can include analytical or probabilistic aspects. Temporal aspect can also be included (Chen et al., 2020). This paper focuses on some of these methods, in particular, Bayesian network, Petri net and Markov chain. First, a brief description in the context of domino effect is given. Then the comparative study is detailed: the criteria of comparison and the case study used. In the last part, the first results are presented and improvement are suggested before concluding.

2. Graph Theory models

In graph theory applied to risk assessment, equipment or infrastructures are symbolized by nodes (or vertices). Nodes can be connected by links (or edges) if the equipment they represent can interact with each other.

2.1. Bayesian Network

The Bayesian network (BN) is a probabilistic model that represents the dependency relationships between different random variables in a directed acyclic graph. Figure 1 (a) is a case of a really simple network. Each node can have several states that characterize plant i. It can, for example, be in a normal state S_{i1} or a damaged state S_{i2}, and it is the states of the parent nodes that will determine the propagation probabilities. A conditional probability table is annexed to each node to compute the probabilities. One of the strengths of this tool, is that based on the observation of a situation (evidences), the probabilities can be updated. It allows for detecting the most likely causes and consequences (Weber et al., 2012).

Initially, BN aren't able to deal with time-dependant probabilities, however, Dynamic Bayesian Networks are an improved version that can compute temporal escalation on top of spatial escalation (Khakzad, 2015).

2.2. Petri Net

In Petri Nets (PN), transitions are a new type of element present on the graph. Pictured by a rectangle and placed between nodes, it embodies the conditions required for the evolution of the situation. Tokens, on a graph, dots in nodes, represent the state of the PN. In Figure 1 (b), the system is in state $p1$ and would need to meet conditions defined by $t1$ to get in state $p2$. Transition conditions can be probabilistic or deterministic. Also, for more realism, multiple conditions can be set and combined in a transition (Murata, 1989). Stochastic PN are an extension of the traditional PN that incorporates randomness to represent uncertainty or variability in the modeling of systems.

For PN, estimation of scenarios and quantification of the most probable case is necessarily carried out with simulations, e.g. Monte-Carlo simulations (Weber et al., 2012).

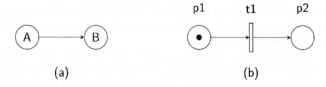

(a)   (b)

Figure 1 - (b) Basic Bayesian Network, (b) Basic Petri Net.

2.3. Markov Chain

Markov Chains (MC) are Markov processes with discrete time or discrete state space. The essential property of those processes is that the probability of an event depends only on the state attained in the previous event (Cox, 2017). There is an independence between past and future states as future state are affected only by the present state.

Piecewise Deterministic Markov Processes (PDMPs) are a specific class of Markov processes that combine the deterministic and stochastic elements of the Markov model. These processes are characterized by the fact that they evolve deterministically for a certain period of time, after which they undergo a "jump" to a new state (Fearnhead et al., 2018). The deterministic part of the process can be used to model physical properties, while the stochastic part can be used to model uncertainties. This duality makes PDMPs suitable for risk assessment.

Stochastic finite state machines (SFSMs) represent another variant of Markov processes that has elements of both determinism and randomness. In SFSMs, the temporal transitions are probabilistic, not predetermined. Meaning that the future state cannot always be precisely predicted, adding a degree of uncertainty to the system.

3. Frame of comparison

Each method is compared on specific points using the same situation. From an initial situation, the aim is to obtain the sets of events produced by each method.

3.1. Comparison criteria

To compare the methods, it is important to have reference points. These criteria can be divided into three big categories: those about the input data, those about the model itself and those about the output data.

The completeness and accuracy of the input data required to run the model may be limited. Depending on the actual situation modelled some information may be unknown. Some models expect all the data to run while others can handle this uncertainty factor.

The accessibility of the tool is another point to take into account. The time required for a new user to understand how the tool works is important for the spread of the model within companies. Even for an experienced user, a method that allows faster modelling is preferable. Other than the handiness for the user, the capacity for them to access the equations and to modify the method itself is to be studied, whether it is to update a step to make it more precise or to add new options.

A feature like sensitivity must be considered. This is the ability of the method to output least probable scenarios with high consequences. A model might find pointless to output some inconceivable sets of events. That would be a mistake as the essence of domino effect is to examine unlikely situations with terrible effects.

Similarly, reachability analysis has to be performed. Particularly, state reachability which determine whether a particular state or set of states in a system can be reached from

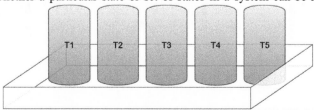

Figure 2 - Case study where five tanks are aligned and can interact with their closest neighbor.

another state. It can be used to compare the consistency of simulations within a run and between methods.

Computation time is an obvious element to compare and is directly correlated to the power of calculation required to run the model. It is crucial for complex infrastructures but might not be relevant in the case studied as the situations considered are fairly simple and may sometimes be negligable. Finally, the nature of the results, their precision and their accuracy have to be compared.

3.2. Case study

The studied situation is the one depicted on Figure 2. Five identical tanks are aligned and equidistant from each other. They contain the same flammable compound. If one of them is on fire, the heat can ignite the adjacent tanks. Initially, each tank has only two states, either on fire or not. A schematic representation of the situation is shown on Figure 3. The situation is the one described by Khazad and Khan in chapter 3 of Cozzani and Reniers (2021)

The spread conditions are determined with a dose-response relationship. The probability of an escalation from tank i to tank j is given by equation (1).

$$P = 1 - \frac{Q_T}{Q_{ij}} \tag{1}$$

With Q_T the heat radiation threshold of the tank j and Q_{ij} the intensity of heat radiation received by the tank j from tank i.

4. Results and discussion

4.1. Results

The situation was modelled using BN on GeNIe 4.1 (BayesFusion, LLC, 2023). In order to get the most of the tool, the dynamic option was used instead of a classic BN that simulate the time step. Figure 4 is the dynamic BN created. Each link has a number representing the time order of the interaction.

The equivalence of the time step is not defined but is considered the order of magnitude of the minute. The initial conditions are an equal chance of spontaneous ignition for all

Figure 3 – Network representation of the case study where five tanks are aligned and can interact with their closest neighbor.

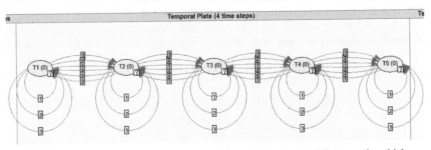

Figure 4 - Dynamic Bayesian Network of the first case study: five equidistant tanks which can spread fire to their closest neighbor.

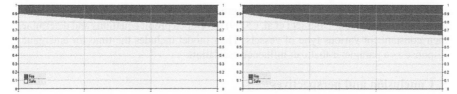

Figure 5 - Evolution of fire probabilities (dark gray) for the DBN for an edge tank (T1 or T5) on the left, and for the central tank (T3) on the right. Light gray represents the non-fire probability.

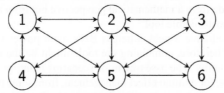

Figure 6 - Case study where six tanks are aligned and can interact with their closest neighbor.

tanks, set at 10 %; the spontaneous ignition is then zero for next time steps. This reflects the risk on long time span.

As the layout is symmetrical, the results are symmetrical too. Fire probabilities of an edge tank (T1 or T5) and the central tank (T3) are compared in Figure 5. As expected T3 is the most exposed tank and has a higher probability of catching fire. After 3 timesteps, the fire probability reaches 36 % for T3 versus 26 % for T1 or T5.

For PDMP, the same case was modelled using PyCATSHOO (Chraibi, 2018). The tool is less visual and produces raw data which is less appealing for the user.

4.2. Discussion

The DBN fire probability of each tank matches the results previously obtained by Cozzani and Reniers (2021). However, the process for obtaining them was laborious as all previous states are treated for the calculation, unlike a Markovian process where just the last state impacts the probabilities of future states.

The case study can be gradually complexified to make it more realistic. First, mitigation measures can be added to the model. Mitigation measures are barriers that reduce the probability of escalation. The heat radiation received is decreased or the threshold is increased, causing an overall diminution of the probability. Also, the mitigation measures can delay the spread of the fire; completely protecting a tank for a certain amount of time. However, barriers can also be defective, and their success is subject to a certain probability.

The next step would be to change the layout of the tanks. Introducing distances between tanks in the equations allows for a more realistic model. It is no longer necessary for the tanks to be equidistant. More complex layouts can be studied. The layout shown in Figure 6 can, for example, be modelled with also more interactions between the tanks and possible cumulative effects.

In real chemical plants, tanks are placed inside spillage retention basins to limit the spillage if a leak occurs. An illustration of spillage retention is shown in Figure 2. However, in the case of a flammable liquid spill, a pool fire would affect not one but all the tanks. The propagation probabilities are updated accordingly. Another risk is that one of the tanks will explode due to the pressure increase caused by the heat.

Finally, equations can be updated again for greater realism, taking into consideration time aspects of a fire spread. Landucci et al. (2009) developed probit equations and determined their constant for various type of vessels. Their model includes the time for emergency response as a parameter that can influence escalation.

5. Conclusion and perspectives

Several tools using graph theory for risk analysis have been described. The aim of this study is to compare these different methods for domino effect assessment. The comparison is not made from a mathematical perspective but from an industrial one. The goal is to select the most suitable tool.

PDMPs provide a predictive aspect, whereas BN's main power resides in the update, thanks to evidence. Therefore, combining the tools might be the right decision to take advantage of their benefits. The assessment of scenarios being given by PDMP is then injected into BN. Thus, for domino effect management, from some observations, the most probable causes and consequences can be obtained. The Petri Net model still has to be created in order to complete the comparison. The discussed improvement to model more realistic case studies would upgrade the comparison.

References

N. Alileche, 2015. Étude des effets dominos sur une zone industrielle. INSA de Rouen, Rouen (France).

BARPI, 2006. BLEVE dans un dépôt de GPL en raffinerie, Le 4 janvier 1966 Feyzin (69) – France (No. 1), ARIA. Ministère chargé de l'environnement, France.

BayesFusion, LLC, 2023. GeNIe Modeler Programmer's Manual (Software manual V4.1.R0).

C. Chen, G. Reniers and N. Khakzad, 2020. A thorough classification and discussion of approaches for modeling and managing domino effects in the process industries. Safety Science 125, 104618.

H. Chraibi, 2018. Getting started with PyCATSHOO V1.2.2.8 Document version V1. (Software manual No. V1.1). EDF R&D, Paris Saclay (France).

D. R. Cox, 2017. The Theory of Stochastic Processes, First edition. ed. CRC Press, Boca Raton, FL (United States of America).

V. Cozzani and G. L. L. Reniers (eds.), 2021. Dynamic risk assessment and management of domino effects and cascading events in the process industry. Elsevier, Amsterdam, Netherlands ; Cambridge, MA, USA.

P. Fearnhead, J. Bierkens, M. Pollock and G. O. Roberts, 2018. Piecewise Deterministic Markov Processes for Continuous-Time Monte Carlo. Statist. Sci. 33.

N. Khakzad, 2015. Application of dynamic Bayesian network to risk analysis of domino effects in chemical infrastructures. Reliability Engineering & System Safety 138, 263–272.

G. Landucci, G. Gubinelli, G. Antonioni and V. Cozzani, 2009. The assessment of the damage probability of storage tanks in domino events triggered by fire. Accident Analysis & Prevention 41, 1206–1215.

T. Murata, 1989. Petri Nets: Properties, Analysis and Applications. Proceedings of the IEEE 77.

A. Necci, V. Cozzani, G. Spadoni and F. Khan, 2015. Assessment of domino effect: State of the art and research Needs. Reliability Engineering & System Safety 143, 3–18.

G. Reniers and V. Cozzani (eds.), 2013. Domino effects in the process industries: Modeling, prevention and managing. Elsevier, Amsterdam; Boston (Mass.).

P. Weber, G. Medina-Oliva, C. Simon and B. Iung, 2012. Overview on Bayesian networks applications for dependability, risk analysis and maintenance areas. Engineering Applications of Artificial Intelligence 25, 671–682.

Flavio Manenti, Gintaras V. Reklaitis (Eds.), Proceedings of the 34th European Symposium on Computer Aided Process Engineering / 15th International Symposium on Process Systems Engineering (ESCAPE34/PSE24), June 2-6, 2024, Florence, Italy

Coping with Sustainability, Circularity and Complexity in Optimizing Industrial Symbiosis Networks among Distributed Chemical Processes

Thérèse Lee Chan[a*], David A. Janes[b] and Kyle Joshua[a]

*a*The University of the West Indies, St. Augustine, Trinidad and Tobago
*b*NN, Haddon House, Hucknall, NG15 7ED, UK
*Therese.Lee@sta.uwi.edu

Abstract

For the optimal design and operation of decentralized industrial symbiosis (IS) systems, a multi-criteria decision support tool employing multi-objective optimization (MOO) was developed on a MATLAB® platform. Initial studies had considered exchanging high-purity process carbon dioxide between plants in the IS network (ISN). However, when streams of different concentrations (e.g., spent water) were kept separate, the modelled networks became more difficult to solve. An exploratory examination was undertaken to consider how to model the sharing of contaminated spent water streams between plants in a smaller ISN. The optimization objectives were to minimize fresh material and transportation costs. MOO procedures from the optimization toolboxes and bespoke coding of popular MOO methods were investigated. Multi-criteria decision methods were used to select the 'most appropriate' of the non-dominated solutions. The 'digraph' function was then used to generate network diagrams displaying source-sink connections and the amount of flow between plants in the ISN. It was found that bespoke-coded scalarized methods, like the ε-constraint method, were more robust than methods relying on the packaged MATLAB MOO functions. Thus, a way was resolved for handling the optimization of more complex ISN models in a numerical computing environment.

Keywords: industrial symbiosis, network analysis, multi-objective optimization.

1. Introduction

Process systems engineers have turned to methods and tools such as multi-objective optimization (Scotti et al. 2017) and network analysis (Tan et al. 2023) to quantitatively assess and improve the sustainability of systems of chemical plants. Such techniques can be applied to investigate improving the exchange of CO_2 of decentralized CO_2 reuse systems on petrochemical clusters to reduce emissions (Lee Chan and Janes 2023). However, increasing network complexity in the hope of achieving synergetic benefits is likely to present more problematic analysis.

By filtering current and potential industrial symbiosis (IS) scenarios on the Point Lisas Industrial Estate (PLIE) in Trinidad and Tobago, Lee Chan and Janes (2023) quantified existing instances of sharing by-product process CO_2 and found that there are further IS opportunities for reusing valuable high-purity process CO_2 to reduce emissions. To build on this, further research aimed at future resource developments of the distributed petrochemical-manufacturing cluster was conducted. Case studies were undertaken to analyze the sharing of waste streams (e.g., contaminated water) and valuable by-product streams (e.g., process CO_2) through reuse between different petrochemical plants in the PLIE network. To assist in the initial studies, multi-criteria decision support tools had been developed utilizing multi-objective optimization (MOO) algorithms on a MATLAB® platform. The optimization sought to minimize costs, waste emissions, as well as fresh materials. The graph and network functions in MATLAB could then be used to generate network diagrams that display the connections between the source and sink plants as well as the flow rates between plants in the optimized IS network (ISN). But, modelling exchanges of several materials at different levels of purity would introduce greater complexity to the modelled ISNs. The most reported type of eco-industrial park (EIP) optimization studies is water exchange networks (Tiu and Cruz 2017). Boix et al. (2015) comprehensively reviewed the literature on MOO of water allocation network in EIPs. Rather our motivation was how to perform both MOO and network graphing conveniently in our chosen numerical computing environment, MATLAB.

Therefore, work was undertaken to see what simplifications and improvements to the concepts, methods and tools used to model and optimize more complex multi-material ISN models could realistically be employed. Particularly for non-evolutionary MOO methods, decision analysis is required to select 'the most appropriate' solution from a non-dominated solution set or Pareto front (PF). For example, this can be a solution in a smooth PF, where the cost has been rapidly reducing while the other objectives are hardly varying. Hence, to explore the extraction of a 'compromise' solution from the PF, some compromise methods (Kundu et al. 2013) and multi-criteria decision-making (MCDM) methods (Kolios et al. 2016) were investigated. The latter methods allow for the decision maker to include additional weightings in extracting the solutions. Therefore, for the MCDM method the number of plant linkages was incorporated into the selection to represent social and IS aspects. As the original aim of a numerical computing environment for combining packaged evolutionary MOO with network graphing and analysis could be achieved with either Scilab or Python and their relevant associated toolboxes, the findings might be transferable to these as well as GNU Octave.

2. Methodology

2.1 Model Development

This exercise built on the 'current case' in Lee Chan and Janes (2023), but this case study introduced a melamine plant (M) and considered only water reuse among some of the plants. A cut-down version of the petrochemical cluster, consisting of one ammonia plant (A1), one methanol plant using Davy technology (M1) and another Lurgi technology methanol plant (M2) was used. Four types of water qualities: boiler blowdown, wastewater, process water and boilerfeedwater makeup, were modelled. The representative water contaminant was total dissolved solids (TDS). The flow rates of water, in kg/h, to and from the processes were corroborated against sources cited in Lee Chan and Janes (2023). As before, the levelized cost of pipe-borne water transport, in USD/kg, was assessed from the distance between the sources and sinks and the pipeline and pumping requirements. A mixed-integer linear programming (MILP) model of the network was created, but now with four water streams with different levels of TDS. So, an equation that ensures the source purity requirement is achieved, Eq. (1), and two extra objectives to reduce the freshwater requirements and the total levelized cost of water transportation, as represented by Eq. (2) and Eq. (3) respectively, were added to the existing MILP optimization model. In these, R is the flow rate of fresh material, W is the flow rate of waste material, F is the flow rate of medial material, X is the TDS in the water and C is the levelized transportation cost. Index i refers to the source, j refers to the sink, k indicates the source quality and p the destination quality, whilst q refers to the material type.

$$\sum_{j,p} R_{j,p}^q X_R^q + \sum_{j,k} F_{i,j,k,p}^q X_{i,k}^q \leq F_{j,p}^q X_{j,p}^q \tag{1}$$

$$Min \sum_{j,p} R_{j,p}^q \forall p \tag{2}$$

$$Min \sum_{i,j,k,p} F_{i,j,k,p}^q C_{i,j,k,p}^q + \sum_{j,p} R_{j,p}^q C_{j,p}^q + \sum_{i,k} W_{i,k}^q C_{i,k}^q \forall q \tag{3}$$

The petrochemical cluster model contained 230 constraints, 120 continuous variables and 100 binary variables for algorithmic control purposes.

2.2 Model Optimization and MCDM PF Analysis

The optimization algorithms fell into two groups: packaged evolutionary MOO functions available in the MATLAB optimization toolboxes (MathWorks 2007) as well as bespoke code using scalarized MOO methods. Options within the packaged optimization algorithms were varied and the use of parallel computing was investigated. For each algorithm an attempt was made to generate a non-dominated solution set or PF. Two single objective optimization (SOO) models were created with freshwater minimization and cost reduction as the respective objective functions. The built-in MILP solver, 'intlinprog' was used to generate the SOO solutions, which were used as initial points for the optimization and global optimization toolbox solvers. To generate a four-point PF with 'fgoalattain' varying weights were used. For comparison, three scalarized MOO methods (viz, weighted sum, weighted metric and ε-constraint) were each coded to generate 25-point PFs. As these bespoke-coded methods required starting and ending points, the SOO solutions were used. The networks were optimized using MATLAB (ver. R2023a).

Two compromise methods (fuzzy LP and global criterion method (GCM) and three MCDM methods (ELECTRE-I, TOPSIS, and PROMETHEE-II) were employed to explore the extraction of a '*compromise*' solution from the PF. Additionally, a social and IS indicator, the eco-connectance (*EC*), was incorporated in the MCDM methods. The dimensionless EC, as represented by Eq. (4), is a modified form of the 'density' of the graph (Zhang et al. 2016) and it represents the ratio of byproduct and waste links in the network (N_w) compared to maximum possible links in the network, which is a function of the number of plants (N_p). *EC* was calculated from graph and network algorithm functions in MATLAB. For a simple graph with no self-looping, the closer EC is to one, indicates a more cohesive network.

$$EC = N_w / [N_p (N_p - 1)] \tag{4}$$

3. Results

The generated SOO solutions for the MILP model are shown in Table 1. When the initial points were used as starting points in the toolboxes, the 'gamultiobj' and 'paretosearch' functions produced a PF with only the initial points. The built-in function, 'fminimax' produced one point that was the lowest out of all the solutions obtained on the PF.

Table 1: SOO results for reduced water network

Objective Function	Cost (US$/h)	Freshwater consumption (kg/h)
Cost	102	91823
Freshwater consumption	124	90509

Without seeding with the SOO points, the 'gamultiobj' gave solutions within the SOO solution costs but greater than the SOO freshwater consumption. Both the 'fminimax' and 'fgoalattain' functions yielded solutions greater than the SOO solutions. A well-defined PF was only obtained with the 'gamultiobj' function; however, the run-time was longest. Using parallel computing decreased the runtime for solving the models by 50 % - 80 %. However, even with parallel computing, the 'gamultiobj' took five times longer to solve than the other built-in functions.

As shown in Figure 1, the 4-point PF values generated with 'fgoalattain' varied roughly by 0.3 % – 1 % from the PFs generated using the scalarized MOO methods. The runtime for the weighed sum and weighted metric methods were about the same, whereas the runtime for the ε-constraint method was 7 times greater. The 'fgoalattain' with varying weights method, although with 4 points only on the PF, had a runtime which was 111 times greater than the ε-constraint method with 25 points on the PF.

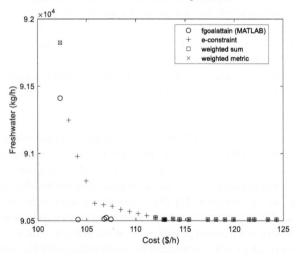

Figure 1: PF for bespoke and packaged methods

Because the ε-constraint method gave the widest spread of points on the PF, the solutions from this method were used in the extraction of a single solution for the network. For the MCDM methods, a social and IS indicator was factored into the selection slate. Firstly, in scenario S1, equal weightings for the three criteria: freshwater consumption, cost and the number of plant links, were applied. In scenario S2, the cost was weighted twice as much as the other two criteria. Table 2 shows the non-dominated solutions extracted from the PF using the various methods. It was found that the PROMETHEE-II (S2) results were similar to the Fuzzy LP, while the PROMETHEE-II (S1) results were like the GCM results. The solution with the lowest cost for scenarios S1 and S2 is highlighted in Table 2.

Table 2: Non-dominated solutions extracted from the PF

Method	Freshwater Consumption (kg/h)	Cost ($)	No. of Plant Links
Fuzzy LP	90690	105	-
GCM	90509	113	-
TOPSIS (S1& S2)	90509	122	8
PROMETHEE-II (S1)	90509	115	7
PROMETHEE-II (S2)	90629	106	4
ELECTRE-I (S2 & S2)	90509	118	6

The corresponding network graph of interplant exchanges is depicted in Figure 2. Flows of fresh material and flows to waste are not shown. Figure 2 showed that there was reuse of both process and utility water amongst the plants. There was water reuse within all the plants except the melamine plant. The network was analyzed from an IS and sustainability purview and the results obtained are shown in Table 3.

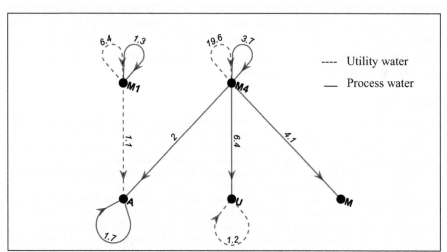

Figure 2: Network with water flows in t/h

The PROMETHEE-II (S2) solution has a lower *EC*, which is a function of plant links, since more links probably increases transportation costs. However, the existence of IS in the network, as spent-water exchanges, can be quantified by the *EC*. By computing the hub and authority centrality of the plants, the most important source (M4, from which 96 % of reused water originates) and sink (U, the destination for 51 % of reused water) can be identified. This reinforces other work by Zhang et al. (2016) and Tan et al. (2023) on using network analysis to provide granularity when quantifying IS options.

Table 3: IS and Sustainability indicators for 'most appropriate' compromise solution

Type of Indicator	Indicator	Value
IS	Eco-connectance, EC^*	0.2
Environmental	Fraction of waste utilized	0.5
Social	No. of plant linkages*	4
Economic	Cost of freshwater	Million US\$0.8/y
Circular	Percentage of process water reused	74
Circular	Percentage of utility water reused	10

* Calculated after removing self-looping.

Of all the MOO methods evaluated with this network, the ε-constraint method was the most systematic in obtaining a broad PF. The Fuzzy LP was judged the most pragmatic of the methods, which did not require an expansive non-dominated solution set, for determining a single compromise solution. To obtain 'a most appropriate' compromise solution according to the decision-maker's preference, the PROMETHEE-II method was the most practicable of the three MCDM methods explored.

4. Conclusions

When increasing complexity of the ISN made the MILP representation more challenging to solve, the bespoke code coped better and outperformed the algorithms in the toolboxes. The results show how MOO coupled with MCDM methods can be successfully used in a numerical computing platform for investigating ISNs. The next step is to incorporate exchanges of discarded water into the larger CO_2-reuse model of the PLIE in Lee Chan and Janes (2023) and apply the ε-constraint and PROMETHEE-II methods to realize triple bottom-line benefits (e.g.: reduced CO_2 emissions, new revenue streams and skilled jobs) and increased materials circulation.

References

M. Boix, L. Montastruc, C. Azzaro-Pantel and S. Domenech, 2015, Optimization methods applied to the design of eco-industrial parks: a literature review, Jour. of Cleaner Production 87: 303-317.
A. Kolios, V. Mytilinou, E. Lozano-Minguez and K. Salonitis, 2016, A Comparative Study of Multiple-Criteria Decision-Making Methods under Stochastic Inputs, Energies 9: 566.
P. Kundu, S. Kar, and M. Maiti, 2013, Multi-objective Multi-item Solid Transportation Problem in Fuzzy Environment, Applied Mathematical Modelling 37 (4): 2028-2038.
T. G. Lee Chan and D. A. Janes, 2023, Uncovering and Filtering Symbiosis Networks for Carbon Dioxide Utilization in Trinidad and Tobago, Carbon Capture Science & Technology 7: 100109.
MathWorks. 2007. Optimization Toolbox 3: User's Guide. MA, USA: The MathWorks Inc.
F. Scotti, N. Fabricatore, P. Sepiacci and D. Manca, 2017, A MOO approach towards Sustainable Process Design: Integrating the Three Pillars of Sustainability, In Computer Aided Chemical Engineering, edited by A. Espuña, M. Graells and L. Puigjaner, 637-642, Elsevier.
M. D. Tan, P. Ibarra-Gonzalez, I. Nikolic and A.Ramirez, 2023, Determining the Performance and Network Properties of Petrochemical Clusters, In Computer Aided Chemical Engineering, edited by A. C. Kokossis, M. C. Georgiadis and E. Pistikopoulos, 1211-1216, Elsevier.
B. T. C. Tiu and D. E. Cruz, 2017, An MILP model for optimizing water exchanges in eco-industrial parks considering water quality, Resources, Conservation and Recycling 119: 89-96.
Y. Zhang, H. Zheng, H. Shi, X. Yu, G. Liu, M. Su, Y. Li, Y. Chai, 2016, Network analysis of eight industrial symbiosis systems, Frontiers of Earth Science. 10 (4): 352-365.

Flavio Manenti, Gintaras V. Reklaitis (Eds.), Proceedings of the 34th European Symposium on Computer Aided Process Engineering / 15th International Symposium on Process Systems Engineering (ESCAPE34/PSE24), June 2-6, 2024, Florence, Italy

Prototyping cloud application for regional green transformation supported by prospective life cycle assessment

Yuichiro Kanematsu,[a*] Shoma Fujii,[bc] Yuko Oshita,[b] Satoshi Ohara,[bc] Atsushi Komori,[d] Daisuke Shimotoku,[e] Katsura Iizuka,[e] Junya Kawase,[e] Hiroki Kobayashi,[e] Yasunori Kikuchi[abc]

[a]Presidential Endowed Chair for "Platinum Society", The University of Tokyo, 113-8656 7-3-1 Hongo, Bunkyo-ku, Tokyo, Japan
[b]Institute for Future Initiatives, The University of Tokyo, 113-8654 7-3-1 Hongo, Bunkyo-ku, Tokyo, Japan
[c]Department of Chemical System Engineering, The University of Tokyo, 113-8656 7-3-1 Hongo, Bunkyo-ku, Tokyo, Japan
[d]Engineering Advancement Association of Japan, 106-0041 1-11-9 Azabudai, Minato-ku, Tokyo, Japan
[e]Information Technology Center, The University of Tokyo, 277-0882 6-2-3 Kashiwanoha, Kashiwa-shi, Chiba, Japan
kanematsu@platinum.u-tokyo.ac.jp

Abstract

Regional green transformation (GX) requires collaborative planning among local entities, integrating various technologies and life cycle thinking. A cloud-based information system prototype was developed in this study to expedite GX planning through prospective life cycle assessment (LCA), incorporating simulators, visualization tools, and local databases. The information system's conceptual design includes separate activity and data models. These models focus on the regional system's basic design, allowing planners to configure device installations, simulate mass/energy balances, and generate inventory data for LCA. Rationales are derived from previous case studies involving prospective LCA. The activity model covers local supply-demand analysis, alternative generation, mass & energy simulation, evaluation, and installation planning. The data model defines essential datasets for simulators used in prospective LCA of emerging technologies. The information system's function requirements, including prototypes for applications like GIS-based visualizers and energy flow diagrams, were defined using activity and data models. Datasets were integrated from statistical open data, and a technology database was created for matching technology with regional supply/demand. Simulators for specific technologies are being developed on a local server with plans for cloud integration, and the simulation results can used as the data to perform LCA. The entire system architecture based on an academic cloud infrastructure was discussed and the tools mentioned above will be integrated into a holistic application in near future.

Keywords: Life cycle assessment, Renewable energy, Local resource circulation

1. Introduction

Global and national targets and statements have been set for the promotion of carbon neutrality and resource circulation, and efforts at the regional level are essential to achieve these goals. While a few regions have made progress in introducing advanced technologies and mechanisms, many regions have only stated targets and are struggling to come up with concrete plans for installing the technologies needed to achieve these targets. Prospective life cycle assessment (LCA) is effective and necessary for the proof of concept of emerging technologies (Arvidsson *et al.*, 2018) required for carbon neutrality and resource circulation. Although there are an increasing number of studies of prospective LCA in academic research, there exists many challenges in the actual applications (Bergerson *et al.*, 2020). In order to achieve the implementation of the technology in a large number of regions, a mechanism to support and significantly accelerate the implementation of prospective LCA is needed, and the use of information technology is one of the essential elements. In this study, cloud-based information system was prototyped to accelerate the planning of regional GX based on prospective LCA, by integrating simulators, visualization tools and databases for local resources, energies and green technologies.

2. Methods

2.1. Conceptual Design of Information System for Supporting Regional GX

As a base of conceptual design of the information system, activity model and data model were separately developed to structurally visualize the planning procedure and the data relations. These models focus on the basic design phase of the regional system that the planner can determine the major configurations of devices to be installed into the region and can simulate the mass/energy balances in the system, which can be used as the inventory data for LCA. The rationales of the models were extracted from the previous case studies of system design based on prospective LCA such as combined heating and power using woody biomass (Kanematsu *et al.*, 2017a), mobile heat storage system with zeolite boiler (Fujii *et al.*, 2022), and the trial of their regional implementation (Kikuchi et al, 2020). The IDEF0 functional modeling method and UML class diagrams had been applied for the activity model and data model respectively in our previous research (Kanematsu *et al.*, 2017b), and improved through the current research activities.

2.2. Prototyping of the Modules of Cloud Application: RE-CODE

Based on the activity and data models, the function requirements of the information system were defined, and the entire system architecture were conceptually designed. Several prototypes of the modules required to functionalize the information system for accelerating regional GX were developed. It was identified that the cloud-based system is suitable for the entire system architecture in order to realize the required functions and promote the co-creation between the developers, system users and involved stakeholders. The system were named as RE-CODE, there "RE" involving the means region, resource, renewables, revitalize and so on, with "CODE" means co-design and program code. The prototype modules in RE-CODE were designed and developed supposing to build on the cloud-based information infrastructure.

3. Results and Discussions

3.1. Defined Functional Requirements and the Conceptual Design of RE-CODE

The activity model was defined as consisting of four planning tasks: local supply-demand analysis, alternative generation, mass/energy simulation, and evaluation, with entire management and review. The data model defined the datasets for simulators, which are essential for prospective LCA of emerging technologies. Figure 1 conceptually shows the activity model and required datasets.

Based on these models, we identified the need for tools to support each of the four activities included in the planning task, and organized into the following four main modules: *View, Match, Sim*, and *Value*. *View* is a tool for analyzing and visualizing regional supply and demand, and integrates data from multiple data sources, including supply potential of resources, industrial and residential demand, and their future estimates. *Match* is a tool for matching technologies and regions. This tool proposes elemental technologies and their combinations that can contribute to solving problems by taking advantage of the strengths of the region, based on the analysis results of *View*. *Sim* is a simulation tool for material/energy balance, which simulates the changes in material and energy flows when multiple combinations of technologies proposed by *Match* are introduced to a region as candidates. *Value* is an evaluation tool that uses the simulation results from *Sim* as inventory data for LCA and Input-Output Analysis (IOA).

Additionally, we found it desirable to configure the entire system as a cloud-based system. It is because the datasets required for planning are dispersed among various owners, such as energy demand data by residents or industries, unused wasted resources from agriculture, or state-of-the-art technology specifications from device developers. Timely, " mdx" (https://mdx.jp/), an academic cloud system jointly developed by several Japanese research institutes for the purpose of promoting transdisciplinary researches and activities, has been operational in 2022. We started to use mdx as the infrastructure for the development and operation.

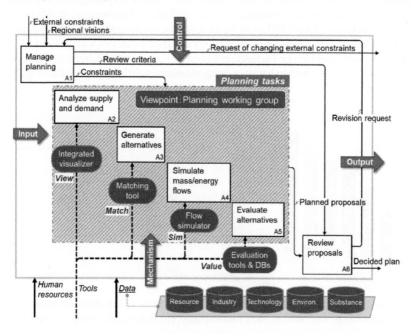

Figure 1. Activity model and related data sets for planning installation of GX technologies

3.2. Developed Prototypes for Modules of RE-CODE

3.2.1. RE-CODE View: Regional Supply-Demand Analyzer and Visualizer

Prototype web system that integrates open data on renewable resource potential and facility installation records published by different ministries, such as the Ministry of Environment and the Ministry of Economy, Trade and Industry, and visualizes them on a single web interface (Figure 2-a). In addition, a portion of the data can be visualized on Geographic Information System (GIS). A visualization combining bubble maps and pie charts were applied so that the characteristics of each municipality can be seen at a glance. (Figure 2-b) As a visualization tool for the demand side, we constructed a tool to calculate the actual statistical energy consumption at the basic municipality level and visualize it as a Sankey flow diagram. In Japan, energy consumption statistics are only available on a prefectural basis. A program was developed that can estimate energy consumption in minimum municipality level by combining population statistics with industry statistics such as the number of employees and production volume.

3.2.2. RE-CODE Match: Matching Tool Between Region and Technology

RE-CODE Match aims to propose technologies that match the characteristics of a region using the results of a supply-demand analysis by RE-CODE View. We identified that this tool should have functions to search and propose environmental technologies and their combination that can utilize resources in which the region has strengths or contribute to improve the energy consumption structure. Technology database in which the device development companies can register their own technologies including premature ones, will be developed and combined. Comprehensive and systematic categorization of technology categories is important for efficient storage and searching of technology data. In addition, to promote future decarbonization and resource recycling, it is important to consider the installation of technologies that are still under development. In this purpose, technology readiness level (TRL) can be an indicator for determining when they can be installed. Therefore, information on technology categories and TRLs was organized with reference to the Clean Energy Technology Guide by IEA Energy Technology Perspective (IEA, 2023), which has both exhaustive categorizations including future technologies and information on TRLs.

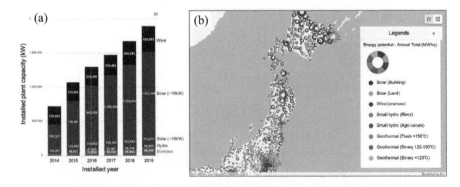

Figure 2. Prototyped web interface of RE-CODE View. (a) Installation history of renewable power plant of each municipality, (b) Renewable energy potential

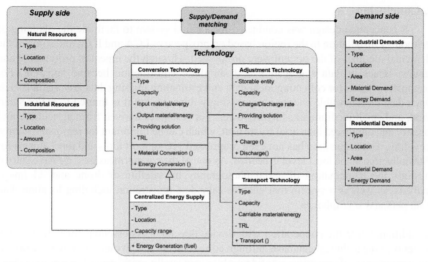

Figure 3. Major entities and data attributions considered in supply/demand matching
and simulation

3.2.3. RE-CODE Sim and Value: Region-level Simulation and Evaluation Tool for Technology Installation Planning

RE-CODE Sim is a tool to calculate changes in mass/energy flows when various sets of technologies proposed by *Match* are installed to a region. It enables regional simulation by connecting multiple process unit models, similarly with chemical process simulators, including resource acquisition, transport, energy/material conversion, storage, demand-side entities and so on. *RE-CODE Value* performs LCA based on the mass/energy balance information calculated by *Sim*, and evaluates environmental and economic impacts at the regional level. Premature technologies often change in scale and performance due to their development stage. Prospective LCA should be possible by constructing model structures that can treat such technological parameters as variables in the simulation, though conventional LCA have treated these parameters as given ones based on inventory data from actual operating process. For this purpose, the technology database described in previous section is being designed to store parameters and their changes as well. Figure 3 shows the major entities and data attributions considered in supply/demand technology matching and simulation.

The simulator for woody biomass CHP (Combined Heating and Power), which had been prepared for our own LCA research and were not designed for external users, were re-programmed for integration into a cloud system. As a test of the effect of the simulator, the application of the reconstructed woody biomass CHP simulator to a LCA in different regions resulted in a significant speed-up. While the initial case study required a total of more than 6 months for basic investigation, data collection, model construction, and visualization, the application to a different region allowed the same LCA to be performed in only 3 days, it is approximately 60 times faster. To support the combined simulation of multiple technologies, commonization of the model structure that enables seamless connection between various technology unit models is required and under construction.

4. Conclusion

A conceptual design was conducted for a cloud system to facilitate the planning of technology installation to the region based on prospective LCA and IOA, and some of the elemental modules of the system were prototyped. Through the repeat of prototyping and review, issues in data aggregation and simulator construction became apparent. For example, methods for collecting local data and estimating missing data are urgent issues. Open data on renewable energy is increasingly released, but it is limited to major solar, wind, and small/medium-sized hydropower. For resources derived from agriculture and forestry and unutilized industrial waste heat, which can be important for regional resource recycling, data acquisition has not even progressed yet. support tools and mechanisms for data collection at the local level is needed. As one of the countermeasures, we have started to study the combination of aerial photography by satellite or drone and AI image analysis, as well as a system that enables easy data registration including location data from personal smartphones.

In addition, while the cooperation with device developers is essential for enriching the contents of the technical database, through communication with them we have reaffirmed the importance of ensuring confidentiality, especially with regard to cutting-edge technologies. We plan to implement measures to ensure from both of software and hardware issues, that is confidentiality in data processing and security on the infrastructure side. It is also found to be necessary to design incentives for data providers so that they can benefit from the data.

Acknowledgements

This work is supported by MEXT/JSPS KAKENHI (JP21K17919) and JST COI-NEXT (JPMJPF2003). Activities of the Presidential Endowed Chair for "Platinum Society" at the University of Tokyo are supported by Mitsui Fudosan Corporation, Sekisui House, Ltd., the East Japan Railway Company, and Toyota Tsusho Corporation.

References

R. Arvidsson, A. M. Tillman, B. A. Sandén, M. Janssen, A.Nordelöf, D. Kushnir, S. Molander, 2018, Environmental Assessment of Emerging Technologies: Recommendations for Prospective LCA. Journal of Industrial Ecology 22, 1286–1294

JA. Bergerson, A. Brandt, J. Cresko, M. Carbajales-Dale, H. L. MacLean, H. S. Matthews, S. McCoy, M. McManus, S. A. Miller, W. R. Morrow III, I. D. Posen, T. Seager, T. Skone, S. Sleep, 2020, Life cycle assessment of emerging technologies: Evaluation techniques at different stages of market and technical maturity. Journal of Industrial Ecology 24, 11–25

S. Fujii, T. Nakagaki, Y. Kanematsu, Y. Kikuchi, 2022, Prospective life cycle assessment for designing mobile thermal energy storage system utilizing zeolite, Journal of Cleaner Production, 365, 132592

IEA, ETP Clean Energy Technology Guide, https://www.iea.org/data-and-statistics/data-tools/etp-clean-energy-technology-guide, last accessed on 28/12/2023

Y. Kanematsu, K. Oosawa, T. Okubo, Y. Kikuchi, 2017a, Designing the scale of a woody biomass CHP considering local forestry reformation: A case study of Tanegashima, Japan, Applied Energy, 198, 160-172

Y. Kanematsu, T. Okubo, Y. Kikuchi, 2017b, Activity and Data Models of Planning Processes for Industrial Symbiosis in Rural Areas, Kagaku Kōgaku Ronbunshū, 43(5), 347-357 (in Japanese)

Y. Kikuchi, M. Nakai, Y. Kanematsu, K. Oosawa, T. Okubo, Y. Oshita, Y. Fukushima, 2020, Application of technology assessments to co-learning for regional transformation: a case study of biomass energy systems in Tanegashima, Sustainability Science, 15, 1473-1494

Flavio Manenti, Gintaras V. Reklaitis (Eds.), Proceedings of the 34th European Symposium on Computer Aided Process Engineering / 15th International Symposium on Process Systems Engineering (ESCAPE34/PSE24), June 2-6, 2024, Florence, Italy
 http://dx.doi.org/10.1016/B978-0-443-28824-1.50579-2

On Numerical Stability of Relaxations of Generalized Disjunctive Programs

Miloš Bogataj[a], Zdravko Kravanja[a]

Faculty of Chemistry and Chemical Engineering, University of Maribor, Smetanova ulica 17, SI-2000 Maribor, Slovenia
milos.bogataj@um.si

Abstract

In this paper we present an approach that guarantees equally tight, if not tighter, continuous relaxations of mixed-integer (non)linear programs obtained by the reformulation of Generalized Disjunctive Programs than those obtained by the Hull Reformulation. The approach allows to solve cases where the the functions are not defined at a particular point or even over a larger part of the domain of the global variables. The numerical difficulties are avoided by the translation of variables. An algorithm is presented that optimizes the values of the non-zero points to which the disaggregated variables are driven when the corresponding binary variables are zero. The different MINLP reformulations obtained, i.e., the proposed reformulation, Big-M reformulation, and Hull reformulation, are discussed and compared in terms of their efficiency based on the results of numerical studies.

Keywords: Generalized Disjunctive Programming, Mixed-Integer Nonlinear Programming, Continuous Relaxation, Hull Reformulation, Big-M.

1. Introduction

This Generalized Disjunctive Programming (GDP) paradigm finds applications in various fields of engineering where decisions involve simultaneous continuous and discrete interactions. It was introduced as an alternative representation of the Mixed-Integer Nonlinear Programming (MINLP) model (Türkay and Grossmann, 1996; Lee & Grossmann, 2000; Grossmann and Lee, 2003). Although the GDP framework provides a higher-level representation of the relationships between the discrete and continuous aspects of a model, solving these models directly is not straightforward. Commonly, a reformulation of GDP into its MINLP counterpart is used. This can be achieved by either the Big-M reformulation (BMR) or Hull Reformulation (HR). The latter generally provides tighter continuous relaxation of the obtained MINLP (Lee and Grossmann, 2000); however, at an expense of increased model size. In addition, if a constraint $r(x) \leq 0$ in a disjunction of a GDP is nonlinear, it requires the introduction of the perspective function $yr(x/y)$, where y is a binary variable, or its numerically more stable approximation, Eq. 1, (Sawaya and Grossmann, 2007).

$$yr(x/y) \leq 0 \approx ((1-\varepsilon)y+\varepsilon)f(x/((1-\varepsilon)y+\varepsilon)) - \varepsilon r(0)(1-y) \leq 0 \tag{1}$$

One of the downsides is that either of the perspective function formulations introduces additional nonlinear terms for each linear term originally present in $r(x)$. To avoid this, Bogataj and Kravanja (2018) introduced a reformulation that preserves the nonlinear functions in their original form. The reformulation is based on the translation of variables introduced by Ropotar and Kravanja (2009). So far, however, the continuous relaxations obtained by HR have generally been tighter.

In this work we focus on reformulation of nonlinear GDPs that contain problematic functions that are undefined either at a single point or over a larger part of the domain of global variables. The most common examples of such functions in engineering are logarithmic and rational functions, the simples being $1/x$.

2. Proposed reformulation

The proposed GDP to MINLP reformulation addresses three goals. The first goal is to provide a reformulation that avoids numerical difficulties that arise when one or more constraints in the disjunctive terms are undefined at a particular point or over a larger part of the domain of global variables. The second goal is to provide a reformulation that preserves the form of the local constraints. The third and final goal is to provide a reformulation that guarantees a tight continuous relaxation of the resulting MINLP. To keep the derivation short, let us consider the following problem (GDP), which consists of an objective function $f(\mathbf{x})$, a global constraint $g(\mathbf{x})$ and a disjunction with two terms containing local constraints $r_1(\mathbf{x})$ and $r_2(\mathbf{x})$.

$$\min Z = f(\mathbf{x})$$

s.t.

$$g(\mathbf{x}) \leq 0 \qquad\qquad\qquad\qquad\qquad\qquad\qquad\qquad\qquad\qquad\text{(GDP)}$$

$$\begin{bmatrix} Y_1 \\ r_1(\mathbf{x}) \leq 0 \end{bmatrix} \vee \begin{bmatrix} Y_2 \\ r_2(\mathbf{x}) \leq 0 \end{bmatrix}$$

$$Y \in \{True, False\}, \quad Y_1 \veebar Y_2, \quad \mathbf{x} \in \square^{\,n}, \quad \mathbf{x}^{LO} \leq \mathbf{x} \leq \mathbf{x}^{UP}$$

The proposed Mixed-Integer Reformulation (MIR) follows the general idea of HR. However, three major exceptions are noticeable. First, the local constraints are expressed with disaggregated variables $\mathbf{x}^D$ without the use of the perspective function. Second, the bounding constraints on disaggregated variables (Eqs. 2–3) are augmented to fix disaggregated variables to predetermined non-zero values $\mathbf{x}^F$ if $y_j = 0$, and allow them to take any value between the lower and upper bounds if $y_j = 1$. Third, the aggregation constraint (Eq. 4) is augmented so that the value $x^F_{i,j}$ is subtracted from the value of the corresponding disaggregated variable if $y_j = 0$.

$$\min Z = f(\mathbf{x})$$

s.t.

$$g(\mathbf{x}) \leq 0$$

$$r_j\left(x^D_{i,j}\right) \leq 0 \qquad\qquad\qquad j = 1,2$$

$$x^D_{i,j} \leq x^{UP}_{i,j} y_j + x^F_{i,j}(1 - y_j) \qquad i = 1,\dots,n,\, j = 1,2 \qquad (2) \qquad\qquad \text{(MIR)}$$

$$x^D_{i,j} \geq x^{LO}_{i,j} y_j + x^F_{i,j}(1 - y_j) \qquad i = 1,\dots,n,\, j = 1,2 \qquad (3)$$

$$x_i = \sum_{j=1}^{2}\left(x^D_{i,j} - x^F_{i,j}(1 - y_j)\right) \qquad i = 1,\dots,n \qquad (4)$$

$$\sum_{j=1}^{2} y_j = 1$$

$$y \in \{1,0\}, \quad x^D_{i,j} \in \square, \quad x^{LO}_{i,j} = x^{LO}_i \leq x_i \leq x^{UP}_i = x^{UP}_{i,j}$$

3. Illustrative Example

The example considered in this work is a convex nonlinear GDP example composed of a quadratic objective function, and a single disjunction with three terms (GDP-E). The optimal solution to the problem is $Z = 6.8237$, $\mathbf{x} = (3.7069, 4.1506)$, $\mathbf{Y} = $ (*False, True, False*). The problematic constraints within each term are those with logarithmic functions.

$$\min Z = (x_1 - 3)^2 + (x_2 - 3)^2 + \sum_{i=1}^{3} \gamma_i$$

s.t.

$$\begin{bmatrix} Y_1 \\ -\log(x_1) + x_2 \leq 0 \\ (x_1 - 1)^2 - x_2 - 1 \leq 0 \\ \gamma_1 = 8 \end{bmatrix} \vee \begin{bmatrix} Y_2 \\ -\log(x_1 - 3) - x_2 + 4 \leq 0 \\ 0.5(x_1 - 4)^2 + x_2 - 5 \leq 0 \\ \gamma_2 = 5 \end{bmatrix} \vee \begin{bmatrix} Y_3 \\ -\log(x_1 - 6) + x_2 - 3 \leq 0 \\ (x_1 - 6.5)^2 - x_2 + 1.5 \leq 0 \\ \gamma_3 = 3 \end{bmatrix} \text{(GDP-E)}$$

$$Y \in \{True, False\}, \quad Y_1 \veebar Y_2 \veebar Y_3$$
$$x_1, x_2 \in \Box, \quad 0 \leq x_1 \leq 8, \quad -1 \leq x_2 \leq 5$$

4. Numerical results

Big-M reformulation (BMR): The most important thing when applying the BMR is to determine the appropriate values of Big-M parameters. They should be large enough to make a particular constraint redundant when $y = 0$, so that the entire feasible region of the problem is preserved. At the same time, they should be small enough to ensure a tight continuous relaxation of the problem. A common approach is to maximize the value of each constraint $r(\mathbf{x}) \leq 0$, s.t. $\mathbf{x}^{LO} \leq \mathbf{x} \leq \mathbf{x}^{UP}$ by which the following Big-M parameters $M_{j,k}$ = $(14_{1,1}, 49_{1,2}, 14_{2,1}, 8_{2,2}, 113_{3,1}, 44.75_{3,2})$, where $j = 1, 2, 3$ is the term in disjunction and $k = 1, 2$ is index of a constraint in the particular term of the disjunction. Note, however, that the constraints containing logarithmic functions are not easily subjected to this approach. For example, in constraint $r_{1,1}(\mathbf{x})$, the term $-\log(x_1)$ approaches ∞ as x_1 approaches 0, and becomes the dominant term in the constraint, thus making the Big-M parameter seemingly infinite. To avoid this, the Big-M parameter was determined by bounding the critical variable to the δ-vicinity ($\delta = 10^{-9}$) of a point at which the function is undefined. Nevertheless, solving the problem using BMR when the domains of problematic constraints do not coincide leads to reduction of feasible region and potential cut-off of the optimal solution. In the given example, a solution $Z = 13.5812$, $\mathbf{x} = (6.1253, 2.0981)$, $\mathbf{y} = (0, 0, 1)$ was identified as optimal. The reason is that no matter how large the Big-M parameters associated with the critical functions are, the only part of the feasible region in which all the critical functions are defined is when $x_1 \geq 6.0000 + \delta$.

Modified Hull Reformulation (MHR): The HR (Lee and Grossmann, 2000) requires that the continuous variables assume the value 0 if a disjunctive term is not selected, i.e., $y = 0$. Therefore, it is required that all constraints in disjunctions are defined at 0. This is clearly a difficulty in the given example. To overcome this problem, we propose a modified formulation of the perspective function (Eq. 5). The bounding constraints on the disaggregated variables and the aggregating constraint are the same as in MIR. Eq. 5 is an extension of the one proposed by Sawaya (2006) and allows continuous variables to take values different than 0 when $y = 0$. It is also easy to show the reformulation is identical to the HR when parameter x^F is 0.

$$yr(x/y) \le 0 \approx ((1-\varepsilon)y+\varepsilon)f\left(x/((1-\varepsilon)y+\varepsilon)\right)-\varepsilon r(x^F/\varepsilon)(1-y) \le 0 \qquad (5)$$

The GDP-E was formulated as an MINLP using BMR, MHR ($\varepsilon = 10^{-6}$) and the proposed MIR. First, apart from the BMR, the models were solved with 10,000 uniformly distributed values of the parameter x^F per disjunctive term. All x^F values were feasible points. The distribution of the obtained objective functions is shown in Figure 1. The results show that the values of x^F clearly affect the tightness of the continuous relaxation in both MINLP reformulations, indicating that neither reformulation yields a strict hull relaxation. While MIR leads to tighter relaxations ($3.850 \le Z_R \le 5.085$) compared to the MHR ($3.466 \le Z_R \le 3.527$), the deviation around the mean value is significantly lower in the latter case. We attribute the "looseness" of the MHR to the effect of the last term in Eq. 5, which acts as a considerably large Big-M parameter for small ε and large x^F values.

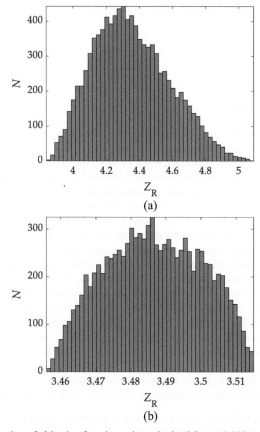

Figure 1: Distribution of objective function values obtained from 10,000 randomly selected x^F points: (a) MIR, (b) MHR.

Second, each of the 10,000 x^F values were optimized with the goal of obtaining the tightest possible continuous relaxation of the MINLP problem. The optimization was based on an algorithm that iterates between two nonlinear problems (NLPs). The first

NLP is relaxed MINLP with respect to MHR or MIR. Note that the problem is convex if GDP is convex. The second NLP corresponds to its nonconvex derivative, in which the aggregating constraint is replaced by Eq. 6 and the bounding constraints on disaggregated variables are omitted. The algorithm iterates between the two NLPs and resets the value of the parameters x^F to the current solution (values of the disaggregated variables) of the optimization problem. The algorithm terminates once the difference between the values of the objective functions is less than tolerance (e.g. 10^{-5}).

$$x_i = \sum_j x_{i,j}^D y_j \tag{6}$$

The proposed algorithm was used to obtain the values of the x^F parameters shown in Table 1. Regardless of the initial random value, the same optimal values were obtained in all 10,000 cases. Note that none of the values listed in Table 1 correspond to the optimal solution of the GDP problem or to the minimum of a particular disjunction with respect to the objective function. The values of the objective functions when solving the continuous relaxation of the corresponding MINLPs are 3.6604 for MHR and 5.1928 for MIR. Thus, in both cases, the continuous relaxation is tightened. The optimization of the x^F parameters took on average 1 pass (2 NLPs) in the case of MIR and 3 passes (6 NLPs) in the case of MHR. As a sidenote, the optimal values of the x^F parameters can also be determined by iteratively solving the convex, relaxed MINLP alone. In our experience, however, up to 20 NLPs must be solved before the algorithm terminates. This is not problematic for the small example considered in this paper but can contribute significantly to the solution time of larger problems.

Table 1: Values of optimal x^F parameters.

$x^F_{i,j}$	MHR					
	$x^F_{1,1}$	$x^F_{1,2}$	$x^F_{1,3}$	$x^F_{2,1}$	$x^F_{2,2}$	$x^F_{2,3}$
	0.811	0.989	4.156	−0.932	5.000	2.012
$x^F_{i,j}$	MIR					
	$x^F_{1,1}$	$x^F_{1,2}$	$x^F_{1,3}$	$x^F_{2,1}$	$x^F_{2,2}$	$x^F_{2,3}$
	0.305	3.206	6.050	−0.516	4.685	1.702

In addition to the illustrative example presented in Chapter 3, the proposed approach was tested on several examples from the literature, such as different instances of illustrative examples, e.g., Circles (Lee and Grossmann, 2000), and various instances of a Strip Packing Problem (Trespalacios and Grossmann, 2016), and Process Synthesys Problem (Türkay and Grossmann, 1996, Sawaya and Grossmann, 2007). The aim was to cover the diversity of GDPs, i.e., from purely linear GDPs to purely nonlinear GDPs. The results of these experiments show that the proposed MIR in conjunction with the proposed algorithm to optimize x^F values provides as tight a continuous relaxation as HR, regardless of the GDP type.

5. Conclusions

In this paper, we have presented an approach to reformulate GDP problems into MI(N)LP problems. The strength of the proposed approach is that the points at which the local constraints in disjunctions are not defined, if such constraints exist, do not pose a numerical problem. According to the results obtained, it provides at least as tight a continuous relaxation as HR. Moreover, the proposed approach avoids the use of the perspective function when local constraints are nonlinear; therefore, the reformulation of

GDP is identical for linear and nonlinear constraints. We could argue that this simplifies the implementation of the proposed approach compared to HR. More importantly, the proposed reformulation does not introduce additional nonlinearities. A drawback of the proposed approach is that, at the time of this publication, an algorithmic approach is needed to determine the values of the x^F parameters.

This research provided some answers and new insights into GDP to MI(N)LP reformulations. However, it also opened up several additional topics for future research. The first is to determine whether an algorithmic approach can be avoided when determining the optimal values of the x^F parameters. Furthermore, it is tempting to answer the question whether and under which conditions the optimal values of the x^F parameters can be used to tighten the bounds on disaggregated variables. Last but not least, future research will try to determine the role of x^F parameters in the Logic-Based Outer Approximation algorithm, namely their potential role in providing valid and good linearization points.

Acknowledgements

The authors would like to acknowledge Slovenian Research and Innovation Agency (ARIS), Programme P2-0414.

References

F. Trespalacios, I.E. Grossmann, 2016, Symmetry breaking for generalized disjunctive programming formulation of the strip packing problem. Annals of Operations Research, 258(2), 747–759

I.E. Grossmann, S. Lee, 2003, Generalized convex disjunctive programming: Nonlinear convex hull relaxation. Computational optimization and applications, 26(1):83–100.

M. Bogataj, Z. Kravanja Z., 2018, Alternative mixed-integer reformulation of Generalized Disjunctive Programs, Computer-aided chemical engineering 43, 549–544.

M. Ropotar, Z. Kravanja Z., 2009, Translation of Variables and Implementation of Efficient Logic-Based Techniques in the MINLP Process Synthesizer MIPSYN, AIChE Journal, 55 (11), 2896– 2913.

M. Türkay, I.E, Grossmann, 1996, Logic-based MINLP algorithms for the optimal synthesis of process networks. Computers & Chemical Engineering, 20(8), 959–978.

N. Sawaya, 2006, Thesis: Reformulations, relaxations and cutting planes for generalized disjunctive programming, Carnegie Mellon University.

N.W. Sawaya, I.E. Grossmann, 2007, Computational implementation of non-linear convex hull reformulation. Computers & Chemical Engineering, 31(7), 856–866.

S. Lee, I.E. Grossmann, 2000, New algorithms for nonlinear generalized disjunctive programming. Computers & Chemical Engineering, 24, 2125–2141.

Flavio Manenti, Gintaras V. Reklaitis (Eds.), Proceedings of the 34th European Symposium on Computer Aided Process Engineering / 15th International Symposium on Process Systems Engineering (ESCAPE34/PSE24), June 2-6, 2024, Florence, Italy

Biological analogues in advanced water treatment with application in 3D printed graphene oxide and metal-halide $Bi_xO_yCl_z$/AgCl composite heterogeneous photocatalysis

Evans M. N. Chirwa,[a] Shepherd M. Tichapondwa,[a] Fisseha A. Bezza,[a] Emmanuel O. Ichipi,[a] Rachel Mugumo,[a] Osemeikhian Ogbeifun,[a] Dorcas O. Adenuga,[a] Zakhele A. Khumalo,[a] Emomotimi E. Bamuza-Pemu[a]

[a]*Water Utilisation and Environmental Engineering Division, Department of Chemical Engineering, University of Pretoria*
Email: evans.chirwa@up.ac.za

Abstract

Engineering can be made simple and more impactful by observing and understanding how organisms in nature solve eminent problems. For example, scientists around the world have observed green plants thriving without organic food inputs using the complex photosynthesis process to kick start a biochemical food chain. Observations have also been conducted on bacteria multiplying in diverse environments, some so unimaginable for life to exist. In several studies, complex biochemical pathways for detoxification and degradation of pollutants were emulated in AOPs and photocatalytic processes. This includes the development of heterogeneous nanoparticle materials for photocatalytic reactions and solar desalination for recovery of water mimicking the z-scheme photochemical process used by plants. How plants split water to H^+ and O_2 to produce the reducing equivalents ($\sim e^-$) is still a subject of intensive research. If a material is found that is capable of releasing $H_2(g)$ from water, that will solve the world's energy crisis for forthcoming generations. From the fundamental energy transduction processes in microorganism, the research group from the Water Utilisation Group at the University of Pretoria has studied and developed fundamental processes for degradation and remediation of unwanted compounds such as disinfection byproducts (DBPs), volatile organic compounds (VOCs) and pharmaceutical products from water. The research entailed the derivation, synthesis and characterisation of visible-light activated metal-halide heterogeneous photocatalysts for degradation of hard-to-degrade organic pollutants, intermediates and their congeners from wastewater and water from impaired sources. The processes of low energy photocatalysis and 3D printed graphene oxide solar desalination and degradation of compounds were evaluated as developments towards future applications.

Keywords: biological analogues, z-scheme, heterogenous photocatalysis, 3D printed graphene, organics degradation.

1. Introduction

While investigating the photoelectrolysis of water, the discovery by Fujishima and Honda in 1972 of the photocatalytic splitting of water on *n*-type rutile titanium dioxide (TiO_2) electrodes opened the doors to numerous possibilities that the field of photocatalysis presents (Hashimoto *et al.*, 2005). The limitation of TiO_2 photocatalysis is due to its wide band-gap energy which is mostly activated using high-frequency UV light produced by high-pressure mercury lamps. Many studies have recently been undertaken to unravel the underlying principles of oxidative degradation of organic pollutants in aqueous phase (Mzimela et al., 2023), photodegradation pathways, as well as identification of intermediates produced during photocatalysis (Bamuza-Pemu and Chirwa, 2010).

Based on the predominant scientific understanding of the enzymatic redox processes in living cells, the redox processes in a photocatalytic semiconductor particle during the oxidation of water at the valance band (h^+) and reduction of oxygen at the conduction band (e^-) is presented as a set of equations, Eqs. (1-7):

$$TiO_2 + h\nu \rightarrow TiO_2 \ (e^-_{CB} + h^+_{VB}) \tag{1}$$

$$TiO_2(h^+_{VB}) + H_2O_{ad} \rightarrow TiO_2 + {}^{\bullet}OH_{ad} + H^+ \tag{2}$$

$$TiO_2(h^+_{VB}) + OH^- \rightarrow TiO_2 + {}^{\bullet}OH_{ad} \tag{3}$$

$$TiO_2 \ (e^-_{CB}) + O_2 \rightarrow TiO_2 + O_2^- \tag{4}$$

$$O_2^- + H^+ \rightarrow HO_2^{\bullet} \tag{5}$$

$$TiO_2(h^+_{VB}) + R\text{-}H \rightarrow TiO_2 + \text{oxidized products} \tag{6}$$

$${}^{\bullet}OH + R\text{-}H \rightarrow \text{oxidized products} \tag{7}$$

The photogenerated electrons that are available to reduce oxygen to water are passed on through the Redox reactions, Eqs.(1-5). The photogenerated h^+ oxidise organic pollutants, Eq.(6), and oxidation of organic compounds by ${}^{\bullet}OH$ generated indirectly by photolytic reactions is illustrated by Eq.(7). The mineralization process is believed to involve the initial oxidation of surface hydroxyl groups ($>Ti^{IV}OH$) on the TiO_2 to hydroxyl radicals ($>Ti^{IV} OH^{\bullet+}$), which oxidizes the pollutant and any intermediate(s).

Alternatively, visible-light activated metal-halide heterogeneous photocatalysts are suggested derived based on BiOCl stoichiometry. These studies have one theme in common, i.e., the catalysts activation following a model similar to the photoenergy transduction and electron generation using the z-scheme photosynthetic process in green plants. Surface interaction models followed standard Langmuir isotherms, however interactive conversion of species was highly non-linear with multi-species rate limiting levels following the simulation routine derived by Khuzwayo and Chirwa (2016). Complementary photocatalytic performance matrices were established to estimate parameters based on the Taguchi orthogonal arrays (Sendin et al., 2004).

The aim of this study was to develop efficient visible-light driven photocatalysts for degradation of toxic organics in water based on known processes from nature. Examples being the $AgCl/Bi_xO_yCl_z$ (Adenuga et al., 2023) and porphyrin@$Bi_{12}O_{17}Cl_2$ (Ogbeifun et al., 2023). Batch results for the above photocatalysts showed 80.3% and 83.4% degradation of phenol, respectively, after 6 hours exposure to visible-light.

2. Experimental Methods

2.1. Synthesis of Heterogeneous Metal-Halide Photocatalysts

The synthesised $Bi_{24}O_{31}Cl_{10}$ (0.2 g) was added into 50 mL of water with continuously stirring. A 10 mL solution containing 50 mg cetyltrimethyl ammonium chloride (CTAC) was added to the suspension and stirred for 1 h. $AgNO_3$ (27 mg) dissolved in 10 mL water

Biological analogues in advanced water treatment with application in 3D   3477
printed graphene oxide and metal-halide Bi$_x$O$_y$Cl$_z$/AgCl composite
heterogeneous photocatalysis

was slowly added into the Bi$_{24}$O$_{31}$Cl$_{10}$/CTAC suspension and stirred continuously for 2 h. The collected precipitate was washed with ethanol and water before being dried at 60 °C for 8 h. This resulted in 10% AgCl on a mass basis being deposited on the BOC to form a composite photocatalyst. The process is illustrated in Figure 1.

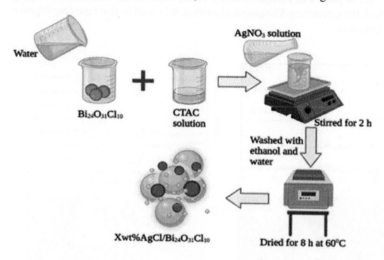

Figure 1. Schematic diagram illustrating the preparation process of Xwt%AgCl/BOC heterojunction photocatalyst.

2.2. Reactor Studies

All experiments were conducted in batch with different doses of the photocatalyst under visible-light with UV irradiation as a control. For systems with ultimate catalyst dose, the concentration of test compounds was varied to determine the effect of loading on reaction rates. Effective photocatalytic reaction was measured from the point when the light was turned on as time zero.

2.3. Photocatalyst Characterization Studies

The crystal structure of the synthesized photocatalysis was determined using SEM. The composition of synthesized materials was verified by SEM-EDX, XRD, XPS and FTIR. Particle size distribution and surface area was determined by the Mastersizer 3000 — Particle Size Analyzer and BET analysis. XRD, SEM-EDX and XPS characterization results are shown in Figure 2 whereas particle size and surface area relationship data is discussed in Section 3.

2.4. Parameter Analysis and Optimisation

The program Sugal 2.1 by Hunter (1995) was interfaced with the simulation program using Modified Sugal GA subroutine (Chirwa, 2001). The Genetic Algorithm uses the fitness function, $f_i(\sigma)$, and an evolutionary search engine to find the best parameters for the system of equations (Eqs. 8-9):

$$RSS = \frac{1}{n-q}\sum_{i=1}^{n}\left(y_i^{obs} - y_i^{pred}\right)^2 \qquad (8)$$

$$f_i(\sigma) = [RSS]^{-1} \qquad (9)$$

where RSS = residual sum of squares, $f_i(\sigma)$ = fitness function, n = number of points to evaluate, q = number of parameters, y_i^{pred} = model prediction for a given set of parameters, and y_i^{obs} = a corresponding experimental value. The genetic algorithm was terminated with a coarse set of parameters within vicinity of the true optima. A faster converging gradient method, the Levenberg-Marguardt algorithm, was used to fine tune convergence to the global optimum.

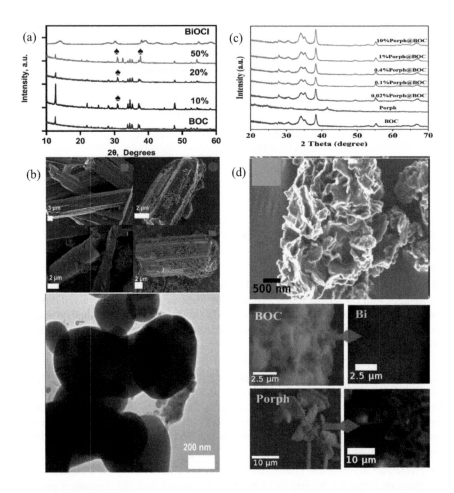

Figure 2. (a-b) Composition characterization using XRD and SEM for a BiOCl/AgCl system, and (c-d) XRD and SEM-EDS for the synthesized porphyrin@Bi$_{12}$O$_{17}$Cl$_2$ photocatalyst.

3. Results and Discussion

3.1. Catalyst Performance Data - BiOCl/AgCl system

The compound *BiOCl/AgCl* was tested on phenol degradation under visible light irradiation and is reported in Figure 3a. Experiments were carried out under photolysis

Biological analogues in advanced water treatment with application in 3D   3479
printed graphene oxide and metal halide $Bi_xO_yCl_z$/AgCl composite
heterogeneous photocatalysis

and adsorption conditions to investigate the individual effects of light and photocatalyst. The results show negligible degradation of phenol illustrating that light and photocatalysts are required for photocatalytic degradation to take place. The compound porphyrin@$Bi_{12}O_{17}Cl_2$ achieved similar results as demonstrated by Figure 3b.

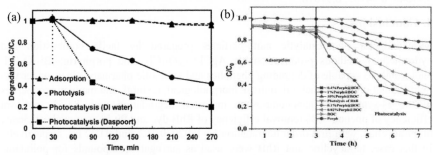

Figure 3. (a) Degradation of phenol as a model compound using the BiOCl/AgCl system, and (b) degradation of RhB dye by the porphyrin@$Bi_{12}O_{17}Cl_2$ photocatalyst.

The results in Figure 3a show clearly that photocatalytic degradation of phenol in a complex matrix was highest under visible light using the *BiOCl/AgCl* heterogeneous photocatalyst. Notably, no degradation was observed in the absence of light even in the presence of the heterogeneous photocatalyst.

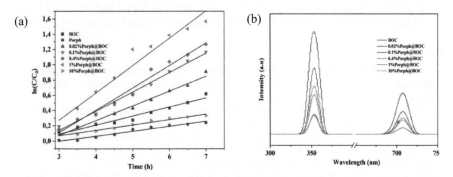

Figure 4. (a) Correlation of date to the pseudo-first order rate kinetic which yielded the optimum operational condition for a z-scheme photocatalytic model using Rhodamine B (RhB) dye, and (b) light absorption conditions for different structural compositions.

3.2. Catalyst Performance Data - porphyrin@$Bi_{12}O_{17}Cl_2$

Similar results were observed with the porphyrin@$Bi_{12}O_{17}Cl_2$ photocatalyst (Figure 3b). In this version of photocatalyst, the best reaction was achieved with a 1% of porphyrin to the BiOCl composite. It was demonstrated here that there is still room of improvement in the development of metal-halide heterogeneous photocatalysts through inclusion of organic reactive compounds that were never studied before.

3.3. Suggested Operational Model

The kinetics of RhB dye degradation were determined from the data obtained in the degradation study to be *pseudo-first order* kinetic equation. *First-order kinetic* $-\ln C/C_o = kt$ where C_0 and C are the initial and final concentrations of RhB dye, k, the rate constant, and t, the time, was used to fit the experimental data. The *pseudo-first order* kinetic was confirmed from the linear curve in Figures 4 (a) and (b). The R^2 values for 0.02%Porph@BOC, 0.1%Porph@BOC, 0.4%Porph@BOC, 1%Porph-@BOC, 10%Porph@BOC and BOC were found to be 0.9566, 0.97107, 0.97808, 0.99063, 0.97548, 0.94701, 0.97018.

4. Conclusions

Semiconductor photocatalytic nano-particles prepared by facile combustion and hydrothermal methods produced stable $AgCl/Bi_{24}O_{31}Cl_{10}$ and porphyrin@$Bi_{12}O_{17}Cl_2$ photocatalysts capable of degrading phenolics and antibiotic pharmaceuticals under vis-light irradiation. The structural, optical, morphological, textural, and magnetic properties of the as-synthesised nanocomposites indicated degradation with 83.5% removal efficiency of phenol, 98% removal efficiency of RhB dye and 99.5% removal efficiency of tetracycline, with first-order degradation $k = 0.020$, 0.362, and 0.032 h^{-1}, respectively. In this case, tetracycline and RhB were used as surrogate compounds for pollutants emanating from major industrial polluters around the world. The derived heterogeneous photocatalysts exhibited excellent chemical stability and recyclability after five runs without need for any significant alteration in its structural and morphological properties.

5. Acknowledgements

The study was funded by the National Research Foundation (NRF) through Grant No's. SRUG2204072544 and EQP180503325881 and Rand Water Company, through Grant No. RW01413/18 awarded to Prof E.M.N. Chirwa, and The NRF Thuthuka Fund Grant No. TTK18024324064 awarded to Prof S.M. Tichapondwa at the University of Pretoria

References

D.O. Adenuga, S.M. Tichapondwa, and E.M.N. Chirwa, 2023, Influence of wastewater matrix on the visible light degradation of phenol using $AgCl/Bi_{24}O_{31}Cl_{10}$ photocatalyst, Advances in Science, Engineering and Technology, 30, 98922–98933.

E.E. Bamuza-Pemu, E.M.N. Chirwa, 2010, Photocatalytic degradation of geosmin: Reaction pathway analysis, Water SA, 38, 5, 689-696.

F.A. Bezza, S.A. Iwarere, S.M. Tichapondwa, E.M.N. Chirwa, 2023, Fabrication and Application of Ag, Black TiO 2 and Nitrogen-Doped 3D Reduced Graphene Oxide (3D Black TiO_2/Ag/N@rGO) Evaporator for Efficient Steam Generation, Catalysts, 13, 3, 514.

E.M.N. Chirwa, 2001, Modeling Chromium(VI) Reduction in Pure and Coculture Biofilm Reactors, PhD Thesis, University of Kentucky, Lexington Kentucky.

A. Fujishima, K. Honda, 1972, Electrochemical photolysis of water at a semiconductor electrode, *Nature*, 238, 37-38.

K. Hashimoto, H. Irie, and A. Fujishima, 2005, TiO_2 Photocatalysis: A Historical Overview and Future Prospects, Japanese Journal of Applied Physics, 44, 8269.

Z. Khuzwayo, E.M.N. Chirwa, 2016, Modelling and simulation of photocatalytic oxidation mechanism of chlorohalogenated substituted phenols in batch systems: Langmuir–Hinshelwood approach, Journal of hazardous Materials, 300 (2015), 459-466.

N. Mzimela, S.M. Tichapondwa, E.M.N. Chirwa, 2022, Visible-light-activated photocatalytic degradation of rhodamine B using WO_3 nanoparticles, RSC Advances, 12, 34652-34659.

O. Ogbeifun, S.M. Tichapondwa, E.M.N. Chirwa, 2023, Self-assembled micro and nano rod-shaped porphyrin@$Bi_{12}O_{17}Cl_2$ composite as an efficient photocatalyst for degradation of organic contaminants, Discover Nano, 18, 137, 1.

O.H. Sendin, C.G. Moles, A.A. Alonso, and J.R. Banga, 2004, Chapter D4 - Multi-Objective Integrated Design and Control using Stochastic Global Optimization Methods, Computer Aided Chemical Engineering, 17, 2004, 555-581.

Flavio Manenti, Gintaras V. Reklaitis (Eds.), Proceedings of the 34th European Symposium on
Computer Aided Process Engineering / 15th International Symposium on Process Systems
Engineering (ESCAPE34/PSE24), June 2-6, 2024, Florence, Italy

Design optimal experiments for parameter identification of a dynamic model with perturbed inputs

Ran Wang,[a] Antonio Armaou,[a,b,c]*Robert Rioux,[a,d]

[a]*Department of Chemical Engineering, Pennsylvania State University, University Park, PA 16802, USA*
[b]*Department of Mechanical Engineering, Pennsylvania State University, University Park, PA 16802, USA*
[c]*Department of Chemical Engineering, University of Patras, Patras, 26504, Greece*
[d]*Department of Chemistry, Pennsylvania State University, University Park, PA 16802, USA*
armaou@psu.edu

Abstract

An optimization approach for sensor placement and input sequences to improve parameter identifiability in spatiotemporally dependent experiments, modelled by partial differential equations, is developed. Robust design criteria using bilevel optimization are applied in the approach. The determinant (D-optimality), the smallest eigenvalue (E-optimality) or the inverse of condition value (modified E-optimality) of the Fisher information matrix are applied as criteria. A greedy algorithm is used in the optimization procedure to avoid extremely long calculation time. The developed approach is illustrated towards the identification of kinetic parameters in a transient axial dispersion reactor model with perturbed inlets. Improvement of the parameter identifiability for the model is investigated fitting synthetic data generated by high-fidelity simulations with preset kinetic parameters. The performance of the three objective functions is also compared.

Keywords: parameter identification, robust design, perturbed inputs.

1. Introduction

To adequately model chemical processes using first principles, experimental observations or their combination, we often need to consider both the spatial and temporal codependencies of the desired variables (such as species concentrations, temperature, etc.). Parameters in the time and space-varying partial differential equations (PDEs) of the resultant dynamic model can be more accurately identified using measured time-varying output profiles (observations) under persistently perturbed inputs. (Narendra and Annaswamy, 1987) In such cases, the locations of sensors for data collection and the time distribution of the perturbed inputs are important for parameter identifiability. (Uciński and Patan, 2007) Model-based design of experiments (MBDoE) is widely used to maximize the information potential from the collected data. Optimization criteria based on information are widely applied in MBDoE for accurate parameter identification. (Franceschini and Macchietto, 2008) Initial model parameters may have a strong effect on the performance of MBDoE if objective functions are directly optimized in the criteria. However, little information is usually provided for the initial parameters. This effect of the initial parameters can be mitigated using a robust design criterion, which has been applied in lumped parameter system. (Asprey and Macchietto, 2002)

In this study, a robust design procedure for optimization of sensor location and perturbed input to improve parameter identifiability of appropriate models for distributed parameter systems is proposed. The sensor location and the input sequence leading to a maximum of the objective function for the worst set of parameters are regarded as the optimal design, which aims to maintain acceptable parameter identification accuracy in a wide range of the model parameters. Different optimality criteria are compared in the study.

The procedure is tested in transient kinetic study cases with pseudo-random binary sequence (PRBS) perturbations at the reactor inlet. The parameter identifiability is investigated using synthetic data.

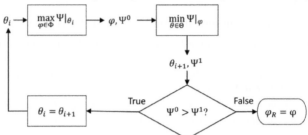

Figure 1 Schematic of robust design method for accurate parameter identification.

2. Method

2.1. Design of experiments for parameter identifiability

The sensor location, x_s, or the perturbed input at the boundary condition, $u_{in}(t)$, are optimized by a robust design procedure using a max-min criterion on the Fisher information matrix (FIM) as shown in Eq 1. (Asprey and Macchietto, 2002). The optimized experimental conditions from robust design, φ_R, are optimized through searching the experimental conditions, φ, which maximize the objective function, Ψ, at worst set of model parameters, θ. The determinant, the smallest eigen value and the inverse of 2-norm condition number of FIM are used as objective functions, Ψ, for a D-optimality, an E-optimality and a modified E-optimality design (Balsa-Canto et al., 2008), respectively. The FIM is determined by Eq. 2, where y is the observation of the experiment and W is its diagonal weight matrix. Though a better design may be obtained using Newton-based and global search algorithms, a greedy algorithm (Asprey and Macchietto, 2002) demonstrated in Figure 1 is applied to avoid significantly longer time to identify the global optimal solution of the problem for the bilevel optimization problem. In the algorithm, the experimental condition, φ, is first optimized for the maximal objective function value at certain model parameters, θ_i. Then, model parameters for the smallest objective function value are searched at the optimized experimental condition, φ_i. If the objective function value decreases between the two steps, the iteration continues. Otherwise, the optimized experimental condition is regarded as the result of the robust design. The determinant of FIM may be extremely large or small if there are too many observation points. Therefore, the natural logarithm of the determinant is used as the objective function. An upper limit of 1000 and a lower limit of -1000 are set to the objective function to avoid the occurrence of infinite value. The interior-point method in function fmincon of MatLab is used to solve the optimization in each iteration.

$$\varphi_R = \arg \max_{\varphi \in \Phi} \min_{\theta \in \Theta} \Psi; \varphi = x_s, u_{in} \tag{1}$$

$$FIM = J^T W J; J_{ij} = \frac{\partial y_i}{\partial \theta_j} \tag{2}$$

2.2. Investigation of practical parameter identifiability of the model

The practical identifiability of the model parameters is investigated using synthetic data as shown in Figure 2. The synthetic data is generated by high-fidelity simulations with preset parameters, where white Gaussian noise with a signal to noise ratio (SNR) of 35dB is added to emulate real experiments. Then, the same model (denoted as M in Fig.2) will be used to fit these synthetic data and derive fitted parameter values and their 95% confidence intervals. If the deviation between fitted and preset parameters' values is small and the corresponding confidence interval is narrow, the parameter is practically identifiable. To quantitively evaluate the deviation and the confidence interval respectively, we propose two criteria, $E_1 = \left| log_{10} \frac{\theta_f}{\theta_s} \right|$, and $E_2 = \frac{\delta}{\theta_f}$, where θ_f denotes the fitted model parameter, θ_s is the preset parameter, and δ represents the half width of the confidence interval. Therefore, if values of both E_1 and E_2 are small, parameters are practically identifiable. Conversely, if E_1 or E_2 is large, parameters are unidentifiable. In the following test case, parameters are regarded as accurately identified if $E_1 < 0.12$ and $E_2 < 0.25$.

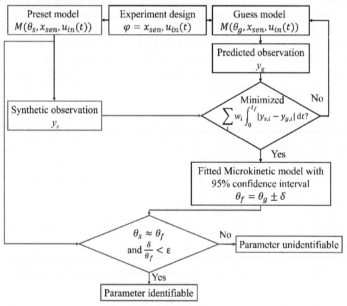

Figure 2 Schematic of investigation procedure for practical identifiability of parameters.

3. Results

3.1. Transient kinetic study case for test of the robust design

The proposed MBDoE and parameter identifiability investigation procedures are tested in a transient kinetic study for general reaction $2A + B_2 \rightleftharpoons 2AB$, where two reactants are simultaneously pulsed into the reactor under a molar ratio of 2 for A and B_2 with PRBS perturbation as demonstrated in Figure 3. Inert gas is

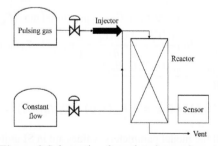

Figure 3 Schematic of emulated experimental apparatus for synthetic transient kinetic study.

constantly fed intro the reactor. Other operation conditions are summarized in Table 1. Kinetic constants, k, and total concentration of active sites, C_t, are estimated using the objective function of sum of squared errors of concentration profiles as shown in Eq. 3; C_s and C_g denote the synthetic time-varying concentration profiles at the sensor location generated by preset parameters and corresponding estimated profiles. The total number for observation points in the time-varying concentration profiles, n_t, is

Table 1 Operating conditions for kinetic study

Operation conditions	Value
Pulsing gas flow rate, Q_P	10 mL/min
Carrier gas flow rate, Q_c	100 mL/min
Temperature, T	423.15 K
Total Pressure, P_T	1.06 atm
Length of packed bed, L_b	10 mm
Inner diameter of reactor, D_i	3.9 mm
Bed void fraction, ε	0.57
Mass of packed catalyst, m_c	67 mg
Diameter of catalyst, d_p	0.1 mm
Concentration of total active sites, C_t	0.4mol/kg

set as 1001. An isothermal axial dispersion model assuming ideal gas is used for the reactor model (Yang et al., 2018). Material balance equations are shown as Eq. 4 to Eq. 6, where C represents concentration, t denotes time, x is axial coordinate. The superficial velocity in the gas phase is calculated according to mass balance of an inert component. The surface reaction rate, r_{surf}, is calculated by microkinetic model as shown in Table 2. The kinetic constants' values are constrained by the thermodynamic equilibrium of overall reaction. The axial dispersion coefficient, D_L, is calculated by Ruthven's (1984) correlation, and diffusion coefficient are estimated by Fairbanks and Wilke's (1950) equation.

Table 2 Microkinetic model of surface reactions and preset values for synthetic study

Step	Elementary steps	Kinetic equations	Preset values
S1	$A+* \rightleftharpoons A*$	$r_1 = k_1 P_A \theta_v - k_{-1}\theta_A$	$r_1 = 1.75 \times 10^{-4} P_A \theta_v - 0.5\theta_A$
S2	$B_2+* \rightleftharpoons B_2 *$	$r_2 = k_2 P_{B_2}\theta_v - k_{-2}\theta_{B_2}$	$r_2 = 1.75 \times 10^{-4} P_{B_2}\theta_v - 0.5\theta_{B_2}$
S3	$B_2 * \rightleftharpoons 2B *$	$r_3 = k_3 \theta_{B_2}\theta_v - k_{-3}\theta_B^2$	$r_3 = 4\theta_{B_2}\theta_v - 0.4\theta_B^2$
S4	$A * + B * \rightleftharpoons AB * + *$	$r_4 = k_4\theta_A\theta_B - k_{-4}\theta_{AB}\theta_v$	$r_4 = 0.1\theta_A\theta_B - 7.4 \times 10^{-31}\theta_{AB}\theta_v$[a]
S5	$AB * \rightleftharpoons AB +*$	$r_5 = k_5\theta_{AB} - k_{-5}P_{AB}\theta_v$	$r_5 = 0.1\theta_{AB} - 3.5 \times 10^{-5} P_{AB}\theta_v$

[a]here, $k_{-4} = \frac{k_4 k_1 k_5}{k_{-1}k_{-5}}\left(\frac{k_2 k_3}{k_{-2}k_{-3}K_r}\right)^{\frac{1}{2}}$, where K_r is the equilibrium factor for overall reaction.

$$\min f = \sum_i^{n_t} \sum_j \frac{C_{max,all}^2}{C_{max,i}^2}(C_{s,i,j} - C_{g,i,j})^2 + \frac{C_{max,all}^2}{C_{max,i}^2}(C_{s,i,j+1} - C_{s,i,j} - (C_{g,i,j+1} - C_{g,i,j}))^2 \tag{3}$$

$$C_{max,i} = \max(C_{s,i}); C_{max,all} = \max(\max(C_{s,i})); i = A,AB,B_2$$

$$\frac{\partial C_i}{\partial t} = D_{L,i}\frac{\partial^2 C_i}{\partial x^2} - \frac{1}{\varepsilon}\frac{\partial u_S C_i}{\partial x} - \frac{1}{\varepsilon}r_{surf}(k, C_i, \theta_m); i = A,AB,B_2; m = A,AB,B_2,B \tag{4}$$

$$\frac{\partial \theta_m}{\partial t} = \frac{r_{surf}(k, T, C_i, \theta_m)}{C_t} \tag{5}$$

$$C_i(x,0) = 0, x \neq 0; \theta_m(x,0) = 0; C_i(0,t) = u_{in,i}(t), \frac{\partial C_i}{\partial x}(L_b,t) = 0 \tag{6}$$

All the model parameters' values are in SI units. The PDEs are discretised in space using the method of lines in the form of the second order upwind scheme into 101 points.

Function lsqnonlin and ode23tb in MatLab are used for fitting and solving the ordinary differential equations derived from the discretization.

3.2. Practical identifiability improvements of different optimality

Practical identifiability improvements of robust designs are tested in cases when optimizing sensor locations alone or together with input perturbations. For input perturbations, there are assumed to be totally 8 pulses. Therefore, the time interval of each pulse in a PRBS perturbation can be optimized for robust design. The initial guess position of sensor for MBDoE is at $x_s=0.07L_b$. Then, 16 time intervals for 8 pulses are randomly generated, creating a perturbation at the reactor inlet and result in the collection of concentration profiles by the sensor in Figure 4. When perturbations are being optimized, these generated time intervals also perform as initial guesses for robust design. An optimized density function for the PRBS perturbation will be derived in the design.

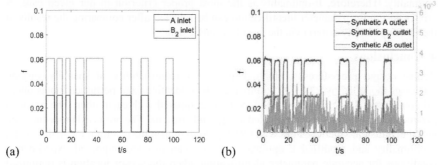

Figure 4 Perturbations at the reactor inlet (a) and corresponding synthetic outlet concentration profiles (b) collected by sensor at $x=0.07L_b$

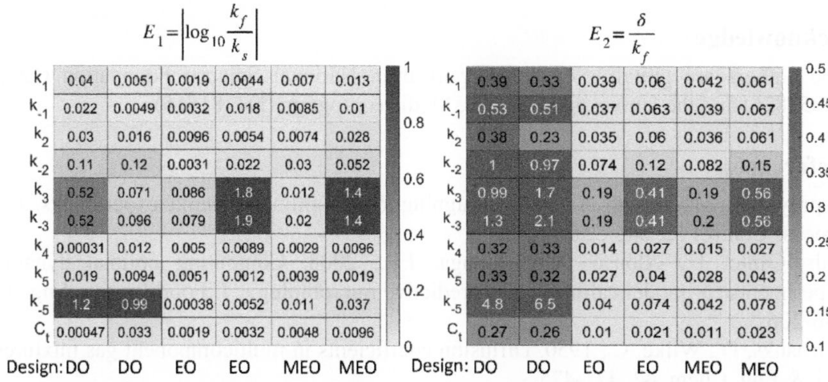

$$E_1=\left|\log_{10}\frac{k_f}{k_s}\right| \qquad E_2=\frac{\delta}{k_f}$$

k_1	0.04	0.0051	0.0019	0.0044	0.007	0.013	k_1	0.39	0.33	0.039	0.06	0.042	0.061
k_{-1}	0.022	0.0049	0.0032	0.018	0.0085	0.01	k_{-1}	0.53	0.51	0.037	0.063	0.039	0.067
k_2	0.03	0.016	0.0096	0.0054	0.0074	0.028	k_2	0.38	0.23	0.035	0.06	0.036	0.061
k_{-2}	0.11	0.12	0.0031	0.022	0.03	0.052	k_{-2}	1	0.97	0.074	0.12	0.082	0.15
k_3	0.52	0.071	0.086	1.8	0.012	1.4	k_3	0.99	1.7	0.19	0.41	0.19	0.56
k_{-3}	0.52	0.096	0.079	1.9	0.02	1.4	k_{-3}	1.3	2.1	0.19	0.41	0.2	0.56
k_4	0.00031	0.012	0.005	0.0089	0.0029	0.0096	k_4	0.32	0.33	0.014	0.027	0.015	0.027
k_5	0.019	0.0094	0.0051	0.0012	0.0039	0.0019	k_5	0.33	0.32	0.027	0.04	0.028	0.043
k_{-5}	1.2	0.99	0.00038	0.0052	0.011	0.037	k_{-5}	4.8	6.5	0.04	0.074	0.042	0.078
C_t	0.00047	0.033	0.0019	0.0032	0.0048	0.0096	C_t	0.27	0.26	0.01	0.021	0.011	0.023
Design:	DO	DO	EO	EO	MEO	MEO	Design:	DO	DO	EO	EO	MEO	MEO
φ:	x_s	x_s&u_{in}	x_s	x_s&u_{in}	x_s	x_s&u_{in}	φ:	x_s	x_s&u_{in}	x_s	x_s&u_{in}	x_s	x_s&u_{in}

(a)   (b)

Figure 5 Heat maps for (a) deviations between preset and estimated parameters' values and (b) ratio of half width of 95% confidence intervals and corresponding estimated parameters in different robust designs.

The Investigation for practical parameter identifiability is summarised in Figure 5. When the D-optimality is applied, the derived optimal time intervals and sensor location are at the initial value because the calculated objective function is easy to reach the set lower limit. However, almost all the model parameters are not identifiable according to E_2 values in Figure 5(b). When sensor location alone is optimized, the result x_s is $0.955L_b$ for

E-optimality, and $0.885L_b$ for modified E-optimality. All the parameters are practically identifiable in these two cases. The E-optimality criterion will provide the experimental conditions for more accurate parameter identification owing to narrower confidence intervals as shown in Figure 5(b).

When time intervals of perturbations are optimized together with sensor location, their optimal values are close to the initial guesses though they are not exactly the same. Therefore, the shape of the perturbation will not change too much from the initial guess. The optimized sensor locations change to $0.517L_b$ for E-optimality and $0.500L_b$ for modified E-optimality. Parameter k_3 and k_{-3} are no longer identifiable in these cases. However, other parameters are still accurately identified. The greedy algorithm still provides proper designs for parameter identification though it does not reach the global optimal solution. The E-optimality still perform little better than the modified E-optimality. Therefore, E-optimality is the most proper criterion in our given case. A proper design for parameter identification can be selected after comparing the results of the three optimality criteria via the use of synthetic data.

4. Conclusions

Robust design procedures to improve parameter identifiability of spatially varying processes modelled by PDEs by optimizing sensor locations and perturbed inputs under different optimality criteria are developed and compared with each other. The practical parameter identifiability is investigated using synthetic data. The proposed procedures are tested in transient kinetic studies with PRBS perturbation at the reactor inlet. In this study, E-optimality and modified E-optimality criteria can provide improved experimental conditions for accurate parameter identification when the sensor location is optimized alone or together with the input sequence. Furthermore, the use of E-optimality criteria results a minor performance enhancement compared to modified E-optimality.

Acknowledge

The authors are grateful for the support from National Science Foundation (Grant #2053826) and the University of Patras, Medicus program (No. 81816).

References

Asprey, S.P., Macchietto, S., 2002. Designing robust optimal dynamic experiments. J. of Process Control 12, 545-556.

Balsa-Canto, E., Alonso, A.A., Banga, J.R., 2008. Computing optimal dynamic experiments for model calibration in predictive microbiology. J. Food Process Eng. 31, 186-206.

Fairbanks, D., Wilke, C., 1950. Diffusion coefficients in multicomponent gas mixtures. Ind. & Eng. Chem. 42, 471-475.

Franceschini, G., Macchietto, S., 2008. Model-based design of experiments for parameter precision: State of the art. Chem. Eng. Sci. 63, 4846-4872.

Narendra, K.S., Annaswamy, A.M., 1987. Persistent excitation in adaptive systems. Int. J. Control 45, 127-160.

Ruthven, D.M., 1984. Principles of adsorption and adsorption processes. Wiley.

Uciński, D., Patan, M., 2007. D-optimal design of a monitoring network for parameter estimation of distributed systems. J. Global Optim. 39, 291-322.

Yang, M., Wang, L., Kamali Shahri, S.M., Rioux, R.M., Armaou, A., 2018. Investigation of CO2 Sorption Mechanisms in Isothermal Columns via Transient Material and Energy Balance PDE Models. Ind. Eng. Chem. Res. 57, 10303-10314.

Flavio Manenti, Gintaras V. Reklaitis (Eds.), Proceedings of the 34th European Symposium on Computer Aided Process Engineering / 15th International Symposium on Process Systems Engineering (ESCAPE34/PSE24), June 2-6, 2024, Florence, Italy

Priority Planning for Methane Emissions Abatement via Marginal Abatement Cost Curves (MAC) and Shapley-Shubik Power Index

Adeline Shu Ting Tan,[a] Jaya Prasanth Rajakal,[a,c] Mohammad Lameh,[b] Dhabia Al-Mohannadi,[b] Bing Shen How,[a] Viknesh Andiappan[a]

[a]*Faculty of Engineering, Computing and Science, Swinburne University of Technology, Jalan Simpang Tiga, 93350, Kuching, Sarawak, Malaysia*

[b]*Department of Chemical Engineering, Texas A&M University at Qatar, Education City, PO Box 23874, Doha, Qatar*

[c]*School of Engineering and Technology, Sunway University, Jalan Universiti, Bandar Sunway, 47500 Petaling Jaya, Selangor, Malaysia*

vmurugappan@swinburne.edu.my

Abstract

Methane is the second largest emitted greenhouse gas next only to carbon dioxide. Methane is also a more potent greenhouse gas with higher global warming potential. The oil and gas sector is a major contributor to the methane emissions. Given the impact of methane emissions on global warming, there is an urgent need to report and mitigate these emissions from the sector. This necessitates the need for systematic tools to strategies the methane emissions reduction. This work proposes an integrated marginal abatement cost (MAC) and Shapley-Shubik methodology to determine the most cost-effective selection and deployment strategy of methane abatement technologies to meet the set emissions reduction targets. A case study from the Malaysian oil and gas sector is used to demonstrate the applicability of the aforementioned methodology.

Keywords: Methane emissions, Oil and gas system, Marginal abatement cost curve, Shapley-Shubik power index, Decision support tool

1. Introduction

Methane is one of the important greenhouse gases (GHGs) responsible for global warming and associated climate change effects. Methane emissions contributes about 30% to the current global warming (IEA, 2022). Notably, methane is a more potent GHG which has more than 80% higher global warming potential compared to carbon dioxide for 20-year period. Therefore, methane is viewed as a key GHG that determines the pace towards peak atmospheric temperature. This calls for concerted global effort to mitigate the methane emissions and its impact on climate change and global warming. Recognizing the above-stated challenge, the global methane pledge was signed at COP26 in 2021. The pledge mandates a 30% methane emissions reduction by signatory countries by 2030 (UNFCCC, 2021).

The major sources of methane emissions include agriculture, energy, and waste sectors. The oil and gas industry, in particular, is the largest emitter of methane emissions. It accounts for about 25% of the total global methane emissions. (IEA, 2022). There is a growing advocacy for reporting and reduction of these methane emissions from oil and gas systems. Most of these emissions are from venting, incomplete flaring, and leaks in the existing infrastructure. There are several abatement technologies available to mitigate each source of methane emissions, while each of them differs in terms of cost and its abatement capacity. This complicates the decision-making which to be selected or prioritised to ensure optimal decisions are made.

The Marginal Abatement Cost (MAC) method is a systematic cost-based approach in identifying emissions reduction technologies. MAC have been widely used in the past to illustrate the economics of climate change mitigation and have contributed to decision making in the context of climate policy (Huang et al., 2016). The concept of abatement curves has been applied since the early 1990s to illustrate the cost associated with emissions reduction (Kesicki, 2010). Additionally, MAC offers visual representation of emissions reduction and cost of abatement through a graphical plot that arranges the abatement options from the lowest to highest cost, prioritizing the most cost-effective option. Its utility has been showcased in various field, including but not limited to glass manufacturing in China (Xian et al., 2023), dairy industry in Switzerland (Huber et al., 2023), and energy sector in Russia (Keiko et al., 2022).

However, MAC method has limitations in that it does not provide insights into which of these abatement options are of utmost importance for achieving emissions reduction targets and offer a more robust long-term strategy. As such, this work employs Shapley-Shubik Power Index to determine the criticality of each abatement option in achieving methane emissions reduction targets. It was originally designed to determine the influencing power of each voter in affecting the voting outcome (Matsubara, 1989), but has now been applied to aid game-theoretic decisions for prioritization (Yahya et al., 2021). In this regard, the use of Shapley-Shubik Power Index in this work is anticipated to allow decision-makers to prioritize the deployment of abatement options that offer long-term methane emissions reduction.

2. Problem Statement

A formal problem statement can be defined as follows: The given oil and gas system consists of a set of methane emissions sources. In order to mitigate these emissions, a set of abatement technologies are considered. The proposed approach aims to determine the optimal selection and criticality of the abatement technologies in meeting the emissions reduction target. The above stated problem is solved considering the economic objective through minimizing the costs. The methodology used to solve the problem is described in Section 3.

3. Methodology

Figure 1 shows the general framework used to perform the analysis. The framework can be viewed as an integrated Marginal Abatement Cost (MAC) and Shapley-Shubik methodology. Initially, the MAC methodology, as introduced by Meier et al. (1982), is utilized to determine the most cost-effective pathway for methane emissions reduction in the given oil and gas system. Subsequently, criticality of each pathway for achieving the specified emissions reduction target is quantified using the Shapley-Shubik power index method, developed by Shapley and Shubik (1954). In this integrated analysis, the pathways determined from the mini-MAC profile are assessed based on their contribution to the overall emissions reduction, which sets the "score" for each selected abatement technology to perform the criticality assessment. The details of conducting the mini-MAC and Shapley-Shubik analysis are presented in the following subsections.

3.1. Selection of Abatement Technology using MAC analysis

The datasets pertaining to the cost and emissions profile of the source (i.e., methane emissions sources) and sinks (i.e., abatement options) are compiled. The methane emissions sources are characterized by the flow rate of methane emitted. Likewise, the abatement technologies are characterized by their emissions reduction potential, capital cost, operating cost, credits earned from methane recovery. These parameters serve as input for the MAC analysis. MAC curve can be developed by formulating the algorithm in a simple flowsheet. The output is a marginal abatement cost profile that determines the source-sink combination, which contributes to the low-cost methane emissions reduction pathway.

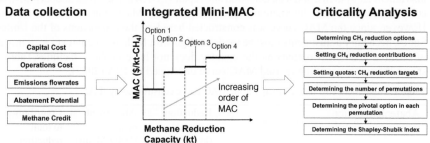

Figure 1. Overview of the proposed methodology for this present work.

3.2. Criticality of Abatement Technology using Shapley-Shubik power index

The Shapley-Shubik power index is used to determine pivotal abatement options to achieve urgent methane emissions reduction targets. In this work, the algorithm to determine the power index is coded using Python. The total number of abatement options considered is represented by $n \in N$. Their respective contributions to methane emissions reduction are represented by F_n, as shown in Eq. (1).

$$\left[q : F_{n=1}, F_{n=2}, F_{n=3}, ..., F_{n=N} \right] n \in N \tag{1}$$

In Eq. (1), a quota, q is included. The quota q, in this case, may refer to a methane emissions reduction target that the oil and gas facilities need to meet. Following this, the number of permutations is determined. The number of permutations represents the possible sequences in which these abatement options can be introduced. As mentioned earlier, the order in which these options are implemented may affect the long-term strategy for reducing methane emissions. The number of permutations can be determined using $N!$ All permutations (or sequences of options) are then listed. For each permutation, the contribution F_n, is one-by-one added according to its sequence until its cumulative contribution reaches quota, q. The pivotal option, is the last option added to the given sequence when it reaches quota, q.

The pivotal option for other remaining permutations would differ as this depends on their order of entry into a given sequence and their contribution to meeting the quota. Hence, it is essential to determine the number of times each option is pivotal for all possible permutations. After obtaining the number of times each option is pivotal, the Shapley-Shubik power index (α_p) is calculated using Eq. (2).

$$\alpha_p = \frac{\text{Number of times an Option is Pivotal}}{N!} \tag{2}$$

4. Case Study

This section delves into a case study to demonstrate the proposed methodology outlined in Section 3. The methane emissions from the upstream segment in Malaysian oil and gas system is taken for the analysis. The sources of these emissions include venting, equipment leaks, blowdown operations, well workovers, and pneumatic devices. The total emissions in Malaysian oil and gas system upstream segment are estimated to be 377 kt in 2022 (IEA, 2022). Severable abatement options to reduce these methane emissions are available. These can be aggregated as installation of flares, installation of vapor recovery units, replacement of compressor seals and rods, replacement of pneumatics with instrument air systems, and leak detection and repair (LDAR). This work adopts the MAC curve developed by the International Energy Agency for Malaysian oil and gas system. However, since the MAC curve was constructed based on the proportions of the United States, necessary adjustments must be made to align with Malaysian context i.e., removal of onshore abatement options as the country does not have onshore facilities.Table 1 shows the summary of the revised MAC curve developed by IEA (2022).

Table 1. Abatement cost data extracted from MAC curve constructed by IEA.

Abatement option	Reduction potential (kt)	Abatement cost (USD/MBtu)	Contribution to total reduction
Install flares (A)	115	2.2	44%
Replace compressor seal or rod (B)	0.05	-16.3	0.02%
Replace with instrument air system (C)	25.80	-18	9.93%
Upstream LDAR (D)	56.20	-59.2	21.61%
Vapor recovery units (E)	63	-23.4	24.22%

5. Results

The MAC results show that the abatement technologies in the upstream segment can reduce 260 kt, which is 68.96%% of the total methane emissions in the Malaysian oil and gas system. It can be noted that installation of flares accounts for about 44% of this emissions reduction followed by installation of vapour recovery units, LDAR, and replacement with instrument air system at 24.23%, 21.61%, and 9.93% respectively. The replacement of compressor seal and rod only reduces 0.02% of the emissions reduction. In the case of cost of reduction, LDAR yields a net revenue of 59.2 USD/MBtu. Likewise, installation of vapour recovery units, installation of instrument air systems, and compressor seal replacement yields a net revenue of 23.4 USD/MBtu, 18 USD/MBtu, and 16.3 USD/MBtu, respectively; while installation of flares leads to an expense of 2.2 USD/MBtu. As shown in MAC profile, the deployment of upstream LDAR results in the highest overall cost saving, followed by the vapor recovery unit.

The Shapley-Shubik analysis is performed to determine the criticality of each abatement technologies in achieving a range of emissions reduction targets. The abatement technologies - installation of flares, the replacement of compressor seal and rod, replacement with instrument air system, LDAR, and installation of vapour recovery units are referred to as Options A, B, C, D, and E respectively. Figure 2 shows the results of the Shapley-Shubik analysis. The results show that Option D and Option E show a similar power index as the methane emissions reduction goal increases from 10% to 60%, implying that these options possess symmetrical influence regardless of the changes in the reduction goal. This can be explained as Option D and Option E exhibits very close abatement potential of 56.2 and 63 kt, respectively, and their contribution to emissions reduction is nearly interchangeable. In addition, it can be observed that Option D and Option E show the greatest influence at 10% and 60% reduction targets (37.7 kt and 226.2 kt emissions reduction, respectively), with a power index of 33.3% and an even standing with Option A. This is owing to the fact that at 10% reduction, the abatement potential for all three options can single-handedly achieve the target. However, as the reduction target increases to 20%, Option D and Option E become less pivotal and require combining effort with other abatement options to achieve the target.

Following Options D and E, the deployment of instrument air system (Option C) exhibits as the third highest cost saving. However, based on the results shown in **Error! Reference source not found.**, Option C only becomes pivotal at 20% as it can meet the target by coupling with Option D and E. At this point, Option C shows similar power index as Option D and E due to the fact that it will only meet the target by combining with either option. However, as moving to a higher target of 30% and 40%, Option C was not needed as it will not be able to meet these targets by only combining with Option A, Option D, or Option E. At 50% reduction target, Option C becomes pivotal again and shows the same power index as Option D and Option E (16.7%). This implies that the contribution between these three options to emissions reduction has become similar, where these three options will have to combine with Option A to achieve the target.

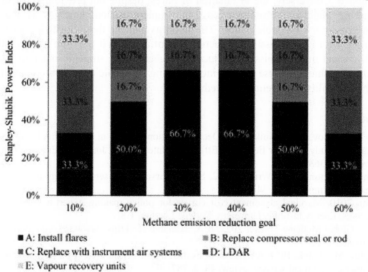

Figure 2. Shapley-Shubik Power Index for each abatement option at different methane emissions reduction target.

Moving on to the installation of flares (Option A) that constantly exhibits high power index in all reduction scenario. Option A shows the highest power index of 66.7% at 30% and 40% reduction goal, which outweighs Option D and Option E, as Option A possesses a significantly higher reduction potential (115 kt). In this case, Option D and Option E can only be pivotal when Option A is installed. However, at 50% target, Option A becomes less pivotal with power index dropped to 50%. This can be explained as at this point, combining either Option D or Option E with Option A will no longer meet the target, hence the involvement of Option C is necessary resulting in a reduction of power index for Option A. . At 60% reduction target - Option A, Option D, and Option E show an even standing, inferring that these options shared a same level of importance in the coalition and all pathways are necessary to meet the emissions reduction target. Therefore, Option C becomes insignificant and can be removed from this scenario.

The Shapley-Shubik results indicate that Option A is the most pivotal abatement technology in achieving the emissions reduction targets despite a higher abatement cost of 2.2 USD/MBtu. On the other hand, the MAC analysis by IEA prioritised pathways in this order; D, E, C, B and A for the case of Malaysian oil and gas upstream segment, which is based on cost-effectiveness. However, the integrated MAC Shapley-Shubik analysis in this work prioritise the deployment based on their significance in meeting a given emissions target, especially when become more stringent over time.

6. Conclusion

This work has presented an integrated approach that utilizes the economic dimensions of the MAC method and the systematic decision support from the Shapley-Shubik power index analysis to determine the criticality of cost-efficient abatement options for methane emissions reduction in oil and gas systems. The findings indicate that, in order to achieve the emissions reduction targets, the implementation of LDAR, which yields the highest cost saving will need to be combined with other abatement options at reduction goal of 20% or above. Conversely, the installation of flares, despite not providing cost savings and requiring additional abatement cost for implementation, emerges as the most important among the available option. The findings indicate that prioritizing abatement technologies with high emissions reduction potential, even if they are more costly, is essential to meet urgent emissions reduction targets. While strategic planning plays a crucial role in achieving these targets, incorporating economic considerations is vital to ensure the feasibility of the emissions reduction.

References

A. Keiko, F. Veselov, A. Solyanik, 2022, Decarbonization Options in the Russian Energy Sector: A Comparative Study on Their Economic Efficiency, International Journal of Energy Economics and Policy, 12(4), 368-378.

A. Meier, A.H. Rosenfeld, J. Wright, 1982, Supply curves of conserved energy for California's residential sector, Energy, 7, 4, 347-358.

F. Kesicki, 2010, Marginal abatement cost curves for policy making–expert-based vs. model-derived curves, Energy Institute, University College London, 1-8.

IEA, 2022, Global Methane Tracker 2022, IEA, available at <https://www.iea.org/reports/global-methane-tracker-2022>.

L.S. Shapley, M. Shubik, 1954, A method for evaluating the distribution of power in a committee system, American political science review, 48, 3, 787-792.

N. Matsubara, 1989, Conflict and Limits of Power, The Journal of Conflict Resolution, 33(1), 113-141.

N.S.M. Yahya, L.Y. Ng, V. Andiappan, 2021, Optimisation and planning of biomass supply chain for new and existing power plants based on carbon reduction targets, Energy, 237, 121488.

R. Huber, M. Tarruella, D. Schäfer, R. Finger, 2023, Marginal climate change abatement costs in Swiss dairy production considering farm heterogeneity and interaction effects, Agricultural Systems, 207, 103639.

S.K. Huang, L. Kuo, K.L. Chou, 2016, The applicability of marginal abatement cost approach: A comprehensive review, Journal of Cleaner Production, 127, 59-71.

UNFCC, 2021, World Leaders Kick Start Accelerated Climate Action at COP26, UNFCCc, available at <https://unfccc.int/news/world-leaders-kick-start-accelerated-climate-action-at-cop26>.

Y. Xian, Z. Hu, K. Wang, 2023, The least-cost abatement measure of carbon emissions for China's glass manufacturing industry based on the marginal abatement costs, Energy, 284, 129159.

Flavio Manenti, Gintaras V. Reklaitis (Eds.), Proceedings of the 34th European Symposium on Computer Aided Process Engineering / 15th International Symposium on Process Systems Engineering (ESCAPE34/PSE24), June 2-6, 2024, Florence, Italy

FermentAI: Large Language Models in Chemical Engineering Education for Learning Fermentation Processes

Fiammetta Caccavale,[a] Carina L. Gargalo,[a] Krist V. Gernaey,[a] Ulrich Krühne[a]*

[a]*PROSYS, Dept. of Chemical and Biochemical Engineering, Technical University of Denmark, Søltofts Plads, Building 228 A, 2800 Kgs. Lyngby, Denmark.*
ulkr@kt.dtu.dk

Abstract

Recent developments in artificial intelligence (AI), leading to the release of continuously improving large language models (LLMs) provide the opportunity for educators to automate repetitive tasks with stimulant experiences for the students. In fact, the ability of LLMs to extract content and key information from text offers a powerful tool for enhancing the learning experience. In this work, we present an example of how LLMs can be used to automate educational processes. We implement *FermentAI*, a virtual tutor (VT) to answer students' questions about fermentation for a Master's Degree course taught at the Technical University of Denmark. The model used is a pre-trained sequence-to-sequence model. The prompt provided to the LLM is composed of a question and its context, the curated information for the model to generate the answer. The context is retrieved through semantic search by calculating the cosine similarity between the query question and a dataset of historical questions. The primary objective of this work is to create an interactive, freely available, and accurate tool that students can use to ask questions about fermentation. The VT is integrated into BioVL, an online educational platform for (bio)chemical processes developed by the authors. The code and data are open-source on GitHub.

Keywords: Large Language Models, AI in Education, Chatbots in Engineering Curriculum, Education 4.0, Prompt Engineering.

1. Introduction

Education 4.0 represents a significant shift in the education sector through the incorporation of cutting-edge technology, including virtual reality, artificial intelligence (AI), and online platforms, into the learning process. Its primary objective is to prepare students to face the challenges resulting from this digital transformation and to thrive in a digital and automated world. This new paradigm prioritizes interactive and personalized learning experiences that promote digital literacy, critical thinking, and creativity. In addition, it aims to produce tech-savvy professionals who can adapt to rapidly changing landscapes and drive progress.

If applied correctly and ethically, AI could enable educators to automate repetitive tasks with stimulant experiences for the students. Particularly, natural language processing (NLP) systems have gained considerable interest in educational research and practice, due to their ability to learn and output natural language. Among others, these models have been used in applications for essay scoring, discourse analysis (e.g., between students), intelligent tutoring systems, and tools that support collaborative learning activities (Ferreira et al., 2019). Recent years have witnessed the rise of large language models

(LLM), which are NLP models trained on massive amounts of text, mostly available online (Brown et al., 2020). The result of this large-scale training is that these models obtain knowledge about a wide range of topics and, hence are suitable for being applied in many different contexts and fields. This ability to extract content and key information from text offers a powerful tool for enhancing the learning experience. They could be used to identify knowledge gaps, aid formative assessment, provide personalized feedback, and facilitate the grading process, resulting in reducing educators' workload and providing more accurate and consistent evaluations (Hopfenbeck et al., 2023; Kasneci et al., 2023). Other AI-driven tools that could highly benefit students' learning are chatbots and virtual tutors (VT). The benefits of these applications on learning include the fact that, if deployed online, students could continually have access to them to clarify easily answered questions, not needing the mediation of a teacher, and therefore and therefore reducing the workload related to some of the teacher's responsibilities. Given all these new trends in the field, it follows that AI is becoming an integral part of new educational platforms in an effort to successfully deploy Education 4.0.

This work presents an initial investigation of how LLMs can be used to automate educational processes. We implemented *FermentAI*, a VT for answering students' questions about fermentation. This aims to provide students with an open-access interactive tool that is trained on curated data and therefore returns high-quality and relevant responses. *FermentAI* is integrated into BioVL (Caño de las Heras et al., 2022), users can chat with it at: www.biovl.com/fermentAI. To foster transparency and knowledge transfer, code and data are available on GitHub at: https://github.com/FiammettaC/FermentAI.

2. Data

The data used for the model development is from the "Process Adaptation in Fermentation Based Biomanufacturing" (28455 course, 2023) Master's Degree course taught at the Technical University of Denmark (DTU). The main purpose of the course is to introduce the used methods and tools when transferring a cell from a lab or research environment to pilot and full scale. Students should therefore acquire a better understanding of the interactions between the cells and the reactor, and learn how to aim for optimal conditions for the cells to grow in large scale. Some of the learning objectives of the course include: (i) simulate different reactor operating modes and interpret the simulation results; (ii) describe the effect of introducing basic process control on a process in a bioreactor; (iii) design and implement a basic strategy for data collection and handling on a fermentation process; and (iv) distinguish between basic AI tools for fermentation data processing.

In this work, a dataset composed of question-answer pairs is collected. The data is retrieved from past exams administered in the aforementioned course, where the answers are curated by the teachers. The set of questions and answers have a conversational nature and are therefore deemed suitable for this type of application.

3. Methods

The model implemented in this work, *FermentAI*, is based on a pre-trained LLM, FLAN-T5 (Chung et al., 2022), and is used to perform a question-answering task. The Hugging Face library is used for the pre-trained model implementation. The pre-trained model, FLAN-T5, is chosen because of the extensive fine-tuning on multiple downstream tasks performed, especially question-answering, and its manageable size.

For this task, we perform zero-shot learning, meaning that we do not provide additional examples to the LLM to be able to perform the given task. The prompt provided to the

FermentAI is composed of a question (asked by the student) and its context, containing the curated information for the model to answer the question. This is done because in-context learning, which means enriching the prompt with some context, usually improves the quality of the generation. The context is retrieved through semantic search by calculating the cosine similarity, measuring the cosine of the angle between two vectors, of the query question and the set of historical questions populating the dataset. The algorithm then returns the most similar historical question (similarity closest to 1) and returns its context. This means that for each question the students ask, the algorithm calculates the most similar historical question and retrieves its context, which is the answer that was previously given to the historical question. Then the question and the context are given as prompt, providing the VT the necessary information to answer the questions asked. A schematic of the input given to the model is presented in Figure 1.

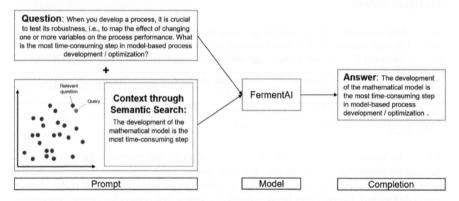

Figure 1: Schematics of the *FermentAI* pipeline. The context is retrieved through semantic search by calculating the cosine similarity between the query question and all historical questions stored in the dataset. The prompt is prefixed by the following instruction: "*Based on the HISTORICAL ANSWER, please answer this QUESTION*".

We benchmark the results of the small model (google/flan-t5-small with 77M parameters), the base model (google/flan-t5-base with 248M parameters), and the xl model (google/flan-t5-xl with 2.85B parameters) to investigate whether a larger model, and therefore more parameters, can be beneficial in the specific domain and task performed. We then highlight the trade-off between performance and runtime speed, to facilitate other researchers working on similar applications. The model can be used with a CPU, although the deployed version makes use of GPUs.

At this stage of the project, we chose not to fine-tune the model but to provide the context to enrich the prompt of the LLM to save computing resources. The two approaches will be further assessed and benchmarked in the future.

To evaluate the responses generated by the model, we calculated two metrics widely used to evaluate QA models, the F1 score and cosine similarity. The F1 score is the harmonic mean of precision and recall score; it is implemented by taking into account the set of predicted tokens and therefore has the drawback that the order in which the tokens are predicted does not count. The cosine similarity is a metric often used to calculate document similarity in the NLP field.

4. Results and Discussion

3.1 Quantitative evaluation: model performance

The results of the model evaluation of the model on a subset of data are shown in Table 1. The cosine similarity is generally quite high, meaning that the generated output is similar to the original answers. Table 1 also shows that the F1 scores are not as high as the cosine similarity: however, this does not necessarily mean that the model is not able to perform the task. The metric compares the set of tokens produced to the ones in the original answer, and therefore possible explanations for the low F1 scores could include that the model tries to exclude redundant or not meaningful information, generate synonyms of words, or paraphrase the content of the original answer. Moreover, the used metrics, especially the F1 score, are affected by the length of the completion compared to the original answer.

Table 1: Average results of *FermentAI* model given the prompt (student's question and context, retrieved through semantic search given historical answers). The results are calculated over a subset of questions (N=10) with a single high-performance GPU (NVIDIA GeForce RTX 2060).

Model	F1 score	Cosine similarity	Runtime/completion
Flan-T5 small	0.62	0.83	3.3 s
Flan-T5 base	0.74	0.94	9.3 s
Flan-T5 xl	0.64	0.82	82.0 s

One of the major issues of the model is the length of the output, which could be a challenging parameter to tune. In fact, if the minimum number of characters expected for the generation is too high, there is the risk that the model will repeat itself if the answer is straightforward. On the other hand, a fixed parameter that is too short would also mean that some sentences are cut and left unfinished. This issue will be further investigated in the future.

The fourth column in Table 1 compares the runtime necessary for one completion. It is important to notice that, generally, larger models have a longer runtime, meaning that they will output the answer more slowly. This has to be taken into consideration and addressed properly to ensure a fast and smooth experience for students.

At this stage of the implementation, to expert evaluation, the results are considered satisfactory. We plan to benchmark various approaches in the future, such as comparing prompt engineering and instruction fine-tuning, to investigate what is the best strategy to adopt in this use case and whether it can be generalized to different applications. Fine-tuning could be beneficial in fields that use language in an idiosyncratic manner, such as in our specific case. Finally, more quantitative metrics will also be used.

3.2 Qualitative evaluation: further analyses

An initial qualitative evaluation of the model revealed that the answers generated are coherent with the question asked and generally complete. For example, to the given prompt: *"QUESTION: When processing time series data, stationarity is important. How do you define stationarity? HISTORICAL ANSWER: Stationary data is time series data that keeps the same statistical properties. Non-stationary data will have properties that change as a function of time"*, the three models generated, respectively: (small) "non-stationary data will have properties that change as a function of time", (base) "stationary data is time series data that keeps the same statistical properties. Non-stationary data will have properties that change", and (xl) "stationary data is data that has the same statistical properties over a long period of time". We can observe that all generated answers are correct, although they are formulated differently, where the most complete is arguably the completion generated by the base model, supporting the results previously discussed. However, rigorously evaluating the models implemented in educational systems is very important; therefore, we plan to further evaluate the performance of the models and assess the fit of the VT for the given task. We plan to perform two tests with students: first, a small-scale test where only a few students are asked to get familiar with the platform and extensively interact with it. This is needed to establish whether the model can sustain a long QA session or if it gets repetitive after a few answers concerning the same topic (suggesting that the model might have limited knowledge regarding a topic). This small-scale test would also allow us to gain insights into the platform itself, whether it is user-friendly and intuitive whether further improvements to the interface are needed. Afterward, we aim to test the model with a larger set of volunteering students from DTU, as well as experts in the subject, such as the teachers of the course.

3.3 Deployment of the model online and code availability

FermentAI is integrated into BioVL (Caño de las Heras et al., 2022), an online educational platform dedicated to teaching (bio)chemical processes. Anybody can freely chat with the implemented VT at: www.biovl.com/fermentAI. The VT is currently in the form of a chatbot, however, future developments envisage an avatar or human-like agent, where students can utter the questions and the VT will voice an answer.

To foster transparency and knowledge transfer, the code and the pre-processed data are open-source, stored in a public repository and shared publicly on GitHub at: https://github.com/FiammettaC/FermentAI.

3.4 Transferability to other domains of chemical and biochemical engineering

Although the project presented has a quite specific application, i. e. answering questions related to the Process adaptation in Fermentation Based Biomanufacturing course taught at DTU, the approach discussed in this work could be applied to other domains within chemical and biochemical engineering. Similar models could be used, for example, to answer questions related to process control or thermodynamics, given that the dataset is curated to include discursive answers. At this stage the model could not, in fact, return or correct equations. However, provided the availability of high-quality domain data, it could explain the theory and answer simple questions, which could relieve some of the pressure from the teachers and allow them to focus on less trivial tasks.

3.5 Reflection and possible implications regarding the use of AI in Education

Finally, a reflection regarding the ethical and fair use of AI is indispensable. Emerging research in the field suggests that the use of AI in Education has the potential to support teaching and learning and improve student performance; however, its misuse, which may result from algorithmic bias and lack of clear regulations, could inhibit human rights and result in the reinforcement of existing inequalities (Prinsloo, 2020; Yang et al., 2021). Thus, although the expectations and promise of how AI can contribute to advancing education are substantial, it must be remembered that AI is not infallible, and attention should be put into its implementation to avoid unintended consequences. Therefore, developing these solutions requires understanding the possible issues and limitations, as well as the time and effort it takes to safely develop, test and use these types of systems. Moreover, even though an AI-powered system in Education could be used fairly and ethically, we should also reflect on whether these systems could benefit students and improve their education on a case-by-case basis. Extensive testing and model validation should be performed before rolling out these models in an educational context.

5. Conclusion

This work presented *FermentAI*, an educational virtual tutor to answer questions about fermentation processes. The data used to test the model is composed of the exam questions (and answers) from the "Process Adaptation in Fermentation Based Biomanufacturing" Master's Degree course taught at DTU.

The model used is a pre-trained LLM, FLAN-T5, fine-tuned on multiple downstream tasks, including question-answering. Instead of fine-tuning the model on our domain-specific data, we performed prompt engineering, enriching the prompt given to the model with the context retrieved through semantic search from a database of historical questions. The performance of the model, calculated using F1 score and cosine similarity, is considered to be satisfactory. However, more qualitative assessment is needed, therefore the model will be extensively evaluated in the future, including tests with students.

Moreover, some considerations that researchers and developers should make to ensure fair and ethical application of AI in Education were discussed. Finally, we discuss some of the implications of using AI in Education, by providing some advantages and limitations. We hope that this effort will encourage researchers and practitioners working in this field to contribute with reflections and resources to ensure a more ethical and safe transition to a reality where AI models are fully embedded in the educational system, to safeguard learners and where every aspect of the 'digital contract' is transparent.

References

T. Brown, B. Mann, N. Ryder, M. Subbiah, J.D Kaplan, P. Dhariwal, A. Neelakantan, P. Shyam, G. Sastry, A. Askell, and S. Agarwal, 2020, Language models are few-shot learners. Advances in neural information processing systems, 33, pp.1877-1901.

S. Caño de las Heras, C.L. Gargalo, F. Caccavale, B. Kensington-Miller, K.V. Gernaey, S. Baroutian, and U. Krühne, 2022, From Paper to web: Students as partners for virtual laboratories in (Bio) chemical engineering education. Frontiers in Chemical Engineering, 4, p.959188.

H.W. Chung, L. Hou, S. Longpre, B. Zoph, Y. Tay, W. Fedus, E. Li, X. Wang, M. Dehghani, S. Brahma, and A. Webson, 2022, Scaling instruction-finetuned language models. arXiv preprint arXiv:2210.11416.

R. Ferreira-Mello, M. André, A. Pinheiro, E. Costa, C. Romero, 2019, Text mining in education, Wiley Interdisciplinary Reviews: Data Mining and Knowledge Discovery 9, e1332.

T.N. Hopfenbeck, 2023, The future of educational assessment: self-assessment, grit and ChatGTP?. Assessment in Education: Principles, Policy & Practice, 30(2), pp.99-103.

E. Kasneci, K. Seßler, S. Küchemann, M. Bannert, D. Dementieva, F. Fischer, U. Gasser, G. Groh, S. Günnemann, E. Hüllermeier, and S. Krusche, 2023, ChatGPT for good? On opportunities and challenges of large language models for education. Learning and individual differences, 103, p.102274.

P. Prinsloo, 2020, Of 'black boxes' and algorithmic decision-making in (higher) education–a commentary, Big Data & Society 7, 2053951720933994.

S.J. Yang, H. Ogata, T. Matsui, N.-S. Chen, 2021, Human-centered artificial intelligence in education: Seeing the invisible through the visible, Computers and Education: Artificial Intelligence 2, 100008.

28455 course: Process adaptation in Fermentation Based Biomanufacturing (28455), available at: https://kurser.dtu.dk/course/2023-2024/28455?menulanguage=en, Accessed: 27/11/2023.

Hugging Face Flan-T5 implementation, available at: https://huggingface.co/docs/transformers/model_doc/flan-t5, Accessed: 27/11/2023.

Flavio Manenti, Gintaras V. Reklaitis (Eds.), Proceedings of the 34th European Symposium on Computer Aided Process Engineering / 15th International Symposium on Process Systems Engineering (ESCAPE34/PSE24), June 2-6, 2024, Florence, Italy

Interactive Coding Templates for Courses and Undergraduate Research Using MATLAB Live Scripts

Ashlee N. Ford Versypt*, Carley V. Cook, Austin N. Johns

Department of Chemical and Biological Engineering, University at Buffalo, The State University of New York, 507 Furnas Hall, Buffalo, NY, 14228, USA
ashleefv@buffalo.edu

Abstract

Undergraduate students in core chemical engineering courses spend a significant amount of time solving problems. For courses or research experiences early in undergraduate study, students generally have not yet taken advanced mathematics, numerical methods, or programming courses, making it challenging to address realistic problems without such tools. The resources provided in this paper aim to enable students, who are still in the early parts of their curriculum, to solve realistic problems in their coursework or research with the aid of faculty-provided interactive coding templates built in the MATLAB live script format. These files combine executable MATLAB code, formatted explanatory text and equations, images, and code output directly in a single file. Here, these MATLAB live scripts are referred to more generically as interactive coding templates because they could alternatively be provided in other coding languages (such as Jupyter Notebooks for Python or Julia). The paper details a set of interactive coding templates for use in training undergraduate students in the introductory chemical engineering material and energy balances course and in an undergraduate research experience on the topic of biomedical applications of systems engineering tools. Each interactive coding template provides background information about the topic, the equations or a diagram defining the technique, an example problem with worked solution, and fully functional code that can solve the example problem and can be extended to new problems that use the same types of numerical methods.

Keywords: MATLAB live script, numerical methods, undergraduate education, undergraduate research.

1. Introduction

Undergraduate students in core chemical engineering courses spend a significant amount of time solving problems. Often assignments and examinations focus on analytical solutions to simplified problems. More complicated realistic problems require the use of computers to determine numerical solutions. For early courses such as material and energy balances (MEB), students often have not yet taken advanced mathematics, numerical methods, or programming courses; learning to program is typically not an explicit learning objective of the core chemical engineering courses. We aim to enable students to solve realistic problems early in the curriculum with instructor-provided interactive coding templates built in the MATLAB live script format. Interactive coding templates typically provide background information about the topic, the equations or a diagram defining the technique, an example problem with a worked solution, fully functional code that can solve the example problem, and a clear pattern or instructional notes for interacting with or editing the code to solve new problems of the same type. Several previous resources have provided interactive coding templates for use in engineering courses, including a conference paper by our team that focused on providing and surveying MATLAB and Python-based interactive coding templates for courses across the chemical engineering curriculum and training faculty to use these materials (Johns et al. 2023). Readers are encouraged to see the references and detailed table surveying the literature in this previous publication (Johns et al. 2023) and the associated repository of open-access materials that we developed featuring nine interactive coding templates demonstrating numerical methods through examples from MEB, fluid mechanics, heat transfer, separations, thermodynamics, and reaction engineering (Ford Versypt et al. 2022). We also have previously developed graphical user interfaces for use in engineering education (Eastep et al. 2019; Bara et al. 2020); however, a disadvantage of these tools is that users cannot easily modify the original problem statement to adapt to new problems, which is very straightforward using interactive coding templates. Distinct from the previously published materials, our emphasis here is on early undergraduates (first- and second-year students) and providing templates that students can use to solve a variety of problems encountered in their first core chemical engineering course, MEB. Beyond coursework, undergraduates interested in joining research teams in computer-aided process engineering are often discouraged from doing so until they have completed a suite of advanced mathematics courses. To onboard students with limited mathematics and programming backgrounds into research that involves describing dynamic processes through systems of ordinary differential equations (ODEs), we provide the same type of interactive coding templates to reduce the barrier to entry into mathematical systems engineering research.

We developed a set of MATLAB live scripts for training undergraduate students in the introductory chemical engineering MEB course and in an undergraduate research experience on the topic of biomedical applications of systems engineering tools. The MATLAB live script files combine executable MATLAB code, formatted explanatory text and equations, images, and code output directly in a single file. Students are instructed on the interactive coding template and then are assigned various problems to work on their own, starting from the interactive coding template rather than from a blank MATLAB file. The pedagogical emphasis is on the covered topic rather than on learning to program or the details of the numerical methods. For the MEB course, our interactive coding templates focus on solving linear systems of equations. For undergraduate research, the topic is applying conservation balances to populations of cells and amounts of chemical species in living organisms and solving these dynamic problems with systems of ODEs. Undergraduates with a wide range of mathematics and programming backgrounds have successfully used interactive coding templates as they study realistic applications with linear systems of equations and systems of ODEs.

2. MATLAB live scripts for material and energy balances course

Classically in the MEB course systems of linear equations are solved algebraically by hand or via spreadsheets as in three popular textbooks (Felder, Rousseau, and Bullard 2016; Liberatore 2019; Murphy 2023). The material developed here supplements the section in the Liberatore (2019) textbook titled Systems of linear equations, specifically as a MATLAB Live Script-based alternative to the subsection titled "Solving systems of linear equations in a spreadsheet."

In the MEBLinearSystems repository (Johns and Ford Versypt 2022a), we have three MATLAB live script files for use directly in MEB courses or for introducing systems of linear equations more broadly. The first file is Systems_of_Linear_Equations.mlx (Figure 1), which includes explanatory text and instructions, a worked example, and an interactive example. The second file contains the corresponding solution to the interactive example and is named Systems_of_Linear_Equations_sol.mlx. We have created an explanatory video (Johns and Ford Versypt 2022b) narrating the solution. Systems_of_Linear_Equations.mlx includes an interactive example section (Figure 1) that can also be used as a template for solving other systems of linear equations, such as those encountered in homework assignments in MEB courses.

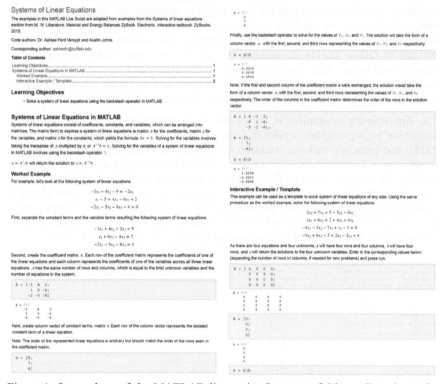

Figure 1. Screenshots of the MATLAB live script Systems_of_Linear_Equations.mlx: explanatory text and instructions, a worked example, and an interactive example. Content is split into two columns to fit within this manuscript.

The third file Lecture_With_Examples.mlx is a lecture to introduce the topic, even before students learn about material balances. The lecture includes the explanatory text and worked examples from Systems_of_Linear_Equations.mlx and five additional examples from three MEB textbooks: (Liberatore 2019; Felder, Rousseau, and Bullard 2016; Murphy 2023). The GitHub repository includes a README.md file for summarizing the information above and two additional files for viewing on GitHub or static sharing: Lecture_With_Examples.pdf and Systems_of_Linear_Equations_sol.pdf. The .mlx files can be run interactively via MATLAB after downloading from GitHub.

3. MATLAB live scripts for onboarding undergraduate researchers

We have had 51 undergraduate research scholars in the Ford Versypt Lab since it started in fall of 2014. Since spring of 2022, 14 new undergraduate researchers were trained using the MATLAB live scripts and onboarding materials described in this section. Prior to that four 1st year students helped write the solution codes, and one graduate student drafted the instructional portions of the interactive coding templates. Collectively, these 18 undergraduate students studied chemical engineering, biomedical engineering, and nursing, with a wide range of mathematics and programming backgrounds. Generally, these students had no prior knowledge of MATLAB or ODEs.

The Ford Versypt Lab uses applied mathematics and process systems engineering methods to model tissues, treatments, and toxicology. We introduce new undergraduate students to a suite of techniques for these topics in mathematical systems biology. We start with training on applying conservation balances to populations of cells and amounts of chemical species in living organisms and solving these problems with systems of ODEs. During the training period, students meet weekly with Dr. Ford Versypt as a group. They learn from each other's issues and receive feedback about their progress. Then we provide guidance for an open exploration period for the students to investigate topics of their interest that use the techniques and templates.

The first training assignment is to use the Write_system_of_ODEs.mlx (Figure 2) interactive coding template, available from our UGResearch repository (Ford Versypt 2023). We introduce material balances through the acronym IOGA for In – Out + Generation = Accumulation. We provide a worked example of a system of ODEs for tracking the concentrations of three chemical species (Figure 2). Students are tasked with using the interactive coding template to solve numerous ODEs from chemical engineering to practice adapting the template for new problems. We use Chapter 10 of the Felder, Rousseau, and Bullard (2016) textbook, which provides several examples with worked solutions to ODEs from dynamic chemical engineering applications.

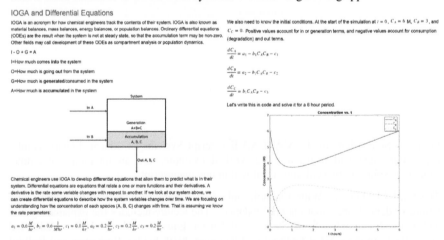

Figure 2. Screenshots of the MATLAB live script Write_system_of_ODEs.mlx: problem statement and output figure.

The second assignment in the training period introduces the use of ODEs for systems biology applications. Students are assigned to read Peskov et al. (2019), which reviews the process of building mechanistic mathematical models for systems biology for applications to cancer treatment via the immune system, so called "immuno-oncology". Figure 1 in Peskov et al. (2019) is particularly useful for students as it illustrates the types of biological interactions in complex cancer systems that can be modeled with ODEs to track the cell populations and chemical interactions relevant to cancer treatments. We ask students to explain how the population balance principles introduced in assignment one apply to the illustrations for the cancer system (Peskov et al. 2019).

The third assignment tasks students with reading de Pillis, Gu, and Radunskaya (2006), which is an in-depth published example for systems dynamics of cancer chemotherapy and immunotherapy tracking the populations of four types of cells and the concentrations of two types of treatments. We prompt them to connect the IOGA concepts and the illustrations from Peskov et al. (2019) to the system of ODEs defined in de Pillis, Gu, and Radunskaya (2006). The repository includes a file titled Intro_to_Bio_ODEs.mlx, which reproduces the results of Figure 7 of de Pillis, Gu, and Radunskaya (2006). Students explore this file to see how a larger system of ODEs can be solved in much the same way as the examples in the first assignment.

The fourth and final training assignment is for students to adapt a partial solution available in our file dePillisSoln.mlx for the de Pillis, Gu, and Radunskaya (2006) model into a full solution for various scenarios to match the results in Figures 6 – 14 of the publication. The purposes of this exercise are for students to encounter issues with reproducible research computing and to gain practice with editing interactive coding templates to simulate other equations, parameter values, or conditions.

After the one-month training period, students enter the exploration period for the remainder of the academic term. Here is the prompt to the students:

> Using what you've learned so far about mathematical biology, MATLAB, and using ODEs and IOGA to describe biological problems from a chemical engineering perspective, you'll spend the rest of the term working on a topic area of your choice.
>
> 1. Choose a biomedical topic (note: this is likely an iterative process)
> 2. Search the literature to find two mathematical biology papers that involve ODE models for your selected biomedical topics. These two papers should have different equations. Each paper should list the full equations, parameters, and show some output plots.
> 3. Your task by the end of the term is to use MATLAB to replicate the two models that you find. You are encouraged to use the interactive coding template Write_system_of_ODEs.mlx available online (Ford Versypt 2023) to solve the systems of ODEs for each model. In your final presentation and report, you'll discuss the pros/cons of each model for the biomedical topic and any issues you encountered in reproducing them. You'll think about future directions that could involve merging the two models or otherwise expanding them to address new aspects of the biomedical topic.

Weekly feedback on topic selection and candidate papers is provided by Dr. Ford Versypt along with additional instruction in oral and poster presentations, searching the literature, and writing technical reports. After students select their papers, they meet weekly with graduate mentors to report on progress and to troubleshoot technical issues. At the end of the term, they deliver written and oral reports on the topic background and their progress in using MATLAB live scripts to explore published models and their completed codes for the project and plans for future extensions. By using MATLAB live scripts, students focus on the learning goals related to the research concepts instead of being hindered by programming or analytical mathematics proficiency. Senior students also appreciate that the templates enable them to quickly make progress towards using advanced techniques.

4. Conclusions

MATLAB live script resources to enable MEB students to solve linear systems of equations and for undergraduate researchers to solve systems of ODEs were developed by the Ford Versypt Lab and have been shared in two GitHub repositories with links provided in the References section (Johns and Ford Versypt 2022a; Ford Versypt 2023), respectively. We acknowledge that many are shifting from MATLAB to alternative software (Johns et al. 2023). We used MATLAB because of our institution's adoption of MATLAB. Transferring MATLAB live script content to Jupyter Notebooks is a relatively straightforward process (Johns et al. 2023). The emphasis on the materials presented here is on training students without advanced mathematics or programming skills to use interactive coding templates for classes of problems routinely encountered in first chemical engineering courses or in undergraduate research focused on dynamic systems. Similar types of materials could be developed for onboarding new researchers or industry professionals studying and solving realistic problems in contexts that do not have programming or advanced mathematics as a learning objective or prerequisite. Others are encouraged to reuse or adapt these materials as needed.

Acknowledgements

The authors acknowledge support of U.S. National Science Foundation grant 2133411 and the University at Buffalo. Ford Versypt Lab members are acknowledged for participating in or mentoring for undergraduate research.

References

J. E. Bara, A. N. Ford Versypt, R. B. Getman, C. A. Kieslich, and R. S. Voronov. 2020. Apps for chemical engineering education: off-the shelf and do-it-yourself development options. *Chem Eng Ed* 54 (3):137-42.

L. G. de Pillis, W. Gu, and A. E. Radunskaya. 2006. Mixed immunotherapy and chemotherapy of tumors: modeling, applications and biological interpretations. *J Theoretical Biology* 238 (4):841-62. doi: 10.1016/j.jtbi.2005.06.037.

C. V. Eastep, G. K. Harrell, A. N. McPeak, and A. N. Ford Versypt. 2019. A MATLAB app to introduce chemical engineering design concepts to engineering freshmen through a pharmaceutical dosing case study. *Chem Eng Ed* 53 (2):85-90.

R. M. Felder, R. W. Rousseau, and L. G. Bullard. 2016. *Elementary Principles of Chemical Processes*. 4th ed. Hoboken, NJ: John Wiley & Sons, Inc.

A. N. Ford Versypt. "UGResearch." https://github.com/ashleefv/UGResearch. doi: 10.5281/zenodo.10157864.

A. N. Ford Versypt, R. P. Hesketh, A. N. Johns, and M. D. Stuber. "ChESS2022." https://github.com/ashleefv/ChESS2022. doi: 10.5281/zenodo.7477475.

A. N. Johns, and A. N. Ford Versypt. "MEBLinearSystems." https://github.com/ashleefv/MEBLinearSystems. doi: 10.5281/zenodo.10157856.

A. N. Johns, and A. N. Ford Versypt. "[YouTube Video] Solving Systems of Linear Equations Using a MATLAB Live Script." https://youtu.be/78n8XaCBt9w.

A. N. Johns, R. P. Hesketh, M. D. Stuber, and A. N. Ford Versypt. 2023. Numerical Problem Solving across the Curriculum with Python and MATLAB Using Interactive Coding Templates: A Workshop for Chemical Engineering Faculty. Proceedings of the ASEE Annual Conference, Baltimore, MD. https://peer.asee.org/43749.

M. W. Liberatore. 2019. *Material and Energy Balances ZyBook*: Electronic textbook: ZyBooks.

R. M. Murphy. 2023. *Introduction to Chemical Processes: Principles, Analysis, Synthesis*. 2nd ed. New York, NY: McGraw Hill.

K. Peskov, I. Azarov, L. Chu, V. Voronova, Y. Kosinsky, and G. Helmlinger. 2019. Quantitative Mechanistic Modeling in Support of Pharmacological Therapeutics Development in Immuno-Oncology. *Frontiers in Immunology* 10:924. doi: 10.3389/fimmu.2019.00924.

Flavio Manenti, Gintaras V. Reklaitis (Eds.), Proceedings of the 34th European Symposium on Computer Aided Process Engineering / 15th International Symposium on Process Systems Engineering (ESCAPE34/PSE24), June 2-6, 2024, Florence, Italy

Teaching Process Design – Quo Vadis?

Daniel R. Lewin,[a*] Thomas A. Adams II,[b] Dominik Bongartz,[c] Grégoire Léonard,[d] Seyed Soheil Mansouri,[e] Fernando G. Martins,[f] Iqbal I. Mujtaba,[g] and Edwin Zondervan[h]

[a]*Department of Chemical Engineering, Technion I. I. T., Haifa 32000, Israel*
[b]*Department of Energy and Process Engineering, Norwegian University of Science and Technology, Norway*
[c]*Department of Chemical Engineering, KU Leuven, Belgium*
[d]*Department of Chemical Engineering, University of Liège, Belgium*
[e]*Department of Chemical and Biochemical Engineering, Technical University of Denmark, Denmark*
[f]*LEPABE, Chemical Engineering Department, University of Porto, Portugal*
[g]*Chemical Engineering Department, University of Bradford, UK*
[h]*Department of Chemical Engineering, University of Twente, Netherlands*

Email for correspondance: dlewin@technion.ac.il

Abstract

The capstone course in chemical process design, together with its associated design project is the acid test to gauge the mastery of trainee chemical engineers. There is no other component in the chemical engineering curriculum that performs this function to this degree. This paper presents the results of an international survey to investigate the current teaching practices with regards to instruction in chemical process design. The results indicate that virtually all capstone courses have substantial group-based design projects. Process simulation is used extensively, while the targeted technical skills are often still classical design and economic evaluation techniques. Heat integration is also very highly considered (93% of respondents) perhaps reflecting awareness of global energy issues. Interestingly, the way teaching session time is distributed between activities (e.g. lecturing versus active learning techniques) falls into a clear bimodal distribution, reflecting distinct teaching philosophies and styles.

Keywords: Capstone design, Process design instruction, Design project, Active learning.

1. Introduction

"The design course will become even more important given the challenges posed by increasing relevance of designing sustainable process and energy systems. Chemical Engineering as a discipline should recognize this fact and not treat process design a second-class course as is done by a number of universities." *Ignacio Grossmann, CMU*

Process design is a core component of chemical and biochemical engineering education. In most universities and institutions, the process design course either involves or is followed by an extensive design project. The design project is often considered a core activity in the education of future chemical engineers because it develops their skills in creative, innovative, and critical thinking beyond the boundaries of their acquired knowledge, as well as in collaboration in a team. It also integrates the various technical topics into a single project, evidencing the interdependence between classes that are usually taught separately and leading the students to acquire a general overview of chemical engineering activities. Such skills are likely to be crucial to empower students to develop process technologies that respond to the relevant future challenges in process design and/or of the world. These future challenges include accommodating alternative raw materials and energy resources, alternative or more flexible production schedules, engineering ethics, health and safety and addressing sustainability concerns (Lewin and Zondervan, 2022) including UN sustainable development goals. Some schools already integrate several of these challenges in process design courses and design projects, e.g., water and energy conservation as well as CO_2 capture, storage and utilization, and biologics manufacturing (El-Halwagi, 2017; Osman et al., 2020; Léonard et al., 2017). At the same time, process design tools are also evolving, including, for example, increased emphasis on combination with data, digital twin concepts, or integration with virtual and augmented reality tools (Wu et al., 2022; Carberry et al., 2023).

Given this changing landscape in the field of process design, we present the outcomes of an extensive survey conducted on teachers/instructors of process design around the world to understand the state of the art in teaching process design in chemical and biochemical engineering. Similar surveys were conducted by Silverstein et al. (2013), and by Ford et al. (2023), with the second of these focussed only on university practice in the USA. Changes in subject matter, methodology and teaching strategies in the last decade apparent from the responses of our survey are highlighted to understand recent trends, as well as develop a vision on how process design could be taught in the future.

2. The 2023 Survey on Process Design Teaching Practice

2.1. About the survey

A survey to learn about the teaching practice of chemical process design was sent to more than 160 academic colleagues around the world, most of which are known to be associated with their institutions' efforts in teaching chemical process design. A particular effort was made to reach out to the leading schools teaching chemical engineering in the highest-ranked universities (e.g., the top 10 schools in the QS World University Rankings of 2021 and 2023). At the time of writing, we have received 50 responses to our survey, including at least 50% of the top 10 schools in the QS World Rankings for 2021 and 2023.

The purpose of the survey was to learn how chemical process design is taught in universities around the world. The central question is to determine to what extent design activities are taught in one or two design-specific courses at the end of the degree in chemical engineering (i.e., capstone design), rather than exposing students to chemical engineering design during the entire degree. The survey consisted of three parts: I – general questions; II – questions on how process design is taught (specifically in capstone design); III –questions on how the process design project – if there is one – is administered and assessed.

We shall now provide a review of the results extracted from the 50 responses that we received, of which 56% were from European universities, 20% from North America, 12% from South America and the remaining 12% from Asia and Australasia. The responders are on the whole seasoned teachers of process design, with an average teaching experience of 13 years of teaching. The chemical engineering programs lead to either BSc or MSc, with an average degree length of 4.4 years. The average class size taught by the responders is 57, but with a large standard deviation (45).

2.2. What is taught in the capstone process design course

"No one thinks the courses are easy and most students are glad they took them after they have graduated but find them challenging when they are taking them." *Marnie Jamieson, University of Alberta*

As shown in Table 1, the technical skills taught in the capstone design course are those one would expect, with most institutions teaching the economic considerations associated with process design (e.g., plant cost estimation and profitability analysis), as well as technical design skills (e.g., heat integration, process synthesis, and design heuristics). Subjects more related to individual unit operations are somewhat less prevalent in the reported curricula, even when including systems of these units (e.g., separation sequencing and reactor selection and reactor network design). The less commonly included subjects are (surprisingly) safety, and to an even lesser extent, plantwide control and LCA. Not shown in the table are the soft skills that are taught in the course.

Table 1. Which technical skills are taught in the capstone design course.

Technical Skill	% Responders
Plant cost estimation	95
Heat integration	93
Process synthesis	89
Design heuristics	89
Profitability analysis	86
Techno-economic assessment methods	80
Equipment sizing	73
Separation sequence design	73
Reactor selection/reactor network design	68
Flowsheet optimization/superstructure optimization	57
Safety	55
Plantwide control	32
Life Cycle Analysis (LCA)	32

Table 2 lists the tasks expected to be addressed by students in the design project. These follow naturally from the skills taught in the capstone design course, with a strong emphasis on equipment sizing, plant cost estimation and profitability analysis.

Table 2. Which technical skills are addressed by students in the design project.

Technical Skill	% Responders
Comparing design alternatives	100
Equipment sizing	96
Plant cost estimation	96
Profitability analysis	94
Flowsheet synthesis	89
Flowsheet simulation	89
Environmental constraints	64
Pinch analysis	62
Heat exchanger network design	60
Safety analysis	55
Optimization	47
Carbon footprint analysis	38
Uncertainty/sensitivity analysis	34
Comparing alternative raw materials	32
Process control	32

The respondents were asked to list the textbooks that are used to teach the capstone chemical design course, and as seen in Table 3, many schools do not rely on a single book, which makes sense, given the nature of process design. The leading texts that are used the most are Seider et al (2017), Sinnot and Towler (2020), and Turton et al (2020), in that order.

Table 3. Which textbooks are used in the capstone design course.

Textbook	% Responders
Seider et al. (2017)	66
Sinnot and Towler (2020)	58
Turton et al. (2020)	54
Peters et al. (2003)	44
Biegler et al. (1997)	38
Smith (2005)	36
Couper et al. (2012)	20
Kemp and Lim (2020)	14
Adams (2022)	10

"The origins of Chemical Engineering lie in Industrial Chemistry, however in the era of digitalization: as an educator, to establish a balance between process simulation and conventional hand or spreadsheet calculation is sometimes a challenge." *Asad Sahir, IIT Ropar.*

Several questions were directed at elucidating which simulation software packages are used in the capstone design course, and how students are instructed in their usage. 78% of the responders indicated that simulation software is used extensively, with a further 16% stating that it is used to a small degree. Table 4 indicates that 58% of the respondents are using ASPEN Plus, with the rest relying on other packages. With regards to training, 54% of the responders indicated that the use of simulation is taught either as part of the capstone course or in a separate course that is taught in parallel. 40% of the respondents indicate that the use of simulation is taught separately before the capstone design course. Only 2% of the respondents report that students are expected to acquire these skills on their own with no support.

Table 4. Which simulation software is used in the capstone design course.

Simulation software	% Responders
Aspen Plus	58
Aspen HYSYS	16
Honeywell UniSim	8
AVEVA PRO/II	6
gPROMS	4
CHEMCAD	2
GAMS	2

2.3. How is the capstone process design course taught.

"Although most of the students learn how to do the expected tasks/calculations mechanically using process simulation, often they do not achieve 'junior competencies' on process design as expected at the end of the course (e.g., why they should do the different tasks as they do them?). The previous background of the students (e.g., lack of emphasis on 'decision making' in previous courses), and the time/effort allocated to this topic are real constraints." *Antonio Espuña, UPC - Technical University of Catalonia*

The core skills for process design are taught systematically year-by-year for the entire degree in 36% of the cases. A capstone design course is taught in the second to last year of the degree in 46% of the cases, and in the last year of the degree in 74% of the cases. The capstone design courses are taught by professors and lecturers, with the assistance of TAs in 42% of the cases, industrial adjuncts in 44% of the cases, and some assistance from the simulator providers in 8% of the cases. In most cases, the capstone process design class is taught using a weekly combination of lectures (average length of 2.1 hours), recitations/exercises (average length of 1.1 hours), laboratories (average length of 1.2 hours), meetings with students (average length of 1.2 hours), and office hours (average length of 1.3 hours).

The design project is included as part of the capstone design course by 57% of the respondents, another 41% having the design project as a separate course, and only 2% having no design project. The average project group size is 5.3 students (standard deviation, STD = 4). The distribution of assessment of student mastery by categories is listed in Table 5, where the average weights and their standard deviations (STD) are presented. The large variance is due to 25% of the responders indicating that students are not examined in their courses, with the project grade being heavily dependent on the project and course performance of the students.

Table 5. How are the students of the capstone design course assessed?

Category	Average Weight (%)	STD (%)
Course progress	9	10
Project (group assessment)	32	21
Project (individual assessment)	16	21
Project presentation	15	16
Soft skills assessment	5	7
Midterm exam	7	11
Final Exam	16	19

Figure 1 shows the distribution of total meeting time used in the capstone design course by lecturers and TAs to present materials, with the rest used for Q&A, and other in-class activities (e.g., problem solving). The responses received indicate bimodal distributions in the time-utilization for active learning in both lectures, shown in Fig. 1(a), and recitations/exercises, shown in Fig. 1(b) – with a close to even split between those who utilize the time in favor of hands-on problem solving by students, and those who favor more traditional usage of the time to transmit information by lecturing. The positive impact of active learning on learning outcomes in process design education have been reported by Lewin and Barzilai (2021). These distributions are closely related to the even split between responders using recorded lectures and those who are not.

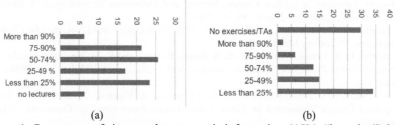

(a)   (b)

Figure 1. Percentage of time used to transmit information (AKA "lecturing") by (a) teachers in lectures, and (b) TAs in recitations/exercises.

3. Conclusions

From the 50 responses received to our survey, it is clear that process design is perceived as a central activity in chemical engineering, with the focus being on practical process synthesis and the associated techno-economic analysis as applied to industrial-scale problems. This skill set is unmatched by any other activity in the chemical engineering curriculum (Kiss and Webb, 2021). Results regarding soft skills, which can be ideally trained in the process design education, were not reported here due to space constraints but will be detailed in a later version of the paper. Finally, it appears that carbon footprint analysis, LCA and process control currently receive low priority in the process design and design project. To meet the UN SDG on sustainable production and consumption and to be in line with Industry 5.0, these subjects should be taken more seriously in future teaching of process design and in the design project.

References

T. A. Adams II, 2022, *Learn Aspen Plus in 24 Hours*, 2nd Edition, McGraw-Hill.

L. Biegler, I. Grossmann, and A. W. Westerberg, 1997, *Systematic Methods of Chemical Process Design*, Prentice Hall.

D. E. Carberry, K. Bagherpour, J. M. Woodley, C. Beenfeldt, M. P. Andersson, U. Krühne, and S. S. Mansouri, 2023, "A Strategic Plan for Developing eXtended Reality Tools to Teach Unit Operations in Chemical Engineering: Defining Needs, Technology Selection and Project Resources," *Digital Chemical Engineering*, 8, 100104.

J. R. Couper, W. R. Penney, J. R. Fair, 2012, *Chemical Process Equipment Selection and Design*, 3rd Edition, Elsevier.

M. M. El-Halwagi, 2017, *Sustainable Design Through Process Integration*, 2nd Edition, Elsevier.

L. P. Ford, J. Cole, K. D. Dahm, B. K. Vaughen, M. V. Jamieson, L. J. Landherr, D. L. Silverstein, T. J. Vogel, C. W. West, and S. W. Thiel, 2023, "How We Teach: Capstone Design," presented at *2023 ASEE Annual Conference & Exposition*, Baltimore, Maryland, Paper 37520.

I. C. Kemp and J. S. Lim, 2020, Pinch *Analysis and Process Integration – A User Guide in Process Integration for the Efficient Use of Energy*, Butterworth-Heinemann

A. A. Kiss and C. Webb, 2021, "The Manchester Perspective on using the Design Project to Enhance the Education of Chemical Engineering Students," *Journal of Chemical Technology and Biotechnology*, 96, 1453-1464.

G. Léonard, S. Belboom, D. Toye, M-N. Dumont, A. Léonard, and G. Heyen, 2017, "Recent Evolutions and Trends in the Use of Computer Aided Chemical Engineering for Educational Purposes at the University of Liège," *Computer Aided Chemical Engineering* , 40, 2941-2946.

D. R. Lewin and A. Barzilai, 2021, "Teaching Process Design to Chemical Engineering Undergraduates – an Evolution," *Chem. Eng. Educ.*, 55(3), 157-172.

D. R. Lewin and E. Zondervan, 2022, "Motivating Students to Design Emission-free Processes," *Chem. Eng. Trans.*, 96, 19-24.

A. I. Osman, M. Hefny, M. I. A. Abdel Maksoud, A. M. Elgarahy, and D. W. Rooney, 2021, "Recent Advances in Carbon Capture Storage and Utilisation Technologies: A Review," *Environmental Chemistry Letters*, 19, 797-849.

M. S. Peters, K. D. Timmerhaus, and R. E. West, 2003, *Plant Design and Economics for Chemical Engineers*, 5th Edition, McGraw-Hill.

W. D. Seider, D. R. Lewin, J. D. Seader, S. Widagdo, R. Gani, and K. M. Ng, 2017, *Product and Process Design Principles: Synthesis, Analysis and Evaluation*, 4th Edition, John Wiley and Sons.

D. L. Silverstein, L. G. Bullard L.G., W. D. Seider, and M. A. Vigeant, 2013, "How We Teach: Capstone Design," presented at *120th ASEE Annual Conference & Exposition*, Atlanta, Georgia.

R. Sinnot and G. Towler, 2020, *Chemical Engineering Design*, 6th Edition, Elsevier.

R. Smith, 2005, *Chemical Process Design and Integration*, John Wiley and Sons.

R. Turton, J. Shaeiwitz, D. Bhattacharyya, and W. Whiting, 2020, *Analysis, Synthesis, and Design of Chemical Processes*, 5th Edition, Addison-Wesley.

F.-Y. Wu W.-S. Lu, X.-Y. Wang, J.-L. Yang, C. Li, L. Cheng, and Z. Xie, 2022, "Enhanced Virtual Reality Plant: Development and Application in Chemical Engineering Education," *International Journal of Emerging Technologies in Learning*, 17 (14), 205-220.

Flavio Manenti, Gintaras V. Reklaitis (Eds.), Proceedings of the 34th European Symposium on Computer Aided Process Engineering / 15th International Symposium on Process Systems Engineering (ESCAPE34/PSE24), June 2-6, 2024, Florence, Italy

Serious games for active learning in Optimization of Chemical Processes

Ismael Díaz[a], Emilio J. González[a], María González-Miquel[a], Manuel Rodríguez[a]

aDepartamento de Ingeniería Química Industrial y del Medio Ambiente, Universidad Politécnica de Madrid, C/ José Gutiérrez Abascal 2, Madrid 28006, Spain
ismael.diaz@upm.es

Abstract

Optimization of Chemical Processes is a course that demands a thorough understanding of mathematical concepts and intensive use of programming tools. In recent years, new cohorts of students have shown a decreased interest and motivation for the subject. To mitigate it, a modification of course activities is proposed based on active learning methodologies. These methods have previously demonstrated a positive impact on students' engagement and motivation. In this work, active learning is implemented by means of serious games, offering additional advantages such as a positive impact on the work climate and teamwork collaboration, among others. This paper details three examples of serious games, ranging from simple word search games (aimed at fostering the remembering and understanding of important concepts) to complex escape room activities (designed to address open problems and promote students' creativity).

Keywords: Optimization, active learning, serious games

1. Introduction

The primary objective of this study is to show the efforts made to improve Gen Z students' motivation towards the subject Optimization of Chemical Processes taught at Universidad Politécnica de Madrid (Spain). In the last years, a decrease in student's engagement and motivation was perceived leading to a shift towards a more active approach by the incorporation of serious games. The main novelty of this work is presenting some examples of how serious games of variable complexity can be used to address the previous issues. In sections 1.1 and 1.2 the problem is presented along with the expected impacts of introducing serious games. Section 2 is fully devoted to describing the activities developed and implemented. Key findings are presented in Section 3 and the final conclusions in Section 4.

1.1. Characteristics of the new generation of students (Gen Z)

The present higher education landscape witnesses a marked shift in the characteristics of students compared to previous generations like Baby boomers, Gen X, and Gen Y. Generation Z is the term coined to describe people born between 1995 and 2010, whose identity has been built based on the ubiquitous access to internet and a pervasive use of social media with a fast access to a vast amount of information. The latter, along with the rise of global problems such as climate anxiety and the shifts in the financial and labor markets, have greatly influenced their behavior and preferences (Billings et al., 2016). Young people today are defined, among others, by their increasing interest in the sustainability and green transition, being more socially inclusive and showing more concerns about mental health, coupled with a pragmatic decision-making approach and a desire for immediate feedback. Unfortunately, these distinctions with respect to previous generations of students are usually overlooked in the design of higher education courses, which could be one of the reasons behind the disaffection of Gen Z students with the higher education system.

Contrary to the assumption of being the first "native digital generation", Generation Z students generally exhibit limited technological proficiency, many of them being reluctant to programming or using scientific software. Precisely, the intensive use of algebraic programming and mathematics is the main characteristic of the course Optimization of Chemical Processes analyzed in this paper. This fact, exacerbated by the impact of the COVID19 pandemic, has resulted in a perceived worse students' motivation in the last years which has affected students' learning and performance. On the other hand, following ABET recommendations, it is important to foster not only analytical and problem-solving learning, but it is also necessary to promote soft skills such as teamwork and communication among others.

1.2. Serious games and active learning

To address the identified challenges, an effective teaching approach is the implementation of active learning methodologies (Rodríguez et al., 2018), understood as instructional methods that engage students in the learning process.

An active learning methodology helping to address previous issues is the use of serious games, defined in 1970 by Clarck C. Abt "as games that have an explicit and carefully thought-out educational purpose and are not intended to be played primarily for amusement" (Abt, 1970). The theoretical foundations of using game-based learning are well established (Krath et al., 2021). It has been observed to positively impact people's behavior, cognitive skills, and motivation. According to the existing literature some key game design aspects have been identified (goals, feedback, social play, etc.) being the root for three different games designed and implemented in the course (word search, a conference-like activity, and the escape room). For the interested reader, more details about the advantages of using serious games in chemical engineering courses can be found in our recent paper (Díaz et al., 2024).

For the specific course on Optimization of Chemical Processes, a range of activities has been formulated based on Bloom's taxonomy (Figure 1). Foundational-level activities focus on recall and comprehension, utilizing crossword games to revisit previously taught concepts. These activities, conducted throughout the semester, served the purpose of revisiting specific concepts previously taught. Moving towards the application of the knowledge, a conference-like activity has been developed. In this activity, students are required to set new exercises regarding different real life problems, not restricted to chemical engineering applications, also participating as co-evaluators of other students, thus forcing them to analyze other's solutions. The exercises are submitted in a paper format, there is a review process and finally their work is presented in a poster session. Finally, an activity requiring high level thinking was implemented at the end of the semester in the form of a modular escape room. In this activity, students must solve different quizes regarding general concepts but also formulate and solve diverse optimization problems, leveraging programming skills cultivated during the course. In all the activities, game-based elements were added in order to foster competition, challenge and teamwork, positively impacting student's engagement and the work climate in the classroom. As it can be seen in Figure 1, the role of the teacher in the activities is also evolving during the semester. At the beginning, the teacher plays an important role presenting concepts, tools, etc., giving more prominence to the students as the course progresses. In the last activities, students are in the center of the learning process being responsible for their own learning (creating problems, analyzing solutions, etc.).

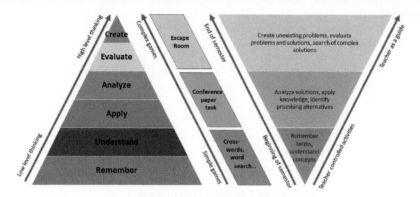

Figure 1. Context of the games developed according to Bloom's taxonomy, adapted from Díaz et al. 2024.

2. Implementation of serious games in Optimization of Chemical Processes

2.1. The non-gamified subject

The course Optimization of Chemical Processes is taught as a compulsory course during the first semester of the master's degree in chemical engineering (Universidad Politécnica de Madrid, Spain). Students attending this course have very different process system engineering (PSE)-related backgrounds, depending on the university they come from. Many of them have not used any programming software in the last years. The number of students is normally between 25-30.

Prior to the COVID19 pandemics, the course structure involved a combination of master classes and practical sessions. At the beginning of the semester some general concepts (convexity, optimality, etc.) were presented along with the programming tool (Python/Pyomo). Subsequently, a block about linear programming and mixed-integer linear programming was introduced in the syllabus, where the students delved into the main algorithms (simplex, branch and bound, etc.) and problems (transport, allocation, diet, etc.). Afterwards, the students explored the non-linear block where, again, general concepts, algorithms and problems were worked during the lessons. The last segment introduced advanced concepts such as mixed integer non-linear programming and multi-objective optimization methods.

2.2. Simple games to promote remembering and understanding.

At the end of crucial lessons, simple games were created to reinforce important concepts (an example is presented in Figure 2). In the non-gamified course, revisiting concepts was done by dedicating 10-15 min of each lesson for re-teaching the concepts. Now, the same time is dedicated to a competition for the fastest student to solve the game. The result is that students are actively looking for previous concepts in their mind, trying to find as many of them in the shortest time, instead of being passive listening the same concepts again. Another advantage from these games is that students are obtaining instant feedback of the concepts they may have missed. Both winning and non-winning students benefit from this approach, as non-winning students pay more attention to the explanation about the concepts they may have overlooked, contributing to a more effective learning experience.

Figure 2. Example of word search.

2.3. A conference-like activity to apply knowledge and identify real problems.

Throughout the semester, students are tasked with solving many problems (simpler at the beginning, becoming more difficult during the semester) whose objective is to become proficient in using algebraic modelling tools (Python/Pyomo). The Python environment was chosen because of the great number of resources available to learn and solving problems and being open source. However, it is important for them to know that optimization is used in many different real-life situations. Therefore, a task was scheduled where they played the role of PSE professionals attending a conference.

In pairs, the students are firstly required to present an original optimization model they have devised. The constraints are that the problem must be original, and it can be solved using the methods and tools worked during the course. Teachers then evaluate the models proposed based on criteria such as difficulty and originality, marking them as "rejected" (the students must completely re-do the task to pass it), "major revisions" (the student mark is going to be between 5-6.5 out of 10), "minor revisions" (mark between 6.5-8) and "accepted" (8-10).

Two weeks later, the conference takes place, where the students are required to bring a poster to the classroom to share the problem and solution with the rest of "professionals" attending the conference. For one hour, students interact with each other, asking questions and making explanations. Finally, both students and teachers evaluate each poster considering both poster design and oral communication skills. The final grade of each pair of students (each poster) is the result of averaging teacher and other students mark within the limits of the initial range provided. For instance, if a pair obtain a designation of "major revisions" but they deliver a compelling poster presentation, their mark will be close to 6.5, but if they do not convey the message properly, they will obtain a 5.

2.4. An escape-room to foster creativity

Attending to Bloom's taxonomy, the highest level of cognitive skills is obtained when an individual can evaluate and create new problems. This is the aim of the escape room designed to be implemented in the last session of the course. Traditionally, this last session was devoted to solving exam-like problems and go over the main concepts of the course. Now, this session is dedicated to face the students to incomplete problems in the form of quizzes, evaluating the way they can set new optimization problems from restricted information. This escape-room also allows teachers to gauge the extent to which students are adept at solving problems using the subject's tool.

The game is designed to be modular. Initially, each team receives a red box, common to all groups, which contains another box inside. The outer box is initially secured with a chain and a code lock (shown at the top left in Figure 3). The groups also received a letter providing the context of the story. This letter contains the information to solve an initial linear programming whose solution is the numerical code needed to unlock the red box. Inside it, they find different quizzes and items that provide the constraint of an incomplete problem (mixed integer programming). The correct solution of the new problem is again the numerical code needed to open a smaller box. Once the second box is opened, teams encounter theoretical questions and a puzzle related to the classical problem classification tree of optimization problems. The ordered sentence derived from the solution is obtained, and instructions are provided for problem number 3. The solution (temperature 479.73 K) corresponds to the positions of letters in the ordered sentence (4 =P, 7 =X, 9 =K, 7 =X, 3 =M). The final code is obtained by applying a decoder to the previous code.

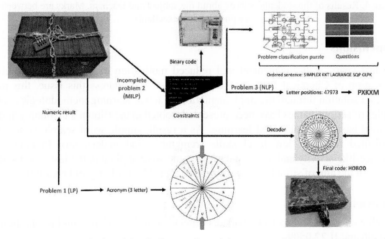

Figure 3. Escape room designed for the last session of the course, adapted from Díaz et al. 2024.

3. Results

At the end of the semester, students are asked to participate in a global survey regarding both the subject and the instructors. As it can be seen in Figure 4, the subject global mark reached a minimum during the course 2020/2021 which can be attributed to the shift to remote teaching methods used amid the pandemics. During the following two courses, some serious games were gradually introduced in the subject, what seems to be welcomed by the students according to the results obtained. However, there is not a clear trend on the mark given to the teachers. The results from students' survey also show that they perceive game-based activities as more motivating. This is especially important for the case of students who did not keep the subject up to date. In previous years, these students usually "disconnected" from the course activities and the group, being more prone to work alone. The introduction of game-based activities based on group collaboration encourages them to continue working because they want to participate in the activities. It is important to highlight that all the activities were designed with a try-fail-try again philosophy. Teachers do not intend to use these activities for grading the students (evaluation activities are the same in the gamified and non-gamified approaches), but rather to encourage students to attempt the activities, get the feedback, learn from experience and then do it again.

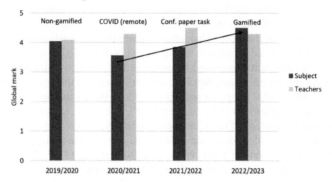

Figure 4. Results of the students' survey about the subject and teachers. Marks are between 0 (very poor) and 5 (excellent).

4. Conclusions

In the last years, a disengagement and reduced motivation of students in the subject Optimization of Chemical Processes was perceived. To address this issue, this paper proposes a solution through the implementation of active learning methodologies. Three examples of serious games have been presented, rooted in the Bloom's taxonomy and the theoretical basis of game-based learning. As a result, simple word search games were implemented to foster low level skills (remember and understand). In contrast, a conference-like activity and an escape room game were applied in the last lessons of the course with the aim of stimulate critical thinking, problem solving and creativity.

Acknowledgement

The authors are grateful to Universidad Politécnica de Madrid for funding the projects IE23.0506 and IE22.0509.

References

Abt, C.C., 1970. Serious Games. American Behavioral Scientist 14, 129–129. https://doi.org/10.1177/000276427001400113

Billings, D. M., Kowalski, K., Shatto, B., Erwin, K., 2016. Moving on From Millennials: Preparing for Generation Z. The Journal of Continuing Education in Nursing, 47(6), 253–254. doi:10.3928/00220124-20160518-05

Díaz, I., González, E.J., González-Miquel, M., Rodríguez, M., 2024. Application of serious games in chemical engineering courses. Education for Chemical Engineers 46, 22–32. https://doi.org/10.1016/j.ece.2023.10.002

Krath, J., Schürmann, L., Von Korflesch, H.F.O., 2021. Revealing the theoretical basis of gamification: A systematic review and analysis of theory in research on gamification, serious games and game-based learning. Computers in Human Behavior 125, 106963. https://doi.org/10.1016/j.chb.2021.106963

Rodríguez, M., Díaz, I., Gonzalez, E.J., González-Miquel, M., 2018. Motivational active learning: An integrated approach to teaching and learning process control. Education for Chemical Engineers 24, 7–12. https://doi.org/10.1016/j.ece.2018.06.003

Flavio Manenti, Gintaras V. Reklaitis (Eds.), Proceedings of the 34th European Symposium on Computer Aided Process Engineering / 15th International Symposium on Process Systems Engineering (ESCAPE34/PSE24), June 2-6, 2024, Florence, Italy

Simulated-Experimental Cross Validation of Multistage Batch Distillation for Water/Propylene Glycol Separation as Educational Exercise

Giulia Tonsi*, Elisa Zanella, Arian Grainca, Andrea Bonetti, Pietro Cassinerio, Carlo Pirola

Università degli Studi di Milano, Department of Chemistry, Via Golgi 19, 20133, Milan (MI), Italy
giulia.tonsi@unimi.it

Abstract

This study describes an educational exercise concerning the multistage batch distillation of the mixture water-propylen glycol (PG). The research study consisted of three primary components: practical experimentation using a batch distillation setup, computer simulations, utilizing the AVEVA PRO/II™ software, and the development and operation of a multistage system. The initial experiment was centred around the process of distillation involving mixtures of n-heptane/toluene and water/PG. This phase aimed to establish a fundamental understanding that would be crucial for conducting further simulations using the AVEVA PRO/II™ platform. The utilisation of these simulations is the basic background in customizing the design and optimizing the performance parameters of the multistage distillation plant, hence guaranteeing the highest possible level of separation efficiency.

Keywords: Simulation software, AVEVA ProII, batch distillation, binary mixture.

1. Introduction

Distillation is one of the most used separation technologies. It can be performed in batch or continuous configuration. Batch distillation (M. Mujtaba, 2004) is the most used configuration in educational laboratory and multistage batch distillation represents the higher-level experiment in the education of this separation technique. In the field of chemical engineering, computer simulation is largely used, and it can be a powerful complementary tool for innovative educational lessons. The application of computer simulation to batch distillation is a challenging topic for students, due to the complexity of both vapor liquid interpretation and the in-silico design of these experiments.

The aim of this work is to report the experimental activity for the study of the separation of a binary mixture by batch multistage distillation through the interpretation of the collected data, based on the correct thermodynamic model of fluid phase equilibria involved, and through the correct set-up of the simulation representation. Two different mixtures were tested: one completely organic (n-heptane/toluene) and one composed by water and an organic compound (water/propylene glycol), that is more challenging due to the high latent heat of water evaporation. The experimental plant and methodology, the analysis of the thermodynamic approach for the non-ideal behavior of the mixture and the simulation interpretation will be presented. This didactic methodology embraces the mission of the third-year course titled "Industrial Plant with Laboratory" hold during the Industrial Chemistry Bachelor program at the University of Milano, Chemistry Department. As reported in a previous work of our group (C. Pirola, 2019), the pedagogical objectives of this procedure are mainly related to: the learning of the principles of experimental bench scale plants and the correct experimental procedures, the elaboration of the equilibria data to propose a suitable thermodynamic approach, and the interpretation of the experimental distillations results using a process simulation software (AVEVA PRO/II Simulation datasheet).

2. Experimental section

2.1. Mono-stage batch distillation

The initial step of this work is the data collection of n-heptane/toluene mono-stage batch distillation. A distillation laboratory scale apparatus has been set up, equipped with: heating mantle to give the required heat for the distillation, round bottom flask of 500 mL, Claisen distillation head for the condensation of the vapour and the control of vapours temperature with a thermocouple, pressure controller and vacuum pump to perform and control under vacuum distillations, round bottom flask with stopcock-equipped-inlet and three-way stopcock-equipped adapter to collect samples in vacuum conditions.

The distillations were conducted as follow:

- In a round bottom flask a certain quantity of n-heptane and toluene was weighed to obtain 100-200 mL of solution of known composition.
- The chosen experimental pressure was set.
- The heating was started to allow the boiling of the mixture.
- Samples of the accumulate distillate were taken at certain intervals time and the composition was determined using gas chromatographic (GC) analysis.

The same apparatus was then used to distil water/propylene glycol (PG) mixtures, in order to evaluate the feasibility of the separation of this mixture, and to further validate the AVEVA PRO/II™ batch simulation setup.

2.2. Multistage batch distillation

The multistage batch distillation experimental setup was similar to the one described for the mono-stage distillation. A distillation column (h = 35 cm, internal diameter = 3 cm, filled with 0.6 cm ceramic Raschig rings) was added to increase the number of theoretical stages, and equipped with a distillation head (Figure 1) connected directly to the top of the column to allow the setting of the reflux. In the left part, the temperature of the rising vapour was measured by the thermocouple. The vapour was condensed in the top left condenser to allow the liquid to fill the space above the first stopcock. Tuning the two stopcocks was possible to set the quantity of liquid refluxed or taken as distillate, changing the value of R. In the right part the sampling zone and the vacuum and N_2 inlet. were located.

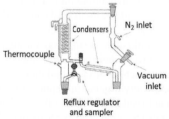

Figure 1: distillation head scheme

The experimental procedure used in the multistage distillation process was similar to the one described for the mono-stage distillation with the addition of the setting of the reflux ratio (R). Once the liquid was started to condense in the top left condenser, the two stopcocks were tuned to modify the flow rate of reflux (L) and the flowrate of the distillate

(D) to obtain a certain value of R (R=L/D). To measure the R value the left three-ways valve was turned in the position of sampling stopping the reflux of the liquid back into the column. The sampling time was measured to determine the flowrate of L. The values of D were obtained considering the weight of the cuts distilled and the times of sampling. The values of L and D were calculated in mol*min^{-1}.

3. Software simulation section

3.1. Mono-stage batch distillation

To start with software simulation the right thermodynamic approach has to be determined using experimental VLE data taken from literature (S. J. Ashcroft et al., 1979; Fendu et al., 2014), and comparing them with the data given by the software using different models (IDEAL, NRTL and UNIQUAC) for the calculation of the activity coefficients.

Firstly, the thermodynamic model, the substances involved, and the unit of measure were set, and then the "batch distillation" unit was selected (Figure 2b). For the mono-stage batch distillation, the settings present in Table 1 were used and the two different operating policies (START UP and CUT-n) followed during the experimental distillation were indicated.

Table 1: *setting and policies used for the simulation of the mono-stage batch distillation with ProII^{TM} (example of simulation data of n-heptane/toluene distillation).*

ProII COMMAND	DESCRIPTION (Example of input data)
STREAMS	
Feed	Flowrate, composition, T and P of the initial mixture (0.754 mol/min, hep/tol=70/30, 20 °C, 760 torr)
Residue	Content of the still-pot (residue) at the end of the distillation (0.008 mol/min)
Accum-res	Residue of the condenser holdup (1.04 * 10^{-6} mol/min)
Cuts	All the cuts sampled along the distillation process (number of cuts = 7)
BATCH DISTILLATION WINDOW	
Number of theoretical stages	This type of configuration simulates the Claisen distillation with just condenser and reboiler (number of theoretical stages = 2)
Batch cycle time	This value is used to normalize the exiting flowrates of the unit (cycle time = 1 min)
Initial pressure profile	Pressure of the distillation (760 torr) and pressure drop in the plant (0 torr per tray)
Liquid holdup	Holdup in the condenser (0.0001 g)
START UP POLICY	
Charge	Liquid charged in the reboiler, and the modalities (100 cm^3, instantaneous amount)
Distil	Initial vapor rate of the distillation (3.0 g/min)
Run until	Time for which the policy is kept (10 min)
CUT-n POLICIES (simulation data for n=1)	
Distil	Vapor rate (3.35 g/min, from experimental test) and reflux ratio (R=0)
Run until	Time for which the policy is kept (4 min, from experimental test)
End cut	It indicates the stream to destinate the cut (CUT 1)

The simulated data for the different experimental runs conducted were compared with the experimental composition profile to verify and adjust the settings until the best fitting of the data. The same procedure was used for both n-heptane/toluene and water/propylene glycol (PG) mixtures.

3.2. Multistage batch distillation

The simulations for the two mixtures distilled in the multistage plant were conducted at R = ∞ and R = finite.

In the first case, the simulations for R = ∞ were conducted using a continuous distillation column (Figure 2a) setting a very high reflux ratio (R = 100). It was considered that almost all the product is taken from the bottom of the column, and just a small fraction distilled on top to simulate the sampling. The numbers of separating stages were determined trying different configurations starting from the value obtained with the McCabe and Thiele method (Erich Krell, 1982)). In the case of R=finite, the simulations of the multistage batch plant were similar to the mono-stage batch case, with some additional consideration, both for setting and policies (Table 2).

Table 2: *setting and policies used for the simulation of the multistage batch distillation (R=finite) with AVEVA ProII™ (example of simulation data of water/PG distillation).*

ProII COMMAND	DESCRIPTION (Example of simulation data)
STREAMS	
Feed	Flowrate, composition, T and P of the initial mixture (7.753 mol/min, water/PG molar ratio=80/20, 50 °C, 250 torr)
Residue	Content of the still-pot (residue) at the end of the distillation (0.001 mol/min)
Accum-res	Residue of the condenser hold-up (8.76 * 10^{-5} mol/min)
Cuts	All the cuts sampled along the distillation process (number of cuts = 12)
BATCH DISTILLATION WINDOW	
Number of theoretical stages	These values have been estimated starting from the McCabe and Thiele method (number of theoretical stages = 4)
Batch cycle time	Used to normalize the exiting flowrates of the unit (cycle time = 600 min)
Initial pressure profile	Pressure of the distillation (250 torr) and pressure drop in the plant (0 torr per tray)
Liquid holdup	Condenser liquid holdup (4 g) and tray holdup (different values were tried until the best simulation profile was found, 4 g)
START UP POLICY	
Charge	Liquid charged in the reboiler, and the modalities (220 g, instantaneous amount)
Distil	Initial vapor rate of the distillation (1.0 g/min)
Run until	Time for which the policy is kept (10 min)
CUT-n POLICIES (simulation data for n = 1)	
Distil	Top vapor rate (1.25 g/min, from Eq(1)) and reflux ratio (R = 0.5)
Run until	Effective experimental distillation times were used, or quantity of distillate taken from every cut (10.018 g)
End cut	It indicates the stream to destinate the cut (CUT 1)

A parameter that as to be defined is the value of top vapour rate. It was calculated starting from the values of R_{min} found with the McCabe and Thiele method and using the Equation (1), where the mean values of D (mol*min^{-1}) were obtained in the different experimental distillations, while the possible values of L (mol*min^{-1}) were calculated with the formula of the reflux ratio (R=L/D).

$$\text{Top vapour rate} = L + D \tag{1}$$

Different values of R were tried until the best simulation profile was obtained.

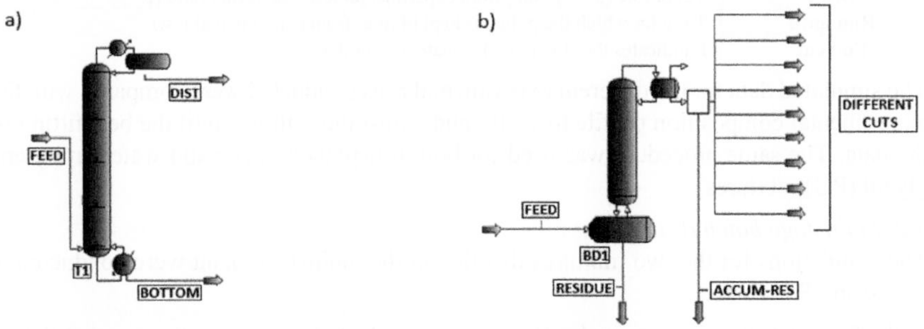

Figure 2: *Simulated plants use in PRO II to study a) multistage batch distillation with R=∞ and b) mono and multistage batch distillation with R=finite.*

4. Results and discussion

In this section are presented results obtained with the simulation software and the comparison with the experimental data.

From the comparison of the experimental VLE data with the simulated ones using different thermodynamic models the following xy diagrams were obtained. In the case of n-heptane/toluene mixture (Figure 3a), the NRTL model was chosen for the simulation due to its best fitting with the experimental data. For the water/PG mixture instead (Figure 3b), UNIQUAC model showed the lowest error, and so it was chosen for the simulation part of the work.

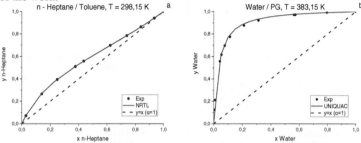

Figure 3: *Comparison between the experimental values of liquid-vapour equilibria and those simulated on AVEVA ProII^{TM} with the model that best fits the data: a) n-heptane/toluene mixture at 298.15 K, b) water/PG mixture at 383.15 K.*

Using these thermodynamic models, the simulations of the mono-stage distillation were performed. A good fitting of the experimental data was obtained, both in the case of n-heptane/toluene mixture and water/PG one, with a maximum error observed around 3%. In the Figure 4 two examples about the profile comparison for the two mixtures are reported.

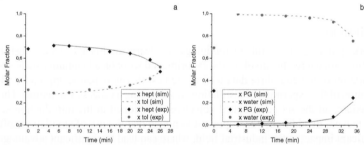

Figure 4: *Comparison of simulated and experimental data obtained with the mono-stage batch distillation: a) n-heptane/toluene mixture, initial molar ratio hept/tol=70/30, p=760 torr and b) Water/PG mixture, initial molar ratio water/PG=70/30, p=255 torr.*

In the case of multistage apparatus, the results obtained from the R = ∞ simulations showed good comparability with the experimental ones (Table 3 confirming the number of separating stages calculated at R = ∞ using McCabe and Thiele method (5-6 trays).

Table 3: *comparison between experimental and simulated results (for different number of stages) of the R = ∞ distillation of n-heptane/toluene mixtures*

	χ_{hept} **exp**	χ_{hept} **sim with 4 trays**	χ_{hept} **sim with 5 trays**	χ_{hept} **sim with 6 trays**
Dist 1	0.706	0.571	0.639	**0.695**
Dist 2	0.780	0.761	**0.796**	0.827
Dist 3	0.810	0.191	**0.825**	0.852

Simulations of multistage batch distillation at R = finite are in accord with the experimental results obtained, both in the case of n-heptane/toluene mixture and water/PG one. In Figure 5 two examples about the profile comparison for the two mixtures are reported.

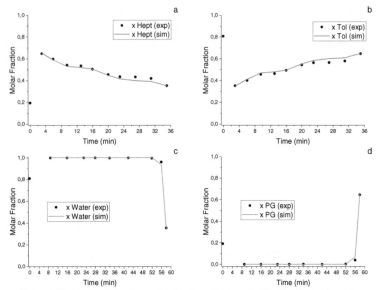

Figure 5*: comparison of simulated and experimental data for the multistage batch distillation apparatus: a) n-heptane/toluene mix, initial molar ratio hept/tol=20/80, p=760 torr, R=4 and b) water/PG mix, initial molar ratio water/PG=80/20, p=250 torr, R=0.5.*

5. Conclusions

This work provides a useful methodology to learn multistage batch distillation optimization procedure, that involves the experimental work on a laboratory scale system, the elaboration of the equilibria data to find the best thermodynamic approach, and the interpretation of the experimental distillations results using a process simulation. Through this procedure, all the set pedagogical objectives mentioned in the introduction section can be achieved. In addition, it is important to notice that the use of simulation software has significant impact in the industrial field, where can lead to significant advantages.

References

S. J. Ashcroft, A. D Clayton, and R. B. Shearn, 1979, Isothermal Vapor-Liquid Equilibria for the Systems Toluene-n-Heptane, Toluene-Propan-2-ol, Toluene-Sulfolane, and Propan-2-ol-Sulfolane, Journal of Chemical and Engineering Data, Vol. 24, No. 3

AVEVA PRO/II Simulation – The Trusted Steady-State Process Simulator. Datasheet

E. M. Fendu* and F. Oprea, 2014, Vapor–Liquid Equilibria for Water + Propylene Glycols Binary Systems: Experimental Data and Regression, Journal of Chemical and Engineering Data.

E. Krell, 1982, Calculation of separating stages by the McCabe-Thiele method in batch operation, Handbook of laboratory distillation, 2nd edition, 108

M. Mujtaba, 2004, Batch distillation, design, and operation – Series on chemical engineering, Vol.3

C. Pirola, 2019, Learning distillation by a combined experimental and simulation approach in a three steps laboratory, Education for Chemical Engineers, 28, 54–65.

Flavio Manenti, Gintaras V. Reklaitis (Eds.), Proceedings of the 34th European Symposium on
Computer Aided Process Engineering / 15th International Symposium on Process Systems
Engineering (ESCAPE34/PSE24), June 2-6, 2024, Florence, Italy

An Open-Source Software for Low-Code Implementation of Fuzzy Logic for Process Engineering

Raphael A. Santana[a], Vitor A. O. Silva[a], Tiago F. Souza[a], Vitor M. V. Cruz[a],
Ana M. F. Fileti[a], Flávio Vasconcelos da Silva[a,*]

[a]*University of Campinas (UNICAMP), School of Chemical Engineering, Chemical
Systems Engineering Department – Albert Einstein Ave., 500, Campinas – SP, 13083-
852, Brazil*
flaviovs@unicamp.br

Abstract

Fuzzy logic is suitable and widely applied to modeling and controlling multivariable
processes with non-linearities and susceptible to uncertainties. Furthermore, fuzzy logic
has been utilized in risk analysis and process safety. The main reason for widely applying
fuzzy logic in modeling, control, risk analysis, and process safety is using human
experience to evaluate the processes through linguistic variables, which are naturally
diffuse and imprecise. Implementing fuzzy logic for the previously mentioned situations
requires using some programming languages. However, a lack of programming skills is
a barrier to the engagement of engineers, educators, and students in applying fuzzy logic
in several engineering areas. In this context, this paper aims to evidence the development
and characteristics of open-source software for low-code implementation of fuzzy logic
to process control, modeling, risk analysis, and process safety. This software, named
FuzzyWise, is entirely based on the Python language. It provides a comprehensive library
that offers a range of tools for creating various fuzzy systems through the code editor or
using an intuitive and versatile interface, allowing users to download the source code for
use in other applications. The FuzzyWise will empower engineers, educators, and
students in process engineering to implement fuzzy logic effectively.

Keywords: fuzzy logic, process engineering, open-source software, low-code software,
engineering education.

1. Introduction

Fuzzy logic has emerged as a very powerful tool in dealing with complex problems and
uncertainty, particularly in engineering application in problems that lays on lack of data
and dependence on specialists knowledge (Simão and Shawn, 2007).
The theory of fuzzy logic introduces the notion of fuzzy sets, referred to as membership
functions, which determine the degree of membership of a specific element within a set.
This concept serves as a gateway to explore and apply human reasoning. There are a lot
of real-world problems where engineers and scientists do not have mathematical models
to describe, but it has specialists observations: "when the temperature of a turbine is cool
and the pressure is weak, the action of the throttle is positively large". Through that kind
of description, the fuzzy logic allows to simulate human decision making, mathematically
translating the human reasoning through various methods.
There are several Python libraries available for implementing fuzzy logic, but a solid
understanding of the Python language is essential. It wouldn't be sufficient to merely
comprehend the concept of fuzzy logic; acquiring proficiency in utilizing the Python

language would be equally crucial. In this regard, there are graphical UI, such as the Fuzzy Logic Toolbox in Matlab, that facilitate the application of fuzzy logic. However, it's important to note that a paid subscription is required to access this toolbox.

In this context, the current study seeks to create a completely free, intuitive, and low-code application for implementing fuzzy inference systems across diverse scenarios in process engineering. Also, aims to establish a library that consolidates various methods in fuzzy logic, thereby facilitating the dissemination of the concept.

2. Fundamentals and Methodology

2.1. Fuzzy Logic

The fuzzy logic was introduced by Zadeh (1965) as a mechanism for modelling human conceptualizations that involve uncertainties not representable by the traditional probability theory. Unlike boolean logic, where an observation either belongs or does not belong to a set (1 or 0), the fuzzy logic extends this characterization using degrees of membership. In this concept, observations partially belong to one or more sets defined by linguistic variables (Vilela, Oluyemi and Petrovski, 2020). For instance, a temperature of 40 °C might be 80% a part of the "hot" set and 20% of the "warm" set. Consequently, for each value in a universe of discourse, the membership function assigns a value between 0 and 1, describing various types of mathematical functions, such as triangular, trapezoidal, and gaussian. Figure 1 illustrates these previously mentioned membership functions.

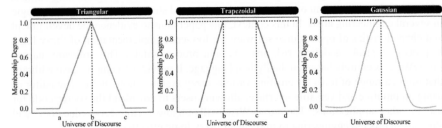

Figure 1: Triangular, trapezoidal, and gaussian membership functions.

Given that the entire universe of discourse for input and output variables is represented by a set of membership functions (fuzzy sets) through the capture of human knowledge, the fuzzy inference system is the process that uses fuzzy logic to map input variables to output variables once a fuzzy set. This process is inherently computational and comprises three fundamental blocks: Fuzzification, Inference Mechanism (including operation, implication and aggregation), and Defuzzification (Figure 2).

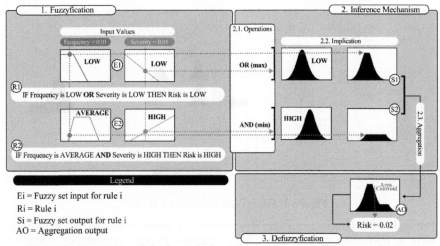

Figure 2: Illustration of the fuzzy logic system and fuzzy inference mechanism.

1. **Fuzzification:** This initial step involves mapping the universe of discourse, establishing the correspondence between each numerical value of the variables through appropriate membership functions.
2. **Inference Mechanism:** Based on the fuzzified variables, the mechanism evaluates the fuzzy rules activated from a predefined rule base. Each rule defines an implication between conditions using logical operators such as intersection (AND), union (OR), and complement (NOT). Then, all activated rule implications are aggregated. The rules structure depends on the inference method employed. The most commonly used methods are the Mamdani method and the Takagi-Sugeno method (Santana *et al.*, 2022). Mamdani uses linguistic variables for both inputs and outputs ("**IF input 1 is A AND/OR input 2 is B THEN output is C**"), while Takagi-Sugeno defines the output of a rule directly as a crisp value through the weighted average of inputs ["**IF input 1 is A AND/OR input 2 is B THEN output is a_1(input 1) + b_1(input 2)**"].
3. **Defuzzification:** For the Mamdani inference method it is necessary to transform the fuzzy output obtained by implication into a crisp value. The most common method for this conversion is the centroid.

2.2. FuzzyWise Architecture

This section elaborates on the methodology employed to develop FuzzyWise, providing a detailed insight into the systematic approach adopted for the software implementation, as can be seen in Figure 3.

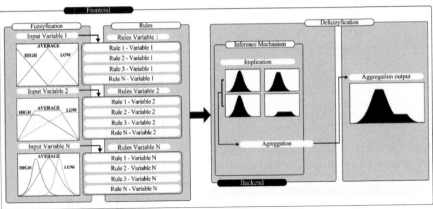

Figure 3: FuzzyWise architecture diagram.

The backend architecture of FuzzyWise serves as a robust computational framework, adept at overseeing intricate fuzzy logic processes through meticulously optimized algorithms developed for a newly created Python library. Its scalability guarantees steadfast decision-making across different scenarios, maintaining computational efficiency. On the frontend, developed using the PyQt5 library, FuzzyWise offers users an intuitive interface to input linguistic variables and witness real-time evaluations of fuzzy logic. The incorporation of responsive design and graphical representations enhances user comprehension, rendering complex fuzzy logic concepts easily accessible.

3. Results and Discussion

To showcase the capabilities of FuzzyWise, we analyzed a common case study widely used in risk analysis and process safety, specifically focusing on the risk matrix depicted in Figure 4.

Risk Matrix		Severity				
		Negligible	Low	Moderate	High	Catatrophic
Frequency	Low	Very Low	Low	Medium	Medium	High
	Moderate	Low	Medium	Medium	High	High
	High	Low	Medium	High	Very High	Very High

Figure 4: Representation of the case study risk matrix.

The illustrated risk matrix relates the frequency and severity of a general event to determine the consequence risk associated with the event. Only relying on the risk matrix has the following limitation: the determined risk value is merely qualitative. In order to overcome this limitation, fuzzy logic can be applied to determine the quantitative risk values (Almeida et al., 2023). Based on the risk matrix illustrated in Figure 4, a fuzzy inference system can be developed to model the relation between input variables (frequency and severity) and output (consequence risk).

The results will be presented as the sequential steps necessary for implementing the ongoing case study under investigation, with each step thoroughly elucidated. It is worth noting that identical results can be obtained by employing the FuzzyWise library in any code editor through the terminal.

Step 1: Creating the Input Variables - Fuzzification

Figure 5: FuzzyWise variable creation.

Step 2: Adding Membership Functions

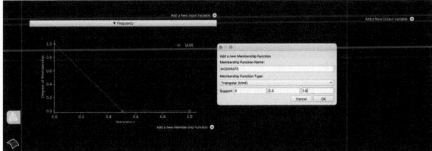

Figure 6: FuzzyWise membership functions creation.

Step 3: Rules and Inference Mechanism

Figure 7 shows a comprehensive overview of the input variables, universe of discourse, associated membership functions support, output variable, and inference method.

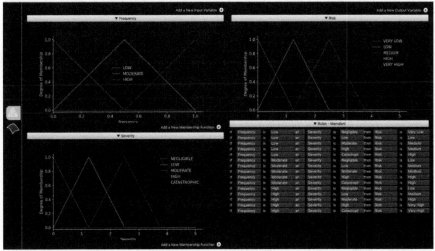

Figure 7: Interface representation of the case study implementation using FuzzyWise.

Step 4: Defuzzification and Response Surface

Tuning the fuzzy system is a critical step, and retrieving the real-time response surface as soon as it is updated can significantly enhance the specialist's ability to quickly achieve the desired configuration. Therefore, Figure 8 shows the response surface for the case study under discussion.

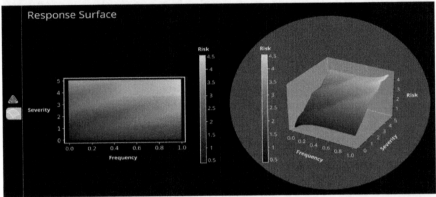

Figure 8: Response surface for the implemented case study.

The response surface is presented in two dimensions for improved user understanding, with an additional interactive 3D representation for a more engaging and insightful exploration of the results. This approach enhances the visual appeal and facilitates a comprehensive data analysis, promoting intuitive interpretation. The implementation of the case study is detailed in a tutorial video available on FuzzyWise Online Library.

4. Conclusion

FuzzyWise is an open-source software that enables implementing fuzzy logic systems without prior knowledge of any programming languages. The user-friendly graphical interface of this software makes it possible to implement fuzzy logic systems by directly defining the following parameters: fuzzy system input and output variables and their membership functions, inference method, defuzzification method, and rule base. The characteristics previously mentioned about FuzzyWise are the main contributions related to developing this software since there is a lack of open-source softwares for low-code implementation of fuzzy logic. The available version of FuzzyWise has limitations, such as the possibility of using only the Mandani or Takagi-Sugeno inference method. Therefore, software improvements will enable the development of the most diverse systems based on fuzzy logic.

References

Simões, M. G., & Shaw, I. S. (2007). Controle e modelagem fuzzy. Editora Blucher.
Zadeh, L. A. (1965). Fuzzy sets. Information and control, 8, 338-353.
Vilela, M., Poluem, G. F., & Petrovski, A. (2020). Sensitivity analysis applied to fuzzy inference on the value of information in the oil and gas industry. International journal of applied decision sciences, 13, 344-362.
Santana, R., Vianna, S. S. V., & Silva, F. V. (2022). A novel approach in fuzzy bowtie analysis applying Takagi–Sugeno inference for risk assessment in chemical industry. Journal of Loss Prevention in the Process Industries, 80, 104892.
Almeida, R. S., da Silva, F. V., & Vianna, S. S. (2023). Combining the bow-tie method and fuzzy logic using Mamdani inference model. Process Safety and Environmental Protection, 169, 159-168.

Flavio Manenti, Gintaras V. Reklaitis (Eds.), Proceedings of the 34th European Symposium on Computer Aided Process Engineering / 15th International Symposium on Process Systems Engineering (ESCAPE34/PSE24), June 2-6, 2024, Florence, Italy

Merging digitalization tools for training the new generation of bio-chemical engineers: challenges and perspectives

Oscar Andrés Prado-Rubio,[a,b*] Jakob K. Huusom[b]

[a]*Departamento de Ingeniería Química, Universidad Nacional de Colombia – 170003 Manizales, Colombia, *oaprador@unal.edu.co*
[b]*Department of Chemical and Biochemical Engineering, Technical University of Denmark (DTU), DK-2800 Lyngby, Denmark*

Abstract

Digitalization is reshaping the qualifications required for a growing industry 4.0. Efforts are necessary to introduce those skills into the biochemical engineers' competences. Future engineers need to feel comfortable designing and using digitalization tools to drive developments in biomanufacturing. In this contribution, we discuss the challenges of building digital objects for novel pilot units, to be used for student exercises and research towards more digital assisted operation within the context of digital twins. Besides, relevant topics for digitalization strategy are discussed as planning, team assembly, and infrastructure upgrades. For illustration, obstacles of digitalization of novel membrane technologies with time-variant nature and limited process understanding are discussed, focusing on the modelling approaches from whiter hybrid models to pure data-driven representations. Perspectives on the future needs and potential implications are presented.

Keywords: Digitalization, digital object, dynamic ultrafiltration

1. Introduction

Activities in Digitalization strategies are increasing at an outstanding rate in both Academia and Industry. Academic publications in Digital twins for Chemical Engineering have grown almost exponentially in the last 10 years (Source: Scopus). Besides, the Digital twins market is reported between 10 - 13 billion USD (2022-2023), with a CAGR of up to 61 % for 2027 (Markets and Markets, 2023). The current picture of software development for digital twins has grown by 71 % between 2020 and 2022, and from a survey, 29 % of worldwide manufacturing companies are implementing their digitalization strategies and 63 % are developing them. An important driver for digitalization lies in the less capex-intensive upgrades required, where disruptive technologies are not necessarily linked to high investments and it is expected that only 40 % to 50 % of the cases require equipment replacement (McKinsey Digital, 2015). It is known that biomanufacturing processes are still operated relying on recipes and workers' experience with limited monitoring and automation (Bähner et al., 2021). Therefore, digitalization has great potential to propel the next generation of bioprocesses, where interactive communication between the real-plant, high-fidelity digital objects (core of digital twins) and users becomes a powerful decision-support tool useful from enhanced process/product development, up to partially automated or self-optimizing operation. However, biomanufacturing is progressing in digitalization at a slower pace compared to telecommunications and finances, due to the complex monitoring which limits process understanding, lack of confidence in digital technologies and it is not entirely clear the cost of implementation (Deloitte, 2017). As the foundation for building the required understanding and transforming biomanufacturing through digitalization, a key step is to assemble a skilled and empowered team on digital competencies to set up governance and steering into designing quick-release digitalization strategies. Biochemical engineers are important players in digitalizing biomanufacturing. Nevertheless, it has been pointed out that there is a big gap between available technologies and harnessing them for PSE teaching/training practices (Lewin *et al.*, 2023). Also, in a time of graduates considered digital natives, this does not mean they are competent in technologies required in digitization of the manufacturing sector areas such as big data, internet of things, cloud technology, data analytics/intelligence, artificial intelligence, and physical-to-digital conversion. Then, there is a call to narrow the skills gap in future biochemical engineers for an industry going through a digital transformation.

The Department of Chemical and Biochemical Engineering at DTU has been maturing a Digitalization strategy. This includes the transformation of the pilot units hall for both teaching and research (Jones et al., 2022). In this contribution, a discussion is made around challenges encountered in constructing digital objects aiming for future digital twins to assist students to develop the skills for dealing with digital tools/infrastructures, explore the potential of hybrid modelling combining data and first principles; and ultimately enhance their capabilities for problem solving designing or using dockable digital entities. As illustrating cases, experiences with two novel dynamic membrane technologies are presented, where different approaches have been investigated to develop digital objects capable of predicting best operation scenarios (so-called critical flux), membrane rejection, fault detection, and forecast fouling rate under uncertain operation. Finally, some perspectives are presented on the digital objects' deployment and impact.

2. Developing digital objects for novel membrane technologies

As part of the digitalization strategy, the department has defined a first project aiming to develop digitalization tools on the equipment available in the pilot hall. The target is to have a) a cloud-based system for data acquisition, storage, analysis and usage by digital objects, and b) Visualization tools for training. The project execution could lead to identifying future directions from technical, scientific, and even philosophical perspectives for education in the pilot hall. For illustration, we have investigated two novel membrane technologies referred to as high-frequency backshock/backwash and vibrating membranes. Those technologies impose challenges at different complexity levels that are common to other dynamic systems or under development intensified processes with limited process understanding. A sketch of how the technologies work is shown in Figure 1. In the high-frequency backshock/backwash system, two fouling mitigation strategies are applied at different frequencies. Both strategies involve reversing the transmembrane pressure to use permeate for cleaning. In the vibrating membrane, high-frequency membrane vibration creates a high shear rate at the membrane surface which mitigates fouling formation. Both technologies have shown remarkable performance for biomanufacturing, but their operation is not straightforward and could benefit from digitalization. Relevant to this contribution, the three main aspects of the strategy for the first goal are depicted in Figure 2; answering the questions Who (People), Through (Infrastructure), and What (Building digital objects). Those aspects are discussed in the following sections, focusing on the Digital Object implementation.

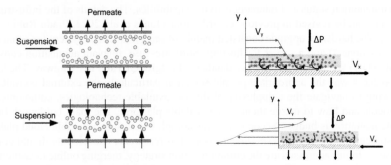

(a)   High-frequency backshock/backwash   (b)   Vibrating membrane system

Figure 1. Illustration of the antifouling mechanisms in two dynamic ultrafiltration systems.

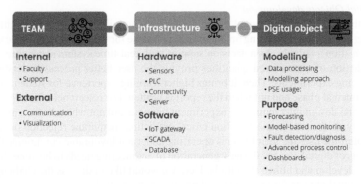

Figure 2. Approach for building digital objects for pilot units

2.1. Setting-up the correct team

The team involved included the head of the department, faculty members with experience in relevant areas (i.e., process control, pilot unit operation, equipment maintenance), the University IT department and support researchers with projects in the area. In this manner, there was a combination of management capabilities and technical support to define specific activities and materialize them. Important topics where external consultancy is relevant are infrastructure, communication, and visualization. In an early stage, the main challenge is to establish a common reference language, due to the broad spectra of disciplines within the team. This difficulty was mitigated by performing workshops and regular meetings between key internal and external members. On the other end, the digital object developers must be trained or under training in digitalization tools complemented by experienced researchers in the technology of interest. This could be challenging with novel technologies where the process understanding should be built along the digital object development, therefore iteration is unavoidable. Also, it becomes a major endeavour accounting for the large number of units in a pilot laboratory. There, stepwise implementation is the most reasonable approach to build the required experience.

2.2. Infrastructure upgrade

To build the cloud-based system, hardware and software infrastructure upgrades are required, this is capex-intensive. The pilot plants were evaluated to determine their instrumentation status and interconnectivity capabilities. The details of the infrastructure upgrade can be revised in previous contributions (Jones et al., 2022; Prado-Rubio et al., 2023). The hardware upgrade consisted mainly of sensors, PLCs, a system for connection (Cloud-connect) and a server for hosting. Software-wise, relevant acquisition consisted of SCADA (WinCC + Kubernetes), database (PostgreSQL) and IoT gateway. The key to the success was the appropriate people selection particularly the external consultancy, allowing to navigate the complexity of diverse available technologies, communication protocols and how to merge them into a scalable platform. The main bottleneck before implementation is budget. Secondly, it was complex to design a flexible cloud platform for students doing defined experiments as well as researchers developing digital objects. Sensitive topics addressed are the communication strategy, merging online measurements and metadata, space-efficient database design, SCADA design and objective-driven digital objects development.

2.3. Digital Objects development

Having the end in mind, digital objects representing pilot units can use different modelling approaches depending on the ultimate purpose for the user (student/researcher) and information available. As a decision support tool, real-time system states forecasting plus prediction of unmeasured quantities provide the user better process understanding while running experiments. Then, it brings higher learning experience for students during the experimental phase and not when the report is written. For researchers, it can facilitate experimental design intervening the experiment ongoing and not when data are analysed. Particularly, in the membrane filtration cases, predicting membrane rejection or fouling rate can alert the user the membrane is operating under not favourable conditions. Due to the benefits of digital objects, the new generation of engineering needs to become stronger in how to develop and utilize such tools. Here we would like to discuss the challenges of building digital objects for the mentioned novel membrane technologies.

2.3.1. Monitoring and data pre-processing

Monitoring in biomanufacturing is complex. Normally, only regulatory variables (e.g., T, P, F, L, pH) are monitored at high frequency. On the contrary, supervisory variables (i.e., concentrations) if available, are monitored at a lower frequency especially if offline lab analysis is required. There are interesting developments in PAT for biomanufacturing and membrane technology, however, majorly are expensive or not massively available. In dynamic filtration, the first obstacle is to have the infrastructure to store the data at the required frequency to capture the systems' fast dynamics (i.e., less than 1 second), thus being able to perform long experimental campaigns relevant at pilot scale. After significant experimentation performed with the high-frequency backshock/backwash system, modelling showed the selected sampling time (allowed by PLC memory) was insufficient (Prado-Rubio & von Stosch, 2017). This is corrected by having the cloud-based acquisition system as implemented for the vibrating membrane. Another challenge regarding the high-frequency backshock/backwash system is signal pre-processing. First, when information has not been recorded, then algorithms must be designed for signal reconstruction necessary for modelling (Prado-Rubio & von Stosch, 2017). Secondly, system information is hidden within complex signals and noise elimination might imply losing system information. To overcome this issue, wavelet feature extraction has shown to be handy (Zadkarami et al., 2023). This approach requires hyperparameters tuning, but it can be made based on historical data. Then, conventional signal preprocessing techniques can be used.

2.3.2. Modelling approaches for digital object development

The modelling challenge lies in process understanding (defines whiteness), information available for parameter estimation and tuning/solving procedures fast enough to be used in real-time. For the investigated novel membrane technologies, there are two extremes which define the modelling approach based on the available information. The spectra of modelling approaches investigated for the dynamic systems are shown in Figure 3.

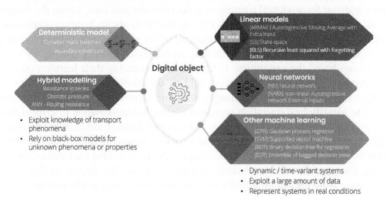

Figure 3. Investigated modelling approaches for the novel dynamic membrane systems

First, information availability could not be a limitation in the case of well-understood processes (e.g., dextran filtration with no fouling) operated in controlled experiments (minimum uncertainty). In this scenario, digital objects can include a strong deterministic part (López-Murillo et al., 2021). Thus, online measurements and metadata are used to build a whiter hybrid model to describe membrane flux, dynamic concentration profiles and solute rejection. As a model backbone, there is a mass balance in the boundary layer (PDE) coupled with Darcy's law to estimate the membrane flux. So, black box models are used to determine the osmotic pressure and membrane intrinsic rejection. In this way, knowledge of transport phenomena is harnessed and just complemented by data-driven models for model parameters. This hybrid model provides parameters interpretability and system insights very useful for design. As a drawback, due to the absence of fouling the system is time-invariant, and the challenge is considerably lower.

On the other hand, if the high-frequency backshock/backwash system is under uncertainty of real industrial application, the lack of concentration monitoring and dynamic operation forced the usage of darker hybrid approaches or fully data-driven model (Díaz et al., 2017; Prado-Rubio & von Stosch, 2017). The flux is modelled through Darcy's law considering the osmotic pressure. Data-driven approaches are used to model the time-variant transport resistance. In that way, the fouling rate can be estimated in a wide range of operating conditions. Those approaches have shown high accuracy (>95%), comparable with machine learning results from the literature. Despite the performance, there are some drawbacks as a) there are still missing guidelines for model selection and how much data is required, b) models underperformance during validation, c) training time could be a problem in real-time applications, and d) it is uncertain when to perform a recalibration. To overcome the last issues, we have proposed to use online system identification which has shown comparable quality to machine learning techniques but it can be trained in real-time and perform fouling rate forecasting (Prado-Rubio et al., 2023).

3. Conclusions and Perspectives

The increasing interest in digitalization is driving advances in biomanufacturing. Then, education must cope with the future skills required in Industry 4.0, towards the development and usage of digital assisted tools. Relevant skills to be further developed for students are programming in different environments and numerical methods tuning for real-time applications. On the other hand, the implementation of digital objects becomes relevant for students' training as a decision-support tool, where the forecasting capabilities of states and unmeasured KPIs can enable to obtain better experimental data and learning experience during the experiments. This is because the students can focus on the experience insights instead of dealing recipe-based tasks or solving by trial-and-error/intuition-based the experiment bottlenecks, accelerating their learning curve. As a take-home message, the digital objects could be the combination of approaches. From one side, hybrid models and data-hungry machine learning could be used for process design or to identify best operation scenarios (through determination of critical flux and faulty conditions), either for automatic operation or as decision support tool for users. As an alternative, the data inexpensive method as online system identification could be used for short horizon forecasting complementing results from hybrid approaches. Due to the emerging nature of this field, research projects involving the design of digital objects facilitate increasing the required understanding to massify their implementation.

Acknowledgements
This research was founded by Novo Nordisk Foundation grant NNF19SA0035474.

References

Bähner, F. D., Prado-Rubio, O. A., & Huusom, J. K. (2021). Challenges in Optimization and Control of Biobased Process Systems: An Industrial-Academic Perspective. *Industrial and Engineering Chemistry Research*, *60*(42), 14985–15003.

Deloitte. (2017). Digital Transformation : Are chemical enterprises ready? In *Deloitte* (Issue January).

Díaz, V. H. G., Prado-Rubio, O. A., Willis, M. J., & von Stosch, M. (2017). Dynamic hybrid model for ultrafiltration membrane processes. In *Computer Aided Chemical Engineering* (Vol. 40).

Jones, M. N., Stevnsborg, M., Nielsen, R. F., Carberry, D., Bagherpour, K., Mansouri, S. S., Larsen, S., Gernaey, K. V., Dreyer, J., Woodley, J., Huusom, J. K., & Dam-Johansen, K. (2022). Pilot Plant 4.0: A Review of Digitalization Efforts of the Chemical and Biochemical Engineering Department at the Technical University of Denmark (DTU). *Computer Aided Chemical Engineering*, *49*, 1525–1530.

López-Murillo, L. H., Grisales-Díaz, V. H., Pinelo, M., & Prado-Rubio, O. A. (2021). Ultrafiltration intensification by dynamic operation: Insights from hybrid modeling. *Chemical Engineering and Processing - Process Intensification*, *169*, 108618.

Markets and Markets. (2023). *Digital Twin Market Size, Share, Industry Report, Revenue Trends and Growth Drivers*.

McKinsey Digital. (2015). *Industry 4.0 How to navigate digitalization of the manufacturing sector*.

Prado-Rubio, O. A., Hui, W. F., Stevnsborg, M., Pinelo, M., & Huusom, J. K. (2023). Digital-twin development for a novel vibrating membrane aiming at fractionating fermentation broths. *Computer Aided Chemical Engineering*, *52*, 2575–2580.

Prado-Rubio, O. A., & von Stosch, M. (2017). Towards Sustainable Flux Determination for Dynamic Ultrafiltration through Multivariable System Identification. *Computer Aided Chemical Engineering*, *40*, 2719–2724.

Zadkarami, M., Safavi, A. A., Gernaey, K. V., Ramin, P., & Prado-Rubio, O. A. (2023). Designing a fault detection classifier framework for an industrial dynamic ultrafiltration membrane process using wavelet-based feature analysis. *Process Safety and Environmental Protection*, *174*, 1–19.

Flavio Manenti, Gintaras V. Reklaitis (Eds.), Proceedings of the 34th European Symposium on Computer Aided Process Engineering / 15th International Symposium on Process Systems Engineering (ESCAPE34/PSE24), June 2-6, 2024, Florence, Italy

Virtual Reality and Digital Twins for Enhanced Learning in Chemical Engineering

Andrea Galeazzi,[a] Paolo Marenghi,[b] Lamberto Duò,[c] Maurizio Galardo,[d] Renato Rota,[a] Susanna Sancassani,[b] Flavio Manenti,[a,*]

[a]Politecnico di Milano, CMIC Department "Giulio Natta", Piazza Leonardo da Vinci 32, 20133 Milano, Italy
[b]Politecnico di Milano, METID, Piazza Leonardo da Vinci 32, 20133 Milano, Italy
[c]Politecnico di Milano, Department of Physics, Piazza Leonardo da Vinci 32, 20133 Milano, Italy
[d]AVEVA / Schneider-Electric, Via Macchi 35, 20124 Milano, Italy
*flavio.manenti@polimi.it

Abstract

This study explores the implementation of digital twin technology in engineering education at Politecnico di Milano, through the EYEducation Project in collaboration with AVEVA/Schneider-Electric. The project integrates immersive virtual reality and digital twins into the M.Sc. chemical engineering program at Politecnico di Milano, utilizing Dynsim for dynamic simulation of chemical processes and AVEVA XR for 3D plant experiences. A case study involving a valve switch in a process line illustrates the practical application and benefits of digital twins. This approach significantly enhances the educational experience by providing students with a realistic, interactive learning environment. It effectively bridges the gap between theoretical knowledge and practical skills, showcasing the transformative potential of digital twins in modern engineering education. The integration of this technology marks a pivotal advancement in preparing students for real-world industrial operations.

Keywords: Digital twin, Immersive environment, Process dynamics, Series of Operations, Digitalization in education programs.

1. Introduction

In recent years, Virtual Reality (VR) has emerged as a significant trend in the educational sector, recognized for its potential to transform learning experiences. Despite its promising aspects, particularly in establishing connections between research and education, VR has yet to realize its full impact in technical higher education. VR creates immersive experiences that transport users to a dimension entirely distinct from the physical world. However, its effective application in educational settings, along with the implications for teaching methodologies, remains a topic of exploration.

The effectiveness of VR in education is contingent on integrating it into curricula designed to achieve specific learning outcomes. This requires a reevaluation of teaching and learning practices to leverage the new types of content VR offers. Innovative pedagogies are essential to harness the potential of VR, with an emphasis on blending practical and theoretical aspects of learning.

A cognitive perspective on pedagogy views knowledge as a combination of information and process structures, vital for skills such as reasoning, problem-solving, comprehension, and language use. Learning, from this perspective, is seen as an evolution of cognitive structures through internal mental activities. It involves students in recursive processes that blend experiences, abstractions, inference, problem solutions, and information recombination. This approach moves beyond linear learning models to a recursive, networked vision where direct experience plays a central role.

The teacher's role is crucial in creating an environment conducive to learning, linking knowledge to practical and experiential domains, and fostering student autonomy. VR can be an effective tool in this context, facilitating a transformative learning process as described in the Kolb Cycle. This cycle suggests that learning is a process of knowledge creation through the transformation of experience, connecting theoretical concepts through observation and reflection on experiences.

Further, the application of pedagogical methods like Inquiry-Based Learning (IBL) and Problem-Based Learning (PBL) can be enhanced with VR. These methods focus on autonomous research by students and learning through problem-solving, respectively. Scenario-Based Learning (SBL) also benefits from VR, where learning is encouraged through simulated scenarios requiring students to perform actions based on different roles.

These pedagogical approaches, combined with VR, can provide a learning experience that goes beyond content reference to actual interaction within a 'real' learning environment. The integration of VR in learning processes presents new opportunities and challenges, necessitating a reassessment of content-sharing approaches and student engagement strategies. As VR becomes more prevalent, educational environments may evolve to accommodate more interactive and collaborative methods, potentially redefining traditional classroom settings to allow direct interaction with virtual 3D content (Halabi, 2020; Liljaniemi and Paavilainen, 2020; Paravizo and Braatz, 2019).

2. Digital Twin

In engineering terms, a "digital twin" represents the digital manifestation of a physical entity. This concept transcends traditional boundaries, finding relevance in diverse engineering fields such as process/chemical, electric/electronic, and mechanical engineering. Digital twins can span in terms of complexity and representativeness of the physical asset, depending on the specific application. In this work, it is intended as a dynamic, interactive representation that reflects the multifaceted behavior of a plant across various operational scenarios, including complex processes like start-ups and emergency shutdowns. In this case, it goes beyond providing a mere realistic field representation, evolving into a fully immersive environment where interactions with unit operations and instrumentation are seamlessly linked with the process simulation.

The essence of a digital twin lies in its integration of four key areas of digitalization: Process Simulation, Data Analytics, Immersive Environment, and Decision-Making Process. Process simulation, the core component, accounts for the constant dynamic state of plants, driven by various internal and external factors. Data analytics play a critical role in ensuring the reliability and accuracy of the digital twin by analyzing, interpreting, and reconciling plant data. The immersive environment component is vital for creating a realistic virtual plant experience, requiring high-quality visualizations and advanced gaming technology for implementation. Finally, the decision-making process in a digital twin involves an intricate series of operations and controls that dictate the actions and effects within the plant, achieved through integrated process control systems within the simulation environment. This comprehensive blend of simulation, data analysis, immersive technology, and decision-making processes forms the cornerstone of the digital twin concept, transforming it into a pivotal tool in modern engineering education and practice.

To understand more in detail how the digital twin technology is built it is necessary to have an overview of the whole digital twin framework, from raw plant data acquisition to process decision implementation. Such a framework is schematized in Figure 1 and it is possible to grasp the link with raw process data. However, one of the key enablers of the digital twin technology is data analysis (Romagnoli and Sanchez, 1999) coupled with machine learning methods (Ferranti et al., 2021; Galeazzi et al., 2022, 2021). This whole pipeline, shown in Figure 1, is beneficial to immersive reality experiences, providing more accurate representations of real industrial assets and operations, thus aiding in education or operators training and finally, decision making.

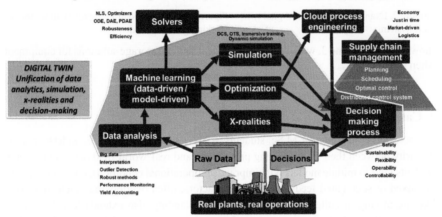

Figure 1. Flow diagram of a digital twin system, integrating data analytics, simulation, and decision-making in cloud engineering.

3. Implementation

Implementing a VR-based learning environment requires careful planning to meet specific technological and spatial requirements. The initial step involves setting up a demo station that's compatible with the simulation software. The learning space is designed to support immersive experiences for groups of up to four, allowing for both interaction and observation.

The VR software architecture is structured simply yet encompasses complex interdisciplinarity for case studies and scenarios. It includes a dynamic simulation suite for plant behavior, complete with control logic and user interaction capability, and a high-level virtual simulation suite for a realistic 3D plant model. These are linked via custom bridging software.

For hardware, a robust workstation with an advanced processor, ample RAM, significant storage, and a high-quality graphics card is essential. The chosen Oculus Rift S headset offers a cost-effective, immersive VR experience and requires a PC connection.

Classrooms are set up on two campuses, equipped with necessary technical infrastructure, ensuring enough space for safe movement and interaction with the VR system. Workstations are designed for both individual and collaborative work on simulations, as

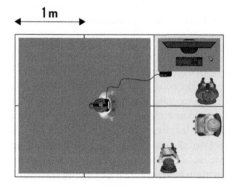

Figure 2. Example usage of the digital twin VR system.

Figure 3. VR workstation representation for a working group of students.

shown in Figure 2 and 3, with clear space delineations and storage solutions for equipment when not in use.

4. Case study

The selected case study for M.Sc. students, a valve line bypass switch, underscores the disparity between their programming proficiency and real-world field operations. Many students tend to initiate models with impractical operational conditions, either employing premixed or segregated feeds directly into reactors, often overlooking practical aspects like pre-mixing in collectors. This gap in understanding also extends to valve switch systems within industrial settings, as students using process simulators typically neglect the significance of valves, concentrating solely on essential units and disregarding the operational context. However, as the emphasis shifts towards operational efficiency and sustainability, the need to consider a more realistic environment becomes paramount, and this is where digital twins play a pivotal role.

The digital twin valve switch exercise offers students an immersive VR-based tutorial, enabling them to gain practical experience in simulated plant operations. In this virtual environment, students step into the shoes of avatars equipped with standard safety gear, collaborating closely with a virtual DCS engineer. Together, they embark on a series of tasks aimed at bypassing a malfunctioning automatic flowrate control valve (FV_10540), shown in Figure 4.

This hands-on operation sequence entails identifying the correct intervention points, ensuring that the flowrate remains within specified limits, and proficiently managing both automatic and manual valves to redirect the flow through a designated bypass line. Within this interactive VR setting, students have access to all the necessary equipment, can engage in real-time communication, and make critical adjustments in coordination with the control room. The process includes isolating the automatic valve by closing adjacent manual valves, opening the bypass valve, and draining the liquid from the isolated section. Upon successful completion of these tasks, students verify the operation's success with the control room and, if necessary, make adjustments to the flowrate. This immersive

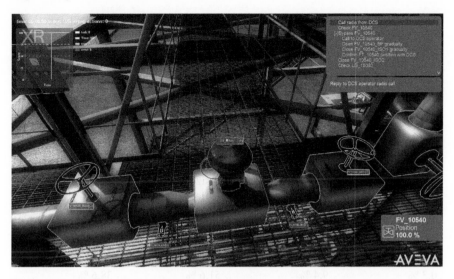

Figure 4. Interactive training scenario showcasing a valve bypass operation. The central red valve, identified as *FV_10540*, is the target of the exercise due to its malfunction. To successfully navigate the tutorial, participants must isolate this valve by adjusting the neighboring manual isolation valves and initiate flow through the bypass by engaging the manual wheel valve located on the extreme right of the scene.

exercise, typically completed within a timeframe of 22 to 28 minutes, significantly enhances students' practical understanding of process management and control in field operations.

5. Impact

The effectiveness of incorporating digital twins into engineering education was assessed through a questionnaire administered after the VR-based valve switch exercise conducted at Politecnico di Milano, involving 69 M.Sc. students. The primary objective of this survey was to gauge how the VR experience impacted the students' understanding of chemical plant operations and its efficacy as an instructional tool.

The questionnaire encompassed a range of inquiries aimed at evaluating the extent to which the VR environment enhanced the students' comprehension of chemical plant operations, process operation management, and unit operations. It also sought to ascertain the perceived value of VR as both an educational and training resource, along with its capacity to provide unique insights when compared to traditional classroom instruction, laboratory exercises, and real-world plant visits. Additionally, the survey explored the student's perceived benefits of VR in terms of its contribution to ongoing education, future career prospects, and overall knowledge acquisition, including its ability to clarify the structural intricacies of chemical plants and the sequencing of unit operations. However, understanding the actual benefits is no simple task and it would require a meta-analysis on the application of such tools, or, possibly, asking in the future to the same group of people how and if they received a career benefit through the usage of these immersive experiences.

The findings from the survey underscored a strong endorsement of the VR experience among the students. A significant majority recognized its role in enhancing their knowledge, which is directly applicable to their academic pursuits and future professional endeavours. Most students found VR to be a valuable tool for comprehending the complexity of plant structures and operations, surpassing traditional learning methods. However, they also acknowledged the irreplaceable value of real plant visits. The feedback provided insights into potential enhancements of VR, particularly in terms of its collaborative features to better simulate real-world teamwork in plant operations. With a remarkable positive response rate exceeding 90%, this study signifies a significant advancement in engineering education, demonstrating the successful integration of digital twin technology. Furthermore, students reflected on how the VR experience reshaped their perception of operation timelines, emphasized the importance of teamwork, and indicated their comfort and proficiency with VR technology.

Table 1. Average questionnaire results from the mandatory answers of 23 questions asked to a sample of 69 M.Sc. students after the VR-based valve bypass experience.

Strongly disagree	Disagree	Agree	Strongly agree
0.3 %	9.4 %	51.6 %	38.6 %

6. Conclusions

In summary, the EYEducation Project at Politecnico di Milano successfully integrated digital twins into the M.Sc. curriculum using Schneider-Electric/Aveva's software in a 3D environment. This pioneering approach received positive feedback from 69 Chemical Engineering M.Sc. students, highlighting its efficacy in bridging theory and practical knowledge. Challenges identified include improving virtual team collaboration. The project convincingly demonstrated the practicality of tasks like valve switching, emphasizing their real-world importance. Future efforts will expand digital twin integration in advanced engineering education, marking a promising step forward in preparing students for modern industry demands.

References

F. Ferranti, F. Manenti, G. Vingerhoets, M. Vallerio, 2021. Value chain planning optimization: a data driven digital twin approach. 16th IFAC Symposium on Advanced Control of Chemical Processes ADCHEM 2021 54, 572–577.

A. Galeazzi, R. Nasti, G.L. Bozzano, L. Verotta, S. Marzorati, F. Manenti, 2021. A Cloud Computing Application for the Supercritical Carbon Dioxide Extraction Using Coffee Grounds Silverskin, 31 European Symposium on Computer Aided Process Engineering. Elsevier, pp. 1035–1040.

A. Galeazzi, K. Prifti, F. Gallo, F. Manenti, 2022. A Methodology for The Optimal Surrogate Modelling of Digital Twins Using Machine Learning, 32 European Symposium on Computer Aided Process Engineering. Elsevier, pp. 1543–1548.

O. Halabi, 2020. Immersive virtual reality to enforce teaching in engineering education. Multimed Tools Appl 79, 2987–3004.

A. Liljaniemi, H. Paavilainen, 2020. Using Digital Twin Technology in Engineering Education – Course Concept to Explore Benefits and Barriers. Open Engineering 10, 377–385.

E. Paravizo, D. Braatz, 2019. Using a game engine for simulation in ergonomics analysis, design and education: An exploratory study. Applied Ergonomics 77, 22–28.

J.A. Romagnoli, M.C. Sanchez, 1999. Data processing and reconciliation for chemical process operations. Elsevier Science & Technology.

Author Index

Printed and bound by CPI Group (UK) Ltd, Croydon, CR0 4YY

03/10/2024

01040328-0003